RELATIONSHIP OF UNITS

(Values in boldface are exact.)

Length

1 in. = **2.54** cm
1 ft = **30.48** cm
1 yd = **91.44** cm

Volume

1 liq oz = **29.57353** mL
1 liq qt = **946.352946** mL
1 gallon = **3.785411784** L

Mass

1 oz = **28.349523125** g
1 lb = **453.59237** g

Pressure

$1 \text{ mm Hg} = 1 \text{ torr} = \frac{1}{760} \text{ atm}$

Energy

1 cal = **4.184** joule

STRONG AQUEOUS ACIDS

Hydrochloric acid, HCl
Hydrobromic acid, HBr
Hydriodic acid, HI
Nitric acid, HNO_3
Sulfuric acid, H_2SO_4

STRONG, HIGHLY SOLUBLE AQUEOUS BASES

Sodium hydroxide, NaOH
Potassium hydroxide, KOH

STRONG, SLIGHTLY SOLUBLE AQUEOUS BASES

Calcium hydroxide, $Ca(OH)_2$
Magnesium hydroxide, $Mg(OH)_2$

PHYSICAL CONSTANTS

Atomic mass unit (amu) = 1.6606×10^{-24} g

Avogadro's number = 6.022045×10^{23}

Gas constant, R = $6.24 \times 10^4 \dfrac{\text{mm Hg mL}}{\text{mol K}}$

Molar volume = 22.41383 L/mol (ideal gas, at 273.15 K and 760 mm Hg)

ABBREVIATIONS OF UNITS

amu	atomic mass unit
atm	atmosphere of pressure
Bq	becquerel
°C	degree Celsius
cal	calorie
cc	cubic centimeter
Ci	curie
cm	centimeter
cm^3	cubic centimeter
D	rad
dL (dl)	deciliter
eq	equivalent
eV	electron-volt
°F	degree Fahrenheit
ft	foot
g (Gm)	gram
gal	gallon
GeV	gigaelectron-volt
Gy	gray
in.	inch
J	joule
K	kelvin
kcal	kilocalorie
keV	kiloelectron-volt
kg	kilogram
km	kilometer
kPa	kilopascal
L	liter
lb	pound
m	meter
M	mol/L (molarity)
mcg (μg, γ)	microgram
meq	milliequivalent
MeV	megaelectron-volt
mg	milligram
μg, (mcg, γ)	microgram
mi	mile
mL (ml)	milliliter
μL (μl, λ)	microliter
mm	millimeter
μm	micrometer
mm Hg	millimeter of mercury
mmol	millimole
mol	mole
mOs	milliosmole
oz	ounce
Pa	pascal
ppb	parts per billion
ppm	parts per million
pt	pint
qt	quart
s	second
T	Kelvin temperature
t_c	Celsius temperature
t_f	Fahrenheit temperature
yd	yard

NORMAL RANGES OF VALUES FOR SOME CONSTITUENTS OF ADULT BLOOD

Constituent	Range of Values[a]	
	Conventional	SI
Albumin, serum	3.5–5.0 g/dL	35–50 g/L
Ammonia, plasma	12–55 μmol/L	12–55 μmol/L
Bilirubin, serum (total)	Up to 1.0 mg/dL	Up to 17 μmol/L
Blood urea nitrogen (BUN) (Urea = BUN × 2.14)	8–25 mg/dL	2.9–8.9 mmol/L
Calcium	8.5–10.5 mg/dL	2.1–2.6 mmol/L)
Carbon dioxide content	24–30 meq/L	24–30 mmol/L
pCO_2	25–45 mm Hg	4.7–6.0 kPa
Chloride ion, serum	100–108 meq/L	100–108 mmol/L
Cholesterol, fasting (age and sex-dependent)	120–220 mg/dL	3.10–5.68 mmol/L
Creatinine	0.6–1.5 mg/dL	53–133 μmol/L
Globulin, serum	2.3–3.5 g/dL	23–35 g/L
Glucose, fasting	70–110 mg/dL	3.9–5.6 mmol/L
Lipids, triacylglycerols	40–150 mg/dL	0.4–1.5 g/L
Magnesium ion	1.5–2.0 meq/L	0.8–1.3 mmol/L
Osmolality	280–296 mOsm/kg water	280–296 mmol/kg
Oxygen pressure, pO_2	75–100 mm Hg	10.0–13.3 kPa
pH	7.38–7.42	7.38–7.42
Phosphorus, inorganic	3.0–4.5 mg/dL	1.0–1.5 mmol/L
Potassium	3.5–5.0 meq/L	3.5–5.0 mmol/L
Protein, total	6.0–8.4 g/dL	60–84 g/L
Sodium	135–145 meq/L	135–145 mmol/L
Uric acid	3.0–7.0 mg/dL	0.18–0.42 mmol/L

[a] The ranges of values are from various sources but mostly from *The New England Journal of Medicine,* Vol. 314 (January 2, 1986), pages 39–49, and December 18, 1986, page 1606).

Fundamentals of General, Organic, and Biological Chemistry

About the Author **John Holum** is on the faculty of Augsburg College, Minneapolis, Minnesota. He did his under-graduate work at St. Olaf College and earned the Ph.D. (organic chemistry) at the University of Minnesota. Additional studies were taken as sabbatical leaves at California Institute of Technology and Harvard University. In 1974 he was given the Distinguished Teaching Award of the Minnesota Section of the American Chemical Society. He is a member of Phi Beta Kappa, Phi Lambda Upsilon, Sigma Xi, and Sigma Pi Sigma. The National Science Foundation has awarded him several research grants and a Science Faculty Fellowship. He is the author or coauthor of several texts in chemistry, all published by John Wiley and Sons. He has also authored papers for the *Journal of the American Chemical Society,* the *Journal of Organic Chemistry,* and the *Journal of Chemical Education.* He has been active on the Examinations Committee and the Committee on Chemistry for Professional Health Care Students of the Division of Chemical Education of the ACS, and he has spoken often at Divisional and Regional meetings, as well as at conferences of the Two-Year College Chemistry Association. His textbooks in chemistry for professional health care students have been widely used in America and abroad for 25 years.

JOHN R. HOLUM
Augsburg College

Fundamentals of General, Organic, and Biological Chemistry

Fourth Edition

John Wiley & Sons

New York   Chichester   Brisbane   Toronto   Singapore

Cover photograph by Erwin and Peggy Bauer/Bruce Coleman

Cover and text design by Ann Marie Renzi
Production supervised by Lucille Buonocore, Dawn Reitz, and Marcia Samuels
Photo researched by Mary Schoenthaler
Illustrations by John Balbalis with the assistance of the Wiley Illustration Department
Manuscript edited by Genevieve Scandone under the supervision of Priscilla Todd

Copyright © 1978, 1982, 1986, 1990 by John Wiley & Sons, Inc.

All rights reserved. Published simultaneously in Canada.

Reproduction or translation of any part of
this work beyond that permitted by Sections
107 and 108 of the 1976 United States Copyright
Act without the permission of the copyright
owner is unlawful. Requests for permission
or further information should be addressed to
the Permissions Department, John Wiley & Sons, Inc.

Library of Congress Cataloging in Publication Data:

Holum, John R.
   Fundamentals of general, organic, and biological chemistry /
John R. Holum. — 4th ed.
      p. cm.
   Includes indexes.

   1. Chemistry.   I. Title.
QD31.2.H62   1990
540—dc20   89-14685

Printed in the United States of America
10 9 8 7 6 5 4 3

Preface

The Central Theme Is the Molecular Basis of Life The programs of study for a number of careers have two requirements that this book addresses: that students take just one year of chemistry and that this study include several topics in biochemistry and physiological chemistry. Almost never more than a year of high school chemistry, if that, is a prerequisite for these programs. The college-level course in chemistry to meet these demands thus faces severe constraints, and only the tightest control over which topics to include and at what level makes such a course possible.

This control requires an overarching, organizing theme on which to base the hard decisions about what to include and in what order. Such a theme — the molecular basis of life — has served in the preparation of this fourth edition, just as it has served for over 25 years in previous editions of this book and its shorter companion, *Elements of General and Biological Chemistry.*

Students Like the Theme We believe that no other text remains so consciously faithful to a consistent theme. We also know from years of experience that students are grateful for the careful effort to make the chemistry they study as relevant as possible to their professional needs.

This text provides coverage of all the topics viewed as major by teachers actively involved in teaching chemistry to health care professionals. These topics are listed in the Report of the Committee on Chemical Education for the Health Professions established by the Division of Chemical Education, American Chemical Society. See J. M. Daly and J. L. Sarquis, "A Syllabus for a Two-Semester Chemistry Course for Health Professions," *Journal of Chemical Education,* August 1987, page 699.

We Accept the Career Orientation of Our Students Our students are overwhelmingly career-oriented, and we capitalize on this rather than fight it. The book thus takes abundant opportunities to point out why a topic in question, one that seems utterly remote from a career — atomic and molecular structures come to mind — has to be studied. It isn't difficult for students to see that if life does have a molecular basis, we cannot talk about it until we know what it means to be a molecule. Students study acids, bases, and buffers not as things in themselves but as substances whose interactions profoundly affect their own health.

The First Eleven Chapters Are Devoted to Topics in General Chemistry In terms of pages, slightly under half of this book is about chemical principles, atomic and molecular structure, and types of inorganic substances — particularly acids, bases, salts, buffers, and redox reactions and their associated equilibria.

The early chapters have been changed in five important ways. At the urgings of professors who used previous editions, I have made room for some additional material in the general chemistry chapters. Because not all teachers would want to (or would have the students who could) use the new topics, I have made it quite easy to leave them out. First, there is more on how to write Lewis structures of molecules to make it easier for those who wish to deal later and in more detail with mechanisms of reactions.

A second change in the general chemistry section is the addition of a unit on the Henderson-Hasselbalch equation, with an emphasis on its application to the carbonate buffer in the body. (To help with the solving of log problems, an expanded Appendix A now includes a unit on how the pocket calculator can be used to find logs or antilogs.)

The third change in the general chemistry section is a new but quite short chapter on redox reactions, including reduction potentials and cell potentials. This chapter will help those who wish to teach a Special Topic in Chapter Twenty-Six ("Biochemical Energetics") on the redox potentials of biological equilibria. (All Special Topics, incidentally, now have Review Exercises.) Included in this new chapter are Special Topics on cells and batteries.

The fourth change did not increase the book's length. It merely brought forward the material on multiple bonds and hybrid orbitals from the organic chapters to Chapter Four.

The fifth change actually shortened the book a bit. I have removed the unit on the normalities of acids and bases, so titration problems are now worked strictly as mole and molarity problems. (The concept of an equivalent of an ion with respect to its charge has to be retained, but not equivalent weights of acids and bases.)

The Organic Chemistry Chapters, Twelve through Eighteen, Remain Essentially the Same   The theme of the course continues in these chapters as students are often shown that biochemicals have the functional groups being studied in simple systems. I continue to believe that the soundest pedagogical approach is to introduce these groups, one after the other, as they occur among the *simplest,* monofunctional compounds. Large, complex structures such as glucose or hemoglobin or DNA can be sources of terror rather than wonder when they are introduced too early.

Only the minimum organic chemistry can be included, because the available time has to be very carefully allotted. Thus alkyl halides are barely mentioned because this system occurs nowhere among the biochemicals to be studied later. Very little is done with aromatic chemistry, because the details of aromatic electrophilic substitution reactions will not be exploited later. (What it means to be *aromatic* and some of the characteristic reactions of the benzene ring are studied, because this ring does occur in some amino acids and proteins.)

The emphasis in the chapters on organic chemistry is on the chemical properties of functional groups rather than on strategies for making organic compounds. We emphasize three types of reactants — water, oxidizing agents, and reducing agents — the major types of reactants that abound in all living things.

We do look briefly at certain mechanisms of reactions so that students can see that they are rational, that the reactions don't just happen by the operation of "lassos." However, the elaborate paraphernalia of mechanistic terminology that students who go on in chemistry must learn is here kept to the barest of levels. Thus the chapters on organic chemistry do not constitute a survey of organic chemistry such as might be obtained in even a one-term course. These chapters are wholly devoted to preparing the students using this text for the biochemistry and molecular biology that follows — no more, no less. Professors who actually teach this kind of course overwhelmingly approve this approach. They know full well the constraints of time if any meaningful biochemistry is to be taught.

The Biochemistry Chapters, Nineteen through Twenty-Nine, Make Relevant All That Went Before   Chapters Nineteen through Twenty-Nine focus everything from the earlier chapters onto a study of the principal organic substances found in cells — carbohydrates, lipids, proteins, and nucleic acids — and their chief functions as chemicals when they are in cells.

The changes in the biochemistry chapters consist mostly in bringing the discussions up to date. There are also new Special Topics:

The Greenhouse Effect

Ozone in Smog

Ozone in the Stratosphere

The Omega-3 Fatty Acids and Heart Disease

Genetic Fingerprinting and Crime Prosecution

Redox Potentials of Biological Oxidations

Condensing Esters: A Major C—C Bond-Making Reaction

The discussion of viruses and of genetic engineering have been expanded somewhat.

A Substantial Amount of Rewriting Has Been Done   There are innumerable small changes in the text. The preparation of this edition included a rewriting of the entire book, sentence by sentence, in an effort to improve its clarity and readability for students. Of course, not every sentence was changed, but every sentence was scrutinized to see whether a worthwhile change could be made.

Just as in this Preface, a secondary heading is no longer merely a title, but rather a descriptive sentence concerning the subtopic. Students find this very helpful.

The Design of This Edition Is Like That of the Third Edition   Margin comments are used sometimes as reminders, sometimes to restate a point, and sometimes to give data or structures.

There are **Special Topics** on matters of current interest, and a list is provided following the Table of Contents. One new Special Topic in the general chemistry chapters is on radon as an air pollutant.

Key terms are highlighted in boldface at those places where they are defined and then discussed. At the end of the book, there is a complete glossary of all these terms. The accompanying *Study Guide* has separate glossaries for each chapter.

Each chapter has a **Summary** which uses the key terms in a narrative survey. Each main section of each chapter also begins with a **summary statement** that announces what is coming and that serves during test review periods to highlight the major topics.

A large number of **Examples** appear throughout the book, and nearly all are immediately followed by **Practice Exercises**. At the end of each chapter is a large set of **Review Exercises** grouped under descriptive headings. (As we have said, there are Review Exercises now for all Special Topics, too.) The **factor-label** method is used for nearly all computations. The answers to all Practice Exercises and to selected Review Exercises are given in Appendix D.

The **Appendix on Mathematical Concepts** has been enlarged, as we said, to provide a study of how to use the pocket calculator to work log problems.

Continuing a long tradition, we have tried to make the **Index** the most thorough, most cross-referenced index in any text of this type.

John R. Holum
Augsburg College

Acknowledgments

Over the many years of preparing instructional materials, my wife Mary and our daughters, Liz, Ann, and Kathryn, have been my strongest supporters. I am pleased to say "thank you" to them for being such nice people.

Here at Augsburg College, I have enjoyed consistently strong support from Dr. Earl Alton, Chemistry Department Chair, Dr. Ryan LaHurd, the Academic Dean, and Dr. Charles S. Anderson, President. My freedom to write stems in no small measure from the freedom that these caring people have accorded me. I greatly appreciate the helpful comments that Professor Arlin Gyberg of our Chemistry Department makes from time to time.

Nice people abound at John Wiley & Sons, too. They do good work. I think particularly of the support of my Executive Editor, Dennis Sawicki. I also wish to thank his Administrative Assistant, Jo Ann Spear.

Chief illustrator John Balbalis has been skillful, artistic, and faithful in handling art work for many years. Now that we have gone to four colors, I asked Mr. Balbalis to prepare an explanation of how the consistent use of color has pedagogical power. You will find what he wrote on page xi.

Picture editor Mary Schoenthaler cheerfully solved problems and made this facet of production worry-free. The designer, Ann Marie Renzi, rose to the challenge of using added color to heighten student interest and make the book much more user-friendly. Copy editor Genevieve Scandone and supervising editor Priscilla Todd have been souls of diplomacy as they have smoothed out stylistic and grammatical problems. Sandra Olmsted provided very valuable assistance at the proofreading stage, but I must exempt her from all responsibility for any errors that remain. Such errors are mine, and I would truly appreciate your telling me about them. Finally, my thanks to Lucille Buonocore, Dawn Reitz, and Marcia Samuels, supervisors of production, who managed with skill and patience the interfacing of all these people with the compositing and printing work.

All in all, John Wiley & Sons always assembles an impressive team, and I count myself to be fortunate indeed for having become associated with this publisher.

The professional critiques of teachers are part of the process of preparing a manuscript. I am pleased to acknowledge and to thank the following people for their work.

Carlo Alfare
Mercer County Community College

Richard Beitzel
Bemidji State University

Herman DeHaas
University of Maine

Stanley Grenda
University of Nevada at Las Vegas

Arlin Gyberg
Augsburg College

G. Olof Larson
Ferris State University

Marvin Lofquist
Ferris State University

Robert G. Martinek, Manager
Chicago Laboratory
Illinois Department of Public Health

Kevin Mayo
Temple University

Robert Nelson
Georgia Southern College

Sandra Olmsted
Augsburg College

Louis Perlgut
California State University, Long Beach

Suzanne Rottman
The University of Maryland

James Schreck
University of Northern Colorado

Michael Strauss
University of Vermont

Neal Thorpe
Augsburg College

Harry Ungar
Cabrillo College

J.R.H.

SUPPLEMENTARY MATERIALS FOR STUDENTS AND TEACHERS

The complete package of supplements that are available to help students study and teachers to plan the course and operate the associated laboratory work includes the following.

Laboratory Manual for Fundamentals of General, Organic, and Biological Chemistry, fourth edition. This revision has been prepared by Professor Sandra Olmsted. An instructor's manual is a section in the general Teachers' Manual described below.

Study Guide for Fundamentals of General, Organic, and Biological Chemistry, fourth edition. This softcover book contains chapter objectives, chapter glossaries, additional worked examples and exercises, sample examinations for each chapter, and the answers to Review Exercises.

Teachers' Manual for Fundamentals of General, Organic, and Biological Chemistry, fourth edition. This softcover supplement is available to teachers, and it contains all the usual services for *both the text and the laboratory manual*. The lists of books and selected readings that formerly appeared in the text are now gathered in one place in the Teachers' Manual.

Test Bank. Available in both hard copy and software (Macintosh® and IBM® compatible) versions, this carefully prepared test resource contains 1000 questions in all.

Transparencies. Instructors who adopt this book may obtain from Wiley, without charge, a set of transparencies that duplicate key illustrations from the text.

J.R.H.

THE PEDAGOGICAL USE OF COLOR IN THE ILLUSTRATIONS

Color in its fullest range has been made an integral part of the illustrations with this edition. It is used to focus attention on key aspects of a figure and to identify and relate items appearing within a variety of different contexts. Conventional colors have been assigned to the chemical elements, for instance, and are associated with them in representations of individual atoms or as components of three-dimensional ball-and-stick and space-filling molecular models, as well as in miscellaneous schematic forms. Orbital theory is visually heightened with a unique color for each of the *s, p,* and *sp* orbital types. The many and varied chart categories throughout the book are organized and recognized by different colors. Chemical concepts and their related physical structures at the organic chemistry, biochemical, and anatomical levels are clarified with appropriate colors in their relevant parts. Throughout the illustration program the basic consideration has been to use color as a means of organizing information and facilitating its communication to the student.

John Balbalis

Contents

Index to Special Topics

Goals, Methods, and Measurements

What these trumpeter swans know by instinct we know by intellect: life goes along better when we work with nature, not against her. The more we know about life at its molecular level, the more intelligently are we able to work with nature. This book is about the molecular basis of life.

1.1 CHEMISTRY AND THE MOLECULAR BASIS OF LIFE

The theme of this book is the molecular basis of life.

Centuries ago, people surely noticed that many *different* animals drank at the same water holes, breathed the same air, ate the same kinds of food, and enjoyed the same salt licks. Ancient farmers knew that the droppings of animals nourished plants, and that animals prospered by eating plants. Some animals could eat weaker animals and grow.

Evidently, at some deep level of existence, living things can exchange parts. These parts are not organs and tissues but much smaller things, extremely tiny particles called molecules made of even smaller particles called atoms. All of life, whether plant or animal, has a *molecular* basis, and chemistry has been the route to its discovery. **Chemistry** is the study of that part of nature that bears on substances, their compositions and structures, and their abilities to be changed into other substances. There are so many different substances that we have to have a plan of study.

■ Well over 6 million chemical substances are known.

Our Strategy Life at the molecular level involves molecules and chemical reactions that are often complicated. The symbols we use for them, however, are actually less complex than many symbol systems you have already mastered. Anyone who has never seen a map, for example, would no doubt be dismayed, but you learned how to read and understand dozens of maps by mastering just a few map symbols. Our symbols for molecules are like maps because the same pieces of molecules, like molecular "map signs," occur over and over again. It will be a good idea, therefore, before we study some of the most complicated molecules in nature (Chapters 19 through 29), to learn these "signs" among simpler substances. Our chapters on organic compounds (Chapters 11 through 18) do this.

As we said earlier, molecules are made of atoms. It really isn't possible to understand molecules without first learning about atoms and how their own (even tinier) parts get reorganized into molecules. This study occurs mainly in the first third of the book, together with essential background about a variety of substances such as acids, bases, salts, and solutions. All these studies rest on experimental evidence that involved taking measurements, so many of our topics rely on measured quantities. In this chapter we'll learn about some of the measurements that have been useful.

■ The atoms of all the kinds of matter are made of varying combinations of just three extremely tiny particles: electrons, protons, and neutrons.

Our plan, therefore, is to use Chapters 1 through 10 to study some of the basic principles that underlie all of chemistry. Then, in Chapters 11 through 18, we will learn the molecular "map signs" of the major substances in living systems. In Chapters 19 through 29 we'll apply all this to a broad study of how nature uses substances to sustain living processes. Expect to learn a great deal about how nature works, and be prepared to be surprised at how enjoyable this can be. Expect also to discover that chemistry stands in service to a large number of careers and professions besides research in chemistry: agriculture, forestry, home economics, engineering, medicine, nursing, dentistry, veterinary science, dietetics, nutrition, inhalation therapy, physical therapy, public health, science education, pharmacy, clinical lab work, crime lab work, consumer products safety, and many others. Little wonder that chemistry is often referred to as the *central science*. It's at the heart of understanding so many aspects of nature, and knowledge of it is at the heart of so many ways in which people can help people and enjoy doing it.

1.2 FACTS, HYPOTHESES, AND THEORIES IN SCIENCE

Scientific theories speak to one general question, "How does nature work?"

One of the most common activities of scientists is the gathering of information and facts by observing nature. Some facts are reproducible and some aren't. Both kinds are important in science. A *reproducible fact* is one that can be observed over and over by independent observers. It might be an event such as a chemical reaction that can be carried out again and again, or it might be some property of a substance, like its temperature, that anyone can check as often as they please.

■ In science, the most reliable facts are those that can be observed in repeated observations or measurements.

Just because a fact isn't reproducible does not necessarily make it unimportant or untrue. We cannot rerun yesterday just to check weather measurements, for example. But if we are confident about our instruments and our ability to keep records, yesterday's weather maps can be trusted.

Hypotheses and Theories Are Used to Explain Facts   Scientists are forever interested in underlying causes. "How does nature work?" "What must be true about what we cannot see in nature to account for what we see?" Facts and observations, therefore, are seldom interesting all by themselves. They are valued, instead, as building blocks for *hypotheses.*

■ The aim in testing a hypothesis is not to prove the hypothesis but to discover the truth about it.

A **hypothesis** is a conjecture that explains a set of facts in terms of a common cause. A hypothesis also serves as the basis for designing additional tests or experiments that should disclose the truth about the hypothesis. Is it right or wrong? A mechanic might listen to a funny noise in your car engine, do some tests, and conclude — make a hypothesis — that a spark plug is defective. This suggests a test: replace the plug and see whether the sound disappears. In medicine, every preliminary diagnosis is a hypothesis based on observed or reported facts. A preliminary diagnosis always suggests what new information should be sought, like further lab tests or X rays.

Sometimes hypotheses are considered on a large scale. In the history of nutrition science, for example, a number of quite different ailments simply did not fit the notion that *all* diseases are caused by germs. In searching for other causes, trace substances in certain foods were discovered that were vital to health, and the vitamin theory developed. After much research, this theory became so solidly based on experiments and tests that everybody now regards it as simply another fact, that we need various vitamins to be healthy. What really clinched this promotion from theory to fact was *chemical* research, the discoveries of the chemical structures of the vitamins and how they worked at the molecular level of life. When we know the *chemistry* of an illness we finally know what it is.

A theory differs in scope from a hypothesis. A **theory** is an explanation for a large number of facts, observations, and hypotheses in terms of one or a few basic assumptions of what the world is like. One of the broadest, grandest theories about how our world works is that all matter is made of tiny, invisible particles called atoms. We'll get into this theory in the next chapter.

The Scientific Method Bases Conclusions on Evidence   Often in the history of science, isolated facts and human reason have been used to construct testable hypotheses and, then theories, and it is popular now to call this approach to questions the **scientific method.** This method, however, is as much an attitude of mind as a procedure, an attitude of trying as hard as possible to let observations and facts control reasoning. Reason and logic are wondrous tools for constructing hypotheses and theories. Reason and logic might strongly suggest what is true, but neither discovers facts. Experience, observations, and experiments do that.

■ It was once perfectly logical to believe that the earth does not move and that the sun moves around it.

The scientific method is not some mechanical, cut-and-dried operation applied in a uniformly orderly way to problems. Chance discoveries, hunches, lucky guesses, false leads, and wishful thinking are found repeatedly in the history of science along with many wrong theories, beautifully logical in their day but now discarded. There is seldom anything tidy about a scientific study, but underlying it will be the will to base conclusions — whether hypotheses or grand theories — on observations, measurements, and facts.

In any scientific study, asking the right question of nature is critical all in itself. Asking "*How* does nature work?" leads, for example, to more progress in understanding nature than asking "*Why* does nature work?" If we ask, for example, "*Why* do we get sick?" instead of "*How* do we get sick?" we can get bogged down in speculations that people have never resolved to everyone's satisfaction. Historically, answers to "*Why* do we get sick?" have ranged widely — "Because of evil spirits," for example, or "Because of sin," or "Because an enemy put a hex on me." Not that asking "Why?" isn't important to us, but the value of the "*How?*" question is that it gets at *mechanism.* Knowing the physical or chemical *mechanisms* of various illnesses doesn't answer all serious and important questions, but it has certainly helped to reduce pain and suffering in the world and to raise living standards. Science cannot claim to address all important questions, but it has been extremely successful with those that ask "How?" Scientists, of course, still use the language of "Why?" After all, both "Why?" and "How?" are ways of asking "What causes . . . ?" But almost always "Why?" means "How?" in science.

To know and describe *how* nature works, we use the results of measurements. This is why we have to learn about the business of measurements very early in our study.

1.3 PROPERTIES AND PHYSICAL QUANTITIES

A physical property differs from a chemical property by being observable without changing a substance into a different substance.

A **property** is any characteristic of something that we can use to identify and recognize it when we see it again. The observations of some properties, however, change an object or a sample of a substance into something else. We can measure, for example, how much gasoline it takes to drive a car 100 miles, but this measurement uses up the gasoline. As it burns it changes into water and carbon dioxide (the fizz in soda pop). A property that, when observed, causes a substance to change into new substances is called a **chemical property,** and what is being observed is called a **chemical reaction.** A chemical property of iron, for example, is that it rusts in moist air; it changes slowly into a reddish, powdery substance, iron oxide, quite unlike metallic iron. **Chemistry** is the study of these kinds of changes in substances, how they occur, and how atoms become reorganized as they happen.

Properties such as color, height, or weight that can be observed without changing the object into something different are called **physical properties.** We usually rely on such properties to recognize and name things. For example, some physical properties of liquid water are that it is colorless and odorless; that it dissolves sugar and table salt but not butter; that it makes a thermometer read 100 °C (212 °F) when it boils (at sea level); and that if it is mixed with gasoline it will sink, not float. If you were handed a glass containing a liquid having these properties, your initial hypothesis undoubtedly would be that it is water. Think of how often each day you recognize things (and people) by simply observing physical properties.

Notice how much a description of water's properties depends on human senses, our abilities to see, taste, feel, and to sense hotness or coldness. Our senses, however, are limited, so inventors have developed instruments that extend the senses and make possible finer and sharper observations. These devices are equipped with scales or readout panels, and the data we obtain by using them are called *physical quantities.*

A **physical quantity** is a property to which we can assign both a numerical value *and a unit.* Your own height is a simple example. If it is, say, 5.5 feet, its numerical value, 5.5, and its unit, feet, together tell us at a glance how much greater your height is than an agreed-upon reference of height, the foot.

The unit in a physical quantity is just as important as the number. If you said that your height is "two," people would ask, "Two what?" If you said "two yards," they would know what you meant (provided they knew what a yard is). (But they might ask, "*Exactly* two yards?") This example shows that we can't describe a physical property by a physical quantity without giving both a number and a unit.

■   2 = a number
2 yards = a physical quantity

$$\text{Physical quantity} = \text{number} \times \text{unit}$$

Physical Quantities Are Obtained By Measurements   A **measurement,** is an operation by which we compare an unknown physical quantity with one that is known. Maybe, as you were growing up, someone measured your height by comparing it with how many sticks, perhaps one-foot rulers, it took to equal your height. Usually the number of sticks did not match your height exactly, so fractions of sticks called inches (each with their own fractions) were also used. It's probably quite obvious to you by now that somebody has decided what an inch, a foot, or a yard is and that the rest of us have agreed to these definitions. And that's just what they are, definitions. We'll learn those that are the most useful in chemistry in the next section.

1.4 UNITS AND STANDARDS OF MEASUREMENT—THE INTERNATIONAL SYSTEM OF UNITS

The most fundamental quantities of measurement are called base quantities, and each has an official standard of reference for one unit.

Mass, Length, Time, and Temperature Degree Are Base Quantities   The most fundamental measurements in chemistry are those of mass, volume, temperature, time, and quantity of chemical substance.

Mass is the measure of the inertia of an object. Anything said to have a lot of inertia such as a train engine, a massive boulder, or an ocean liner is very hard to get into motion, or if it is in motion, it is difficult to slow it down or make it change course. It is this inherent resistance to any kind of change in motion that we call **inertia,** and *mass* is our way of describing inertia quantitatively. A large inertia means a large *mass*.

■ *Quantitative* describes something expressible by a number and a unit.

A large mass doesn't always mean a large *weight.* Your mass does not depend on where you are in the universe, but your weight does. Your weight is a measure of the gravitational force of attraction that the earth makes on your body. This gravitational force is less on the moon, which is a smaller object than the earth—about one-sixth less. But the mass of an astronaut, the fundamental resistance to any change in motion, is the same on the moon as on the earth. When we use a laboratory balance to *weigh* something, we are actually measuring mass because we are comparing two weights *at the same place on the earth* and, therefore, under the same gravitational influence. One weight is the quantity being measured, and the other is a "weight" (or set of weights) built into the weighing balance. Although we commonly call the result of the measurement a "weight," we'd more properly call it the *mass* of the object or the sample. (We'll generally speak of masses, not weights, in this book.)

Large inertia goes with large mass.

A traditional two-pan balance showing a small container on the left pan and some weights on the right pan.

Volume of cube = $(l)^3$

The **volume** of an object is the space it occupies, and space is described by means of a more basic physical quantity, length. The volume of a cube, for example, is the product of (length) $\times$ (length) $\times$ (length), or (length)^3. **Length** is a physical quantity that describes how far an object extends in some direction, or it is the distance between two points.

A fundamental quantity such as mass or length is called a **base quantity** and any other quantity such as volume that can be described in terms of a base quantity is called a **derived quantity.**

Another base quantity in science is **time** — our measure of how long events last. We need this quantity to describe how rapidly the heart beats, for example, or how fast some chemical reaction occurs.

Still another important physical quantity is **temperature degree,** which we use to describe the hotness or coldness of an object.

All these base quantities are necessary to all sciences, but chemistry has a special base quantity called the *mole* that describes a certain amount of a chemical substance. It consists of a particular (and very large) *number* of tiny particles without regard to their masses or volumes. We will not study this base quantity further until we know more about these particles.

Every Base Quantity Has a Reference Standard of Measurement   To measure and report an object's mass, its temperature, or any of its other base or derived physical quantities, we obviously need some units and some references. By international treaties among the countries of the world, the reference units and standards are decided by a diplomatic organization called the General Conference of Weights and Measures, headquartered in Sèvres, a suburb of Paris, France. The General Conference has defined a unit called a **base unit** for each of seven base quantities, but we need units only for the five that we have already mentioned: mass, length, time, temperature, and mole. We also need some units for the derived quantities, for example, for volume, density, pressure, and heat. The standards and definitions of base and derived quantities and units together make up what is now known as the **International System of Units** or the **SI** (after the French name, *Système Internationale d'Unités*).

■ The other two SI base quantities are electric current and luminous intensity. Their base units are called the ampere and the candela, respectively.

Each base unit is defined in terms of a **reference standard,** a physical description or embodiment of the base unit. Long ago, the reference (such as it was) for the *inch* was "three barleycorns, round and dry, laid end to end." Obviously, which three barleycorns were picked had a bearing on values of length under this "system." And if the barley corns got wet, they sprouted. You can see that a reference standard ought to have certain properties if it is to serve the needs of all countries. It should be entirely free of such risks as corrosion, fire, war, theft, or plain skulduggery, and it should be accessible at any time to scientists in any country. The improvement that the SI represents over its predecessor, the *metric system,* is not so much in base units as in their reference standards.

The SI base unit of length is called the **meter,** abbreviated **m,** and its reference standard is called the *standard meter.* Until 1960, the standard meter was the distance separating two thin scratches on a bar of platinum–iridium alloy stored in an underground vault in Sèvres. This bar, of course, could have been lost or stolen, so the new reference for the meter is based on a property of light, something available *everywhere,* in all countries, and that obviously can't be lost or damaged. This change in reference didn't change the actual length of the meter, it only changed its official reference.[1]

■ An alloy is a mixture of two or more metals made by stirring them together in their molten states.

In the United States, older units are now legally defined in terms of the meter. For example the yard (yd), roughly nine-tenths of a meter, is defined as 0.9144 m (exactly). The foot (ft), roughly three-tenths of a meter is defined as 0.3048 m (exactly).

In chemistry, the meter is usually too long for convenience, and submultiples are often used, particularly the **centimeter,** or **cm,** and the **millimeter,** or **mm.** Expressed mathematically, these are defined as follows.

[1] The SI now defines the standard meter as how far light will travel in 1/299,792,458 of a second. It is thus based on the speed of light as measured by an "atomic clock."

Figure 1.1
The SI standard kilogram mass. Shown here is the U.S. copy of the reference standard kept at the International Bureau of Weights and Measures in France. The U.S. copy is at the National Bureau of Standards in Washington, D.C. It is made out of a very corrosion-resistant alloy of platinum and iridium.

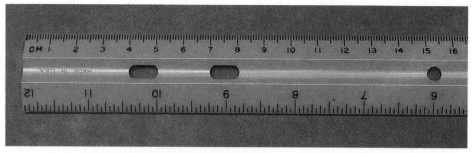

Common ruler marked in inches and centimeters. Notice that there are ten 1-millimeter spaces marked between the centimeter divisions.

TABLE 1.1   Some Common Measures of Length[a]

SI	U.S. Customary
1 kilometer (km) = **1000** meters (m) 1 meter = **100** centimeters (cm) 1 centimeter = **10** millimeters (mm)	1 mile (mi) = **5280** feet (ft) = **1760** yards (yd) 1 yard = **3** feet (ft) 1 foot = **12** inches (in.)

1 meter = 39.37 inches
          = 3.280 feet
          = 1.093 yards
	1 foot = 30.48 centimeters
	          = 0.3048 meter
	1 inch = **2.54** centimeters

[a] Numbers in boldface are exact.

$$1 \text{ m} = 100 \text{ cm} \quad \text{or} \quad 1 \text{ cm} = 0.01 \text{ m}$$
$$1 \text{ m} = 1000 \text{ mm} \quad \text{or} \quad 1 \text{ mm} = 0.001 \text{ m}$$
$$1 \text{ cm} = 10 \text{ mm} \quad \text{or} \quad 1 \text{ mm} = 0.1 \text{ cm}$$

Notice that the subunits are in fractions based on 10. The millimeter, for example, is one-tenth of a centimeter. As we'll often see, this makes many calculations much easier than they were under older systems (where, for example, the inch was one-twelfth of a foot, and the foot was one-third of a yard).

The inch (in.) is about two and a half centimeters; more exactly,

$$1 \text{ in.} = 2.54 \text{ cm} \quad \text{(exactly)}$$

Paper clip — 0.4 g

Penny — 3.1 g

■ Except when noted otherwise, the avoirdupois (advp) system of masses in Table 1.2 is used for common mass units in all calculations in this text.

Table 1.1 gives several important relationships between various units of length.

The SI base unit of mass is named the **kilogram,** abbreviated **kg,** and its reference is named the *standard kilogram mass*. This is a cylindrical block of platinum–iridium alloy housed at Sèvres under the most noncorrosive conditions possible (Figure 1.1). This is the only SI reference that could still be lost or stolen, but no alternative has yet been devised. Duplicates made as much like the original as possible are stored in other countries. One kilogram has a mass roughly equal to 2.2 pounds, and Table 1.2 gives a number of useful relationships among various units of mass, including some old apothecaries' units.

The most often used units of mass in chemistry are the kilogram, the **gram (g),** the **milligram (mg),** and the **microgram (μg).** These are defined as follows.

$$1 \text{ kg} = 1000 \text{ g} \quad \text{or} \quad 1 \text{ g} = 0.001 \text{ kg}$$
$$1 \text{ g} = 1000 \text{ mg} \quad \text{or} \quad 1 \text{ mg} = 0.001 \text{ g}$$
$$1 \text{ mg} = 1000 \text{ μg} \quad \text{or} \quad 1 \text{ μg} = 0.001 \text{ mg}$$

Lab experiments in chemistry usually involve grams or milligrams of substance.

■ One cubic meter holds a little over 250 gallons.

The SI unit of volume, one of the important derived units, is the cubic meter, m^3, but this is much too large for convenience in chemistry. An older unit, the **liter,** abbreviated **L,** is accepted as a *unit of convenience*. The liter occupies a volume of 0.001 m^3 (exactly), and one

1 kg of butter

One drop of water is about 60 mg.

TABLE 1.2 Some Common Measures of Mass[a]

SI

1 kilogram (kg) = **1000** grams (g)
1 gram = **1000** milligrams (mg)
1 milligram = **1000** micrograms (μg, γ, or mcg)[b]

U.S. Customary (avoirdupois)[c]

1 short ton = **2000** pounds (lb avdp)
1 pound = **16** ounces (oz avdp)
1 ounce = **16** drams (dr avdp)
1 dram = 437.5 grains (grain)[d]

Apothecaries'

1 pound (lb ap) = **12** ounces (oz ap, or ℥) = **5760** grains
1 ounce = **8** drams (dr ap, or ℨ) = **480** grains
1 dram = **60** grains

Other Relationships

1 kilogram = 2.205 lb avdp	= 2.679 lb ap	= 15,432 grains
= 35.27 oz avdp	= 32.15 oz ap	
1 lb avdp = 453.6 grams	1 lb ap = 373.2 grams	
1 oz avdp = 28.35 grams	1 oz ap = 31.10 grams	
1 grain = 0.0648 gram	= 64.8 milligrams	
1 gram = 15.43 grains	1 dr ap = 3.887 grams	

[a] Numbers in boldface are exact.

[b] The microgram is sometimes called a *gamma* in medicine and biology.

[c] These are the common units in the United States, not the apothecaries' units.

[d] The National Bureau of Standards has adopted no symbol for *grain*. Pharmacists usually symbolize it by *gr*. There is another apothecaries' weight called the *scruple* (20 grains), but it is no longer listed in the *U.S. Pharmacopoeia*.

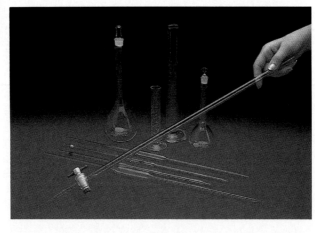

Figure 1.2
Some apparatus used to measure liquid volumes. In the back are two volumetric flasks flanking two graduated cylinders. Lying on the surface are four volumetric pipets, and the hand holds a buret.

liter is almost the same as one liquid quart; 1 quart (qt) = 0.946 L. Even the liter is often too large for convenience in chemistry, and two submultiples are used, the **milliliter (mL)** and the **microliter (μL)**. These are related as follows:

$$1 \text{ L} = 1000 \text{ mL} \quad \text{or} \quad 1 \text{ mL} = 0.001 \text{ L}$$
$$1 \text{ mL} = 1000 \text{ } \mu\text{L} \quad \text{or} \quad 1 \text{ } \mu\text{L} = 0.001 \text{ mL}$$

In routine chemistry work, the milliliter is by far the most common unit you will encounter. Table 1.3 gives several other relationships among units of volume. Figure 1.2 shows apparatus used to measure volumes in the lab.

The SI unit of time is called the **second**, abbreviated **s**. The SI *definition*, however, involves complexities of atomic physics that are entirely beyond our needs. Fortunately, the

TABLE 1.3 Some Common Measures of Liquid Volume[a]

SI	
1 cubic meter (m^3) =	**1000** liters (L)
1 liter	= **1000** milliliters (mL)
1 milliliter	= **1000** microliters (μL, λ, or lambda)
U.S. Customary and Apothecaries'	
1 gallon (gal)	= **4** liquid quarts (liq qt)
1 liquid quart	= **2** liquid pints (liq pt)
1 liquid pint	= **16** liquid ounces (liq oz) (fluidounce, f℥, fl oz, in the apothecaries' system)
1 liquid ounce	= **8** fluidrams (f℈) = **480** minims (♏)
1 fluidram	= **60** minims (♏)
Other Relationships	
1 cubic meter	= 264.2 gallons
1 liter	= 1.057 liquid quarts = 2.113 liquid pints
	= 33.81 liquid ounces
1 milliliter	= 16.23 minims
1 liquid ounce	= 29.57 milliliters
1 liquid quart	= 946.4 milliliters
1 fluidram	= 3.696 milliliters
Miscellaneous Approximate Equivalents (unofficial)	
1 liquid pint	= 2 cups = 4 gills
1 cup	= 16 tablespoonfuls = 250 mL
1 tablespoon	= 3 teaspoonfuls = 15 mL
1 teaspoonful	= 5 mL

[a] The apothecaries' system uses the U.S. Customary system for liquid measures. Numbers in boldface are exact.

duration of the SI second is the same as before, for essentially all purposes. The second is 1/18,400 of a mean solar day. Decimal-based multiples and submultiples of the second are used in science, but so are such deeply entrenched old units as minute, hour, day, week, month, and year.

The SI unit for degree of temperature is called the **kelvin, K.** (Be sure to notice that the abbreviation is K, not °K.) This degree used to be called the **degree Celsius (°C),** and even earlier the **degree centigrade** (also °C). Then it was defined as 1/100 the interval between the freezing point of water (named 0 °C) and the boiling point of water (named 100 °C). The most extreme coldness possible is −273.15 °C, and this is named 0 K on the Kelvin scale. The kelvin is the name of the degree on this scale, and it is identical with the Celsius degree. Only the *numbers* assigned to points on the scale differ. See Figure 1.3, where the scales are compared.

Because 0 K corresponds to −273.15 °C, we have the following simple relationships between kelvins and degrees Celsius (where we follow common practice of rounding 273.15 to 273).

$$°C = K − 273$$

or

$$K = °C + 273$$

■ The *kelvin* is named after William Thomson, Baron Kelvin of Largs (1842–1907), a British scientist.

PRACTICE EXERCISE 1 Normal body temperature is 37 °C. What is this in kelvins?

The Kelvin scale is used in chemistry mostly to describe temperatures of gases. The Celsius scale is more popular for most other uses. (It is even rapidly supplanting the old, familiar Fahrenheit scale in medicine.) The **degree Fahrenheit (°F)** is five-ninths the size of the degree Celsius. To convert a Celsius temperature, t_C, to a Fahrenheit temperature, t_F, we can use either of the following equations:

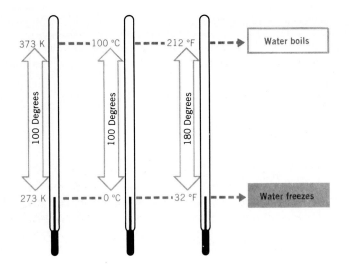

Figure 1.3
Relationships between the Kelvin, Celsius, and Fahrenheit scales of temperature.

TABLE 1.4 Some Common Temperature Readings in °C and °F

	°F	°C
Room temperature	68	20
Very cold day	−20	−29
Very hot day	100	38
Normal body temperature	98.6	37
Hottest temperature the hands can stand	120	49

$$t_C = \frac{5 \ °C}{9 \ °F} (t_F - 32 \ °F)$$

$$t_F = \frac{9 \ °F}{5 \ °C} \times t_C + 32 \ °F$$

Table 1.4 gives some common temperatures in both °C and °F.

1.5 SCIENTIFIC NOTATION

Scientific notation expresses very large or very small numbers in exponential forms to make comparisons and calculations easier.

The typical human red blood cell has a diameter of 0.000008 m. Whether we want to write it, say it, or remember it, 0.000008 m is an awkward number, and to make life easier scientists have developed a method called **scientific notation** for recording very small or very large numbers. In scientific notation (sometimes called exponential notation), a number is written as the product of two numbers. The first is a decimal number with a value usually between 1 and 10, although sometimes a wider range is used. Following this number is a times (×) sign and then the number 10 with an exponent or power. For example, we can write the number 4000 as follows.

■ Appendix A has a review of exponential numbers.

$$4000 = 4 \times 1000 = 4 \times 10 \times 10 \times 10$$
$$= 4 \times 10^3$$

■ When the decimal point is omitted, we assume that it is after the last digit in the number.

Notice that the exponent 3 is the number of places to the left that we have to move the decimal point in 4000 to get to 4, which is a number in the desirable range.

$$4 \underset{3 \quad 2 \quad 1}{\underbrace{0 \ 0 \ 0}}$$

$$4 \underset{4 \quad 3 \quad 2 \quad 1}{\underbrace{2 \ 1 \ 9 \ 5}}.$$

If our large number is 42,195, the number of meters in a marathon distance, we can rewrite it as follows after figuring out that we have to move the decimal point four places to the left to get a decimal number between 1 and 10.

$$42{,}195 \ m = 4.2195 \times 10^4 \ m$$

In rewriting numbers smaller than 1 in scientific notation, we have to move the decimal point to the *right* to get a number in the acceptable range of 1 to 10. This number of moves is the value of the *negative* exponent of 10. For example, we can rewrite 0.000008 as

1 2 3 4 5 6

$$0.000008 = 8 \times 10^{-6}$$

You should not continue until you are satisfied that you can change large or small numbers into scientific notation. For practice, do the following exercises.

PRACTICE EXERCISE 2

Express each number in scientific notation. Let the decimal part be a number between 1 and 10.

(a) 545,000,000   (b) 5,670,000,000,000   (c) 6454
(d) 25   (e) 0.0000398   (f) 0.00426
(g) 0.168   (h) 0.00000000000987 (See footnote 2.)

Prefixes to the Names of SI Base Units Are Used To Specify Fractions or Multiples of These Units   If we rewrite 3000 m as 3×10^3 m and try to pronounce the result, we have to say "three times ten to the third meters." There's nothing wrong with this, but it's clumsy. This is why the SI has names for several exponential expressions — not independent names but prefixes that can be attached to the name of any unit. For example, 10^3 has been assigned a prefix name of *kilo-*, abbreviated *k-*. Thus 1000 or 10^3 meters can be called 1 kilometer. Abbreviated, this becomes 10^3 m = 1 km.

With just a few exceptions, the prefixes set by the SI go with exponentials in which the power is 3, 6, 9, 12, 15, and 18 or with -3, -6, -9, -12, -15, and -18. These are all divisible by 3. Table 1.5 has a list of the SI prefixes and their symbols. Those given in boldface are so often encountered in chemistry that they should be learned now.

---

[2] Some of the numbers in this exercise illustrate a small problem that the SI is trying to get all scientists to handle in a uniform way. In part (h), for example, you might have gotten a bit dizzy trying to count closely spaced zeros. The SI recommends — and most European scientists have accepted the suggestion — that in numbers having four or more digits, the digits be grouped in threes separated by thin spaces. For large numbers, just omit the commas. Thus 545,000,000 would be written as 545 000 000. The number 0.00000000000987 becomes 0.000 000 000 009 87. It will be a while before you see this usage very often in the United States, but when you do you'll now know what it means. Incidentally, European scientists use a comma instead of a period to locate the decimal point. You might see this yourself soon when you first weigh anything in the lab. If the weighing balance was made in Europe, a reading such as 1,045 g means 1.045 g.

TABLE 1.5 SI Prefixes for Multiples and Submultiples of Base Units[a]

	Prefix	Symbol
$1\ 000\ 000\ 000\ 000\ 000\ 000 = 10^{18}$	exa	E
$1\ 000\ 000\ 000\ 000\ 000 = 10^{15}$	peta	P
$1\ 000\ 000\ 000\ 000 = 10^{12}$	tera	T
$1\ 000\ 000\ 000 = 10^{9}$	giga	G
$1\ 000\ 000 = 10^{6}$	**mega**	**M**
$1\ 000 = 10^{3}$	**kilo**	**k**
$100 = 10^{2}$	hecto	h
$10 = 10^{1}$	deka	da
$0.1 = 10^{-1}$	**deci**	**d**
$0.01 = 10^{-2}$	**centi**	**c**
$0.001 = 10^{-3}$	**milli**	**m**
$0.000\ 001 = 10^{-6}$	**micro**	**μ**
$0.000\ 000\ 001 = 10^{-9}$	nano	n
$0.000\ 000\ 000\ 001 = 10^{-12}$	pico	p
$0.000\ 000\ 000\ 000\ 001 = 10^{-15}$	femto	f
$0.000\ 000\ 000\ 000\ 000\ 001 = 10^{-18}$	atto	a

[a] The most commonly used prefixes and their symbols are in boldface. Thin spaces instead of commas are used to separate groups of three zeros to illustrate the format being urged by the SI (but not yet widely adopted in the United States).

■ $1 \text{ dL} = 1 \times 10^{-1} \text{ L} = 1/10$ liter
But $1/10$ liter $= 100$ mL
Therefore,

$1 \text{ dL} = 100 \text{ mL}$

Notice that there are four prefixes that do not go with powers divisible by 3. The SI hopes their usage will gradually fade away, but this hasn't happened yet. The two in boldface have to be learned. However, *centi* is used almost entirely in just one physical quantity, the centimeter. *Deci* is limited almost completely to another physical quantity, the deciliter (100 mL or $\frac{1}{10}$ L), and you won't see it often in strictly chemical situations. (Clinical chemists often use it because it saves space on clinical report sheets to abbreviate 100 mL to just dL.)

To take advantage of the SI prefixes, we sometimes have to modify a rule used in converting a large or small number into scientific notation. The goal in this conversion will now be to get the exponential part of the number to match one with an SI prefix even if the decimal part of the number isn't between 1 and 10. For example, we know that the number 545,000 can be rewritten as 5.45×10^5, but 5 isn't divisible by 3, and there isn't an SI prefix to go with 10^5. If we counted 6 spaces to the left, however, we could use 10^6 as the exponential part.

■ We usually put a zero in front of a decimal point in numbers that are less than 1, such as in 0.545. This zero just helps us remember the decimal point, and it doesn't count as a significant figure.

$$5\overset{\curvearrowleft}{\,}4\overset{\curvearrowleft}{\,}5\overset{\curvearrowleft}{\,}0\overset{\curvearrowleft}{\,}0\overset{\curvearrowleft}{\,}0\overset{\curvearrowleft}{\,}0 = 0.545 \times 10^6$$
$$654321$$

Now we could rewrite 545,000 m as 0.545×10^6 m or 0.545 Mm (megameter), because the prefix *mega,* abbreviated M, goes with 10^6. We also could have rewritten 545,000 as 545×10^3, and then 545,000 m could have been written as 545 km (kilometers) because *kilo* goes with 10^3.

EXAMPLE 1.1	**REWRITING PHYSICAL QUANTITIES USING SI PREFIXES**

Problem: Bacteria that cause pneumonia have diameters roughly equal to 0.0000009 m. Rewrite this using the SI prefix that goes with 10^{-6}.

Solution: In straight exponential notation, 0.0000009 m is 9×10^{-7} m, but -7 is not divisible by 3 and no SI prefix goes with 10^{-7}. If we move the decimal six places instead of seven to the right, however, we get 0.9×10^{-6} m. The prefix for 10^{-6} is *micro* with the symbol μ, so

$$0.0000009 \text{ m} = 0.9 \times 10^{-6} \text{ m} = 0.9 \ \mu\text{m}$$

The diameter of one of these bacteria is 0.9 micrometer (0.9 μm).

PRACTICE EXERCISE 3

Complete the following conversions to exponential notation by supplying the exponential parts of the numbers.

(a) $0.0000398 = 39.8 \times$ _____   (b) $0.000000798 = 798 \times$ _____
(c) $0.000000798 = 0.798 \times$ _____   (d) $16500 = 16.5 \times$ _____

PRACTICE EXERCISE 4

Write the abbreviation of each of the following.

(a) milliliter   (b) microliter   (c) deciliter
(d) millimeter   (e) centimeter   (f) kilogram
(g) microgram   (h) milligram

PRACTICE EXERCISE 5

Write the full name that goes with each of the following abbreviations.

(a) kg   (b) cm   (c) dL   (d) μg
(e) mL   (f) mg   (g) mm   (h) μL

PRACTICE EXERCISE 6

Rewrite the following physical quantities using the standard SI abbreviated forms to incorporate the exponential parts of the numbers.

(a) 1.5×10^6 g   (b) 3.45×10^{-6} L   (c) 3.6×10^{-3} g
(d) 6.2×10^{-3} L   (e) 1.68×10^3 g   (f) 5.4×10^{-1} m

PRACTICE EXERCISE 7   Express each of the following physical quantities in a way that uses an SI prefix.

(a) 275,000 g   (b) 0.0000625 L   (c) 0.000000082 m

1.6 ACCURACY AND PRECISION

The way in which the number part of a physical quantity is expressed says something about the precision of the measurement but nothing about its accuracy.

Most people use the terms *accuracy* and *precision* as if they meant the same thing, but they don't. **Accuracy** refers to the closeness of a measurement (or the average of several measurements) to the true value. In an accurate measurement, the instrument is faithful and its user knows how to use it. **Precision** means the degree to which successive measurements agree with each other. It also means the fineness of the measurement when only one is made.

Figure 1.4 illustrates the difference between accuracy and precision in the measurement of someone's height. Each dot represents one measurement. In the first set of results, the dots are tightly clustered close to or exactly at the true value, and obviously a skilled person was at work with a carefully manufactured meterstick. This set illustrates both high precision and great accuracy. In the second set, a skilled person, without realizing it, evidently used a faulty meterstick, one that was mislabeled by a few centimeters. The precision is as great as that shown by the first set, because the successive measurements agree well with each other. But they're all untrue, so the accuracy is poor. In the third set of measurements, someone with a good meterstick did careless work. Only by accident do the values average to the true value, so the accuracy, in terms of the average, turned out to be high, but the precision is terrible and no one would really trust the average. The last set displays no accuracy and no precision.

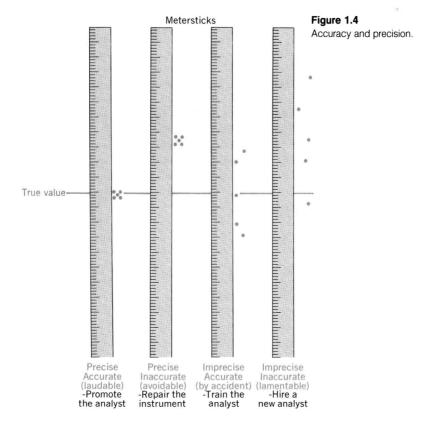

Figure 1.4
Accuracy and precision.

No matter what physical quantities we use, we want to be able to judge how accurately and precisely they were measured. Concerning accuracy, we have a problem, because when we read the value of some physical quantity in a report or a table, we have no way of telling *from it alone* if it is the result of an accurate measurement. Someone might write, for example, "4.5678 mg of antibiotic," but in spite of all its digits we can't tell from this report alone if the balance was working or if the person using it knew how to handle it and read it correctly. A skilled and careful experimenter frequently checks the instruments against references of known accuracy. Thus the question of *accuracy* is a human problem. We learn to trust the *accuracy* of data by employing trained people, giving them good instruments, requiring that they prove they are doing consistently accurate work, and rewarding consistently good results.

The Digits Known To Be Correct in a Quantity Are All But One of Its Significant Figures We can indicate something about the precision of a measurement by the way in which we write its value. We do this by the way we round off the value to leave it with a certain number of *significant figures*. The number of **significant figures** in a physical quantity is the number of digits known with complete certainty to be correct plus one more. For example, the quantity "4.56 mg of antibiotic" has three significant figures. The first two, the 4 and the 5, are known to be correct, but the analyst is acknowledging a small uncertainty in the last digit. Unless otherwise stated, the uncertainty is assumed to be *one* unit of the last digit, so this report means that the mass of the sample is closer to 4.56 mg than to 4.55 mg or 4.57 mg. If the mass had been reported to be 4.560 mg, then it has four significant figures. The 4, 5, and 6 are certainly true, but there is some uncertainty in the last digit, 0. The true mass is closer to 4.560 mg than to 4.559 mg or 4.561 mg. Thus "4.560 mg" discloses a greater precision or fineness of measurement than 4.56 mg. Sometimes you'll see a report with a value such as 4.560 ± 0.001 mg or 4.560 ± 0.005. The symbol ± stands for "plus or minus," and what follows it, like 0.001 or 0.005, indicates how much uncertainty is carried in the last digit.

■ The ± sign in 4.560 ± 0.001 mg means that the physical quantity is in the range of 4.559 to 4.561 mg.

Figuring out how many significant figures are in a number is easy, provided we have an agreement on how to treat zeros. Are all the zeros counted as *significant* in such quantities as 4,500,000 people, or 0.0004500 L, or 400,005 m? We will use the following rules to decide.

1. Zeros sandwiched between nonzero digits are always counted as significant.

Thus both 400,005 and 400.005 have six significant figures.

2. Zeros that do no more than set off the decimal point on their *left* are never counted as significant figures.

■ The quantities 4056 g and 4506 g both have four significant figures.

■ The other zeros are needed to locate the decimal points in these numbers, and they definitely are important in this sense. They just have nothing to do with precision.

Although such zeros are necessary to convey the general *size* of a quantity, they don't say anything about the *precision* of the measurement. Thus such quantities as 0.045 mL, 0.0045 mL, and 0.00045 mL all have only two significant figures.

3. Trailing zeros to the *right* of the decimal point are always significant.

Trailing zeros are any that come to the right of a decimal point at the very end of the number, as in 4.56000. This number has three trailing zeros, and because they are to the right of the decimal point, all are significant. The number 4.56000 has six significant figures and represents considerable precision or fineness of measurement.

4. Trailing zeros that are to the *left* of the decimal point are counted as significant only if the author of the book or article has somewhere said so.

The zeros in 4,500,000 are trailing zeros, but are they significant? Suppose this number stands for the population of a city. A city's population changes constantly as people are born and die, and as they move in and out. No one could claim to know a population is *exactly* 4,500,000 — not 4,499,999 and not 4,500,001, but 4,500,000. Most scientists handle this problem by restating the number in scientific notation so that any desired trailing zeros can be placed *after* the decimal point. By doing this, scientists can give as many or as few of such zeros to convey the proper degree of precision. If the census bureau feels that the population is known to be closer to 4,500,000 than to 4,400,000 or to 4,600,000 people, and that no better precision than this is possible, then it should show only two significant figures in the result. It should report the population as 4.5×10^6 people. Giving the population as 4.50×10^6 people indicates greater precision — to three significant figures. There are four significant figures in 4.500×10^6.

Not everyone agrees with this way of handling trailing zeros that stand to the *left* of the decimal point, so you have to be careful. Some say that they aren't significant unless the decimal point is actually given, as in 45,000. L. When the decimal point is the last item in a number, however, it is easily forgotten at the time of making the record. This problem is avoided by switching to scientific notation so that all trailing zeros come after the decimal point. This is the practice we will usually follow in this book, unless noted otherwise, or unless the context makes the intent very clear.

A Few Rules Govern The Rounding Off of Calculated Physical Quantities When we mathematically combine the values of two or more measurements, we usually have to round the result so that it has no more significant figures than allowed by the original data. Normally, such rounding is done at the *end* of a calculation (unless specified otherwise) to minimize the errors introduced by rounding. There are four simple rules for rounding.

1. When we multiply or divide quantities, the result can have no more significant figures than carried by the least precise quantity (the one with the fewest significant figures).
2. When we add or subtract numbers, the result can have no more decimal places than are in the number having the fewest decimal places.
3. When the first of the digits to be removed by rounding is 5 or higher, round the digit to its left *upward* by one unit. Otherwise, drop it and all others after it.
4. Treat exact numbers as having an infinite number of significant figures.

An *exact number* is any that we define to be so, and we usually encounter exact numbers in statements relating units. For example, all the numbers in the following expressions are exact and, for purposes of rounding calculated results, have an infinite number of significant figures.

> ■ We use the period in the abbreviation of inch (in.) to avoid any confusion with the preposition *in*, which has the same spelling.

$$1 \text{ in.} = 2.54 \text{ cm} \quad \text{(exactly, as defined by law)}$$
$$1 \text{ L} = 1000 \text{ mL} \quad \text{(exactly, by the definition of mL)}$$

The significance of having an infinite number of significant figures lies in our not letting such numbers affect how we round results. It would be silly to say that the "1" in "1 L" has just one significant figure when we intend, by definition, that it be an exact number.

| EXAMPLE 1.2 | ROUNDING THE RESULT OF A MULTIPLICATION OR A DIVISION |

Problem: A floor is measured as 11.75 m long and 9.25 m wide. What is its area, correctly rounded?

Solution:
$$\text{Area} = (\text{length}) \times (\text{width})$$
$$= 11.75 \text{ m} \times 9.25 \text{ m}$$
$$= 108.6875 \text{ m}^2 \quad \text{(not rounded)}$$

> ■ Resist the impulse that some owners of new calculators have of keeping all the digits they paid for.

But the measured width, 9.25 m, has only three significant figures whereas the length, 11.75 m, has four. We have to round the calculated area to three significant figures.

$$\text{Area} = 109 \text{ m}^2 \quad \text{(correctly rounded)}$$

| EXAMPLE 1.3 | ROUNDING THE RESULT OF AN ADDITION (OR A SUBTRACTION) |

Problem: Samples of a medication having masses of 1.12 g, 5.1 g, and 0.1657 g are mixed. How should the total mass of the resulting sample be reported?

Solution: The sum of the three values, obtained with a calculator, is 6.3857 g, which shows four places following the decimal point. However, one mass is precise only to the first decimal place, so we have to round to this place. The final mass should be reported as 6.4 g. Notice that the value of the second sample mixed, 5.1 g, says nothing about the third or fourth decimal places. We don't know whether the mass is 5.101 g or 5.199 g, or what; the sample just wasn't measured precisely. This is why we can't know anything beyond the first decimal place in the sum.

PRACTICE EXERCISE 8   The following numbers are the numerical parts of physical quantities. After the indicated mathematical operations are carried out, how must the results be expressed?

(a) 16.4×5.8 (b) $5.346 + 6.01$
(c) 0.00467×5.6324 (d) $2.3000 - 1.00003$
(e) $16.1 + 0.004$ (f) $(1.2 \times 10^2) \times 3.14$

(g) $9.31 - 0.00009$ (h) $\dfrac{1.0010}{0.0011}$

1.7 THE FACTOR–LABEL METHOD IN CALCULATIONS

In calculations involving physical quantities, the units are multiplied or canceled as if they were numbers.

Many people have developed a mental block about any subject that requires the use of mathematics. They know perfectly well how to multiply, divide, add, and subtract, but the problem is in knowing *when,* and no pocket calculator tells this. We said earlier that the inch is defined by the relationship, 1 in. = 2.54 cm. This fact has to be used when a problem asks for the number of centimeters in some given number of inches, but for some people the problem arises in knowing whether to divide or multiply.

Science teachers have worked out a method called the *factor–label* method for correctly setting up such a calculation and *knowing* that it is correct. The **factor–label method** takes a relationship between units stated as an equation (such as 1 in. = 2.54 cm), expresses the relationship in the form of a fraction, called a **conversion factor,** and then multiplies some given quantity by this conversion factor. In this multiplication, identical units (the "labels") are multiplied or canceled as if they were numbers. If the remaining units for the answer are right, then the calculation was correctly set up. We can learn how this works by doing an example, but first let's see how to construct conversion factors.

The relationship, 1 in. = 2.54 cm, can be restated in either of the following two ways and both are examples of conversion factors.

$$\frac{2.54 \text{ cm}}{1 \text{ in.}} \quad \text{or} \quad \frac{1 \text{ in.}}{2.54 \text{ cm}}$$

If we read the divisor line as "per," then the first conversion factor says "2.54 cm per 1 in." and the second says "1 in. per 2.54 cm." These are merely alternative ways of saying that "1 in. equals 2.54 cm." Any relationship between two units can be restated as two conversion factors. For example,

■ Some call the factor-label method the cancel-unit or the factor-unit method.

■ When we divide both sides of the equation 2.54 cm = 1 in. by 2.54 cm, we get

$$\frac{2.54 \text{ cm}}{2.54 \text{ cm}} = \frac{1 \text{ in.}}{2.54 \text{ cm}}$$

This only restates the relationship of the centimeter and the inch; it doesn't change it. The use of a conversion factor just changes units, not actual quantities.

$$1 \text{ L} = 1000 \text{ mL} \qquad \frac{1000 \text{ mL}}{1 \text{ L}} \quad \text{or} \quad \frac{1 \text{ L}}{1000 \text{ mL}}$$

$$1 \text{ lb} = 453.6 \text{ g} \qquad \frac{453.6 \text{ g}}{1 \text{ lb}} \quad \text{or} \quad \frac{1 \text{ lb}}{453.6 \text{ g}}$$

PRACTICE EXERCISE 9 — Restate each of the following relationships in the forms of their two possible conversion factors.

(a) 1 g = 1000 mg   (b) 1 kg = 2.205 lb

Suppose we want to convert 5.65 in. into centimeters. The first step is to write down what has been given, 5.65 in. Then we multiply this by the one conversion factor relating inches to centimeters that lets us cancel the unit no longer wanted and leaves the unit we want.

$$5.65 \text{ in.} \times \frac{2.54 \text{ cm}}{1 \text{ in.}} = 14.4 \text{ cm} \qquad \text{(rounded correctly from 14.351 cm)}$$

Notice how the units of "in." cancel. Only "cm" remains, and it is on top in the numerator where it has to be. Suppose we had used the wrong conversion factor.

■ The arithmetic is correct, but the result is still all wrong.

$$5.65 \text{ in.} \times \frac{1 \text{ in.}}{2.54 \text{ cm}} = 2.22 \frac{(\text{in.})^2}{\text{cm}} \qquad \text{(correctly rounded)}$$

That's right. We *must* do to the units exactly what the times sign and the divisor line tell us, and (in.) times (in.) equals $(\text{in.})^2$ just as $2 \times 2 = 2^2$. Of course, the units in the answer, $(\text{in.})^2$/cm, make no sense, so we know with certainty that we can't set up the solution this way. The reliability of the factor–label method lies in this use of the units (the "labels") as a guide to setting up the solution. Now let's work an example.

EXAMPLE 1.4 — USING THE FACTOR–LABEL METHOD

Problem: How many grams are in 0.230 lb?

Solution: From Table 1.2, we find that 1 lb = 453.6 g, so we have our pick of the following conversion factors.

$$\frac{453.6 \text{ g}}{1 \text{ lb}} \quad \text{or} \quad \frac{1 \text{ lb}}{453.6 \text{ g}}$$

To change 0.230 lb into grams, we want "lb" to cancel and we want "g" in its place in the numerator. Therefore we pick the first conversion factor; it's the only one that can give this result.

$$0.230 \text{ lb} \times \frac{453.6 \text{ g}}{1 \text{ lb}} = 104 \text{ g} \qquad \text{(correctly rounded)}$$

There are 104 g in 0.230 lb. (We rounded from 104.328 g to 104 g because the given value, 0.230 lb, has only three significant figures. Remember that the "1" in "1 lb" has to be treated as an exact number because it's in a definition.)

PRACTICE EXERCISE 10 — The *grain* is an old unit of mass still used by some pharmacists and physicians, and 1 grain = 0.0648 g. How many grams of aspirin are in an aspirin tablet containing 5.00 grain of aspirin?

Often there is no one conversion factor that does the job, and two or more have to be used. For example, we might want to find out how many kilometers are in, say, 26.22 miles, but our tables don't have a direct relationship between kilometers and miles. However, if we can find in a table that 1 mile $= 1609.3$ m and that 1 km $= 1000$ m, we can still work the problem. We'll see in the next example how we can string two (or more) conversion factors together before doing the calculation that gives the final answer.

| EXAMPLE 1.5 | USING THE FACTOR–LABEL METHOD.   STRINGING CONVERSION FACTORS |

Problem: How many kilometers are there in 26.22 miles, the distance of a marathon race? Use the following relationships.

$$1 \text{ mile} = 1609.3 \text{ m}$$
$$1 \text{ km} = 1000 \text{ m}$$

Solution: The given relationships provide the following sets of conversion factors.

$$\frac{1 \text{ mile}}{1609.3 \text{ m}} \quad \text{or} \quad \frac{1609.3 \text{ m}}{1 \text{ mile}}$$

and

$$\frac{1 \text{ km}}{1000 \text{ m}} \quad \text{or} \quad \frac{1000 \text{ m}}{1 \text{ km}}$$

Now let's write down the given, 26.22 mile, and pick a conversion factor that lets us cancel "mile."

$$26.22 \text{ mile} \times \frac{1609.3 \text{ m}}{1 \text{ mile}}$$

If we paused to carry out this calculation, the answer would be in meters (m), not in kilometers (km). Therefore *before doing this calculation,* use another conversion factor that lets us cancel "m." In principle, we could keep on doing this—stringing out conversion factors—until we found the unit that we wanted for the answer.

$$26.22 \text{ mile} \times \frac{1609.3 \text{ m}}{1 \text{ mile}} \times \frac{1 \text{ km}}{1000 \text{ m}} = 42.20 \text{ km} \quad \text{(correctly rounded)}$$

The marathon distance is 42.20 km.

PRACTICE EXERCISE 11   Using the relationships between units given in tables in this chapter, carry out the following conversions. Be sure that you express the answers in the correct number of significant figures.

(a) How many milligrams are in 0.324 g (the aspirin in one normal tablet)?
(b) A long-distance run of 10.0×10^3 m is how long in feet? (This is the 10-km distance.)
(c) A prescription calls for 5.00 fluidrams of a liquid. What is this in milliliters?
(d) One drug formulation calls for a mass of 10.00 drams (10.00 dr avdp). If only an SI balance is available, how many grams have to be weighed out? (The dr avdp, or dram avoirdupois, is defined in Table 1.2.)
(e) How many microliters are in 0.00478 L?

On page 10, equations were given relating degrees Celsius and degrees Fahrenheit. The use of these equations illustrates further examples of how units no longer wanted cancel, as you can demonstrate by using those equations to work the following Practice Exercises.

PRACTICE EXERCISE 12   A child has a temperature of 104 °F. What is this in degrees Celsius?

PRACTICE EXERCISE 13   If the water at a beach is reported as 15 °C, what is this in degrees Fahrenheit? (Would you care to swim in it?)

1.8 DENSITY

One of the important physical properties of a liquid is its density, its amount of mass per unit volume.

Properties Are Called Extensive or Intensive According to Their Dependence on The Sample Size Both the mass of some chemical sample and its volume are examples of **extensive properties,** those that are directly proportional to the size of the sample. Length is also an extensive property. An **intensive property** is independent of the sample's size. Temperature and color are such intensive properties, for example. Generally, intensive properties disclose some essential quality of a substance that is true for any sample size, and this is why scientists find intensive properties particularly useful.

An Object's Density Is the Ratio of Its Mass to Volume One useful intensive property of a substance, particularly if it is a fluid, is its density. **Density** is the mass per unit volume of a substance:

$$\text{Density} = \frac{\text{mass}}{\text{volume}}$$

The density of mercury, the silvery liquid used in most thermometers, is 13.60 g/mL, making mercury one of the most dense substances known. The density of liquid water is 1.0 g/mL. Table 1.6 gives the densities of several common substances.

Don't make the mistake of confusing *heaviness* with *denseness.* A pound of mercury is just as heavy as a pound of water or a pound of feathers because a pound is a pound. But a pound of mercury occupies only 1/13.6 the volume of a pound of water.

The density of a substance varies with temperature, because for samples of most substances the volume but not the mass changes with temperature. Most substances expand in volume when warmed and contract when cooled. The effect isn't great if the substance is a liquid or a solid. For example, the density of mercury changes only from 13.60 g/mL to 13.35 g/mL when its temperature changes from 0 °C to 100 °C, a density change of only about 2%.

TABLE 1.6 Densities of Some Common Substances

Substance	Density (g/cm³)
Aluminum	2.70
Bone	1.7–2.0
Butter	0.86–0.87
Cement, set	2.7–3.0
Cork	0.22–0.26
Diamond	3.01–3.52
Glass	2.4–2.8
Gold	18.88
Iron	7.87
Marble	2.6–2.8
Mercury	13.55
Milk	1.028–1.035
Wood, balsa	0.11–0.14
ebony	1.11–1.33
maple	0.62–0.75
teak	0.98

TABLE 1.7   Density of Water at Various Temperatures

Temperature °C	Density (g/mL)
0	0.99987
3.98	1.00000
10	0.99973
20	0.99823
25	0.99707
30	0.99567
35	0.99406
45	0.99025
60	0.98324
80	0.97183
100	0.95838

Table 1.7 gives the density of water at several temperatures. Notice that, when rounded to two significant figures, the density of water is 1.0 g/mL in the (liquid) range of 0 °C to 30 °C (32 to 86 °F). Remember that 1 mL = 1 cm³, and the kilogram mass, in fact, was originally meant to be the mass of 1000 cm³ (1000 mL) of water at its temperature of maximum density (3.98 °C). This is why the density of water (in SI units) comes out to have such a simple value.

One of the uses of density is in calculating what volume of a liquid to take when the problem or experiment specifies a certain mass. Often it is easier (and sometimes safer) to measure a volume than a mass, as we will note in the next example.

EXAMPLE 1.6	**USING DENSITY TO CALCULATE VOLUME FROM MASS**

Problem: Concentrated sulfuric acid is a thick, oily, and very corrosive liquid that no one would want to spill on the pan of an expensive balance, to say nothing of the skin. It is an example of a liquid that is usually measured by volume instead of by mass, but suppose an experiment called for 25.0 g of sulfuric acid. What volume (in mL) should be taken to obtain this mass? The density of sulfuric acid is 1.84 g/mL.

Solution: The given value of density means that 1.84 g acid = 1.00 mL acid. This gives two possible conversion factors:

$$\frac{1.84 \text{ g acid}}{1 \text{ mL acid}} \quad \text{or} \quad \frac{1 \text{ mL acid}}{1.84 \text{ g acid}}$$

The "given" in our problem, 25.0 g acid, should be multiplied by the second of these conversion factors to get the unit we want, mL.

$$25.0 \text{ g acid} \times \frac{1 \text{ mL acid}}{1.84 \text{ g acid}} = 13.6 \text{ mL acid}$$

Thus if we measure 13.6 mL of acid, we will obtain 25.0 g of acid. (The pocket calculator result is 13.58695652, but we have to round to three significant figures.)

PRACTICE EXERCISE 14   An experiment calls for 16.8 g of methyl alcohol, the fuel for fondue burners, but it is easier to measure this by volume than by mass. The density of methyl alcohol is 0.810 g/mL, so how many milliliters have to be taken to obtain 16.8 g of methyl alcohol?

SPECIAL TOPIC 1.1   SPECIFIC GRAVITY AND ITS APPLICATIONS

The **specific gravity** of a liquid is the ratio of the mass contained in a given volume to the mass of the identical volume of water at the same temperature. If we arbitrarily say that the "given volume" is 1.0 mL, then the water sample has a mass of 1.0 g (or extremely close to this over a wide temperature range). This means that dividing the mass of some liquid that occupies 1.0 mL by the mass of an equal volume of water is like dividing by 1, but all the units cancel. Specific gravity has no units, and a value of specific gravity is numerically so close to its density that we usually say they are numerically the same. This fact has resulted in a rather limited use of the concept of specific gravity, but one use occurs in medicine.

In clinical work, the idea of a specific gravity surfaces most commonly in connection with urine specimens. Normal urine has a specific gravity in the range of 1.010 to 1.030. It's slightly higher than water because the addition of wastes to water usually increases its mass more rapidly than its volume. Thus the more wastes in 1 mL of urine the higher is its specific gravity.

Figure 1.5 shows the traditional method to measure the specific gravity of a urine specimen, by using a urinometer. Its use, however, has largely been supplanted by a method, the use of a refractometer, that needs only one or two drops of urine for the measurement. The refractometer is an instrument that measures the ratio of the speed of light through air to its speed through the sample being tested. This ratio can be correlated with the concentration of dissolved substances in the urine. (*How* the refractometer does this is beyond the scope of our study.)

One of the important functions of the kidneys is to remove chemical wastes from the blood stream and put them into the urine being made. The kidney's mechanism for doing this does not remove those substances from the blood that ought to remain in the blood. The clinical significance, therefore, of a change in the concentration of substances dissolved in the urine is that it indicates a change in the activity of the kidneys. This might be the result of kidney disease so that substances that should stay in the blood leak into the urine being made. Or it might mean that somewhere else in the body wastes are being generated more rapidly than the kidneys can remove them.

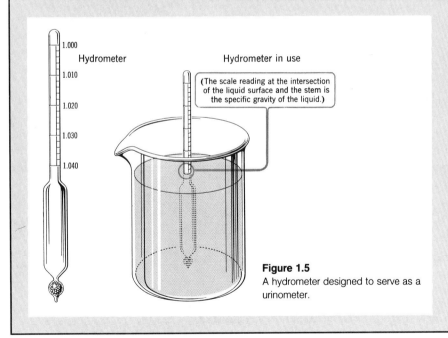

Hydrometer   Hydrometer in use

(The scale reading at the intersection of the liquid surface and the stem is the specific gravity of the liquid.)

Figure 1.5
A hydrometer designed to serve as a urinometer.

PRACTICE EXERCISE 15   After pouring out 35.0 mL of corn oil for an experiment, a student realized that the mass of the sample also had to be recorded. The density of the corn oil is 0.918 g/mL. How many grams are in the 35.0 mL?

Specific gravity is a property of a fluid that is very similar to density. It is not used very often in chemistry, but in clinical work the specific gravity of liquid specimens (such as urine) helps to reveal the nature of an illness, as described in Special Topic 1.1.

SUMMARY

Chemistry and the molecular basis of life Down at the level of nature's tiniest particles, we find the "parts"—molecules—that nature shuffles from organism to organism in the living world. One of the many ways of looking at life is to examine its molecular basis, the way in which well-being depends on chemicals and their properties.

Scientific facts and physical quantities Scientific facts are usually capable of being checked by independent observers, and these facts often are physical quantities that pertain to physical properties, whether these are extensive or intensive properties. Physical properties—those that can be studied without changing the substance into something else—include mass, volume, time, temperature, color, and density. For our purposes, the important base quantities are (with the names of the SI base units given in parentheses) mass (kilogram), length (meter), time (second), temperature degree (kelvin), and quantity of chemical substance (mole). Except for temperature, all are extensive properties, those that depend on the size of a sample.

The liter is an important derived unit for volume, and volume is another extensive property. An important intensive physical property is the density of something, the ratio of its mass to its volume. It is usually reported in units of grams per milliliter (g/mL).

Special prefixes can be attached to the names of the base units to express multiples or submultiples of these units. To select a prefix we have to be able to put very large or very small numbers into scientific notation.

Precision and accuracy Whether we obtain data from direct measurements or by calculations, we have to be careful not to imply too much precision by using the incorrect number of significant figures. When we add or subtract numbers, the decimal places in the result can be no more than the least number of decimal places among the original numbers. When we multiply or divide, we have to round the result to show the same number of significant figures as are in the least precise original number.

Factor-label method The units of the physical quantities involved in a calculation are multiplied or canceled as if they were numbers. To convert a physical quantity into its equivalent in other units, we multiply the quantity by a conversion factor that permits the final units to be correct. The conversion factor is obtained from a defined relationship between the units.

REVIEW EXERCISES

The answers to Review Exercises that require a calculation and whose numbers are marked with an asterisk are given in Appendix D. The answers to all other Review Exercises are given in the *Study Guide to Fundamentals of General, Organic, and Biological Chemistry*, 4th edition.

Molecular Basis of Life

1.1 Give some common experiences that illustrate that at some deep level of existence we can use the same "parts" as, say, a kitten.

1.2 Life, besides having a molecular basis, can be studied in terms of other bases. What are some? (One, for example, is the psychological basis.)

Scientific Method

1.3 You're driving down a dry highway (and sober), and the car starts to respond poorly to the steering wheel. You probably devise what—what is the better term—a theory or a hypothesis? Why?

1.4 What initially was called the vitamin *theory* eventually became part of established fact. Briefly, why did this happen?

1.5 What mental attitude goes along with the use of the scientific method?

1.6 You're studying at home, alone, at night when suddenly the lights in your room go out. Assuming that you instinctively use the scientific method in such a situation, what do you do next? And then after that?

Physical Quantities, Properties, and Measurements

1.7 What is meant by the word *property*?

1.8 How does a *physical property* differ from a *chemical property*?

1.9 How does a physical quantity differ from a number?

1.10 What is meant by the *inertia* of some object, and how is its inertia related to its mass?

1.11 Why is *volume* considered to be a less basic quantity than *length*?

1.12 What general name do we give to any fundamental quantity in terms of which less fundamental quantities are defined?

1.13 Name the five base quantities to be used in this book.

1.14 What is the name of the base unit for each of the following quantities?
(a) time   (b) mass
(c) temperature degree   (d) length
(e) quantity of chemical substance

1.15 What relationship does a *reference standard* have to a *base quantity*?

1.16 What are some of the properties that a reference standard should have, ideally?

1.17 Which reference standard in the SI is least ideal in terms of its being secure from any kind of physical or chemical loss?

1.18 What are the names and symbols for the common submultiples that we will use in this book for each of the following base units?
(a) meter   (b) liter
(c) kilogram

1.19 How many centimeters make 1 m?

1.20 How many millimeters make 1 cm?

1.21 How many grams are in 1 kg?

1.22 How many milligrams are in 1 g?

1.23 Is the yard slightly shorter or slightly longer than the meter?

1.24 Is the liquid quart slightly smaller or slightly larger than the liter?

Temperature Degrees and Temperature Scales

1.25 The value -273.15 °C is a peculiar number to pick to be equivalent to 0 K. Why was it selected?

1.26 Suppose you took an unmarked, unetched thermometer and immersed it in a slush of ice and water until the mercury level stopped changing and then you marked the mercury level with a wax crayon. What is the name of this line in the Celsius system? In the Fahrenheit system? On the Kelvin scale?

1.27 Suppose that you repeated the experiment of Exercise 1.26 only this time immersed the unmarked thermometer in boiling water (at sea level), and you marked the mercury level after it stopped changing. What is the name given to this mark in each of the three temperature scales?

1.28 How many scale divisions are there between the two marks created by the experiments described in Exercises 1.26 and 1.27 when the distances are subdivided into (a) Fahrenheit degrees, (b) Celsius degrees, (c) kelvins?

1.29 How do the kelvin and the degree Celsius compare in size?

1.30 How do the degree Celsius and the degree Fahrenheit compare in size?

*1.31 Water freezes at 0 °C and it boils at 100 °C. What are these values in kelvins?

1.32 Many people would find a temperature of 294 K to be comfortable. What is this in degrees Celsius?

*1.33 A German recipe calls for baking batter at 210 °C. What Fahrenheit setting should you use?

1.34 A weather report from a station in Alaska gave the outside temperature as -40 °F. What is this in °C?

*1.35 The pool temperature at an Austrian health spa is 31 °C. What is this in °F?

1.36 An infant's temperature is 38.5 °C. Is this normal? (Do a calculation. Normal temperature is considered to be 98.6 °F.)

*1.37 Wishing to make an outside temperature of 109 °F seem less hot to a friend visiting from Europe, you tell him what it is in °C. What number do you report? (Will this gesture work?)

1.38 Anesthetic ether is a vapor above 94.3 °F. What is this in °C?

SI Prefixes and Scientific Notation

1.39 Rewrite the following physical quantities with their units abbreviated.
(a) 26 micrograms of vitamin E
(b) 28 millimeters wide
(c) 5.0 deciliters of solution
(d) 55 kilometers in a distance

(e) 46 microliters of solution
(f) 64 centimeters long

1.40 Rewrite the following physical quantities with their units written out in full.
(a) 125 mg of water   (b) 25.5 mL of coffee
(c) 15 kg of salt   (d) 12 dL of iced tea
(e) 2.5 μg of ozone   (f) 16 μL of fluid

1.41 Rewrite the following data in scientific notation in which the decimal part of the number is between 1 and 10.
(a) 0.013 L   (b) 0.000006 g
(c) 0.0045 m   (d) 1455 s

1.42 Express each of these quantities in scientific notation and limit the decimal part of the number to a number between 1 and 10.
(a) 24,605 m   (b) 654,115 g
(c) 0.0000000095 L   (d) 0.00000568 s

1.43 Use a suitable SI prefix to express each of the quantities in Exercise 1.41.

1.44 Reformulate the numbers in the quantities of Exercise 1.42 so that they can be expressed in units that employ suitable SI prefixes.

Accuracy, Precision, and Significant Figures

1.45 According to one almanac, the population of the United States in 1790 was 3,939,214. Rewrite this figure in scientific notation retaining only three significant figures.

1.46 When a meterstick was used to take five successive measurements of a person's height, the following data were recorded: 172.7 cm, 172.9 cm, 172.6 cm, 172.6 cm, 172.8 cm. The meterstick had earlier been checked against an official reference standard and found to be good. The true value of the height was verified as 172.7 cm.
(a) Can the measurements be described as *accurate*? Why?
(b) Can they be described as *precise*? Why?

1.47 Examine the following numbers.
(A) 3.7200×10^3 (B) 3720   (C) 3.720
(D) 0.03720   (E) 37,200   (F) 0.00372
(G) 3.720×10^3 (H) 0.0372   (I) 3.72×10^9
(a) Which of these numbers has three significant figures? Identify them by their letters.
(b) Which has four significant figures?
(c) Which of them has five significant figures?

1.48 If we multiply $3.4462 \times 55.1 \times 10^8$, how many significant figures can we permit the answer to have?

1.49 If we add 0.00014 to 1.36, how many places after the decimal point can we permit to stand in the answer?

1.50 Rewrite the following number according to the number of significant figures specified by each part.

$$144,549.09$$

(a) seven   (b) five   (c) four
(d) three   (e) one   (f) two

1.51 The relationship between the gram and the microgram is given by

$$1 \text{ g} = 100,000 \ \mu\text{g}$$

How many significant figures are considered to be in each number?

Converting Between Units

1.52 Write each of the following relationships between units for physical quantities in the forms of two conversion factors.
(a) 1 mile = 5280 ft
(b) 1 dram = 60 grains
(c) 1 lb = 453.6 g
(d) 1 ounce = 480 grains
(e) 1 m = 39.37 in.
(f) 1 liquid ounce = 480 minims

1.53 Given the relationships of Exercise 1.52, which of the two following calculated answers is more likely to be correct in each part? You should be able to make this kind of judgment without actually doing a calculation.
(a) 250 minims = 0.520 liquid ounce or 1.20×10^4 liquid ounce
(b) 3.50 ounce = 0.00729 grain or 1.68×10^3 grain
(c) 0.350 lb = 159 g or 0.000772 g

1.54 What are the units in the result of the following calculation?

$$1.0 \text{ kg} \times 1 \frac{m}{\sec} \times 1 \frac{m}{\sec}$$

(The resulting units are the SI units for energy, a derived quantity.)

*1.55 Convert each of the following physical quantities into the units specified. Use tables in this chapter to find relationships between units.
(a) 75.5 in. into centimeters (the height of an adult male)
(b) 50.5 kg into lb avdp (the mass of an adult female)

1.56 Using relationships between units found in this chapter, convert each of the following quantities into the new units specified.
(a) 70.0 kg into lb avdp (the mass of an adult male)
(b) 64.0 in. into centimeters (the height of an adult female)

*1.57 A 500-mL bottle of soda contains how many liquid ounces (to three significant figures)?

1.58 If a gas tank holds 16.0 U.S. gallons, how many liters does it hold?

*1.59 Driving a car with a mass of 4.6×10^3 lb, you come to a bridge with a sign that reads "Closed to all vehicles weighing more than 1.5×10^3 kg." Should you cross? (Do the calculation assuming that "lb" means "lb avdp.")

1.60 A foreign car has a mass of 915 kg. What is this in lb avdp?

*1.61 If you can get 32 equal-sized butter pats from a quarter-pound (0.25 lb avdp) stick, what is the mass of each pat in grams?

1.62 The *carat* is a measurement jewelers use to describe the mass of a precious stone. 1 carat = 200 mg. What is the mass in milligrams of a diamond rated as 0.750 carat?

*1.63 Mount Everest in Nepal is the highest mountain in the world — 29,028 ft. What is this in meters? In kilometers?

1.64 The highest mountain in the United States is Alaska's Mount McKinley at 6194 m. How high is this in feet? In miles?

Density

1.65 Why is density called an intensive property?

1.66 If dissolving something in water increased the mass of the system by 0.5 g for each 0.5 mL increase in its volume, how would the density be affected?

1.67 Within limits, dissolving a solid in water increases the mass of the system more rapidly than the volume. What does this do to the density of the system, cause it to increase, decrease, or remain the same?

*1.68 Taking the density of lead to be 11.35 g/cm³, how many pounds (lb avdp) of lead fill a milk container with a volume of 1.00 qt?

1.69 Aluminum has a density of 2.70 g/cm³. A milk carton with a volume of 1.00 qt could hold how many grams of aluminum? How many kilograms? How many pounds (lb avdp)?

*1.70 To avoid spilling any liquid onto an expensive balance, a student obtained 30.0 g of acetic acid by measuring a corresponding volume. The density of acetic acid is 1.06 g/mL. What volume in milliliters was taken?

1.71 In an experiment to test how well methyl alcohol works as an antifreeze, a technician took 275 mL of this liquid. Its density is 0.810 g/mL. How many grams of methyl alcohol were taken?

Specific Gravity (Special Topic 1.1)

1.72 What is the difference between density and specific gravity?

1.73 What fact about water makes the density of some object and its specific gravity the same (or very nearly so, depending on the number of significant figures used)?

1.74 In which fluid does a urinometer float sink farther, one of low density or one of high density?

1.75 It is possible to dissolve 2.0 g of salt in 100 mL of water with hardly any change in the total volume. Calculate the specific gravity of the resulting salt solution if no change in volume occurs.

1.76 An abnormally high specific gravity of a urine specimen tells us what about the specimen?

CHAPTER TWO

Matter and Energy

The mind of this slalom racer makes kinetic energy and chemical energy work splendidly together, and even his mental work is fueled by reserves of chemical energy. In this chapter we begin our study of the molecular basis of energy for living.

2.1   STATES AND KINDS OF MATTER

Elements and compounds always have definite compositions, but mixtures do not.

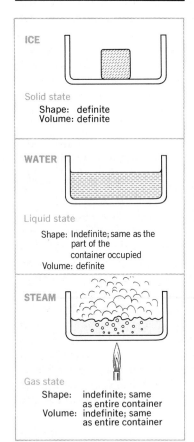

ICE

Solid state
Shape: definite
Volume: definite

WATER

Liquid state
Shape: Indefinite; same as the
       part of the
       container occupied
Volume: definite

STEAM

Gas state
Shape: indefinite; same
        as entire container
Volume: indefinite; same
        as entire container

Figure 2.1
The three physical states of matter—
solid, liquid, and gas—are illustrated by
ice, liquid water, and steam.

Matter is anything that occupies space and has mass. This includes literally everything, and because there is such a huge variety of matter, making some sense out of it might seem impossible. Throughout history, however, we humans have had a powerful impulse to sort and classify whenever we face what is very complex. Biologists, for example, created kingdoms, phylla, species, subspecies, and groups for plants and animals. One reason for sorting, classifying, and naming is simply to be able to find and recognize different things again, but another reason is to focus our minds on possible explanations for what we see around us.

The States of Matter Are Solids, Liquids, and Gases   One useful way to classify matter is according to the **states of matter,** meaning its possible physical conditions of aggregation. We recognize three such states, solid, liquid, and gas, which are illustrated very familiarly by ice, liquid water, and steam. Each state can be defined by an ability to hold a shape and have a definite volume, as Figure 2.1 illustrates. Solids have both definite shapes and volumes. Liquids have definite volumes but indefinite shapes; they take the shapes of their containers. Gases have no definite shapes or volumes. They fill whatever enclosed space they are in.

Having pointed out the almost obvious about the three states, we ask, "What's behind this?" "What is it that makes solids have definite shapes but which seems to be weaker in liquids and still weaker in gases?" Such a question tries to get to the bottom of things. That's what this course is about, getting to the bottom of things in nature, and we'll do this for the states of matter in a later chapter. We have some more sorting and classifying to do first.

The Three Kinds of Matter Are Elements, Compounds, and Mixtures   The materials in any sample of matter have the broad name of **substances.** Most matter consists of two or more substances mixed together, and each contributes something to the overall properties of the sample. Freshly squeezed orange juice, for example, consists of water, vitamin C, a little fruit sugar, citric acid, some of the pulp of the fruit, and other substances. If you remove any of them, you would notice the change (although the removal of some, like the vitamins, might not be noticed right away). You probably can sense that if we want to "get to the bottom" of orange juice, we have to study its individual substances. The best way, in fact, to begin a study of the physical and chemical properties of any sample of matter is to study what it's made of.

There are basically two broad kinds of substances, *elements* and *compounds.* We'll briefly survey what defines these next and then return to them for an in-depth study in later chapters.

Elements Cannot Be Changed into Simpler Substances   As their name implies, elements are elementary. An **element** is a substance that cannot be broken down into simpler substances. Many familiar things are elements, like aluminum, copper, gold, iron, and chromium, or the oxygen and the nitrogen in air. Water isn't an element because we can break it down into oxygen and hydrogen. Both are elements, and we can make them recombine again to give water. Hydrogen burns in oxygen, and water forms.

A list of the known elements is inside the front cover of this book. There are just a few over 100 of them, but we'll be concerned with only about a dozen. Over 90% of the bulk mass of nearly all living things consists of substances made from only four elements: carbon, nitrogen, hydrogen, and oxygen.

Just 90 elements occur naturally; the rest have been made by physicists who used very expensive equipment. These synthetic elements plus a few that occur naturally have a special property called **radioactivity,** the ability to emit one kind of dangerous radiation or another. We will return to their special properties in Chapter Ten.

■   Some naturally occurring elements, such as uranium and radium, are radioactive, too.

■ Mercury is a metallic element but a liquid at room temperature. It's the fluid used in most thermometers.

■ The current U.S. nickel coin is actually an alloy of copper (75%) and nickel (25%).

■ Diamonds consist of one form of pure carbon.

At room temperature, all but 13 elements are solids, 2 are liquids and 11 are gases. All but about 20 elements are metals. A **metal** is any substance that has a shiny surface when polished, can be hammered into sheets and drawn into wires, and is a good conductor of electricity.

Sometimes two or more metals are melted, mixed together, and allowed to cool to give a solid mixture of metals called an **alloy.** Steel, for example, is actually the name for a family of alloys — chromium steel, nickel steel, and many others. Each steel alloy has particularly useful properties, like unusual resistance to corrosion, or to breaking under large stretching forces. A few alloys are used to replace bones or to strengthen them, and they must be unusually resistant to corrosion.

Several of the solid elements, like carbon and sulfur, plus all of the gaseous elements are classified as **nonmetals.** The solid nonmetals cannot be worked into sheets or wires, and they do not conduct electricity as well as the metals. Metals and nonmetals have somewhat opposite *chemical* properties, as we will study in the next chapter.

Compounds Are Made from Elements   Chemical **compounds** are substances that are made from two or more elements that have combined in a very special way; they are *always* combined in a proportion by mass that is both definite and unique for the compound. When water, for example, is broken down into its elements, hydrogen and oxygen are invariably obtained in a mass ratio of 2.0 g of hydrogen to 16.0 g of oxygen. The vitamin C in orange juice, as well as the citric acid and the fruit sugar, are all chemical compounds. Their constituent elements are carbon, hydrogen, and oxygen, but the proportions are different for each. Table salt is also a compound. Its elements are sodium and chlorine. Interestingly, both are dangerous elements; sodium (Figure 2.2) is a shiny metal (only when freshly cut) that combines with both the oxygen and the moisture in humid air, and chlorine (Figure 2.3) is a greenish-yellow poisonous gas. The two combine violently, as you can see in Figure 2.4, to give salt, sodium chloride, a compound needed by all animals. How can sodium chloride be so different from its elements? We'll see in the next chapter. We still have some more sorting to do.

Figure 2.2
The shiny, metallic luster of sodium will soon fade, because this soft, easily cut metal reacts quickly with both oxygen and moisture in air.

Figure 2.3
Chlorine, a pale yellowish-green gas, is a poison. Warring sides used it in World War I as a weapon.

Figure 2.4
When a small piece of sodium metal, spread on the tip of a pointed glass rod, is thrust into chlorine, the reaction produces an instant shower of light and heat as sodium chloride forms.

Mixtures Have Variable Compositions   The third and last kind of matter is the **mixture.** A mixture consists of two or more substances that are present in a proportion that can vary considerably. Orange juice is thus a mixture. Even its pulp is a mixture of compounds.

Chemical Reactions Change Substances into Other Substances   Compounds are made by **chemical reactions,** events in which substances called **reactants** change into different substances called **products.** Reactants and products almost always have at least some physical properties that are quite different. Sodium, chlorine, and sodium chloride certainly illustrate this. Chemical reactions always feature at least some changes in physical properties as reactants change over into products.

Laws of Chemical Combination Govern Chemical Composition   Sodium chloride is a *compound,* not just a mixture of elements. It isn't even possible to have a mixture of sodium metal and chlorine gas. We say that they are too *reactive* to coexist. Yet it is possible to break down sodium chloride into sodium and chlorine. (It's done by passing a current of electricity through *molten* salt in such a way that the sodium and chlorine emerge into separate containers.) This is also a chemical reaction, because different substances are made. Every time this is done, or every time sodium and chlorine are allowed to react to form sodium chloride, the ratio of chlorine that reacts with sodium is invariably 1.5421 g of chlorine to 1.0000 g of sodium. You can obtain a sample of sodium chloride from any place in the world, and it would have this ratio of chlorine to sodium. And no matter in what proportion you might initially mix sodium and chlorine, the reacting proportion would be exactly 1.5421 g of chlorine to 1.0000 g of sodium. You might have either chlorine or sodium left over, depending on how carefully you mixed these elements, but for every 1.0000 g of sodium that reacts, 1.5421 g of chlorine would react as well, to form 2.5421 g of sodium chloride.

Compounds are like this, so much so that we will now make this behavior part of the *definition* of a compound. A **compound** is a substance made from two (or more) elements in a definite proportion by mass. This is, in fact, the first of the scientific laws that we study, the **law of definite proportions.**

■ Huge quantities of both sodium and chlorine are made annually by passing electricity through molten salt (sodium chloride).

> **Law of Definite Proportions**   In a given chemical compound, the elements are always combined in the same proportion by mass.

In a sense, elements also obey this law, because an element consists of 100% of itself. Chemists call elements and compounds **pure substances** because their compositions are constant in this way.

The proportions of the constituents in a mixture can vary widely. For example, we can prepare mixtures (solutions) of sugar and water, two compounds, in almost any proportion we please. Moreover, we can separate the two simply by letting the water evaporate — a physical change because only a change in physical state occurs. Mixtures, in general, require only physical changes to be separated into their components.

Another law of chemical combination was suggested when we pointed out that 2.5421 g of sodium chloride forms when 1.0000 g of sodium combines with 1.5421 of chlorine. The mass of the product is the sum of the masses of the reactants. This mass relationship between reactants and products has always been observed for chemical reactions, and these observations are behind the **law of conservation of mass.**

Lemonade is little more than lemon-flavored sugar – water, and its sweetness can be varied from nearly sour to syrupy sweet.

> **Law of Conservation of Mass**   In any chemical reaction, the sum of the masses of the reactants always equals the sum of the masses of the products.

Any widespread regularity in nature generally suggests some very basic truth about the world in which we live, and the laws of chemical combination were examples of a regularity that demanded an answer to the question: "What must be true about substances to explain these laws?" John Dalton was the first to offer an answer, as we'll see next.

2.2 ATOMS AND CHEMICAL SYMBOLS

Dalton saw that the laws of chemical combination virtually compel the belief that atoms exist.

John Dalton (1766 – 1844), an English scientist, was the first to find a reasonable explanation for both definite proportions in compounds and the conservation of mass in reactions. In this section we will first study Dalton's atomic theory and then see how to symbolize elements and chemical reactions.

Dalton's Atomic Theory Proposed Indestructible Atoms   Dalton reasoned that matter must be made of very tiny, individual particles that undergo a variety of chemical reactions *without breaking apart or losing any mass.* In order to explain the *definite* compositions observed for compounds, he said that these tiny particles simply cannot exist as major fragments of themselves. Each particle is an unbreakable unit.

The idea of a tiny, invisible, unbreakable particle had been around for centuries, because ancient Greek philosophers had proposed it. The Greek word for "not cut" is *atomos,* and from this term came our word *atom.* Dalton revived this ancient belief in "not cuttable" particles with the enormously important difference that he had solid evidence — the laws of chemical combination.

The chief postulates of **Dalton's atomic theory** are the following.

1. Matter consists of definite particles called **atoms.**

2. Atoms are indestructible.

3. All atoms of one particular element are identical in mass.

4. Atoms of different elements have different masses.

5. By becoming stuck together in different ways, atoms form compounds in definite ratios *by atoms.*

The only way, said Dalton, that we can observe definite ratios *by mass* in compounds is that compounds possess definite ratios of atoms, each kind of atom having its own unique and definite mass.

The elements iron and sulfur can be made to combine to form iron(II) sulfide in the ratio of 1.000 g of iron to 0.574 g of sulfur. Dalton would have explained this definite mass ratio as illustrated in Figure 2.5. The large circles labeled "Fe" represent iron atoms and the smaller circles labeled "S" stand for sulfur atoms. If we assume that the *atoms* of these two elements combine in a ratio of one atom of iron to one atom of sulfur, each atom with its own mass, *then the mass ratio can't help but be a constant.*

John Dalton

Figure 2.5
Mass ratio versus atom ratio in iron(II) sulfide. If the mass of one sulfur atom is 0.574 times the mass of one iron atom, then combining sulfur and iron atoms in a simple 1 to 1 ratio (by atoms), regardless of how much this is scaled up, must result in a constant ratio by mass.

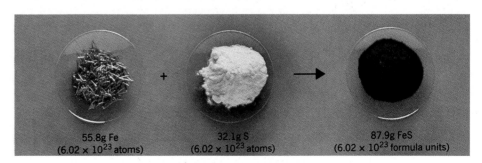

55.8g Fe
(6.02 × 10²³ atoms)

32.1g S
(6.02 × 10²³ atoms)

87.9g FeS
(6.02 × 10²³ formula units)

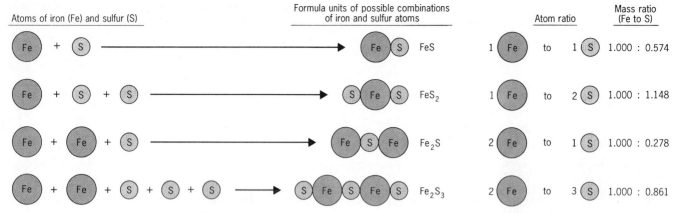

Figure 2.6
Possible multiple proportions for combinations of iron atoms and sulfur atoms. If atoms remain essentially intact (and suffer no detectable loss in mass) when they form compounds, then they must assemble in *whole-number ratios by atoms*, regardless of the masses of the individual atoms.

The Discovery of the Law of Multiple Proportions Compelled Belief in Atoms

Powerful evidence for Dalton's atomic theory came from the study of different compounds that can be made from the same elements but in different mass ratios. The mineral pyrite, for example, is made from iron and sulfur, like iron(II) sulfide, but the ratio by mass in pyrite is 1.000 g of iron to 1.148 g of sulfur. The mass ratio in iron(II) sulfide is 1.000 g of iron to 0.574 g of sulfur. Notice that 1.148 is exactly twice the size of 0.574. In other words, there is a simple *whole-number* ratio between the grams of sulfur combined with 1.000 g of iron in the two compounds. If Dalton is right, there *must* be a simple whole-number ratio because atoms combine as whole units, as whole particles. Figure 2.6 shows why this is so. It shows several possible combinations of intact iron and sulfur atoms. Three of the four are known compounds, the first two and the fourth.

Two compounds of tin and oxygen further illustrate the special relationship among compounds made from the same elements. In one compound of tin and oxygen, 1.000 g of oxygen is combined with 3.710 g of tin. In another, 1.000 g of oxygen is combined with 7.420 g of tin. Now compare 7.420 g of tin with 3.710 g of tin.

$$\frac{7.420}{3.710} = \frac{2}{1}$$

The ratio of the quantities of tin in the two compounds that combine with the same mass of oxygen is a simple, whole-number ratio, 2 to 1. These and several other examples led to the third law of chemical combination, the **law of multiple proportions.**

■ Pyrite is often found as golden crystals embedded in rock samples. Many a novice gold miner felt a quickened heartbeat on finding what more experienced miners called fool's gold.

■ Tin is the metal used to coat the inner surfaces of ''tin'' cans. Tin, unlike iron and less expensive steels, won't rust in an environment of food juices.

> **Law of Multiple Proportions** Whenever two elements form more than one compound, the different masses of one that combine with the same mass of the other are in the ratio of small whole numbers.

The many examples that illustrated this law, combined with Dalton's astute interpretations, virtually compelled scientists to believe that atoms exist. Since Dalton's time, so much additional evidence has accumulated that the existence of atoms is taken as fact, not theory.

Chemical Formulas Give a Substance's Composition

Chemists use special symbols for compounds called **chemical formulas,** which tell us at a glance which elements are present and in what ratio by atoms. For constructing these formulas, each element has been assigned an **atomic symbol** consisting of one or two letters. Those with which we will most

TABLE 2.1 Names and Symbols of Some Common Elements[a]

C	Carbon	Al	Aluminum	Cl	Chlorine	Ag	Silver *(argentum)*
H	Hydrogen	Ba	Barium	Mg	Magnesium	Cu	Copper *(cuprum)*
O	Oxygen	Br	Bromine	Mn	Manganese	Fe	Iron *(ferrum)*
N	Nitrogen	Ca	Calcium	Pt	Platinum	Pb	Lead *(plumbum)*
S	Sulfur	Li	Lithium	Zn	Zinc	Hg	Mercury *(hydrargyrum)*
P	Phosphorus	Si	Silicon	As	Arsenic	K	Potassium *(kalium)*
I	Iodine	Co	Cobalt	Cs	Cesium	Na	Sodium *(natrium)*
F	Fluorine	Ra	Radium	Cr	Chromium	Au	Gold *(aurum)*

[a] The names in parentheses in the last column are the Latin names from which the atomic symbols were derived.

often work are given in Table 2.1, and the complete list of atomic symbols appears in a table inside the front cover of this book.

Many elements, like those in the first column of Table 2.1, have single-letter symbols, usually (but not invariably) the capitalized first letter. Because there are more elements than letters in the alphabet, several elements have names beginning with the same letter — for example, carbon, calcium, chlorine, chromium, cobalt, and copper. Many atomic symbols, therefore, consist of the first two letters with the first letter *always* capitalized and the second letter *always* in lowercase. Examples are in the second column of Table 2.1. The third column shows how the first letter and some letter in the name that stands beyond the second place are combined to make a symbol. Thus chlorine has the symbol Cl and chromium has the symbol Cr. The last column of Table 2.1 lists some elements named long ago when Latin was the almost universal language of educated people, and so the symbols of some elements were derived from Latin names, as shown.

Students often find the symbols for sodium (Na) and potassium (K) the trickiest, so be sure to take some extra time to fix these firmly in mind.

Empirical Formulas Give the Ratios of Atoms in Compounds Chemists employ more than one kind of chemical formula, and we'll learn about one now, the *empirical formula*. The formula FeS for iron(II) sulfide is an example. This compound has a ratio of 1 Fe atom to 1 S atom. Its empirical formula, therefore, combines the atomic symbols, Fe and S, without spaces between them in a 1 to 1 ratio.

In pyrite, the ratio is 1 atom of iron to 2 atoms of sulfur, and the empirical formula of pyrite is written as FeS_2. The 2 is called a *subscript,* and subscripts in formulas always *follow* the symbols to which they refer. In Fe_2S_3, the empirical formula of another compound of iron and sulfur (given in Figure 2.6), the ratio is 2 atoms of Fe to 3 atoms of S. You can see that formulas give more direct chemical information than names.

The subscript 1 is always "understood" in chemical formulas. We write the formula of iron(II) sulfide as FeS, not as Fe_1S_1. We do not write the formula as Fe_2S_2 or as Fe_3S_3 either. An **empirical formula** shows the elements present in a compound by the atomic symbols used, and it shows their ratios by atoms using the *smallest* whole numbers that can be used to represent the ratios.

We might have conveyed the identical information about FeS by writing the formula as SFe, instead, but symbols for metal elements are generally placed first. Finally, always remember that empirical formulas disclose *ratios*, not absolute numbers. The actual numbers of combined atoms in FeS even in a speck barely visible under a microscope are extremely large because atoms are exceedingly tiny.

It is too early in our study to go much more into the rules for writing either formulas or names, so don't worry about this phase yet. For the present, just be sure you can spot the difference between say, FeS and fes, or that you can tell that CO can't possibly be the symbol for an element (the second letter is not in lowercase) but that Co might be. CO is the formula of carbon monoxide, a compound made of carbon, C, and oxygen, O, and Co is the atomic symbol of cobalt.

■ Among the trickier, but still common, pairs of chemical symbols are:

P = phosphorus

K = potassium

S = sulfur

Na = sodium

I = iodine

Fe = iron

As we said, whenever a compound is made from a metal and a nonmetal, the symbol for the metal is placed first. Often compounds are made of two nonmetals, so we will learn a rule that applies when one of the nonmetals is carbon. The symbols for carbon monoxide, CO, and methane, CH_4 (natural gas), illustrate the rule. When a formula involves carbon and another nonmetal, the symbol for carbon comes first. Let's now work an example to illustrate how to use these rules and to become more familiar with chemical formulas and the use of subscripts.

EXAMPLE 2.1   **WRITING CHEMICAL FORMULAS FROM ATOMIC COMPOSITIONS**

Problem: Aluminum, a metal with the symbol Al, and sulfur, a nonmetal with the symbol S, form a compound in which the atom ratio is 2 atoms of Al to 3 atoms of S. Write the formula.

Solution: The symbol for aluminum has to come first because aluminum is a metal. The answer is Al_2S_3 in which the "2" goes with Al and the "3" with S.

EXAMPLE 2.2   **WRITING CHEMICAL FORMULAS FROM ATOMIC COMPOSITIONS**

Problem: Carbon, a nonmetal with the symbol C, and chlorine, another nonmetal but with the symbol Cl, form a compound in which the ratio of atoms is 1 of C to 4 of Cl. Write the formula.

Solution: By convention, the symbol of carbon comes first, so the answer is CCl_4. (The subscript, 1, of carbon is understood.)

PRACTICE EXERCISE 1   Write the formula of the compound between sodium (a metal) and sulfur in which the atom ratio is 2 atoms of sodium to 1 atom of sulfur.

PRACTICE EXERCISE 2   Give the names of the elements that are present and the ratio of their atoms in K_2CO_3.

Formula Units Are Particles That Correspond To The Formula of a Compound   If Fe stands for an atom, what kind of particle does FeS stand for? The most general name we can give to the particle with the composition of the formula of a compound is **formula unit.** Other names such as *molecule* or *set of ions* or *ion group* will be used when we are farther along in our study. *Formula unit* includes all of these more special names. One formula unit of FeS is made of one iron atom and one sulfur atom. In fact, we can extend the term *formula unit* to include atoms. The chemical formula for sodium is given simply by its symbol, Na; hence, one formula unit of sodium is one atom of sodium.

Chemical Equations Use Formulas To Describe Reactions   Now that we know something about chemical formulas, we can learn how to use them in describing chemical reactions by means of chemical equations. A **chemical equation** is a special shorthand description of a reaction; it groups the symbols of the reactants, separated by plus signs, on one side of an arrow and places the symbols of the products, also separated by plus signs, on the arrowhead side of the arrow. A very simple example is the formation of iron(II) sulfide from iron and sulfur.

$$Fe + S \longrightarrow FeS$$

Translation:

iron reacts with sulfur
in a ratio of 1 atom of
Fe to 1 atom of S..........to give.......iron(II) sulfide

Thus the + sign separating reactants means *reacts with;* and the arrow means *to give.*

A more complicated example of an equation is the one for the formation of aluminum sulfide, Al_2S_3, from aluminum and sulfur.

$$2Al + 3S \longrightarrow Al_2S_3$$

Translation:

aluminum reacts with sulfur
in a ratio of 2 aluminum
atoms to 3 sulfur atoms..........to give......1 formula unit of aluminum sulfide

The numbers in front of the formulas are called **coefficients.** They specify the proportions of the formula units involved in the reaction. As with subscripts, whenever a coefficient is 1, the 1 isn't written; it is understood.

Our objective here is simply to recognize equations and translate them, not to write them. (That will come later.) An essential feature of any chemical equation, however, is that it be a **balanced equation,** one in which all atoms present in the reactants occur somewhere among the products. For example, in the equation for the formation of Al_2S_3, there are 2 Al atoms on the left and 2 on the right in Al_2S_3. Similarly, there are 3 S atoms on the left and 3 on the right. The unbreakability of atoms and the conservation of mass in chemical reactions ensures this kind of balance. As Dalton said so long ago, when reactions occur the atoms of the reactants rearrange; they do not break up or disappear.

Chemical Reactions Always Convert Substances into Different Substances   It is one matter to notice that a change has occurred in some system but another matter to decide whether the change is a physical change or a chemical reaction. The absolutely necessary and sufficient condition that determines whether the event was a chemical reaction is that substances change into other substances. However, to tell whether this has happened, we rely on changes in physical appearances or physical properties. As a chemical reaction occurs, the physical properties associated with the reactants disappear and those of the products emerge. Such changes might be in color, in odor (but always be very cautious when checking odors), or in physical state — a gas might bubble out, or a new-appearing solid might separate out. If the event seems to be able to occur, once started, without any further intervention and it releases heat, usually this means it is a *chemical* change. Most chemical reactions that "go by themselves" release heat. If none of these tests decides the matter, then more sophisticated measures must be used, steps that positively identify different compounds.

2.3 FORMS OF ENERGY

The chemical energy that substances have because of their chemical nature can change into heat, light, sound, electrical, or kinetic energy when chemical reactions occur.

We have to be interested in energy in our study of chemistry, because almost all reactions either require energy in order to occur or they release energy. **Energy** is the ability to cause various kinds of changes. We say that things have energy when they have the ability to cause changes. Energy comes in a variety of forms, having names that we associate with the kind of change, names such as light, sound, heat, electricity, and work.

■ *Kinetic* is from the Greek *kinetikos,* meaning "of motion."

Moving Objects Have Kinetic Energy   One kind of energy is called **kinetic energy,** the energy associated with motion. A moving car has kinetic energy; so does an avalanche, or a falling star, or a running child. The kinetic energy (K.E.) of a moving object can be calculated by the equation

$$K.E. = \tfrac{1}{2}mv^2$$

■ Velocity, a derived unit, is distance per period of time, and in the SI its units are meters per second (m/s).

A great amount of play energy comes from the chemical energy in a sandwich.

where m is the mass of the moving object and v is its velocity. Thus the kinetic energy of a moving object is directly proportional to its mass and to the *square* of its velocity. If you double the velocity of a moving car, its kinetic energy increases by a factor of four (because $4 = 2^2$). The energy quadruples, not doubles, and this is why a small increase in velocity can be much more dangerous than the numbers might indicate.

When the brakes are applied to a moving car, all the kinetic energy of the car is converted into heat, and the brake shoes and brake drums become hotter. If the brakes squeal, a small amount of the kinetic energy changes into sound energy. Sound energy is associated with the ability to change the noise level. You can see by these simple examples that we can convert energy from one form into another. It is conceivable that the brake drums could get so hot that they would glow in the dark. Now some of the car's kinetic energy is being converted into light. Light energy is related to the ability to change the level of illumination.

Total Energy Is Conserved As Changes Occur   Consider now a sliced turkey sandwich and a small child. What an astonishing amount of activity is made possible by this sandwich! If the child receives energy for its activities from such a source, it must mean that substances can have a special kind of energy—energy in storage, so to speak. A simpler example of stored energy is a piece of paper. You can hold it in your hands comfortably, until someone puts a match to it. Now the paper burns, giving off heat and light (and maybe a little sound). If such energy can come from the paper, the paper must have possessed it in some way, because scientists have learned something very fundamental about energy: the **law of conservation of energy.**

> **Law of Conservation of Energy**   Energy can be neither created nor destroyed; it can only be transformed.

The chemical energy in paper becomes heat energy.

Chemical Energy Resides in the Forces That Hold Atoms Together in Substances   Burning a piece of paper doesn't create energy from nothing; it releases it from storage. Generally speaking, it is stored in the forces that hold the atoms together, forces called chemical bonds that undergo adjustments when the substances undergo a chemical reaction. The energy residing in the paper or the sandwich even when it is at room temperature and doing nothing is called **chemical energy.**

Chemical energy is one of the kinds of **potential energy.** This is energy that something possesses simply by virtue of its location or because of its chemical composition. A boulder poised at the edge of a high cliff is not in motion, but anyone immediately below it fears its potential for causing change—its potential energy, which it possesses not only because of its mass but also because of its location.

The substances in a peanut butter sandwich or in a piece of paper have chemical energy not because of their locations but because they have chemical properties. One of the chemical properties is that these substances can combine with oxygen from the air, undergo energy-releasing chemical reactions, and liberate their chemical or stored energy in other forms such as heat. If the reactions of the substances in the peanut butter sandwich occur under the very special conditions of a human body, then some of the energy—about half—is released not as heat but as the kinetic energy in the form of muscles in motion, or in other forms useful to the body.

2.4   HEAT ENERGY

The human body can absorb or release large quantities of heat with little change in temperature because its water content gives it a high heat capacity.

Heat is the energy that transfers from one object to another when the two are at different temperatures and in some kind of contact. We say that heat flows from the object with the higher temperature to the one with the lower temperature. If left to itself, the flow continues until both objects reach the same intermediate temperature. Heat is thus a temperature-changing capacity possessed by any object. To get heat to flow, all we have to do is put the object next to one with a lower temperature.

Heat is also a physical-state changing capacity. A block of ice at 0 °C in contact with a warm radiator will not itself undergo a change in temperature. It will simply melt — change its physical state from solid to liquid. As long as the freshly melted water is in contact with some ice, its temperature is the same as that of the ice. The temperature at which a solid changes into a liquid is called the **melting point** of the solid.

If you put a pan of water at 100 °C on a hot burner, the flame's higher temperature won't raise the temperature of the water. It will cause the water to boil and change its state from liquid to gas (vapor). The temperature at which this occurs is called the **boiling point.** Thus when an object at a higher temperature is in contact with one at a lower temperature either a change in state or a change in temperature occurs. In either case, heat flows.

The Calorie Is One Unit of Heat Energy
It takes a certain amount of heat to make the temperature of 1 g of water change from 14.5 °C to 15.5 °C, and the name of this quantity is the **calorie,** abbreviated **cal.**[1]

One degree is a small change, and one gram of water isn't much — about 16 drops — so the calorie is an extremely small amount of heat. It is often convenient, therefore, to use a multiple of the calorie called the **kilocalorie, kcal.**

$$1 \text{ kcal} = 1000 \text{ cal}$$

Each Substance Has a Thermal Property Called Its Specific Heat
All other substances require specific quantities of heat in order for the temperature of a one-gram sample to change by one Celsius degree. The general name for this thermal property is **specific heat,** defined by the following equation,

$$\text{Specific heat} = \frac{\text{cal}}{\text{g } \Delta t} \tag{2.1}$$

where cal = calories, g = mass in grams, and Δt = the change in temperature in Celsius degrees. Translated into words, Equation 2.1 says that "The specific heat equals the calories absorbed (or released) per gram per Celsius degrees of temperature change." The units in Equation 2.1 give us the units for specific heat, cal/g °C.

The specific heats of several substances are given in Table 2.2. Notice that metals have very low values; for example, the specific heat of iron is 0.1 cal/g °C (to one significant figure).

[1] Although the specific Celsius degree, the one between 14.5 and 15.5 °C, is specified in this formal definition, a one-degree transition anywhere between the 0 °C and 100 °C marks requires virtually an identical quantity of heat.

TABLE 2.2 Specific Heats of Some Substances

Substance	Specific Heat (cal/g °C)[a]
Ethyl alcohol	0.58
Gold	0.031
Granite	0.192
Iron	0.12
Olive oil	0.47
Water (liquid)	1.00

[a] These values are good in the temperature range of several degrees Celsius on either side of room temperature.

■ Turning up a burner on a pan of boiling water won't cook the potatoes faster, because it doesn't raise the temperature. It just boils the water away faster. (*Then* the temperature soars as the potatoes turn blacker and blacker.)

■ In nearly all popular books on nutrition and diet, the word *calorie* actually means *kilocalorie.*

■ The symbol Δ is the Greek capital *delta.* Pronounce Δt as "delta tee." When Δ is in front of any other symbol, it means a *change* in the value of whatever the other symbol represents. Thus ΔE refers to a *change* in energy; Δm is a change in mass.

In other words, it takes only one-tenth of a calorie to make the temperature of a 1-g sample of iron rise by 1 °C. Put another way, the 1 cal that raises the temperature of only 1 g of water by just 1 °C can raise the temperature of the same mass of iron by 10 °C, ten times as much. Iron undergoes a much larger change in temperature than the same mass of water by the gain or loss of a relatively small amount of heat. In the next section we will see how tremendously important the high specific heat of water is to all living things. But first, to get a better understanding of the concept of specific heat, we will work an example using it.

■ To two significant figures, water's specific heat is 1.0 cal/g °C over the entire range of 0 to 100 °C.

EXAMPLE 2.3   USING SPECIFIC HEAT DATA

■ A large iron nail has a mass of about 25.4 g.

Problem: The specific heat of iron is 0.106 cal/g °C in the temperature range pertaining to this problem. If a 25.4-g piece of iron at 20.0 °C received 115 cal of heat, what would its temperature change to?

Solution: What we need to find is the value of Δt, and we can use Equation 2.1. *It is essential that we carry along all the units as we place data into this equation, because we have to be sure that they will cancel properly to leave the answer in the correct unit.* NEVER OMIT THE UNITS OF PHYSICAL QUANTITIES DURING CALCULATIONS UNTIL THEY CANCEL OR MULTIPLY PROPERLY TO GIVE THE CORRECT FINAL UNITS. THE UNITS ARE OUR CHIEF CHECK ON SETTING UP A SOLUTION CORRECTLY.

$$\text{Specific heat of iron} = \frac{0.106 \text{ cal}}{\text{g °C}} = \frac{115 \text{ cal}}{25.4 \text{ g} \times \Delta t}$$

To solve this for Δt we have to cross-multiply. If you think this mathematical procedure is something you can't do, turn to Appendix A where it is described using this particular problem. Cross-multiplication gives us

$$\Delta t = \frac{(115 \text{ cal}) \times (\text{g °C})}{(25.4 \text{ g}) \times (0.106 \text{ cal})}$$

Notice how we can cross-multiply units just like numbers and that now all the units except °C cancel. After doing the arithmetic, we get

$$\Delta t = 42.7 \text{ °C} \quad \text{(rounded from 42.71282127)}$$

In other words, 115 cal of heat will raise the temperature of a 25.4-g piece of iron by 42.7 °C. Therefore its new temperature is 20.0 °C + 42.7 °C = 62.7 °C.

PRACTICE EXERCISE 3

Suppose that the same amount of heat used in the example, 115 cal, was absorbed by 25.4 g of water instead of iron, with the initial temperature also 20.0 °C. What will be the final temperature of the water in degrees Celsius? (The specific heat of water in this range is 0.998 cal/g °C.) This exercise demonstrates the superior ability of water to absorb heat, compared to iron, without experiencing a large change in temperature.

Heat Capacity Can Provide a Thermal "Cushion"   The high specific heat of water is a major factor in the human body's ability to withstand large swings in outside temperature. If your body's core temperature changes even a few degrees from normal, 37.0 °C, you could die. Because the adult body is about 60% water, however, it has a substantial thermal "cushion" called its *heat capacity.*

    All objects have this thermal property of heat capacity. Its value is proportional to the total mass of the object, so heat capacity is an extensive property. The **heat capacity** of an object is the quantity of heat that it can absorb (or release) per degree change in Celsius temperature. Its common units are calories per degree Celsius (cal/°C). For calculating purposes, we can define it by the following equation:

■ Notice the difference between *specific heat* and *heat capacity.* Specific heat is the heat capacity of a substance *per gram.*

$$\text{Heat capacity} = \frac{\text{cal}}{\Delta t} \qquad (2.2)$$

TABLE 2.3 Heats of Vaporization of Some Substances

Substance	Heat of Vaporization (at the boiling point) (cal/g)
Benzene	94.1
Chloroform	59.0
Ethyl alcohol	204
Ethyl chloride	93
Diethyl ether	84
Gasoline	76–80[a]
Water	539.6

[a] This is the range in values for the individual compounds present in gasoline.

The estimated heat capacity of a 70-kg adult male is 5×10^4 cal/°C. If such a person generated this much heat without being able to get rid of any, his temperature would rise by only 1 °C. In contrast, the temperature of the same mass of iron would rise by about 10 °C, a change that, if it occurred in a human, would cause death. You can see how the body's relatively high heat capacity helps the system protect itself against harmful fluctuations in temperature. The heat generated by the body each day, however, is so great that additional mechanisms are needed. To understand how they work, we have to study other thermal properties of substances, particularly their heats of vaporization.

Heats of Vaporization and Fusion Are the Energies Needed To Boil or To Melt Substances The change of a liquid to its gaseous or vapor state is called either **vaporization** or **evaporation,** and the associated verbs are *to vaporize* and *to evaporate.* The opposite change, the conversion of a vapor to its liquid form, is called **condensation,** and the verb is *to condense.* To vaporize a liquid requires a constant addition of heat, as you no doubt have experienced when you have boiled water on the stove. Of course, a liquid doesn't have to be at its boiling point to evaporate. Wet clothing does dry out, and if it is next to the skin, much of the heat needed for evaporation is taken from the body. You've also experienced this, no doubt, whenever you've noticed how cold wet jeans can feel.

The heat needed to change 1 g of a substance from its liquid to its gaseous form is called its **heat of vaporization.** Its value varies somewhat with the temperature at which the liquid is evaporating. For water at its boiling point, the heat of vaporization is 539.6 cal/g; at body temperature (37 °C), water's heat of vaporization is about 580 cal/g. Table 2.3 gives the heats of vaporization for several substances at their boiling points. Notice that the value for water is considerably higher than for the others. As we will see in greater detail in the next section, this fact means that the body can get rid of a lot of heat by letting a little water evaporate from the skin.

■ The use of the word *vapor* is usually limited to talking about the gaseous form of something that at ordinary temperatures is a liquid or a solid. Thus we speak of "water vapor," but we don't refer to air as a vapor.

■ Gaseous water, below 100 °C, can be called *water vapor,* but when the temperature of gaseous water is about 100 °C (water's boiling point), it's called *steam.*

EXAMPLE 2.4 **USING HEAT OF VAPORIZATION DATA**

Problem: How much heat in calories is needed to convert 10.0 g of liquid water to steam at 100 °C?

Solution: We're given 10.0 g of water, and we know that the heat of vaporization is 539.6 cal/g. This value means that we have available the following two conversion factors:

$$\frac{539.6 \text{ cal}}{1 \text{ g}} \quad \text{or} \quad \frac{1 \text{ g}}{539.6 \text{ cal}}$$

(Treat the "1" in these conversion factors as an exact number.) Therefore, to get the answer in the right units, we have to multiply 10.0 g by the first factor:

$$10.0 \text{ g} \times \frac{539.6 \text{ cal}}{1 \text{ g}} = 5396 \text{ cal} \quad \text{(unrounded)}$$

Because 10.0 has only three significant figures, we have to round the answer and use scientific notation to express the result as 5.40×10^3 cal. This is the same as 5.40 kcal, because

$$5.40 \times 10^3 \text{ cal} \times \frac{1 \text{ kcal}}{10^3 \text{ cal}} = 5.40 \text{ kcal}$$

PRACTICE EXERCISE 4

How much heat in kilocalories is needed to evaporate 1.0 kg of water from the body at 37 °C? The heat of vaporization of water at this temperature is 5.8×10^2 cal/g.

Changing a solid to its liquid state also requires a characteristic quantity of heat called the heat of fusion. The **heat of fusion** of a substance is the heat needed to change 1 g of it to a liquid at the same temperature, the melting point. Table 2.4 gives heats of fusion for some common substances, and notice again the unusually high value for water. As we'll see in a later chapter, these high values for water's heats of fusion and vaporization are an indication of how strongly water's formula units cling to each other.

Ice is much more effective in an icepack than liquid water, even if the liquid is at essentially the same temperature, because of the high heat of fusion of water, 79.67 cal/g. The melting of a small amount of ice draws considerable heat without any change in temperature, but if the water is a liquid, its absorption of heat can occur only if its temperature rises. We have learned that the specific heat of liquid water is (rounded) 1.0 cal/g °C. Its heat of fusion is (also rounded) 80 cal/g. If *liquid* water at roughly 0 °C is to be used to absorb 80 cal and yet rise in temperature only 1 °C, then 80 g of liquid would be needed. But if *solid* water at roughly 0 °C can be used, then only 1 g is needed to absorb 80 cal because this much heat is needed to melt the ice.

TABLE 2.4 Heats of Fusion of Some Substances

Substance	Heat of Fusion (cal/g)
Benzene	30
Ethyl alcohol	24.9
Gold	15.0
Iron	65.7
Sulfur	10.5
Water	79.67

EXAMPLE 2.5

USING HEAT OF FUSION DATA

Problem: How much heat is needed to melt an ice cube with a mass of 30.0 g (about 1 ounce) if the ice temperature is 0 °C?

Solution: The value for the heat of fusion of ice, 79.67 cal/g, makes available to us two conversion factors.

$$\frac{79.67 \text{ cal}}{1 \text{ g}} \quad \text{or} \quad \frac{1 \text{ g}}{79.67 \text{ cal}}$$

If we multiply the given, 30.0 g, by the first factor, the remaining unit will be "cal."

$$30.0 \text{ g} \times \frac{79.67 \text{ cal}}{1 \text{ g}} = 2390 \text{ cal}$$

We have to express the answer as 2.39×10^3 cal to show the right number of significant figures, three. Thus one ice cube, by melting, can absorb considerable heat. If this heat were removed from 250 mL of liquid water—about one glassful—with an initial temperature of 25 °C (77 °F), the water temperature would drop by about 10 °C and become 15 °C (59 °F).

PRACTICE EXERCISE 5

An icepack was prepared using 375 g of ice at 0 °C. As this ice melts, how much heat in calories and in kilocalories will be removed from the surroundings?

One important fact must be remembered about all these thermal properties of water. If a certain quantity of heat has to be absorbed to cause a change of state or a change of temperature in one direction, then exactly the same quantity has to be released to go in the opposite direction. For example, if 80 cal have to be absorbed by ice at 0 °C to *melt* one gram, then to *freeze* one gram of water at the same temperature requires that we remove 80 cal. Similarly, if 540 cal must be absorbed by liquid water at 100 °C to vaporize one gram, then when the same mass of steam at 100 °C condenses it releases the identical quantity of heat. This is why steam is so much more dangerous in contact with the skin than very hot water, although both are life-threatening. When *steam* contacts the much cooler skin, it condenses and all of its heat of vaporization is released, some into the skin itself.

PRACTICE EXERCISE 6   If 16.4 g of steam change to the liquid state at 100 °C, how many kilocalories of heat are released?

Chemical Reactions That Give Off Heat Are Exothermic   In a very broad sense, chemical reactions are either spontaneous or they are not. Spontaneous events are those that, once started, continue with no further human intervention. Combustion (burning) is a common example. The flame from a tiny match can initiate a gigantic forest fire. A reaction such as combustion that continuously releases heat is called an **exothermic** reaction, and most (but not all) spontaneous reactions are exothermic.

■ *exo,* out
endo, in
therm, heat

Many chemical reactions can be made to take place if we continuously supply them with heat. Reactions that require a continuous input of heat are called **endothermic** reactions.

2.5 METABOLISM AND BODY TEMPERATURE

Heat generated by metabolism is lost by radiation, conduction, convection, and the evaporation of water.

Warm-blooded creatures, like people, maintain their internal, core temperatures within a few tenths of a degree. In this section we will apply the principles of specific heat and heat capacity to explain some of the mechanisms for doing this.

Basal Metabolism Supports Basal Activities   The minimum activities inside the body that must take place just to maintain muscle tone, control body temperature, circulate the blood, breathe, make compounds or break them down, and otherwise operate tissues and glands during periods of rest are called the body's **basal activities.** The sum total of all the chemical reactions that supply the energy for the basal activities is called the body's **basal metabolism.** The rate at which chemical energy is used for basal activities is called the **basal metabolic rate,** and it is customarily given in kcal/min or in the units of kcal/kg h (kilocalories per kilogram of body weight per hour).

■ Other units of time could also be used.

Measurements of basal metabolic rates are taken when the person is lying down, has done no vigorous exercise for several hours, has eaten no food for at least 14 hours, and is otherwise awake but at complete rest. A 70-kg (154-lb) adult male has a basal metabolic rate of 1.0 to 1.2 kcal/min. The rate for a 58-kg (128 lb) woman is 0.9 to 1.1 kcal/min. Under other activities, the metabolic rate is higher, of course, as the data in Table 2.5 show. We'll show how these data can be used to estimate the daily calorie needs of an individual who spends various segments of each day in known activities.

EXAMPLE 2.6   **COMPUTING DAILY CALORIE NEEDS**

Problem: A woman student was found to have a basal metabolic rate of 1.1 kcal/min. During a typical day, she spent 6.0 hr sleeping, 6.0 hr in class and lab, 8.0 hr in seated activities such as eating, studying, and resting, 2.0 hr in walking at a rate of 3.0 mph, and 2.0 hr in moderately strenuous recreational activities. How many calories of energy were needed during these 24 hours to sustain these activities? Assume that the data for a 58-kg woman apply to this individual. Assume also that the values at the higher end of each range in Table 2.5 apply.

Solution: The best approach is to construct a table as follows (remembering that an hour has 60 minutes).

Activity	Rate of Energy Expenditure	Minutes	Energy
Sleep, 6.0 hr	1.1 kcal/min	360 min	396 kcal
Class/lab, 6.0 hr	2.0 kcal/min	360 min	720 kcal
Seated, 8.0 hr	2.0 kcal/min	480 min	960 kcal
Walking, 2.0 hr	3.9 kcal/min	120 min	468 kcal
Exercise, 2.0 hr	5.9 kcal/min	120 min	708 kcal
Total			3252 kcal

The total has to be rounded to two significant figures. Thus the woman used 3.3×10^3 kcal in the day.

PRACTICE EXERCISE 7 A 70-kg adult male student carried out the same activities as those described for the female student in Example 2.6. Assuming that his basal metabolic rate was 1.2 kcal/min, and assuming that his other activities used energy at the rates given by the higher ends of the ranges, what were his energy needs for the day?

The Body Has Several Mechanisms for Losing Heat The higher the metabolic rate, the more heat the body must release to preserve its temperature. Because of the relatively high heat of vaporization of water at body temperature, the evaporation of water becomes an important vehicle for this release.

TABLE 2.5 Average Energy Expenditures by Individuals According to Daily Activities[a]

Categories of Activities	Rate of Energy Expenditure (kcal/min)	
	Man (70 kg)	Woman (58 kg)
Sleeping, reclining	1.0–1.2	0.9–1.1
Very light Seated and standing activities; painting trades, auto and truck driving; laboratory work; typing; playing musical instruments; sewing and ironing	1.2–2.5	1.1–2.0
Light Walking on level, 2.5–3 mph; tailoring; pressing; garage work; electrical trades; carpentry; restaurant trades; cannery workers; washing clothes; shopping with light load; golf; sailing; table tennis; volleyball	2.5–4.9	2.0–3.9
Moderate Walking 3.5–4 mph; plastering; weeding and hoeing; loading and stacking hay bales; scrubbing floors; shopping with heavy load; cycling; skiing; tennis; dancing	5.0–7.4	4.0–5.9
Heavy Walking with load uphill; tree felling; work with pick and shovel; basketball; climbing; football	7.5–12.0	6.0–10.0

[a] Data are for mature, adult men and women and are from *Recommended Dietary Allowances*, 8th ed. (Committee on Dietary Allowances, Committee on Interpretation of the Recommended Dietary Allowances, Food and Nutrition Board, National Research Council, National Academy of Sciences. Washington, D.C., 1974).

TABLE 2.6 Water Budget of the Human Body

Water Intake		Water Outgo	
As drink	1.2 L	Evaporation	
In food	1.0 L	from skin	0.5 L
Made by metabolism	0.3 L	from lungs	0.5 L
		Urine	1.4 L
		Feces	0.1 L
Total intake	2.5 L	Total outgo	2.5 L

Table 2.6 shows the daily water exchange of a typical adult male. Notice particularly how much water is lost by evaporation, 40% or 1.0 L. Because 1.0 L of water has a mass of 1.0 kg, 1.0 kg of water evaporates. We learned earlier that the heat of vaporization of water *at body temperature* is 5.8×10^2 cal/g, which translates to 5.8×10^2 kcal/kg. Thus as 1.0 kg of water evaporates from the body, 5.8×10^2 kcal of heat are removed from the body each day by this mechanism. Compare this with the 20×10^2 to 40×10^2 kcal per day of food energy taken in by eating from which roughly half does appear as heat. In other words, very roughly half of the heat that must be lost by the body each day is carried away in the body water that evaporates. (Half of 20×10^2 kcal is 10×10^2 kcal, and the figure of 5.8×10^2 kcal is 58% of this.)

Evaporation occurs two ways. When the sweat glands work and beads of perspiration emerge, the evaporation is called **sensible perspiration.** Evaporation that does not involve the sweat glands is called **insensible perspiration** because we do not notice that it happens. Both forms help to cool the body, but in hot weather and during strenuous exercise, sensible perspiration accelerates. Either form, of course, cannot be sustained without the intake of ample fluids.

Radiation, Conduction, and Convection Also Carry Heat Away   The body has other mechanisms for releasing heat besides perspiration. One is by **radiation,** the same heat transfer that occurs at a radiator or a hot clothing iron. Radiation from the body is like light radiation except it isn't visible light but infrared radiation. The uncovered head in cold weather radiates as much as half of the body's heat production. This is why experienced mountaineers say, "If your feet are cold, put on your hat." The hat helps the entire body retain heat.

■ Infrared radiation is sometimes referred to as heat rays.

Conduction is the direct transfer of heat from a warmer body to a colder object. It happens, for example, when we place an ice pack on an inflamed area of the skin, or when we sit on a cold surface, or when we put bare hands onto cold machinery or tools.

Finally, **convection** is another mechanism for losing heat from the body. This happens whenever we let the wind or a draft sweep away the warm, thin layer of air next to the skin. Both waffle-weave undergarments and heavy wool slacks or sweaters are filled with tiny pore spaces that trap this layer of warm air. Air is a very poor conductor of heat, so as long as the warm air layer is held close to the skin, little heat is lost by convection.

Body Temperature and Metabolic Rate Are Connected   One reason why the body tries to maintain a steady temperature is that even small changes in temperature affect the rates of chemical reactions, including those of metabolism. If the body's core temperature increases—a condition called **hyperthermia**—metabolic processes speed up. To sustain this, the body needs more oxygen—about 7% more for every one degree Fahrenheit increase. To deliver this oxygen, the heart must work harder, so a sustained condition of hyperthermia creates problems for the heart.

■ hyper- = over or above
therm = heat
hypo- = under or below

The opposite of hyperthermia is **hypothermia**—a condition of a lower than normal body temperature. Under this condition, the rates of metabolism slow down, including those reactions that keep vital functions working normally. Special Topic 2.1 describes the progression of events when someone is a victim of hypothermia.

| SPECIAL TOPIC 2.1 | HYPOTHERMIA |

The body responds to a fall in its temperature by trying to increase its rate of metabolism so that more heat is generated internally. Uncontrollable shivering is the outward sign of this response, and it sets in with a drop in temperature of only 2 to 3 °F (measured rectally). If the temperature continues to drop, the shivering will be violent for a period of time. Then loss of memory — amnesia — sets in at about 95 to 91 °F. The muscles become more rigid as the core temperature drops to the range of 90 to 86 °F, and the individual must have outside help immediately. The victim no longer has any ability to take life-saving steps. The heartbeat becomes erratic, unconsciousness sets in (87 to 78 °F), and below 78 °F death occurs by heart failure or pulmonary edema.

Death by hypothermia has often been called death by *exposure,* and it can happen even if the air temperature is above freezing. If you become soaked by perspiration or rain and the wind comes up, an outside temperature of

40 °F is dangerous. Those who fall into cold water (32 to 35 °F) seldom live longer than 15 to 30 minutes.

The legendary Saint Bernard dogs who brought little casks of brandy to blizzard victims in the Swiss Alps were more likely agents of death than of life to anyone who drank the brandy. A shot of brandy in a hypothermic individual worsens the situation. Alcohol *enlarges* blood capillaries. When the capillaries near the skin's surface, which are loaded with the most-chilled blood in the hypothermic body, suddenly enlarge, the chilled blood moves quickly to the body's core. This rapid drop in *core* temperature is particularly life-threatening.

If a victim of hypothermia is conscious and able to swallow food or drink, administer warm, nonalcoholic fluids and sweet foods. As quickly as possible, get the victim dry and out of the wind. Get into a dry sleeping bag with the victim, so that your own body warmth can be used. It is a genuine medical emergency and prompt aid is vital.

SUMMARY

Matter Matter, anything with mass that occupies space, can exist in three physical states: solid, liquid, and gas. Broadly, the three kinds of matter are elements, compounds, and mixtures. Elements and compounds are called pure substances, and they obey the law of definite proportions. Mixtures, which do not obey this law, can be separated by operations that cause no chemical changes, but to separate the elements that make up a compound requires chemical reactions.

A chemical reaction is an event in which substances change into different substances with different formulas. Elements can be classified as metals or nonmetals.

Dalton's atomic theory The law of definite proportions and the law of conservation of mass in chemical reactions led John Dalton to the idea — now regarded as well-established fact — that all matter consists of discrete, noncuttable particles called atoms. The atoms of the same element, said Dalton, all have the same mass, and those of different elements have different masses. When atoms of different elements combine to form compounds, they combine as *whole* atoms; they do not break apart. Dalton realized that when different elements combine in different proportions by atoms, the resulting compounds must display a pattern now summarized by the law of multiple proportions.

Symbols, formulas, and equations Every element is given a one- or two-letter symbol, and it can stand either for the element or for one atom of the element. The symbol for a compound is called a formula. The empirical formula (one kind of formula) consists of the symbols of the atoms in one formula unit, with the smallest whole-number subscripts used to show the proportions of the different atoms present.

To describe a chemical reaction, the symbols of the substances involved as reactants, separated by plus signs, are on one side of an arrow that points to the symbols of the products, also separated by

plus signs. The equation is balanced when all atoms showing in the formulas of the reactants are present in like numbers in the formulas of the products. Coefficients, numbers standing in front of formulas, are employed as needed to achieve the correct balance. In both formulas and equations, the numbers used for subscripts and coefficients are generally the smallest whole numbers that show the correct proportions.

Forms of energy When something is able to cause a change in motion, position, illumination, sound, or chemical composition, it has energy of one form or another — kinetic energy (energy of motion), light, sound, potential energy, and chemical energy (a special form of potential energy). Energy is not created nor does it disappear into nothing; it can only be transformed from one type into another or from one place to another. Spontaneous chemical reactions are usually exothermic — they release heat — but many reactions can be made to occur by continuously heating the reactants. These are endothermic reactions.

Heat energy Heat is the form of energy that transfers because of temperature differences. This transfer causes changes either in the temperatures or in the physical state, such as melting or freezing, boiling or condensing.

The heat that changes the temperature of one gram of a substance by one degree Celsius is called the substance's specific heat. When the substance is water, the quantity of heat is defined as the calorie.

The heat capacity of an object — an extensive property — is the heat that the whole object will absorb or release as its temperature changes by one degree Celsius.

Heat and metabolism Because the body contains so much water, and because water has a relatively high specific heat, the body has a high heat capacity. Its temperature doesn't change much as heat is absorbed or released. The body loses heat by radiation, conduction, convection and the evaporation of water. The body's loss of heat by the evaporation of water takes advantage of water's relatively high heat of vaporization. Because of water's relatively high heat of fusion, an ice pack is roughly 80 times more efficient than the same mass of ice-cold water in cooling an inflamed area of the body. Without

proper management of the body's heat budget, a condition of hyperthermia (a temperature increase) or hypothermia (a temperature decrease) will develop. Hyperthermia increases the rate of metabolism, because heat accelerates reactions. This eventually strains the heart. Hypothermia slows down body reactions, and this is also life-threatening.

REVIEW EXERCISES

The answers to the Review Exercises that require a calculation and whose numbers are marked by an asterisk are given in Appendix D. The answers to all other Review Exercises appear in the *Study Guide* that accompanies this book.

States and Kinds of Matter

2.1 If we think about a warm room, bathed in sunlight, we might imagine that energy itself occupies space. Why don't we call it matter?

2.2 What are the names of the three states of matter?

2.3 In terms of shapes and volumes, how do solids differ from gases?

2.4 We can push a hand through a basin of water, but we can't move our hand through a block of ice. Yet the same formula units (molecules) are present in both. What can we say about the relative *mobilities* of the formula units of water in these two states?

2.5 Unless the wind is strongly against us, we can move through air with no noticeable difficulty. Air consists of a mixture of the formula units of nitrogen and oxygen, both gases. What can we say about the relative *mobilities* of these formula units as contrasted with the formula units in a liquid such as water?

2.6 Indium is a substance that can be given a shiny finish, and it conducts electricity well. Is indium more likely to be a metal or a nonmetal?

2.7 Phosphorous is a dark-reddish, powdery substance that doesn't conduct electricity. Is it more likely to be a metal or a nonmetal?

2.8 What is the essential difference between a chemical reaction and a physical change?

2.9 Which of the following events are physical changes?
(a) The splintering of rock into gravel.
(b) The change in the color of leaves during the fall season.
(c) The decay of plant remains on a forest floor.
(d) The eruption of an oil well just "brought in" by drillers.
(e) The seeming disappearance of sugar as it is stirred into coffee or tea.
(f) The swing of a compass needle near another magnet.
(g) The formation of a raindrop in a cloud.

2.10 What fact is true about all elements and distinguishes them from compounds and mixtures?

2.11 Roughly, how many elements are known: 80, 100, 200, or 2000?

2.12 Roughly, how many elements are not solids under ordinary room conditions, but are either liquids or gases: 2, 13, 44, 75, 180, or 1885?

2.13 What important facts about compounds distinguish them from either elements or mixtures?

2.14 What is meant in chemistry when something is described as a *pure substance?* What two kinds of substances are called *pure?*

2.15 What is the general name given to the event by which elements are changed into compounds?

2.16 Hydrogen reacts with oxygen to give water. What are the *reactant(s)* and the *product(s)* in this event?

2.17 What is an alloy?

2.18 What important mass relationship between reactants and products in a chemical reaction is always observed?

Dalton's Atomic Theory

2.19 If a sulfur atom had the same mass as an iron atom, in what *mass* ratio of iron to sulfur in iron(II) sulfide would the atom ratio be 1 to 1?

2.20 In compounds consisting of just two elements, the mass ratios of the elements are never found to be simply 1 to 1. Which postulate of Dalton's atomic theory is based on this fact?

*2.21 Platinum forms two compounds with oxygen. In one, the combining ratio is 6.10 g of platinum to 1.00 g of oxygen. In the other, the combining ratio is 12.2 g of platinum to 1.00 g of oxygen. By means of a calculation, show how these two compounds illustrate the law of multiple proportions.

2.22 Two compounds of the elements tin and chlorine are known. When they are broken down into the separate elements, the following mass data are obtained from 100.0-g samples of each compound.

Compound A: 62.20 g of tin and 37.40 g of chlorine

Compound B: 45.56 g of tin and 54.44 g of chlorine

(a) From compound A, for every 1.000 g of tin, how many grams of chlorine are obtained?
(b) From compound B, for every 1.000 g of tin, how many grams of chlorine are obtained?
(c) What is the ratio of the mass of chlorine that combines with 1.000 g of tin in compound B to the mass that combines to make compound A?
(d) What law of chemical combination is illustrated by the results of part (c)?

2.23 What, fundamentally, must happen in order for some change to be described as chemical and not physical?

2.24 What are some observations or measurements that we can make to determine if a given change is chemical and not just physical?

Chemical Symbols, Formulas, and Equations

2.25 The symbol BN stands for a compound (boron nitride), not an element. How can we tell this *from the symbol itself?*

2.26 What are the symbols of the following elements?
(a) iodine (b) lithium (c) zinc
(d) lead (e) nitrogen (f) barium

2.27 Write the symbols for the following elements:
(a) carbon (b) chlorine (c) copper
(d) calcium (e) fluorine (f) iron

2.28 What are the symbols of the following elements?
(a) hydrogen (b) aluminum (c) manganese
(d) magnesium (e) mercury (f) sodium

2.29 Write the symbols for the following elements:
(a) oxygen (b) bromine (c) potassium
(d) silver (e) phosphorus (f) platinum

2.30 The symbol S represents the *element* sulfur. What else does this symbol stand for?

2.31 What are the names of the elements represented by the following symbols?
(a) P (b) Pt (c) Pb (d) K
(e) Ca (f) C (g) Hg (h) H
(i) Br (j) Ba (k) F (l) Fe

2.32 Give the name of each element represented by the following symbols:
(a) S (b) Na (c) N (d) Zn
(e) I (f) Cu (g) O (h) Li
(i) Mn (j) Mg (k) Ag (l) Cl

2.33 One formula unit of water is made from two hydrogen atoms and one oxygen atom. Which of the following formulas is the best for water?
(a) HO_2 (b) H_2O (c) 2HO (d) H_2O_4 (e) H_4O_2

2.34 Suppose that we wrote the formula of iron(II) sulfide as Fe_2S_2 instead of FeS. Would this violate a natural law — for example, the law of definite proportions — or a convention, or both?

2.35 What essential feature of FeS makes it a compound, not a mixture?

2.36 Write a balanced equation that symbolizes the following description of a chemical reaction: Iron combines with sulfur to give FeS_2.

Energy

2.37 Matter is a *thing*. What is energy?

2.38 Kinetic energy refers to what kind of energy? What is the equation that defines kinetic energy?

2.39 What is the law of conservation of energy?

2.40 If energy is conserved, what happens to the kinetic energy in a rock avalanche or slide?

2.41 A stick of dynamite lying on the ground has no potential energy that relates to its *location*, but it still has potential energy. What kind?

2.42 A lighted candle represents the conversion of chemical energy into what two other forms?

2.43 Is chemical energy one form of potential energy or a form of kinetic energy?

*2.44 In the equation for kinetic energy, if *m* is in kilograms and *v* is in meters per second (m/s), the calculated value of the kinetic energy has the units of kg m²/s², and these units define the SI unit of energy called the joule (J). The relationship between the joule and the calorie is 1 cal = 4.184 J (exactly).
(a) How much kinetic energy, in joules, does a large station wagon with a mass of 1.97×10^3 kg (2.17 ton) have when it is traveling at a velocity of 24.4 m/s (55.0 mph)?
(b) How much energy does this station wagon have in calories? In kilocalories?

2.45 Referring to the information about kinetic energy and the joule given in Exercise 2.44, what velocity in m/s does a compact car with a mass of 910 kg have if its kinetic energy is 5.86×10^5 J?

Heat Energy

2.46 *Heat* is the name we give to the form of energy that transfers from one object to another in what two kinds of situations?

2.47 What is the name of the temperature reading at which a substance changes from the solid to the liquid state?

2.48 The numerical value of the specific heat of granite is 0.192. What are the units (as studied in this book)?

2.49 Consider a body of water with a volume of 10^5 m³. Which would be the larger value for this, its heat capacity or its specific heat? What relationship exists between heat capacity and specific heat?

2.50 The specific heat of gold is 0.031 cal/g °C. In order to calculate the heat capacity of a given bar of gold, what additional information is needed?

*2.51 What is the heat capacity of 1.00 g of water? Of 10.0 g of water?

2.52 The specific heat of gold is 0.031 cal/g °C and that of olive oil is 0.471 cal/g °C. Suppose that you had 10.0-g samples of each at a temperature of 20.0 °C, and that each sample absorbed 25.0 cal of heat. First judge which sample would experience a greater rise in temperature, and then calculate the final temperatures of each.

*2.53 Describe two circumstances in which water can absorb heat and not experience a change in temperature.

2.54 The numerical value for the heat of fusion of gold is 15. What are the units (as used in this book)?

2.55 Which substance would experience a greater change of its mass from the solid to the liquid form upon absorbing 25 cal of heat, gold (at its melting point) or ice (at 0 °C)? Explain.

2.56 If ice at 0 °C can absorb heat without any change in temperature, why doesn't this constitute a violation of the law of conservation of energy?

2.57 Why is ice at 0 °C far superior as a coolant in an ice pack than as the same mass of liquid water at 0.0005 °C?

2.58 Which could melt more ice, the heat in 100 g of water as steam at 100.0001 °C or as a liquid at 99.9999 °C? Explain.

2.59 What two terms can be used for the change of a liquid to its vapor state at any temperature at which this occurs?

2.60 What happens to the heat that changes water to steam at 100 °C when the steam condenses?

2.61 Water in the gaseous state is sometimes called *steam* and sometimes *water vapor*. Under what circumstance is each term used?

2.62 Would the physical change of steam to liquid water at just under 100 °C be properly described as an endothermic or an exothermic change?

2.63 What kind of change, exothermic or endothermic, is necessary to make ice at 0 °C change to liquid water?

2.64 Give an example of an exothermic chemical change.

*2.65 The specific heat of gold is 0.031 cal/g °C. If a bar of gold with a mass of 1.0 g at 25 °C is given the same quantity of heat as is needed to melt 0.10 g of ice at 0 °C, what will be the new temperature of the bar of gold?

2.66 The specific heat of iron is 0.119 cal/g °C. If a piece of iron with a mass of 1.00 g at 20.0 °C is given the same quantity of heat as is needed to vaporize 0.100 g of water at 100 °C, what will be the new temperature of the iron?

*2.67 The heat of vaporization of ethyl alcohol is 204 cal/g. How many grams of ethyl alcohol can be vaporized by the heat released when 100.0 g of steam (at 100 °C) condenses?

2.68 Ethyl chloride is sometimes used as a local anesthetic when boils are lanced. Because its boiling point is very low (12 °C), it quickly evaporates when sprayed on the skin at the site of the boil. The energy for this evaporation comes from the skin, which experiences a local drop in temperature — the desired response. At the lower temperature, the chemical reactions needed to send a pain signal don't occur rapidly enough to matter. The heat of vaporization of ethyl chloride is 93 cal/g. Suppose that a physician sprays 2.0 g of ethyl chloride on a boil, and that the affected site has a mass of 5.0 g. Further suppose that the specific heat of the exposed site is the same as that of water, 1.00 cal/g °C, and that the temperature at the site is initially 37 °C. If only the heat at this site and none from the surrounding air goes to make the ethyl chloride evaporate, what will the final temperature of the exposed site be, in °C and in °F? (A fall of skin temperature to 50 °F always causes it to feel numb and soon to lose all sense of touch and pain.)

Metabolism and Body Temperature

2.69 List six activities that are basal activities of the body.

2.70 What constitutes the body's *basal metabolism,* in general terms?

2.71 What does the term *basal metabolic rate* mean?

2.72 To one significant figure, what is the basal metabolic rate for adults in kcal/min?

2.73 What are the ways in which water becomes part of the body and, to two significant figures, how many liters of water are involved by each route?

2.74 What percent of the water lost by the body is lost by a change of state?

2.75 What name is given to the loss of body water by the evaporation that does not involve the sweat glands?

2.76 Name the body's three mechanisms for losing heat that do not involve evaporation directly.

2.77 What is the difference between radiation and conduction as means for losing heat from the body?

2.78 Wearing woolen clothing minimizes heat loss from the body by what mechanism?

2.79 What is hypothermia, and why is it dangerous to life?

2.80 What is hyperthermia, and how can it be life-threatening?

*2.81 Suppose that an adult woman with a weight of 58 kg carried out the following activities over a period of one day:

Sleeping, 8.0 h   Light activities, 3.0 h

Very light activities, 12.0 h   Heavy activities, 1.0 h

How many kilocalories are expended for these activities? Use the higher of the two rates (in kcal/min) given in Table 2.5 as the basis for your calculations. (Thus the metabolic rate for sleeping would be taken as 1.1 kcal/min. Remember there are 60 min/h.)

2.82 Suppose that an adult male with a weight of 70 kg performed the following activities in a 24-hour day:

Sleeping, 8.0 h   Moderate activities, 4.0 h

Very light activities, 4.0 h   Heavy activities, 8.0 h

What is his energy requirement in kilocalories for this period? Use the higher of the two rates in the data of Table 2.5.

*2.83 The National Academy of Sciences uses the following conversion factors for the energy content of foods: proteins, 4.0 kcal/g; carbohydrates, 4.0 kcal/g; food fat, 9.0 kcal/g. If a 1-cup serving of milk (250 g) contains 8.4 g of protein, 12 g of carbohydrate, and 9.6 g of food fat, what is the energy content of this serving in kilocalories?

2.84 A 100-g portion (about ⅔ cup) of roasted, salted peanuts contains, besides some undigestible food fiber, the following: protein, 26 g; carbohydrate, 19 g; food fat, 50 g.
   (a) What is the energy content of this portion in kilocalories? (Use the conversion factors given in Exercise 2.83.)
   (b) If a man walking at 3.5 mph needs 5.0 kcal/min to maintain this activity, how many hours does he have to walk to "work off" the kilocalorie intake of the 100-g serving of peanuts?
   (c) How far does he have to walk, in miles?

Hypothermia (Special Topic 2.1)

2.85 How can an increase in the rate of metabolism help meet the challenge of hypothermia?

2.86 Being soaked to the skin and in the wind is more dangerous than being soaked and in still air. Explain.

2.87 Giving a hypothermic individual a shot of brandy or whiskey increases the danger to the person. Explain.

CHAPTER THREE

Atomic Theory and the Periodic System of the Elements

Since the Nobel-prize-winning work of Niels Bohr, the popular imagination has seen atoms as tiny solar systems with electrons whizzing around an atomic nucleus like planets around a sun. We study a better model of the atom in this chapter.

3.1 THE NUCLEAR ATOM

The particles that make up atoms—nuclei and electrons—have opposite electrical charges, but the atom itself is uncharged.

Like most successful theories in science, Dalton's atomic theory opened many areas for further study. Dalton had used the mass relationships of the elements in compounds with such success that many scientists sought ways to measure the relative masses of the atoms of all the elements. Other scientists became increasingly interested in what atoms themselves might be made of. The quest for a deeper knowledge about atoms was on.

The Major Subatomic Particles Are Electrons, Protons, and Neutrons Dalton had said that atoms cannot be broken, but this meant only that they are not broken *in chemical reactions.* He couldn't have known of other ways to split atoms; these weren't developed until early in the 1930s, when scientists treated various elements to a number of high-energy conditions and found that atoms are made of smaller, *subatomic particles.* Several have been identified, but only three are needed to account for the masses and the chemical properties of atoms. These three **subatomic particles** are the **electron, proton,** and **neutron.** Their electrical conditions and their masses are summarized in Table 3.1.

■ The proton and the neutron appear to be made of still smaller particles that physicists have named *quarks.*

Two of the subatomic particles, the proton and the electron, carry electrical charge. You no doubt have had many experiences with the *fact* if not the vocabulary of such charges. For example, if you have ever received a shock after walking across a carpet (or touching a bare wire!), the spark that gave this shock was a movement of an electrical charge.

There are fundamentally two kinds of charge. They give rise to two important phenomena, and you have probably experienced both. Have you ever tried to flick away a small thin piece of plastic, the kind used to wrap record albums, only to have it stick stubbornly to your fingers? Most annoying! You shake your hand harder, but it still sticks. This is because you are momentarily carrying one kind of electrical charge, and the plastic has picked up the opposite kind. *Opposite charges attract.* This is the first of two rules of behavior of electrical charges that are among the most important rules in all of chemistry. Maybe you have seen your hair stand on end after blow-drying it. The individual hairs act as if they repel each other, because each hair has picked up the *same* kind of charge. *Like charges repel*—this is the second of the two rules about electrical charges. Attracting and repelling are opposites, so we designate one kind of charge as positive and the other as negative, and give them + and − signs.

Like charges repel.

The proton has one unit of positive charge, $1+$. The electron has one unit of negative charge, $1-$. Electrons tend to repel each other, because they are like-charged; protons also tend to repel each other for the same reason. (Whether they actually succeed in pushing each other apart depends on how free they are to move.) Electrons and protons tend to attract each other, because they are oppositely charged. The neutron has no charge—hence its name.

The Atomic Mass Unit Is About 1.66×10^{-24} g Table 3.1 gives the masses of the three subatomic particles both in grams and in a unit new to our study, the **atomic mass unit** or **amu.** This unit was invented to let us express the masses of protons and neutrons in numbers that are simpler than those we have to use when we employ the gram unit:

$$1 \text{ amu} = 1.6605665 \times 10^{-24} \text{ g}$$

TABLE 3.1 Properties of Three Subatomic Particles

Name	Mass in grams	Mass in amu	Electrical Charge	Common Symbols
Electron	$9.1093897 \times 10^{-28}$ g	0.0005485712 amu	$1-$	e^-
Proton	$1.67262305 \times 10^{-24}$ g	1.00727605 amu	$1+$	p^+ or p
Neutron	1.674954×10^{-24} g	1.008665 amu	0	n

■ No known atom has more than 108 electrons, and they contribute only about 0.02% to the mass of such an atom.

Protons and neutrons have masses of 1.0 amu each, when we round to two significant figures. The electron has a mass only 1/1836 the mass of the proton. This is so small, relatively speaking, that we ignore it in working out relative masses of atoms. We say, for example, that the mass of an atom (in amu) is made up entirely of the sum of the masses of its neutrons and protons. This sum of neutrons and protons is called the atom's **mass number.**

> Mass number = number of protons + number of neutrons

An Element's Atomic Number Equals the Number of Protons in One of Its Atoms

As we learned in the last chapter, an **element** is a *substance* that cannot be further broken down by chemical means into simpler substances, and it consists of *atoms*. At **atom** is the smallest sample of an element that has its chemical properties. We can now add that *all the atoms of a given element have the same number of protons.* This number is called the **atomic number** of the element.

■ An alphabetically arranged list of the elements with their atomic numbers is inside the front cover.

> Atomic number = number of protons in each atom of an element

Thus each element has its own unique atomic number, and to date the atomic numbers run to 108. Element number 6, for example, is carbon. Every atom of carbon has six protons.

Most Elements in Nature Are Mixtures of Isotopes

Although all atoms in any given element have identical numbers of protons, they usually do not have the same number of neutrons. For almost any given element, the numbers of neutrons per atom vary over a small range. These variations are responsible for the existence of isotopes, and nearly all elements are actually mixtures of isotopes. An **isotope** of an element is made up of atoms of the element that not only have identical atomic numbers but also identical mass numbers. In other words, all atoms of any particular *isotope* of a given element have identical numbers of neutrons as well as identical numbers of protons. The atoms of an element's different isotopes vary only in numbers of neutrons.

■ The element fluorine (at. no. 9) consists of just one isotope; its mass number is 19.

There are three isotopes of hydrogen, the simplest element. Its atomic number is 1, so all three have the same number of protons per atom. Always remember that the isotopes of a given element all have the same atomic number as the element. The isotopes of hydrogen differ in the numbers of neutrons per atom, so they differ in mass numbers. One hydrogen isotope has a mass number of 1, another has a mass number of 2, and the third's mass number is 3. The first isotope, occasionally called *protium,* has just one proton in each atom and no neutrons. The second isotope, usually called *deuterium,* has one proton per atom, but also one neutron. (This is why its mass number is 2, because 1 proton + 1 neutron = 2 particles with mass of 1 amu each.) See Table 3.2. As you can see from the last column in this table, deuterium occurs only in a trace amount relative to the chief isotope. For *every* 100,000

■ Hydrogen is the only element whose isotopes have unique names.

TABLE 3.2 **Isotopes of Hydrogen**

Name	Symbol[a]	Protons	Neutrons	Mass Number	Natural Abundance
Hydrogen	^1_1H	1	0	1	99.985%
Deuterium	^2_1H	1	1	2	0.015%
Tritium	^3_1H	1	2	3	trace[b]

[a] Sometimes deuterium is symbolized as ^2_1D and tritium as ^3_1T.

[b] Tritium is radioactive and decays (which we will study in Chapter 10). It occurs only in cosmic rays and as part of short-lived radioactive wastes from atomic power plants.

■ Before the atomic age with its bomb tests and power plant wastes, there was only 1 tritium atom for every 10^{17} to 10^{18} atoms of ordinary hydrogen.

■ About 250 isotopes occur naturally. About 1100 more have been made using nuclear reactors. Many synthetic isotopes are used in medicine.

atoms of hydrogen in nature, 99,985 have a mass number of 1 and only 15 have a mass number of 2. The third isotope of hydrogen, called *tritium,* has a mass number of 3 (1 proton + 2 neutrons), but it is radioactive and very rare. It is largely a product of atomic reactors and their atomic wastes, but it is also found in cosmic rays.

The existence of isotopes, fortunately, does not really complicate the chemistry of an element because *isotopes of a given element have the same chemical properties.* When an element undergoes *chemical* changes, the atoms of its various isotopes do not react differently nor do they separate from each other. We can use, therefore, a common atomic symbol for an element in nearly all situations. When we need a symbol that specifies just one isotope, we use the atomic symbol but add the specific mass number and atomic number as a left superscript and a left subscript, as illustrated in the following:

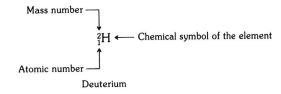

Mass number ⎤
$^{2}_{1}$H ← Chemical symbol of the element
Atomic number ⎦
Deuterium

INTERPRETING SYMBOLS FOR ISOTOPES

Problem: The atoms of one of the isotopes of carbon have six protons and seven neutrons. Write the symbol for this isotope.

■ You aren't expected to memorize the atomic numbers or mass numbers that go with the elements, although you're bound to learn a few through repeated usage.

Solution: We need the chemical symbol, which is C, and we also need the atomic number, which is given by the number of protons, 6. The mass number is the sum of the protons and neutrons.

$$\text{Mass number} = \text{protons} + \text{neutrons}$$
$$= 6 + 7$$
$$= 13$$

The symbol, therefore, is $^{13}_{6}$C.

PRACTICE EXERCISE 1

The most abundant isotope of oxygen consists of atoms with eight protons and eight neutrons. Write its special symbol.

PRACTICE EXERCISE 2

How many neutrons and protons are in the atoms of each of the following isotopes?

(a) $^{17}_{8}$O   (b) $^{14}_{7}$N   (c) $^{37}_{17}$Cl   (d) $^{35}_{17}$Cl

PRACTICE EXERCISE 3

If $^{12}_{6}$C is the correct symbol for one isotope of carbon, what is incorrect about the symbol $^{14}_{7}$C for another isotope?

Ernest Rutherford (1871–1937)

All Atoms Have Nuclei That Hold Their Protons and Neutrons The impression of the atom that one might get from Dalton's theory is that it is a hard sphere, like a billiard ball (only very small). In 1911, British scientists working under Ernest Rutherford found evidence that pointed to a softer image. They found that when streams of certain subatomic particles from a radioactive element were allowed to strike a very thin metal foil, most of the particles sailed right through with no change in course. Only a few bounced back, and many went through with various angles of deflection. It was as though the metal foil were mostly empty space, like chain-link fencing, but that at some places there were particles massive enough to bounce the subatomic "bullets" back again. See Figure 3.1. By studying the angles at which many of the particles careened through the foil, Rutherford deduced that the massive particles in the foil were positively charged and contained virtually all the mass of an atom. Thus, he concluded, an atom must be mostly empty space around a dense, massive inner core, to which he gave the name **nucleus.**

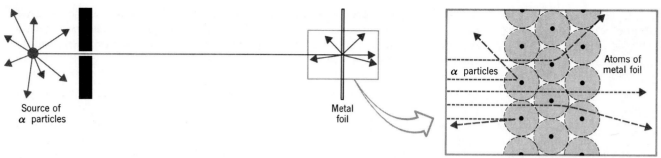

Figure 3.1
The discovery of the atomic nucleus. The α (alpha) particles consist of two protons and two neutrons, a "package" that some radioactive elements emit in high-energy streams called alpha rays. Most of the α-particles passed through the foil, although some were deflected. A few particles bounded right back as though they had hit something far more massive than an electron.

■ Rutherford's discovery of the nucleus earned him the 1908 Nobel prize in chemistry and, in 1930, the title Baron Rutherford of Nelson.

We now know that any given atom has only one nucleus and that all the atom's protons and neutrons are located in it. The protons cause the positive charge on the nucleus and the *number* of protons equals the size of this charge. In other words, the atomic number of an element turns out to be equal to the size of the positive charge carried by the element's atomic nuclei.

Atomic number = +charge on nucleus = number of protons

Now we need to find out where the electrons are in atoms. This knowledge will help us understand many chemical properties of substances at the molecular level of life.

3.2   WHERE AN ATOM'S ELECTRONS ARE—AN OVERVIEW

The electrons in an atom are confined to particular energy levels outside the nucleus.

■ We may seem far from the molecular level of life right now, but remember that an apple seed doesn't look much like an apple, and right now we're planting seeds of concepts and ideas for everything that follows.

When elements combine to form compounds, some electrons of the element's atoms become relocated with respect to atomic nuclei. To understand this, we have to learn where an atom's electrons initially are. Only then can we think about how they might relocate to give the more stable arrangements of electrons and nuclei in compounds.

The electrons of an atom are *not* in or on its nucleus. They are outside the nucleus but very close by. The *number* of electrons equals the atomic number of the atom. We said earlier that the atomic number equals the number of protons and thus the size of the positive charge on the nucleus. But there must be exactly as many electrons as protons, because we know that atoms are electrically neutral.

Atomic number = number of protons = number of electrons

Thus the nucleus of an atom with six protons has a total positive charge of 6+. There must be a total of 6− of negative charge to balance this charge so that the atom is electrically neutral. This requires six electrons, because each electron has a charge of 1−.

Niels Bohr (1885–1962)

An atom's electrons do not occur simply at random in the space near its nucleus. They are constrained to particular patterns, and the specific arrangement of electrons about a nucleus is called the atom's **electron configuration.** When we know it, we can understand a great deal about the chemical properties of an element.

The Bohr Atom Was an Early Atomic Model   In 1913, only two years after Rutherford's discovery of the nucleus, Niels Bohr (1885–1962), a Danish physicist, suggested two postulates concerning electron configurations. Bohr's first postulate was that electrons are confined to what came to be called *allowed energy states.* This says that electrons cannot be just anywhere like buzzing mosquitoes. They can only be in particular places, much as tennis balls on a stairway can only be on the level places, not suspended between them. Bohr's allowed energy states, in fact, are commonly called *energy levels.* And like a stairway, the lower energy states are more stable places to be than are the higher states. In other words, each of the allowed energy states or energy levels of an atom corresponds to some different energy value.

Bohr's second postulate was that as long as the atom's electrons remain in allowed energy states, the atom neither radiates nor absorbs any energy associated with the electrons' movements. Not that it isn't possible to make an electron move from one allowed state to another. This is what happens, for example, when an iron fireplace poker is heated until it glows in the dark. Before being heated, the iron atoms are nearly all in their *ground state* arrangement of electrons; all their electrons are in the lowest energy states available. The heat causes electrons in iron atoms to shift to higher energy states called *excited states.* This is partly how the iron actually soaks up heat energy. As soon as atoms have become excited in this way, the electrons begin to shift back to lower states *and the difference in energy between the excited state and the lower state is emitted as light.*

Scientists had known long before Bohr that the emitted light did not possess every conceivable value of light energy, but had only certain values. This is what led Bohr to believe that atoms had only certain allowed energy states.

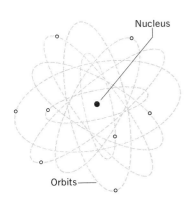

Light quantum emitted

Nucleus

Orbits

The Bohr "solar system" model

The precise quantity of energy that is emitted when one electron changes from a higher to a lower energy state is called a **quantum** of energy, and sometimes a **photon** of energy. Sometimes electricity rather than heat is used to generate excited atoms that then emit light. Sodium vapor lamps or mercury vapor lamps along highways work this way. And you know that the sodium vapor lamps have a characteristic color. Excited sodium atoms don't emit all colors of light, just yellow light, and the yellow light from sodium lamps is characterized by photons of just two, very nearly equal values of energy.

To help people understand his postulates, Bohr suggested an analogy. He pictured an atom's electrons as being in very rapid motion around the nucleus and following paths, called *orbits,* much as planets move in orbits around the sun. This picture of an atom is an example of a scientific **model,** a mental construction — often involving a picture or drawing — used to explain a number of facts. The **Bohr model** of the atom was quickly dubbed the "solar system" model, and it is still commonly used in the media to accompany almost any discussion of things atomic.

The solar system picture of the atom is no longer accepted, but Bohr's two fundamental postulates behind the model are still firmly fixed in atomic theory.

■ Heisenberg won the 1932 Nobel prize in physics.

■ The idea that the very act of measuring something actually alters what is being measured has profound implications for the fields of psychology, sociology, poll taking, and even television news.

Heisenberg's Uncertainty Principle   The Bohr model worked well only for one element, hydrogen. The problem, as a German physicist, Werner Heisenberg (1901–1976), soon realized, is that calculations based on the model assume that the location of an electron and its energy can both be precisely known at any given instant. This is untrue.

The electron is small enough that any act of measuring its location gives it a nudge and changes its energy, and any attempt to find its energy changes its location. This is why both the location and energy of an electron cannot be known simultaneously. There is always some uncertainty about either the location of an electron or its energy, and this is one way of stating what came to be called the **Heisenberg uncertainty principle.**

TABLE 3.3 The Principal Energy Levels

Principal level number	1	2	3	4	5	6	7
Maximum number of electrons observed in nature[a]	2	8	18	32	32	18	8

[a] In theory, levels 5, 6, and 7 could accommodate 50, 72, and 98 electrons, respectively. Levels 1, 2, 3, and 4 are filled in theory as well as among certain elements by the numbers of electrons given.

Because of Heisenberg's insight, scientists gave up the idea that an electron moves in a fixed orbit. Instead, the locations of moving electrons came to be described in terms of probabilities. The question became, In what particular parts of the space surrounding a nucleus is it *likely* that an electron will be? It's like asking: If I go out a certain distance from the nucleus in one particular direction, what are the chances of an electron being there? The answer depends first and foremost on what energy state we're talking about.

3 —
2 —
1 —
Principal energy levels

Electrons in Atoms Are Confined to Principal Energy Levels The specific energy states in which electrons can be are now usually called the **principal energy levels.** They roughly correspond to certain successive distances from the atom's center. These levels are numbered, beginning with level 1 for the lowest energy level, the one nearest the nucleus. An electron in level 1 has the least quantity of energy it can have in the atom. Just as nature has a powerful tendency to take up positions having the lowest possible energy, so an atom's electrons nearly always are in the lowest allowed levels — in the ground state.

There Are Limits on the Numbers of Electrons in the Principal Energy Levels Not all electrons can crowd into level 1. Electrons, remember, are like-charged and so they repel each other. Each principal energy level has a limit to its number of electrons, and the limit for level 1 is only two. At level 2, the limit is eight electrons, a larger number because there is more room farther from the nucleus. Table 3.3 summarizes the maximum number of electrons that can be in the various principal energy levels.

The Principal Energy Levels Are Electron Shells If you've ever studied a whole onion, you know that it exists in sections, each one a hollow sphere with thick walls, each successively larger than the one just inside it. They all have a common center, so they are called concentric spheres. We can think of an atom's principal energy levels as concentric spheres, too, and each with a definite thickness. This is why the principal energy levels are often called **electron shells.** The first principal energy level is thus the first shell.

To summarize, the electrons of an atom reside in principal energy levels or shells that occur concentrically around the atom's nucleus. It's a rather simple picture, and it lacks some details that we will need to relate an atom's structure to its chemical properties. These details are the concern of the next section. Bear in mind that we intend to get to the bottom of certain chemical properties of the elements common to living systems, and that these properties can be related to the electron configurations in the formula units of elements and compounds.

3.3 ATOMIC ORBITALS

The principal energy levels have sublevels made up of regions called atomic orbitals.

Electron Shells Have Sublevels The thickness of an electron shell allows for some fine structure. All the electron shells except the first (the one corresponding to the lowest energy) have a small number of **sublevels.** It's as though an atom is an apartment house for electrons (with the nucleus in the basement) and each floor is a principal energy level or shell. Each floor can have one, two, three, four, or five apartments called sublevels. The electrons of an atom are thus in sublevels, but the sublevels also have particular structures.

Sublevels Have Regions Called Orbitals

Each sublevel has a certain definite number of spaces, called **atomic orbitals,** where electrons can be. They are particularly shaped spaces that can hold up to two electrons apiece, no more. It's as though each apartment (sublevel) has a certain number of rooms (orbitals) for electrons, but no room can hold more than two electrons. To specify the location of an electron we have to name its main energy level, its sublevel, and its orbital. We need not specify the location any more precisely.

Heisenberg said that if we give up wanting to know *precisely* where an electron is within an orbital, we can know what is more important, the energy of the electron. The importance of energy derives from this major fact about our world: nature, given the opportunity, tends to change in whichever direction results in a more stable, lower energy arrangement of things. If we can find out that one arrangement of electrons and nuclei is more stable (has lower energy) than another, we can then know which of the two arrangements nature will prefer. This is at the heart of understanding chemical reactions, because they tend to illustrate nature's preference for the more stable arrangements of its parts.

An Orbital Can Hold Two Electrons If They Have Opposite Spin

The final complexity in electron configurations is that electrons are *spinning* particles. Like the earth, electrons spin about an axis. Unlike the earth, they have the option of spinning in one or the other of two opposite ways. When an atomic orbital holds two electrons, they can be present only if one electron spins in a direction opposite that of the other. Part of the reason is that spinning electrons behave like tiny magnets. By spinning oppositively, the two tiny magnets have a magnetic attraction for each other. This helps to overcome the electrical repulsion between two like-charge electrons when they are in the same small space.

Wolfgang Pauli (1900–1958), an Austrian-born physicist, was the first to realize the limitations on the number and spins of electrons in the same orbital, and we call the rule the **Pauli exclusion principle.**

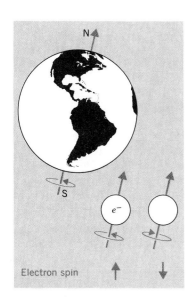

Electron spin

■ Wolfgang Pauli won the 1945 Nobel prize in physics.

Pauli Exclusion Principle   An orbital can hold as many as two electrons, but only if they have opposite spin.

Orbitals Have Unique Shapes

Now let's look more closely at the kinds of rooms, the atomic orbitals, available in the atoms's electron apartments (sublevels). It turns out that at principal level 1, there is only one sublevel and it constitutes an entire atomic orbital. It's as though the ground floor — the first principal energy level — of the apartment house has only one apartment (a sublevel) and it consists of just one room (orbital). This orbital is called the 1s orbital — 1 for principal energy level 1 and s for a German word of no interest here, but we can think of it as meaning "spherical."

Each atomic orbital has a particular shape. These shapes have been deduced from the mathematical operations used to calculate the probabilities of finding electrons. The shape of an orbital is simply what you get when you wrap an imaginary envelope around enough of a particular space to enclose a region of high probability — say, 90% — of having an electron somewhere within it.

Figure 3.2 shows the shape of the 1s orbital. It looks like a sphere when viewed from the outside. The nucleus is in its center. The surface of the sphere encloses a space within which the probability of finding an electron belonging to level 1 is greater than 90%. An electron in a 1s orbital moves about — very rapidly, in fact. But we can't know *exactly* how or where because we would rather know about the 1s electron's energy (at least its energy relative to other electrons). It is thus more important that we know if an electron is in a 1s state than to know precisely where in this state it is.

The fact that an electron does move rapidly about within an orbital gives us another useful image, that of an **electron cloud.** An electron moves so rapidly within an orbital that the influence of its negative electrical charge is evened out within the orbital, somewhat as a

Figure 3.2

The 1s orbital. (a) Imagine that the space around a nucleus is made up of layer upon layer of extremely thin, concentric shells. At each distance away from the nucleus there is a point on the curve that indicates the probability of finding a 1s electron at this distance. Notice that the probability is zero for a zero distance — the electron is not on the nucleus. The probability reaches a maximum at the radius marked a_0, which is 52.9 pm (1 pm = 10^{-12} m). (b) One of the thin spheres described in part a encloses a space within which the total probability of finding an electron is large, say, 90%. This sphere is the "envelope" discussed in the text, and its shape is the shape of the 1s orbital.

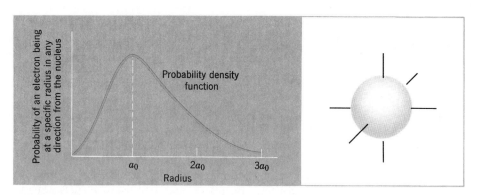

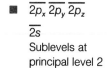

■ $\overline{2p_x}\ \overline{2p_y}\ \overline{2p_z}$
$\overline{2s}$
Sublevels at
principal level 2

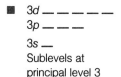

■ $3d$ _ _ _ _ _
$3p$ _ _ _
$3s$ _
Sublevels at
principal level 3

cloud is an evened-out distribution of moisture in a volume of very humid air. Thus the spherical shape of a 1s orbital is the same as the shape of the electron cloud associated with this orbital.

Principal level 2 has two sublevels. One sublevel consists of only one orbital. It is named the 2s orbital, and it corresponds to slightly less energy than that of the other sublevel. The 2s orbital looks like a sphere from the outside, which is why it is designated an s orbital — it resembles the s orbital at level 1. The other sublevel holds three orbitals. They all correspond to the same energy, but they are pointed at right angles to each other, as seen in Figure 3.3. Each looks like two small spheres pierced by one of the axes — x, y, and z. Orbitals that have this kind of shape are named p orbitals, and when they belong to level 2, they are named the 2p orbitals — the $2p_x$, the $2p_y$, and the $2p_z$. We say that each of them has two *lobes*, and where these lobes touch is where the three axes — x, y, and z — touch. This point between lobes is called a *node*.

Principal level 3 has three sublevels. (You may notice that the number of sublevels at a principal level is the same as the number of the principal level. At level 1, there is one sublevel; at level 2, there are two sublevels; and now at level 3, there are three sublevels.) One of the sublevels at level 3 is an orbital all by itself — the 3s orbital; it is of the s-type because it looks from the outside like the other s orbitals. At the second sublevel of level 3, there are p-type orbitals — the $3p_x$, the $3p_y$, and the $3p_z$. They resemble the p orbitals of level 2. Finally, the

Figure 3.3

The orbitals at principal energy level 2. From the outside, the 2s orbital looks like a 1s orbital, seen in Figure 3.2. However, its radius is larger. Each of the 2p orbitals has the same shape and energy as the others, but they are oriented along the three different axes.

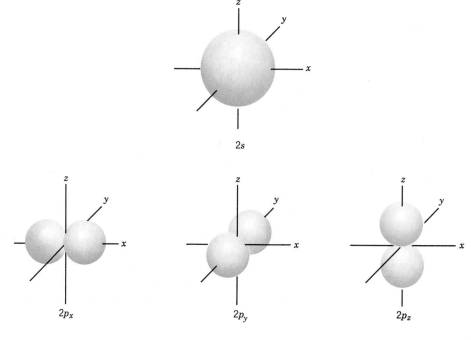

Figure 3.4
The atomic orbitals, showing their relative energies and the order in which the sublevels fill in accordance with the aufbau rules.

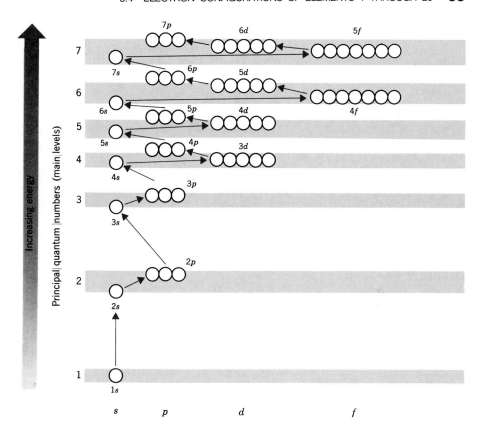

third sublevel at level 3 is made up of five orbitals called *d* orbitals. Having mentioned them, we'll not give them individual names nor deal with them further here. We won't be needing them for the elements that are most important in our study.

At principal level 4, there are four sublevels, one 4*s* orbital, three 4*p* orbitals, five 4*d* orbitals, and seven of a new type, called *f* orbitals. We'll not be needing the *f* orbitals in our study either.

Think of the names of individual orbitals as addresses of individual electrons. An electron in, say, the 3*p_y* orbital is located in principal level 3, in a sublevel that consists of *p* orbitals, and in the specific *p* orbital whose axis is the *y* axis.

The relative energies that electrons have in the various orbitals are indicated by the circles in Figure 3.4. The thick, horizontal stripes correspond to the principal energy levels. (Don't worry about the arrows in this figure yet.) Notice that the 3*d* orbitals actually correspond to slightly lower energies than the 4*p* orbitals. There are other peculiarities such as this that we have to leave to more advanced treatments. We are now ready to describe the electron configurations of the atoms of several key elements.

■ 4*f* __ __ __ __ __ __ __
　4*d* __ __ __ __ __
　4*p* __ __ __
　4*s* __
Sublevels at
principal level 4

3.4 ELECTRON CONFIGURATIONS OF ELEMENTS 1 THROUGH 20

The electrons of an atom fill into the lowest-energy atomic orbitals available, spreading out among orbitals of the same energy.

The kind of question we raise in this section is what is the most stable distribution of the electrons among the orbitals of, say, element 13, aluminum? (Remember, we need to know electron configurations to *understand* why different elements have certain chemical properties.) We will learn here how to figure out the electron configuration of an atom of any of the first 20 elements using just the atomic number and a few rules called the *aufbau rules*. The Pauli exclusion principle is one of these rules.

■ *Aufbau* = "building up" in German.

Electrons Spread Out among Orbitals of the Same Sublevel Another aufbau rule concerns where electrons go when orbitals of the same energy are available, like the *p*-type orbitals at level 2 and higher. **Hund's rule** handles this question.

> **Hund's Rule.** Electrons at the same sublevel spread out among the sublevel's orbitals as much as possible.

This rule makes sense because electrons are like-charged and they would tend to be as far from each other as possible. Therefore, when it makes no difference in terms of the orbital energies, electrons spread out among the same set of orbitals. It is also true than when they do spread out like this, they have the same spins. To illustrate, the distribution on the left is more stable than the one on the right.

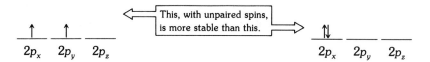

As a symbol for the direction of spin, we use an arrow, which can point either down ($\downarrow$) or up ($\uparrow$). However, because two electrons in the same orbital *must* have opposite spins, we seldom need such arrows. Usually, the symbol used for a pair of electrons in the same orbital is a superscript number as in $1s^2$.

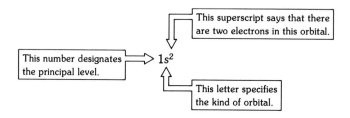

We can summarize the **aufbau rules** as follows.

1. The atomic number tells us how many electrons to distribute.
2. Electrons are placed into the orbitals of *lowest* energy that are available, provided that
   (a) No more than two electrons go into the same orbital, and then only if they have opposite spin (Pauli exclusion principle).
   (b) Electrons are spread out as much as possible — retaining the same spins — when orbitals of the *same* sublevel are open (Hund's rule).

Let us now apply these rules to a few elements, beginning with the simplest, hydrogen, atomic number 1.

The Aufbau Rules Let Us Construct The Electron Configurations of Elements 1 Through 20 A hydrogen atom has one electron. We have learned that the $1s$ orbital has the lowest associated energy, so this is where the electron resides.

$$\textbf{H} \quad 1s^1$$

meaning $\quad 1s \;\uparrow$

Helium has atomic number 2 and therefore its atoms have two electrons. Both can (and must) go into the $1s$ orbital.

■ Helium is a gas used to fill dirigibles such as the Goodyear blimp. It is much less dense than air, and it won't burn.

He $1s^2$

meaning $1s$ ⇅

Lithium, atomic number 3, has three electrons in each atom. The first two fill the $1s$ orbital. The third electron must go to the next lowest orbital, the $2s$. Here is where the arrows in Figure 3.4 help; they show the order of filling of the orbitals, and notice that the order goes from lowest energy successively upward to higher energy values.

Li $1s^22s^1$

meaning $2p$ __ __ __
           $2s$ ↑
           $1s$ ⇅

■ Think of the three lines at the $2p$ sublevel as representing, in order, the $2p_x$, $2p_y$, and the $2p_z$ orbitals.

Beryllium, atomic number 4, has four electrons per atom. The first two fill the $1s$ orbital, and the last two fill the $2s$ orbital. None enters a $2p$ orbital, because these orbitals are at a higher energy level (Figure 3.4), and we must fill the lower energy orbitals first.

Be $1s^22s^2$

meaning $2p$ __ __ __
           $2s$ ⇅
           $1s$ ⇅

■ Borax, a cleansing agent, contains boron.

Boron, atomic number 5, has five electrons per atom. The first four fill the $1s$ and the $2s$ orbitals, exactly as in beryllium (number 4), and boron's fifth electron enters a $2p$ orbital. We don't know which of the three takes it, so we just arbitrarily assign it to the $2p_x$ orbital.

B $1s^22s^22p_x^1$

meaning $2p$ ↑ __ __
           $2s$ ⇅
           $1s$ ⇅

■ All but a handful of the roughly six million compounds of carbon are classified as *organic compounds*.

The next element, carbon (atomic number 6), is of central importance at the molecular level of life, because its atoms make up most if not quite all of the "backbones" of molecules, other than water, that are in living cells.

C $1s^22s^22p_x^12p_y^1$

meaning $2p$ ↑ ↑ __
           $2s$ ⇅
           $1s$ ⇅

Notice that carbon illustrates the application of Hund's rule. The last two electrons go into *separate* orbitals at the $2p$ sublevel.

■ Air is about 79% nitrogen.

Nitrogen, number 7, is another very important element among biological chemicals. It also illustrates Hund's rule.

N $1s^22s^22p_x^12p_y^12p_z^1$

meaning $2p$ ↑ ↑ ↑
           $2s$ ⇅
           $1s$ ⇅

■ Air is about 21% oxygen.

Oxygen (atomic number 8) illustrates that we don't start with level 3 until level 2 is filled. Oxygen's eighth electron goes into a $2p$ orbital, not the $3s$.

$$\textbf{O} \quad 1s^2 2s^2 2p_x^{\,2} 2p_y^{\,1} 2p_z^{\,1}$$

$$\text{meaning} \quad 2p \ \uparrow\downarrow\ \uparrow\ \uparrow$$
$$2s \ \uparrow\downarrow$$
$$1s \ \uparrow\downarrow$$

■ Fluorine is so reactive that it burns with water.

Fluorine (atomic number 9) has nine electrons, and we continue to fill the $2p$ orbitals.

$$\textbf{F} \quad 1s^2 2s^2 2p_x^{\,2} 2p_y^{\,2} 2p_z^{\,1}$$

$$\text{meaning} \quad 2p \ \uparrow\downarrow\ \uparrow\downarrow\ \uparrow$$
$$2s \ \uparrow\downarrow$$
$$1s \ \uparrow\downarrow$$

■ Neon is the gas in "neon" lights.

With the next element, neon (atomic number 10), we complete the filling of all the atomic orbitals at level 2.

$$\textbf{Ne} \quad 1s^2 2s^2 2p_x^{\,2} 2p_y^{\,2} 2p_z^{\,2}$$

$$\text{meaning} \quad 2p \ \uparrow\downarrow\ \uparrow\downarrow\ \uparrow\downarrow$$
$$2s \ \uparrow\downarrow$$
$$1s \ \uparrow\downarrow$$

Level 2 now has its maximum of eight electrons, two at the $2s$ sublevel and six at the $2p$ sublevel.

With element 11, sodium, we start to fill the third main level.

$$\textbf{Na} \quad 1s^2 2s^2 2p_x^{\,2} 2p_y^{\,2} 2p_z^{\,2} 3s^1$$

$$\text{meaning} \quad 3s \ \uparrow$$
$$2p \ \uparrow\downarrow\ \uparrow\downarrow\ \uparrow\downarrow$$
$$2s \ \uparrow\downarrow$$
$$1s \ \uparrow\downarrow$$

The aufbau rules, as least as far as we have developed them, continue to apply through element 18, argon.

■ The electron configurations of all the elements through number 103 are in Appendix B.

We won't be concerned with the electron configurations of elements beyond element 20, calcium, because nearly all the elements that are important at the molecular level of life are among the first 20. These include potassium (19) and calcium (20). If you look again at Figure 3.4, you will see that the $4s$ orbital accepts electrons before the $3p$. Therefore the electron configuration of potassium is $1s^2 2s^2 2p^6 3s^2 3p^6 4s^1$. (Notice that when a p sublevel has all its orbitals filled, we can save a little space by writing p^6 instead of showing the individual orbitals with two electrons each.)

When we write the electron configuration of an element, we do so for any of its isotopes. Atoms of isotopes of the same element differ only in their numbers of neutrons, but these are in the nucleus and have nothing to do with electron configurations. Because isotopes have the same electron configurations, they have the same chemical properties.

| EXAMPLE 3.2 | **WRITING AN ELECTRON CONFIGURATION** |

Problem: Phosphorus, atomic number 15, is another element important at the molecular level of life. Write its electron configuration.

Solution: With 15 electrons, we know that both levels 1 and 2 are filled; they take $2 + 8 = 10$ electrons. The remaining five must be in level 3.

$$1s^2 2s^2 2p^6 3s^2 3p_x{}^1 3p_y{}^1 3p_z{}^1$$

meaning $3p$ ↑ ↑ ↑

$3s$ ⇅

$2p$ ⇅ ⇅ ⇅

$2s$ ⇅

$1s$ ⇅

PRACTICE EXERCISE 4   Using the one-line representation rather than the system with arrows, write the electron configuration of each of the following elements. Use the table inside the front cover to find out their atomic numbers.

(a) magnesium   (b) chlorine   (c) argon   (d) calcium

3.5   ATOMIC WEIGHTS

The atomic weight of an element is the average mass, expressed in atomic mass units, of the atoms of the isotopes of the elements as they occur naturally.

Because atoms combine as whole particles when they form compounds, chemical reactions involve whole-number proportions *by atoms*. Iron, for example, can combine with sulfur according to the following equation.

$$\text{Fe} + \text{S} \longrightarrow \text{FeS}$$
Iron   Sulfur   Iron(II) sulfide

If we want to carry out this reaction in the lab, we have to try to bring iron and sulfur together in a ratio of one to one *by atoms*. If atoms were as big as cups and saucers, it would be easy to get this ratio simply by counting. But atoms are too small to count, at least to count *directly*. Atoms are so small that even if we had a sample of iron consisting of 6.02×10^{23} atoms, the sample would have a mass of only 55.8 g. Even if we could see, handle, and count atoms, it would take nearly 200 thousand billion centuries to assemble a pile of iron atoms this size, counting at a rate of two atoms per second. Obviously, we need an indirect method for counting particles this small.

You probably know that it is possible to count such things as pennies by weighing them. All we need is to measure the mass of one penny or, if the pennies are of different ages and have not all worn down similarly, the average mass of several pennies. If a penny has an average mass of say, of 3.00 g (to pick a round number), and a pile of pennies has a mass of 300 g, you can tell that there are 100 pennies in the pile. We do something like this to count atoms by weighing them.

Chemists count — well, at least estimate — the number of atoms in a sample by weighing the sample and then doing a calculation. If we know the number of atoms per gram, we can multiply this ratio by the grams of the sample and get the number of atoms.

$$\text{Grams of sample} \times \frac{\text{atoms}}{\text{gram}} = \text{number of atoms in sample}$$

It would appear that all we now need is a good figure for the number of atoms per gram for each element.

Isotopes complicate this somewhat in the way that well-worn pennies mixed with newly minted pennies complicate the estimation of the number of pennies in a sackful. Isotopes do this because the atoms of the isotopes of a given element have different masses. What we need is the average mass of all the atoms of the various isotopes that make up a naturally occurring sample of an element. Consider, for example, the element magnesium, which consists of three isotopes,

$$^{24}_{12}\text{Mg}, \quad ^{25}_{12}\text{Mg}, \quad \text{and} \quad ^{26}_{12}\text{Mg}.$$

In naturally occurring magnesium, regardless of its origin on planet earth, 78.70% of all atoms are magnesium-24; 10.13% are magnesium-25; and 11.17% are magnesium-26. Most of the atoms have a mass number of 24, so we'd naturally expect that the mass of the "average" atom would be closer to 24 than to 25 or 26 amu. And this is true; the accepted value for the average atomic mass of magnesium is 24.305 amu.

■ Most scientists use the expression *atomic weight* instead of the technically better term, *atomic mass*.

The average atomic mass (in amu) of the atoms of an element, as they occur naturally, is called the **atomic weight** of the element. Dalton said that the atoms of different elements differ in mass. The atomic weights provide a way to describe how different.

A Table of Atomic Weights and Numbers appears inside the front cover. Notice that the atomic weight of carbon is 12.001. We just saw that the atomic weight of magnesium is 24.305. In other words, an atom of magnesium is roughly twice as heavy as an atom of carbon. If we wanted to obtain samples of magnesium and carbon that had the same numbers of *atoms*, we would have to take twice as much magnesium *by weight* than carbon. Then the ratio would be one to one by atoms and we wouldn't even have to know the actual number of atoms. It would be very large, we can be sure of that, but when our interest is in the one to one atom ratio, the actual number doesn't matter. We'll return to the measurement of substances used in reactions in Chapter 5. We've introduced the concept of atomic weight here because it's needed in the next section.

Notice in the Table of Atomic Weights and Numbers that atomic weights are reported to varying numbers of significant figures. Often this means that the proportions of the isotopes of an element do vary slightly, very slightly, from place to place on the planet. (Footnotes to the table discuss this further.) When we use atomic weights from this table, we will usually round the values to the first decimal place.

3.6 THE PERIODIC LAW AND THE PERIODIC TABLE

In a given family of representative elements, the atoms of all members have the same outside-level electron configurations.

If each of the 108 elements were completely unlike any of the others, the study of chemistry would be far more difficult. Fortunately, chemists have found that the elements can be sorted into a small number of families whose members have much in common. Dimitri Mendeleev, a Russian scientist, was the first to notice this as he worked on writing a chemistry textbook for his students, published in 1869.

Many Properties of the Elements Vary Periodically with Their Atomic Numbers

Dimitri Mendeleev (1834–1907)

■ *Periodic* means the recurrence of something in a regularly repeating way, such as lampposts or sunsets.

When he organized some of the physical and chemical properties of the elements known in his time, Mendeleev observed that the properties seemed to go through cycles from the elements of lowest atomic weight to the highest. The cycles weren't geometrically perfect, but there were definite rises and falls. One improvement, which came with the discovery of atomic numbers a few decades after Mendeleev's work, was to use atomic numbers instead of atomic weights as the basis for arranging the elements in order. The temperatures at which the first 20 elements boil, for example, illustrate the kind of rise and fall that Mendeleev noted. These temperatures do not keep rising ever higher as the atomic numbers increase. Instead, as seen in Figure 3.5a, they fluctuate with the atomic numbers.

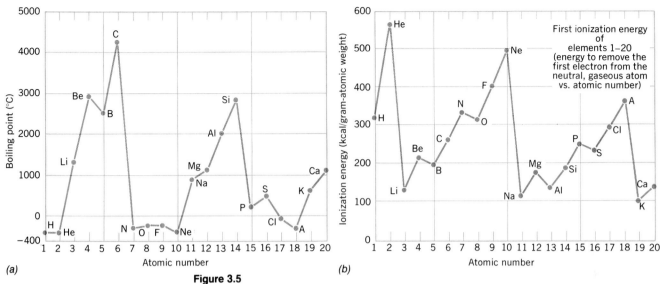

Figure 3.5
Two properties of elements 1 through 20 that show periodic fluctuations. (a) Boiling points versus atomic numbers. (b) Ionization energies versus atomic numbers.

The ionization energies of the elements display a similar rising and falling in values, as seen in Figure 3.5b. An element's ionization energy is the energy needed to make one electron leave each atom in a sample whose mass equals the element's atomic weight in grams. Notice that in the plot of boiling points versus atomic numbers, helium, neon, and argon are at the bottoms of cycles. They are at the tops in Figure 3.5b. They seem to form a set of elements that have similar properties.

The combining abilities of the atoms of one element for atoms of another also go through a cyclical rise, fall, rise, fall pattern. For example, most of the first 20 elements form binary compounds with hydrogen. A **binary compound** is one made of only two elements.

An atom of atomic number:	3	4	5	6	7	8	9	10
can bind these many H atoms:	1	2	3	4	3	2	1	0
The formulas are:	LiH	BeH_2	BH_3	CH_4	NH_3	H_2O	HF	—

■ CH_4 is methane, the natural gas used for heating and cooking. NH_3 is ammonia.

This pattern repeats itself as we go to still higher atomic numbers.

An atom of atomic number:	11	12	13	14	15	16	17	18
can bind these many H atoms:	1	2	3	4	3	2	1	0
The formulas are:	NaH	MgH_2	AlH_3	SiH_4	PH_3	H_2S	HCl	—

In both series, we see an increase in the number of hydrogens from 1 to 4 and then we see the number fall back again. The number of hydrogens doesn't just keep rising to ever higher values as we go to elements of higher atomic numbers.

Just as neon (10) and argon (18) seem to be similar with respect to boiling points and ionization energies, they also similarly form no compound with hydrogen. Neither does helium. Elements 6 and 14 are similar in their ability to bind four hydrogen atoms, and they similarly share high boiling points (Figure 3.5a). Periodically, with increasing atomic number, physical and chemical properties recur — more or less. This is the essence of the **periodic law,** one of the important laws of nature.

Periodic Law. The properties of the elements are a periodic function of their atomic numbers.

The Periodic Table Organizes the Elements To Show Off Their Periodic Properties

The heart of Mendeleev's discovery was that elements of similar properties would line up in vertical columns if horizontal rows made of their symbols (and arranged in order of increasing atomic weight) were interrupted by breaks at the right places. The result was a table of the elements called the **periodic table.** Its modern form is shown inside the front cover of this book. It incorporates elements discovered since the time of Mendeleev, and it arranges the elements in order of their atomic numbers, not atomic weights. Each horizontal row in the periodic table is called a **period** and each vertical column is called a **group.**

In constructing his periodic table, Mendeleev had the boldness to leave blanks in the columns whenever this seemed necessary to get elements to line up vertically in families. He even went so far as to declare that these blanks represented elements that had not yet been discovered — and he was right. In order to achieve the best vertical sorting into families, he even switched some pairs of elements from their order of increasing atomic weights. He listed, for example, tellurium (atomic weight 127.6) *before* iodine (atomic weight 126.9), because iodine seemed to fit far better with fluorine, chlorine, and bromine in group VIIA than with oxygen, sulfur, and selenium in group VIA. When atomic numbers were discovered, it was gratifying to find that placing tellurium before iodine put these elements in the correct order according to increasing atomic numbers.

You have probably noticed that the periods in the periodic table are not all the same length and that several are broken. This is necessary if the highest priority is to be the nature of the vertical columns or groups — the members of these groups must, as much as possible, have similar chemical properties. Thus period 1 is very short, containing only hydrogen and helium, and like the next two periods it is separated into two parts.

The groups have both numbers and letters.[1] Some groups have roman numerals followed by the letter A — IA, IIA, IIIA, and so forth up to VIIA. These plus group 0 are called the **representative elements.** The other groups, clustered near the middle of the periodic table, use roman numerals followed by the letter B (except for a cluster in the middle designated as VIII). The B series plus VIII are called the **transition elements.** The two rows of elements placed outside the table are the **inner transition elements.** (The table would not fit well on the page if the inner transition elements were not handled in this way.) Elements 58 through 71 constitute the *lanthanide* series, named after element 57, which just precedes this series. The series of elements 90 to 103 is the *actinide series.*

Several of the groups of representative elements also have names. Those in group IA, for example, are called the **alkali metals,** because they all react with water to give an alkaline or caustic (skin-burning) solution. If we let M represent any alkali metal, the general equation for this reaction is

$$2M + 2H_2O \longrightarrow 2MOH + H_2$$

| Alkali metal | Water | Alkali metal hydroxide | Hydrogen |

For example, if M is sodium, Na, the alkali metal hydroxide that forms is sodium hydroxide, NaOH, commonly known as lye.

The elements in group IIA are called the **alkaline earth metals,** because they are commonly found in "earthy" substances such as limestone. For example, calcium carbonate or $CaCO_3$ is a compound of calcium, an alkaline earth metal of group IIA, and this compound is the chief substance in limestone.

The elements in group VIIA are called the **halogens** after a Greek word signifying salt-forming ability. Chlorine of group VIIA, for example, is present in a chemically combined form in table salt, NaCl (sodium chloride).

■ Notice in the periodic table that Co (at. no. 27) has a *higher* atomic weight than Ni (at. no. 28).

■ Hydrogen isn't a member of group IA in any chemical sense, but it is often located in the periodic table where it gives this appearance.

■ NaOH flakes are an ingredient in one kind of drain cleaner. Use it very carefully and keep it out of reach of children.

[1] We are using here the column labels most widely employed in the United States. The International Union of Pure and Applied Chemistry has adopted different designations for the vertical columns, but this had encountered stiff opposition in this country largely because it does not readily adapt to teaching how electron configurations correlate with the column numbers.

The elements in group 0, all gases, were discovered after Mendeleev's work. Except for a few compounds that xenon and krypton form with fluorine and oxygen, these elements chemically react with nothing. For this reason they are called the **noble gases** (*noble* signifying limited activity).

Other groups of representative elements are named simply after the first member — for example, the **carbon family** (group IVA), the **nitrogen family** (group VA), and the **oxygen family** (VIA).

PRACTICE EXERCISE 5 Referring to the periodic table, pick out the symbols of the elements as specified.

(a) A member of the carbon family: Sr, Sn, Sm, S
(b) A member of the halogen family: C, Ca, Cl, Co
(c) A member of the alkali metals: Rn, Ra, Ru, Rb
(d) A member of the alkaline earth metals: Mg, Mn, Mo, Md
(e) A member of the noble gas family: Ac, Al, Am, Ar

Electron Configurations Are Behind the Periodic Table's Organization Mendeleev's observation and his periodic law aroused considerable interest in finding underlying causes for the similarities of members of the same groups or families. The very fact of the periodic table arrangement begs the question, "What must be true about the structures of the atoms of the elements to make *families* of elements possible?"

A strong clue is given in Table 3.4. Here the numbers of electrons in the principal energy levels of several representative elements are given, family by family. Notice the **outside levels,** the highest numbered main levels that hold electrons. When we look at the outside

TABLE 3.4 Electron Configurations among Four Families of Representative Elements

Family	Element	Number	Principal Level Number						
			1	2	3	4	5	6	7
Group IA	Lithium	3	2						
The alkali metals	Sodium	11	2	8					
	Potassium	19	2	8	8				
	Rubidium	37	2	8	18	8			
	Cesium	55	2	8	18	18	8		
	Francium	87	2	8	18	32	18	8	
Group IIA	Beryllium	4	2						
The alkaline earth metals	Magnesium	12	2	8					
	Calcium	20	2	8	8				
	Strontium	38	2	8	18	8			
	Barium	56	2	8	18	18	8		
	Radium	88	2	8	18	32	18	8	
Group VIIA	Fluorine	9	2						
The halogens	Chlorine	17	2	8					
	Bromine	35	2	8	18				
	Iodine	53	2	8	18	18			
	Astatine	85	2	8	18	32	18		
Group O	Helium	2							
The noble gases	Neon	10	2						
	Argon	18	2	8					
	Krypton	36	2	8	18				
	Xenon	54	2	8	18	18			
	Radon	86	2	8	18	32	18		

levels, family by family, we see two very striking facts. First, the atoms of the same family all have the same number of electrons in their outside levels and, second, these numbers differ from family to family.

All atoms of group IA metals have one electron in the outside level. In group IIA, all atoms have two outside level electrons. In fact, *among the representative elements, the group number (I, II, and so forth through VII) corresponds to the number of electrons in the outside level.* The group number for the noble gases used to be VIII, so giving this group number 0 doesn't make it as much an exception to this rule as it might seem. Helium, the first element in this group, has just two electrons in its outside level, but this level (number 1) cannot hold more than two anyway.

The electron configurations of the series B elements, such as the various transition elements, have their own fairly regular patterns, but our study will not require much knowledge of them. We can mention that as we go from element 21 (Sc, scandium) through element 30 (Zn, zinc) — the transition elements in period 4 — the 4s orbital usually holds one or two electrons whereas the five 3d orbitals successively fill. You can see this by consulting Appendix B, where you will also be able to see how the transition elements in period 5 (elements 39 through 48) experience the successive filling of the 4d orbitals. As soon as the d orbitals fill among each of these transition elements, we reenter the region of the representative elements of the table. The progressive fillings of 4f and 5f orbitals take place among the lanthanide and actinide series, as Appendix B shows.

EXAMPLE 3.3   **FINDING INFORMATION IN THE PERIODIC TABLE**

Problem: How many electrons are in the outside level of an atom of iodine?

Solution: Until you become more familiar with the locations of certain elements in the table, you'll have to use the Table of Atomic Weights and Numbers (inside the front cover) to find the atomic number of a given element. Doing this, we find that the atomic number of iodine is 53. Now we use the periodic table and find that iodine is in group VIIA. Being one of the A-type elements, we know that iodine is a *representative* element, which means that its group number is the same as the number of outside level electrons, 7.

PRACTICE EXERCISE 6

How many electrons are in the outside level of an atom of each of the following elements?

(a) potassium   (b) oxygen   (c) phosphorus   (d) chlorine

Metals and Nonmetals Are Segregated in the Periodic Table   Another use of the table is to tell us at a glance which elements are metals and which are not. As seen in Figure 3.6, the nonmetals are all in the upper right-hand corner. All the noble gases (group 0) and the halogens (group VIIA) are nonmetals. The great majority of all elements are metals. The few

Figure 3.6
Locations of metals, nonmetals, and metalloids in the periodic table.

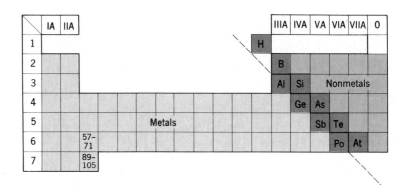

lying along the borderline between metals and nonmetals are sometimes called **metalloids,** and they have properties that are partly metallic and partly nonmetallic.

If you compare the locations of the elements in Figure 3.6 with the electron configurations given in Table 3.4, you will see that all the nonmetals, except hydrogen and helium, have four to eight electrons in their outside levels. All the elements that are metals, except for hydrogen and helium, have atoms with one, two, or three outside-level electrons. Only among some elements with high atomic numbers do we find metals with more than three outside-level electrons. Tin and lead of group IVA are common examples.

Other Uses of the Periodic Table Perhaps the most noteworthy consequences of having a set of elements in the same group is that they tend to form compounds of similar formulas, and that such compounds have at least some similar properties. We have already learned that the alkali metals form compounds called hydroxides that have the general formula *MOH* and that all these are caustic substances. Thus, if we had never handled rubidium hydroxide, RbOH, we would be very careful with it, because it is the hydroxide of an alkali metal. (And it actually is very caustic.)

All the binary compounds involving the halogens (group VIIA) and hydrogen have the common formula H*X* (where *X* can be F, Cl, Br, or I). If we know that a solution in water of, say, HCl could give an acid burn to skin, we would be very careful when handling similar solutions of HF, HBr, and HI. These solutions are able to destroy or neutralize the caustic properties of the alkali metal hydroxides according to the following general equation:

$$H X + M O H \longrightarrow M X + H_2O$$

For example, hydrochloric acid, HCl, and sodium hydroxide, NaOH, react as follows:

$$HCl + NaOH \longrightarrow NaCl + H_2O$$

Water (H_2O) and sodium chloride (NaCl), or table salt, form in this reaction, and we know that a solution of salt in water can give neither an alkali burn nor an acid burn to the skin. Because the reaction of an acid with an alkali destroys a characteristic property of any alkali and any acid, it is an important reaction and deserves a special name. We call it **neutralization.** Substances that can neutralize acids are generally called **bases,** so the reaction of hydrochloric acid with sodium hydroxide is an example of an acid–base neutralization.

These examples are intended to show how useful the periodic table can be, especially when taken together with the sorting of the elements made possible by the periodic law. One purpose of our study is to learn the chemical properties of important substances, and the periodic table helps us to organize the information for easier study. We will often be able, for example, to write *general* equations that apply to several reactions, instead of having to learn each and every reaction, because members of the same family of elements have similar properties.

■ Rubidium, Rb, has atomic number 37 and is in group IA.

■ Pure HCl is a gas called hydrogen chloride. It dissolves in water to form a solution called hydrochloric acid

SUMMARY

Atomic structure Atoms, which are electrically neutral particles, are the smallest representatives of an element that can display the element's chemical properties. Each atom has one nucleus—a hard inner core—surrounded by enough electrons to balance the positive charge on the nucleus. All the atom's protons and neutrons are in the nucleus, and each of these subatomic particles has a mass of 1.0 amu. The mass of the electron is only 1/1836 the mass of a proton. The proton has a charge of $1+$, the electron's charge is $1-$, and the neutron is electrically neutral. The atomic number of an element is the number of protons in each atom. It also equals the number of electrons in one atom.

Isotopes Nearly all elements occur as a mixture of a small number of isotopes. The isotopes of an element share the same atomic number, but their atoms have small differences in their numbers of neutrons. To characterize an isotope fully, we have to specify both the atomic number and the mass number—the number of protons plus neutrons.

Atomic orbitals The places where electrons can be in an atom are organized as principal energy levels, which consist of sublevels, which are made up of orbitals. An atomic orbital is a volume of space near the nucleus within which the probability is very high that a particular electron can be. The shape of an orbital comes from wrapping an imaginary envelop about that much of the space within which the overall probability is at least 90%.

Principal level (or shell) 1 has only one sublevel. (It is its own sublevel.) And this sublevel has just one orbital. (It is its own orbital.) This orbital is the 1s orbital, the 1 standing for principal level 1, and the s specifying the shape of the orbital—spherical. At level (shell) 2, there are two sublevels—the s and the p types. Any s sublevel, no matter at which principal level, has just one orbital. A p-type sublevel always has three orbitals, designated as p_x, p_y, and p_z, to correspond to the three coordinate axis along which they three point. Each p-orbital consists of two lobes of equal size and shape. Level 3 has s-, p-, and d-type sublevels. (Sublevel d consists of 5 orbitals.) Levels 4 and higher have all these plus an f-type sublevel (with 7 orbitals). Since our study focuses almost exclusively on the representative elements 1 through 20, we'll not need more information on d- or f-type orbitals.

Each occupied orbital can be viewed as an electron "cloud." It isn't possible to obtain precise information simultaneously about an electron's location and energy, but the knowledge of where electrons most likely are—information obtained from electron configurations—is sufficient for understanding chemical properties.

As long as electrons remain in their orbitals, an atom neither absorbs nor radiates energy. However, an atom can absorb the energy that corresponds exactly to the difference in energy between two orbitals, provided the orbital of higher energy has a vacancy. The absorbed energy makes an electron move to the higher orbital. When it drops back down, this energy is radiated as a quantum or photon of light.

Electron configurations To write an electron configuration of an atom, we follow certain rules (aufbau rules). We place its electrons one by one into the available orbitals, starting with the one of lowest energy, the 1s orbital. According to the Pauli exclusion principle, each orbital can hold two electrons (if their spins are opposite), but where two or more orbitals are available at the same sublevel, electrons spread out (Hund's rule).

Atomic weights The atomic weight of an element is the average mass (in amu) of the atoms of all its isotopes as they occur naturally together. If we weigh out samples of elements in the same mass ratios as their atomic weights, we obtain the elements in one to one ratios by atoms.

Periodic properties Because many properties of the elements are periodic functions of atomic numbers, the elements fall naturally into groups or families that we can organize into vertical columns in a periodic table. Atoms of the representative elements that belong to the same family have the same number of outside-level electrons—a number that corresponds to the group number itself. (Helium does not fit this generalization.)

The horizontal rows of the periodic table are called periods. The long periods that contain transition and inner transition elements involve the systematic filling of inner orbitals. The nonmetallic elements are in the upper right hand corner of the periodic table, and the metals—the great majority of the elements—make up the rest of the table. (At the border between metals and nonmetals occur the elements—the metalloids—that have both metallic and nonmetallic properties.)

The metal hydroxides formed from the group IA metals (alkali metals) have the general formula, MOH and are all bases. They neutralize acids, like hydrochloric acid, in the same way.

REVIEW EXERCISES

The answers to Review Exercises marked with asterisks are in Appendix D. The answers to all other Review Exercises appear in the *Study Guide* that accompanies this book.

The Nuclear Atom

3.1 What are the names, electrical charges, and masses of the three subatomic particles? (Use the amu as the unit of mass, and omit the mass of the lightest of the three.)

3.2 Name two subatomic particles that attract each other.

3.3 What subatomic particles have forces of repulsion between them?

3.4 We will learn in the next chapter that it is possible for particles of an atomic size to have unequal numbers of electrons and protons. If particle M has 13 protons and 10 electrons, what is the electrical charge on M?

3.5 It costs energy to make an electron leave an atom, but which of the following changes would cost the *least* energy, and why?
  (a) Removal of an electron from a particle having 12 protons and 12 electrons.
  (b) Removal of an electron from a particle having 12 protons and 11 electrons.

3.6 Particle M has 13 protons and 10 electrons, and particle Y has 8 protons and 10 electrons. Do they attract each other, repel each other, or leave each other alone? Explain.

3.7 The atomic mass unit is roughly on the order of what size, 10^{-230} g, 10^{-23} g, 10^{-3} g, or 10^{23} g?

3.8 To five significant figures, calculate the mass in grams of a sample of 6.0220×10^{23} hydrogen atoms, each one having just one proton. Ignore the mass of the electron. How does the result compare with the atomic weight of hydrogen? (To two significant figures, are the results the same or different?)

*3.9 The mass of one proton, which we said was 1.0 amu, is actually 1.00727605 amu, and the mass of one neutron is 1.008665 amu.
  (a) What is the total mass in amu of a helium nucleus that consists of two protons and two neutrons? (Calculate to seven significant figures.)
  (b) The observed mass of one helium *atom* is 4.002604 amu. Given that the mass of one electron is 0.0005486 amu (and that a helium atom has two electrons), calculate the observed mass of one helium *nucleus*.
  (c) Calculate the difference in amu between the observed mass of the helium nucleus and the mass you calculate by sum-

ming the masses of two protons and two neutrons. (Retain five significant figures.) You no doubt notice that the observed mass is less that the calculated mass. This difference is real. What we haven't discussed within the chapter is the Einstein relationship between mass and energy. Einstein found that mass can be converted to energy, and energy to mass. His famous equation, $E = mc^2$, gives the relationship, where E is the energy obtained when an amount of mass, m, "disappears" into energy; c in the Einstein equation is the velocity of light.

(d) For each amu loss in mass, 1.49454×10^{-10} joule of energy is released. Using the result of part (c), calculate the joules of energy released when two protons and two neutrons come together — fuse — to form *one* helium nucleus. The result doesn't seem to be very much, does it? However, go to the next part.

(e) Calculate the number of joules of energy that would be released if 6.0220×10^{23} helium nuclei form — about a total of 4 g of helium. This much energy could keep a 100-watt light bulb going for roughly 900 years. These calculations give an idea of the huge energy potentially available by nuclear fusion, the same kind of process that is believed to generate the energy of the sun.

Isotopes

3.10 Elements and isotopes are *substances,* not tiny particles — although they consist of such particles. What is the distinction between the terms *element* and *isotope of an element?*

3.11 What are the names and the compositions of the nuclei of the three isotopes of hydrogen? What do these nuclei have in common? In what specific way do they differ? In *atoms* having these nuclei, what else is the same?

3.12 Which of the following are isotopes? (Use the hypothetical symbols for your answer.)

M has 12 protons and 13 neutrons

Q has 13 protons and 13 neutrons

X has 12 protons and 12 neutrons

Z has 13 protons and 12 neutrons

3.13 Write the atomic symbol for the isotope of oxygen (atomic number 8) that has a mass number of 18.

3.14 Write the atomic symbol for the isotope of cobalt (atomic number 27) that has 33 neutrons. (This is a radioactive isotope that is used in cancer treatment.)

3.15 Carbon, atomic number 6, has three isotopes that are found in nature. The most abundant (98.89%) has a mass number of 12. The isotope with a mass number of 13 makes up 1.11% of naturally occurring carbon. The third isotope — obviously present in the merest trace, because 98.89% + 1.11% = 100.00% — makes possible the dating of ancient artifacts.
(a) What is the same about these isotopes?
(b) In what specific feature of atomic structure do they differ?

3.16 Later, when we want to describe some *chemical* reaction of sulfur, which consists principally of two isotopes (mass numbers 32 and 34), we will use the symbol S. Why won't we have to use the special symbols $^{32}_{16}$S and $^{34}_{16}$S?

The Bohr Atom Model

3.17 Briefly describe the picture of atomic structure that emerged from Niels Bohr's theory.

3.18 What features of Bohr's theory are still valid?

3.19 What does the term *allowed energy state* mean?

3.20 What is meant by the term *ground state?*

3.21 If an electron drops from a higher energy state into a ground state, what else happens?

Where Electrons Are in Atoms

3.22 Some kind of contact, if only by photons, is made between one making a measurement and what is being measured. If you sent energy into an atom to get precise information about the location of an electron, could you also get precise information about the electron's energy?

3.23 Heisenberg found that what physical quantities of an electron cannot be known with precision and accuracy at the same instant?

3.24 What can still be known (actually, calculated) about an electron's position if we cannot think of it as traveling in a definite orbit?

3.25 How many sublevels and how many orbitals are at principal level 1?

3.26 At principal level 2, how many sublevels are there? How many orbitals are in each? What symbols are used for these orbitals?

3.27 How many sublevels are at principal level 3? How many orbitals are in each?

3.28 When one electron is in an *s*-type sublevel at principal level 4, what symbol is used for this?

Electron Configurations

3.29 What is the maximum number of electrons that can be in each?
(a) Principal level 2
(b) The *p*-type orbitals of principal level 3
(c) The 4*s* orbital
(d) Principal level 3

3.30 Write the one-line electron configuration of silicon (atomic number 14).

3.31 Using only the information in Figure 3.4, and the fact that krypton has atomic number 36, write the one-line electron configuration of a krypton atom.

3.32 The electron configuration of iron is $1s^2 2s^2 2p^6 3s^2 3p^6 3d^6 4s^2$. Using only this information, answer the following questions.
(a) What is the atomic number of iron?
(b) Is principal level 3 completely filled? If not, which sublevel is partially filled?
(c) Are there likely to be any electrons in this atom with unpaired spin? If not, why? If there are, where are they likely to be and why?

3.33 Suppose that we have the following sublevels and orbitals available.

$$2p \; \underline{\;\;} \; \underline{\;\;} \; \underline{\;\;}$$
$$2s \; \underline{\;\;}$$

(a) Name and state the aufbau rules that are illustrated if we have one, two, or three electrons to distribute.
(b) Besides the rules needed for part (a), what is the name and the statement of the aufbau rule that would be illustrated if six electrons have to be distributed?

3.34 Consider the two possible electron configurations:

$$1s^2 2s^2 2p_x{}^2 2p_y{}^2 2p_z{}^2 3s^1 \quad \text{and} \quad 1s^2 2s^2 2p_x{}^2 2p_y{}^2 2p_z{}^2 3p_x{}^1$$
$$\mathbf{1} \qquad\qquad\qquad\qquad \mathbf{2}$$

(a) Would atoms having these configurations be atoms of the *same* element or atoms of different elements? How can you tell?
(b) Which is more stable, **1** or **2**? Explain.
(c) What does it take to convert the atom in the more stable of these two states into the other state?

3.35 Write the one-line electron configurations of the elements that have the following atomic numbers, using only these numbers and the aufbau rules.
(a) 11   (b) 8   (c) 17   (d) 20

3.36 Write the one-line electron configurations of the elements that have the following atomic numbers.
(a) 12   (b) 19   (c) 9   (d) 3

Atomic Weights

3.37 Mass numbers are always whole numbers. Atomic weights almost never are. Explain.

3.38 Iodine, which is needed in the diet to have a healthy thyroid gland, occurs in nature as only one isotope, $^{127}_{53}$I. Using just this information, what is the atomic weight of iodine (to three significant figures)?

3.39 Bromine, in the same chemical family as iodine, occurs in nature as a nearly one-to-one mixture of two isotopes, $^{79}_{35}$Br and $^{81}_{35}$Br. Using just this information, what is the atomic weight of bromine (to two significant figures)?

3.40 To two significant figures, the atomic weight of magnesium is 12 and the atomic weight of sulfur is 24.
(a) How much heavier are sulfur atoms than magnesium atoms?
(b) If we counted out in separate piles 10^{23} atoms of magnesium and the identical number of sulfur atoms, which pile of atoms would have the larger mass, and by what factor?
(c) If we weighed out 2.0 g of magnesium and we wanted a sample of sulfur that had the identical number of atoms, how many grams of sulfur should we weigh out?

*3.41 How much heavier are carbon atoms than hydrogen atoms (on the average)? Calculate the answer to two significant figures. Use data from the Table of Atomic Weights and Numbers inside the front cover.

*3.42 Carbon atoms and oxygen atoms can chemically combine to form particles consisting of these atoms in a ratio of one to one.

(The substance that forms is a poisonous gas, carbon monoxide.)
(a) How much heavier are oxygen atoms than carbon atoms (to three significant figures)?
(b) If all the atoms in a sample of 12.0 g of carbon are to combine entirely with oxygen atoms, how many grams of oxygen are needed?

The Periodic Table

3.43 What general fact about the chemical elements makes possible the stacking of these elements in the kind of array seen in the periodic table?

3.44 What do the terms *group* and *period* refer to in the periodic table?

3.45 Without consulting the periodic table, is an element in group VA a representative or a transition element?

3.46 Without consulting the periodic table, is an element in period 2 a representative or a transition element?

3.47 How does the modern form of the periodic law differ from Mendeleev's form?

3.48 How would period 4 of the periodic table be different if the elements were arranged in their order of increasing atomic weights?

3.49 Suppose that an atom has the following electron configuration:

$$1s^2 2s^2 2p^6 3s^2 3p^6 3d^5 4s^1$$

Without consulting the periodic table, answer the following questions.
(a) Is this element a representative or a transition element? How can you tell?
(b) What is the number of its outside level, and how many electrons are in it?
(c) Is the element a metal or a nonmetal? How can you tell?

3.50 The atoms of an element have the following electron configuration.

$$1s^2 2s^2 2p^6 3s^2 3p^6 3d^{10} 4s^2 4p_x{}^1 4p_y{}^1 4p_z{}^1$$

Without using the periodic table, answer the following questions.
(a) What is the group number of this element? How can you tell?
(b) Is the element a metal or a nonmetal? How can you tell?

3.51 Give the group number and the chemical family name of the set of elements to which each of the following belongs.
(a) sodium   (b) bromine   (c) sulfur   (d) calcium

3.52 For each of the following elements give the group number and the name of the family to which it belongs.
(a) iodine   (b) phosphorus   (c) magnesium   (d) lithium

3.53 Considering the pattern described on page 61 for the formulas of the binary compounds of the representative elements in periods 2 and 3 of the periodic table, what are the likely formulas for the binary compounds with hydrogen of the following elements?
(a) K   (b) Ca   (c) Ga   (d) Ge
(e) As   (f) Se   (g) Br

3.54 The accompanying diagram shows a section of the periodic table, except that hypothetical atomic symbols are used. The numbers are atomic numbers, but not all the numbers are given symbols. Without referring to an actual periodic table, answer the following questions.

7	8	9	10
15 *W*	16 *X*	17 *Y*	18 *Z*
33	34	35	36

(a) What elements, if any, are shown as belonging to the same family as *Y*? Write the number(s).

(b) What elements, if any, are in the same period as *W*? Write the number(s).

(c) Above the first horizontal row, write the group numbers for the elements of this row.

(d) If the outside level of an atom of number 33 has five electrons, how many electrons are in the outside level of an atom of number 15? Of number 16? Of number 36?

(e) If element 9 (let's give it the symbol *M*) has a compound with hydrogen with the formula H*M*, what is a good possibility for the formula of a compound between hydrogen and number 17?

(f) If number 10 is one of the noble gases, which is also a noble gas, 9, 11, or 36?

(g) If number 18 is a nonmetal, and number 33 is a metalloid, are the elements represented here metals or nonmetals?

CHAPTER FOUR

Chemical Compounds and Chemical Bonds

Iron pyrite, a compound of iron and sulfur, forms exceptionally regular crystals, seen here reflecting a multicolored background. The tiniest pieces of iron pyrite can stack comfortably together only in a very regular manner. We will learn more about how atoms combine to form compounds in this chapter.

4.1 ELECTRON TRANSFERS AND IONIC COMPOUNDS

Strong forces of attraction exist between oppositely charged ions in a large number of chemical compounds.

In this chapter we ask a fundamental question: What holds things together? How come rock salt is hard, water is squishy, and air seems to move out of our way at will? Atoms, we have learned, are electrically *neutral,* so how can they become stuck together strongly enough to account for the existence of compounds? The answer, in brief, is that atoms are able to reorganize their electrons and nuclei into new particles in which there are net electrical forces of attraction called **chemical bonds.** The two rules — unlike charges attract and like charges repel — will serve us very well as we move through this study of compounds.

Two Kinds of Compounds Are Ionic and Molecular There are two important ways by which electrons and nuclei can become reorganized relative to each other. One way leads to a new kind of small particle called a molecule. A **molecule** is an electrically neutral particle consisting of two or more atomic nuclei surrounded by a swarm of enough electrons to make the particle electrically neutral. **Molecular compounds** are those whose smallest particles are molecules with nuclei from *different* elements. Sugar, vitamin C, cholesterol, aspirin, and water are examples of molecular compounds. So, too, are the substances that make up muscle fibers, many hormones, and such familiar plastics as polyethylene, nylon, and rubber.

■ *Molecule* is from a Greek term meaning *little mass.*

A few elements consist of molecules, too. Both the nitrogen and the oxygen in the air we breathe, for example, are elements, and they consist not of separate, individual atoms but of molecules. The nitrogen molecule has two nitrogen nuclei, and its symbol is N_2. Similarly, oxygen occurs as molecules that have two oxygen nuclei. Oxygen thus occurs normally as O_2. You may have heard of ozone, a dangerous air pollutant. Its molecules have *three* oxygen nuclei, and its formula is O_3.

■ Molecules made from two atoms are called **diatomic molecules.**

The other way to reorganize atoms into compounds produces tiny particles of opposite electrical charge called *ions,* and these strongly attract each other. Compounds consisting of oppositely charged ions are called *ionic compounds,* and we will study these next.

■ *Ion* is from the Greek *ienai,* to go or to move. Ions, unlike atoms, can move in response to electrical forces.

Electron Transfers Between Atoms Can Produce Ions Sodium chloride (table salt) is a typical ionic compound. We learned in Section 2.1 that the parent elements of this compound, sodium and chlorine, cannot be stored in each other's presence because they react violently. Their atoms undergo the following changes in their electron configurations. (These are the *overall* changes — the net results. To simplify this discussion, we're ignoring the fact that the element chlorine consists of molecules, Cl_2, instead of individual atoms.)

■ For purposes of illustration, we have picked the sodium-23 and chlorine-35 isotopes.

$$\left(\begin{array}{c}11\ p^+\\12\ n\end{array}\right)1s^22s^22p^63s^{\text{①}} + \left(\begin{array}{c}17\ p^+\\18\ n\end{array}\right)1s^22s^22p^63s^23p_x^{\ 2}3p_y^{\ 2}3p_z^{\ 1} \longrightarrow$$

One sodium atom
Na

One chlorine atom
Cl

$$\left[\left(\begin{array}{c}11\ p^+\\12\ n\end{array}\right)1s^22s^22p^6\right]^+ + \left[\left(\begin{array}{c}17\ p^+\\18\ n\end{array}\right)1s^22s^22p^63s^23p_x^{\ 2}3p_y^{\ 2}3p_z^{\ 2}\right]^-$$

Outer octet

Outer octet

One sodium ion
Na^+

One chloride ion
Cl^-

It is very, very important to realize now that the new particle with the sodium nucleus is no longer a sodium *atom,* because it no longer is electrically neutral. Although it has the sodium nucleus with its $11+$ charge, it now has only 10 electrons. These can cancel only $10+$ of the nuclear charge, so this new particle has a new charge of $1+$.

Similarly, the new particle with a chlorine nucleus isn't an atom either. It carries a net electrical charge of $1-$. The chlorine nucleus has 17 protons for $17+$ but surrounding it are now 18 electrons for $18-$, so the net charge on this new particle is $1-$.

Electrically charged particles at the atomic level of size are called **ions.** In the reaction of sodium with chlorine, electrons relocate relative to atomic nuclei to give sodium ions and chloride ions. These particles, not intact atoms, constitute sodium chloride. Before we see how ions organize themselves into crystals, it will be useful to learn how monatomic ions such as these are named.

Names and Formulas of Monatomic Ions   When an ion has just one nucleus, it is called a *monatomic ion.* Such ions are named after the parent element, either the same name or something close to it.

All ions derived from metals have the same name as the element (plus the word *ion*). Some particularly important metal ions are the sodium ion, Na^+, the potassium ion, K^+, the magnesium ion, Mg^{2+}, and the calcium ion, Ca^{2+}. Notice that the formula of an ion, when set separately, always includes the electrical charge as a right superscript.

The transition metals can exist as ions with more than one amount of charge. Ions of iron, for example, can exist as Fe^{2+} or as Fe^{3+}. Each has to have a name, of course, so the amount of charge is written into the ion's name with a roman numeral. Fe^{2+} is named the iron(II) ion, and Fe^{3+} is the iron(III) ion. These are the modern names. The iron ions were once (and still often are) called the ferrous ion (Fe^{2+}) and the ferric ion (Fe^{3+}). The two ions that copper can form are Cu^+, the copper(I) ion (cuprous ion), and Cu^{2+}, the copper(II) ion (cupric ion). Notice that in the older names, the *-ous* ending goes with the ion of the lower charge and the *-ic* ending is for the ion with the higher charge.

■ The *metal* elements in groups IVA and VA can form positively charged ions.

Monatomic ions derived from nonmetals have names that end in *-ide,* as in the *chloride ion,* whose parent element is chlorine. Other important monatomic ions from nonmetals are the fluoride ion, F^-, bromide ion, Br^-, iodide ion, I^-, oxide ion, O^{2-}, and sulfide ion, S^{2-}.

The names, symbols, and electrical charges of several common ions are given in Table 4.1, and they must be learned now. (A complete list of the ions mentioned in this book is in Appendix C.)

Ionic Compounds Have Ionic Bonds Between Symmetrically Arrayed Ions   It isn't physically possible to arrange a chemical meeting between just one atom of sodium and one of chlorine. Any visible sample, even the tiniest speck, has upward of at least 10^{18} atoms. Therefore when actual samples of these elements are mixed, a storm of electron transfers occurs, and countless numbers of oppositely charged ions form.

■ A 0.1-mg sample of NaCl has about 10^{18} pairs of ions.

The new sodium ions repel each other, of course, because like charges repel. The chloride ions also repel each other for the same reason. Sodium ions and chloride ions, however, attract each other, because unlike charges attract. Out of all these attractions and repulsions, the storm of new ions subsides into firm, hard, and regularly shaped crystals of sodium chloride. Spontaneously, the unlike charged ions, Na^+ and Cl^-, nestle together as closest neighbors and like-charged ions stay just a little farther apart, as seen in Figure 4.1. If the ions are to make maximum use of their forces of attraction and minimize their forces of repulsion, they *must* come together in as symmetrical an array as possible. This is why crystals of sodium chloride have such a definite shape.

What has formed by the coming together of Na^+ and Cl^- ions is an example of an ionic compound. **Ionic compounds** are orderly aggregations of oppositely charged ions, and the force of attraction between these ions is called the **ionic bond.** Ionic bonds are very strong, but you also know that crystals such as salt crystals can be pulverized without too much difficulty. A sharp blow can make one layer of ions shift over so that suddenly like-charged ions

Sodium chloride forms crystals with perfect 90° angles.

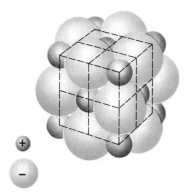

Figure 4.1
The structure of a sodium chloride crystal. The sodium ions are surrounded by chloride ions as nearest neighbors, and like-charged ions are just a little farther apart.

TABLE 4.1 Some Important Ions[a]

Group	Element	Symbol for Neutral Atom	Symbol for Its Common Ion	Name of Ion
IA	Lithium	Li	Li^+	Lithium ion
	Sodium	Na	Na^+	Sodium ion
	Potassium	K	K^+	Potassium ion
IIA	Magnesium	Mg	Mg^{2+}	Magnesium ion
	Calcium	Ca	Ca^{2+}	Calcium ion
	Barium	Ba	Ba^{2+}	Barium ion
IIIA	Aluminum	Al	Al^{3+}	Aluminum ion
VIA	Oxygen	O	O^{2-}	Oxide ion
	Sulfur	S	S^{2-}	Sulfide ion
VIIA	Fluorine	F	F^-	Fluoride ion
	Chlorine	Cl	Cl^-	Chloride ion
	Bromine	Br	Br^-	Bromide ion
	Iodine	I	I^-	Iodide ion
Transition Elements	Silver	Ag	Ag^+	Silver ion
	Zinc	Zn	Zn^{2+}	Zinc ion
	Copper	Cu	Cu^+	Copper(I) ion (cuprous ion)[b]
			Cu^{2+}	Copper(II) ion (cupric ion)
	Iron	Fe	Fe^{2+}	Iron(II) ion (ferrous ion)
			Fe^{3+}	Iron(III) ion (ferric ion)

[a] Other common ions are listed in Table 4.3

[b] The names in parentheses are older names, but still often used.

momentarily become closest neighbors. Now the net force — at least along this layer — is one of repulsion, not attraction, and the crystal splits apart.

The ionic bond does not extend in any single, unique direction. The force of attraction from Na^+, for example, radiates equally in all directions, like light from a light bulb. One particular Na^+ ion doesn't belong to any particular Cl^- ion. There is no such thing as a separate, discrete particle consisting of just one Na^+ ion and one Cl^- ion that belong exclusively to each other. We mention this because the formula used for sodium chloride, NaCl, might be incorrectly interpreted this way.

The formula for sodium chloride or for any ionic compound is meant only to disclose the ratio of the ions present. The ratio in sodium chloride is one to one. It *must* be one to one, because the net electrical charge of a compound is zero — always — and the charge of 1 + on one sodium ion is balanced exactly by the charge of 1 − on one chloride ion. As we said, ionic compounds are represented by formulas that give only the *ratios* of the particles present, so the chemical formulas of ionic compounds are always *empirical* formulas. (We have to make this distinction now because we'll soon learn about other kinds of formulas.)

■ *Empirical* is from the Latin *empiricus,* something experienced.

How To Name Binary Ionic Compounds   A binary ionic compound is one made of the ions of just two elements, like sodium chloride, NaCl, or calcium oxide, CaO. As these examples suggest, they are easy to name. We just write the name of the metal ion, then the name of the nonmetal ion, omitting the word *ion,* of course. A binary compound of the iron(III) ion and the bromide ion is called iron(III) bromide. (The older name is ferric bromide.)

The formula of an ionic compound gives the ratio of the ions. This ratio must be one that permits all opposite charges to cancel, because compounds are electrically neutral. A compound of calcium ions, Ca^{2+}, and oxide ions, O^{2-}, can have them only in a ratio of one to one.

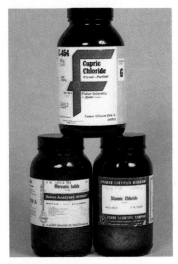

The older system of naming compounds can still be found on the bottles of lab chemicals.

In this way, the 2 + on the calcium ion cancels the 2 − on the oxide ion. So the formula is CaO. By convention, the positive ion is written first, and the charges are omitted. They are "understood."

Calcium chloride, a compound of calcium ions and chloride ions, must have *two* chloride ions for every calcium ion because it takes two Cl^- ions to give enough negative charge to cancel the charge of 2 + of a calcium ion. To show this ratio, we write the formula of calcium chloride as $CaCl_2$. The 2 is called a **subscript,** and subscripts are used to specify ratios of ions (or atoms) present. Subscripts follow and are placed half a line below the symbols they go with. The subscript 1 is always omitted; it is always understood because just writing a symbol means that you're taking at least one of it.

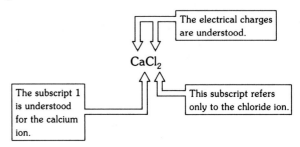

Remember, in empirical formulas, like those of ionic compounds, the subscripts are the smallest whole numbers that express the correct ratio. We don't write Ca_2Cl_4 for calcium chloride, even though it gives the correct ratio.

EXAMPLE 4.1

WRITING FORMULAS FROM NAMES OF IONIC COMPOUNDS

■ Aluminum oxide is a buffing powder for polishing metals.

Problem: Write the formula of aluminum oxide.

Solution: We first use the name to identify the ions, including their electrical charges, Al^{3+} and O^{2-}. We know that 3 + isn't canceled by 2 −, so we can't simply write AlO. The lowest common multiple of 2 and 3, however, is 6 ($2 \times 3 = 6$). Therefore if we can pick the smallest number of aluminum ions that give a total of 6 + and the smallest number of oxide ions that give a total of 6 −, we will have the ratio. This requires 2 Al^{3+}, because $[2 \times (3+) = 6+]$, and it requires a 3 O^{2-}, because $[3 \times (2-) = 6-]$. The ratio in aluminum oxide, therefore, is 2 Al^{3+} to 3 O^{2-}, and writing the aluminum first in the formula gives us the answer:

$$Al_2O_3$$

The strategy in Example 4.1 to find and use the lowest common multiple of the numbers in the charges on the ions always works. Try Practice Exercise 1 to develop experience in using this approach.

PRACTICE EXERCISE 1

Write the formulas of the following compounds.

(a)   Silver bromide (a light-sensitive chemical used in photographic film)
(b)   Sodium oxide (a very caustic substance that changes to lye in water)
(c)   Ferric oxide (the chief component in iron rust)
(d)   Copper(II) chloride (an ingredient in some laundry-marking inks)

EXAMPLE 4.2

WRITING NAMES FROM FORMULAS OF IONIC COMPOUNDS

Problem: Write the name of $FeCl_2$, using both the modern and the older forms.

Solution: The symbol Fe stands for one of the two ions of iron, but which? What charge does it bear, in other words, in $FeCl_2$? This is a situation in which we have to use our knowledge of the charge on one of the ions, Cl^-, to figure out the charge on the other. The Cl_2 part of $FeCl_2$ tells us that there must be a total negative charge of $2-$, because $2 \times (1-) = 2-$. The lone Fe part of $FeCl_2$ must therefore provide $2+$ in charge, so we must be dealing with the Fe^{2+} ion—named either the iron(II) ion or the ferrous ion. The compound is named either iron(II) chloride or ferrous chloride.

PRACTICE EXERCISE 2

Write the names of each of the following compounds. When a name can be given in a modern form or an older form, write both.

(a) CuS   (b) NaF   (c) FeI_2 (d) $ZnBr_2$ (e) Cu_2O

The technique used in Example 4.2 of finding the electrical charge on one ion from the known charge on the other in an ionic compound greatly reduces the number of ions that have to be memorized. The next exercise gives some practice in this.

PRACTICE EXERCISE 3

What are the charges on the *metal* ions in each of these substances?

(a) Cr_2O_3 (a green pigment in stained glass)
(b) HgS ("Chinese red," a bright, scarlet-red pigment)
(c) $CoCl_2$ (an ingredient in invisible ink)

Ions Have Different Radii Than Their Parent Atoms   We're now going to take a short side trip into the matter of the sizes and shapes of small particles. At the molecular level of life, the shapes and sizes of ions and molecules are as important as anything else about them, and these are determined by several factors—which atomic nuclei are involved, what electron clouds they have, electron configurations, and the kind and amount of any net electrical charge.

■ Monatomic ions are spherical, and the *radius* of a sphere is the distance from its center to its surface.

Notice in Figure 4.1 that sodium ions and chloride ions have quite different sizes. When a metal ion forms from a metal atom, the electron cloud that remains shrinks because the positive nuclear charge now exceeds the negative charge of this cloud. The nuclear charge now pulls the cloud more tightly toward itself. This is why metal ions are always smaller than their parent atoms. You can see more examples of this in Figure 4.2, which gives the radii of the atoms and ions of some of the representative families of the elements. Notice how the sodium *ion* has a radius (95 pm) only about half as large as the sodium *atom* (186 pm).

When one or more electrons are added to the electron cloud of an atom to make a negative ion, the cloud expands. Negative ions derived from nonmetal atoms are thus always larger than their parent atoms. The radius of the Cl^- ion, 181 pm, is almost twice as large as the radius of the Cl *atom*, 99 pm. You can see similar increases in Figure 4.2 among the group VIA and VIIA elements.

The sizes of the Na^+ and Cl^- ions are such that the final shape of the sodium chloride crystal is that of a cube. These ions form cubic crystals. So do K^+ and Cl^- ions. Other combinations of ions form crystals with different but still regular shapes.

Many Common Substances Are Ionic Compounds   Many familiar substances besides sodium chloride are ionic compounds. Sodium bicarbonate in baking soda, barium sulfate in "barium X-ray cocktails," sodium hydroxide in lye and drain cleaners, and calcium sulfate in plaster and plaster of paris, are other examples. When prepared foods are advertized as "low in sodium," it means that they are low in sodium ion, certainly not the extremely reactive sodium atom. This, incidentally, hints at how profoundly chemical properties differ between atoms and their ions. Something "rich in calcium" is rich in calcium ions, not calcium atoms. Every fluid in every living thing, whether plant or animal, contains dissolved ions. Even among the largest molecules in living things—those of proteins, for example—there are often a few or several electrically charged sites. People in professional health care fields speak of the "electrolyte balance" of this or that body fluid. An **electrolyte** is any substance that can furnish ions in a solution in water. Thus, at the molecular level of life, ions are everywhere.

■ The principal ions in blood are Na^+ and Cl^-, but many others are also present.

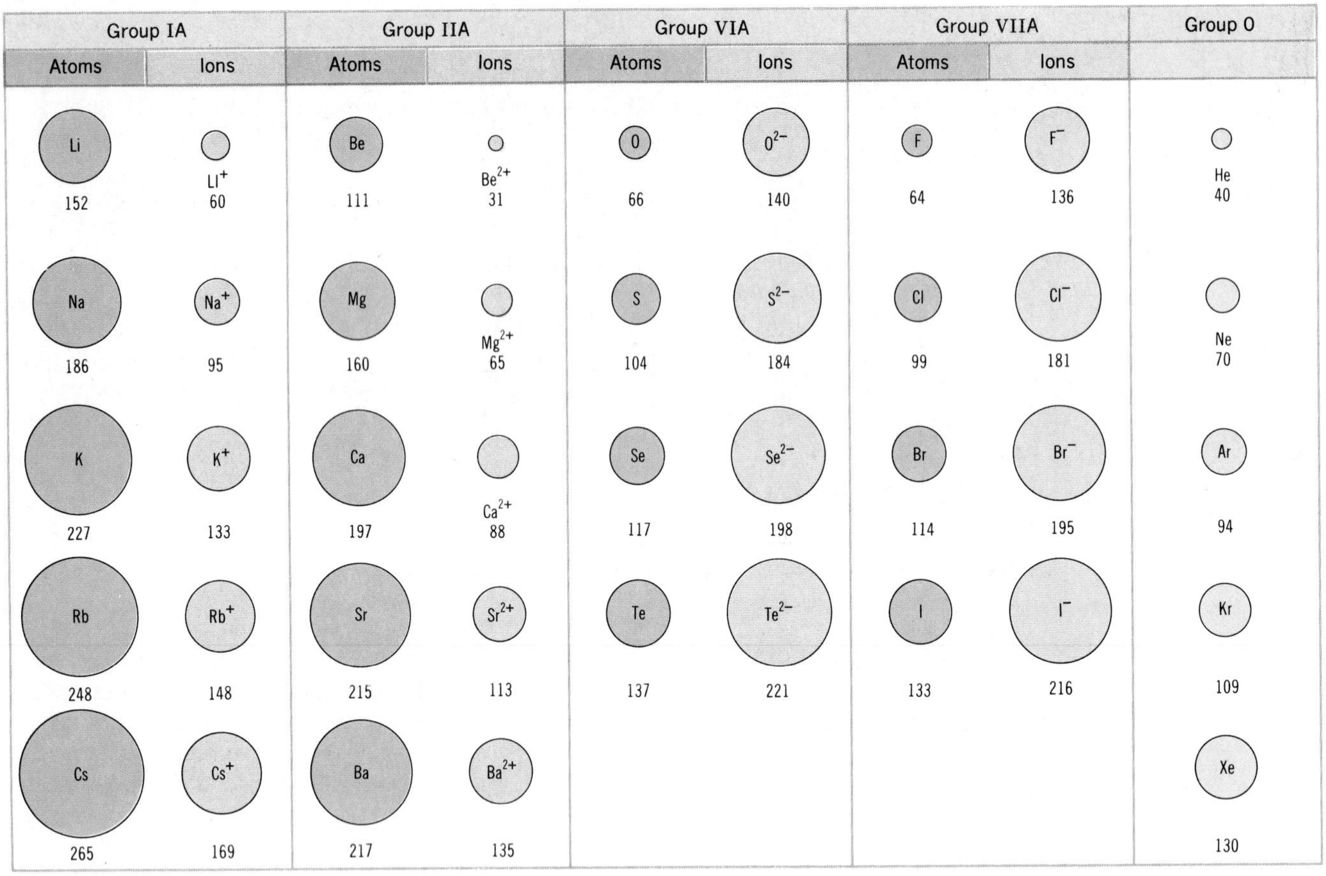

Group IA		Group IIA		Group VIA		Group VIIA		Group 0
Atoms	Ions	Atoms	Ions	Atoms	Ions	Atoms	Ions	
Li 152	Li$^+$ 60	Be 111	Be^{2+} 31	O 66	O^{2-} 140	F 64	F$^-$ 136	He 40
Na 186	Na$^+$ 95	Mg 160	Mg^{2+} 65	S 104	S^{2-} 184	Cl 99	Cl$^-$ 181	Ne 70
K 227	K$^+$ 133	Ca 197	Ca^{2+} 88	Se 117	Se^{2-} 198	Br 114	Br$^-$ 195	Ar 94
Rb 248	Rb$^+$ 148	Sr 215	Sr^{2+} 113	Te 137	Te^{2-} 221	I 133	I$^-$ 216	Kr 109
Cs 265	Cs$^+$ 169	Ba 217	Ba^{2+} 135					Xe 130

Figure 4.2
Atomic and ionic radii of some representative elements. The radii are given in picometers, pm (10^{-12} meter).

4.2 IONS AND THE OCTET RULE

Atoms and ions whose outside energy levels hold eight electrons are substantially more stable than those that do not.

The formation of sodium and chloride ions raises several questions. Does sodium always form singly charged ions, Na$^+$? Why not Na^{2+} ions? We could ask similar questions about chlorine. Indeed, we could ask, why do they form ions at all? Not all elements do. In this section we'll learn about a pattern in nature that answers these questions in terms of a very general principle, nature's preference for what is the most stable, lowest energy condition in a given circumstance.

Atoms of the Noble Gases Have the Most Stable Electron Configurations In the previous chapter we learned that the group 0 elements, the noble gases, are the least reactive, most stable of all elements. If you look back to Figure 3.6, you will see that these elements also have the highest ionization energies. This means that they require far greater amounts of energy than their neighbors to suffer the loss of an electron. They are stable as atoms.

Noble gas atoms do not form positive ions. They don't form negative ions either. There is evidently something quite stable about the two kinds of electron configurations found among these atoms. One is the **outer octet,** eight electrons in whichever principal level happens to be the *outside* level. The other is a *filled* level 1 when it is the *outside* level (as in helium). These two noble gas configurations are conditions of unusual chemical stability. They will help us

■ The noble gases are
  Helium   He
  Neon   Ne
  Argon   Ar
  Krypton   Kr
  Xenon   Xe
  Radon   Rn

understand why ions have the charges they do and why the elements in the same chemical family, if they form ions at all, form ions of the *same* charge.

Monatomic Ions of the Representative Elements Have Noble Gas Configurations A sodium atom, in group IA, has one electron in its outside level — level 3 — but after losing this electron, it has a new outside level — the former inner level number 2, which has eight electrons. As the sodium ion, the particle has an outer octet, and it also has the electron configuration of a member of the noble gas family — neon. Whatever causes an outer octet to lend stability to the neon *atom* evidently is at work in the sodium *ion*, because the sodium ion is an unusually stable particle, too. (It's stable provided that there is something oppositely charged nearby, so that the overall system is electrically neutral.)

A chlorine atom, in group VIIA, has seven electrons in its highest occupied energy level, number 3. When it accepts one electron, its outside level acquires an outer octet. Thus the chloride *ion* has the same electron configuration as an atom of one of the noble gases, argon. The chloride ion, provided that an oppositely charged system is nearby, is also a particle of unusual chemical stability.

When we put sodium and chlorine together, the electron transfers between sodium and chlorine generate particles with noble gas configurations. In other words, these two chemicals — given the opportunity in terms of each other's actual presence — spontaneously change in a direction that leads to greater stability for both. They change from particles that don't have noble gas configurations to those that do. It does not matter that the new particles are charged. The atoms sacrifice neutrality for stability.

We have to emphasize that we don't mean that ions are stable in isolation. It isn't possible to have a bottle of just sodium ions. Matter in bulk must *always* be electrically neutral to be stable. But these ions are electrically and oppositely charged, so they *must* attract each other. As the crystal of sodium chloride forms, ions of one charge are surrounded by ions of the opposite charge. It is in such an environment that we can say that the ions are exceptionally stable.

We haven't explained *why* a noble gas configuration is stable. We are only pointing out that for some reason it is. The pattern we noted for the formation of sodium chloride is so general for the reactions of the representative metals and nonmetals that it almost amounts to a law of nature called the **octet rule.**

■ Just why noble gas configurations are so stable is still not fully understood.

■ G. N. Lewis (1875 – 1946), was chiefly responsible for the development of the octet rule.

> **Octet Rule** The atoms of the reactive representative elements tend to undergo those chemical reactions that most directly give them electron configurations of the nearest noble gas.

The Charges on Representative Ions Correlate with the Periodic Table Notice the phrase "most directly" in the octet rule. What does it mean, and why is it there? To answer these questions, consider another way by which a sodium atom could acquire an outer octet. We could imagine a sodium atom getting seven more electrons to give an outer octet at level 3, instead of losing one electron to get an outer octet at level 2. But the sodium nucleus, with a charge of $11+$ and already (in the atom) hanging onto eleven electrons, cannot possibly attract and hold an extra seven electrons. All metal atoms have just a few outside level electrons, so changing to ions "most directly" for all metal atoms means losing a few electrons rather than gaining many. Thus all metals form *positively* charged ions by giving up electrons. The *representative* metals always give up only as many as needed to strip the electron configuration to that of the noble gas nearest the metal in the periodic system.

The atoms of members of the same family of elements have the same outside level electron configurations. The left half of Table 4.2 reminds us of this. It also reminds us that, for the representative elements (those in the A series, such as group IA, IIA, and so forth), the group number tells us the number of outside level electrons. Therefore, all members of the

TABLE 4.2 Electron Configurations of Ions and Comparable Noble Gases

Group	Common Element	Atomic Number	ATOMS Electron Configurations (Main Levels Only)						Ion	IONS Electron Configurations (Main Levels Only)						Nearest Noble Gas
			1	2	3	4	5	6		1	2	3	4	5	6	
IA Alkali metals	Li	3	2	1					Li$^+$	2						Helium
	Na	11	2	8	1				Na$^+$	2	8					Neon
	K	19	2	8	8	1			K$^+$	2	8	8				Argon
IIA Alkaline earth metals	Mg	12	2	8	2				Mg^{2+}	2	8					Neon
	Ca	20	2	8	8	2			Ca^{2+}	2	8	8				Argon
	Ba	56	2	8	18	18	8	2	Ba^{2+}	2	8	18	18	8		Xenon
VIA Oxygen family	O	8	2	6					O^{2-}	2	8					Neon
	S	16	2	8	6				S^{2-}	2	8	8				Argon
VIIA Halogens	F	9	2	7					F$^-$	2	8					Neon
	Cl	17	2	8	7				Cl$^-$	2	8	8				Argon
	Br	35	2	8	18	7			Br$^-$	2	8	18	8			Krypton
	I	53	2	8	18	18	7		I$^-$	2	8	18	18	8		Xenon
0 Noble gases	He	2	2						The noble gases do not form stable ions							
	Ne	10	2	8												
	Ar	18	2	8	8											
	Kr	36	2	8	18	8										
	Xe	54	2	8	18	18	8									

■ The calcium ion is essential to bones, and it is vital to the transmission of nerve impulses.

same family of elements will gain or lose electrons in the same way and form ions of identical charges. The right half of Table 4.2 shows this.

For representative metal elements, *the positive charge on the ion is the same as the group number.* For example, the ions of the group IA metals all have charges of $1+$, Li$^+$, Na$^+$, K$^+$, Rb$^+$, and Cs$^+$. Two ions, Na$^+$ and K$^+$, are particularly important in the fluids of living systems. The ions of the group IIA metals have charges of $2+$, for example, Mg^{2+}, Ca^{2+}, and Ba^{2+}. We will be interested in only one element in group IIIA, aluminum, and its ion has a charge of $3+$, Al^{3+}.

For the ions of the transition metals there is no simple correlation between their group numbers and the size of their positive charges. Generally, the charges vary from $1+$ to $3+$, and several transition metals can exist as ions of more than one charge, as we have noted.

Nonmetal atoms, with outside levels already close to octets, are nearer to noble gas configurations by means of gaining a few electrons rather than by losing many. They accept only as many electrons as will build the electron configuration to that of the noble gas nearest them in the periodic system. Thus the nonmetallic elements of groups VIA have outside levels of six electrons and so need two more electrons for noble gas configurations. Group VIA elements, therefore, form monatomic ions with charges of $2-$. See Table 4.2 again. Group VIIA elements, with outside levels of seven electrons, need just one more electron for outer octets. So their monatomic ions all have charges of $1-$.

■ The nitride ion, N^{3-} occurs with ions of group IIA metals in salt-like compounds; e.g., Mg$_3$N$_2$, magnesium nitride.

The nonmetal elements in groups IVA and VA form ions so rarely that we will assume they don't form ions at all. If we encounter an exception, we will be careful to note it. These elements evidently have outside levels too far from octets and would have to gain more electrons than their nuclear charges can attract and hold.

The octet rule, the periodic table, and the aufbau rules enable us to figure out the electron configurations of the ions that are most likely to exist for any of the first twenty elements. When we can do this, we can also figure out the charges on these ions. We will work some examples to show how.

| EXAMPLE 4.3 | **USING THE OCTET RULE** |

Problem: When nutritionists speak of the calcium requirement of the body, they always mean the calcium *ion* requirement. Calcium has atomic number 20. What charge does the calcium ion have, and what is the symbol of this ion?

Solution: There are two methods for solving this kind of problem, and you should learn both. The first is to write the electron configuration of the atom and the second is to exploit the periodic table.

Using the aufbau rules, we write the electron configuration of element 20, remembering that $4s$ fills before electrons go into $3d$.

$$1s^2 2s^2 2p^6 3s^2 3p^6 4s^2$$

The atom has two electrons in the outside level (level 4) and eight electrons in the next level down, two $3s$ electrons plus six $3p$ electrons. Only by losing *both* of the $4s$ electrons can this atom get a new outside level that holds the octet. Losing one electron won't do. Neither will losing three or more. Therefore the only stable ion that calcium can form is one with the following electron configuration:

$$1s^2 2s^2 2p^6 3s^2 3p^6$$

By losing two electrons the net charge on the particle becomes $2+$, so the symbol for the calcium ion is Ca^{2+}.

The second way to arrive at this answer is to find the position of calcium in the periodic table, group IIA. Because all the group IIA elements have two outside-level electrons and all can most directly acquire configurations of the nearest noble gases by losing two electrons, all the group IIA ions bear charges of $2+$. Therefore the group IIA ions are Be^{2+}, Mg^{2+}, Ca^{2+}, Sr^{2+}, Ba^{2+}, and Ra^{2+}.

| EXAMPLE 4.4 | **USING THE OCTET RULE** |

Problem: Oxygen can exist as the oxide ion in such substances as calcium oxide, an ingredient in cement. What is the symbol for the oxide ion, including its electrical charge?

Solution: As in Example 4.3, we will solve this in two ways. First, the electron configuration of an oxygen atom is

$$1s^2 2s^2 2p_x^2 2p_y^1 2p_z^1$$

The outside level—number 2—has a total of six electrons, just two short of an octet and a neon configuration. We could also say that the oxygen atom has six too many electrons to have the helium configuration. However, gaining two electrons to become like neon is much simpler than losing six, so oxygen achieves a noble gas configuration most directly by accepting two electrons from some metal atom donor. The new configuration, then, is

$$1s^2 2s^2 2p_x^2 2p_y^2 2p_z^2$$

The symbol for the oxide ion is O^{2-}.

To get this answer using the periodic table, we find oxygen in group VIA, so its outside level has six electrons. It must pick up two electrons, not just one and not more than two, to have a noble gas configuration. These two extra electrons give the particle a charge of $2-$, so we can write O^{2-} directly.

EXAMPLE 4.5   **USING THE OCTET RULE**

Problem: Hardly any element is involved in more compounds than carbon. (Roughly six million carbon compounds are known.) Can carbon atoms change to ions? If so, what is the symbol of the ion?

Solution: We will just use the shorter method of solving this. When we find carbon's place in the periodic table, we see that it is in group IVA. This tells us that carbon atoms have four outside-level electrons. To achieve a noble gas configuration, a carbon atom either must lose these four electrons (and become helium-like) or gain four electrons (and become neon-like). In one or two very rare situations, carbon can do the latter—become the C^{4-} ion. Because this is so rare we ignore it, and to make things simpler, we will stick to the rule that any *nonmetal* atoms in groups IVA and VA do not form ions.

■ The methanide ion, C^{4-}, apparently occurs in Be_2C, beryllium methanide, a brick-red solid.

PRACTICE EXERCISE 4

Write the electron configuration of an atom of each of the following elements, and from this deduce the charge on the corresponding ion. If the atom isn't expected to have a corresponding ion, state so. The numbers in parentheses are atomic numbers. Do not use the periodic table for this practice exercise.

(a) potassium (19)   (b) sulfur (16)   (c) silicon (14)

PRACTICE EXERCISE 5

Write the electron configurations of the *ions* of the elements in Practice Exercise 4 that can form ions.

PRACTICE EXERCISE 6

Relying on their locations in the periodic table, write the symbols of the ions of each of the following elements. Always remember that no symbol of an ion is complete without its electrical charge. (The numbers in parentheses are atomic numbers.)

(a) cesium (55)   (b) fluorine (9)
(c) phosphorus (15)   (d) strontium (38)

Electron Transfer Reactions Are Examples of Redox Reactions   Chemical reactions, like chemical substances, can be usefully classified, meaning that we can make helpful generalizations about them. The reaction that we have just studied, between sodium and chlorine, illustrates one very broad family of reactions, the *redox reaction,* or **oxidation-reduction reaction.** We'll pause long enough, therefore, to introduce the major terms concerning it, but we cannot study it in any depth here.

The redox reaction is today defined in terms of changes in *oxidation numbers.* For all monoatomic ions, the **oxidation number** is simply the electrical charge on the ion, both the sign and amount. For example, the oxidation number of sodium in NaCl is $+1$ because there is a charge of $1+$ on the sodium ion. The oxidation number of chlorine in NaCl is -1 because the chloride ion has a charge of $1-$. In $FeCl_3$, the oxidation number of iron is $+3$. The oxidation numbers in MgS are $+2$ for magnesium and -2 for sulfur. *The oxidation number of an element is zero.* A **redox reaction** is defined as one in which oxidation numbers change.

Let's return to the reaction of sodium with chlorine and see how it illustrates a redox reaction. When a sodium atom, Na, transfers an electron to a chlorine atom, Cl, the oxidation number of sodium changes from 0 to $+1$. We define any change that makes an oxidation number more positive as an **oxidation.** We say that the sodium atom is oxidized to the sodium ion. Of course, this occurs here only because an electron leaves, so in electron-transfer reactions, *oxidation means the loss of electrons.*

When a chlorine atom accepts an electron and changes from Cl to Cl^-, the oxidation number of chlorine changes from 0 to -1. We define any change that makes an oxidation number more negative as a **reduction.** This can't take place without the particle accepting an electron, so *reduction means the gain of electrons.*

A reduction cannot occur without an oxidation of something else. Electrons don't just leave from or go to outer space; they *transfer.* A reaction that involves a reduction also *must* involve an oxidation, and any such reaction is a redox reaction.

■ The earliest examples of oxidation involved oxygen itself as the oxidizing agent; hence, the name.

■ People used to call the conversion of ores, like iron ore, to the metal a *reduction* of the ore to the metal. This is where we got the general name, reduction.

The reactant that causes the reduction of something is called the **reducing agent.** Sodium is the reducing agent in the reaction with chlorine. The reactant that oxidizes something else is called an **oxidizing agent.** Chlorine is the oxidizing agent in the reaction with sodium.

$$Na + Cl \longrightarrow Na^+ + Cl^-$$

Reducing   Oxidizing
agent   agent

Notice that an oxidizing agent is always itself reduced in a redox reaction, and that a reducing agent is always itself oxidized.

Redox reactions are at the heart of biological oxidations, the chain of chemical reactions whereby we use oxygen from the air to oxidize chemicals obtained by the partial breakdown of food molecules. These oxidations provide energy in forms the body can use.

| EXAMPLE 4.6 | ANALYZING A REDOX REACTION |

Problem: The reaction of calcium with sulfur is a redox reaction in which calcium ions and sulfide ions form to make calcium sulfide, CaS.

$$Ca + S \longrightarrow CaS$$

Determine the oxidation numbers of calcium and sulfur in CaS, and decide what is the oxidizing agent and what is the reducing agent in this redox reaction.

Solution: From Table 4.1 (and soon, it must be said, from memory) we know that the charge on Ca in CaS must be 2+ and that the charge on S in CaS must be 2−. Calcium, therefore, has an oxidation number of +2 in CaS, and sulfur's oxidation number in this compound is −2. Because the reactants are both elements, they have oxidation numbers of 0. We can see that calcium's oxidation number becomes more positive, so calcium is oxidized. Sulfur's oxidation number becomes more negative, so it is reduced. Calcium is the reducing agent and sulfur is the oxidizing agent.

PRACTICE EXERCISE 7   Identify by their chemical symbols what is oxidized and what is reduced in the following reactions. Also identify what is the oxidizing agent and what is the reducing agent.

(a) $Mg + S \rightarrow MgS$

(b) $CuCl_2 + Zn \rightarrow ZnCl_2 + Cu$ (*Hint:* Both $CuCl_2$ and $ZnCl_2$ are compounds of the chloride ion. From this information, you should be able to deduce the charges on the metal ions in these compounds.)

4.3 ELECTRON SHARING AND MOLECULAR COMPOUNDS

When electron density concentrates enough between two atomic nuclei there is a chemical bond — a covalent bond — between them.

Nature has ways besides the ionic bond to organize chemical bonds, and our purpose in this section is to learn about one of them. It usually occurs between atoms of nonmetals.

Compounds of Nonmetals Are Not Ionic   For ionic compounds, both kinds of ions, positive and negative, are needed. Atoms of nonmetals cannot become positive ions, however, because too many electrons would have to be lost from their outside levels to achieve noble gas configurations. The nonmetals in groups IVA and VA, moreover, almost never become negative ions, because they would have to gain too many electrons to get outer octets. Yet several million compounds, probably over 90% of all compounds, involve only nonmetals atoms! These compounds consist of particles called molecules. A **molecule,** as we

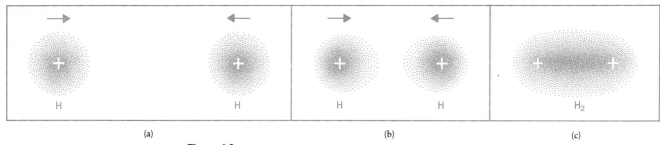

(a)   (b)   (c)

Figure 4.3
Formation of the covalent bond in hydrogen, H_2. (From J. E. Brady and J. R. Holum, *Fundamentals of Chemistry*, 3rd ed., John Wiley & Sons, New York, 1988. Used by permission.)

said, is a small, electrically neutral particle consisting of at least two nuclei and enough electrons to make the whole system neutral. A compound that consists of molecules is called a **molecular compound,** and we have noted that several elements consist of molecules, too. Our question now is, "What holds these and larger molecules together?"

Electron Clouds Can Become Dense Between Suitable Atoms   We'll consider the simplest molecule, H_2, first. Imagine two isolated hydrogen *atoms* moving directly toward each other, as visualized in Figure 4.3a. As they get closer, the electron clouds of their 1s electrons begin to sense the other atom's positively charged nucleus. This attraction distorts the two electron clouds so that they bulge toward the sides of the atoms that are nearing each other, as seen in Figure 4.3b. As the atoms continue toward collision, their electrons spend more and more of their time on facing sides of the atoms. Their two nuclei, however, sense the like-charged nature of each other, so the collision can never fully develop. Instead, as shown in Figure 4.3c, the atoms brake so that their two nuclei are at a short distance apart.

　　The atoms do not rebound, like two billiard balls, because the electron density between their two nuclei is now too great. The nuclei are attracted toward this electron cloud, and the cloud is attracted to the two nuclei. Because of the pair of electrons concentrated more or less between them, the two nuclei now have a bond between them, and a molecule is born, H_2.

　　The language used to describe such a pair of electrons is *shared pair*. Neither of the shared electrons any longer belongs exclusively to just one of the nuclei, as they did well before the atoms came together. The two now belong to both nuclei, and we say that the nuclei share the two electrons. The bond created by this sharing of electron pairs between atomic nuclei is called the **covalent bond.**

　　The whole new package, the two protons and two electrons of H_2, is electrically neutral, as molecules *must* be. Unlike a single pair of ions, like Na^+ and Cl^- in NaCl, a molecule is a discrete and separate particle that can enjoy independent existence. It can move around as a unit. But it is so small that it takes a huge number to have an actual sample of a molecular substance. A sample of just 2 g of H_2, for example, consists of over 6×10^{23} molecules of H_2.

　　The covalent bonds in larger molecules are like those in H_2. They involve the electron density of a pair of electrons that becomes concentrated between two nuclei. The nuclei are attracted into this region and held there at a very small distance apart. We'll see in the next section how the stability of a noble gas configuration influences the number of covalent bonds an atom can form.

▪ A region of *high electron density* is one with a thick or dense electron cloud.

▪ *Co-* from cooperative; *-valent* from the Latin *valere,* to be strong, signifying strong binding.

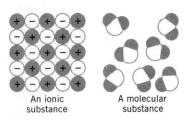

An ionic substance   A molecular substance

4.4   MOLECULES, LEWIS STRUCTURES, AND THE OCTET RULE

The electron pairs of covalent bonds are counted with the other valence electrons in computing octets.

Like atoms and ions, molecules need symbols, and one approach is to represent a molecule by an electron-dot structure. We start with electron-dot symbols for atoms.

Electron-Dot Structures Give Valence-Shell Electrons in Atoms The **valence shell** of an atom is another name for the *original* outside level of an atom. *Electron-dot symbolism* is a scheme to draw attention to valence shell electrons and to the presence or absence of octets. The electrons of the valence shell are represented by dots placed around the atomic symbol. These are kept separated and at the corners of an imaginary square until there are four dots. The fifth, sixth, seventh, and eighth electrons are placed so as to create pairs of electrons. Because of the great contributions of G. N. Lewis, an American chemist, to the theory of the covalent bond, electron-dot structures are usually called **Lewis structures.**

For the representative elements, we can tell how many electron dots must be used from the group numbers of these elements, which tell us how many electrons are in their valence shells. All group IA elements require just one electron dot. Those in group VIIA need seven. (Remember that those of group 0, the noble gases, need eight, with the exception of helium, which needs two. These exceptions are unimportant because the noble gases do not ordinarily form compounds.) The electron-dot structure of hydrogen is simply H· and of helium is He:. The electron-dot structures or Lewis structures of the atoms in the second period of the periodic table are as follows.

■ It doesn't matter which sides of the symbols get the pairs.

$$\text{Li·} \quad \text{·Be·} \quad \text{·B·} \quad \text{·C·} \quad \text{:N·} \quad \text{:O·} \quad \text{:F:} \quad \text{:Ne:}$$

Notice how, after the first four dots have gone into place, additional dots are paired with others. More importantly, notice how the number of dots always equals the group number of the atom (these all being of the representative elements).

EXAMPLE 4.7	**WRITING THE ELECTRON-DOT SYMBOL OF A REPRESENTATIVE ATOM**

Problem: What is the electron dot symbol of sulfur, S?

Solution: Sulfur is in group VIA of the periodic table, so its atoms must have six electrons in their valence shells. We write the first four as the corners of an imaginary square,

$$\text{·S·}$$

and we add the last two to create two pairs. (It doesn't matter which of the possible pairs are created.)

$$\text{:S·}$$

PRACTICE EXERCISE 8   Write the electron-dot symbols for the atoms of the period 3 elements of the periodic table.

PRACTICE EXERCISE 9   Write the electron-dot symbol for antimony, Sb, atomic number 51.

The Formation of Ions Can Be Shown by Electron-Dot Symbolism The electron transfer that occurs when sodium and chlorine react can be shown by electron-dot symbolism as follows.

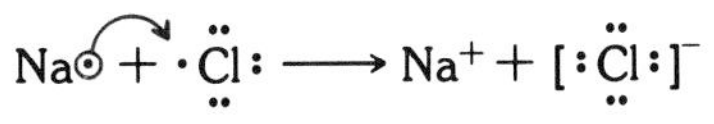

$$\text{Na·} + \text{·Cl:} \longrightarrow \text{Na}^+ + [\text{:Cl:}]^-$$

The valence shell of sodium loses its electron, so no dot remains. (Only valence shells, the *original* outside levels, are given electron dots.) The valence shell of chlorine accepts this electron and an octet forms. To show that this electron is fully the property of chlorine, we put brackets about the symbol of the ion.

The reaction between magnesium and chlorine can similarly be represented.

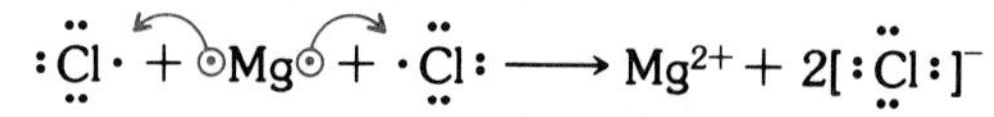

$$:\ddot{Cl}\cdot + \odot Mg\odot + \cdot \ddot{Cl}: \longrightarrow Mg^{2+} + 2[:\ddot{Cl}:]^-$$

Each chlorine atom has room in its valence shell for only one more electron, so two chlorine atoms are needed to take care of the two electrons of one magnesium atom.

EXAMPLE 4.8   **REPRESENTING A REACTION IN ELECTRON-DOT SYMBOLISM**

Problem: Sodium sulfide is an ionic compound of the sodium ion, Na^+ and the sulfide ion, S^{2-}. How could its formation be represented in electron-dot symbolism?

Solution: We first write the Lewis symbols for sodium and sulfur.

$$Na\cdot \qquad \cdot \ddot{S}\cdot$$

To achieve an octet, S needs two electrons, so we need two Na atoms. We can therefore write (remembering the brackets),

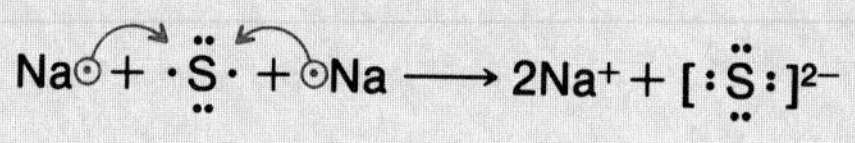

$$Na\odot + \cdot \ddot{S}\cdot + \odot Na \longrightarrow 2Na^+ + [:\ddot{S}:]^{2-}$$

PRACTICE EXERCISE 10   Represent the formation of calcium oxide by electron-dot symbolism. It consists of Ca^{2+} and O^{2-} ions.

Lewis Structures of Molecules Display Noble Gas Configurations for the Atoms Present   The formation of H_2 can be represented in electron-dot symbolism as follows.

$$H\cdot + \cdot H \longrightarrow H:H$$

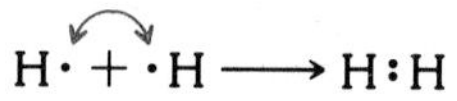

The shared pair of electrons is shown between the two atomic symbols. Since they are shared, they both count for each hydrogen when assessing whether a noble gas configuration is achieved. Each hydrogen atom acquires the helium configuration by this sharing of the electron pair. What we see here is a general rule; noble gas configurations also dominate the formation of covalent bonds as they did of ions. Atoms that form covalent bonds tend, by the sharing of electron pairs, to acquire as many electrons as needed to achieve noble gas configurations.

We can represent the formation of the diatomic halogen molecules in electron-dot symbolism as follows. We will also carry the symbolism one step farther in these examples. It is customary to represent any shared pair of electrons — any covalent bond — by a short line, a "dash" bond.

■ Remember, only the outside-level electrons are shown. The inside-level electrons are just understood to be there.

Fluorine, F_2	$:\ddot{F}\cdot + \cdot\ddot{F}: \longrightarrow :\ddot{F}:\ddot{F}:$	or $:\ddot{F}-\ddot{F}:$
Chlorine, Cl_2	$:\ddot{Cl}\cdot + \cdot\ddot{Cl}: \longrightarrow :\ddot{Cl}:\ddot{Cl}:$	or $:\ddot{Cl}-\ddot{Cl}:$
Bromine, Br_2	$:\ddot{Br}\cdot + \cdot\ddot{Br}: \longrightarrow :\ddot{Br}:\ddot{Br}:$	or $:\ddot{Br}-\ddot{Br}:$
Iodine, I_2	$:\ddot{I}\cdot + \cdot\ddot{I}: \longrightarrow :\ddot{I}:\ddot{I}:$	or $:\ddot{I}-\ddot{I}:$

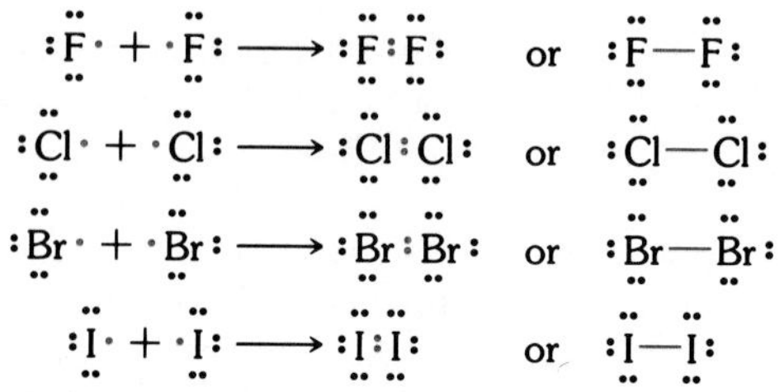

By counting the shared electron pairs of the covalent bonds for either atom, we can see that each halogen atom in these diatomic molecules has achieved a noble gas configuration, an outer octet.

Hydrogen chloride, HCl, is a diatomic molecule with one covalent bond, and its formation can be represented as follows.

$$H\cdot + \cdot \ddot{\underset{\cdot\cdot}{Cl}}: \longrightarrow H:\ddot{\underset{\cdot\cdot}{Cl}}: \quad \text{or} \quad H—\ddot{\underset{\cdot\cdot}{Cl}}:$$

Again we see the noble gas configurations made complete for H and Cl by the sharing of an electron pair.

The atoms of the nonmetals of groups IVA, VA, and VIA must form more than one covalent bond to acquire octets. Of particular importance at the molecular level of life are atoms of carbon, nitrogen, oxygen, and sulfur. Their Lewis symbols are

$$\cdot \underset{\cdot}{\overset{\cdot}{C}}\cdot \qquad \cdot \underset{\cdot}{\overset{\cdot\cdot}{N}}\cdot \qquad \cdot \underset{\cdot}{\overset{\cdot\cdot}{O}}: \qquad \cdot \underset{\cdot}{\overset{\cdot\cdot}{S}}:$$

You can see at a glance from these symbols how many electrons each must get by sharing to acquire octets. Carbon has four electrons so it needs four more, and if it combines with hydrogen (which has just one electron per atom to share), it *must* have four hydrogen atoms to get the necessary four additional electrons.

■ Methane is the chief constituent of natural gas.

$$H\cdot + \cdot \underset{\underset{H}{\cdot}}{\overset{\overset{H}{\cdot}}{C}}\cdot + \cdot H \longrightarrow H:\underset{\underset{H}{\cdot\cdot}}{\overset{\overset{H}{\cdot\cdot}}{C}}:H \quad \text{or} \quad H—\underset{\underset{H}{|}}{\overset{\overset{H}{|}}{C}}—H$$

Methane

Similarly, a nitrogen atom, which has five electrons and needs a share of three more to have an octet, combines with three hydrogen atoms. And oxygen and sulfur combine with two. We will let a small "x" represent the electron donated by a hydrogen atom to the shared pair to make it easier to see the originals of the pairs.

■ Ammonia is an important nitrogen fertilizer.

$$H\overset{\cdot\cdot}{\underset{\overset{\cdot x}{H}}{N}}H \; \text{or} \; H—\underset{\underset{H}{|}}{\overset{\cdot\cdot}{N}}—H \qquad H\overset{\cdot\cdot}{\underset{\overset{x\cdot}{H}}{O}}: \; \text{or} \; H—\underset{\underset{H}{|}}{\overset{\cdot\cdot}{O}}: \qquad H\overset{\cdot\cdot}{\underset{\overset{x\cdot}{H}}{S}}: \; \text{or} \; H—\underset{\underset{H}{|}}{\overset{\cdot\cdot}{S}}:$$

Ammonia   Water   Hydrogen sulfide

The valence shell electrons that are not covalent bonds are called **unshared pairs.** Often they become involved in chemical reactions, and we'll have to bring them into the discussions as needed.

The symbols for methane, ammonia, water, and hydrogen sulfide that show the sequence in which the atoms are joined together are called **structural formulas** or simply **structures.** A formula of a molecular substance, such as H_2O, which gives the composition of one molecule is called a **molecular formula.**

The kinds of formulas we used for ionic compounds, empirical formulas, are almost never used for molecular compounds. This is because when molecules react, they often change in only one part of their structure, and we need the fuller information of a structural formula to show this. Thus the *empirical* formula of butane, a familiar lighter fluid, is C_2H_5. This tells us nothing more than that butane is made of carbon and hydrogen in the indicated two to five ratio by atoms, which are the smallest *whole* numbers we could use. But one molecule of butane has the composition of C_4H_{10}, which is its *molecular* formula. The fourteen atoms in this formula are organized in the molecule in the following structural formula or structure.

$$
\begin{array}{c}
\quad\ \ \overset{\displaystyle H}{|}\ \ \overset{\displaystyle H}{|}\ \ \overset{\displaystyle H}{|}\ \ \overset{\displaystyle H}{|} \\
H-C-C-C-C-H \\
\quad\ \ \underset{\displaystyle H}{|}\ \ \underset{\displaystyle H}{|}\ \ \underset{\displaystyle H}{|}\ \ \underset{\displaystyle H}{|}
\end{array}
$$

Structural formula of butane, C_4H_{10}

Sometimes the empirical and molecular formulas of a molecular compound happen to be the same, as in water, ammonia, and methane. But this isn't very common.

EXAMPLE 4.9	**USING THE OCTET RULE AND ELECTRON-DOT STRUCTURES TO FIGURE OUT STRUCTURAL FORMULAS**

■ Phosphine is present in the very unpleasant odor of decaying fish.

Problem: Phosphine is a very poisonous compound of phosphorus and hydrogen. What is its most likely structure?

Solution: We need the electron-dot structures for the atoms first.

$$H\cdot \qquad \cdot\ddot{\underset{\cdot}{P}}\cdot$$

We can see that phosphorus, in group VA, needs three more electrons (like nitrogen—N and P are in the same family). To get them, it *must* have three hydrogen atoms. The structural formula of phosphine, therefore, must be

$$
\begin{array}{ccc}
H\!:\!\ddot{P}\!:\!H & & H-\overset{\displaystyle ..}{\underset{\displaystyle |}{P}}-H \\
\ \ \ddot{H} & \text{or} & \quad\ \ H
\end{array}
$$

PRACTICE EXERCISE 11

Silicon and hydrogen form a simple compound called silane that has one Si atom per molecule. What is the structural formula of silane?

■ Ethylene is used to make polyethylene plastics.

In Many Molecules Two or Three Pairs of Electrons Are Shared in Double or Triple Bonds Ethylene is C_2H_4. Its structure is

$$
\begin{array}{ccc}
\overset{\displaystyle H}{\diagdown}\ \ \overset{\displaystyle H}{\diagup} & & H\underset{x}{\overset{x}{\ }}\ \ \overset{x}{\underset{x}{\ }}H \\
\quad C\!=\!C & \text{or} & \ \ C\!:\!:\!C \\
\overset{\displaystyle \diagup}{H}\ \ \overset{\displaystyle \diagdown}{H} & & H\ \ \ \ \ \ H
\end{array}
$$

We have again used a tiny "x" to represent an electron supplied by a hydrogen atom. Each bond with one shared pair, like the bond from H to C, is called a **single bond.** You can see that each carbon supplied four electrons, as its location in group IVA requires. Now notice that each carbon atom has an octet. This would not have been possible without placing two pairs of electrons between the carbon symbols. When two pairs of electrons are shared, the result is called a **double bond.** Such bonds are extremely prevalent in nature.

The nitrogen molecule has a **triple bond,** because three pairs of electrons are shared between the nitrogen nuclei. We can think of N_2 forming as follows.

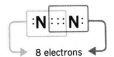

8 electrons

$$:\!\ddot{N}\!\cdot\ \longleftrightarrow\ \cdot\ddot{N}\!: \longrightarrow\ :\!N\!:\!:\!:\!N\!: \qquad \text{or} \qquad :\!N\!\equiv\!N\!:$$

All six valence shell electrons between the two nitrogen nuclei count toward the octet of each nitrogen. The triple bond is not as common as single and double bonds, but acetylene, C_2H_2, the fuel for oxyacetylene torches, has one.

$$H:C:::C:H \quad \text{or} \quad H—C≡C—H$$

Acetylene

Many molecules have two double bonds. Carbon dioxide, CO_2, is a common example. Its Lewis structure is

$$:O::C::O: \quad \text{or} \quad :O=C=O:$$

Carbon dioxide

Be sure that you can recognize how each atom in CO_2 has an octet.

Sometimes the Octet Rule Fails The octet rule is not really a law of nature because it fails sometimes. We will just cite, by structures, some examples of such failures without making something big out of them. We will seldom encounter failures of the octet rule when only the row 1 and the row 2 elements of the periodic table are involved. This means that H, C, N, and O will never give us trouble on this score. Their valence shells can never hold more than eight electrons (just two for hydrogen, of course).

Some failures of the octet rule involve more than eight valence shell electrons in the structure. These can occur when a "central" nonmetal atom is from period 3 (or higher) of the periodic table. These atoms have their valence electrons at principal energy level 3 (or higher), *which can hold more than eight electrons*. Sulfur hexafluoride, SF_6, and phosphorus pentachloride, PCl_5, are examples of octet rule failures of this type.

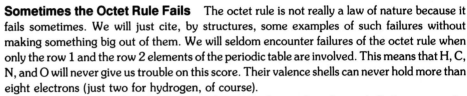

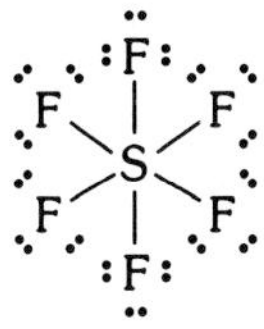

12 electrons
around S and
8 electrons
around each F

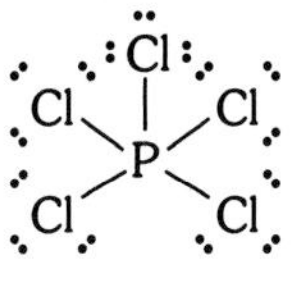

10 electrons
around P and
8 electrons
around each Cl

A few failures of the octet rule involve fewer than eight electrons around a central atom. The classic examples are beryllium chloride, $BeCl_2$, and boron trichloride, BCl_3. The Lewis structure of Be is simply $·Be·$, because Be is in group IIA. We can represent the formation of $BeCl_2$ as follows.

$$:\ddot{C}l· \curvearrowright ·Be· \curvearrowleft ·\ddot{C}l: \longrightarrow :\ddot{C}l:Be:\ddot{C}l:$$

Only four valence electrons are around the Be atom in this structure.

The formation of BCl_3 is represented as follows.

$$·B· + 3·\ddot{C}l: \longrightarrow :\ddot{C}l:\overset{\displaystyle :\ddot{C}l:}{B}:\ddot{C}l:$$

Boron has only six electrons in its valence shell in BCl_3.

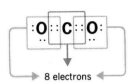

■ SF_6 is a colorless, odorless, tasteless, nonflammable, nontoxic, and unusually stable gas used to insulate high-voltage generators and switches.

■ Boron is the first member of group IIIA.

4.5 POLYATOMIC IONS AND A FIRST LOOK AT ACIDS AND BASES

Many important ions are electrically charged clusters of atoms held together by covalent bonds.

A **polyatomic ion** is a cluster of atoms held together by covalent bonds, but which has a net electrical charge. The ammonium ion, NH_4^+, is a particularly important example, because it and substances like it have functions at the molecular level of life. To understand this ion, we must expand our understanding of the covalent bond.

A Shared Electron Pair Can Originate from One Atom   The electron-dot structure of ammonia, NH_3, is

$$H : \overset{\cdot\cdot}{\underset{\overset{\cdot\cdot}{H}}{N}} : H \qquad or \qquad H - \overset{\cdot\cdot}{\underset{\overset{|}{H}}{N}} - H$$

Now notice that the nitrogen atom in this molecule has one unshared pair in the valence shell. Both electrons of this pair hold a fourth nucleus of hydrogen in the ammonium ion. The nucleus of a hydrogen atom, of course, is just a bare proton, and we can symbolize it here as H^+, a hydrogen ion, because its a hydrogen atom minus its $1s$ electron. Then we can visualize the formation of NH_4^+ from NH_3 and H^+ as follows.

$$H - \overset{\cdot\cdot}{\underset{\overset{|}{H}}{N}} - H + H^+ \longrightarrow \left[H - \overset{\overset{H}{|}}{\underset{\overset{|}{H}}{\overset{\cdot\cdot}{N}}} - H \right]^+ \quad or \quad \left[H - \overset{\overset{H}{|}}{\underset{\overset{|}{H}}{N}} - H \right]^+ \quad or \quad NH_4^+$$

Ammonia   Hydrogen   Ammonium
                    ion   ion

The new bond to the fourth hydrogen is a covalent bond like the other bonds, because it's an electron-pair bond. Sometimes it's useful, however, to have a special name for a covalent bond for which *both* shared electrons come from one atom. When we want to indicate this, we call the bond a **coordinate covalent bond.**

The ammonium ion bears a net charge of $1+$ because we have added the $1+$ charge of H^+ to a particle, NH_3, that has zero charge. The resulting cluster of atoms, all held together by covalent bonds, is therefore an example of a **polyatomic ion.** It can exist in solution, or it can be present in a solid, ionic compound, like ammonium chloride, NH_4Cl.

In the structure of the ammonium ion, the nitrogen still has an octet, only now all four electron pairs of the octet are involved in covalent bonds. All four of these bonds are equivalent. The molecule cannot remember which bond formed in which way, so you can see that a coordinate covalent bond and a covalent bond are not different *once they have formed.*

Before considering other polyatomic ions we want to introduce two families of compounds that are not just sources of polyatomic ions, but are also involved either in supplying or in combining with the hydrogen ion that we used to make NH_4^+. We will introduce here two major families of compounds, acids and bases.

Compounds That Furnish Hydrogen Ions Are Called Acids   If you're wondering where we got the hydrogen ion, H^+, to make NH_4^+, there is a large family of substances called **acids** that provide it. The hydrogen ion is an ion furnished by all common acids in water. For example, hydrochloric acid is actually a one to one mixture of hydrogen ions and chloride ions in water. Sulfuric acid, H_2SO_4, in water furnishes hydrogen ions and a polyatomic ion, the sulfate ion, SO_4^{2-} (and some HSO_4^- ions). Nitric acid provides, besides the hydrogen ion, the nitrate ion, NO_3^-.

■ We briefly introduce acids and bases here. They are the subjects of two later chapters, but you'll probably be using them in the lab before then.

■ Even dilute solutions of nitric, sulfuric, and hydrochloric acids will quickly eat holes in blue jeans.

Dilute solutions of these acids all have very tart tastes (but don't experiment with them unless your instructor shows you what to do — some acids are poisons and can harm teeth!). The tartness of lemon juice is caused by citric acid, and the tartness of vinegar is caused by acetic acid. Another property common to acids is that they corrode metals such as iron. The reason that acids have properties in common is that all supply hydrogen ions.

Compounds That Combine with Hydrogen Ions Are Called Bases Ammonia, which can react with and bind hydrogen ions is an example of a base. It's just one of several bases. The most characteristic property of **bases** is their ability to combine with hydrogen ions. If we represent hydrochloric acid by its separated ions, H^+ and Cl^-, its reaction with ammonia, a base, can be written as follows:

■ Hydrochloric acid is the acid in the stomach's gastric juice.

$$NH_3 \quad + [H^+ + Cl^-] \longrightarrow [NH_4^+ + Cl^-]$$

Ammonia   Hydrochloric acid   Ammonium chloride

■ Ammonia, a gas when pure, is available in the lab as solutions in water called *aqueous ammonia*.

Chemical Formulas Involving Polyatomic Ions Table 4.3 lists several of the important polyatomic ions. Their names and formulas should be learned. In many of the reactions of compounds made of polyatomic ions, the ions stay together as intact units. Therefore they are shown as units in chemical formulas, as in the following examples:

NH_4Cl	ammonium chloride, an ingredient in smelling salts
$NaOH$	sodium hydroxide, a raw material for making soap
NH_4NO_3	ammonium nitrate, a fertilizer
$NaNO_2$	sodium nitrite, a preservative in bacon and bologna
Na_3PO_4	sodium phosphate, a powerful cleaning agent

TABLE 4.3 Some Important Polyatomic Ions

Name	Formula
Ammonium ion	NH_4^+
Hydronium ion[a]	H_3O^+
Hydroxide ion	OH^-
Acetate ion	$C_2H_3O_2^-$
Carbonate ion	CO_3^{2-}
Bicarbonate ion[b]	HCO_3^-
Sulfate ion	SO_4^{2-}
Hydrogen sulfate ion[c]	HSO_4^-
Phosphate ion	PO_4^{3-}
Monohydrogen phosphate ion	HPO_4^{2-}
Dihydrogen phosphate ion	$H_2PO_4^-$
Nitrate ion	NO_3^-
Nitrite ion	NO_2^-
Hydrogen sulfite ion[d]	HSO_3^-
Sulfite ion	SO_3^{2-}
Cyanide ion	CN^-
Permanganate ion	MnO_4^-
Chromate ion	CrO_4^{2-}
Dichromate ion	$Cr_2O_7^{2-}$

[a] This ion is known only in a water solution.

[b] Formal name: hydrogen carbonate ion.

[c] Common name: bisulfate ion.

[d] Common name: bisulfite ion.

Na_2CO_3 sodium carbonate, washing soda

$NaHCO_3$ sodium bicarbonate, baking soda (not baking *powder*)

Whenever a formula has more than one polyatomic ion, we place parentheses about it and put a subscript *outside* the closing parenthesis. One example is ammonium sulfate.

$$(NH_4)_2SO_4$$

        This 2 specifies that there are two ammonium ions for every sulfate ion.

Other compounds whose formulas require parentheses are the following.

$Ca(NO_3)_2$ calcium nitrate

$Mg_3(PO_4)_2$ magnesium phosphate

$Al_2(SO_4)_3$ aluminum sulfate

Appendix C contains a summary of the rules for naming the kinds of compounds we have been using thus far, but notice from these examples that nothing new has been added to what we have already covered. We make names of ionic compounds from the names of their ions (omitting *ion*) in the usual way.

PRACTICE EXERCISE 12   Spend some time memorizing the names and formulas of the polyatomic ions that your instructor has assigned, and then drill yourself by writing the formulas of the following compounds.

(a)   potassium bicarbonate
(b)   sodium monohydrogen phosphate
(c)   ammonium phosphate

PRACTICE EXERCISE 13   Write the name of each of the following compounds.

(a) $NaCN$ (b) KNO_3 (c) $NaHSO_3$ (d) $(NH_4)_2CO_3$ (e) $NaC_2H_3O_2$

4.6   WRITING LEWIS STRUCTURES

As much as possible, Lewis structures are written so that all atoms have valence shell octets.

Learning how to write Lewis structures is one way to gain a better sense of where electrons are in molecules. This is useful to our study, because chemical reactions rearrange valence electrons as bonds break and reform.

Chemists have reduced the writing of a Lewis structure to several simple steps. The first step is to write a *skeletal structure,* one that roughly groups the atoms in the way they are arranged in the molecule, but without any valence electrons. This is often the trickiest step, and sometimes you have to make an educated guess. For example, sometimes the formula suggests what might be the centrally located atom. Hydrogen can never be the central atom because its valence shell is principal energy level 1; once a covalent bond extends from H, there can be no more bonds from it. Thus in H_2O oxygen must be the central atom. Otherwise, oxygen isn't often the central atom. Here are the skeletal structures for H_2O, CO_2, and NO_2.

■ NO_2 is the air pollutant that gives the red-brown color to smog.

$$H \ O \ H \qquad O \ C \ O \qquad O \ N \ O$$

But it isn't as simple with something like carbonic acid, H_2CO_3. Which of the following is the correct grouping simply is not obvious.

■ Carbonic acid forms by a reaction of CO_2 with water. It isn't a stable acid, and it cannot be isolated and made pure.

What we need is a guideline, a rule of thumb that can help us out in most situations like this. The key word in carbonic acid is *acid*, plus the fact that its formula, H_2CO_3, contains both oxygen and hydrogen. Such acids are classified as *oxoacids*, and in all the oxoacids that we study, H is always joined covalently to O. The third atom in the formula of an oxoacid — C in carbonic acid — is the central atom. You can see that all these factors are satisfied in the correct skeletal structure of carbonic acid.

EXAMPLE 4.10   WRITING SKELETAL STRUCTURES

Problem: Write the skeletal structure of nitric acid, HNO_3.

Solution: This is an acid with both H and O, so we know that one oxygen atom holds the hydrogen atom. The central atom is N, so we can now write the skeletal structure by grouping the O atoms around the N and placing H near one of the O atoms. (It does not matter which one.)

$$
\begin{array}{c}
\text{O} \\
\text{H O N O}
\end{array}
$$

PRACTICE EXERCISE 14   Write the skeletal structure of sulfuric acid, H_2SO_4, probably the most important acid used in industry, and phosphoric acid, H_3PO_4.

The second step in writing a Lewis structure is to add up all of the valence electrons. The total equals the number of dots that must be used. Use the locations of the elements in the periodic table to find the number of their valence electrons.

EXAMPLE 4.11   ADDING UP VALENCE ELECTRONS

Problem: How many dots must appear in the Lewis structures of H_2CO_3, HNO_3, and H_2SO_4?

Solution:

H_2CO_3	H has 1 valence electron, so for 2 H	$2 \times 1 =$	2
	C (group IVA) has 4, so for 1 C	$1 \times 4 =$	4
	O (group VIA) has 6, so for 3 O	$3 \times 6 =$	18
	Total valence electrons		24
HNO_3	H has 1 valence electron, so for 1 H	$1 \times 1 =$	1
	N (group VA) has 5, so for 1 N	$1 \times 5 =$	5
	O (group VIA) has 6 each, so for 3 N	$3 \times 6 =$	18
	Total valence electrons		24
H_2SO_4	H has 1 electron, so for 2 H	$2 \times 1 =$	2
	S (group VIA) has 6, so for 1 S	$1 \times 6 =$	6
	O (group VIA) has 6, so for 4 O	$4 \times 6 =$	24
	Total valence electrons		32

PRACTICE EXERCISE 15   How many valence electrons are in H_3PO_4, phosphoric acid?

In the third step, we start to place the electrons *by pairs* into the skeletal structure. Do this in the following order. Put *one* pair in each bond. Then use pairs to complete the octets of all atoms attached to the central atom. Finally, if necessary, complete the octet of the central atom using as many pairs as needed. (Remember to limit the electrons by any H atom to two.)

EXAMPLE 4.12   **PLACING ELECTRON PAIRS INTO SKELETAL LEWIS STRUCTURES**

Problem: Fill in the electron pairs for the skeletal structure of sulfuric acid.

Solution: If you worked Practice Exercise 14, you found the skeletal structure to be the following:

$$
\begin{array}{c}
O \\
H\ O\ S\ O\ H \\
O
\end{array}
$$

(You might have placed the H atoms by different oxygens. This would not matter.) In Example 4.11 we calculated that there are 32 valence electrons—32 dots—to distribute. So first we put electron pairs into each bond.

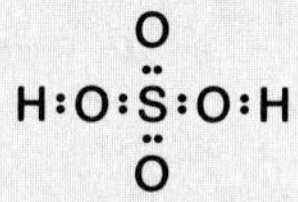

$$
\begin{array}{c}
O \\
H\!:\!O\!:\!\overset{\cdot\cdot}{\underset{\cdot\cdot}{S}}\!:\!O\!:\!H \\
O
\end{array}
$$

This used up 12 electrons. Now we finish the octets for the oxygen atoms.

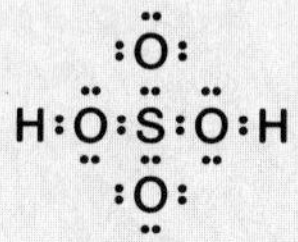

$$
\begin{array}{c}
:\!\overset{\cdot\cdot}{O}\!: \\
H\!:\!\overset{\cdot\cdot}{\underset{\cdot\cdot}{O}}\!:\!\overset{\cdot\cdot}{\underset{\cdot\cdot}{S}}\!:\!\overset{\cdot\cdot}{\underset{\cdot\cdot}{O}}\!:\!H \\
:\!\overset{\cdot\cdot}{O}\!:
\end{array}
$$

This uses up 20 more electrons. We have used the 32 electrons we had to place, 12 + 20. And we see that the central atom has an octet. So we have answered the problem, but we can still change this structure to one with dash bonds and write the Lewis structure of sulfuric acid as follows.

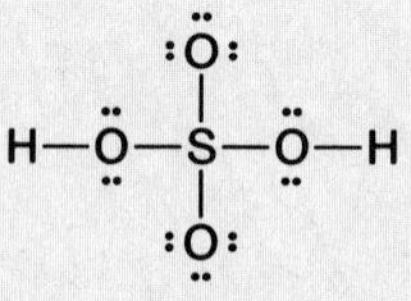

$$
\begin{array}{c}
:\!\overset{\cdot\cdot}{O}\!: \\
| \\
H\!-\!\overset{\cdot\cdot}{\underset{\cdot\cdot}{O}}\!-\!S\!-\!\overset{\cdot\cdot}{\underset{\cdot\cdot}{O}}\!-\!H \\
| \\
:\!\overset{\cdot\cdot}{O}\!:
\end{array}
$$

PRACTICE EXERCISE 16   One of the oxoacids of chlorine is chloric acid, $HClO_3$. Chlorine is its central atom. Write its skeletal structure, calculate the total number of valence electrons, fill them in (remembering to complete the octet of the central atom), and display the Lewis structure using dash bonds.

In many applications of the steps just given, you run out of electrons before you complete all the octets. This is a sign that *double or triple bonds have to be created.* (Be and B are exceptions, remember.)

| EXAMPLE 4.13 | CREATING DOUBLE BONDS IN WRITING A LEWIS STRUCTURE |

Problem: Write the Lewis structure of carbon dioxide, CO_2.

Solution: Its correct skeleton was given earlier,

$$O \quad C \quad O$$

Its total number of valence electrons is 16. (Two O atoms contribute $6 \times 2 = 12$ electrons, and the C contributes 4 electrons for a total of 16.) So we fill these in as follows according to Steps 2 and 3.

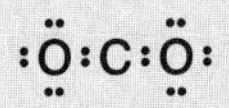

$$:\ddot{O}:C:\ddot{O}:$$

We have now used up all 16 electrons, but the central atom does not have an octet. There are only 4 electrons around C, and we've run out of valence electrons.

The procedure now is to move a nonbonding pair of electrons on an oxygen into an existing carbon-oxygen bond.

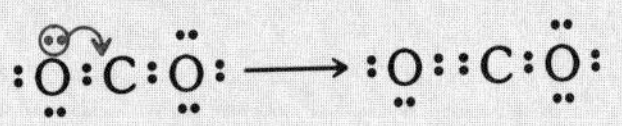

$$:\ddot{O}:C:\ddot{O}: \longrightarrow :\ddot{O}::C:\ddot{O}:$$

But carbon still doesn't have an octet. So we move another pair, taking it from the other oxygen, and the result is two double bonds in CO_2.

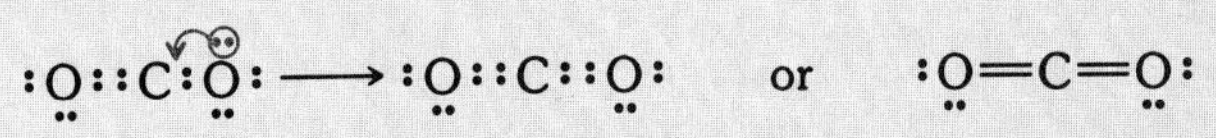

$$:\ddot{O}::C:\ddot{O}: \longrightarrow :\ddot{O}::C::\ddot{O}: \quad \text{or} \quad :\ddot{O}=C=\ddot{O}:$$

PRACTICE EXERCISE 17   Write the Lewis structure for sulfur trioxide, SO_3, an air pollutant.

Lewis Structures of Polyatomic Ions Also Show Noble Gas Configurations We need only a small modification of our preceding steps to construct Lewis structures of polyatomic ions. These modifications concern the total of the valence shell electrons that are to be inserted into a skeletal structure.

1.   For each negative charge on the ion, we have to add an electron to the count. A charge of $1-$ means adding 1 electron. A charge of $2-$ means adding 2 electrons, and so forth.

2.   For each positive charge on an ion, we subtract an electron.

Let's see how this works with the sulfate ion, $SO_4{}^{2-}$.

| EXAMPLE 4.14 | WRITING THE LEWIS STRUCTURE OF A POLYATOMIC NEGATIVE ION |

Problem: What is the Lewis structure of $SO_4{}^{2-}$?

Solution: First, we total the valence shell electrons.

For S (group VIA), 6 electrons	$1 \times 6 = 6$
For each O (group VIA), 6 electrons	$4 \times 6 = 24$
For each negative charge, add 1 electron	$2 \times 1 = \underline{2}$
Total valence shell electrons	32

Next we write a reasonable skeletal structure. We use S as the central atom and arrange the O atoms around it symmetrically.

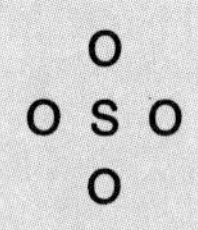

$$O$$
$$O \quad S \quad O$$
$$O$$

Next, we insert electron pairs into the covalent bonds. This will use up 8 electrons out of the 32.

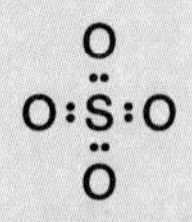

$$O$$
$$O : S : O$$
$$O$$

Now we place electron pairs around the oxygens to give each an octet. This will use up all the remaining 24, so this gives the final structure of the sulfate ion. We don't have to create double bonds. To show that the ion carries a charge of $2-$, we'll place brackets about it and place the $2-$ charge as a right superscript.

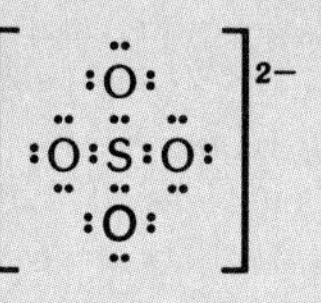

$$\left[\begin{array}{c} :\ddot{O}: \\ :\ddot{O}:\ddot{S}:\ddot{O}: \\ :\ddot{O}: \end{array} \right]^{2-} \qquad \text{The sulfate ion, } SO_4{}^{2-}$$

PRACTICE EXERCISE 18   Write the Lewis structures of the following ions.

(a) H_3O^+ (b) OH^-

PRACTICE EXERCISE 19   Write the Lewis structures of the following ions. Each will require that you form a double bond. Remember, it won't matter which electron pair is moved into position as the second bond of the double bond so long as proper octets are realized.

(a) $CO_3{}^{2-}$ (b) NO_3^-

4.7 SHAPES OF MOLECULES

As valence-shell electron pairs act to stay as far apart as possible, they set the overall shapes of molecules.

At the molecular level of life, the shapes of molecules are as important to chemical properties as structures. You have probably heard about hormones, and that each hormone picks out the cells of particular tissues of the body for its unique action. But the hormone is not made in that target tissue. It's made elsewhere and carried in the blood stream. How does a molecule of a hormone know where to go? It does so in the way your right foot knows when you have (perhaps groggily) put a left shoe on it. The shape of the hormone molecule recognizes where it must beach itself in its watery journey by finding a fitting match to it in a receptor molecule. The hormone's shape fits the receptor's shape, so the presence of the receptor molecule defines the hormone's target cell. This section is an introduction to the way that molecules

■ *Linear* means in a straight line.   acquire their shapes. We'll begin with the water molecule. It is not a linear molecule, with all its atoms lined up in a straight line. It's a bent molecule, and the angle is known, 104.5°.

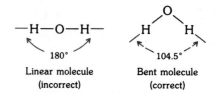

Linear molecule   Bent molecule
(incorrect)   (correct)

The angle formed by two bonds from the same atom is called the **bond angle.**

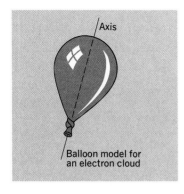

Balloon model for
an electron cloud

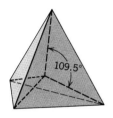

A regular tetrahedron is a four-sided
space bounded by identical equilateral
triangles. Any two lines from the
corners to the midpoint of the space
make an angle of 109.5°.

Figure 4.4
When four identical balloons are tied
off at a common point, their axes will
point to the corners of a tetrahedron.

The VSEPR Theory Is a Simple Explanation for Bond Angles   The easiest way to understand why there is an angle in the water molecule is by a simple and successful theory with a long but very descriptive name — the **valence-shell electron-pair repulsion theory,** or the **VSEPR theory,** for short. *Valence shell,* of course, refers to the original outside energy level of an atom, the shell where covalent bonds originate. *Electron pair* refers to the electrons of the valence shell. As we have learned, there are nearly always four *pairs* of electrons in the valence shell. *Repulsion* refers to the effect that the electron cloud of one pair has on the electron cloud of another in the valence shell.

VSEPR theory says that the shape of a molecule is largely determined by the efforts of the valence-shell electron clouds to stay out of each other's way as much as they can. A good analogy is to imagine that each pair's electron cloud resembles a balloon with an imaginary line or axis running from where it's tied off to the opposite surface. (See the figure in the margin.) Now imagine how four identical balloons *must* arrange themselves most comfortably (and so most stably) if we tie them all close together at one point. The result is shown in Figure 4.4. The balloons are least crowded when their axes make angles of 109.5° with each other. This array is called **tetrahedral** because the axes point to the corners of a regular tetrahedron.

Figure 4.5 shows how VSEPR theory explains the bond angle in the water molecule. In the valence shell of oxygen in H_2O, there are four electron pairs. Two of them are unshared pairs, and the electron clouds of the other two carry and hold one hydrogen nucleus apiece. These hydrogen nuclei shrink the associated clouds somewhat, so they do not repel each other quite as much. Consequently, the actual bond angle in H_2O is not quite as large as the true tetrahedral angle of 109.5°, but it is very close.

VSEPR Theory and the Ammonia Molecule   When nitrogen is the central atom, as it is in ammonia, the VSEPR theory again predicts a tetrahedral bond angle of 109.5°, because there are four valence-shell pairs of electrons. The actual bond angle in ammonia is 107.3°, also quite close. See Figure 4.5

VSEPR Theory and the Methane Molecule   When carbon is the central atom, as in methane, CH_4, VSEPR theory also predicts bond angles of 109.5° for each of the H—C—H bonds. As is also seen in Figure 4.5, theory and fact coincide exactly. The bond angles in methane are all 109.5°.

VSEPR Theory Is Unusually Successful for Systems Like $BeCl_2$, BCl_3, PCl_5, and SF_6, Too   The very simple idea of the VSEPR theory — electron clouds repel each other — accounted beautifully for the bond angles in three molecules of great importance in our study — water, ammonia, and methane. It will apply easily to larger molecules as we move on in our study. But what of those systems with fewer than four electron pairs in the valence shell, like $BeCl_2$ and BCl_3? We learned that there are only two electron pairs around Be in $BeCl_2$, and three around B in BCl_3. And what if there are more than four pairs? There are five around P in PCl_5 and six around S in SF_6, as we learned earlier.

Figure 4.6 illustrates the shapes of all these systems and gives each a technical name. Each shape is exactly what VSEPR theory predicts. When only two electron pairs are in the valence shell — think of just two balloons tied together — the axes of their clouds must point oppositely to give the most comfortable room, so the bond angle in $BeCl_2$ is 180°. When there are just three electron clouds, their axes will be in a plane and point to the corners of a regular triangle, so the bond angle in BCl_3 is 120°. The bond angles and shapes of the rest of the systems in Figure 4.6 follow from the same arguments.

Another accomplishment of VSEPR theory in our study is its illustration of the nature of a *scientific theory.* A theory, which is on a grander, more permanent scale than a hypothesis, explains a great number of facts in terms of just a few underlying causes. In VSEPR theory, we have seen how the shapes and bond angles of many systems are influenced by one simple idea about molecules, electron pairs in valence shells *must* repel each other, because like charges repel.

Figure 4.5
Shapes of molecules that have four pairs of electrons around a central atom.

Number of Bonding Pairs	Number of Nonbonding Pairs	Structure	
4	0	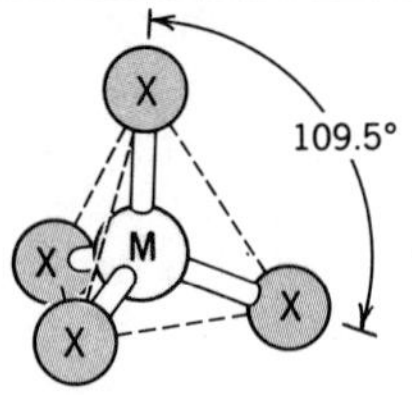	Tetrahedral Example: methane, CH_4
3	1	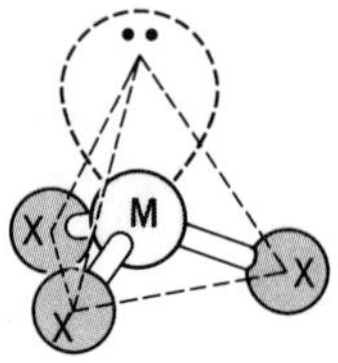	Pyramid-shaped (trigonal pyramidal) Example: ammonia, NH_3
2	2	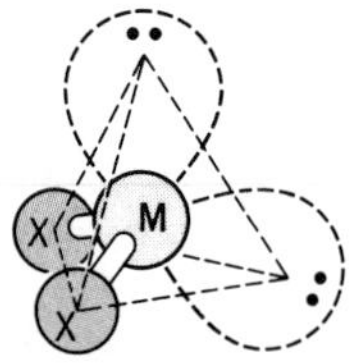	Bent (nonlinear) Example: water, H_2O

4.8 POLAR MOLECULES

Even electrically neutral molecules can attract each other if they are polar.

If molecules are neutral, how can they stick together? Sugar molecules, for example, stack together naturally to make beautiful crystals that are not easy to melt. What holds sugar molecules together in such crystals? We'll introduce the answer here.

Shared Pairs Between Unlike Atoms Are Usually Not Equally Shared   When atoms with different nuclear charges are joined by a covalent bond, the electron cloud of the shared pair usually becomes stabilized nearer one end of the bond than the other. For atoms of the same period in the periodic table, the nucleus with the *larger* positive charge pulls the electron cloud somewhat away from the nucleus of lower positive charge. The positive-charge effect of the nucleus of lower charge is therefore not entirely canceled *where it is.* The electron cloud is too thin in negative charge to do this. In other words, where the electron cloud is too thin, a fraction of a positive charge is still exerting whatever influences any charge can exert. Such a fractional charge is called a *partial charge,* and we use the Greek lowercase letter delta, δ, to stand for *partial.* Thus a partial positive charge has the symbol $\delta+$.

The hydrogen fluoride molecule, for example, has a $\delta+$ charge at its hydrogen end. The hydrogen nucleus has only a charge of $1+$, but the fluorine nucleus has a charge of $9+$, nine times as great. Moreover, because fluorine's other electrons are not concentrated between the two nuclei, they cannot entirely shield the influence of fluorine's nuclear charge from the shared pair. This is why the electron cloud of the shared pair is pulled toward the fluorine end of the H—F molecule. This is why the hydrogen end does not retain enough electron density to neutralize fully the positive charge of the hydrogen nucleus where it is. This is why the hydrogen end has a $\delta+$ charge. Now let's look at the other end.

When the fluorine end of the H—F molecule pulls the electron density of the shared pair toward itself, the total electron density at the fluorine end of the molecule is more than enough

Figure 4.6
Molecular shapes to be expected for different numbers of pairs of valence-shell electrons. (From J. E. Brady and J. R. Holum, *Fundamentals of Chemistry,* 3rd ed., John Wiley & Sons, New York, 1988. Used by permission.)

Number of Electron Pairs	Shape		Example
Two pairs		linear	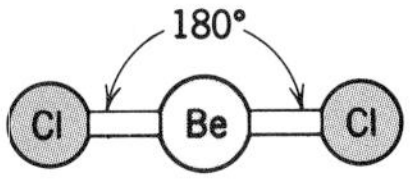
Three pairs	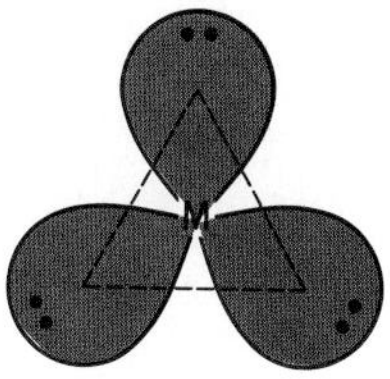	planar triangular	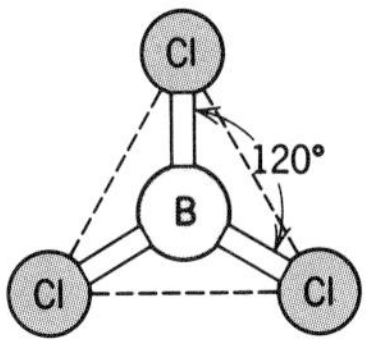
Four pairs	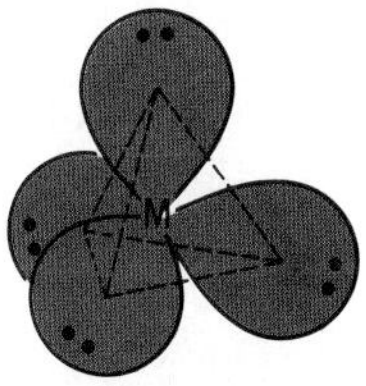	tetrahedral (A tetrahedron is pyramid-shaped. It has four triangular faces and four corners.)	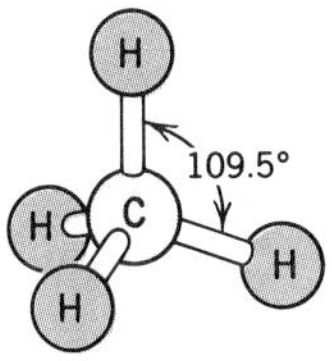
Five pairs	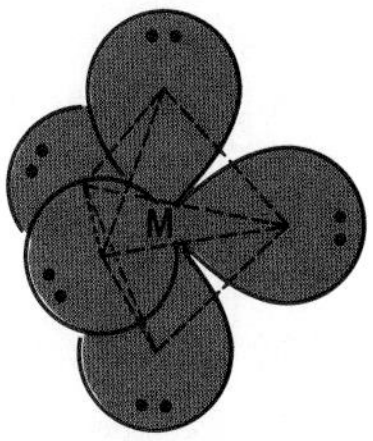	trigonal bipyramidal This figure consists of two three-sided pyramids joined by sharing a common face—the triangular plane through the center.)	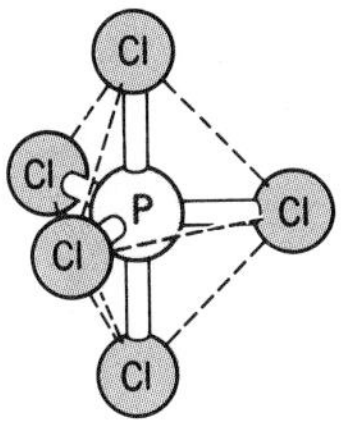
Six pairs		octahedral (An octahedron is an eight-sided figure with *six* corners. It consists of two square pyramids that share a common square base.)	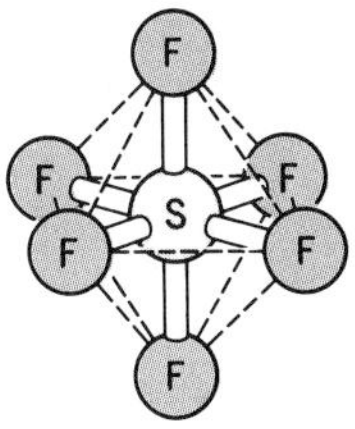

to neutralize the positive charge that is there because of fluorine's nucleus. In other words, the electron cloud is thicker than necessary at this end, and this end of the molecule has a partial negative charge, $\delta-$.

We can't say precisely what the sizes of these fractions are, but because the molecule as a whole is electrically neutral, the algebraic sum of the $\delta+$ and the $\delta-$ must be zero.

Polar Bonds Have Opposite Partial Charges at Either End   When a covalent bond has a $\delta+$ at one end and a $\delta-$ at the other, it is called a **polar bond.** We can symbolize the electrical polarity of the bond in hydrogen fluoride in either of two ways, as seen in structures **1** and **2**.

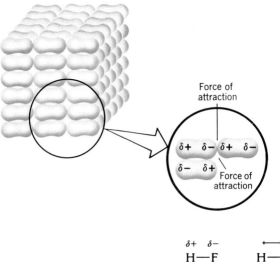

Figure 4.7
Polar molecules attract each other in a crystal of a molecular substance.

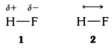

1   **2**

In **2**, the arrow points toward the end of the bond that is richer in electron density. At the other end, there is a hint of the positive character by the merger of the arrow with a plus sign. Because there are two partial, opposite charges in H—F, this molecule is sometimes said to have an **electrical dipole.**

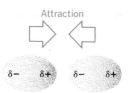

Two polar molecules

Two polar molecules can attract each other.

A magnet is a good analogy of the consequences of being a polar system. It has a magnetic dipole, two poles labeled north and south. Perhaps you have played with toy magnets and know that two magnets can stick to each other *if they are lined up properly.* In fact, if you have a great many magnets and line them up correctly, you can make all of them cling together. You just have to make sure that poles of opposite kind are nearest neighbors and that poles that are alike are as far apart as possible.

Molecules that are electrically polar can stick to each other just like this. Given the freedom to move, they will line up automatically the way magnets can. See Figure 4.7. This is how neutral molecules can stick to each other. How tightly they stick depends on the sizes of the partial charges. It also depends on the shapes of the molecules, because they might interfere with molecules getting close enough for the forces of attraction between opposite partial charges to work. We've already studied some aspects of molecular shape. We now study what can influence the sizes of the partial charges.

When Bonded Atoms Have Different Electronegativities, the Bond Is Polar   The relative ability of an atom of an element to draw electron density toward itself from another atom held to it by a covalent bond is called the **electronegativity** of the element.

Fluorine has the highest electronegativity of all of the elements, because its atoms have the highest nuclear positive charge while being shielded by only level 1 and level 2 electrons. Oxygen, which stands just to the left of fluorine in the periodic table, has the next highest electronegativity. Its atoms have one less charge than fluorine atoms, and also are shielded by only level 1 and level 2 electrons. The element with the third highest electronegativity, you might now guess, lies just to the left of oxygen. It is nitrogen with atoms that have one less charge on their nuclei than oxygen atoms.

Figure 4.8 shows the relative electronegativities of several elements, metals and nonmetals, and their locations in the periodic table. Notice that carbon isn't the element with the fourth highest electronegativity; chlorine ranks fourth. The chlorine atom has a large positive nuclear charge, 17 +. But this doesn't make chlorine even more electronegative than fluorine, because chlorine has level 3 electrons as well as those in levels 1 and 2. These extra electrons evidently provide enough shielding of a chlorine nucleus to make the chlorine atom less able

IA						
H 2.20	IIA	IIIA	IVA	VA	VIA	VIIA
Li 0.97	Be 1.47	B 2.01	C 2.50	N 3.07	O 3.50	F 4.10
Na 1.01	Mg 1.23	Al 1.47	Si 1.74	P 2.06	S 2.44	Cl 2.83
K 0.91	Ca 1.04				Se 2.48	Br 2.74
Rb 0.89	Sr 0.99				Te 2.01	I 2.21

Figure 4.8
Relative electronegativies.

than fluorine to be electronegative. Besides, the covalent bond in a molecule such as H—Cl is a longer bond than it is in H—F. The shared pair has its electron density farther from the chlorine nucleus to start with, and this also makes it harder for this nucleus to pull electron density toward itself. On balance, chlorine is less electronegative than fluorine, but more so than carbon.

Notice in Figure 4.8 that metals have the lowest electronegativities. In fact, the general trend is that as you move to the right in the same period or as you move upward in the same group, the electronegativities become larger. The most electronegative element, as we said, is fluorine; and the least electronegative is cesium, the last element in the group IA family (below rubidium, Rb, in Figure 4.8).

Although you're not asked to memorize any numerical values for electronegativities, you should learn what the trends are in the periodic table. Moreover, we'll be working so often with oxygen, nitrogen, carbon, and hydrogen, that you should memorize the order of their electronegativies, O > N > C > H. We'll see shortly how knowing this can be helpful.

Polar Bonds Make Molecules Polar If the Bond Polarities Do Not Cancel   It's easy to tell if a *bond* is polar; it always is if the atoms that the bond joins have different electronegativities. For diatomic molecules such as H—F and H—Cl that have only one bond, when the bond is polar so is the molecule. Because such diatomics as H—H and F—F involve identical atoms and one bond, we can tell right away that these molecules can't be polar.

Whether larger molecules are polar in an overall sense depends not just on the presence of polar bonds but also on the *geometry* of the molecule. It's possible for the polarities of individual bonds to cancel each other. Consider, for example, the carbon dioxide molecule, **3.**

$$O{=}C{=}O \qquad \begin{array}{c} H \\ \diagdown \\ O{-}H \end{array}$$

$$\textbf{3} \qquad\qquad \textbf{4}$$

Because oxygen is more electronegative than carbon, each carbon-oxygen bond system must be polar. But these two dipoles point in exactly opposite directions, so in an overall sense they cancel each other. This leaves the molecule as a whole nonpolar. The water molecule, **4,** on the other hand, is angular. Its two individual O—H bond polarities can't cancel, and the water molecule is polar, quite polar, in fact.

Another useful way of thinking about the polarity of a molecule uses the idea of a *center of density of charge,* something like a "balance point" for electrical charge. A **polar molecule** is one in which the center of density of positive charge is not at the same place as the center of density of negative charge. We don't have to be able to pinpoint these centers exactly to know if they are in the same place or not. The symmetry of the carbon dioxide molecule, **3,** tells us that all the positive charges on the three nuclei balance around the center of the carbon nucleus. Similarly, all the negative charges contributed by all the electrons must also balance *around the identical point.* Because these two centers are in the same place, the molecule is nonpolar. Wherever these two centers are in the water molecule, **4,** we know that because of the angularity of the molecule they can't be at the same place. Hence, we know that this molecule must be polar.

■ Group IA and IIA elements are so weakly electronegative that they give up electrons entirely to group VIA or VIIA elements and form ions, not polar bonds.

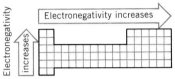

In electronegativity, metals are lowest and nonmetals are highest.

■ Nonbonding valence-shell electrons are often omitted from Lewis structures in general discussions.

EXAMPLE 4.15   **PREDICTING MOLECULAR POLARITY**

Problem: Place $\delta+$ and $\delta-$ signs at the correct ends of each of the bonds in the following structures (whose correct geometries are shown). Then decide whether each molecule as a whole is polar or nonpolar. (Use information in Figure 4.8 as needed.) A three-dimensional view of the carbon tetrachloride molecule is given. This molecule is entirely symmetrical.

■ OF_2 is a colorless, poisonous gas and is one product when fluorine burns(!) in water.

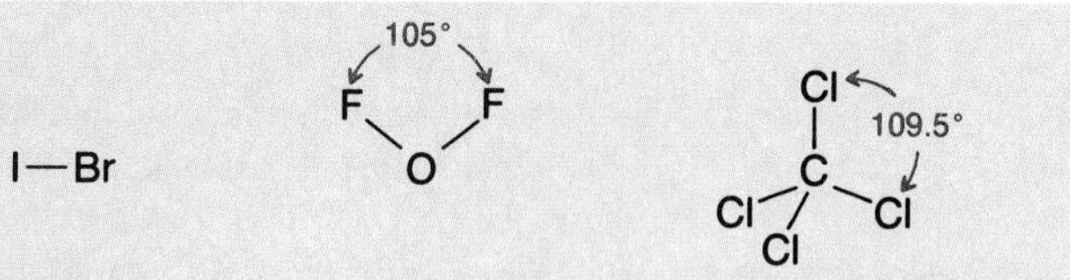

I—Br

Iodine bromide

105°
F⤹ ⤸F
O

Oxygen difluoride

Cl↞
109.5°⤸
C
Cl⁄ \Cl
Cl

Carbon tetrachloride

Solution: Because bromine is more electronegative than iodine, we have to place the partial charges as follows in iodine bromide, and the molecule is polar.

$$\overset{\delta+\ \ \ \delta-}{\text{I—Br}}$$

Because fluorine is more electronegative than oxygen, we have to place the partial charges in oxygen fluoride as follows. Because the molecule is angular, the centers of density of positive and negative charge cannot be at the same location, so the molecule must be (and is) polar.

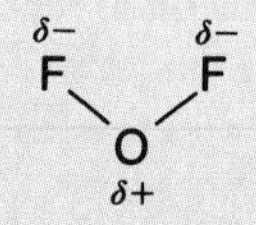

$$\overset{\delta-}{F} \diagdown \underset{\delta+}{O} \diagup \overset{\delta-}{F}$$

Because chlorine is more electronegative than carbon, we have to place the partial charges by each bond in carbon tetrachloride as follows:

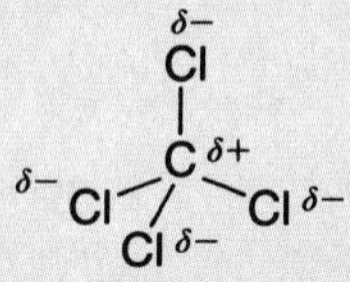

$$\overset{\delta-}{Cl}$$
$$\overset{\delta-}{Cl} \diagup \overset{\delta+}{C} \diagdown \overset{\delta-}{Cl}$$
$$\underset{\delta-}{Cl}$$

Remember, however, that this molecule is symmetrical. Therefore the balance point—the center of charge density—for all positive charge has to be at the center of the carbon nucleus. Similarly, the center of all negative charge density has to be in the identical place—the symmetrical disposition of the chlorine atoms about this center guarantees this result. Hence, the molecule as a whole is not polar.

PRACTICE EXERCISE 20   The structure of chloroform is just like that of carbon tetrachloride (in Example 4.15, above) except that one Cl has been replaced by H. Using the structure of carbon tetrachloride as a model, make the needed changes to draw a structure of chloroform and then place $\delta+$ and $\delta-$ signs by each atom. Finally, decide whether the molecule as a whole is polar.

4.9 MOLECULAR ORBITALS—ANOTHER VIEW OF THE COVALENT BOND

A shared electron pair resides in a molecular orbital formed by the partial overlapping of the spaces of two atomic orbitals.

We earlier described the formation of a hydrogen molecule, H—H, by thinking of two hydrogen atoms, each with a $1s$ electron, approaching each other (Figure 4.3, page 82). In a widely held view of the covalent bond, the $1s$ orbitals partially merge to create a new space for the electrons to be shared. The partial merging of atomic orbitals from different atoms is called

Figure 4.9
The covalent bond in the F—F molecule.

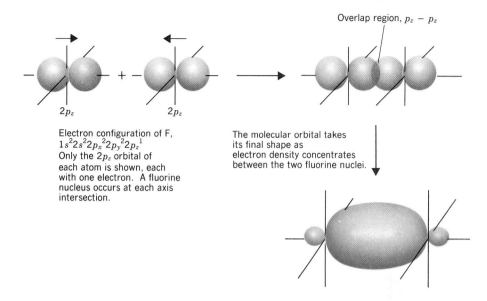

Electron configuration of F,
$1s^2 2s^2 2p_x^2 2p_y^2 2p_z^1$
Only the $2p_z$ orbital of
each atom is shown, each
with one electron. A fluorine
nucleus occurs at each axis
intersection.

Overlap region, $p_z - p_z$

The molecular orbital takes
its final shape as
electron density concentrates
between the two fluorine nuclei.

the **overlapping of orbitals.** The space created by such overlapping of atomic orbitals is called a **molecular orbital,** and it surrounds two nuclei (sometimes more). Like an atomic orbital, a molecular orbital can hold a maximum of two electrons, provided their spins are opposite. The shared electron pair of a covalent bond thus resides in a molecular orbital whose space encloses both nuclei held by the covalent bond.

■ The electron configuration of F is

$$1s^2 2s^2 2p_x^2 2p_y^2 2p_z^1$$

The atomic orbitals that overlap are generally those of valence shell electrons. Figure 4.9 shows how it happens to two fluorine atoms. On the left in the figure, we see two separated fluorine atoms, but only their half-filled p_z orbitals are pictured. (The nodes occur where their nuclei are.) Imagine that these two atoms move toward each other. Eventually, the spaces occupied by facing lobes of the p_z orbitals start to overlap. A molecular orbital forms, and the former two p_z electrons take up residence in it. Thus electron density becomes concentrated between the two nuclei, and the covalent bond in F—F forms.

The Geometry of Atomic Orbitals Decides Bond Angles   The bond angle in the hydrogen sulfide molecule is 92°, almost a right angle (90°). Since sulfur is in the same family as oxygen, shouldn't the angle in H_2S be like that in H_2O, nearly a tetrahedral angle? VSEPR theory would predict this, since the S atom in H_2S, like the O atom in H_2O, has four pairs of electrons, two pairs nonbonding and two bonding. Let's see how molecular orbital theory handles this.

Sulfur is in group VIA, and its electron configuration is

$$S \quad 1s^2 2s^2 2p^6 3s^2 3p_x^2 3p_y^1 3p_z^1$$

■ H$_2$S causes the odor of rotten eggs. It's a very poisonous gas.

■ The atomic number of sulfur is 16, so we have to make places for 16 electrons.

Thus a sulfur atom has two half-filled $3p$ orbitals, *and their axes make an angle of 90° with each other,* as seen in Figure 4.10. Therefore when two hydrogen atoms approach a sulfur atom to form the S—H bonds, the only effective way in which their $1s$ orbitals can overlap with sulfur's $3p$ orbitals is along the two perpendicular axes—also shown in Figure 4.10. Only by this approach can *maximum* overlapping result, and therefore only in this way can the strongest bonds form. Hence, the two resulting S—H bonds should make an angle of 90°. The actual bond angle, as we said, is 92°, which gives nice support to the theory that *the chief cause of a particular bond angle is the angle at which the axes of the atomic orbitals of the central atom cross.*

Second-Row Nonmetals, O, N, and C, Don't Fit the Simple Molecular Orbital View of H$_2$S   Because oxygen is in the same family as sulfur, what works well for H_2S ought to work equally well for H_2O, but it doesn't. As we have learned, the bond angle in H_2O is 104.5°, not 90°, not a good fit.

Figure 4.10
Bonding in H_2S. The H atoms must position themselves so that their $1s$ orbitals overlap with the half-filled $3p$ orbitals of S.

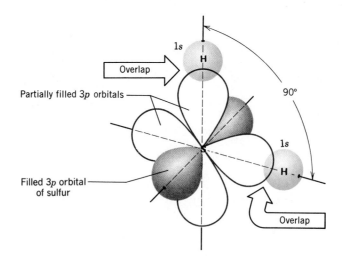

A similar difficulty arises with the bond angles in NH_3. The electron configuration of nitrogen, atomic number 7, is

$$N \qquad 1s^2 2s^2 2p_x^1 2p_y^1 2p_z^1$$

The nitrogen atom has three half-filled $2p$ orbitals, and their axes cross at angles of $90°$. Three hydrogen atoms, each with a $1s$ electron, coming up to overlap with the $2p$ orbitals of N should produce bond angles in NH_3 of $90°$, but they don't. The angles are $107.3°$, very close to what simple VSEPR theory predicts.

So far things are going poorly in extending the molecular orbital theory of H_2S to the hydrides of O and N. It becomes a total disaster when applied to CH_4, whose central atom is carbon with the electron configuration

$$C \qquad 1s^2 2s^2 2p_x^1 2p_y^1$$

Here we have only two half-filled $2p$ orbitals, an empty $2p$ orbital (the $2p_z$), and a filled $2s$ orbital. There is no way we can bring the $1s$ electrons of four hydrogen atoms up to these orbitals of carbon and emerge with bond angles of $109.5°$ in CH_4. Yet the idea of a molecular orbital seems "right," because atomic orbitals were right.

Hybrid Atomic Orbitals Are Used by Some Second-Row Elements To Make Molecular Orbitals

The mismatches between fact and simple molecular orbital theory led scientists to conclude that the atomic orbitals of the *isolated* atoms of O, N, and C are not the actual atomic orbitals used when these atoms form single bonds. Some of their simple atomic orbitals evidently undergo a subtle but important change before they engage in creating molecular orbitals. The result is a mixing of orbital shapes and a small evening out of orbital energy levels. This leads to new atomic orbitals at identical energy levels and with new shapes *and new axes* pointing at different angles.

The mixing of atomic orbitals is called **orbital hybridization.** This term borrows the word *hybrid* from biology, because the new **hybrid orbitals,** like hybrids anywhere, have some resemblances to their "parents." Hybridization occurs because it leads to better overlapping, to stronger bonds, and therefore to more stable molecules. So nature, not being too interested in our efforts to theorize, does its usual thing — it arranges for the most stable systems it can.

The sp^3 Hybrid Orbitals Are One Important Set

One way to form hybrid atomic orbitals for C, N, or O is to mix all the orbitals at level 2, the $2s$ and the three $2p$ orbitals. An important rule about hybridization is that the total number of orbitals is conserved. If we mix four orbitals, we get four new ones.

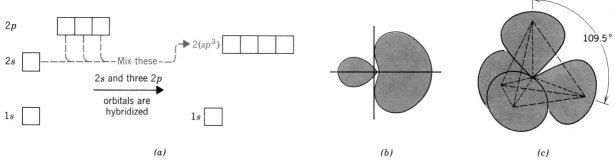

(a)   *(b)*   *(c)*

Figure 4.11

Formation of sp^3 hybrid orbitals. (*a*) The empty atomic orbitals mix (hybridize) to give four new orbitals, sp^3 hybrid orbitals. The four have identical energies, just slightly more than an *s* orbital and slightly less than the *p* orbitals. (*b*) Cross-sectional shape of an sp^3 hybrid orbital. (*c*) Arrangement in space of four sp^3 orbitals (showing only their larger lobes). How many electrons will be placed in these four orbitals will depend on the atomic number of the central atoms. See Figure 4.12.

The mixing of an *s* orbital with three *p* orbitals is called sp^3 hybridization. It produces four new hybrid orbitals named **sp^3 hybrid orbitals.** Figure 4.11 visualizes the process. The four are identical in shape, and their axes make angles of 109.5°. They have a tetrahedral array, in other words, exactly what VSEPR theory would also suggest. Notice that each hybrid orbital has two lobes, like *p* orbitals, but one lobe is much larger, a contribution of the *s* orbital "parent."

Atoms of carbon, nitrogen, and oxygen can all form sp^3 orbitals, but the number of electrons in them depends on which atom is involved. The new electron configurations for the *bonding* states, not the isolated-atom states, of C, N, and O are as follows whenever these atoms participate in the formation of just single bonds.

■ Notice that Hund's rule applies to hybrid orbitals, too. The sp^3 electrons spread out.

C	$1s^2 2(sp^3)^1 2(sp^3)^1 2(sp^3)^1 2(sp^3)^1$	Four half-filled orbitals
N	$1s^2 2(sp^3)^2 2(sp^3)^1 2(sp^3)^1 2(sp^3)^1$	Three half-filled orbitals
O	$1s^2 2(sp^3)^2 2(sp^3)^2 2(sp^3)^1 2(sp^3)^1$	Two half-filled orbitals

These bonding states are illustrated in Figure 4.12.

Figure 4.13 shows how we can imagine the formation of molecules of methane, ammonia, and water. A 1*s* orbital of a hydrogen atom, which holds one electron, overlaps with an sp^3 bonding-state orbital of a central atom, also with one electron, to form the molecular orbital for each bond to H. The bond angles in all these compounds should have the same tetrahedral value, 109.5°. They are a trifle smaller in both ammonia and water, presumably because their nonbonding electron clouds exert squeezing forces.

The sp^3 hybrid orbitals permit the formation of stronger bonds than the original nonhybrid orbitals because their larger lobes extend a little farther from the nucleus. The atomic

Figure 4.12

The bonding orbitals for atoms of carbon, nitrogen, and oxygen when they are involved only in single bonds.

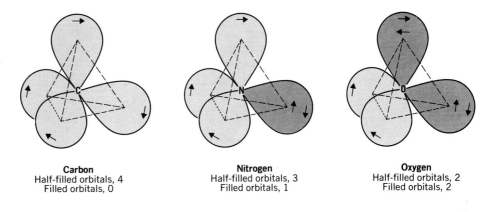

Carbon
Half-filled orbitals, 4
Filled orbitals, 0

Nitrogen
Half-filled orbitals, 3
Filled orbitals, 1

Oxygen
Half-filled orbitals, 2
Filled orbitals, 2

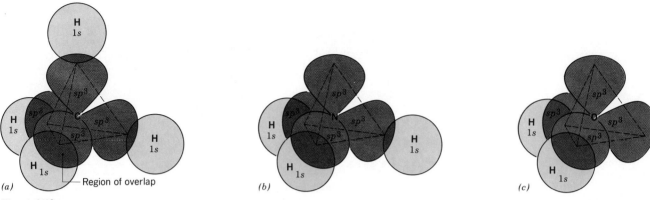

Figure 4.13
The sigma bonds in (a) methane, (b) ammonia, and (c) water.

nuclei of H, therefore, do not have to get quite as close to the central atom nuclei. Thus their mutual repulsion is less, and the system is more stable.

In molecular orbital theory, the bonds we have just described are named **sigma bonds (σ bonds).** Sigma bonds feature the symmetry of a long, straight sausage. We'll next see another kind of molecular orbital with a different symmetry and a different name.

Sometimes Only Two _p_-Orbitals Mix with an _s_-Orbital Sigma bonds are also single bonds. But what about double (or triple bonds) in molecular orbital theory? We'll use ethylene to answer this question.

The bond angles in ethylene are almost exactly $120°$, and all the atoms lie in the same plane. Clearly sp^3 hybrid orbitals will not account for these facts. Moreover, the carbon atoms at a double bond cannot use sp^3 orbitals because they hold three other groups, not four. Different hybrid orbitals are used, and these emerge from the mixing or hybridizing of the $2s$ and just _two_ of the $2p$ atomic orbitals, as shown in Figure 4.14. The third $2p$ orbital is left unchanged, but only for a moment.

Because one _s_ and two _p_ orbitals are mixed, the new hybrid orbitals are called **sp^2 orbitals.** Each carbon of the double bond develops three of them, and it also has one unhybridized $2p$ orbital. Thus there are four orbitals at each carbon with one electron apiece.

The shapes and the distributions of the sp^2 orbitals at carbon are shown in Figure 4.15. Notice how their axes come out at angles that VSEPR theory would have predicted. The axes of these orbitals lie in the same plane, and between them are angles of $120°$. The axis of the unhybridized $2p$ orbital is perpendicular to the plane and intersects it at the point where the three sp^2 orbitals intersect.

Figure 4.16 illustrates how a molecular orbital forms from the overlapping of two sp^2 orbitals, one from each carbon at the double bond. Two electrons are in this molecular orbital and are shared by the two carbons. The result is one of the bonds of the double bond, and it is a sigma bond.

Ethylene

Figure 4.14
Formation of sp^2 hybrid orbitals at a carbon atom. (a) The empty atomic orbitals at level 2. (b) These atomic orbitals have been hybridized to create three sp^2 hybrid orbitals, leaving a _p_ orbital unhybridized. (c) Carbon's six electrons are fed into the available orbitals to create the bonding state of carbon at a double bond.

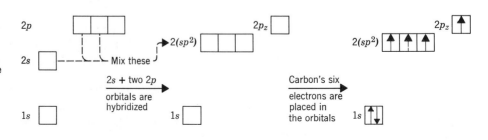

Figure 4.15
The shapes and arrangements of the bonding orbitals at level 2 of carbon when it is in an sp^2 hybridized state. (a) Showing how the three sp^2 hybrid orbitals have their axes in a plane and at angles of 120°. (b) Showing how the unhybridized p orbital fits with the three sp^2 orbitals.

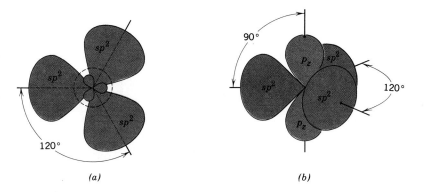

(a)   (b)

Figure 4.16
The sigma-bond network in ethylene. (The $2p$ orbital at each carbon is omitted so that the others can be seen better.)

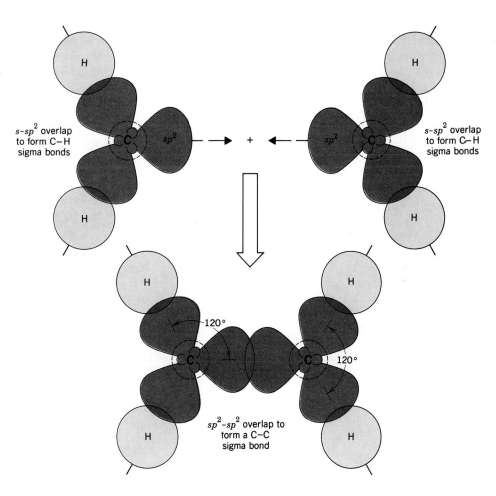

s-sp^2 overlap to form C—H sigma bonds

s-sp^2 overlap to form C—H sigma bonds

sp^2-sp^2 overlap to form a C—C sigma bond

The two groups of CH_2— atoms held so far by this bond would be free to rotate with respect to each other about this bond. Such a rotation would not reduce the degree of overlap and weaken the bond. However, at one stopping point during such a rotation, the two $2p$ orbitals become perfectly aligned, side by side. They are so close to each other that they now overlap *side by side* to create a new kind of molecular orbital, one with two banana-shaped halves, as shown in Figure 4.17. This molecular orbital now holds another shared pair of electrons so it also is a bond, the second bond of the double bond. A covalent bond made by the side-to-side overlap of two p orbitals is called a **pi bond,** or **π-bond.**

The triple bond of an alkyne has two pi bonds and a sigma bond. Special Topic 4.1 discusses this further.

■ F_2 forms by an end-to-end overlap of two p orbitals, so its bond is a sigma bond (Figure 4.9).

■ Carbon has sp hybrid orbitals at a triple bond.

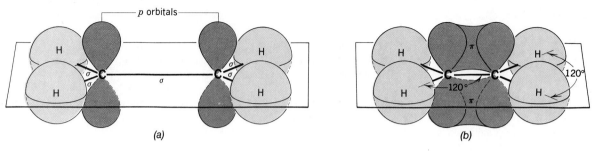

Figure 4.17
How the pi bond forms in ethylene. (*a*) Just before the *p* orbitals overlap side to side, showing the sigma bonds in place (*b*) This side-to-side overlap of two *p* orbitals creates two banana-shaped lobes of the pi bond. One pair of electrons resides in this complex space.

SPECIAL TOPIC 4.1 THE CARBON–CARBON TRIPLE BOND

The triple bond forms from a series of steps very similar to those of the double bond. We'll illustrate how it forms in acetylene, $H—C\equiv C—H$, where it occurs between two carbon atoms.

The $2s$ orbital of carbon and just one of its $2p$ orbitals mix or hybridize, which leaves two of the $2p$ orbitals of carbon unchanged. See Figure 4.18. The new hybrid orbitals are called *sp* hybrid orbitals. In shape they are very similar to sp^2 and sp^3 hybrid orbitals, but their axes point

in exactly opposite directions, not at angles of 109.5° or 120°. Their axes are also at right angles to the axes of the $2p$ orbitals, as seen in Figure 4.19. In this figure we see how the sigma bonds form in acetylene. Notice how two pi molecular orbitals form. They result from the side-to-side overlapping of the $2p$ orbitals. Thus in the triple bond there are one sigma bond and two pi bonds. This is also true in the triple bond of nitrogen, N_2.

Figure 4.18
Formation of *sp* hybrid orbitals at carbon. (*a*) Carbon's empty atomic orbitals. (*b*) The new orbitals after *sp* hybridization. Notice the two unhybridized *p* orbitals. (*c*) After carbon's six electrons have been placed into the orbitals following *sp* hybridization.

Figure 4.19
Showing the molecular orbitals at a carbon–carbon triple bond. (*a*) The sigma-bond network. (*b*) The pi-bond network.

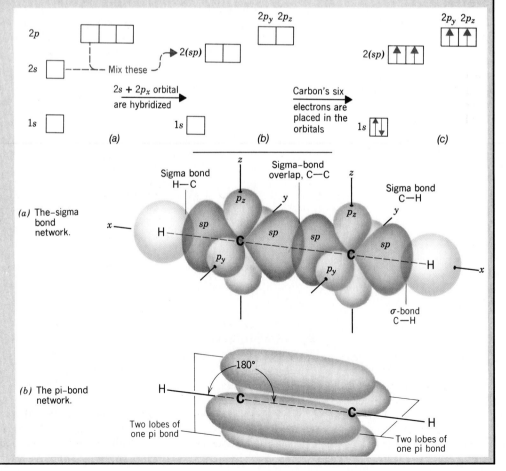

SUMMARY

Ionic bonds and ionic compounds A reaction between a metal and a nonmetal usually goes by the transfer of an electron from the metal atom to the nonmetal atom. The metal atom changes into a positively charged ion and the nonmetal atom becomes a negatively charged ion. The oppositely charged ions aggregate in whatever whole-number ratio ensures that the product is electrically neutral. The electrical force of attraction between the ions is called an ionic bond, and compounds made of ions are called ionic compounds.

Octet rule For the representative elements of the periodic table, we can predict how many electrons transfer by the rule that the resulting ions must have electron configurations of the nearest noble gases. Metal atoms lose their valence-shell electrons to achieve this, and nonmetal atoms gain enough new valence shell electrons to acquire such configurations.

Redox reactions Electron transfers mean changes in oxidation numbers and are called redox reactions. Elements have zero oxidation numbers. Simple, monatomic ions have oxidation numbers that equal their electrical charges. An atom that loses electrons and whose oxidation number becomes more positive is oxidized, and one that gains electrons and a more negative oxidation number is reduced. Anything that causes an oxidation is called an oxidizing agent; a reducing agent is anything that causes a reduction. Metals tend to be reducing agents and nonmetals are oxidizing agents.

Formulas of ionic compounds The empirical formulas of ionic compounds begin with the symbol of the metal ion (without the sign indicating the charge). Subscripts are used to give the ratios of the ions. When two or more polyatomic ions have to be indicated in the formula, parentheses must enclose the symbols for these ions. The names of ionic compounds are based on the names of the ions (except that the word *ion* is omitted). The positive ion is named first, then the negative ion.

Molecular compounds Atoms of nonmetals can form molecules by sharing valence-shell electrons in pairs. Each shared pair constitutes one covalent bond, and each pair is counted as the joint property of both atoms when the system is checked to see if it follows the octet rule. The pair creates a region of relatively high electron density between the two atoms toward which the nuclei are electrically attracted, and this attraction is called a covalent bond.

Lewis structures Molecules have unique structural formulas or structures, which display the sequence in which the atoms are joined. Lewis structures (electron-dot structures) display the valence-shell electrons, both the shared and unshared pairs, in molecules. (The shared pairs are usually replaced by dash bonds.) In nearly all molecules the atoms have noble gas configurations, but a few have fewer than four electron pairs and a few have more than four.

To write a Lewis structure, we must know the skeletal structure as well as the total number of valence-shell electrons present. (Group numbers in the periodic table are used to calculate the latter.) Then electron pairs are placed into the bonds. Next, electron pairs are used to give noble gas configurations to all atoms, doing this for the central atom last. If there aren't enough for the central atom, double (or triple) bonds have to be made by moving electrons pairs from other atoms toward the central atom.

Polyatomic ions In polyatomic ions, the atoms are joined by covalent bonds, but the overall numbers of electrons and protons do not balance. In these ions, coordinate covalent bonds can also occur, bonds whose electron pairs both came from one of the bonded atoms.

The Lewis structures of polyatomic ions can be figured out by the same rules for making other electron-dot structures. In determining the total number of valence-shell elections, add 1 for each negative charge and substract 1 for each positive charge.

Acids and bases Acids are substances that can furnish H^+ ions, and bases are compounds that can combine with H^+ ions. Acids and bases react to neutralize each other.

Molecular shapes and the VSEPR theory Valence-shell electron pairs in molecules stay out of one another's way as much as possible. When there are four pairs, the result is a tetrahedral geometry, or close to it. If only three pairs are present, the geometry is that of a triangle with the three atoms at the corners.

Polar molecules Even though molecules are electrically neutral, they can still be polar. If individual bond polarities, caused by electronegativity differences between the joined atoms, do not cancel, the molecule is polar and it can stick to adjacent polar molecules much as magnets can stick together.

Molecular orbitals Molecular orbitals form by the partial overlapping of atomic orbitals. This creates a space between the two nuclei into which the electron pair of the single covalent bond resides. When the molecular orbital has the symmetry of a straight sausage, it is a sigma bond.

When they form covalent bonds, atoms of carbon, nitrogen, and oxygen use hybrid atomic orbitals instead of the simple atomic orbitals of their isolated atoms. When an s orbital and three p orbitals of the same main level mix (hybridize), four new, equivalent sp^3 hybrid orbitals form whose axes point to the corners of a regular tetrahedron.

When a carbon atom has a double bond, it uses sp^2 hybrid orbitals made by mixing an s and two p atomic orbitals. This leaves the third p orbital of carbon unhybridized. One of the two bonds at the double bond is a sigma bond formed by the overlapping of the sp^2 hybrid orbitals of the two carbons. Then the side-to-side overlap of the unhybridized 2p orbitals creates the other bond, called a pi bond, a double-banana-shaped space above and below the plane of the double bond. One pair of electrons resides in this unusual space.

REVIEW EXERCISES

The *Study Guide* that accompanies this text contains answers to these Review Exercises.

Ions, Ionic Compounds, and Their Names and Formulas

4.1 The term *chemical bond* is another name for what kind of force?

4.2 Define the terms *ionic compound* and *ionic bond*.

4.3 Lithium (group IA) and fluorine (group VIIA) can react to form ionic bonds. Use electron configurations (including the composition of the nuclei) as we did in Section 4.1 for the reaction of sodium and chlorine to show how a lithium atom and a fluorine atom can change to ions.

4.4 Give the correct symbols, including the charges, for the following ions.

(a) potassium ion   (b) aluminum ion
(c) iodide ion   (d) copper(I) ion
(e) barium ion   (f) sulfide ion
(g) sodium ion   (h) ferric ion
(i) oxide ion   (j) lithium ion
(k) silver ion   (l) magnesium ion
(m) cupric ion   (n) bromide ion
(o) calcium ion   (p) iron(II) ion
(q) fluoride ion   (r) chloride ion
(s) zinc ion   (t) barium ion

4.5 Give the names of the following ions. When an ion has more than one name, one older and the other a modern name, write both.

(a) Na^+ (b) Fe^{3+} (c) Li^+ (d) O^{2-}
(e) S^{2-} (f) Ba^{2+} (g) Cu^+ (h) I^-
(i) Al^{3+} (j) K^+ (k) Zn^{2+} (l) F^-
(m) Fe^{2+} (n) Cl^- (o) Ca^{2+} (p) Cu^{2+}
(q) Br^- (r) Mg^{2+} (s) Ag^+

4.6 If the older name of the Hg^{2+} ion is *mercuric ion*, what is the most likely name of Hg^+? (Actually, this ion exists doubled up as Hg_2^{2+}, but the charge is still $1+$ per Hg.)

4.7 An older name for the Sn^{4+} ion is *stannic ion*. Which is the more likely formula for the *stannous ion*, Sn^{2+} or Sn^{5+}?

4.8 The ion Pb^{2+} was once (and often still is) called the *plumbous ion*. What is its modern name?

4.9 The ion Au^{3+} has the older name of *auric ion*. What is its modern name?

4.10 Write the formula of each of the following compounds.

(a) lithium chloride   (b) barium oxide
(c) aluminum sulfide   (d) sodium bromide
(e) cupric oxide   (f) ferric chloride

4.11 What are the formulas of the following compounds?

(a) cuprous sulfide   (b) potassium fluoride
(c) sodium sulfide   (d) calcium iodide
(e) magnesium chloride   (f) ferrous bromide

4.12 Write the names of the following compounds. Wherever two names are possible, a modern name and an older name, write both.

(a) $FeBr_3$ (b) $MgCl_2$ (c) NaF
(d) ZnO   (e) $CuBr_2$ (f) Li_2O

4.13 What are the names of the following compounds? (If both a modern and an older name are possible, give both names.)

(a) KI   (b) CaS   (c) $BaCl_2$
(d) Al_2O_3 (e) $FeCl_2$ (f) AgI

4.14 Which has the smaller radius, a metal ion or the atom of the same metal? Why?

4.15 Why do the radii of both atoms and ions of the same family increase as one goes down the periodic table?

4.16 Which has the smaller radius, an nonmetal ion or the atom of the same nonmetal? Explain.

4.17 Some substances are described as *electrolytes*. What kinds of compounds are most likely to be electrolytes?

4.18 It is common in studies of heart conditions to hear scientists speak of the *sodium level* of the blood. *Level* refers to the concentration, the ratio of substance to volume. To what specifically does *sodium* refer?

Ions and the Octet Rule

4.19 Show how magnesium atoms and fluorine atoms can cooperate to form ions that will aggregate in the correct ratio. (Follow the directions given in Review Exercise 4.3.)

4.20 Write diagrams to show how oxygen atoms and sodium atoms can cooperate to form ions that will aggregate in the correct ratio. (Follow the directions given in Review Exercise 4.3.)

4.21 If *M* is the symbol of some representative metal, and the symbol of its ion is M^{3+}, in what group in the periodic table is *M*?

4.22 An atom of the representative nonmetal *X* can accept two electrons and become an ion. In what group in the periodic table is *X*?

4.23 An element is in group IIA. What charges can its ions have?

4.24 A representative element forms an ion with a charge of $3-$. What group of the periodic table is this element in?

4.25 Two kinds of electron configurations are exceptionally stable, chemically. Describe them in your own words.

4.26 Study the following electron configuration. Is it likely that this atom can be changed to a stable ion? If so, what is the electrical charge on the ion?

$$1s^2 2s^2 2p^6 3s^2 3p^6 3d^{10} 4s^2 4p_x^2 4p_y^2 4p_z^1$$

4.27 Examine the following electron configuration of an atom. Can this atom be changed into a reasonably stable ion? If so, what is the electrical charge on the ion?

$$1s^2 2s^2 2p^6 3s^2 3p^6 3d^{10} 4s^2 4p^6 5s^2$$

4.28 Study the electron configuration given below. Can this atom change into a reasonably stable ion? If so, what electrical charge does the ion have?

$$1s^2 2s^2 2p^6 3s^2 3p^6 3d^{10} 4s^2 4p^6 4d^{10} 5s^2 5p^6$$

4.29 Element M is a transition element. Are its ions more likely to be positively or negatively charged? Explain.

4.30 Using only what can be deduced from electron configurations built from the atomic numbers according to the aufbau rules, write electron configurations of each of the following *ions.* The atomic numbers are given in the parentheses.
(a) calcium ion (20) (b) aluminum ion (13)

4.31 In certain compounds, the hydrogen atom can exist as a negatively charged ion called the *hydride ion.* What is likely to be the electron configuration of this ion? Write a symbol for the ion.

Oxidation and Reduction

4.32 What is the oxidation number of the sodium ion?

4.33 What is the oxidation number of the Pb(IV) ion?

4.34 What is the oxidation number of the metal in each of the following compounds? Write also the chemical symbol of the metal *ion.*
(a) BiF_3 (b) CdI_2 (c) Cr_2S_3
(d) Gd_2O_3 (e) $SnCl_2$ (f) TiF_3

4.35 If the oxidation number of oxygen is always -2 (except in one compound with fluorine, F_2O), what are the oxidation numbers of the other elements in the following compounds?
(a) Mn_2O_7 (b) TiO_4 (c) W_2O_5 (d) Rb_2O

4.36 Consider the following reaction.

$$2Al + 3S \longrightarrow Al_2S_3 \quad \text{(an ionic compound)}$$

For the answer to each of the following parts, write a chemical symbol.
(a) What is reduced?
(b) What is the oxidizing agent?
(c) What is oxidized?
(d) What is the reducing agent?

4.37 Answer each of the parts of this question by writing a chemical symbol. Each part refers to the following reaction:

$$Mg + Br_2 \longrightarrow MgBr_2$$

(a) What is the reducing agent?
(b) What is the oxidizing agent?
(c) Which substance is oxidized?
(d) Which substance is reduced?

4.38 The action of oxygen on FeO can cause the following change:

$$4FeO + O_2 \longrightarrow 2Fe_2O_3$$

(a) What is the oxidation number of Fe in FeO?
(b) What is its oxidation number in Fe_2O_3?
(c) Is Fe oxidized in this reaction?
(d) If so, what is the oxidizing agent? (Write its formula.)
(e) What is reduced by this reaction? (Write its formula.)

Molecules, Molecular Compounds, and Lewis Structures

4.39 In general terms, what is a *molecule,* and in what way or ways is a molecule different from an atom? From an ion?

4.40 How does a molecular compound differ from an ionic compound?

4.41 What provides the electrical force of attraction that is responsible for the covalent bond?

4.42 Describe what happens when two hydrogen atoms form a covalent bond.

4.43 Two helium atoms (atomic number 2) do not combine to give a diatomic molecule, He_2. Offer an explanation.

4.44 State the octet rule. What is it based on?

4.45 Write the electron-dot structures of atoms of (a) cesium (at. no. 55), (b) indium (at. no. 49), (c) bismuth (at. no. 83), and (d) xenon (at. no. 54).

4.46 Use Lewis structures to diagram the formation of MgI_2 from neutral atoms.

4.47 Use Lewis structures to diagram the formation of (a) Cl_2, (b) H_2O, and (c) NCl_3 from neutral atoms.

4.48 The distance between the two nuclei in a single bond is greater than the distance between the same two nuclei when they are joined (in a different molecule) by a double bond. Why should this be so?

4.49 What is a triple bond?

Polyatomic Ions and Formulas Involving Them

4.50 What are the names of the following ions?
(a) HCO_3^- (b) SO_4^{2-} (c) NO_3^-
(d) OH^- (e) NH_4^+ (f) CN^-
(g) HPO_4^{2-} (h) CrO_4^{2-} (i) CO_3^{2-}
(j) MnO_4^- (k) HSO_4^- (l) HSO_3^-
(m) NO_2^- (n) PO_4^{3-} (o) $Cr_2O_7^{2-}$
(p) $H_2PO_4^-$ (q) H_3O^+ (r) $C_2H_3O_2^-$

4.51 Write the formulas of the following ions:
(a) carbonate ion (b) nitrate ion
(c) hydroxide ion (d) ammonium ion
(e) phosphate ion (f) cyanide ion
(g) hydronium ion (h) monohydrogen phosphate ion
(i) nitrite ion (j) bicarbonate ion
(k) bisulfate ion (l) dihydrogen phosphate ion
(m) dichromate ion (n) bisulfite ion
(o) chromate ion (p) sulfate ion
(q) sulfite ion (r) acetate ion

4.52 Write the formulas of the following compounds:
(a) ammonium phosphate
(b) potassium monohydrogen phosphate
(c) magnesium sulfate
(d) calcium carbonate
(e) lithium bicarbonate
(f) potassium dichromate

(g) ammonium bromide

(h) iron(III) nitrate

4.53 What are the formulas of the following compounds?

(a) sodium dihydrogen phosphate

(b) copper(II) carbonate

(c) silver nitrate

(d) zinc bicarbonate

(e) potassium bisulfate

(f) ammonium chromate

(g) calcium acetate

(h) ferric sulfate

4.54 Write the names of the following compounds:

(a) $NaNO_3$ (b) $CaSO_4$

(c) KOH (d) Li_2CO_3

(e) NH_4CN (f) Na_3PO_4

(g) $KMnO_4$ (h) $Mg(H_2PO_4)_2$

4.55 What are the names of the following compounds?

(a) K_2HPO_4 (b) $NaHCO_3$

(c) NH_4NO_2 (d) $ZnCrO_4$

(e) $LiHSO_4$ (f) $Ca(C_2H_3O_2)_2$

(g) $K_2Cr_2O_7$ (h) $NaHSO_4$

4.56 What is the total number of atoms of all kinds in one formula unit of each of the following substances?

(a) $(NH_4)_2SO_4$ (b) $Al_2(HPO_4)_3$ (c) $Ca(HCO_3)_2$

4.57 One formula unit of each of the following substances has how many atoms of all kinds?

(a) $(NH_4)_3PO_4$ (b) $Fe_2(SO_4)_3$ (c) $Ca(C_2H_3O_2)_2$

4.58 Iron(III) glycerophosphate, $Fe_2[C_3H_5(OH)_2PO_4]_3$, has sometimes been used to treat iron deficiency anemia. How many atoms of all kinds are present in one formula unit of this substance?

Acids and Bases

4.59 What is the symbol for the ion supplied by any common *acid*?

4.60 What is the name of the family of compounds whose members can destroy the tartness of an acid and its ability to corrode metals?

4.61 What two kinds of substances react when neutralization occurs?

4.62 In what way does the formation of NH_4^+ by a neutralization illustrate how a coordinate covalent bond forms?

Drawing Lewis Structures

4.63 Predict the simplest molecular formula and draw the corresponding Lewis structure of a compound between hydrogen and (a) Sb, (b) Te, (c) and Sn. (Remember that hydrogen can hold only two electrons in its valence shell.)

4.64 What are the skeletal structures of (a) $SnCl_4$, (b) SCl_2, (c) SbH_3, (d) $AsCl_3$, (e) SO_3^{2-}, and (f) NO_2^-?

4.65 How many dots must appear in the Lewis structures of the compounds given in Practice Exercise 4.64?

4.66 Draw the Lewis structures for the compounds of Practice Exercise 4.64.

4.67 Write the Lewis structure of the cyanide ion, CN^-.

4.68 Write the Lewis structure of formaldehyde, CH_2O. (Its central atom is carbon, which holds the two hydrogens and the oxygen.)

4.69 Sulfurous acid has traditionally been assigned the formula H_2SO_3. What is the Lewis structure of this molecule?

4.70 The molecular formula of hydrazine, a rocket fuel, is N_2H_4. (a) What is its empirical formula? (b) Its structure has only single bonds. Write an electron-dot structure for it.

Shapes of Molecules and VSEPR Theory

4.71 What are the expected arrangements of valence-shell electron pairs when the valence shell holds (a) 4 pairs, (b) 3 pairs, (c) 2 pairs?

4.72 What is the expected bond angle when the bonds at a central atom are (a) four single bonds, (b) three single bonds plus an unshared pair, and (c) two single bonds plus two unshared pairs?

4.73 Describe in your own words how the VSEPR theory explains the bond angle in the water molecule.

4.74 VSEPR theory would predict what bond angles in (a) $SiCl_4$, (b) $AlCl_3$?

4.75 The central atom, N, in NH_3 holds three atoms just like the central atom, B, in BF_3. Why, then, doesn't NH_3 have a planar geometry like BF_3?

Polar Molecules

4.76 Suppose that X and Y can form a diatomic molecule, $X-Y$, and that Y is less electronegative than X.

(a) Is the molecule $X-Y$ polar?

(b) If so, where are the $\delta+$ and the $\delta-$ partial charges located?

4.77 Study the following molecules. For those that are polar, write in $\delta+$ and $\delta-$ where they are properly located.

(a) $H-H$ (b) $H-F$ (c) $F-F$

(d) $Cl-Cl$ (e) $N\equiv N$ (f) $H-I$

4.78 Suppose that X and Y are elements in the same group of nonmetals in the periodic table, but X stands above Y. Which of the two has the higher electronegativity? Explain.

4.79 Suppose that M and Z are in the same period in the periodic table, but M precedes Z. Which of these elements has the higher electronegativity? Explain.

Molecular Orbitals

4.80 Describe in your own words how the molecular orbital in H_2 forms. Does it give rise to a sigma bond? How can one tell?

4.81 Draw figures to illustrate a brief molecular orbital description of how two chlorine atoms develop a covalent bond in Cl_2.

4.82 Discuss how the hydrogen atom and a chlorine atom interact to make a molecular orbital and the $H-Cl$ molecule. Draw figures to illustrate your discussion.

4.83 Examine the following electron configuration and answer the questions about it:

$$1s^2 2s^2 2p^6 3s^2 3p^6 3d^{10} 4s^2 4p_x^2 4p_y^2 4p_z^1$$

(a) Can the atom that has this electron configuration participate in the formation of a covalent bond? If so, how many bonds can it have?

(b) If this atom has the symbol X, what is the structure of its molecular compound with hydrogen?

4.84 What is an sp^3 hybrid orbital? What orbitals are used to make one, and what is its general shape? In what way is it like a p orbital as well as like an s orbital?

4.85 What kinds of orbitals overlap when a C—H bond forms in methane?

4.86 What kind of orbital holds the *unpaired* electrons in a molecule of ammonia? In a water molecule?

4.87 Phosphorus is in the same family as nitrogen and forms the compound phosphine, PH_3, whose structure is similar to that of ammonia. The bond angles in phosphine are 93.7°. What kinds of atomic orbitals on phosphorus are most likely used in forming the P—H bonds? Explain.

4.88 In your own words, using your own drawings, describe what is meant by sp^2 hybridization at carbon.

4.89 Using your own drawing, show how the axes of the four orbitals at an sp^2 hybridized carbon atom (three sp^2 hybrid orbitals plus one $2p$ orbital) are arranged. Indicate the angles.

4.90 If the valence-shell electron-pair repulsion theory (VSEPR) were applied to the electron-occupied orbitals of an sp^2 hybridized carbon atom, what angles would the axes of these orbitals make with each other?

4.91 Consider the molecule BCl_3.
(a) Write the electron configuration of the atomic state of B.
(b) If the boron atom is sp^2 hybridized in BCl_3, what is the electron configuration of the bonding state of the boron atom?
(c) Is there an unhybridized p orbital?
(d) What angles do the axes of the sp^2 hybrid orbitals make with each other?
(e) Is the BCl_3 molecule planar?

The Triple Bond (Special Topic 4.1)

4.92 In molecular orbital terms, what kinds of orbitals does carbon use at a triple bond?

4.93 The triple bond is made up of what kind of molecular orbitals? (Give their Greek names.)

CHAPTER FIVE

Quantitative Relationships in Chemical Reactions

All scientific results in chemistry ultimately rest on quantitative measurements and special equipment to make them. In this chapter we present the SI unit for amount of chemical substance, the mole, and explain how it can be used when working with liquid solutions.

5.1 BALANCED EQUATIONS—A SECOND LOOK

The coefficients of a balanced equation give the ratios by formula units in which the chemicals interact.

In the preceding chapters we looked rather closely at the *structures* of substances. We put the study of structure ahead of the study of chemical properties because structure determines properties. Substances behave as they do because of their structures. In this chapter we get back to properties.

One of the most important properties of substances involves their weight relationships when they react. Quantitative aspects of chemical changes begin with what we learned in Chapter Two; atoms and ions combine only in definite, whole-number proportions when they form compounds. It follows that compounds can likewise react only in whole-number proportions by their formula units. The branch of chemistry that deals with the proportions of reacting chemicals is called **stoichiometry.** The starting place for its study is the balanced equation.

■ "Stoy-kee-ah-meh-tree" from the Greek *stoicheion,* meaning "element," and -*metron,* meaning "measure."

Balanced Equations Tell What Reacts, What Forms, and in What Proportions A chemical equation is a **balanced equation** when all of the atoms given among the reactants appear in identical numbers among the products. In most equations one or more of the formulas is multiplied by some whole number in order to show the correct balance. These multipliers of formulas in chemical equations are called **coefficients.** For example, the formation of water from hydrogen and oxygen has the following equation.

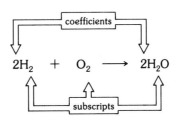

The term, $2H_2O$, means that two units — two molecules — of water form from every two molecules of hydrogen and one molecule of oxygen. Because of the coefficient of 2 in $2H_2O$, there are $2 \times 2 = 4$ atoms of H on the right side of the equation, and $2 \times 1 = 2$ atoms of O. You can see that there are 4 H atoms on the left to balance the 4 on the right, and 2 O atoms on the left balance the 2 on the right.

We are never allowed to change subscripts, once we have the right formulas, just to get an equation to balance. For example, changing H_2O to H_2O_2 makes a change from the formula for water to the formula for hydrogen peroxide, an entirely different substance. We can adjust coefficients, however, in balancing an equation, as we will see in the next worked example.

■ H_2O_2 cannot be made by a direct combination of H_2 and O_2.

EXAMPLE 5.1	BALANCING A CHEMICAL EQUATION

Problem: Sodium, Na, reacts with chlorine, Cl_2, to give sodium chloride, NaCl. Write the balanced equation for this reaction.

Solution: The first step is to set down all the correct formulas in the format of an equation. (Never worry about the coefficients until the correct formulas are down. Then, never change the formulas.)

■ Remember, the formula unit of chlorine is a molecule, Cl_2, not an atom.

$$Na + Cl_2 \longrightarrow NaCl \qquad \text{(unbalanced)}$$

■ $NaCl_2$ doesn't even exist.

So far, we see two chlorine atoms on the left (in Cl_2) but only one on the right. We can't fix this by writing $NaCl_2$, because this isn't the correct formula for sodium chloride. The only way we are allowed to get two Cl atoms on the right is to put a coefficient of 2 in front of NaCl:

$$Na + Cl_2 \longrightarrow 2NaCl \qquad \text{(unbalanced)}$$

Of course, writing 2 in front of NaCl makes it a multiplier for both Na and Cl, so now we have two Na atoms on the right and just one on the left. To fix this, we write a 2 before the Na:

$$2Na + Cl_2 \longrightarrow 2NaCl \qquad \text{(balanced)}$$

Notice particularly how we used a subscript, the 2 in Cl_2, to suggest a coefficient for another formula on the other side of the arrow. This is standard strategy in balancing equations.

EXAMPLE 5.2   **BALANCING A CHEMICAL EQUATION**

Problem: Iron, Fe, can be made to react with oxygen, O_2, to form an oxide with the formula Fe_2O_3. Write the balanced equation for this reaction.

Solution: We first write down the correct formulas in the format of an equation

■ Oxygen, remember, exists as molecules, O_2, not as atoms.

$$Fe + O_2 \longrightarrow Fe_2O_3 \qquad \text{(unbalanced)}$$

Next we exploit subscripts to suggest coefficients. Oxygen has a subscript of 2 in O_2 and a subscript of 3 in Fe_2O_3. To get a balance, we use the 3 as a coefficient for O_2 and the 2 as a coefficient for Fe_2O_3. This is cross-switching the numbers.

$$Fe + 3O_2 \longrightarrow 2Fe_2O_3 \qquad \text{(unbalanced)}$$

Now there are six oxygen atoms on the left (in $3O_2$) and six on the right (in $2Fe_2O_3$). Of course, the coefficient of 2 in the formula on the right also means that there are 4 Fe atoms on the right. To fix this, we simply use a coefficient of 4 on the left, for Fe:

$$4Fe + 3O_2 \longrightarrow 2Fe_2O_3 \qquad \text{(balanced)}$$

PRACTICE EXERCISE 1   In the presence of an electrical discharge, oxygen, O_2, can be changed into ozone, O_3. Write the balanced equation for this reaction.

PRACTICE EXERCISE 2   Aluminum, Al, reacts with oxygen to give aluminum oxide, Al_2O_3. Write the balanced equation for this change.

Sometimes, when we adjust coefficients to balance an equation, we get one whose coefficients can all be divided by the same whole number. Suppose, for example, that we had obtained the following equation for the reaction of sodium with chlorine in Example 5.1:

$$4Na + 2Cl_2 \longrightarrow 4NaCl$$

This equation is balanced and all its formulas are correct, so there is nothing basically wrong with it. Chemists, however, generally (but not always) write balanced equations that use the set of smallest whole numbers as coefficients. We will normally follow this rule.

When the formulas in an equation include polyatomic ions, and when it is obvious that they do not themselves change, treat them as whole units in balancing equations.

| EXAMPLE 5.3 | BALANCING EQUATIONS INVOLVING POLYATOMIC IONS |

Problem: When water solutions of ammonium sulfate, $(NH_4)_2SO_4$, and lead nitrate, $Pb(NO_3)_2$, are mixed, a white solid separates that has the formula $PbSO_4$ (lead sulfate). Ammonium nitrate, NH_4NO_3, is the other product, but it remains dissolved. Represent this reaction by a balanced equation.

Solution: As usual, we start by simply writing the correct formulas in the format of an equation.

■ The symbol (*aq*) stands for aqueous solution, one for which water is the solvent. The symbol (*s*) means a solid, one that forms directly and is not in solution.

$$(NH_4)_2SO_4(aq) + Pb(NO_3)_2(aq) \longrightarrow PbSO_4(s) + NH_4NO_3(aq)$$

Because polyatomic ions are involved, we next examine the formulas to see whether any of them change or whether they all appear to react as whole units. We can see here that they do remain as intact units. The subscript of 2 in $(NH_4)_2SO_4$ suggests that we use 2 as the coefficient in the formula on the right where (NH_4) occurs.

$$(NH_4)_2SO_4(aq) + Pb(NO_3)_2(aq) \longrightarrow PbSO_4(s) + 2NH_4NO_3(aq)$$

This automatically brought into balance the units of (NO_3) on each side of the arrow. The equation is now balanced.

PRACTICE EXERCISE 3

Balance each of the following equations:

(a) $Ca + O_2 \longrightarrow CaO$
(b) $KOH + H_2SO_4 \longrightarrow H_2O + K_2SO_4$
(c) $Cu(NO_3)_2 + Na_2S \longrightarrow CuS + NaNO_3$
(d) $AgNO_3 + CaCl_2 \longrightarrow AgCl + Ca(NO_3)_2$
(e) $Al + H_2SO_4 \longrightarrow Al_2(SO_4)_3 + H_2$
(f) $CH_4 + O_2 \longrightarrow H_2O + CO_2$

5.2 AVOGADRO'S NUMBER

The number of formula units in a sample of any pure substance with a mass equal to its formula weight in grams is 6.02×10^{23}, Avogadro's number.

The coefficients in the equation for the reaction of sodium with chlorine,

$$2Na + Cl_2 \longrightarrow 2NaCl$$

can be interpreted as follows:

$$2 \text{ atoms of Na} + 1 \text{ molecule of Cl}_2 \longrightarrow 2 \text{ formula units of NaCl}$$

However, we can't carry out a reaction on such a small scale, as we noted in Chapter 3. We have to use much larger numbers of particles. The question is, what number should we use as a standard number of formula units? For a reason that we'll soon see, we use 6.02×10^{23} formula units. Like many special numbers, this number has a special name, **Avogadro's number,** after Amadeo Avogadro, an Italian chemist who was interested in stoichiometry.

$$\text{Avogadro's number} = 6.02 \times 10^{23}$$

■ Avogadro's number is known to seven significant figures:

$$6.022137 \times 10^{23}$$

Just as *dozen* can be used to signify 12 of anything, so *Avogadro's number* can be used to signify 6.02×10^{23} of anything—electrons, protons, atoms, virus particles, anything.

The reason for using such a complicated number for a standard number of formula units is because of its relationship to atomic weights. We have seen that 1 amu = 1.6606×10^{-24} g. We also know that the atomic weight of sodium, for example, is 22.99, which means that one atom of sodium has a mass of 22.99 amu. We'll do a simple calculation of how many grams a sample of sodium weighs when it has Avogadro's number of sodium atoms.

$$6.022 \times 10^{23} \text{ Na atoms} \times 22.99 \frac{\text{amu}}{1 \text{ Na atom}} \times 1.6606 \times 10^{-24} \frac{\text{g}}{\text{amu}} = 22.99 \text{ g Na}$$

Thus Avogadro's number of sodium atoms make up a sample of sodium with a mass of 22.99 g, which is numerically equal to the atomic weight of sodium. We can now see the logic of Avogadro's number; this number of atoms delivers a mass in grams numerically equal to something familiar about an element, its atomic weight. For example, Avogadro's number of chlorine atoms has a mass of 35.5 g, which numerically equals the atomic weight of chlorine.

EXAMPLE 5.4	UNDERSTANDING AVOGADRO'S NUMBER

Problem: How many carbon atoms are in 6.00 g of carbon?

Solution: We solve this by working with the basic meaning of Avogadro's number. It's the number of formula units in as many grams of a substance that equal the formula weight. We first look up the atomic weight of carbon, which is 12.0. Therefore, 12.0 g of carbon must have Avogadro's number of carbon atoms, or 6.02×10^{23} carbon atoms. In other words, 12.0 g of carbon = 6.02×10^{23} atoms of carbon. This gives us two conversion factors:

$$\frac{6.02 \times 10^{23} \text{ atoms C}}{12.0 \text{ g C}} \quad \text{or} \quad \frac{12.0 \text{ g C}}{6.02 \times 10^{23} \text{ atoms C}}$$

If we multiply what is given, 6.00 g C, by the first conversion factor, the units "g C" will cancel, and our answer will be in atoms of carbon.

$$6.00 \text{ g C} \times \frac{6.02 \times 10^{23} \text{ atoms C}}{12.0 \text{ g C}} = 3.01 \times 10^{23} \text{ atoms C}$$

Thus 6.00 g of carbon contains 3.01×10^{23} atoms of carbon.

PRACTICE EXERCISE 4   How many atoms of gold are in 1.00 oz of gold? Note, 1.00 oz = 28.4 g.

5.3 FORMULA WEIGHTS AND MOLECULAR WEIGHTS

The formula weight of a chemical is the sum of the atonic weights of all of the atoms in its chemical formula.

Because atoms lose no mass when they combine to form compounds, we can expand the idea of an atomic weight to that of a formula weight for every compound. The **formula weight** of a compound is simply the sum of the atomic weights of all the atoms present in one formula unit. For example, the formula weight of NaCl is calculated as follows, where we round atomic weights to the first decimal place before we use them in a calculation, and we follow a common practice that lets the unit of *amu* be left understood.

■ For the rest of this book, our policy is to round values of atomic weights to their first decimal point before starting any calculations.

1 atom of Na in NaCl gives	23.0
1 atom of Cl in NaCl gives	35.5
Formula weight of NaCl	58.5

Thus one formula unit of NaCl has a mass of 58.5 amu.

The idea of a formula weight is general; it applies to anything with a definite formula, including elements as well as compounds. The formula of sodium, for example, is Na, so we can just as well say that its formula weight is 23.0 as to say that this is its atomic weight. The element chlorine occurs as a diatomic molecule, Cl_2, so its formula weight is twice its atomic weight or $2 \times 35.5 = 71.0$. You should learn, before we continue, that a synonym for formula weight, namely **molecular weight,** is used by many scientists. However, *formula weight* is a more general term, and it's the one that we will use.

EXAMPLE 5.5   **CALCULATING A FORMULA WEIGHT**

Problem: Some baking powders contain ammonium carbonate, $(NH_4)_2CO_3$. Calculate its formula weight.

Solution: First, look up and write down the atomic weights of all the elements present, rounding each to the first decimal place.

$$N, 14.0 \quad H, 1.0 \quad C, 12.0 \quad O, 16.0$$

Notice that in each formula unit of $(NH_4)_2CO_3$ N occurs 2 times, H occurs 8 times, C occurs 1 time, and O occurs 3 times. Therefore,

$$2N \quad +8H \quad +1C \quad +3O \quad = (NH_4)_2CO_3$$
$$2 \times 14.0 + 8 \times 1.0 + 1 \times 12.0 + 3 \times 16.0 = 96.0 \quad \text{(correctly rounded)}$$

The formula weight of ammonium carbonate is 96.0. This means that one formula unit has a mass of 96.0 amu, and it means that Avogadro's number of these units has a total mass of 96.0 g.

PRACTICE EXERCISE 5   Calculate the formula weights of the following compounds:

(a) $C_9H_8O_4$ (aspirin)   (b) $Mg(OH)_2$ (milk of magnesia)

(c) $Fe_4[Fe(CN)_6]_3$ (ferric ferrocyanide or Prussian blue, an ink pigment)

5.4 THE MOLE

The mole is the SI unit for *amount of pure chemical substance* and equals the formula weight of the substance in grams.

The formula weight of any substance, element or compound, taken in grams is called one **mole** abbreviated **mol.** It is the SI base unit for quantity of substance.

■ *Mol* stands for both the plural and the singular.

The actual mass of one mole of a substance depends on the formula weight, *so the actual mass that equals one mole varies from substance to substance.* See Figures 5.1 and 5.2. However, the number of formula units stays the same. Regardless of the substance, if you have 1 mol, you have Avogadro's number of its formula units. Thus 1 mol of the element mercury has a mass of 200.6 g and it consists of 6.02×10^{23} Hg atoms; 1 mol of H_2 has a mass of only 2.01 g, but it consists of 6.02×10^{23} molecules of H_2; and 1 mol of NaCl has a mass of 58.5 g and consists of 6.02×10^{23} formula units of NaCl.

■ What is *constant* about one mole of any substance is not the mass but the number of formula units.

Think of the *mole* as the lab-sized unit of a substance, a quantity of the substance that can be manipulated experimentally and that can be taken in fractions or in multiples. For example, the formula weight of H_2O is 18.0, so 1 mol of H_2O weighs 18.0 g. If we wished, we could weigh out a smaller sample, say 1.80 g, and then we would have 0.100 mol of water, because 1.80 is one-tenth of 18.0. Or we could take 36.0 g of H_2O, and then have 2.00 mol, because 36.0 is 2 times 18.0.

One of the SI prefixes is often used for the mole, the prefix *milli-* signifying one thousandth. The abbreviation of *millimole* is *mmol*.

Figure 5.1
Avogadro's number of atoms are present in each quantity of these elements.

Figure 5.2
Avogadro's number of formula units are present in each of these samples of compounds.

$$1 \text{ mmol} = 0.001 \text{ mol}$$
$$1000 \text{ mmol} = 1 \text{ mol}$$

With the concept of a mole, we can now think about the coefficients in a balanced equation at two levels at the same time. For example, to return to an equation we used in connection with the laws of chemical combination, the reaction of Fe with S, notice that each formula has a coefficient of 1. Beneath each formula in the equation we can see various ways of interpreting these coefficients.

Fe	+ S	$\longrightarrow$ FeS
1 atom of Fe	+ 1 atom of S	$\longrightarrow$ 1 formula unit of FeS
1 dozen atoms of Fe	+ 1 dozen atoms of S	$\longrightarrow$ 1 dozen formula units of FeS
6.02×10^{23} atoms Fe	+ 6.02×10^{23} atoms S	$\longrightarrow$ 6.02×10^{23} formula units of FeS
1 mol of Fe	+ 1 mol of S	$\longrightarrow$ 1 mol of FeS

Notice that the proportions all remain the same, provided we work with *formula units* of one kind or another. All that changes is the *scale* of the reaction — the actual numbers, not their proportions in relationship to each other. *The coefficients in a balanced equation give us the proportions of substances in moles.* We will use this interpretation almost exclusively from here on. Thus to use once more an equation that we have employed before,

$$2Na + Cl_2 \longrightarrow 2NaCl$$

we can now interpret this to mean that for *every 2 mol* of Na that reacts, 1 mol of Cl_2 also reacts and 2 mol of NaCl forms.

There are three kinds of calculations involving moles that have to be learned. One is using an equation's coefficients to determine how many moles of one substance must be involved in a given reaction if a certain number of moles of another are involved. The key step in such a problem is to use the equation's coefficients to set up conversion factors, as we will see in the next example.

EXAMPLE 5.6	USING THE MOLE CONCEPT

Problem: How many moles and how many millimoles of oxygen are needed to combine with 0.500 mol of hydrogen in the reaction that produces water by the following equation?

$$2H_2 + O_2 \longrightarrow 2H_2O$$

Solution: We will calculate the moles of O_2 first and then convert the answer to millimoles. The coefficients tell us that 2 mol of H_2 combines with 1 mol of O_2 in this particular reaction, so we can select between the following conversion factors:

$$\frac{2 \text{ mol } H_2}{1 \text{ mol } O_2} \quad \text{or} \quad \frac{1 \text{ mol } O_2}{2 \text{ mol } H_2}$$

What these ratios tell us is that *for this reaction* 2 mol of H_2 is chemically equivalent to 1 mol of O_2. We have to choose one of these ratios to multiply by the given quantity, 0.500 mol of H_2, to find out how much O_2 is needed. The correct ratio is the second one.

■ The conversion factors involving moles and millimoles are

$$\frac{1000 \text{ mmol}}{1 \text{ mol}} \quad \text{and}$$

$$\frac{1 \text{ mol}}{1000 \text{ mmol}}$$

$$0.500 \text{ mol } H_2 \times \frac{1 \text{ mol } O_2}{2 \text{ mol } H_2} = 0.250 \text{ mol } O_2$$

In other words, 0.500 mol of H_2 requires 0.250 mol of O_2 for this reaction. Since 1 mol = 1000 mmol, we calculate the mmol of O_2 by

$$0.250 \text{ mol } O_2 \times \frac{1000 \text{ mmol } O_2}{1 \text{ mol } O_2} = 250 \text{ mmol } O_2$$

PRACTICE EXERCISE 6   How many moles of H_2O are made from the 0.250 mol of O_2 in Example 5.6? How many millimoles of H_2O are thus made?

PRACTICE EXERCISE 7   Nitrogen and oxygen combine at high temperature in an automobile engine to produce nitrogen monoxide, NO, an air pollutant. The equation is $N_2 + O_2 \rightarrow 2NO$. To make 8.40 mol of NO, how many moles of N_2 are needed? How many moles of O_2 are also needed?

PRACTICE EXERCISE 8   Ammonia, an important nitrogen fertilizer, is made by the following reaction: $3H_2 + N_2 \rightarrow 2NH_3$. In order to make 300 mol of NH_3, how many moles of H_2 and how many moles of N_2 are needed?

The Grams in One Mole Is Called the Molar Mass   The next kind of calculation we have to learn is to convert moles to grams. This is necessary because laboratory balances do

■ We'd need a balance for each number that could be a formula weight.

not read in moles. If they did, we'd need a separate balance marked in moles for each and every possible formula weight! Not too practical.

The calculation uses conversion factors that we can make from a formula weight after we have put units of g/mol after it. This gives us the **molar mass** of the substance, the number of grams per mole. Thus the molar mass of sodium, with an atomic weight of 23.0, is 23.0 g Na/mol Na. We'll see how to use molar mass in the next example.

EXAMPLE 5.7   **CONVERTING MOLES TO GRAMS**

Problem: In Example 5.6 we found that 0.250 mol of O_2 was needed. How many grams of O_2 are in 0.250 mol of O_2?

Solution: We first must calculate the formula weight of oxygen, which is two times its atomic weight (16.0) or $2 \times 16.0 = 32.0$. Therefore the molar mass of oxygen is 32.0 g O_2/mol O_2. This fact gives us the following conversion factors that relate mass of O_2 to moles of O_2.

$$\frac{32.0 \text{ g } O_2}{1 \text{ mol } O_2} \quad \text{or} \quad \frac{1 \text{ mol } O_2}{32.0 \text{ g } O_2}$$

We next multiply what was given, 0.250 mol of O_2, by whichever conversion factor lets us cancel "mol O_2" and leaves us with "g O_2," the desired final unit. This means that we use the first conversion factor.

$$0.250 \text{ mol } O_2 \times \frac{32.0 \text{ g } O_2}{1 \text{ mol } O_2} = 8.00 \text{ g } O_2$$

Thus 0.250 mol of O_2 has a mass of 8.00 g of O_2.

PRACTICE EXERCISE 9   An experiment calls for 24.0 mol of NH_3. How many grams is this?

Often an experiment starts with a goal to make a certain number of grams of some substance. Now we have to be able to convert grams to moles in order to plan the experiment according to some balanced equation. The next worked example shows how to use a molar mass to convert grams to moles.

EXAMPLE 5.8   **CONVERTING GRAMS TO MOLES**

Problem: A student was asked to prepare 12.5 g of NaCl. How many moles is this?

Solution: The relationship between grams and moles of NaCl is given by the molar mass of NaCl. We have already calculated that the formula weight of NaCl is 58.5, so its molar mass is simply 58.5 g NaCl/mol NaCl. Therefore we have these two possible conversion factors:

$$\frac{58.5 \text{ g NaCl}}{1 \text{ mol NaCl}} \quad \text{or} \quad \frac{1 \text{ mol NaCl}}{58.5 \text{ g NaCl}}$$

If we multiply the second ratio by the given, 12.5 g NaCl, the units will cancel properly and the result will be the moles of NaCl in this sample.

$$12.5 \text{ g NaCl} \times \frac{1 \text{ mol NaCl}}{58.5 \text{ g NaCl}} = 0.214 \text{ mol NaCl} \quad \text{(rounded from 0.2136752137)}$$

Thus 12.5 g of NaCl consists of 0.214 mol of NaCl.

PRACTICE EXERCISE 10   A student was asked to prepare 6.84 g of aspirin, $C_9H_8O_4$. How many moles is this?

With the ability to make these kinds of calculations, we can put them together in the context of a very common laboratory situation—how many grams of one substance are needed to make a given amount of another according to some equation? The next worked example illustrates how this is handled.

EXAMPLE 5.9   **MOLE CALCULATIONS USING BALANCED EQUATIONS**

Problem: Aluminum oxide can be used as a white filler for paints. How many grams of aluminum are needed to make 24.4 g of Al_2O_3 by the following equation?

$$4Al + 3O_2 \longrightarrow 2Al_2O_3$$

Solution: It's usually a good idea right at the start of a problem such as this to compute any needed formula weights and write them down for reference. When we do this, we have

Al, 27.0 Al_2O_3, 102.0

Since the equation's coefficients refer to *moles,* we must first find out how many moles are in 24.4 g of Al_2O_3. We learned how to do this in the previous example. The formula weight of Al_2O_3, 102.0, gives us its molar mass, 102.0 g Al_2O_3/mol Al_2O_3. We use this fact in the following calculation.

$$24.4 \text{ g } Al_2O_3 \times \frac{1 \text{ mol } Al_2O_3}{102.0 \text{ g } Al_2O_3} = 0.239 \text{ mol of } Al_2O_3$$

Now we can use the coefficients of the equation, where we see that 4 mol of Al gives 2 mol of Al_2O_3. In other words, we can select one of the following conversion factors.

$$\frac{4 \text{ mol Al}}{2 \text{ mol } Al_2O_3} \quad \text{or} \quad \frac{2 \text{ mol } Al_2O_3}{4 \text{ mol Al}}$$

Now we multiply 0.239 mol of Al_2O_3 by the first factor.

$$0.239 \text{ mol } Al_2O_3 \times \frac{4 \text{ mol Al}}{2 \text{ mol } Al_2O_3} = 0.478 \text{ mol Al}$$

The problem called for the answer in grams of Al, not moles of Al, so we next have to convert 0.478 mol of Al into grams of Al. We studied how to do this in Example 5.7. We use the formula weight of Al to devise the correct conversion factor.

$$0.478 \text{ mol Al} \times \frac{27.0 \text{ g Al}}{1 \text{ mol Al}} = 12.9 \text{ g Al}$$

This is the answer; it takes 12.9 g of Al to prepare 24.4 g of Al_2O_3 according to the given equation.

Before working Practice Exercise 11, think about the overall strategy that we used in this example. As diagrammed in Figure 5.3, we moved the calculations from the grams level to the moles level first. We had to do this because otherwise the equation's coefficients are useless to the solution. Then we used these coefficients to relate the moles of one substance to the moles of another. Finally, we moved back to the grams level so that we could use laboratory balances marked in grams, not moles.

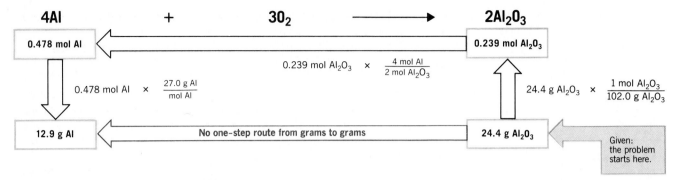

Figure 5.3
All calculations involving masses of reactants and products that participate in a chemical reaction must be worked out at the mole level. There is no one-step route from grams of one substance to grams of another, although one can always use a string of conversion factors.

| PRACTICE EXERCISE 11 | How many grams of oxygen are needed for the experiment described in Example 5.9? Use a diagram of the solution in the style of Figure 5.3 as you work out the answer. |

| PRACTICE EXERCISE 12 | If 28.4 g of Cl_2 are used up in the following reaction, how many grams of Na are also used up, and how many grams of NaCl form? |

$$2Na + Cl_2 \longrightarrow 2NaCl$$

5.5 REACTIONS IN SOLUTION

Virtually all the chemical reactions studied in the lab and occurring in living systems take place in an aqueous solution.

If the particles of one substance are to react with those of another, they must have enough freedom to move about to find each other. Such freedom exists in the gaseous and liquid states but not in the solid state. To get one solid to react with another, chemists usually dissolve them in something. This puts them into a liquid state, and their particles—ions or molecules—can move about. In order to learn in the next section about mass relationships when reactants are in solution, we must first learn the common terms used to describe solutions.

■ Sometimes solids are melted together to cause a reaction.

A Solution Is Made of a Solvent and One or More Solutes A **solution** is a uniform mixture of particles that are atomic, ionic, or molecular size. A minimum of two substances is needed to have a solution. One is called the solvent and all of the others are called the solutes.

The **solvent** is the medium into which the other substances are mixed or dissolved. The solvent is usually a liquid such as water. Unless we state otherwise, we will always be dealing with **aqueous solutions;** *aqueous* designates water as the solvent.

A **solute** is anything that is dissolved by the solvent. In an aqueous solution of sugar, the solute is sugar and the solvent is water. The solute can be a gas. Club soda is a solution of carbon dioxide in water. The solute can be a liquid. Antifreeze, for example, is mostly an aqueous solution of the liquid ethylene glycol. (When we mix two liquids to make a solution, which one we call the solvent is a matter of arbitrary choice. When water is one of the liquids, it is generally called the solvent.)

Solutions Can Be Dilute or Concentrated Several terms are used to describe a solution. A **dilute solution,** for example, is one in which the ratio of solute to solvent is very

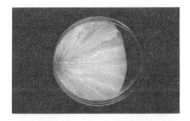

Figure 5.4
Supersaturation. A seed crystal has been added to a supersaturated solution, top photo, and whatever solute was present in solution in excess quickly separates. Any solution that still remains in contact with the crystals (bottom photo) is now a saturated solution.

small, like a few crystals of sugar dissolved in a glass of water. Most of the aqueous solutions in living systems have more than two solutes and they are dilute in all of them.

In a **concentrated solution,** the ratio of solute to solvent is large. Syrup, for example, is a concentrated solution of sugar in water.

Solutions Can Be Unsaturated, Saturated, or Supersaturated   Some solutions are **saturated solutions,** which means that it isn't possible to dissolve more of the solute in them (assuming that the temperature of the solution is kept constant). If more solute is added to a solution already saturated in this solute, the extra solute will just stay separate. If the solute is a solid, it will generally sink to the bottom and remain there.

An **unsaturated solution** is one in which the ratio of solute to solvent is lower than that of the corresponding saturated solution. If more solute is added to an unsaturated solution, at least some of it will dissolve.

It isn't easy, but sometimes a **supersaturated solution** can be made. This is an unstable system in which the ratio of dissolved solute to solvent is actually higher than that of a saturated solution. We can sometimes make a supersaturated solution by carefully cooling a saturated solution. The ability of most solutes to dissolve in water decreases with temperature, so when a saturated solution is cooled some of the now excess solute should separate. But this doesn't always happen, especially if all dust is excluded and the system is not disturbed in any way as it is cooled. If the excess solute does not separate, then we have a supersaturated solution. If we now scratch the inner wall of the container with a glass rod, or if we add a crystal—a "seed" crystal—of the pure solute to the system, the excess solute will usually separate immediately. This event can be dramatic and pretty to watch. See Figure 5.4. The separation of a solid from a solution is called **precipitation,** and the solid is referred to as the **precipitate.**

Solubility Is Usually Given in Grams Solute per 100 g Solvent   The amount of solute needed to give a saturated solution in a given quantity of solvent at a specific temperature is called the **solubility** of the solute in the given solvent. Table 5.1 gives some examples that show how widely solubilities can vary. Notice particularly that a saturated solution can still be quite dilute. For example, only a very small amount of lead sulfate can dissolve in 100 g of water.

The solubilities of most solids increase with temperature, as you can see in Table 5.1. All gases become less and less soluble in water as the temperature rises, assuming that the measurements are made under the same pressure.

TABLE 5.1   Solubilities of Some Substances in Water

Solute	Solubilities (g/100 g water)			
	0 °C	20 °C	50 °C	100 °C
Solids				
Sodium chloride, $NaCl$	35.7	36.0	37.0	39.8
Sodium hydroxide, $NaOH$	42	109	145	347
Barium sulfate, $BaSO_4$	0.000115	0.00024	0.00034	0.00041
Calcium hydroxide, $Ca(OH)_2$	0.185	0.165	0.128	0.077
Gases				
Oxygen, O_2	0.0069	0.0043	0.0027	0
Carbon dioxide, CO_2	0.335	0.169	0.076	0
Nitrogen, N_2	0.0029	0.0019	0.0012	0
Sulfur dioxide, SO_2	22.8	10.6	4.3	1.8 (at 90 °C)
Ammonia, NH_3	89.9	51.8	28.4	7.4 (at 96 °C)

5.6   MOLAR CONCENTRATION

The unit of moles per liter is the most useful unit of concentration when working with the stoichiometry of reactions in solution.

The **concentration** of a solution is the ratio of the quantity of solute to some given unit of the solution. The units can be anything we wish, but for the stoichiometry of reactions in solution, the best units are those of moles of solute per liter of solution. The special name for this ratio is called the solution's **molar concentration,** or **molarity,** abbreviated **M**. The molar concentration of a solution, its molarity, is the number of moles of solute per liter of solution.

$$M = \frac{\text{mol solute}}{\text{L solution}} = \frac{\text{mol solute}}{1000 \text{ mL solution}}$$

■ M = moles/liter
mol = moles

A bottle might, for example, have the label "0.10 M NaCl." If so, we know that the solution in this container has a concentration of 0.10 mol of NaCl per liter of solution (or per 1000 mL of solution). The molarity gives two conversion factors for calculations. In our example they are

$$\frac{0.10 \text{ mol NaCl}}{1000 \text{ mL NaCl solution}} \quad \text{and} \quad \frac{1000 \text{ mL NaCl solution}}{0.10 \text{ mol NaCl}}$$

A Volumetric Flask Is Used to Make a Solution of Known Molarity   Figure 5.5 shows how to make a solution with a known molarity. The grams of solute that have the moles we want are weighed out. This sample is then placed in a *volumetric flask,* a special piece of glassware pictured in the figure. These flasks are available in several fixed capacities; the one selected must allow a final volume of solution that gives the solute the molar concentration we want. The solvent is added until the solute all dissolves and the liquid level exactly reaches the etched mark on the flask, as described in the figure legend.

■ Volumetric flasks as large as 5 L can be purchased as well as many of smaller sizes down to 1 mL.

The concept of molarity will become clearer by studying how to do some of the calculations associated with it. In the next worked example we'll see what kinds of calculations have to be done in order to go into the lab and prepare a certain volume of a solution that has a given molar concentration.

(a)   (b)   (c)   (d)   (e)

Figure 5.5
The preparation of a solution of known molarity. The volumetric flask has an etched line on its neck that marks the liquid level at which the flask will hold the specified volume. *(a)* The solute, accurately weighed, has been placed in the flask. *(b)* Some water (distilled or deionized) is added. *(c)* The flask is agitated so that the solute dissolves. *(d)* Enough water is added to bring the level to the etched line. *(e)* After the flask is stoppered, it is shaken so that the solution will be uniform.

| EXAMPLE 5.10 | PREPARING A SOLUTION OF KNOWN MOLAR CONCENTRATION |

Problem: How much sodium bicarbonate, $NaHCO_3$, is needed to prepare 500 mL of 0.125 M $NaHCO_3$?

Solution: The label indirectly refers to *moles,* but the question asks for the answer in grams. Before we can calculate the grams needed, we have to find out how many moles of $NaHCO_3$ are required. Here is where the given concentration provides what we need most, a conversion factor to calculate the moles of $NaHCO_3$ in the given volume, 500 mL of 0.125 M $NaHCO_3$. Actually, the molarity gives us the following conversion factors, of which we'll need to pick one.

$$\frac{0.125 \text{ mol NaHCO}_3}{1000 \text{ mL NaHCO}_3 \text{ solution}} \quad \text{or} \quad \frac{1000 \text{ mL NaHCO}_3 \text{ solution}}{0.125 \text{ mol NaHCO}_3}$$

If we multiply the given volume, 500 mL of $NaHCO_3$ solution, by the first conversion factor, the volume units will cancel and we will learn how many moles that we need.

$$500 \text{ mL NaHCO}_3 \text{ solution} \times \frac{0.125 \text{ mol NaHCO}_3}{1000 \text{ mL NaHCO}_3 \text{ solution}} = 0.0625 \text{ mol NaHCO}_3$$

In other words, the 500 mL of solution has to contain 0.0625 mol of $NaHCO_3$. So we have to convert 0.0625 mol of $NaHCO_3$ into grams of $NaHCO_3$. To do this we need one of the conversion factors that the formula weight of $NaHCO_3$, 84.0, makes available.

$$\frac{84.0 \text{ g NaHCO}_3}{1 \text{ mol NaHCO}_3} \quad \text{or} \quad \frac{1 \text{ mol NaHCO}_3}{84.0 \text{ g NaHCO}_3}$$

If we multiply 0.0625 mol of $NaHCO_3$ by the first of these factors, then the units of mol $NaHCO_3$ will cancel and our answer will be in what we want, grams.

$$0.0625 \text{ mol NaHCO}_3 \times \frac{8.40 \text{ g NaHCO}_3}{1 \text{ mol NaHCO}_3} = 5.25 \text{ g NaHCO}_3$$

Thus to prepare 500 mL of 0.125 M $NaHCO_3$, we have to weigh out 5.25 g of $NaHCO_3$, dissolve it in some water in a 500-mL volumetric flask, and then carefully add water until its level reaches the mark, making sure that the contents become well mixed.

PRACTICE EXERCISE 13   How many grams of each solute are needed to prepare the following solutions?

(a) 250 mL of 0.100 M H_2SO_4 (b) 100 mL of 0.500 M glucose ($C_6H_{12}O_6$)

Another calculation is to find the volume of a solution of known molar concentration that will deliver a certain quantity of its solute. The next worked example shows how this is done.

| EXAMPLE 5.11 | USING SOLUTIONS OF KNOWN MOLAR CONCENTRATION |

Problem: In an experiment to see whether mouth bacteria can live on mannitol ($C_6H_{14}O_6$), the sweetening agent used in some sugarless gums, a student needed 0.100 mol of mannitol. It was available as a 0.750 M solution. How many milliliters of this solution must be used in order to obtain 0.100 mol of mannitol?

Solution: The two conversion factors that are provided by the given concentration are

$$\frac{0.750 \text{ mol mannitol}}{1000 \text{ mL mannitol solution}} \quad \text{and} \quad \frac{1000 \text{ mL mannitol solution}}{0.750 \text{ mol mannitol}}$$

Therefore

$$0.100 \; \text{mol mannitol} \times \frac{1000 \; \text{mL mannitol solution}}{0.750 \; \text{mol mannitol}} = 133 \; \text{mL mannitol solution}$$

Thus, 133 mL of 0.750 *M* mannitol solution holds 0.100 mol of mannitol.

PRACTICE EXERCISE 14   To test sodium carbonate, Na_2CO_3, as an antacid, a scientist needed 0.125 mol of Na_2CO_3. It was available as 0.800 *M* Na_2CO_3. How many milliliters of this solution are needed for 0.125 mol of Na_2CO_3?

Once solutions of known molar concentration have been prepared, then the most common kind of calculation involves the stoichiometry of some reaction when at least one reactant is in solution. We'll study this in connection with a problem in acid–base neutralization. We earlier learned that an acid is a substance that can furnish H^+ ions and a base is something that can react with H^+ ions in a reaction called an acid–base neutralization. In the next worked example, we'll see how we can do stoichiometric calculations for such a reaction.

EXAMPLE 5.12

STOICHIOMETRIC CALCULATIONS THAT INVOLVE MOLAR CONCENTRATIONS

Problem: Potassium hydroxide, KOH, is a common base. It reacts with hydrochloric acid as follows:

$$HCl(aq) \quad + KOH(aq) \longrightarrow KCl(aq) \quad + H_2O$$

Hydrochloric   Potassium   Potassium
acid   hydroxide   chloride

How many milliliters of 0.100 *M* KOH are needed to neutralize the acid in 25.0 mL of 0.0800 *M* HCl?

Solution: We first calculate the moles of acid present. The molarity of the acid gives us these two conversion factors:

■ Remember, soln = solution.

$$\frac{0.0800 \; \text{mol HCl}}{1000 \; \text{mL HCl soln}} \quad \text{or} \quad \frac{1000 \; \text{mL HCl soln}}{0.0800 \; \text{mol HCl}}$$

We multiply the given, 25.0 mL of HCl solution, by the first factor:

$$25.0 \; \text{mL HCl soln} \times \frac{0.0800 \; \text{mol HCl}}{1000 \; \text{mL HCl soln}} = 0.00200 \; \text{mol HCl}$$

The next step is to find out how many moles of base are needed to neutralize 0.00200 mol of HCl. Here is where we use the coefficients of the balanced equation. They tell us that the ratio is 1 : 1, which means 1 mol of HCl is equivalent chemically (in this equation) to 1 mol of KOH. Thus 0.00200 mol of HCl requires 0.00200 mol of KOH.

Finally, we have to calculate the volume (in mL) of the KOH solution that contains 0.00200 mol of KOH. The molarity of the KOH solution gives us the option of the following conversion factors:

$$\frac{0.100 \; \text{mol KOH}}{1000 \; \text{mL KOH soln}} \quad \text{or} \quad \frac{1000 \; \text{mL KOH soln}}{0.100 \; \text{mol KOH}}$$

We can see that if we multiply 0.00200 mol of KOH by the second conversion factor, we'll have the right units:

$$0.00200 \text{ mol KOH} \times \frac{1000 \text{ mL KOH soln}}{0.100 \text{ mol KOH}} = 20.0 \text{ mL KOH soln}$$

Thus 20.0 mL of 0.100 M KOH solution exactly neutralizes the acid in 25.0 mL of 0.0800 M HCl.

The next worked example shows how to solve a problem in which the mole to mole ratio of acid to base in the equation is not $1:1$.

EXAMPLE 5.13

STOICHIOMETRIC CALCULATIONS THAT INVOLVE MOLAR CONCENTRATIONS

Problem: Sodium hydroxide, NaOH, another common base, can react with sulfuric acid by the following equation:

$$H_2SO_4(aq) + 2NaOH(aq) \longrightarrow Na_2SO_4(aq) + 2H_2O$$

| Sulfuric | Sodium | Sodium |
| acid | hydroxide | sulfate |

How many milliliters of 0.125 M NaOH provide enough NaOH to react completely with the sulfuric acid in 16.8 mL of 0.118 M H_2SO_4 by the given equation?

Solution: Because of the coefficients in the equation, we know that we have to match the moles of sodium hydroxide to the moles of sulfuric acid on a two-to-one basis. Hence, we start by asking how many moles of sulfuric acid are in 16.8 mL of 0.118 M H_2SO_4. Then we will relate this number of moles to the moles of NaOH that match it according to the coefficients. Finally, we will find out how many milliliters of the NaOH solution hold this calculated number of moles of NaOH.

First, then, the moles of H_2SO_4 that are neutralized:

$$16.8 \text{ mL } H_2SO_4 \text{ soln} \times \frac{0.118 \text{ mol } H_2SO_4}{1000 \text{ mL } H_2SO_4 \text{ soln}} = 0.00198 \text{ mol } H_2SO_4$$

Next, the moles of NaOH that chemically match 0.00198 mol of H_2SO_4 according to the coefficients of the equation:

$$0.00198 \text{ mol } H_2SO_4 \times \frac{2 \text{ mol NaOH}}{1 \text{ mol } H_2SO_4} = 0.00396 \text{ mol NaOH}$$

Finally, the volume of 0.125 M NaOH solution that holds 0.00396 mol NaOH:

$$0.00396 \text{ mol NaOH} \times \frac{1000 \text{ mL NaOH soln}}{0.125 \text{ mol NaOH}} = 31.7 \text{ mL NaOH soln}$$

Thus 31.7 mL of 0.125 M NaOH solution is needed to neutralize all the sulfuric acid in 16.8 mL of 0.118 M H_2SO_4.

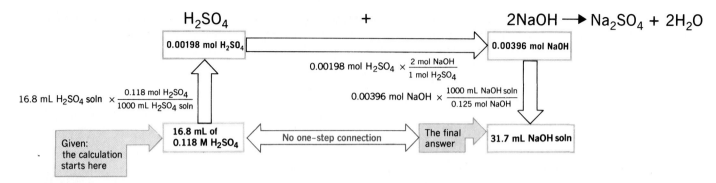

Figure 5.6
The calculation flow diagram for
Example 5.13.

Figure 5.6 provides a pictorial summary — a calculation flowchart — of the steps used to solve the problem of Example 5.13.

PRACTICE EXERCISE 15

Blood isn't supposed to be acidic, but in some medical emergencies it tends to become so. To stop and reverse this trend, the emergency-care specialist might administer a dilute solution of sodium bicarbonate intravenously. Sodium bicarbonate neutralizes acids. For example, it reacts with sulfuric acid (which is *not* present in blood) as follows:

$$2NaHCO_3(aq) + H_2SO_4(aq) \longrightarrow Na_2SO_4(aq) + 2CO_2(g) + 2H_2O$$

How many milliliters of 0.112 M H_2SO_4 will react with 21.6 mL of 0.102 M $NaHCO_3$ *according to this equation?*

5.7 PREPARING DILUTE SOLUTIONS FROM CONCENTRATED SOLUTIONS

The dilution of a fixed volume of a concentrated solution changes only the concentration, not the moles of solute.

Chemicals are often purchased as concentrated reagents that then must be diluted to some desired concentration. We'll study here how to do the calculations needed for the preparation of dilute from concentrated solutions.

One basic idea guides these calculations. The mass or moles of solute in the final volume of the dilute solution will be the same as were in the concentrated solution. We add only *solvent,* not solute.

The calculation begins with three facts. We know what final concentration we want, we know what volume we wish to have, and we know the concentration of the concentrated solution to be diluted. The calculation is to tell us what volume of the concentrated solution must be taken. Since the moles of actual solute are the same in both solutions, we can calculate this amount in the usual way from the volume and molarity data *for both solutions.* In the dilute solution,

■ It costs less to ship concentrated solutions than dilute solutions because less mass of solution is needed per mole of solute shipped.

■ dil = dilute
concd = concentrated

$$\text{mol solute} = \text{liters}_{\text{dil soln}} \times \frac{\text{mol solute}}{\text{liter}_{\text{dil soln}}} = \text{liters}_{\text{dil soln}} \times M_{\text{dil soln}}$$

In the concentrated solution,

$$\text{mol solute} = \text{liter}_{\text{concd soln}} \times \frac{\text{mole solute}}{\text{liter}_{\text{concd soln}}} = \text{liters}_{\text{concd soln}} \times M_{\text{concd soln}}$$

These two expressions for the moles of solute equal each other, as we have said. Therefore,

$$\text{liters}_{\text{dil soln}} \times M_{\text{dil soln}} = \text{liters}_{\text{concd soln}} \times M_{\text{concd soln}}$$

Actually, the unit of liters isn't required. We can use any volume unit that we please provided that it is the same unit on both sides of the equation. Normally the mL unit is used in the lab, so our equation can be restated as follows:

$$\text{mL}_{\text{dil soln}} \times M_{\text{dil soln}} = \text{mL}_{\text{concd soln}} \times M_{\text{concd soln}}$$

The following example shows how this equation is used.

| EXAMPLE 5.14 | DOING THE CALCULATIONS FOR MAKING DILUTIONS |

Problem: Hydrochloric acid can be purchased at a concentration of 1.00 M HCl. How can we prepare 500 mL of 0.100 M HCl?

Solution: What the question really asks is how many milliliters of 1.00 M HCl would have to be diluted to a final volume of 500 mL to make a solution with a concentration of 0.100 M HCl? We first assemble the known data:

$$\text{mL}_{\text{dil soln}} = 500 \text{ mL} \qquad \text{mL}_{\text{concd soln}} = \text{?}$$
$$M_{\text{dil soln}} = 0.100 \ M \qquad M_{\text{concd soln}} = 1.00 \ M$$

Now we use the equation

$$\text{mL}_{\text{dil soln}} \times M_{\text{dil soln}} = \text{mL}_{\text{concd soln}} \times M_{\text{concd soln}}$$
$$500 \text{ mL} \times 0.100 \ M = \text{mL}_{\text{concd soln}} \times 1.00 \ M$$

Rearranging terms to solve for $\text{mL}_{\text{concd soln}}$ gives us

$$\text{mL}_{\text{concd soln}} = \frac{500 \text{ mL} \times 0.100 \ M}{1.00 \ M}$$
$$= 50.0 \text{ mL}$$

In other words, if we take 50.0 mL of 1.00 M HCl, place this in a 500-mL volumetric flask, and add water to the mark, we will have 500 mL of 0.10 M HCl.

Figure 5.7 shows the steps for doing a dilution of 0.200 M $K_2Cr_2O_7$ to give 100 mL of solution with a concentration of 0.0400 M.

PRACTICE EXERCISE 16   Calculate the volume of 0.200 M $K_2Cr_2O_7$ needed to prepare 100 mL of 0.0400 M $K_2Cr_2O_7$, the solution prepared in Figure 5.7.

PRACTICE EXERCISE 17   The concentrated sulfuric acid that can be purchased from chemical supply houses is 18 M H_2SO_4. How could we use this to prepare 250 mL of 1.0 M H_2SO_4?

Handle Concentrated Acids and Bases Very Carefully   When certain very concentrated solutions are diluted with water, a great deal of heat is released, enough to make the system boil. This might spatter hazardous materials onto your clothes or your skin or into your eyes. Concentrated sulfuric acid particularly must be handled very carefully. The only safe course is to *pour the concentrated solution slowly, with stirring, into water.* In this way not all the acid is present at once, and the concentrated and more dense solution more slowly gives off heat as it sinks and dissolves. If done slowly enough, the mixture will not boil and spatter.

If you mistakenly add water *to* a concentrated solution, the first water added tends to float. It interacts where the surfaces meet, and much heat could quickly develop in a small volume of the mixture, enough heat to make the system boil.

Remember, if you ever have to make a dilute aqueous solution from any concentrated acid or alkali, *add the concentrated solution slowly to the water as you stir the mixture and, as always, wear protective eye wear.*

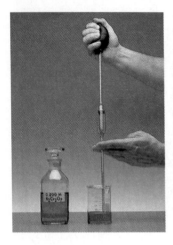
(a)

(b)

(c)

(d)

Figure 5.7
Preparing a dilute solution by dilution. The long glass tube with a bulge in its middle is a volumetric pipet. Like a volumetric flask, it has an etched line on its upper narrow section so that when the liquid level is at this line, the pipet contains the volume printed on it. Notice that suction is being supplied by a suction bulb, not by mouth. The calculated volume of the more concentrated solution is *(a)* withdrawn and *(b)* placed in a volumetric flask. This flask would already contain some of the additional water to be added if the solution in the pipet were a concentrated acid or base. *(c)* Now additional water is added slowly as the new solution is swirled to promote mixing until the final volume is reached. *(d)* Then the new solution is transferred to a dry bottle and labeled.

SUMMARY

Stoichiometry The coefficients in a balanced equation give the proportions of the chemicals involved either in formula units or in moles. A quantity of a substance equal to its formula weight taken in grams is one mole of the substance, so to calculate a molar mass just find the formula weight and attach the units g/mol.

One mole of any pure substance, element or compound, consists of 6.02×10^{23} of its formula units. This number is named Avogadro's number. In working problems involving balanced equations and quantities of substances, be sure to solve them at the mole level where the coefficients can be used. Then, as needed, convert moles to grams.

Solutions A solution has a solvent and one or more solutes, and its concentration is the ratio of quantity of solute to some unit quantity of solvent or of solution.

A solution can be described as dilute or concentrated according to its ratio of solute to solvent being small or large. Whether a solution is unsaturated, saturated, or supersaturated depends on its ability to dissolve more solute (at the same temperature).

Each substance has a particular solubility in a given solvent at a specified temperature, and this is often expressed as the grams of solute that can be dissolved in 100 g of the solvent.

Molar concentration The ratio of the moles of solute per liter (or 1000 mL) of solution is the molar concentration or the molarity of the solution. When we have to prepare one solution by diluting a more concentrated solution, the equation that we use is

$$\text{mL}_{\text{dil soln}} \times M_{\text{dil soln}} = \text{mL}_{\text{concd soln}} \times M_{\text{concd soln}}$$

REVIEW EXERCISES

Answers to the Review Exercises whose numbers are marked by an asterisk are in Appendix D. The *Study Guide* that accompanies this text contains answers to the other Review Exercises. Remember to round atomic weights to their first decimal points *before* using them in any calculations.

Balanced Equations

5.1 Write in your own words what the following equation says.

$$2C + O_2 \longrightarrow 2CO \qquad \text{(carbon monoxide)}$$

5.2 What does the following equation state? Write it in your own words.

$$N_2 + 3H_2 \longrightarrow 2NH_3 \qquad \text{(ammonia)}$$

5.3 What would be a more acceptable way of writing the following balanced equation?

$$8H_3PO_4 + 16NaOH \longrightarrow 8Na_2HPO_4 + 16H_2O$$

5.4 Balance the following equations.
(a) $SO_2 + O_2 \rightarrow SO_3$
(b) $CaO + HNO_3 \rightarrow Ca(NO_3)_2 + H_2O$
(c) $AgNO_3 + MgCl_2 \rightarrow AgCl + Mg(NO_3)_2$
(d) $HCl + Ca(OH)_2 \rightarrow CaCl_2 + H_2O$
(e) $C_2H_6 + O_2 \rightarrow CO_2 + H_2O$

5.5 Balance each of the following equations.
(a) $NaHCO_3 + H_2SO_4 \rightarrow Na_2SO_4 + H_2O + CO_2$
(b) $Fe_2O_3 + H_2 \rightarrow Fe + H_2O$
(c) $Ca(OH)_2 + HNO_3 \rightarrow Ca(NO_3)_2 + H_2O$
(d) $NO + O_2 \rightarrow NO_2$
(e) $Al_2O_3 + H_2SO_4 \rightarrow Al_2(SO_4)_3 + H_2O$

Avogadro's Number

5.6 What is Avogadro's number?

5.7 Why did scientists select Avogadro's number and not some less complicated number to use in defining chemical units for substances?

*5.8 How many molecules are in 6.00 g of H_2O?

5.9 A sample of aspirin ($C_9H_8O_4$) with a mass of 0.180 g (roughly the amount of aspirin in a typical 5-grain tablet) consists of how many molecules of aspirin?

*5.10 One dose of a particular medication contains 6.02×10^{20} molecules. The formula weight of the medication is 150. How many grams are in this dose?

5.11 A sample of impure water contains 3.01×10^{18} molecules of the impurity. How many milligrams of the impurity are present if its formula weight is 240?

Formula Weights

5.12 What law of nature makes it possible to compute formula weights simply by adding all the atomic weights of the atoms given in a formula?

*5.13 Calculate the formula weight of each of the following substances.
(a) NaOH (b) $CaCO_3$ (c) H_2SO_4
(d) Na_2CO_3 (e) $KMnO_4$ (f) Na_3BO_3

5.14 Calculate the formula weight of each of the following substances.
(a) $Mg(HCO_3)_2$ (b) Na_2HPO_4 (c) HNO_3
(d) $KC_2H_3O_2$ (e) $(NH_4)_2SO_4$ (f) $Ca_3(PO_4)_2$

Moles

5.15 How do we calculate the quantity of mass present in 1 mol of any substance?

5.16 What is the relationship between Avogadro's number and 1 mol of any substance?

5.17 What is the practical difficulty in the lab of having balances read in moles instead of in mass units?

5.18 In converting grams to moles or moles to grams, what units are given to the formula weight of, say, H_2O, a molecular compound with a formula weight of 18.0?

5.19 The formula weight of bromine, Br_2, is 159.8. What are the two conversion factors that we can write that use this information?

*5.20 How many grams are in 2.50 mol of each of the compounds listed in Review Exercise 5.13?

5.21 How many grams are in 0.575 mol of each of the compounds given in Review Exercise 5.14?

*5.22 Calculate the number of moles that are in 75.0 g of each of the compounds listed in Review Exercise 5.13.

5.23 How many moles are in 28.6 g of each of the compounds given in Review Exercise 5.14?

Stoichiometry Involving Balanced Equations

*5.24 In the equation for the reaction of iron with oxygen,

$$4Fe + 3O_2 \longrightarrow 2Fe_2O_3$$

what two conversion factors express the *mole* relationship between each of the following pairs of substances?
(a) Fe and O_2 (b) Fe and Fe_2O_3 (c) O_2 and Fe_2O_3

5.25 Ethane, C_2H_6, burns according to the following equation.

$$2C_2H_6 + 7O_2 \longrightarrow 4CO_2 + 6H_2O$$

What two conversion factors express the *mole* relationship between each of the following pairs of compounds?
(a) C_2H_6 and O_2 (b) CO_2 and C_2H_6
(c) H_2O and O_2 (d) C_2H_6 and H_2O

*5.26 Butane, C_4H_{10}, is the fluid used in cigarette lighters. It burns according to the following equation.

$$2C_4H_{10} + 13O_2 \longrightarrow 8CO_2 + 10H_2O$$

(a) How many moles of oxygen are needed to react completely with 4.0 mol of butane?
(b) How many moles of water form from the burning of 10 moles of butane?
(c) To make 16 moles of carbon dioxide by this reaction, how many moles of oxygen are needed?

5.27 In the last step of the most commonly used method to convert iron ore into iron, the following reaction occurs.

$$Fe_2O_3 + 3CO \longrightarrow 2Fe + 3CO_2$$

(a) To make 350 mol of Fe, how many moles of CO are needed?
(b) If one batch began with 35 mol of Fe_2O_3, how many moles of iron are made?
(c) How many moles of CO are required to react with 125 mol of Fe_2O_3?

*5.28 The Synthane process for making methane, CH_4, from coal is as follows, where we use carbon, C, to represent coal.

$$C + 2H_2 \longrightarrow CH_4$$

(a) How many moles of hydrogen are needed to combine with 37.5 mol of C?

(b) How many moles of methane can be made from 86 mol of H_2?

5.29 Gasohol contains ethyl alcohol, C_2H_6O, which burns according to the following equation.

$$C_2H_6O + 3O_2 \longrightarrow 2CO_2 + 3H_2O$$

(a) If 475 g of ethyl alcohol burn this way, how many grams of oxygen are needed?

(b) If 326 g of CO_2 formed in one test involving this reaction, how many grams of ethyl alcohol burned?

(c) If 92.6 g of O_2 are consumed by this reaction, how many grams of water form?

*5.30 An industrial synthesis of chlorine is carried out by passing an electric current through a solution of NaCl in water. Other commercially valuable products are sodium hydroxide and hydrogen.

$$2NaCl + 2H_2O \xrightarrow[\text{electric current}]{} 2NaOH + H_2 + Cl_2$$

(a) How many grams of NaCl are needed to make 775 g of Cl_2?

(b) How many grams of NaOH are also produced?

(c) How many grams of hydrogen are made as well?

5.31 Phosphoric acid, H_3PO_4, is needed to convert phosphate rock into a fertilizer called *triple phosphate*. One way to make phosphoric acid is by the following reaction:

$$P_4O_{10} + 6H_2O \longrightarrow 4H_3PO_4$$

(a) To make 1.00×10^3 kg of phosphoric acid (one metric ton), how many kilograms of P_4O_{10} are needed?

(b) How many kilograms of water are also required?

*5.32 One method that can be used to neutralize an acid spill in the lab is to sprinkle it with powdered sodium carbonate. For example, sulfuric acid, H_2SO_4, can be neutralized by the following reaction:

$$H_2SO_4 + Na_2CO_3 \longrightarrow Na_2SO_4 + CO_2 + H_2O$$

If 45.0 g of sulfuric acid are spilled, what is the minimum number of grams of sodium carbonate that have to be added to it to complete this reaction?

Solutions

5.33 A solution of sodium chloride at 50 °C was found to contain 36.5 g NaCl/100 g water. Using information in a table in this chapter, determine whether this solution was saturated, unsaturated, or supersaturated.

5.34 A solution of barium sulfate at 20 °C contains 0.00024 g $BaSO_4$ per 100 g water. Is it saturated, unsaturated, or supersaturated? Would it be described as dilute or concentrated?

5.35 Suppose you do not know and do not have access to a reference in which to look up the solubility of potassium chloride, KCl, in water at room temperature. Yet you need a solution that you know beyond doubt is saturated. How could such a solution be made?

5.36 Suppose you have a saturated solution of vitamin C in water at 10 °C. Without changing either the quantity of solvent or the quantity of solute, what could you do to make this solution unsaturated? What could you do to find out if this solution could be made supersaturated?

Molar Concentration

5.37 What are the differences between *molecule*, *mole*, and *molarity*?

5.38 What is another term for *molarity*?

5.39 When a volumetric flask is used to prepare a solution having some specified molarity, does the one who makes this solution know precisely how much *solvent* is used? Why is this information unnecessary for the uses to which the solution might be put?

*5.40 Calculate the number of grams of solute that would be needed to make each of the following solutions.

(a) 500 mL of 0.200 M NaCl

(b) 250 mL of 0.125 M $C_6H_{12}O_6$ (glucose)

(c) 100 mL of 0.100 M H_2SO_4

(d) 500 mL of 0.400 M KOH

5.41 How many grams of solute are needed to make each of the following solutions?

(a) 250 mL of 0.120 M Na_2CO_3

(b) 500 mL of 0.100 M NaOH

(c) 100 mL of 0.750 M $KHCO_3$

(d) 250 mL of 0.100 M $C_{12}H_{22}O_{11}$ (sucrose)

*5.42 How many milliliters of 0.10 M HCl contain 0.025 mol of HCl?

5.43 How many milliliters of 1.0 M H_2SO_4 would have to be taken to obtain 0.0025 mol of H_2SO_4?

*5.44 If you need 0.0010 mol of $NaHCO_3$ for an experiment, how many milliliters of 0.010 M $NaHCO_3$ would you have to measure out?

5.45 The stockroom has a supply of 0.10 M H_2SO_4. If you have to have 0.075 mol of H_2SO_4, how many milliliters of this stock solution do you have to take?

*5.46 There is a supply of 1.00 M NaOH in the lab. How many milliliters of this solution have to be taken in order to obtain 10.0 g of NaOH?

5.47 The stock supply of sulfuric acid is 0.50 M H_2SO_4. How many milliliters of this solution contain 5.0 g of H_2SO_4?

Stoichiometry of Reactions in Solution

*5.48 Barium sulfate, $BaSO_4$, is very insoluble in water, a slurry of this compound is the "barium cocktail" given to patients prior to taking X rays of the intestinal tract. It can be made by the following reaction:

$$Ba(NO_3)_2(aq) + Na_2SO_4(aq) \longrightarrow BaSO_4(s) + 2NaNO_3(aq)$$

In one use of this reaction to make barium sulfate—it is collected by filtering the final solution—a chemist used 250 mL of 0.100 M $Ba(NO_3)_2$. How many milliliters of 0.150 M Na_2SO_4 were needed to supply enough solute for this reaction?

5.49 How many milliliters of 0.100 M HCl are required to react completely with (and be neutralized by) 25.4 mL of 0.158 M Na_2CO_3 if they react according to the following equation?

$$2HCl(aq) \ + Na_2CO_3(aq) \longrightarrow 2NaCl(aq) + CO_2(g) + H_2O$$

Hydrochloric   Sodium
acid   carbonate

•5.50 Calcium hydroxide, $Ca(OH)_2$, is an ingredient in one brand of antacid tablets. It reacts with and neutralizes the acid in gastric juice, hydrochloric acid, as follows.

$$Ca(OH)_2(s) + 2HCl(aq) \longrightarrow CaCl_2(aq) + 2H_2O$$

A tablet that contains 2.00 g of $Ca(OH)_2$ can neutralize how many milliliters of 0.100 M HCl?

5.51 A nitric acid spill can be neutralized by sprinkling solid sodium carbonate on it. The reaction is

$$Na_2CO_3(s) + 2HNO_3(aq) \longrightarrow 2NaNO_3(aq) + CO_2(g) + H_2O$$

In one accident, 25.0 mL of 16.0 M HNO_3 (concentrated nitric acid, a dangerous chemical) spilled onto a stone desk top. Will 40.0 g of Na_2CO_3 be enough to neutralize this acid by the given equation? How many grams are needed?

Preparing Dilute Solutions from Concentrated Solutions

•5.52 Concentrated acetic acid is 17 M $HC_2H_3O_2$. How would you prepare 100 mL of 2.0 M $HC_2H_3O_2$?

5.53 Concentrated nitric acid is 16 M HNO_3. How would you prepare 500 mL of 1.0 M HNO_3?

States of Matter, Kinetic Theory, and Equilibria

Heat is the great determiner of the state in which water can exist, whether solid (ice), liquid, or gas (steam). At the geyser basin in Yellowstone National Park, underground heat sends the Clepsydra geyser skyward, and heat from the great forest fire of 1988 reaches up and affects the clouds themselves.

THE GASEOUS STATE

The four properties that completely define the physical state of any gas are pressure, temperature, volume, and moles.

We now move from a study of the *kinds* of matter, elements and compounds, to a study of the *states of matter,* gases, liquids, and solids. We begin with gases because they are the simplest.

All Gases More or Less Obey the Same Set of Physical Laws

What makes gases relatively simple is that, unlike liquids and solids, they all follow the same physical laws. Although different gases have different *chemical* properties, they share the same laws concerning physical properties. These laws describe how four physical quantities interact — volume, temperature, pressure, and the number of moles of a gas.

The volume of a gas, symbolized as V, must be specified, because all gases will spontaneously fill out whatever space we give them. This property is called **diffusion,** and gases, unlike liquids and solids, readily diffuse. Gas volume is usually given in liters (L), sometimes milliliters (mL).

The temperature, T, of a gas is another property that must be known to describe a gas sample. When its temperature changes, so will the gas volume, provided that at least one of the container's walls can move, like the movable piston of an automobile cylinder. Gas temperature has to be given in kelvins (K) to make the calculations simple. If given in degrees Celsius, the temperature in kelvins must then be calculated before other gas law calculations are made.

The pressure of a gas, P, must also be given to describe a specific sample. You're aware of air pressure in bicycle and automobile tires. You've also seen warnings printed on aerosol spray cans — "Do Not Incinerate." If we heat a gas enclosed in a rigid container, its pressure increases, possibly enough to burst the container. Picnickers who put unopened cans of beans on a camp fire soon learn about the power of gas pressure as they pick beans from their hair.

The number of moles of the gas, n, is the fourth physical quantity used to describe a given gas sample. One mole of a gas at some particular pressure and temperature occupies a certain volume, *the same volume (more or less) for any gas.* If we want two moles of the gas at the same pressure and temperature, we need twice the volume.

Volume, temperature, pressure, and moles are the four physical quantities we need to study gases. One of the remarkable facts about all gases is that *when we know any three, the fourth can have only one value,* a value that we can calculate with acceptable precision.

Pressure Describes the Ratio of a Force Acting to the Area It Affects

If we divide the force acting on a given area by the area itself, the result is called the **pressure.** Pressure is force per unit area.

$$\text{Pressure} = \frac{\text{force}}{\text{area}}$$

To understand pressure, we need to learn about the relationship between weight, force, and pressure. The *weight* of an object is related to a special natural force, the force of gravity. The weight of something is a measure of the force it exerts because of the gravitational attraction of the earth. But the effect of a given weight on you, such as that of a book backpack, depends on how the weight is distributed over some area of your body. Imagine balancing a ski pole sideways on your palm. Its weight is distributed over a fairly large area of the hand, so the ratio — force (weight) divided by area — is relatively small and you feel little pressure. (The simple calculations in the margin give a rough idea.) However, if you could balance the pole by its tip on your finger, the entire force (weight) would now be concentrated on a very small area. The pressure you now would feel would be much greater and much more painful. It could be as much as 100,000 times greater, as you can see by the margin calculation. Thus the distinction between force (or weight) and pressure is very important. It's *pressure* that is relevant to gases.

■ Liquids and solids, of course, do not spread out like this.

■ $K = {}°C + 273$

$P = \dfrac{0.69 \text{ lb}}{1.3 \text{ in.}^2}$

$= 5.3 \times 10^{-1} \text{ lb/in.}^2$

$P = \dfrac{0.69 \text{ lb}}{1.6 \times 19^{-5} \text{in.}^2}$

$= 5.3 \times 10^{4} \text{ lb/in.}^2$

Units of Pressure Originated in Air Pressure The pressure exerted by air on the earth's surface gives us our most common units of pressure, the *atmosphere* (atm), the *torr,* and the *millimeter of mercury* (mm Hg).

Because air is matter, it has weight, which means that it is pulled toward the earth by the earth's gravitational attraction. Imagine, now, a perfect cylinder of still air with invisible walls. Its area at the bottom is 1 square inch, it rests on an ocean beach, and it reaches to outer space. This column of air has a weight at sea level of about 14.7 lb when the temperature is 0 °C. Because this weight rests on an area of 1 in.², the pressure exerted by the column of air is the ratio, 14.7 lb/in.². This is normal, sea-level air pressure.

Our air column has less air in it when its bottom rests at a high altitude, like a mountain top, than when it rests on an ocean beach, so air pressure decreases with altitude. At the top of Mt. Everest, the highest mountain on earth, for example, the pressure is about one-third what it is at sea level.

The pushing ability of air caused by its weight is the basis of one way to measure pressure, the mercury or Torricelli **barometer,** named after Evangelista Torricelli (1608 – 1647), an Italian scientist. (See Figure 6.1.) It consists of a glass tube a little less than a meter long, sealed at one end, filled with mercury, and then inverted into a container of mercury. Some mercury immediately runs out of the tube. However, no air can get in to fill the gap that this creates at the top of the tube. There is no air in this gap, and any space where no air or other gas is found is called a **vacuum.**[1] (In other words, virtually nothing inside the tube at its top pushes down on the entrapped mercury. Thus, the outside air pressure on the mercury in the dish is unopposed. It forces mercury to stay in the tube.

The exact height of the column of mercury in the tube fluctuates somewhat with temperature and weather, but at sea level it is about 760 mm. This height is used to define a unit of pressure, the standard atmosphere. One **standard atmosphere, 1 atm,** is the pressure exerted by a column of mercury 760 mm high at a temperature of 0 °C.

■ By *outer space* we mean space beyond the earth's atmosphere, where the atmosphere is so thin as to be almost nonexistent.

■ TV and radio weather reports in the United States use inches of mercury, not mm Hg, as the pressure unit. Because 25.4 mm = 1 in., 760 mm = 29.9 in., so 1 atm = 29.9 in. Hg.

$$760 \text{ mm} \times \frac{1 \text{ in.}}{25.4 \text{ mm}} = 29.9 \text{ in.}$$

---

1 atm = 760 mm Hg   (0 °C)

A smaller unit, widely used by people in the life sciences, is called the **millimeter of mercury,** or **mm Hg** (pronounced *em em aitch gee*).

$$1 \text{ mm Hg} = \frac{1}{760} \text{ atm} \qquad (6.1)$$

Many scientists are uncomfortable about using a measurement of length—the millimeter—to express a measurement of pressure, so they have adopted a new name for the mm Hg, the **torr.**

1 torr = 1 mm Hg   (6.2)

We will use the *mm Hg* unit, but you can see by Equation 6.2 that it's easy to switch from this to *torr.*

The SI unit of pressure is called the **pascal, Pa.** The SI wants all derived units, like pressure, to be based on SI *base* units, like the meter or kilogram. The SI unit for force is called the *newton,* and the SI unit for area is the meter squared (m²). Therefore the SI unit of pressure

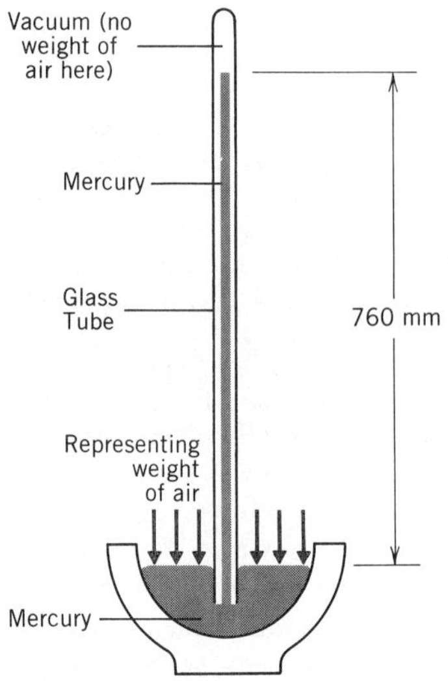

Vacuum (no weight of air here)

Mercury

Glass Tube

760 mm

Representing weight of air

Mercury

Figure 6.1
The Torricelli barometer.

---

[1] The gap does not involve a *perfect* vacuum because this space contains a very small trace of vaporized mercury.

is the ratio of these, newtons/m^2, and is called the *pascal*. The *atmosphere,* in fact, is now defined in relationship to the pascal:

- kPa = kilopascal
  1 kPa = 1000 Pa

$$1 \text{ atm} = 101,325 \text{ Pa} \quad (\text{exactly})$$
$$1 \text{ atm} = 101.325 \text{ kPa} \quad (\text{exactly})$$

- $101,325 \dfrac{\text{Pa}}{\text{atm}} \times \dfrac{1 \text{ atm}}{760 \text{ mm Hg}}$
  $= 133.322 \text{ Pa/mm Hg}$

These show how extremely small the pascal is. It takes over 100,000 pascals to equal just 1 atm. As shown in the margin, 1 mm Hg (1 torr) = 133.322 Pa. During your professional career you may see the pascal or an SI multiple such as the kilopascal (kPa) used more and more, especially in formal scientific articles.

6.2 THE PRESSURE–VOLUME RELATIONSHIP AT CONSTANT TEMPERATURE

When a fixed number of moles of gas is kept at constant temperature, the volume is inversely proportional to the pressure.

Anyone who has used a bicycle pump knows that when the pressure on a gas is increased, the volume decreases. Robert Boyle (1627–1691), an English scientist, discovered that the relationship between P and V is particularly simple if the amount of gas (the sample size in mass) is fixed and the temperature is held constant. Using a device similar to that shown in Figure 6.2, he found that if he doubled the pressure under these conditions, he cut the volume in half. If he decreased the pressure by, say, 50%, the volume increased by 50%.

Whenever one quantity decreases in proportion to an increase in the other we say that they are *inversely proportional* to each other. Boyle discovered that the pressure and volume are inversely proportional (at constant mass and temperature). In time, other scientists found that all the gases they studied had this property, so now we have a law of nature called the **pressure–volume law,** or **Boyle's law.**

> **Pressure–Volume Law (Boyle's Law)** The volume of a fixed quantity of gas is inversely proportional to its pressure at a constant temperature.

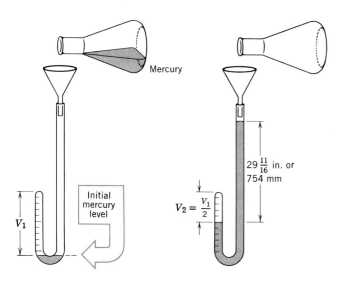

Figure 6.2
J-tube apparatus for pressure–volume data. On the left, the pressures in the two arms of the tubes are the same and equal, say, 754 mm Hg. A volume of gas, V_1, has been trapped in the shorter arm with the sealed end. On the right, enough mercury has been added to make the mercury column in the longer arm extend 754 mm above the top of the shorter mercury column. In other words, the pressure on the entrapped gas is now 754 + 754 mm Hg or twice the initial value. This has squeezed the volume of the gas to half its original size. Higher pressures can be applied to obtain additional Boyle's law data. All that is needed is a longer tube, made of strong material, into which more mercury can be poured.

Mercury

Initial mercury level

V_1

$29\frac{11}{16}$ in. or 754 mm

$V_2 = \dfrac{V_1}{2}$

Put in mathematical form, this law states that

■ The symbol ∝ stands for *is proportional to.*

$$V \propto \frac{1}{P} \quad \text{(} T \text{ and mass constant)} \tag{6.3}$$

Introducing a proportionality constant, C, we can change Equation 6.3 into the following equation,

$$V = \frac{1}{P} \times C$$

or, rearranging terms,

$$PV = C \tag{6.4}$$

The proportionality constant, C, is usually not determined because Equation 6.4 is easily transformed into a more useful form. Whatever its value, C has to be just that, a constant (always assuming the same mass and the same temperature). Thus if P_1 and V_1 are the pressure and volume initially, and we change one of them (at the same T and mass) so that we have new values, P_2 and V_2, then the pressure–volume law tells us that both of the following equations are true:

■ The same constant, C, applies. This is at the heart of Boyle's law.

$$P_1 V_1 = C$$
$$P_2 V_2 = C$$

The two quantities that C equals must equal each other, so we can write the following equation, the equation that is the most useful in doing pressure–volume law calculations.

$$P_1 V_1 = P_2 V_2 \tag{6.5}$$

Equation 6.5 lets us predict how gas volume or pressure will change if we alter one of them. We'll do two worked examples. The first uses a "plugging the numbers into the equation" approach. The second relies more on *a basic understanding* of the the pressure–volume law. You should be able to use either method.

EXAMPLE 6.1   DOING PRESSURE–VOLUME LAW CALCULATIONS

Problem: A given mass of oxygen occupies 500 mL at 760 mm Hg at 20 °C. At what pressure will it occupy 450 mL at the same temperature?

Solution: We have the following data:

$$P_1 = 760 \text{ mm Hg} \qquad P_2 = ?$$
$$V_1 = 500 \text{ mL} \qquad V_2 = 450 \text{ mL}$$

Therefore, using Equation 6.5 directly; we have

$$(760 \text{ mm Hg})(500 \text{ mL}) = (P_2)(450 \text{ mL})$$

To solve for P_2 (that is, to have it stand alone on one side of the equals sign), we divide both sides by 450 mL.

$$\frac{(760 \text{ mm Hg})(500 \text{ mL})}{(450 \text{ mL})} = \frac{(P_2)\cancel{(450 \text{ mL})}}{\cancel{(450 \text{ mL})}}$$

$$P_2 = \frac{(760 \text{ mm Hg})(500)}{(450)}$$
$$P_2 = 844 \text{ mm Hg} \quad \text{(correctly rounded)}$$

Thus the new pressure must be 844 mm Hg.

PRACTICE EXERCISE 1   If 660 mL of helium at 20 °C is under a pressure of 745 mm Hg, what volume will the sample occupy (at the same temperature) if the pressure is changed to 375 mm Hg?

In the next worked example, we'll see how a little reasoning with the fundamental pressure–volume relationship can contribute to your basic understanding of what is happening. Before we discuss it, notice two variations of Equation 6.5. We can solve this equation for P_2 before we enter any numbers into it by dividing both sides by V_2.

$$P_2 = P_1 \times \left(\frac{V_1}{V_2}\right) \qquad (6.6)$$

A ratio of volumes

In other words, *to find the second value of pressure we multiply the given value by a ratio of volumes.* If the problem gives *two* values for volume, both V_1 and V_2, then two ratios are possible, V_1/V_2 or V_2/V_1. You don't have to remember Equation 6.6 to select the correct ratio to multiply by the given pressure. If you remember the basic fact given by the pressure–volume law—P and V vary inversely—you choose the ratio that produces the right kind of change, a pressure-raising or a pressure-lowering change. In Example 6.1, the volume was going to be reduced, so this required that the pressure be increased; when you can make this analysis, you have caught the essence of the pressure–volume law. The volumes given were 500 mL and 450 mL, and only the ratio of 500 mL/450 mL could, when multiplied by the given pressure, yield a *larger* value of pressure. This ratio, 500 mL/450 mL, is a number *larger* than 1. The other ratio, 450 mL/500 mL, is less than 1, so if you used this to multiply by the given pressure, the result would have been a *smaller* pressure. And this would have violated the pressure–volume law's requirement as applied to this problem.

The second variation of Equation 6.5 is like the first. If the problem supplies two values of pressure, P_1 and P_2, and you have to find what a given volume, V_1, changes to, the need is for the appropriate ratio of pressures. By rearranging Equation 6.5, we get

$$V_2 = V_1 \times \left(\frac{P_1}{P_2}\right) \qquad (6.7)$$

A ratio of pressures

In the next worked example, we will see how picking the right ratio of pressures, based on the basic requirement of the pressure–volume law, helps us to solve the problem.

| **EXAMPLE 6.2** | **DOING PRESSURE–VOLUME LAW CALCULATIONS** |

Problem: A sample of nitrogen at 25 °C occupies a volume of 5.65 L at a pressure of 740 mm Hg. If the pressure, at the same temperature, is changed to 760 mm Hg, what is the final volume?

Solution: The pressure is being increased, so the volume will have to decrease; this is what we can predict from the pressure–volume law. Therefore we need a ratio of pressures that is less than 1 to multiply by the given volume. Of the two possible ratios, only 740 mm Hg/760 mm Hg meets this requirement. So, we multiply it by the given volume.

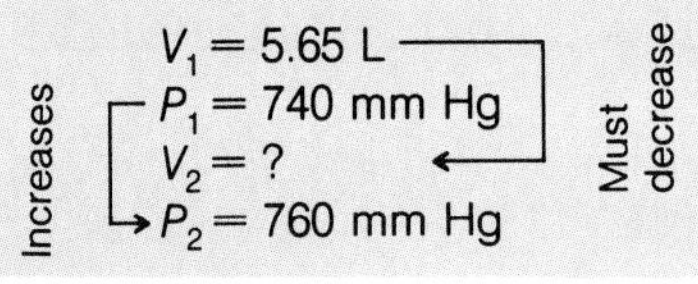

$$V_2 = 5.65 \text{ L} \times \frac{740 \text{ mm Hg}}{760 \text{ mm Hg}}$$

$$= 5.50 \text{ L} \quad \text{(correctly rounded)}$$

Increases

$V_1 = 5.65$ L
$P_1 = 740$ mm Hg
$V_2 = ?$
$P_2 = 760$ mm Hg

Must decrease

Thus increasing the pressure on 5.65 L of nitrogen at 25 °C from 740 mm Hg to 760 mm Hg decreases the volume to 5.50 L.

Notice that the pressure units cancel. Therefore they could be in any units as long as they are the same.

PRACTICE EXERCISE 2   If 2.5 L of a gas is at a pressure of 760 mm Hg and the pressure changes to 730 mm Hg, what is the new volume, assuming that the temperature stays the same and no gas is lost?

6.3   LAW OF PARTIAL PRESSURES

The total pressure of a mixture of gases is the sum of the partial pressures of the individual gases.

The gases in a mixture of gases affect the total pressure more or less independently. John Dalton discovered this, and we state it in the form of the **law of partial pressures** or **Dalton's law.**

Law of Partial Pressures (Dalton's Law)   The total pressure of a mixture of gases is the sum of their individual partial pressures.

$$P_{total} = P_a + P_b + P_c + \cdots \tag{6.8}$$

The **partial pressure** of a gas in a mixture of gases is the pressure that this gas would have if it were all alone in the same container. It's the pressure that this gas would be left to exert if all the other gases disappeared. The subscripts in Equation 6.8, a, b, and c, are identifiers for the individual gases, but in a real situation the formulas of the gases are generally used. For example, the partial pressure of O_2 might be symbolized as P_{O_2} or as PO_2. You'll see both kinds of symbols used.

EXAMPLE 6.3   **USING THE LAW OF PARTIAL PRESSURES**

Problem: At sea level and 0 °C, the partial pressure of the nitrogen in clean, dry air is 601 mm Hg. That is, $P_{N_2} = 601$ mm Hg when the total pressure is 760 mm Hg. If oxygen is the only other constituent, which is virtually true, what is the partial pressure of the oxygen?

Solution: Applying Equation 6.8, we can write

$$P_{Total} = P_{N_2} + P_{O_2}$$

Therefore

$$760 \text{ mm Hg} = 601 \text{ mm Hg} + P_{O_2}$$

Or

$$P_{O_2} = 760 \text{ mm Hg} - 601 \text{ mm Hg}$$
$$= 159 \text{ mm Hg}$$

The partial pressure of oxygen is 159 mm Hg (159 torr).

PRACTICE EXERCISE 3   At the top of Mount Everest (29,000 ft, 8.8 km) the total atmospheric pressure is only 250 mm Hg. Under this total pressure of the air, the partial pressure of the nitrogen is 198 mm Hg. What is the partial pressure of oxygen (assuming no other gas is present)?

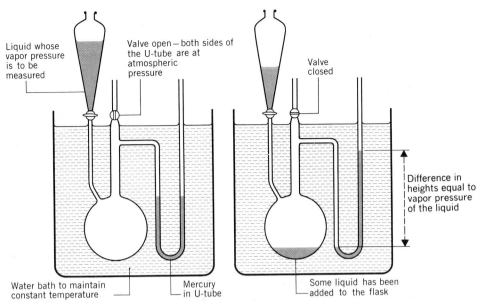

Figure 6.3
Measuring the vapor pressure of a liquid. The liquid whose vapor pressure is to be measured is added to the glass bulb that is connected to an open-end manometer. On the left, just before the liquid is added, the manometer shows that both mercury levels are the same, so the pressure in the bulb equals the atmospheric pressure outside the bulb. At the instant the liquid is added, the second valve is shut, which seals the bulb from the atmosphere. Now the pressure exerted by the developing vapor builds up, which forces one mercury level down and causes the other to rise. The difference in the heights of the two mercury levels equals the vapor pressure of the liquid.

The value of the partial pressure of oxygen you calculated in Practice Exercise 3 is, incidentally, too low to force oxygen from the lungs into the bloodstream at a rate fast enough to sustain normal activity for nearly all humans. Virtually all climbers who intend to do much activity above 15,000 ft need to breathe oxygen-enriched air conducted through a face mask and supplied from a pressurized tank.

Vapors above Liquids Are Gases That Exert Vapor Pressures We learned in Chapter 2 that liquids can change to their vapor states by evaporation. The air space in contact with any liquid therefore includes not only air but the vapor generated by this evaporation. The partial pressure exerted by this vapor is called the **vapor pressure** of the liquid.

■ It's helpful to think of a liquid's vapor pressure as its *escaping tendency.*

To measure the vapor pressure, we have to make sure that the vapor doesn't escape. Figure 6.3 shows how this can be managed, and it shows a simple device, called a **manometer,** that measures pressures other than atmospheric pressure. The U-shaped tube in Figure 6.3 is an example of an *open-end* manometer (meaning that one end is open to the atmosphere). Its two arms contain mercury. When a liquid is admitted to the glass bulb, its vapor pressure forces the mercury level to change as shown. The difference in the heights of the two mercury levels is the vapor pressure of the liquid.

As long as some liquid is present in the bulb, the vapor pressure depends only on the identity of the liquid *and the temperature.* Different liquids have different vapor pressures at a given temperature, and the vapor pressures of all liquids increase with increasing temperature. Table 6.1, for example, shows how the vapor pressure of water changes with temperature.

■ *Humid* means having a high concentration of water vapor.

Water Vapor Is a Component of the Respiratory Gases Air in contact with water always contains water vapor. The air we inhale is usually somewhat humid, and as soon as it

TABLE 6.1 Vapor Pressure of Water

Temperature (°C)	Vapor Pressure (mm Hg)	Temperature (°C)	Vapor Pressure (mm Hg)
18	15.5	32	35.7
20	17.5	34	39.9
22	19.8	36	44.6
24	22.4	37	47.1
26	25.2	38	49.7
28	28.3	40	55.3
30	31.8		

■ The air we breathe is a mixture of gases: 78% nitrogen, 21% oxygen, and traces of water vapor and other gases

makes contact with the warm (37 °C), moist surfaces of lung tissue it picks up even more water vapor. The air we exhale, therefore, is richer in water vapor than the air we inhale; stated technically, the partial pressure of water vapor in exhaled air is greater than that in inhaled air. The data in Table 6.2 give actual values. Inhaled air, as you can see, is mostly nitrogen and oxygen, and the partial pressure of water in inhaled air has been arbitrarily selected to correspond to a relative humidity of 20%.

The partial pressure of carbon dioxide in inhaled air is very low, meaning little carbon dioxide is in this air. The metabolism of the body, however, generates carbon dioxide, which is given up by the blood stream in the lungs. It then becomes part of the exhaled air. Water vapor will also be exhaled. Thus the exhaled air has relatively large values of P_{H_2O} and P_{CO_2}. Notice, however, that regardless of how the individual partial pressures change during breathing, the total pressure remains a constant. The air we breathe obeys the law of partial pressures.

The partial pressure of this water vapor in exhaled air (Table 6.2), 47 mm Hg, is the same as the vapor pressure of water at 37 °C or body temperature (Table 6.1). This means that exhaled air is saturated in water vapor. It holds as much as it can at 37 °C. When the body exports warm water vapor in this way, it also exports heat, as we discussed in Section 2.5.

Gases Collected over Water Contain Water Vapor Another situation in which we need to know about the vapor pressure of water and the law of partial pressures is when we collect a gas over water for some experiment. Figure 6.4 shows how this can be done in the lab.

The measured volume of the gas in the collecting bottle of Figure 6.4 contains water vapor, but to know how much gas we have prepared, we want to know the volume of the gas if

TABLE 6.2 The Composition of Air During Breathing

Gas	Partial Pressure (in mm Hg)		
	Inhaled Air	Exhaled Air	Alveolar Air[a]
Nitrogen	594.70	569	570
Oxygen	160.00	116	103
Carbon dioxide	0.30	28	40
Water vapor	5.00[b]	47	47
Totals	760.00	760	760

[a] Alveolar air is air within the alveoli, thin-walled air sacs enmeshed in beds of fine blood capillaries. Little more than bubbles of tissue, these sacs are the terminals of the successively branching tubes that make up the lungs. We have about 300 million alveoli in our lungs.

[b] A partial pressure of water vapor of 5.00 mm Hg corresponds to air with a relative humidity of about 20%, a familiar weather report term that we will not define further here.

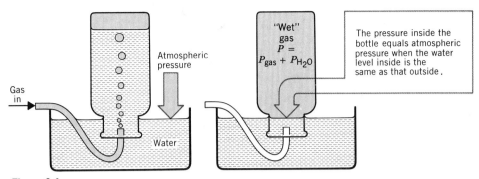

Figure 6.4
The collection of a gas over water produces a gas that contains water vapor so, by Dalton's law, $P_{total} = P_{gas} + P_{H_2O}$. A collecting bottle is first filled with water and then inverted over a basin of water. This water is displaced as the gas bubbles into the bottle. During this time, water vapor effectively saturates the gas and contributes its own partial pressure. (Adapted from J. E. Brady and J. R. Holum, *Fundamentals of Chemistry*, 3rd. ed., John Wiley & Sons, New York, 1988. Used by permission.)

it were dry. For this, we do a calculation. Remember that the measured pressure is the sum of the partial pressures of the gas and the water vapor. The first step, therefore, is to correct the measured pressure by subtracting out the partial pressure of the water. Then we use this corrected value of pressure plus the volume occupied by the wet gas in the bottle in a Boyle's law calculation to find the volume of the gas if it had been collected dry. We'll do an example to show how.

| EXAMPLE 6.4 | CALCULATING A DRY VOLUME FROM A WET VOLUME OF A GAS |

Problem: On a day when the atmospheric pressure was 744 mm Hg, a student collected a sample of oxygen over water at 20 °C by the apparatus shown in Figure 6.4. By making the water level inside the bottle the same as its level outside, the student knew the inside pressure to be 744 mm Hg, too. The volume of the gas was 325 mL. Calculate the partial pressure of the oxygen in the bottle, and then calculate what volume the oxygen would have if all the water vapor were removed and the gas pressure were to become 760 mm Hg.

Solution: To find the value of P_{O_2}, we use the law of partial pressures. From Table 6.1, we find that the vapor pressure of water at 20 °C is 17.5 mm Hg. This is the value of P_{H_2O}.

$$P_{Total} = P_{O_2} + P_{H_2O}$$
$$744 \text{ mm Hg} = P_{O_2} + 17.5 \text{ mm Hg}$$
$$P_{O_2} = 727 \text{ mm Hg} \quad \text{(correctly rounded)}$$

In other words, we have, in effect, *dry* oxygen in a volume of 325 mL at a pressure of 727 mm Hg and a temperature of 20 °C.

The remainder of the problem is to calculate what the volume of this dry oxygen would be at the specified pressure, 760 mm Hg (and 20 °C). This is a straightforward Boyle's law calculation in which we need a volume-*decreasing* ratio of pressures because we are increasing the pressure from 727 mm Hg to 760 mm Hg:

■ We could also calculate V_2 by using Equation 6.5.

$$V_2 = 325 \text{ mL} \times \frac{727 \text{ mm Hg}}{760 \text{ mm Hg}}$$

$$= 311 \text{ mL} \quad \text{(correctly rounded)}$$

Thus the collected oxygen, when dry at 20 °C and 760 mm Hg, would have a volume of 311 mL.

Figure 6.5
Obtaining temperature–volume data for a gas at constant pressure. The temperature of the gas can be changed by varying the temperature of the water bath.

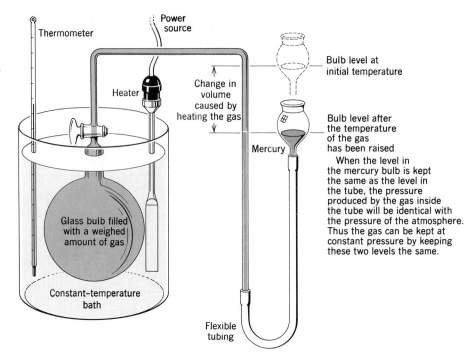

PRACTICE EXERCISE 4   A student prepared a sample of nitrogen, N_2, by collecting it at 740 mm Hg in a 325 mL glass collecting bottle over water at 22 °C. Calculate the partial pressure of the nitrogen, and then find what the dry volume of this nitrogen would be at 22 °C and 760 mm Hg.

6.4   THE TEMPERATURE–VOLUME RELATIONSHIP AT CONSTANT PRESSURE

If the mass and pressure of a gas are kept constant, the volume is directly proportional to the Kelvin temperature.

Because of the excitement over hot-air balloons in his time, the French physicist Jacques Alexander Cesar Charles (1746–1823) became interested in the effect of temperature on the volume of a gas. In order to study only the effect of temperature, he devised a way to keep a fixed mass of gas at a constant pressure. Today, we could carry out such experiments in an apparatus such as illustrated in Figure 6.5.

In Figure 6.6 we see several plots of volumes versus temperatures from different experiments involving different samples of a gas. When the dots are connected, they form several straight lines. Each line shows how a certain quantity of gas changes in volume as the temperature changes. The different lines correspond to different masses of the gas. This particular gas happens to change to its liquid form at −100 °C, so no actual points can be plotted below this temperature. However, down to −100 °C the points are in straight lines, so we can extend the lines to see with considerable confidence how the gas volume would change if it could not liquify when further cooled. All the lines converge to one point, and this point corresponds to each volume being reduced to a hypothetical value of zero.

We say "hypothetical" because it's physically impossible for any matter to have a zero volume, to say nothing of having a *negative* volume! When many gases were studied and when the measurements were further refined, the results were the same. The temperature at which these plots all converged, regardless of the gas, was −273.15 °C. Evidently, this is the coldest temperature possible in nature. The impossibility of having a negative volume for a gas, even one that never liquifies, assures us that −273.15 °C is the lowest temperature we can hope to reach.

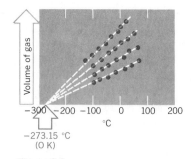

Figure 6.6
Plots of temperature–volume data obtained at constant pressure. For different masses of the same gas, the volume is directly proportional to temperature.

The realization that -273.15 °C is something of an absolute low prompted scientists to invent the Kelvin scale of temperature, a scale that we have already introduced (Section 1.4). It defines the lowest degree of coldness as zero, but otherwise keeps the same intervals of degrees as the Celsius scale. Recall that kelvins, K, are related to degrees Celsius by the equation:

$$K = {}^\circ C + 273$$

When a gas temperature is in kelvins, the direct proportionality between volume and temperature (at constant pressure) can be expressed very simply by the **temperature–volume law** or **Charles' law.**

> **Temperature–Volume Law (Charles' Law)** The volume of a fixed mass of any gas is directly proportional to its Kelvin temperature, if the gas pressure is kept constant.
>
> $$V \propto T \qquad \text{(constant } P \text{ and mass)} \qquad (6.9)$$

Expression 6.9 can be changed into an equation in the usual way by introducing a proportionality constant. We'll call this constant C' (the prime, $'$, to distinguish it from a different constant, C, used with Boyle's law).

$$V = T \times C' \qquad (6.10)$$

Or

$$\frac{V}{T} = C'$$

■ $\dfrac{V_1}{T_1} = C'$ and

$\dfrac{V_2}{T_2} = C'$. Hence

$\dfrac{V_1}{T_1} = \dfrac{V_2}{T_2}$, which is

equation 6.11.

Using subscripts as we did in connection with Boyle's law, we can restate this relationship as follows:

$$\frac{V_1}{T_1} = \frac{V_2}{T_2} \qquad \text{(constant } P \text{ and mass)} \qquad (6.11)$$

Notice that we can transform this equation to calculate a new volume, V_2, by multiplying the old volume, V_1, by a ratio of kelvins:

$$V_2 = V_1 \times \left(\frac{T_2}{T_1} \right)$$

A ratio of kelvins

■ Remember, the temperatures must be in kelvins.

Similarly, a new temperature can be found by multiplying the given temperature by a ratio of volumes.

$$T_2 = T_1 \times \left(\frac{V_2}{V_1} \right)$$

A ratio of volumes

■ The volumes can be in any units as long as they are the same units for both V_1 and V_2.

EXAMPLE 6.5 **DOING TEMPERATURE–VOLUME LAW CALCULATIONS**

Problem: Some of the total anesthetics used in surgery are gases at 37 °C, body temperature. If 1.50 L of a gas is used at 20 °C, to what volume does the gas change when the temperature becomes 37 °C at the same pressure?

Solution: The conditions given are those that let us use the temperature–volume law, but we *must* change degrees Celsius into kelvins in order to use it.

For 20 °C, $T = 20 + 273 = 293$ K (T_1)
For 37 °C, $T = 37 + 273 = 310$ K (T_2)

We also know V_1 to be 1.50 L, so we could plug these given values into Equation 6.11 to find V_2. Or we could note that the temperature is increasing so we need a ratio of temperatures that exceeds 1 to multiply by the given volume in order to ensure that the result is a larger volume than before. This ratio is (310 K)/(293 K). Therefore

$$V_2 = 1.50 \text{ L} \times \frac{310 \text{ K}}{293 \text{ K}}$$

$$= 1.59 \text{ L} \quad \text{(correctly rounded)}$$

Thus the warming of the anesthetic as it enters the patient's lungs causes a rather small increase in volume. Still, anesthesiologists and inhalation therapists must know about it.

PRACTICE EXERCISE 5   A sample of cyclopropane, an anesthetic, with a volume of 575 mL at a temperature of 30 °C, was cooled to 15 °C at the same pressure. What was the new volume?

6.5 THE UNIVERSAL GAS LAW

If we know any three of the four physical quantities of a gas—*P*, *V*, *T*, and *n*—we can use the universal gas law to calculate what the fourth *must* be.

We have kept the size of the gas sample in moles constant so far in our survey of the gas laws. We'll now see what happens if we change it. It has been found that at constant pressure and temperature, the volume of any gas is directly proportional to the number of moles:

$$V \propto n \qquad \text{(at constant } P \text{ and } T) \qquad (6.12)$$

This can be converted into an equation by inserting a proportionality constant, which we'll designate as $C^\bullet$.

$$V = C^\bullet n \qquad \text{(at constant } P \text{ and } T) \qquad (6.13)$$

The Volume–Moles Relationship Is the Same for All Gases   Amadeo Avogadro discovered that the proportionality constant, $C^\bullet$, in Equation 6.13 is the same for all gases under the pressure and temperature restrictions given. For example, 0.500 mol of oxygen and 0.500 mol of nitrogen, both at 25.0 °C and 760 mm Hg, have identical volumes, 12.2 L. Equations 6.12 and 6.13 also mean that identical volumes of gases (at the same T and P) contain identical moles. For example, 45.0 L of oxygen and 45.0 L of nitrogen, both at 25.0 °C and 760 mm Hg, have 1.84 mol. We thus have another gas law, the volume–mole relationship or **Avogadro's law.**

> **Volume–Mole Relationship (Avogadro's Law)**   Equal volumes of gases have equal numbers of moles when compared at the same pressure and temperature.

Instead of learning how to solve problems involving just this law, we now have a basis for learning about a much more general law—actually, it's an equation—that combines the three gas laws we have studied, those of Boyle, Charles, and Avogadro.

The Ratio of *PV* to *nT* Is a Constant, *R*, for All Gases For any gas, it has been found that the result of multiplying P and V and dividing by T is proportional to the number of moles of the gas, n:

$$\frac{PV}{T} \propto n$$

The proportionality constant for this relationship is symbolized by R. Therefore

$$\frac{PV}{T} = nR$$

The usual form in which this is written is

$$PV = nRT \qquad (6.14)$$

■ By rearranging Equation 6.14, we can see that for any gas the ratio of PV to nT is a constant.
$$\frac{PV}{nT} = R$$

This equation is called the **universal gas law** and the constant, **R**, is called the **universal gas constant.**

R Is Calculated from the Molar Volume of a Gas at Standard *T* and *P* To provide a common reference, scientists throughout the world have selected 760 mm Hg and 273 K (0 °C) as the **standard conditions of temperature and pressure,** or **STP** for short. Using these figures for P and T, all we need to calculate R is the actual volume that 1 mol of any gas occupies at STP, the **standard molar volume.** This volume is 22.4×10^3 mL (22.4 L). See Table 6.3. If we use $V = 22.4 \times 10^3$ mL, $T = 273$ K, $P = 760$ mm Hg, and $n = 1.00$ mol, in Equation 6.14, then we can solve for R:

$$R = \frac{PV}{nT}$$

$$= \frac{(760 \text{ mm Hg})(22.4 \times 10^3 \text{ mL})}{(1.00 \text{ mol})(273 \text{ K})}$$

$$= 6.24 \times 10^4 \; \frac{\text{mm Hg mL}}{\text{mol K}} \qquad \text{(universal gas constant)}$$

This particular value of R must always be associated with the particular units of P, V, T, and n used to calculate it. Whenever the universal gas law (Equation 6.14) is used together with this value of R, the pressure must be in mm Hg, the volume must be in mL, and the temperature (as in *all* gas law calculations) must be in K.

TABLE 6.3   Molar Volumes of Some Gases at STP

Gas	Formula	Molar Volume (liters)	Mass (g)
Helium	He	22.398	4
Argon	Ar	22.401	20
Hydrogen	H_2	22.410	2
Nitrogen	N_2	22.413	28
Oxygen	O_2	22.414	32
Carbon dioxide	CO_2	22.414	44

EXAMPLE 6.6   **USING THE UNIVERSAL GAS LAW**

Problem: A sample of oxygen with a volume of 250 mL at a pressure of 7.45×10^4 mm Hg and a temperature of 20 °C is allowed to expand as its pressure falls to 750 mm Hg and the temperature changes to 37 °C (essentially atmospheric pressure and body temperature). How many moles of oxygen are in this sample and what volume will the gas sample have after the expansion?

Solution: The units given here for P and V match the units for these quantities required by the value of the gas constant, R, that we want to use. The temperature value, however, must be translated into kelvins:

$$T = °C + 273$$
$$= 20 + 273 = 293 \text{ K}$$

Now we can calculate the number of moles, using $PV = nRT$

$$(7.45 \times 10^4 \text{ mm Hg})(250 \text{ mL}) = n \times \left(6.24 \times 10^4 \frac{\text{mm Hg mL}}{\text{mol K}} \right) (293 \text{ K})$$

$$n = \frac{7.45 \times 10^4 \times 250 \times \text{mol}}{6.24 \times 10^4 \times 293}$$

$$= 1.02 \text{ mol}$$

Of course, this value of n is the same as under the new conditions:

$$V = ? \qquad P = 750 \text{ mm Hg} \qquad T = 310 \text{ K} \quad n = 1.02 \text{ mol}$$

Therefore

$$(750 \text{ mm Hg})(V) = (1.02 \text{ mol}) \left(6.24 \times 10^4 \frac{\text{mm Hg mL}}{\text{mol K}} \right) (310 \text{ K})$$

$$V = \frac{1.02 \times 6.24 \times 10^4 \times 310 \text{ mL}}{750}$$

$$V = 2.63 \times 10^4 \text{ mL}$$

Thus a huge expansion in volume accompanies the other changes; the new volume is 26,300 mL.

PRACTICE EXERCISE 6   In Example 6.4 we found that the student had collected 311 mL of dry oxygen at 760 mm Hg and 20 °C. How many moles of oxygen were in this sample?

PRACTICE EXERCISE 7   If we use the subscripts 1 and 2 in the usual way to express initial and final conditions, show that the universal gas law can be rewritten as follows whenever we deal with a fixed quantity of gas (that is, when n, the number of moles, is a constant):

$$\frac{P_1 V_1}{T_1} = \frac{P_2 V_2}{T_2} \qquad \text{(at constant } n\text{)}$$

PRACTICE EXERCISE 8   Use the equation derived in Practice Exercise 7 to calculate the final volume of the gas sample that was described in Example 6.6.

PRACTICE EXERCISE 9   Calculate the numerical value of R when we use $P = 1$ atm and $V = 22.4$ L, which are alternative units under standard conditions. (T must always be 273 K.)

6.6 THE KINETIC THEORY OF GASES

All the gas laws can be explained in terms of the model of an ideal gas described by the kinetic theory.

As the gas laws unfolded over the decades, more and more scientists asked the question: "What must gases really be like if these laws are true?" What is particularly remarkable about the gas laws is that they hold for any and all gases, particularly when a gas isn't under high pressure or isn't very cold. (A gas is close to condensing to a liquid under these conditions.) For liquids and solids, there aren't *general* laws like the gas laws.

An *Ideal* Gas Would Obey All the Gas Laws Exactly When the accuracy and precision of measurements are sufficiently high, no gas obeys any of the gas laws *exactly* over all ranges of pressure and temperature. Many come quite close, however, so it was natural for scientists to theorize about a hypothetical gas that would fit the gas law equations exactly under all circumstances. Such a gas is called an **ideal gas,** and scientists used the behavior of real gases to define the following features of the ideal gas.

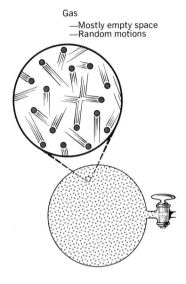

Gas
—Mostly empty space
—Random motions

Model of an Ideal Gas

1. The ideal gas consists of a large number of extremely tiny particles in a state of chaotic, utterly random motion.
2. The particles are perfectly hard, and when they collide they lose no energy because of friction.
3. The particles neither attract nor repel each other.
4. The particles move in accordance with the known laws of motion.

This model says that the fundamental truth about gases is they consist of tiny particles *in random motion,* so it was called the **kinetic theory of gases.**

Theorists used these postulates and the mathematical equations for the laws of motion to see if they could derive the gas laws theoretically. They were splendidly successful. In fact, some historians of science have called the kinetic theory one of the greatest triumphs of the human mind in all of history! We won't develop the equations of the kinetic theory, but we will survey some very useful descriptions of how the kinetic model explains the gas laws.

■ The laws of motion are part of the science of physics, the science of motion and energy.

The Kinetic Theory Explains Gas Pressure and Boyle's Law Theorists could show that the pressure exerted by a gas arises from the innumerable collisions per second that the particles make with each unit of area of the walls of the container. If we imagine, then, that the volume of the container is made less, the wall area battered by the gas particles is also less. More hits per unit wall area therefore occur after the volume has been reduced. Moreover, the reduction in volume does not affect the average speed at which the particles travel, and the particles don't have to travel as far to hit a wall. Thus reducing the volume of the gas increases the frequency with which its particles hit the walls without reducing the strengths of each tiny collision, so the gas pressure must increase. See Figure 6.7.

When the theoretical calculations on which the preceding description is based were carried out, the result was identical with Boyle's pressure–volume law for real gases. This kind of agreement and others like it give us confidence that the model of an ideal gas closely describes real gases, too.

Gas Temperature Is Related to the Average Kinetic Energy of the Gas Particles Theorists were able to use the model of an ideal gas to show that gas temperature is directly proportional to the average kinetic energy of the gas particles. In other words, when we heat a gas and raise its temperature, we cause its particles to move around with greater

Figure 6.7
The kinetic theory and the pressure–volume relationship (Boyle's law). The pressure of the gas is proportional to the frequency of collisions per unit area. When the gas volume is made smaller in part *b*, the frequency of the collisions per unit area of the container's walls increases. This is how the pressure increase occurs.

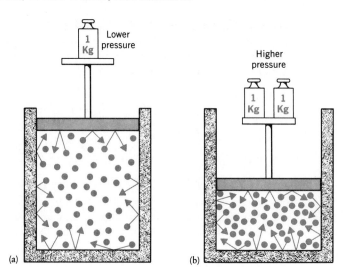

average energy. When we cool a gas, we cause its particles to move with lower average energy.

We know that kinetic energy equals $(1/2)mv^2$, and we know that the mass *(m)* of each particle is unchanging, so the only way that the average kinetic energy can increase is for the average velocity of the particles to increase. Heating a gas, therefore, increases the average kinetic energy of the particles by increasing their average velocity.

In the light of these ideas, it makes sense that if we cool a gas enough, the average kinetic energy of its particles should drop to zero. It could not become less than zero — there's no such thing as *negative* kinetic energy — so the kinetic theory agrees that there ought to be a lower limit to which something can be cooled. As we know, this limit is $-273.15\ °C$, absolute zero.

The Kinetic Theory Explains Charles' Law   If we make the gas particles move with more speed and energy (heat the gas), they will hit the container's walls more frequently and with greater energy. If we want to prevent the pressure from rising — and constant pressure is a condition of Charles' law — we have to let the volume expand. The theoretical calculations along these lines resulted in showing that gas volume at constant pressure is, in theory, proportional to the kelvin temperature, just as Charles and others had earlier shown by experiment.

The Kinetic Theory Also Explains a Pressure–Temperature Law   If we don't let the volume expand when we heat a confined gas, then the pressure of the gas must rise. This relationship between pressure and temperature at constant volume is actually another gas law that we haven't mentioned yet, the **pressure–temperature law** discovered by Joseph Gay-Lussac.

■ This is the law behind the warning not to incinerate aerosol cans.

> **Pressure–Temperature Law (Gay-Lussac's Law)**   The pressure exerted by a fixed quantity of gas is directly proportional to its Kelvin temperature when the gas volume is kept constant.

■ Just after shutting the oven door and telling the guests that the ham was "puffing up" nicely, the unopened can exploded.

Because this law adds nothing to the universal gas law, we will not go into separate calculations involving it. However, as one inexperienced cook discovered, this law goes into dramatic action if you ever leave an unopened can of ham in a hot oven. The increasing steam pressure eventually becomes large enough to rupture the can.

The Kinetic Theory Explains Gas Diffusion   Another property of gases that the kinetic theory explains is the ability of a gas to diffuse or spread out throughout its entire container. Particles in random motion eventually find their way into all the space available. Almost everyone has experienced the diffusion of perfume, cologne, or after-shave fragrances throughout a room.

For us, perhaps the most useful single part of the kinetic theory of gases is the image of particles in rapid, utterly chaotic, random motion. It give us something very fundamental for explaining some features of the liquid and solid states. It also gives us a mechanism for understanding many aspects of how chemical reactions occur, and how the rates of these reactions are affected by many conditions. These are topics that we will take up in the remaining sections of this chapter.

6.7   THE LIQUID STATE AND DYNAMIC EQUILIBRIA

The kinetic picture of molecules in rapid, random motion helps to explain some of the physical properties of liquids.

Molecules of a liquid, like those of a gas, are in a state of constant, chaotic motion, but they are always in touch with one set of neighbors or another. In a liquid we are closer than in a gas to a balance between the forces that attract molecules toward each other and the forces, which arise from collisions, that keep the molecules moving around.

The molecules in a liquid are quite tightly packed, but like marbles or beads in a small box, they can shift around. The packing is so tight that the volume of a liquid is barely changed even under pressures hundreds of times that of the atmosphere. Thus there is no general pressure – volume law for liquids.

There is no general temperature – volume law for liquids either, although liquids do expand slightly when they are heated. The lack of large empty spaces between the molecules of a liquid, a condition sharply in contrast to a gas, explains why there are no laws similar to the gas laws that apply to all liquids.

The Kinetic Theory Helps To Explain Vapor Pressure   We will use the development of a liquid's vapor pressure to introduce one of the major concepts in all of chemistry, a *dynamic equilibrium.*

The vapor pressures of several liquids are plotted against temperature in Figure 6.8. Notice that ether develops high vapor pressures even at low temperatures; liquids like this are called **volatile liquids.** They readily evaporate from open containers at room temperature. In contrast, propylene glycol (in Figure 6.8) has a very low vapor pressure until its temperature is well above the boiling point of water. It is called a **nonvolatile liquid,** because it evaporates very slowly at room temperature.

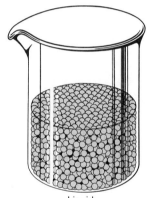

Liquid
Densely packed
Random motions

■   You can leave a nonvolatile liquid such as salad oil uncovered indefinitely with no noticeable loss of the liquid.

Figure 6.8
Equilibrium vapor pressure versus temperature. (Ether was once widely used as an anesthetic. Acetic acid is the sour component in vinegar. Propylene glycol is in several brands of antifreeze mixtures.)

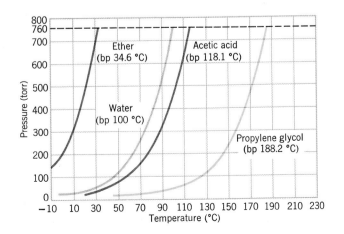

Suppose that we place some ether in the glass bulb of the device in Figure 6.3, page 141 Initially the pressure inside the bulb is the same as outside, atmospheric pressure. For a very brief moment we can imagine that no ether molecules are in the air space above the sample. This situation quickly changes, however, because ether is volatile. Its molecules escape (evaporate) and move around in the space above. As more and more evaporate, they force the mercury level to change. This is the only way that the system can make room for the ether vapor. In other words, the ether is exerting its vapor pressure, and what we have just seen is the kinetic theory's explanation of how it arises.

Eventually, more and more escaped ether molecules get turned around by collisions and return to the liquid ether. Now we have ether molecules coming and going — some leaving the liquid for the vapor and others returning. The two processes are said to *oppose* each other because one reverses the effect of the other. Eventually, the two opposing processes cancel each other, and there is no further change in the vapor pressure. It has reached a steady value.

When a dynamic process — this coming and going — reaches a steady state of no further net change, **dynamic equilibrium** has been established. We say *dynamic* because there is considerable coming and going; and we say *equilibrium* because there is no *net* change. Some very important systems in nature are in dynamic equilibrium or very close to it.

Nature's Synthesis and Use of the Air's Oxygen Illustrates Dynamic Equilibrium

Oxygen gas is consumed as a chemical by several processes in nature: the breathing of all animals (respiration), the burning of things (combustion), the decay of dead plants and animals, and reactions such as rusting. However, essentially as fast as oxygen is consumed, it is replaced by a process in plants called **photosynthesis.** This is the use of solar energy, carbon dioxide, and water by plants to make complex compounds and oxygen. Animals cannot do this. The green pigment in plant leaves, chlorophyll, is essential to the multistep process.

Besides oxygen, carbohydrates are primary products of photosynthesis. We can represent them by something like an empirical formula, $(CH_2O)_n$, where n varies from 3 in the simplest carbohydrates, to 6 in glucose to 12 in table sugar, to several thousands in starch and cellulose. This formula enables us to write an overall equation for photosynthesis as follows (but realize that many steps are involved):

$$nCO_2 + nH_2O \xrightarrow[\text{chlorophyll}]{\text{photosynthesis}} (CH_2O)_n + nO_2$$

The concentration of oxygen in air hasn't changed since measurements were first made decades ago. Evidently, the opposing processes, oxygen use and oxygen regeneration in nature, are in an almost exact equilibrium. If we carelessly destroy enough of the earth's rain forests, however, or poison the phytoplankton in the oceans by wastes, we could seriously endanger this vital balance.

■ Phytoplankton are microscopic marine plants. They account for over half of the photosynthetic work done in nature.

The Earth's Heat Balance Is in Nearly Dynamic Equilibrium

The earth receives energy from the sun; this is a temperature-raising process. The earth also radiates energy to outer space much as a warm pressing iron radiates energy; this is a temperature-lowering process. Globally, there is essentially an almost perfect match between these opposing processes, the coming and going of thermal energy. The earth, therefore, is in a state of thermal equilibrium or very close to it.

You can imagine what it would be like if it weren't. If, for example, the earth radiated *less* energy than it received for a long enough time, the planet would eventually become too hot for life. On the other hand, if the earth radiated *more* energy than it received, it would eventually become too cold for life. Just a few degrees change in the average overall global temperature would be a disaster. Special Topic 6.1 (page 154) describes one effect of just a slight overall warming of the earth's atmosphere.

Dynamic Equilibria Are Described by a Special Vocabulary   To represent a dynamic equilibrium, we use an equation with double arrows, which we can illustrate as follows, using our vapor pressure example:

$$\text{Liquid} + \text{heat} \rightleftharpoons \text{vapor} \tag{6.15}$$

Thus two oppositely pointing arrows signify that we have an equilibrium between the materials to the left and those to the right of arrows.

An equation like 6.15 is called an *equilibrium expression* or an *equilibrium equation*. The change from left to right is called the *forward reaction,* and the opposing change from right to left is called the *reverse reaction*.

Sometimes we include energy as a "reactant" or a "product" in an equilibrium expression, as we did in Equation 6.15. Here it is the heat of vaporization, which we discussed on page 37. It appears on the left side of the arrows because the forward change consumes heat, so heat is like a reactant.

Dynamic Equilibria Can Be Shifted   Once an equilibrium is established, no net change occurs *spontaneously*. But this doesn't mean that we can no longer force a change. The liquid–vapor equilibrium of Equation 6.15, for example, is affected by heating or cooling the system. If we add heat, we know that the vapor pressure will increase, which tells us that some of the liquid will go into the vapor state. During the time that this happens, the rate at which the forward change occurs will be faster than the rate of the reverse change. For a time, the system will not be in equilibrium. We say that the addition of heat *upsets the equilibrium*.

Once we stop adding heat and maintain the temperature of the system at a constant but higher value, the rate at which vapor molecules return to the liquid will catch up, and the opposing rates will become the same again. Both will be faster than they were at the lower temperature, but when both are the same there is no further net change. Once again, we have dynamic equilibrium.

At the higher temperature, of course, the vapor pressure is higher because we have more moles of the gas (the vapor) in the same space. As Figure 6.8 showed, the vapor pressure of any liquid increases with temperature. The vapor pressures plotted in this figure are called the *equilibrium* vapor pressures, which means that each value is the vapor pressure when the liquid and its vapor are in equilibrium at the particular temperature.

Whenever a system at equilibrium changes in response to a disturbance, like the addition or removal of heat, we say that the equilibrium *shifts*. This means that one of the two opposing changes becomes faster than the other. Whichever becomes faster is said to be *favored*. If the forward reaction becomes faster, we say that the equilibrium shifts to the right. And it shifts to the left if the reverse reaction becomes favored for any reason, like cooling a liquid–vapor equilibrium. A disturbance to an equilibrium is called a *stress*.

Shifts in Equilibria Can Be Predicted by Le Chatelier's Principle   The effect that more heat shifts a liquid's vapor pressure equilibrium to the right illustrates an important principle that applies to all equilibria. It's called **Le Chatelier's principle,** after Henri Louis Le Chatelier (1850–1936), a French chemist.

> **Le Chatelier's Principle**   If a system in equilibrium is subjected to a disturbance that upsets the equilibrium, the equilibrium shifts in whichever direction restores equilibrium.

Equilibrium will be restored if the applied stress hasn't been overwhelming. This happens because the rate of the initially unfavored (slower) reaction will eventually catch up to the opposing (faster) reaction. Both then become equal again, and once more we have equilibrium.

SPECIAL TOPIC 6.1

THE GREENHOUSE EFFECT AND EQUILIBRIUM IN THE EARTH'S HEAT BUDGET

About 2% of all the earth's water occurs frozen in the ice caps of the Antarctic and Greenland. If all of it melted, the level of the world's oceans would rise, some think by as much as 250 feet. No one is forecasting that *all* this ice will eventually melt, but Figure 6.9 shows the impact this would have on the coastline of the lower 48 states of the United States. Even an average increase of three or four feet would cause widespread destruction of beaches and other coastal features.

A Global Warming Trend Could Cause the Oceans to Rise   Toward the end of the 1980s scientists throughout the world who specialize in climate became concerned that the earth had entered a warming trend. The cause is an increase in the **greenhouse effect,** the insulating effect that certain gases, the *greenhouse gases,* have on the earth's atmosphere. The greenhouse gases are chiefly carbon dioxide—the most abundant—methane (CH_4), water vapor, nitrous oxide (N_2O), and members of a family of substances called the chlorofluorocarbons or CFCs (e.g., CCl_3F). (The CFCs will be discussed in Special Topic 13.2.)

In a real greenhouse, the glass panes let in solar light energy, which is absorbed by the plants and soil. They become warmer and then radiate some heat energy back again. But the panes transmit heat energy less well than solar light energy (and they prevent heat losses from chilling winds). The space in the greenhouse thus warms and the temperature inside is higher than outside even in winter.

The molecules of the greenhouse gases are able to let the sun's light energy pass to the earth and warm it. But they do not as readily permit the earth's heat energy to radiate back to space. They absorb some of the heat energy and *then reradiate part of it back to the lower atmosphere and earth*. This activity helps to keep the earth warm. The concentrations of the greenhouse gases in the atmosphere have been low enough, however, so that the rates of the earth's heat absorption and heat loss have been equal. Thermal equilibrium thus normally prevails, and the average temperature of the earth has kept extremely constant over centuries of time. There have been fluctuations in this temperature from year to year, of course, but they have tended to cancel.

What concerns scientists today (and governments everywhere) are slow but steady increases in the concentrations of the greenhouse gases. If they continue, the rate at which the earth loses energy will become slightly lower than the rate at which the sun sends energy. If this is now actually happening, the average temperature of the earth's atmosphere will slowly increase with consequences so far-reaching that only educated guesses can be made about their impact on human history.

The Greenhouse Gases Are Released by Both Natural and Human Activities   All the greenhouse gases except the CFCs are produced both by the activities of human beings and by other processes in nature. Methane, for example, is the chief component of natural gas, used widely for home heating (and bunsen burners). It is also a product of underwater bacterial action in swamps, lakes and oceans, and rice paddies.

Carbon dioxide is a product of the natural decay of living things, as well as of forest fires and volcanic erup-

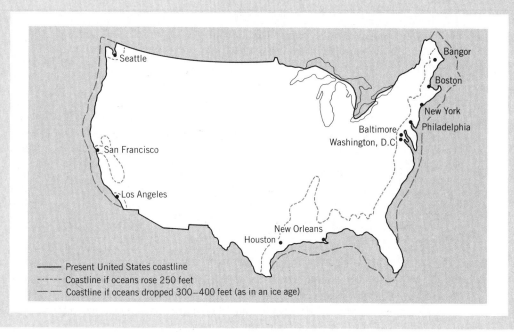

—— Present United States coastline
----- Coastline if oceans rose 250 feet
— — Coastline if oceans dropped 300–400 feet (as in an ice age)

tions. But additional carbon dioxide has been produced at a slowly increasing rate for over a hundred years by the combustion of the fossil fuels (coal, oil, and natural gas) in vehicles, power plants, and furnaces. The concentration of atmospheric carbon dioxide has increased from about 280 ppm (parts per million) to over 340 ppm. (One part per million is the same as 1 microgram of CO_2 per cubic meter of air.) Scientists think that this increase in the carbon dioxide concentration is the chief cause of the 0.5 °C increase in the average earth temperature that occurred between 1861 and 1984. Such an increase seems too small to mention, but scientists now estimate that if present trends in the emissions of greenhouse gases continue over the next century, the global temperature will increase by 3.5 to 4.5 °C. This would give our planet a climate warmer than any it has had for hundreds of thousands of years. At a temperature increase of only 0.3 °C per decade, Chicago's weather would be that of New Orleans in only twenty years! Entire patterns of agriculture would shift to higher latitudes under such a worst-case scenario. Regions now fertile could become deserts. You can see why governments all over the world are deeply concerned about finding ways to reduce the additions of even more greenhouse gases to the atmosphere.

Global Cooling Would Follow Increases in Atmospheric Dusts Just how deeply very small changes in climate in either direction can affect human affairs can be learned from what happened in 1816 in the United States. What is thought to have been the mightiest volcanic eruption in history occurred in 1815, when Tambora, a volcano on the small island of Sumbawa in Indonesia, exploded. It injected pumice and ash high into the atmosphere in a volume estimated to be a quarter to half the volume of Lake Erie, one of the Great Lakes. The particles reflected enough sunlight to cause a small cooling that affected the weather so much that 1816 was called "the year without a summer" in the eastern United States. Crops were killed by frosts in every summer month. Food for both people and farm animals became scarce. Some historians believe that this triggered in 1817 the first large-scale migration of people from the north-eastern United States to the Middle West.

Much earlier in the history of the earth, ice ages have probably been caused by unusual concentrations of dusts and mists in the air thrown up by volcanoes. Thus there are both temperature-raising and temperature-lowering activities occurring in nature. The dynamics are extremely complicated, so it would be difficult to know in advance exactly what will happen. The catch is that if you wait until that future happens, it is too late to do much about its ill effects. The prudent action now is to reduce emissions of carbon dioxide worldwide. Considering the dependence we have all reached on fossil fuels, this reduction will be one of the most difficult but most serious challenges in human history.

It isn't, however, the identical equilibrium that existed before the appearance of the stress. It is a new equilibrium because the actual quantities of materials represented as reactants and products have changed. If the forward reaction has become favored by the stress, then some of the reactants have changed into products. If at one temperature, for example, 20 g of ether exist in an equilibrium in which 18 g is liquid and 2 g is vapor, at a higher temperature we might see 17 g as liquid and 3 g as vapor in equilibrium.

Heat is one of the most common stresses on an equilibrium, either the addition or the removal of heat. As we saw, the addition of heat shifted the vapor pressure equilibrium to the right. Le Chatelier's principle says that it *must* shift to the right. This is the only direction that will absorb the stress. The extra heat is absorbed as heat of vaporization and so, in a sense, is used up.

This is the great value of Le Chatelier's principle; it helps us to predict the way a system at equilibrium *must* change under a given stress. The stress of adding heat to a system at equilibrium speeds up whatever change absorbs this stress. Equilibria *always* change in whichever way absorbs an applied stress. It is as if the system "rolls with any punches."

A Liquid Boils When Its Vapor Pressure Equals the External Pressure Each liquid has a particular temperature at which its equilibrium vapor pressure exactly equals 760 mm Hg. What is now different in the liquid is that its molecules can enter the vapor state not just at the surface but everywhere in the liquid. Bubbles of the vapor can now form *beneath* the surface, and they cause quite a commotion as they rise everywhere. This, of course, is the action called **boiling.** Each bubble is essentially pure vapor with a pressure equal to the opposing pressure of the atmosphere. Since the opposing pressure is no longer able to squeeze the bubbles back to liquid, and since they are much less dense than the liquid, they are free to rise to the surface.

The temperature at which a liquid's equilibrium vapor pressure equals 760 mm Hg (1 atm) is called the liquid's **normal boiling point.** If the liquid is heated where the atmospheric

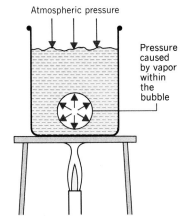

Atmospheric pressure

Pressure caused by vapor within the bubble

The liquid's vapor is the gas inside a bubble formed in a boiling liquid, and its vapor pressure can overcome the opposing pressure of the atmosphere at the boiling point.

COOKING AT HIGH ALTITUDES

As anyone who has tried to cook foods in boiling water at a higher altitude knows, it takes longer than at sea level. Where the atmospheric pressure is lower, water boils at a lower temperature. The chemical reactions caused by cooking are all endothermic. Therefore they do not occur as rapidly at a temperature of, say, 95 °C (roughly the boiling point of water in Denver, Colorado) as they do at 100 °C. No matter how high you turn up the stove setting as you prepare a soft boiled egg using boiling water, you cannot raise the temperature of boiling water above its value at your altitude. Turning up the stove boils the water away *faster,* but it does not raise its temperature.

Of course, you could use a special pan with a tight lid, such as a pressure cooker. Now the steam cannot escape and its pressure can build up until the safety valve is activated. This higher pressure means that the temperature of the boiling water in the pressure cooker is higher than in the open vessel, so the chemical reactions of cooking occur more rapidly.

These same principles are at work in steam sterilization equipment. To ensure that bacteria and viruses on surgical instruments are both quickly and completely destroyed, hospital workers place the instruments in the equivalent of a pressure cooker where the water and steam temperature can be raised well above the normal boiling point of water.

pressure is not 760 mm Hg, boiling, of course, can still occur. It happens at whatever temperature the vapor pressure equals the new pressure, but the associated temperature is not called the *normal* boiling point. For example, in Denver, Colorado, at an elevation of one mile where the atmospheric pressure is usually lower than it is at sea level, water boils at about 95 °C instead of 100 °C. The effect of this on cooking at high altitudes is described in Special Topic 6.2. On the summit of Mount Everest, water boils at only 69 °C!

6.8 THE SOLID STATE AND KINETIC THEORY

Forces of attraction between the particles in a solid are greater than in a liquid or a gas.

Not only are atoms, molecules, or ions tightly packed in a solid, they also have fixed positions and fixed neighboring particles. This does not mean that they are completely at rest; they jiggle and vibrate about their fixed positions. But in the solid the forces of attraction between particles are just too strong to permit any of the movement that occurs in liquids or gases.

A Solid–Liquid Equilibrium Exists at the Melting Point   As the temperature of a solid is increased, the vibrations of the individual particles become more and more intense. Eventually neighboring particles strike each other strongly enough to overcome the forces of attraction. Now the solid passes over into the liquid state; it *melts.* If the temperature of the system is carefully controlled, the rate at which particles leave the solid state and move around as a liquid can be made equal to the rate at which they return and take up fixed positions in the solid again. In other words, at the right temperature, the following equilibrium will exist:

$$\text{Solid} + \text{heat} \rightleftharpoons \text{liquid}$$

The *heat* in this equilibrium is the *heat of fusion* that we described on page 38.

The temperature at which an equilibrium exists between the solid and the liquid states of a substance is called its **melting point.** The forward change in this equilibrium is endothermic, so if we put a stress on the equilibrium by the addition of heat — by raising the temperature — the equilibrium will shift to the right. This shift uses up the stress, the added heat, and Le Chatelier's principle tells us that equilibria shift to absorb stresses. Of course, this shift means that the solid melts.

If we remove heat, if we cool the solid–liquid equilibrium, Le Chatelier's principle tells us that it must now shift to the left. More of the solid forms. Only a leftward shift can provide some heat (heat of fusion) to replace what is lost by cooling, and the equilibrium does what is necessary to replace heat being removed.

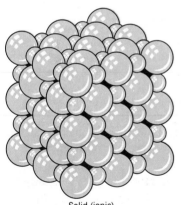

Solid (ionic)
Densely and orderly packed
Vibrations about fixed points

■ Heat of fusion is absorbed by a solid when it melts and the same heat is released when its liquid form solidifies again.

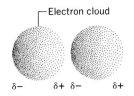

Figure 6.10
London forces. Molecules can be temporarily polarized by coming close to each other, and the force of attraction between such temporary dipoles is called a London force.

Noble Gas	Atomic Weight	Boiling Point (°C)
He	4.00	−269
Ne	20.2	−246
Ar	39.9	−186
Kr	83.8	−152
Xe	131	−107
Rn	222	−62

■ Some reactions, like those that lead to a sunburn, are launched by the photons of a certain energy in light.

London Forces of Attraction Are at Work Even Between Nonpolar Molecules

From time to time we have referred to forces of attraction between ions or molecules. Because oppositely charged ions bear full charges, they generally experience the strongest forces of attraction, and ionic compounds are all solids at room temperature. It is similarly easy to understand how polar molecules, like those of water, can have forces of attraction between them. They have $\delta+$ and $\delta-$ charges that attract each other. However, even the most completely nonpolar substances, such as the noble gases, can be changed into liquids and solids by lowering the temperature enough. This raises the question, "How can forces of attraction develop between nonpolar particles?"

Atoms and molecules have electron clouds. As one particle approaches another on collision course, these somewhat "soft" electron clouds tend to repel each other—at least temporarily—as the collision or near miss develops. See Figure 6.10. This distortion gives the approaching particles a *temporary* polarity, and the distortion is called **polarization.** We say that the particles become temporarily polarized, that they develop temporary dipoles.

In a sample with billions and billions of particles, we can easily imagine that there are innumerable, temporarily polarized molecules. They experience, therefore, a real (although weak) force of attraction called the **London force** (after a physicist, Fritz London). At sufficiently low temperatures, London forces can cause even nonpolar substances to change from a gas to the liquid state or from the liquid to the solid state.

Because London forces are related to electron clouds, the larger the overall electron cloud per molecule, the more polarized the molecule can be. Therefore substances with large molecules or atoms generally can experience larger London forces than those with small molecules or atoms. Because a large electron cloud implies a large formula weight, the rule for the boiling points of nonpolar substances is that *the higher the formula weight, the higher the boiling point.* The boiling points of the noble gases, given in the margin, illustrate this rule.

6.9 THE KINETIC THEORY AND CHEMICAL REACTIONS

The rate of a chemical reaction is dominated by its energy of activation.

In chemical reactions, electrons and nuclei become reorganized. The electron configurations of the reactants switch over to those of the products. If just a very gentle collision were all it took for such an event to occur, no substance would be stable in the presence of anything else. Yet many substances are stable and can be stored in the presence of air, moisture, glass containers, and other potential reactants.

Kinetic Energy Becomes Chemical Energy During Collisions Between Reactant Particles
The kinetic theory helps us understand why some combinations of reactants do nothing, why others react only when heated, and why still other combinations can't be stored under any circumstances. Some reactions, in other words, are extremely slow, others are moderate, and some are explosively fast. The field of chemistry that deals with the rates of chemical reactions is called **kinetics.**

For the particles of two reactants to change each other chemically, they have to collide. Only by a collision can the electrons and nuclei of the reactant particles be forced into the new arrangements of the products. Generally, very light tap-like collisions do not work.

We have to remember that nature operates under a law of conservation of energy. When two moving particles are about to collide, each has a certain kinetic energy. One could imagine a collision in which *both* particles stop. (This happens all the time in highway accidents.) If they stop, their kinetic energies go to zero, because K.E. $= \frac{1}{2} mv^2$ and the value of v is now zero. Where did the kinetic energy go? Is it lost? If so, what of the law of conservation of energy?

Actually, the energy that existed as kinetic energy is not lost; it's transformed into the potential energy of distorted electron clouds. Relatively stable electron–nuclei arrangements are twisted temporarily into less stable arrangements that cannot last. They might, of course, twist back to the original electron–nuclei arrangements of the reactants. When this happens, and it often does, the effect is that the colliding particles simply bounce off each other. The potential energy in the temporary and unstable arrangement at the instant of collision reconverts to kinetic energy much as a bouncing ball can hit a sidewalk, briefly stop, then bounce away — still as a ball and not as some other substance. In other words, some collisions lead to no permanent change.

Following other, perhaps more violent collisions, reactant particles, during the brief moment of deformation, go through a rearrangement of their electrons and nuclei. As the system relaxes into a more permanent state, product particles form. We dub such events successful collisions, because they lead to products. Thus the conversion of the kinetic energy of collision into the potential energy of distorted, unstable configurations makes a chemical reaction possible.

The Minimum Collision Energy for a Reaction Is the Energy of Activation For each chemical reaction, there is a certain minimum collision energy that must develop before the new chemical bonds in the products can form. This minimum energy is called the reaction's **energy of activation.** Figure 6.11, part a illustrates what this means.

■ The collision energy is the sum of the kinetic energies of the colliding particles.

The vertical axis in Figure 6.11 represents changes in the *fraction* of all the collisions that are occurring. The horizontal axis corresponds to values that the collision energy can have, ranging from zero on the left to very large values — approaching infinity — on the right. The reactant particles have a large range of speeds, ranging from very low values (even a zero value for some, for a moment) to very high speeds. Therefore some collisions will be mere taps, whereas others will be extremely violent.

Figure 6.11a shows that in a sample of reactant particles, some collisions will be such slight taps that virtually no distortions of electron clouds can occur. Little if any kinetic energy changes into potential energy. However, the fraction of all collisions that have zero collision energy is essentially zero. Then, to follow the curve to the right, as the collision energy increases, the fraction of the collisions having a particular energy also increases. We eventually reach a maximum value. Beyond it, collisions with increasingly higher energies become less and less likely. The fractions with very high energies decline and the curve moves back down to the base line.

■ The *total* energy — kinetic plus potential — stays constant throughout the change, but it becomes apportioned differently.

Eventually we reach a value of collision energy that provides the exact amount of energy to enable the electron–nuclei rearrangement, the chemical reaction, to occur. This particular collision energy is the energy of activation, symbolized as E_{act} in the figure. When collisions have this much energy, or more, the reaction can take place. Collisions with energies less than the energy of activation cannot cause a chemical change. The colliding particles just bounce away chemically unchanged.

It isn't enough, of course, to have sufficient energy. The colliding particles must hit each other just right, much as the runners in a relay race have to pass the baton correctly regardless of how fast or slowly they are moving at this critical moment in the race.

The **rate of a reaction** is the number of successful collisions that occur each second in each unit of volume of the reacting mixture. Generally, only a small fraction of the collisions have enough energy to be successful. This fraction is represented in Figure 6.11 by the ratio of

Figure 6.11
Energy of activation. (a) Only a small fraction of all the collisions, represented by the ratio of areas, $A/(A + B)$, has enough energy for reaction. (b) This fraction greatly increases when the temperature of the reacting mixture is increased.

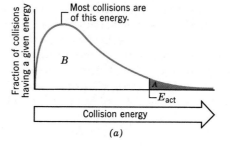

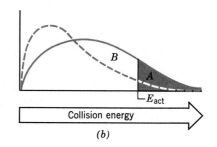

the shaded area marked A to the total area under the curve, $(A + B)$. Thus this ratio is $A/(A + B)$.

You can see from the figure that if the energy of activation were very high, the shaded area on the right would be even smaller, so the fraction $A/(A + B)$ would be much smaller. A high energy of activation, in other words, means a small fraction of successful collisions and a slow rate of reaction.

On the other hand, a reaction with a very small energy of activation would have a large fraction of successful collisions and a high rate of reaction. In the extreme, the fraction might equal 1, which would mean that every collision would be successful no matter how low the energy of the collision. In practical terms, such a reaction would be extremely rapid — an explosion, essentially — because it would mean that simply mixing the reactants causes instantaneous change.

At the other extreme, the energy of activation could be so high that the fraction $A/(A + B)$ might be virtually zero. Now no reaction ever occurs, and the "reactants" are eternally stable in each other's presence.

This analysis tells us that the rate of a reaction depends greatly on its energy of activation. A high energy of activation means a slow rate, and a low energy of activation means a fast rate.

A Slow Reaction Could Still Be Very Exothermic

We must make an important distinction now between a reaction's energy of activation and its *heat of reaction*. We'll use a *progress of reaction diagram* to do this. See Figure 6.12. In such a diagram, the vertical axis gives *relative* values of the potential energies of the substances, either the reactants or the products, depending on which part of the plot gets our attention. The horizontal axis simply shows the direction of the chemical change.

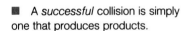

We'll use the combustion of carbon and oxygen to illustrate how to follow a progress of the reaction diagram. It's an exothermic reaction.

$$C + O_2 \longrightarrow CO_2 + \text{heat of reaction}$$

Begin in Figure 6.12 on the left at site A with the unchanged reactants, carbon and oxygen. We know that these are quite stable together at or near room temperature. Coal (mostly carbon), after all, can be stored in air (with its 21% oxygen). To initiate a reaction between carbon and oxygen, we have to heat them (ignite the system). Heat gives their particles higher kinetic energies, and more and more collisions become closer to being successful. In the diagram, we are moving up the curve from A, because the potential energy of the system is increasing. We are climbing an "energy hill."

Eventually we provide sufficient energy of activation, and we are at the top of the energy barrier at location B. The electrons and nuclei of the reactants can now rearrange to give molecules of carbon dioxide. Some of the potential energy in the complex of electrons and nuclei at the top of the energy hill now changes into the kinetic energy of newly forming molecules of carbon dioxide.

There is quite a drop in potential energy now as the reaction progresses to C in the diagram. Some of this potential energy goes to repay the cost of climbing the energy hill, but there is a net excess that is liberated as heat. This net energy difference between the reactants and the products is called the **heat of reaction**. The heat of reaction in this chemical change comes from the conversion of some of the chemical energy in the electron–nuclei arrangements of carbon and oxygen into the kinetic energy of the molecules of CO_2.

As we know, once the reaction of carbon and oxygen starts, it continues spontaneously. The reaction is exothermic, and some of the energy represented in Figure 6.12 in the change from B to C activates (ignites) still unchanged particles of the reactants.

One might think that a rapid exothermic reaction always means a high heat of reaction, but this is not necessarily so. The oxidation of 1 mol of iron, a very slow reaction,

$$4Fe + 3O_2 \longrightarrow 2Fe_2O_3$$

■ Combustion means burning, a reaction with oxygen so rapid that heat, light, and some sound are rapidly released.

■ A *successful* collision is simply one that produces products.

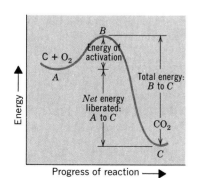

Figure 6.12
Progress of reaction diagram for the exothermic reaction of carbon with oxygen that produces carbon dioxide.

Figure 6.13
Because energies of activation, not the heats of reaction, dominate reaction rates, it is possible to have (a) a fast reaction with a small heat of reaction, or (b) a slow reaction with a large heat of reaction. We can tell that the rate in part a is faster than that in part b because of its smaller E_{act}.

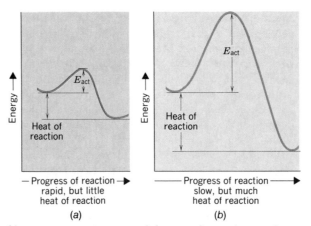

(a) — Progress of reaction →
rapid, but little heat of reaction

(b) Progress of reaction →
slow, but much heat of reaction

liberates over twice as much heat as the oxidation of one mole of carbon. Yet iron oxidizes very slowly, and carbon oxidizes so rapidly that we call it combustion. The reason lies in the energy barriers, the energies of activation. The energy barrier in the oxidation of iron is considerably higher than for the oxidation of carbon, so the rate is slower.

Figure 6.13 explains this in terms of two hypothetical reactions shown in progress of reaction diagrams. The reaction on the right has the higher heat of reaction but also a higher energy of activation. It is the slower reaction. The one on the left has the much lower energy of activation, so its rate will be much faster. Yet it gives off less heat. Thus there is really no simple relationship between how rapidly an exothermic reaction occurs and how large its heat of reaction is. In living systems, there are many highly exothermic changes that happen extremely slowly by themselves. Living systems have ways to switch slow reactions to higher rates, and the chemistry of heredity as well as the work of hormones have much to do with this.

No Net Release of Heat Occurs in Endothermic Reactions   Not all reactions liberate energy. Many won't occur without a continuous input of energy. The conversion of potassium chlorate into potassium chloride and oxygen is an example. Now the heat of reaction has to be shown as if it were a reactant, because the reaction is endothermic.

$$2KClO_3 + \text{heat of reaction} \longrightarrow 2KCl + 3O_2$$

The energy relationships for this reaction are shown in the progress of reaction diagram of Figure 6.14. A good share of the energy of activation (A to B in this figure) is permanently retained by the product molecules as internal or potential energy. The net energy retained is represented in Figure 6.14 by the vertical distance between A and C.

In an endothermic reaction there is a net conversion of kinetic energy (supplied by the steady input of heat) into the potential or chemical energy of the products. Thus you can see that both exothermic and endothermic reactions have energies of activation. But in the exothermic reaction there is still a net release of energy, whereas in the endothermic reaction there is a net absorption of energy.

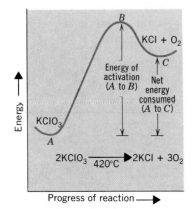

Figure 6.14
Progress of reaction diagram for the endothermic conversion of potassium chlorate into potassium chloride and oxygen.

6.10 FACTORS THAT AFFECT REACTION RATES

Increases in temperature or in concentrations of reactants as well as catalysts make reactions go faster.

A Ten-Degree Increase in Temperature Doubles or Triples Many Rates   If the temperature of a mixture of reactants is raised, their particles acquire higher average kinetic energies. The effect of this on the average energy of collision is shown in Figure 6.11b. It shows that an increase in the temperature makes the curve flatten out. It shifts the maximum of the curve to the right, toward a higher average collision energy, without also increasing the energy of activation. The flattening of the curve thus transfers more of the area under the curve to the right of E_{act}. The fraction of collisions represented by $A/(A + B)$ thus increases, which means that the reaction rate increases. This explains how an increase in the temperature of a mixture of reacting chemicals increases the rate of the reaction.

The effect of temperature on reaction rate is very great. As a rule of thumb, an increase of only 10 °C doubles or triples the rates of most reactions. This is a huge rate acceleration for such a small temperature change, and it has serious implications for health.

Faster Metabolism Requires Faster Oxygen Delivery by the Heart Metabolism, as we learned in Section 2.5, is the sum total of all the reactions in the body. Many of these reactions require oxygen. Medical scientists tell us that an increase in body temperature of only 1 °F increases the rate of metabolism so much that the oxygen requirement of the body increases by 7%. This places an extra strain on the heart, because it has to speed up the delivery of oxygen from the lungs. Although a higher metabolic rate during a fever is part of the mechanism of fighting disease, a prolonged episode has to be prevented.

At Higher Reactant Concentrations, Rates Are Usually Higher Another way to increase the frequency of successful collisions is simply to increase the frequency of all collisions. Even if we don't increase their average violence, by making collisions of *all* kinds occur more often, we will make successful collisions more probable. The way to accomplish this is to increase the concentrations of the reactant particles. It's like going from a stroll down a lonely country lane to an aisle of a very crowded store. An increase in the concentration of people in motion causes an increase in the "excuse-me" kind of bumps and collisions. If the molar concentration of one reactant is doubled, the frequency of all collisions must double because there are twice as many of its particles *in the same volume.*

One of the spectacular results of increasing the concentration of a reactant can be observed by comparing the rate at which something burns in air with the rate of the same reaction in pure oxygen. Air is about 21% oxygen, which means that in every 100 liters of air there are 21 liters of oxygen (and virtually all of the rest is nitrogen). You can make steel wool glow and give off sparks if you direct a bunsen burner flame at it when it is in air. But if glowing steel wool is thrust into pure oxygen, it bursts into flame, as seen in Figure 6.15.

Someone has estimated that if the air we breathe were 30% oxygen instead of 21%, no forest fire could ever be put out, and eventually all of the world's forests would disappear. The higher concentration of oxygen would accelerate combustion too much.

Catalysts Make Reactions go Faster One of the interesting and most important phenomena in all of nature is the acceleration of a reaction rate by a trace amount of some chemical that does not itself permanently change. This phenomenon is called **catalysis,** the chemical responsible for it is called a **catalyst,** and the verb is *to catalyze.*

The catalysts in living systems are called **enzymes,** and a special enzyme is involved in virtually *every* single reaction in any living system. Enzymes are but one family of substances that belong to a very large family of biochemicals called the proteins.

You can easily observe the action of an enzyme if you have access to a slice of raw liver and a dilute solution of hydrogen peroxide, which is sold in drugstores as a bleach and disinfectant. Hydrogen peroxide spontaneously (but slowly) decomposes as follows.

$$2H_2O_2 \longrightarrow 2H_2O + O_2$$

This reaction is so slow at room temperature that if you look at a sample of hydrogen peroxide, you won't notice any bubbling action. However, if you add a tiny slice of liver to the hydrogen peroxide, an enzyme in liver called *catalase* catalyzes this decomposition, and you'll see a vigorous evolution of oxygen. The frothing that you see if you ever use hydrogen

Figure 6.15
Steel wool, after being heated in a flame, burns spectacularly when thrust into pure oxygen.

peroxide to disinfect a wound is the same reaction. Hydrogen peroxide is toxic, and it can form in certain reactions of the metabolism of oxygen. Therefore in the liver (and also in the kidneys), catalase acts to detoxify hydrogen peroxide. The enzyme is not itself permanently changed by this work.

Catalase makes a reaction occur much faster than it would at the same temperature in the absence of a catalyst. A catalyst can also cause a reaction to take place at a much lower temperature than otherwise. A classic illustration is the decomposition of potassium chlorate into potassium chloride and oxygen that we mentioned earlier. Notice in the following equations how the temperature at which the reaction can occur varies according to the presence or absence of manganese dioxide, a catalyst for the decomposition.

■ Sometimes the special conditions for a reaction are written above or below the arrow in the equation.

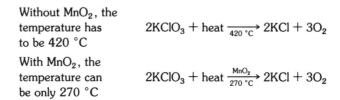

Without MnO_2, the temperature has to be 420 °C

$$2KClO_3 + heat \xrightarrow[420\ °C]{} 2KCl + 3O_2$$

With MnO_2, the temperature can be only 270 °C

$$2KClO_3 + heat \xrightarrow[270\ °C]{MnO_2} 2KCl + 3O_2$$

The rates of the evolution of oxygen are equal under the sets of conditions given here. But the catalyst permits it to happen at a much lower temperature. You can see why catalysts are immensely important in industries that make large quantities of chemicals, like plastics or synthetic gasoline. Energy costs money, and catalysts in trace quantities lower this cost by reducing the energy needed. Catalysts thus make many products less expensive and indirectly extend the world's supplies of energy.

Catalysts Decrease Energies of Activation   With or without the catalyst, the decomposition of potassium chlorate is endothermic, as we saw in Figure 6.14. Figure 6.16 shows the progress of reaction diagram for the same reaction except that the catalyst is present. It illustrates some of the major facts about the entire phenomenon of catalysis. *A catalyst does not change the heat of reaction; it lowers the energy of activation.* This is why the reaction happens faster. The energy barrier is reduced, so the fraction of all collisions that have enough energy is larger with the catalyst than without.

Figure 6.17 uses drawings similar to those in Figure 6.11 to illustrate how a decrease in the energy of activation increases the fraction of successful collisions in a reacting mixture. Exactly *how* a catalyst lowers an energy of activation varies with each reaction.

In summary, a catalyst either makes a reaction go faster at the same temperature or it permits the reaction to go at the same rate at a lower temperature. The catalyst accomplishes this by lowering the energy of activation. Catalysts do not affect the heat of reaction, the net energy released or absorbed by the system as the reaction occurs. Thus we add the effect of a *catalyst* to the *temperature* of the reaction and to the *concentrations* of the reactants as the important factors that govern the rates of reactions.

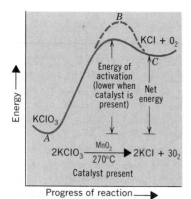

Figure 6.16
Progress of reaction diagram for the endothermic, catalyzed conversion of potassium chlorate into potassium chloride and oxygen. The dashed-line curve shows where the energy barrier went in the uncatalyzed reaction sketched in Figure 6.14. Notice that the net energy consumed, the heat of reaction, is identical to that of the uncatalyzed reaction, but the energy of activation is lower.

Figure 6.17
The effect of a decreased energy of activation on reaction rate. (*a*) This represents a reaction with a high energy of activation and, therefore, a slow rate. Only a small fraction of all collisions, represented by the ratio of areas, $A/(A + B)$, are successful. (*b*) This represents a reaction with a smaller energy of activation than in part *a*. Now the fraction of successful collisions is higher, so the rate is higher.

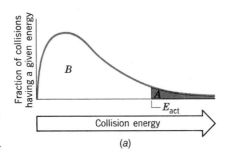

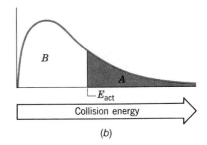

SUMMARY

Gas properties The four important variables for describing the physical properties of gases are moles (n), temperature T (in kelvins), volume (V), and pressure (P). We express pressure—force per unit area—in atmospheres (atm), mm Hg, or torr. Other important physical quantities in the study of gases are partial pressures, standard pressure and temperature (STP = 273 K and 760 mm Hg), and the molar volume at STP (22.4 L).

Gas laws All real gases obey, more or less, some important laws. Gas pressure is inversely proportional to volume (when n and T are fixed)—the pressure–volume law (Boyle's law). Gas volume is directly proportional to the Kelvin temperature (when n and P are fixed)—the temperature–volume law (Charles' law). Gas volume is also directly proportional to the number of moles (when T and P are fixed)—Avogadro's law. In fact, 1 mol of any gas under the same conditions of T and P has as many particles as 1 mol of any other gas. Another gas law is that the total pressure of a mixture of gases equals the sum of their partial pressures (Dalton's law).

Boyle's, Charles', and Avogadro's laws combine in the universal gas law, $PV = nRT$, where R, the universal gas constant, holds for all gases. This law also includes the pressure–volume law (Gay-Lussac's law), which says that the pressure of a gas is directly proportional to its Kelvin temperature (at fixed n and V).

Kinetic theory If we imagine that an ideal gas consists of a huge number of very tiny, very hard particles in random, chaotic motion without attracting or repelling each other, the gas laws can be derived from the laws of motion (with some help from statistics). Out of this kinetic theory of gases came the insight that the Kelvin temperature of a gas is directly proportional to the average kinetic energy of the gas particles.

Liquid state Liquids do not follow common laws as gases do, because essentially no space separates liquid particles from each other. In liquids, there are forces of attraction between the particles caused either by permanent dipoles or temporary dipoles (as in the case of London forces). Liquids can evaporate, and this "escaping tendency" gives rise to vapor pressure. Each liquid has a particular equilibrium vapor pressure that is a constant at each temperature, provided that care is taken to ensure a true dynamic equilibrium exists between the liquid and the vapor state.

When the liquid's vapor pressure equals the pressure of the atmosphere, the liquid boils. The normal boiling point is the temperature at which boiling occurs when the pressure of the atmosphere is 760 mm Hg (1 atm).

Solid state The particles in a solid vibrate about fixed equilibrium points, but if the solid is heated, these vibrations eventually become so violent that the particles enter the liquid state. The temperature at which liquid and solid are in equilibrium is the melting point.

Dynamic equilibria When the rates of two opposing changes, whether physical or chemical, are equal, the system is in dynamic equilibrium. A liquid and its vapor form are in dynamic equilibrium at the boiling point, for example. If some stress, such as the addition or removal of heat, upsets an equilibrium, the equilibrium shifts in whichever direction tends to absorb the stress. If a change is exothermic, the reverse reaction is favored when more heat is added. If a change is endothermic, the forward reaction is favored by the addition of heat.

Kinetic theory and chemical reactions Virtually all chemical reactions have an energy of activation. Reactant particles more frequently surmount this barrier—the reaction happens faster—the more concentrated they are and the more readily their collisions have the proper combined total collision energy. Raising the temperature of a reacting mixture increases the frequency of successful collisions (makes the rate of reaction faster). A catalyst, such as any enzyme, lowers the energy of activation without affecting the overall heat of reaction, so a catalyst also increases the rate of a reaction.

REVIEW EXERCISES

The answers to Review Exercises that require a calculation and whose numbers are marked with an asterisk are given in Appendix D. The answers to the other Review Exercises are given in the *Study Guide* that accompanies this book.

Pressure and Other Variables

6.1 What are the four principal physical quantities used in describing the physical state of any gas?

6.2 What name do we give to the property of a gas that ensures that the gas occupies its entire container, whatever its shape or volume?

6.3 What is the difference between pressure and force?

6.4 What causes the atmosphere to exert a force on the earth?

6.5 What is one standard atmosphere of pressure?

6.6 Why is the high density of mercury an advantage over water for use in a Torricelli barometer?

6.7 How many mm Hg are in 1 atm?

6.8 How many mm Hg are in 1 torr?

6.9 Why doesn't all the mercury run out of a Torricelli barometer?

*6.10 If a force of 300 lb acts on an area of 1 ft^2, what is the pressure in pounds per square inch?

6.11 Which exerts the higher pressure, a force of 150 lb acting on 25 in.^{2} or a force of 50 lb acting on 5 in.^{2}? (Do the calculations.)

*6.12 At the summit of Mount McKinley (20,320 ft, 6194 m), the atmospheric pressure is 0.460 atm. What is this pressure in mm Hg? In torr?

6.13 The highest altitude at which a pilot or plane passenger could survive without a pressurized cabin but while breathing oxygen-enriched air is about 40,000 ft (8 miles, 13 km). The air pressure there is about 150 mm Hg. What is this in atm?

'6.14 If 29.92 in. Hg corresponds to 760 mm Hg, what is the atmospheric pressure in mm Hg on a day when it is reported as 28.95 in. Hg?

6.15 For a measured boiling point to be scientifically useful, the pressure at which it is measured must also be recorded and reported. In one old report the pressure was given as 29.82 in. Hg. What is this in mm Hg? (1 in. Hg = 25.40 mm Hg)

Specific Gas Laws

6.16 What fact about gases did Boyle discover?

6.17 When we say that volume is inversely proportional to pressure, what does *inversely proportional* mean?

6.18 In order for P_1V_1 to equal P_2V_2, what conditions must be true about the measurements at the moments designated by the subscripts 1 and 2?

6.19 What is the law of partial pressures?

6.20 What four gases are in exhaled air?

6.21 Of the four important variables in the study of the physical properties of gases, which are assumed to be held at constant values in each of the following gas laws?
   (a) Boyle's law
   (b) Charles' law
   (c) Law of partial pressures
   (d) Avogadro's law
   (e) Gay-Lussac's law

6.22 Describe in your own words how we can figure out the dry volume of a gas after we have measured its volume when the gas is saturated with water vapor.

6.23 Describe in your own words how the method of ratios works for finding the volume of a gas when we know both its initial volume and pressure and its final pressure.

6.24 Why was a value of −273.15 °C selected as 0 K?

6.25 State the volume–temperature law.

6.26 Describe in your own words how the method of ratios works for finding a new value of the volume of a gas when we know its initial volume and both its initial and final temperatures. (Assume that n and P are constant.)

6.27 What is Avogadro's law?

'6.28 A sample of oxygen with a volume of 525 mL and a pressure of 750 mm Hg has to be given a volume of 475 mL. What pressure is needed if the temperature is to be kept constant?

6.29 What is the new pressure on a sample of helium that has an initial volume of 1.50 L and a pressure of 745 mm Hg if its volume becomes 2.10 L at the same temperature?

'6.30 The value of P_{N_2} at the summit of Mount McKinley (Review Exercise 6.12) is 277 mm Hg on a day when the atmospheric pressure there is 350 mm Hg. Assuming that the air is made up only of nitrogen and oxygen, what is the partial pressure of oxygen in mm Hg up there?

6.31 At an elevation of 40,000 ft (Review Exercise 6.13), the partial pressure of nitrogen is 119 mm Hg on a day when the air

pressure at this elevation is 150 mm Hg. What is the value of P_{O_2}?

6.32 When nitrogen is prepared and collected over water at 30 °C and a total pressure of 739 mm Hg, what is its partial pressure in mm Hg?

6.33 If you were to prepare oxygen and collect it over water at a temperature of 26 °C and a total pressure of 752 mm Hg, what would be its partial pressure?

'6.34 Suppose that you needed 250 mL of dry oxygen at 760 mm Hg and 22 °C. How many milliliters of wet oxygen would you have to collect at this same total pressure and this temperature to have this much dry oxygen?

6.35 Assuming that bunsen burner gas is pure methane (CH_4), if you collect 325 mL of methane over water in a gas-collecting bottle at 740 mm Hg and 26 °C, how many milliliters of dry methane are present?

'6.36 A sample of oxygen was warmed from 15 °C to 30 °C at constant pressure. Its initial volume was 1.75 L. What is its final volume in liters?

6.37 In order to change a 400-mL sample of nitrogen at 25 °C to a 200 mL sample with the same pressure, what must become of the temperature? (Give your answer in degrees Celsius.)

Universal Gas Law

6.38 What are the standard conditions of temperature and pressure?

6.39 What is meant by a *molar volume?* Under what circumstances does it equal 22.4 L?

6.40 What is the equation for the universal gas law?

6.41 At STP how many molecules of hydrogen are in 22.4 L?

6.42 How many millimoles of oxygen would be needed to fill a flask with a volume of 500 mL at a temperature of 24 °C and under a pressure of 745 mm Hg? (These are roughly laboratory conditions.)

6.43 What size flask would be needed (in mL) to hold 10.0 mmol of nitrogen at 20 °C and a pressure of 0.962 atm?

'6.44 When an electric current is passed through water under suitable conditions, the water breaks down into hydrogen and oxygen according to the following equation:

$$2H_2O \longrightarrow 2H_2 + O_2$$

In one experiment, a dry sample of one of these gases was collected. Its volume at 748 mm Hg and 23.0 °C was 875 mL.
   (a) How many moles of this gas were obtained?
   (b) This sample of gas had a mass of 1.136 g. What is the formula weight of this gas? (Remember that a formula weight is numerically equal to the *ratio* of grams to moles.)
   (c) Which gas was it, oxygen or hydrogen?

6.45 Consider the experiment described in Review Exercise 6.44.
   (a) How many moles of hydrogen were obtained?
   (b) What volume was occupied by this sample of hydrogen at 748 mm Hg and 23.0 °C?

'6.46 One source of industrial hydrogen is methane. At a high temperature, methane (CH_4) decomposes ("cracks") as follows into carbon and hydrogen:

$$CH_4 \xrightarrow[\text{heat}]{} C + 2H_2$$

(a) If 1.00 mol of CH_4 is used, how many moles of hydrogen are produced?

(b) If 100 L of methane gas, initially at 740 mm Hg and 20 °C, are used, how many liters of hydrogen will be obtained when they are measured under the same conditions of temperature and pressure?

(c) If a sample of methane with a mass of 50.0 g is cracked, what volume of hydrogen is produced when measured at 750 mm Hg and 25 °C?

6.47 Carbon dioxide can be removed from exhaled air by making the air pass through granulated sodium hydroxide. The reaction is

$$\underset{\substack{\text{Sodium} \\ \text{hydroxide}}}{NaOH} + \underset{\substack{\text{Carbon} \\ \text{dioxide}}}{CO_2} \longrightarrow \underset{\substack{\text{Sodium} \\ \text{bicarbonate}}}{NaHCO_3}$$

After this system had operated for some time, it was found that 12.4 g of NaOH had been used up.

(a) How many moles of CO_2 were responsible for this amount of change?

(b) If 11.6 g of NaOH were used up in a separate operation, how many milliliters of CO_2 gas caused this change if the gas volume was measured at 740 mm Hg and 25 °C?

Kinetic Theory of Gases

6.48 Scientists asked, "What must gases be like for the gas laws to be true?" What was their answer?

6.49 What is true about an ideal gas that is not strictly true about any real gas?

6.50 Dalton's law of partial pressures implies that gas molecules from different gases actually leave each other alone in the mixture, both physically and chemically (except at moments of collisions, when they push each other around). Which one of the three postulates in the model of an ideal gas is based on Dalton's law?

6.51 How does the kinetic theory of gases explain the phenomenon of gas pressure?

6.52 How does the kinetic theory of gases account for Boyle's law (in general terms)?

6.53 Those working out the kinetic theory found that for 1 mol of an ideal gas, the product of pressure and volume is proportional to the average kinetic energy of the ideal gas particles.

(a) To which of the four physical quantities used to describe a gas is the product of pressure and volume for 1 mol of a gas also proportional, according to the universal gas law (which makes no mention of kinetic energy)?

(b) If the product of P and V is proportional both to the average kinetic energy of the ideal gas particles and to the Kelvin temperature, what does this say about the relationship between the average kinetic energy and this temperature?

6.54 What happens to the motions of gaseous molecules at 0 K?

6.55 How does the kinetic theory explain (in general terms) the volume–temperature law?

6.56 The pressure–temperature law (Gay-Lussac's law) can be explained in terms of the kinetic theory in what way (in general terms)?

The Liquid State and Vapor Pressure

6.57 Why aren't there universal laws for the physical behavior of liquids (or solids) as there are for gases?

6.58 How does the kinetic theory explain
(a) How vapor pressure arises?
(b) Why vapor pressure rises with increasing liquid temperature?

6.59 Dimethylsulfoxide (DMSO) is a controversial pain-killing drug permitted by only a few states. Its boiling point is 189 °C. Is it more volatile or less volatile than water? Explain.

6.60 Compare the following expressions.

A	Water + heat	$\longrightarrow$	water vapor
B	Water + heat	$\longleftarrow$	water vapor
C	Water + heat	$\rightleftharpoons$	water vapor

Answer the following questions by using the letter A, B, or C to indicate which expression best represents the answer.

(a) Which expression describes heat being liberated from the system?

(b) Which expression describes the net formation of liquid water from water vapor?

(c) Which expression describes a net endothermic change?

(d) Which expression shows opposing changes?

(e) Which expression, A or B, represents the forward change in expression C? Which represents the reverse change?

(f) Expression C can be the correct description for the water–water vapor system at 1 atm only if the temperature is what?

(g) What is true about the opposing changes in expression C?

(h) What special term applies to expression C? (It does not represent a *reaction* or a permanent *change,* but what?)

6.61 When a liquid and its vapor are in dynamic equilibrium at a given temperature, the rates of what two changes are equal?

6.62 Some solids, like dry ice (solid carbon dioxide), pass directly from their solid state to their vapor state when they absorb heat. This process is called *sublimation.* Write an equilibrium expression for sublimation.

6.63 Why does a liquid's boiling point decrease as the atmospheric pressure decreases?

6.64 The following are some common observations. Using the kinetic theory, explain how each occurs in terms of what molecules are doing.

(a) Moisture evaporates faster in a breeze than in still air.

(b) Ice melts much faster if it is crushed than if it is left in one large block.

(c) Even if hung out to dry in below-freezing weather, wet clothes will become completely dry even though they freeze first.

Le Chatelier's Principle

6.65 What is Le Chatelier's principle?

6.66 Consider the following equilibrium in which all the substances are gases:

$$N_2 + O_2 + heat \rightleftharpoons 2NO$$
$$\text{Nitric oxide}$$

(a) Which reaction, the forward or the reverse, is endothermic?

(b) Which reaction, the forward or the reverse, will be favored by adding heat?

6.67 Consider the following equilibrium that involves a common air pollutant, NO_2. Both substances are gases at room temperature.

$$2NO_2 \rightleftharpoons N_2O_4$$

When the temperature is reduced, this equilibrium shifts to the right.

(a) Which reaction, the forward or the reverse, is exothermic?

(b) This reaction can be shifted in what direction by increasing the pressure on the mixture? Explain in terms of properties of gases and Le Chatelier's principle. (*Hint:* Which reaction, forward or reverse, is a volume-reducing change?)

The Solid State

6.68 Describe the motions made by particles (e.g., ions or molecules) in a solid crystal.

6.69 What is the mechanism whereby heat causes a solid to melt?

6.70 What do we call the temperature at which a solid is in equilibrium with its liquid form?

6.71 At room temperature, nitrogen is a gas, water is a liquid, and sodium chloride is a solid. What do these facts tell us about the relative strengths of electrical forces of attraction in these substances?

6.72 Explain in your own words how a substance such as nitrogen, which consists of nonpolar molecules, can be converted into a liquid and then into a solid by cooling it. How do the needed forces of attraction develop for these changes?

6.73 Why do nonpolar substances of high formula weight generally have higher boiling points than those of low formula weight?

Kinetic Theory, Rates of Reactions, Activation Energy, and Heat of Reaction

6.74 In terms of what we visualize as happening when two molecules interact to form products, how do we explain the existence of an energy barrier to the reaction—an energy of activation?

6.75 Study the accompanying progress of reaction diagram for the conversion of carbon monoxide and oxygen to carbon dioxide, and then answer the questions. The equation for the reaction is

$$2CO(g) + O_2(g) \longrightarrow 2CO_2(g)$$

(a) What substance or substances occur at position A?

(b) What substance or substances occur at position D?

(c) Which letter labels the arrow that represents the heat of reaction?

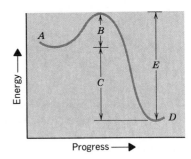

(d) Which letter labels the arrow that stands for the energy of activation?

(e) Is this reaction endothermic or exothermic? How can you tell?

(f) Which letter labels the arrow that would correspond to the energy of activation if the reaction could go in reverse?

6.76 Suppose that the following hypothetical reaction occurs:

$$A + B \longrightarrow C + D$$

Suppose further that this reaction is endothermic and that the energy of activation is numerically twice as large as the heat of reaction. Draw a progress of reaction diagram for this reaction, and draw and label arrows that correspond to the energy of activation and the heat of reaction.

6.77 The reaction of X and Y to form Z is exothermic. For every mole of Z produced, 10 kcal of heat are generated. The energy of activation is 3 kcal. Sketch the energy relationships on a progress of reaction diagram.

Factors That Affect Reaction Rates

6.78 How do we explain the rate-increasing effect of a rise in temperature?

6.79 As a rule of thumb, how much of a temperature increase doubles or triples the rates of most reactions?

6.80 Explain how a rise in body temperature can lead to a strain on the heart.

6.81 How can we increase the frequency of all collisions in a reacting mixture without raising the temperature?

6.82 When an increase in the concentration of one or more reactants causes an increase in the rate of a reaction, how do we explain this?

6.83 When an increase in the rate of a reaction has been caused by an increase in the concentration of one of the reactants, which of the following factors has been changed? (Identify them by letter.)

    A   The energy of activation

    B   The heat of reaction

    C   The frequency of collisions

    D   The frequency of successful collisions

6.84 In what way, if any, does a catalyst affect the following factors of a chemical reaction?

(a) The heat of reaction

(b) The energy of activation

(c) The frequency of collisions

(d) The frequency of successful collisions

6.85 What is the general name for the catalysts found in living systems?

6.86 Once we have selected a particular reaction, we have to accept whatever energy of activation and heat of reaction that goes with it. However, there are three things that we might try to help speed up the reaction. What are they?

Equilibria and the Earth's Heat Budget (Special Topic 6.1)

6.87 How could increasing concentrations of CO_2 in air lead to an increase in the earth's average temperature?

6.88 What has caused increases in the CO_2 level in air of the last several decades?

6.89 What natural phenomena could cause a decrease in the earth's average temperature?

6.90 How could a volcanic eruption on an island of the southwest Pacific Ocean cause an increase in the migration of people from the eastern states to western areas?

The Effect of Altitude on Cooking Times (Special Topic 6.2)

6.91 Cooking an egg involves heat-induced chemical reactions as well as some physical changes. Why does it take longer to prepare a soft-boiled egg in Denver than in New York City?

CHAPTER SEVEN

Water, Solutions, and Colloids

Life is impossible without salt-free water. When salt water freezes, the salt ions are excluded, so a glacier such as this is essentially pure water. One proposal for supplying fresh water to coastal cities in desert countries is to tow huge glaciers to offshore sites and pump the salt-free water to shore facilities.

7.1 WATER

Many physical properties of water relate to its polarity and to the hydrogen bonds between its molecules.

We take in more water than all other materials combined. Our bodies use it as the fluid in all cells, as a heat-exchange agent, and as the carrier in the bloodstream for distributing oxygen and all molecules from food, all hormones, minerals, and vitamins, and all disease-fighting agents.

Water is a superb solvent. It can dissolve at least trace amounts of almost anything, including rock. It is particularly good at dissolving ionic substances and the more polar molecular compounds.

In this chapter we will focus on water and some of the physical properties of aqueous solutions. To understand many aspects of life at the molecular level, we need to know why water dissolves some things well but not others. To do this, we must learn more about the high polarity of the water molecule.

Water's Boiling Point Is Unusually High

In the last chapter we learned an important rule of thumb. The boiling points of similar substances increase with formula weight. However, three simple substances with low formula weights, water, ammonia, and hydrogen fluoride, are striking exceptions. We can see this in Figure 7.1, where the boiling points of the hydrides of the elements in groups IVA through VIIA are plotted against their formula weights.

■ Hydrides are compounds of hydrogen with another element.

Look first at the plot of the boiling points of the hydrides of group IVA — methane (CH_4), silane (SiH_4), and germane (GeH_4) — the lowest plot in Figure 7.1. Their boiling points increase regularly with increasing formula weight, so they nicely follow the rule of thumb to this effect. The plot of the group VA hydrides, however, doesn't follow this rule as well. Ammonia, NH_3, is badly off the straight line on which the other group VA hydrides fall, those of phosphorus, PH_3, arsenic, AsH_3, and antimony, SbH_3. Ammonia boils far higher than "it should." Similarly, hydrogen fluoride, HF, does not fit the plot of the boiling points of the other hydrides of the group VIIA elements, the halogens.

Water departs most of all from the normal trend in the boiling points of its group, VIA. If its boiling point fell on the same line as the boiling points of H_2S, H_2Se, and H_2Te, water "should" boil at about -100 °C. But it actually boils at $+100$ °C.

The plots of Figure 7.1 suggest that forces of attraction *between* molecules in HF, H_2O, and NH_3, but not methane (CH_4), are considerably higher than we could explain on the basis of just London forces (Section 6.7). The molecules of these three hydrides, but not methane, must have permanent dipoles.

Figure 7.1
Boiling points versus formula weights for the binary, nonmetal hydrides of the elements in groups IVA, VA, VIA, and VIIA.

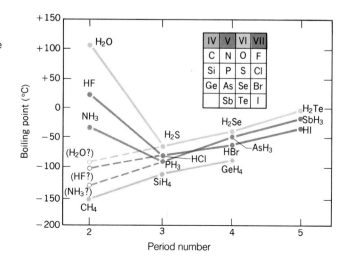

■ The direction of the polarity of the H—O bond is

$$\overset{\longleftarrow}{H—O}$$

Hydrogen Bonds Exist Between Water Molecules

In Chapter 4 we learned that the water molecule has a bent geometry. We also learned that oxygen is much more electronegative than hydrogen, which makes each of the water molecule's two H—O bonds very polar. Because the molecule is bent, these individual polarities do not cancel each other, so the water molecule as a whole is a polar molecule.

The water molecule is so polar, in fact, that between molecules there is a strong enough force of attraction to be called a bond. It's not a covalent bond or an ionic bond, so it has its own name — **hydrogen bond.** It is an electrical attraction between two dipoles whenever molecules have H covalently attached to the most electronegative elements, F, O, and N. The hydrogen bond is a force of attraction between the $\delta+$ on H when held by F, O, or N, and the $\delta-$ on some other O, N, or F atom. This is why HF, H_2O, and NH_3 have boiling points that are ''out of line'' for their molecular sizes.

Here are most of the several possibilities where hydrogen bonds can exist. Only partial structures are shown, and a dotted line is used to represent the force of attraction that we have now named the hydrogen bond. (The solid lines, of course, are covalent bonds.)

$$\overset{\delta+ \quad \delta-}{H—F} \cdots \overset{\delta+ \quad \delta-}{H—F} \qquad \overset{\delta+ \quad \delta-}{H—O} \cdots \overset{\delta+ \quad \delta-}{H—O} \qquad \overset{\delta+ \quad \delta-}{H—O} \cdots \overset{\delta+ \quad \delta-}{H—N}$$

$$\overset{\delta+ \quad \delta-}{H—N} \cdots \overset{\delta+ \quad \delta-}{H—O} \qquad \overset{\delta+ \quad \delta-}{H—N} \cdots \overset{\delta+ \quad \delta-}{H—N}$$

■ In a chain, the important link is the *weakest* link, not the strongest one.

The hydrogen bond is a bridging bond between molecules, as illustrated for water in Figure 7.2. Like all bonds, the hydrogen bond is a force of attraction. However, it is by no means as strong as a covalent bond, being roughly only 5% as strong. But this is strong enough to make a difference not just in water but in such important yet different substances as muscle proteins, cotton fibers, and the chemicals of genes, DNA. In fact, among those biochemicals where hydrogen bonds occur, these weak bonds are more important structurally than any other bond — precisely because they are weak, not strong.

Largely because of the hydrogen bond, water has relatively high heats of fusion and vaporization, as we learned in Section 2.4. An extra large input of heat per gram is necessary to melt or boil water because energy is needed to overcome the force of attraction called the hydrogen bond.

■ H_2O, b.p. 100 °C
NH_3, b.p. −33.4 °C
CH_4, b.p. −161.5 °C

Nitrogen is less electronegative than oxygen, and the H—N bonds in ammonia aren't as polar as the H—O bonds in water. Therefore the hydrogen bonds between molecules in ammonia aren't as strong as those that exist in water. This is chiefly why ammonia doesn't have nearly as high a boiling point as that of water. Despite this lessened polarity of the H—N bond, and as suggested by the plots in Figure 7.1, hydrogen bonding does occur in ammonia. It also occurs in protein molecules and in gene molecules, where H—N bonds abound.

Figure 7.2
Hydrogen bonds in water (· · · · · ·)

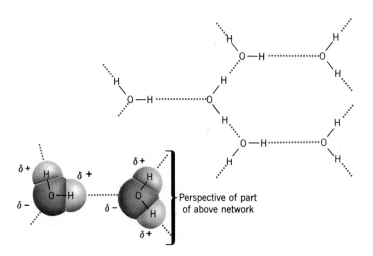

Perspective of part of above network

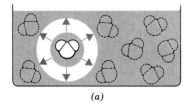

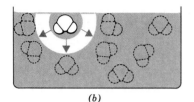

Figure 7.3
Surface tension. (a) In the interior of a sample of water, individual water molecules are attracted equally in all directions. (b) At the surface, nothing in the air counterbalances the downward pull that the surface molecules in water feel.

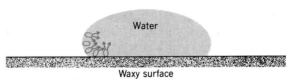

Figure 7.4
Water forms beads on a waxed or greasy surface. Nothing in the surface has enough polarity to attract water molecules to make the water spread out. The net inward pull created by water molecules at the surface creates the bead, because this shape minimizes the total area of the droplet.

A Water Surface Acts Like a Skin Because of Hydrogen Bonding All liquids possess a surface tension, but that of water is unusually high. **Surface tension** is a phenomenon in which the surface acts as though it were a thin, invisible, elastic membrane or skin. It's the reason why some bugs can skitter on the surface of a pond; why parlor magicians can set a steel needle afloat on water; and why water forms tight droplets and doesn't spread out on a waxy surface but does spread out on clean glass. It's also the source of the force that can make a lung collapse under certain conditions.

Because water molecules are polar, they attract each other and tend to jam together where water meets air, as shown in Figure 7.3. The forces of attraction that pull surface molecules downward aren't counterbalanced by forces that pull them upward. There is a net downward pull that causes the surface jam-up of molecules that is responsible for surface tension.

On a greasy or waxed surface, water forms into beads (Figure 7.4) because the inward-pulling forces of attraction in the water bead aren't matched by outward-pulling forces from the nonpolar molecules in wax or grease. These substances are nonpolar because virtually all their covalent bonds are either C—C or C—H bonds, and these bonds are nonpolar.

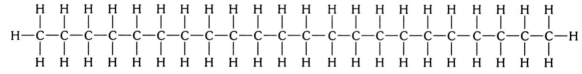

A typical molecule found in paraffin wax

■ Glass consists mostly of silicon and oxygen. Si is less electronegative than H, so the Si—O bond is more polar than the H—O bond.

Glass is rich in silicon–oxygen covalent bonds, so it is a very polar material. The $\delta+$ ends of H—O bonds in water are attracted to the $\delta-$ charges on the oxygens in glass, so water spreads out on a clean, grease-free glass surface (Figure 7.5). Water molecules that are right at

Figure 7.5
The interaction of water with the very polar surface of glass. (a) Water droplets spread on glass in response to polar sites in the glass. (b) When the glass surface is vertical, as in a graduated cylinder, pipet, or buret, water climbs the glass wall for a short distance to form a meniscus. In measuring volumes with these devices, read the bottom of the meniscus.

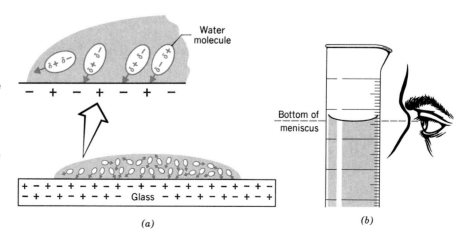

the glass surface find things to be more attracted to on the glass than behind them in the rest of the water sample, so the water spreads out. For the same reason, in a glass graduated cylinder or in a glass pipet, the boundary between the surface of an aqueous solution and the air curves upward at the glass walls.

Surface-Active Agents Reduce the Surface Tension of Water   There are many substances, which are called **surface-active agents** or **surfactants,** that lower the surface tension of water. All soaps and detergents are surfactants, for example. Soapy water won't bead on glass. A magician has to be careful that there is no soap or detergent whatsoever in the water used for the trick with the floating needle.

Water with a surfactant is an excellent cleansing agent, far better than water alone, as you know. Greases and oils are what bind dirt, soil, and harmful bacteria to fabrics, skin, or cooking utensils. Water alone cannot loosen greases and oils, so it is a poor cleansing agent. But surfactant molecules interact with oils and greases to disperse them in water making it possible to wash them away.

At the molecular level of life, there occurs a particularly important situation involving surfactants. The moist membrane of an air sac (an alveolus) in the lungs carries a surfactant that is secreted by the membrane itself. Without it, water molecules would be attracted so strongly to the membrane that the air sac would collapse. If enough air sacs did this, the entire lung would collapses. The membrane surfactant, however, prevents this and so protects the lungs. In some situations this surfactant is depleted or defective and the lungs do collapse. In milder cases, the alveoli shrink, making breathing difficult.

■ All the chemical reactions of digestion use water as a reactant.

Digestion is another process that depends on natural surfactants. Bile, one of the digestive juices, contains an extremely powerful surfactant called a bile salt. Without it, our digestive system would be unable to digest the fats and oils in our diets or to wash them from the particles of other kinds of food. The bile salts are also needed to aid in the absorption of some of the relatively nonpolar vitamins from the intestinal tract, like vitamins A and D. Because the bile salts are manufactured and delivered in bile from the gall bladder, an operation that removes this organ creates special dietary problems with which dieticians and health professionals have to deal.

7.2   TYPES OF HOMOGENEOUS MIXTURES

The sizes of the particles intimately mixed with a solvent determine some physical properties of the mixtures.

Mixtures in which any small sample removed from any place in the mixture has the same composition and properties as any other sample of the same size taken anywhere else are called **homogeneous mixtures.** There are three kinds, *solutions, colloidal dispersions,* and *suspensions,* and all types are found in the body. They differ fundamentally in the sizes of the particles involved, and the differences in size alone can cause interesting and important changes in properties.

In Solutions, the Dispersed Particles Are Smallest   As we learned in Section 5.5, a **solution** is a homogeneous mixture in which the particles of both solvent and solutes have sizes of atoms, or ordinary ions and molecules. They have formula weights of no more than a few hundred and diameters in the range of 0.1 to 1 nm.

■ 1 nm = 10^{-9} m = 1 nanometer

We usually think of solutions as being liquids, but in principle the solvent can be in any state — solid, liquid, or gas — and so can the solute. Table 7.1 is a list of the several combinations that can form a solution. Solutions are generally transparent — you can see through them — but they often are colored. Solutes do not settle out of solutions under the influence of gravity, and they can't be separated from solutions by filter paper.

The blood carries many substances in solution. These include the sodium ion, Na^+, and the chloride ion, Cl^-, as well as molecules of glucose, the chief sugar in blood.

TABLE 7.1 Solutions

Kinds	Common Examples
Gaseous Solutions	
Gas in a gas	Air
Liquid in a gas	(If droplets are present, a colloidal system)
Solid in a gas	(If particles are present, a colloidal system)
Liquid Solutions	
Gas in a liquid	Carbonated beverages (carbon dioxide in water)
Liquid in a liquid	Vinegar (acetic acid in water), gasoline
Solid in a liquid	Sugar in water, seawater
Solid Solutions	
Gas in a solid	Alloy of palladium and hydrogen[a]
Liquid in a solid	Toluene in rubber (e.g., rubber cement)
Solid in a solid	Carbon in iron (steel)[a]

[a] There is some doubt that this is a true solution

In Colloidal Dispersions, the Particle Sizes Are Larger A **colloidal dispersion** is a homogeneous mixture in which the dispersed particles are very large clusters of ions or molecules or are actually **macromolecules** that have formula weights in the thousands and hundreds of thousands. The dispersed particles have diameters in the range of 1 nm to 1000 nm.

■ *Macromolecule* means an extremely large molecule.

Table 7.2 gives several examples of colloidal dispersions, and they include many familiar substances such as whipped cream, milk, dusty air, jellies, and pearls. The blood also carries many substances in colloidal dispersions, including a variety of proteins.

When colloidal dispersions are in a fluid state — liquid or gas — the dispersed particles, although large, are not large enough to be trapped by ordinary filter paper during filtration. They are large enough, however, to reflect and scatter light (Figure 7.6). Light scattering by a colloidal dispersion is called the **Tyndall effect,** after British scientist John Tyndall (1820–1893). This effect is responsible for the milky, partly obscuring character of smog, or the way sunlight sometimes seems to stream through a forest canopy.

■ Solutions do not exhibit the Tyndall effect because the solute particles are too small.

The large, dispersed particles in a fluid colloidal dispersion eventually settle out under the influence of gravity, but this process can take time that can range, depending on the system, from a few seconds to many decades! One of the factors that keeps the particles dispersed is their constant buffeting about by molecules of the solvent. Evidence for this

TABLE 7.2 Colloidal Systems

Type	Dispersed Phase[a]	Dispersing Medium[b]	Common Examples
Foam	Gas	Liquid	Suds, whipped cream
Solid foam	Gas	Solid	Pumice, marshmallow
Liquid aerosol	Liquid	Gas	Mist, fog, clouds, certain air pollutants
Emulsion	Liquid	Liquid	Cream, mayonnaise, milk
Solid emulsion	Liquid	Solid	Butter, cheese
Smoke	Solid	Gas	Dust in smog
Sol	Solid	Liquid	Starch in water, jellies,[c] paints
Solid sol	Solid	Solid	Black diamonds, pearls, opals, metal alloys

[a] The colloidal particles constitute the *dispersed phase.*

[b] The continuous matter into which the colloidal particles are scattered is called the *dispersing medium.*

[c] Sols that adopt a semisolid, semirigid form (e.g., gelatin desserts, fruit jellies) are called **gels.**

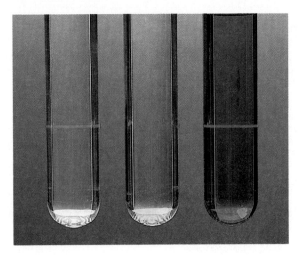

Figure 7.6
Tyndall effect. The tube on the left contains a colloidal starch dispersion, and the tube on the right has a colloidal dispersion of Fe_2O_3 in water. The middle tube has a solution of Na_2CrO_4, a yellow salt. The thin red laser light is partly scattered in the two colloidal dispersions, so it can be seen, but it passes through the middle solution un-changed.

■   Robert Brown (1773–1858), an English botanist, first observed this phenomenon when he saw the trembling of particles inside pollen grains viewed with a microscope.

buffeting can be seen by looking at the colloidal system under a good microscope. You can't actually see the colloidal particles, but you can see the light scintillations caused as they move erratically and unevenly about. This motion of colloidal particles is called the **Brownian movement.**

In the most stable colloidal systems, all the particles bear like electrical charges. In living systems, it's common for colloidally dispersed proteins to be like this, for example. (Other dissolved species of opposite charge, such as small ions, balance the charges on the colloidal particles.) Because like-charged colloidal particles repel each other, they could not coalesce to make larger, heavier, and less soluble particles that would settle out.

Emulsions are colloidal dispersions of two liquids in each other, like oil and vinegar in salad dressing. They usually are not stable; the oil soon separates from the aqueous layer. But sometimes an emulsion can be stabilized by a third component called an *emulsifying agent*. For example, mayonnaise is stabilized by egg yolk, whose protein molecules coat the microdroplets of olive oil or corn oil and prevent them from merging into drops large enough to rise to the surface.

Fluid Suspensions Must Be Stirred To Remain Homogeneous   In **suspensions,** the dispersed or suspended particles are over 1000 nm in average diameter, and they separate under the influence of gravity. They are large enough to be trapped by filter paper. A suspension such as clay in water has to be stirred constantly to keep it from separating. Because of this fact, a suspension is always on the borderline between a homogeneous mixture and one that is heterogeneous (one not uniform throughout). The blood, while it is moving, is a suspension, besides being a solution and a colloidal dispersion. Suspended in circulating blood are its red and white cells and its platelets.

See Table 7.3 for a summary of the chief features of solutions, colloidal dispersions, and suspensions.

7.3   WATER AS A SOLVENT

Water dissolves best those substances whose ions or molecules can strongly attract water molecules.

When crystals of a solid are placed into a potential solvent, the solvent molecules bombard the crystal surfaces. Figure 7.7 shows how such kinetic action would tend to dislodge Na^+ and Cl^- ions from a crystal of sodium chloride. The individual ions, however, have a very stable

TABLE 7.3 **Characteristics of Three Homogeneous Mixtures. Solutions, Colloidal Dispersions, and Suspensions**

Particle Sizes Become Larger		
Solutions	Colloidal Dispersions	Suspensions
All particles are on the order of atoms, ions, or small molecules (0.1—1 nm)	Particles of at least one component are large clusters of atoms, ions, or small molecules, or are very large ions or molecules (1—1000 nm)	Particles of at least one component may be individually seen with a low-power microscope (over 1000 nm)
Most stable to gravity	Less stable to gravity	Unstable to gravity
Most homogeneous	Also homogeneous, but borderline	Homogeneous only if well stirred
Transparent (but often colored)	Often translucent or opaque, but may be transparent	Often opaque, but may appear translucent
No Tyndall effect	Tyndall effect	Not applicable (suspensions cannot be transparent)
No Brownian movement	Brownian movement	Particles separate unless system is stirred
Cannot be separated by filtration	Cannot be separated by filtration	Can be separated by filtration
Homogeneous	to	Heterogeneous

environment in the crystal, where each is surrounded with oppositely charged ions as nearest neighbors. They simply will not leave this environment unless something else substitutes for it. Opposite charges attract each other too strongly. Water, however, can provide a substitute environment.

Water Molecules Can Form Solvent Cages Around Ions Water molecules are very polar, and they have sizable partial charges. The $\delta-$ sites on their oxygen atoms can attract Na^+ ions. Once these ions have been dislodged from a crystal of NaCl, they become surrounded by water molecules whose $\delta-$ ends point toward the positively charged ion. See Figure 7.7. Similarly, water molecules can also attract chloride ions and surround them (Figure 7.7). The $\delta+$ sites of water molecules point toward the negatively charged Cl^- ions. Thus the ions of NaCl become surrounded by cages of water molecules.

No longer do chloride ions have Na^+ ions as nearest neighbors, but they have several water molecules performing the same service, helping to provide Cl^- with an environment of opposite charge. No longer do sodium ions have chloride ions as nearest neighbors; water molecules take their place. This phenomenon whereby water molecules are attracted to solute particles is called **hydration.** When hydration occurs, cages of water molecules develop about each solute particle in solution.

Of all the common solvents, only water has molecules both polar enough and small enough to form effective solvent cages around ions. Of course, in order for water to do this, water molecules must give up some of their attractions for each other. Only ionic substances or compounds made of very polar molecules can break up the hydrogen-bonded network between water molecules. Thus the formation of a solution isn't just the separation of the solute particles from each other. It is also, to some extent, the separation of solvent molecules from each other.

■ *Hydr-* is from the Greek *hydōr,* water.

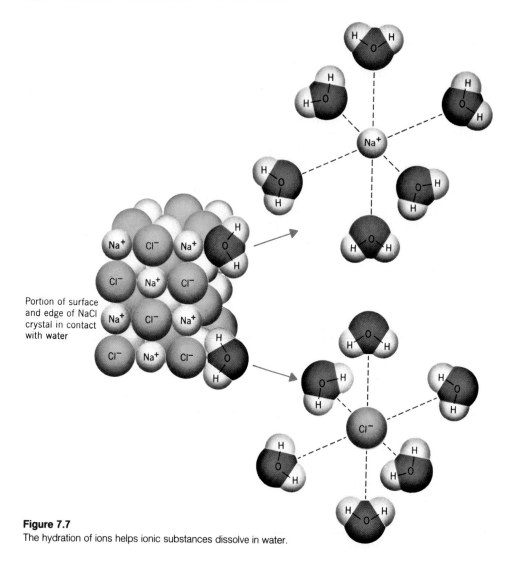

Portion of surface and edge of NaCl crystal in contact with water

Figure 7.7
The hydration of ions helps ionic substances dissolve in water.

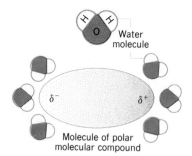

Figure 7.8
The hydration of a polar molecule helps polar molecular substances to dissolve in water.

Polar molecular compounds dissolve in water, too, and Figure 7.8 shows how water hydrates their molecules.

Dynamic Equilibrium Exists in a Saturated Solution   Each potential solid solute and most liquids have a limited solubility in water at a specific temperature. Hundreds of ionic compounds are only slightly soluble, and hundreds seemingly do not dissolve at all. In Section 5.6 we discussed such limits. We called them the *solubilities* of substances in water, the grams of solute in 100 g of water when the solution is saturated.

We can now refine and enlarge our understanding of a saturated solution. A **saturated solution** is one in which there is a dynamic equilibrium between the undissolved and the dissolved solute. We can represent this equilibrium as follows.

$$\text{Solute}_{\text{undissolved}} \rightleftharpoons \text{solute}_{\text{dissolved}} \tag{7.1}$$

In a saturated solution there is coming and going as solute particles leave the undissolved state and go into solution (the forward change) and others, at the same rate, leave the dissolved state and return to the undissolved condition (the reverse change).

Dynamic equilibrium in a saturated solution

■ Usually, when both ions of an ionic compound carry charges of two or three units, the compound isn't very soluble in water. The ions find more stability by remaining in the crystal than they can replace by accepting solvent cages.

The Solubilities of Most Solids Increase with Temperature Suppose we have a saturated solution of some solid at, say, 20° C. It is in contact with undissolved solid resting on the bottom of the container. There is equilibrium. If we increase the temperature of this stable system, what will happen? Will more solid dissolve, or will some come out of solution? The answer is that for most but by no means all solids more will dissolve as the temperature is increased. They have increased solubilities at higher temperatures. The reason is that most solids dissolve endothermically when the solution into which they are dissolving is at or very near the point of being saturated. They require heat to dissolve into a solution already saturated. Thus, for solutes that dissolve endothermically, we can rewrite equilibrium expression 7.1 by introducing an energy term, the *heat of solution.*

$$Solid_{undissolved} + solution + heat\ of\ solution \rightleftharpoons more\ concentrated\ solution$$

The heat of solution is the difference between the energy used to break up the solute and the energy released as the solvent cages form. Figure 7.9 shows what this means on a progress of reaction diagram.

Le Chatelier's principle is at work here. When we heat a saturated solution of anything that dissolves endothermically, the stress we place on this equilibrium is absorbed, as required by Le Chatelier's principle, by a shift of the equilibrium to the right. Only a shift in this direction absorbs the additional heat. Thus more solute dissolves, and the solution becomes even more concentrated. As more and more solute particles move out into the solution at the higher temperature, the rate of their return to the undissolved state also picks up. Eventually, the two rates again become equal (although higher), and equilibrium is restored (assuming that undissolved solute is still present, of course).

A number of ionic compounds have solubilities that decrease with temperature. Calcium hydroxide, $Ca(OH)_2$, is an example, but most of these compounds are sulfates. Only a few are hydroxides. Both the sulfate ion and the hydroxide ion strongly hydrogen-bond to water. One can only speculate, but perhaps higher temperatures interfere too much with this hydrogen bonding to give these ions any advantage in stability by being out in the solution instead of inside the crystalline form.

As we learned in Section 5.5, it's sometimes possible to prepare a supersaturated solution by cooling a saturated solution that contains no undissolved solute. Without the undissolved solute already present to which dissolved solute particles can return, they sometimes simply remain in solution. The system is unstable, of course, as we mentioned on page 123. Just by adding a seed crystal, we can give the excess in solution a place to go, and the excess leaves the dissolved state.

The Ions in Some Crystals Are Hydrated If we let water evaporate from an aqueous solution of any one of several substances, the dry-appearing crystalline residue contains intact water molecules. They are held within the crystals in *definite* proportions. They are true compounds, therefore, because they obey the law of definite proportions. Such water-containing solids are called **hydrates.**

We write the formulas of hydrates in a special way to emphasize that intact water molecules are present. Thus the formula of the pentahydrate of copper(II) sulfate is written as $CuSO_4 \cdot 5H_2O$, where a raised dot separates the two parts of the formula. Table 7.4 lists a number of other common hydrates.

The water indicated by the formula of a hydrate is called the **water of hydration.** It usually can be driven away from the hydrate by heat, and when this is done the residue is sometimes called the **anhydrous form** of the compound. For example,

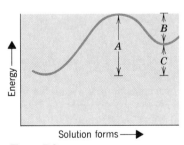

Figure 7.9
Energy relationships in a saturated solution at equilibrium for solid solutes that dissolve endothermically.
A = energy cost to break up the solute crystal
B = energy released as the solvent cages form
C = the net energy cost of forming the solution

$$CuSO_4 \cdot 5H_2O(s) \longrightarrow CuSO_4(s) + 5H_2O(g)$$

Copper(II) sulfate	Copper(II) sulfate	(as steam)
pentahydrate (deep	(anhydrous form is	
blue crystals)	nearly white)	

TABLE 7.4 Some Common Hydrates

Formulas	Names	Decomposition Modes and Temperatures[a]	Uses
$(CaSO_4)_2 \cdot H_2O$	Calcium sulfate hemihydrate (plaster of paris)	$-H_2O$ (163)	Casts, molds
$CaSO_4 \cdot 2H_2O$	Calcium sulfate dihydrate (gypsum)	$-2H_2O$ (163)	Casts, molds, wallboard
$CuSO_4 \cdot 5H_2O$	Copper(II) sulfate pentahydrate (blue vitriol)	$-5H_2O$ (150)	Insecticide
$MgSO_4 \cdot 7H_2O$	magnesium sulfate heptahydrate (epsom salt)	$-6H_2O$ (150)	Cathartic in medicine
		$-7H_2O$ (200)	Used in tanning and dyeing
$Na_2B_4O_7 \cdot 10H_2O$	Sodium tetraborate decahydrate (borax)	$-8H_2O$ (60) $-10H_2O$ (320)	Laundry
$Na_2CO_3 \cdot 10H_2O$	Sodium carbonate decahydrate (washing soda)	$-H_2O$ (33.5)	Water softener
$Na_2SO_4 \cdot 10H_2O$	Sodium sulfate decahydrate (glauber's salt)	$-10H_2O$ (100)	Cathartic
$Na_2S_2O_3 \cdot 5H_2O$	Sodium thiosulfate pentahydrate (photographer's hypo)	$-5H_2O$ (100)	Photographic developing

[a] Loss of water is indicated by the minus sign before the symbol, and the loss occurs at the temperature in °C that is given in parentheses.

Many anhydrous forms readily take up water and re-form their hydrates. Plaster of paris, for example, although not completely anhydrous, contains relatively less water than gypsum. When we mix plaster of paris with water, it soon sets into a hard, crystalline mass according to the following reaction:

$$(CaSO_4)_2 \cdot H_2O + 3H_2O \longrightarrow 2CaSO_4 \cdot 2H_2O$$

Plaster of paris   Gypsum

(Notice that the first 2 in gypsum's formula is a *coefficient* for the *entire* formula, including the $2H_2O$, i.e., a total of four H_2O molecules in $2CaSO_4 \cdot 2H_2O$.)

Some compounds in their anhydrous forms are used as drying agents or desiccants. A **desiccant** is a substance that removes moisture from air by forming a hydrate. Any substance that can do this is said to be **hygroscopic**. Anhydrous calcium chloride, $CaCl_2$, is a common desiccant, and in humid air it draws enough water to form a liquid solution. Any substance this active as a desiccant is also said to be **deliquescent**. Thus calcium chloride is often used to dehumidify damp basements.

7.4 SOLUTIONS OF GASES IN WATER

Pressure, temperature, and sometimes reactions of gases with water affect the solubility of a gas in an aqueous solution.

By some means or another, all living things must exchange gases with their environment. Our bodies, for example, take in oxygen from the air and expel carbon dioxide. The processes

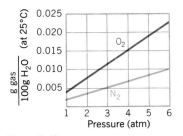

Figure 7.10
The solubilities of oxygen and nitrogen in water versus pressure.

intimately involve aqueous systems, so to understand these vital matters at the molecular level of life we have to look at the factors that affect the solubilities of gases in water.

Gases Are All Less Soluble at Higher Temperatures The solubilities of gases in water always decrease with increasing temperature, as the data in Table 5.1 (page 123) show. This is because the dissolving of gases in liquids, represented by the following equilibrium, is always an exothermic process.

$$\text{Gas}_{\text{undissolved}} + \text{solution} \rightleftharpoons \text{more concentrated solution} + \text{heat of solution}$$

When heat is added, this equilibrium must shift to the left in favor of undissolved gas, in accordance with Le Chatelier's principle. It's the only way that the stress, heat, can be absorbed by the system. A shift to the left, of course, means that gas leaves the solution.

Gases Are More Soluble under Higher Partial Pressures Pressure is a factor that affects solubility only if the solute is a gas. As seen in Figure 7.10, the solubilities of two typical gases are directly proportional to the applied pressure. The equilibrium expression is

$$\text{Gas}_{\text{undissolved}} + \text{solvent} \rightleftharpoons \text{solution} \qquad (7.2)$$

This equilibrium shifts to the right with increasing pressure because only such a change can absorb the volume-squeezing stress of extra pressure — yet another illustration of Le Chatelier's principle.

Similarly, if we reduce the pressure above a liquid that has a dissolved gas, we create a volume-expanding stress, and now equilibrium 7.2 shifts to the left. Dissolved gas now leaves the solution. If we apply both suction and heat to a solution of a gas, we very rapidly degas the solution.

William Henry (1775–1836) was the first to notice that gas solubility is directly proportional to gas pressure, so we now call this relationship **Henry's law** or the **pressure–solubility law.**

Pressure–Solubility Law (Henry's law). The concentration of a gas in a liquid at any given temperature is directly proportional to the partial pressure of the gas on the solution.

Stated in the form of an equation, Henry's law says

$$C_g = k_g P_g$$

where k_g is a constant of proportionality, C_g is concentration, and P_g is partial pressure. The reference is to *partial* pressure because each gas in a mixture of gases, like air, dissolves individually according to its own partial pressure and its own value of k_g.

The value of k_g *for a given gas at a given temperature* is a constant, and it does not change with the partial pressure. Because of this we can quickly change this equation to one that is easier to use in calculations, because it lets us avoid actually having to know k_g. The useful equation for Henry's law is as follows, when the gas stays the same and where the subscripts 1 and 2 refer to two different partial pressures.

$$\frac{C_1}{P_1} = \frac{C_2}{P_2} \qquad \text{(at constant temperature)} \qquad (7.3)$$

(The two sides of 7.3 equal each other because they each equal the same Henry's law constant. This transformation is identical in type to what we did with Charles' law on page 145.)

EXAMPLE 7.1	**USING HENRY'S LAW**

Problem: At 760 mm Hg and 20 °C, the solubility of oxygen in water is 4.30 mg O_2/100 g H_2O. When air is itself saturated with water, the partial pressure of oxygen is 156 mm Hg. How many milligrams of oxygen dissolve in 100 g of water when the water is saturated with air and is in equilibrium with air that is saturated with water vapor?

Solution: The best idea is to collect the data to see what we have.

$$C_1 = 4.30 \text{ g/100 mg} \qquad C_2 = ?$$
$$P_1 = 760 \text{ mm Hg} \qquad P_2 = 156 \text{ mm Hg}$$

Now we can use Equation 7.3.

$$\frac{4.30 \text{ mg/100 g}}{760 \text{ mm Hg}} = \frac{C_2}{156 \text{ mm Hg}}$$

When we solve this for C_2, we get

$$C_2 = 4.30 \text{ mg/100 g} \times \frac{156 \text{ mm Hg}}{760 \text{ mm Hg}}$$

$$= 0.883 \text{ mg/100 g} \quad \text{(answer)}$$

PRACTICE EXERCISE 1

How many milligrams of nitrogen dissolve in 100 g of water when the water is saturated with air and is in equilibrium with air that is saturated with water vapor? The partial pressure of nitrogen in air that is itself saturated with water vapor is 586 mm Hg. The solubility of pure nitrogen in water at 760 mm Hg is 1.90 mg/100 g H_2O.

Solubilities of Some Gases in Water at 20 °C in mg/100 g H_2O

O_2	4.3
CO_2	169
SO_2	10,600
NH_3	51,800

The pressure–solubility relationship for solutions of gases in water is particularly important to people exposed to possible decompression sickness (the bends), as discussed in Special Topic 7.1.

Water Reacts with Some Gases To Aid in Dissolving Them   A number of important gases, like carbon dioxide, sulfur dioxide, and ammonia, are far more soluble in water than are oxygen or nitrogen. At 20 °C, only 4.30 mg of oxygen dissolves in 100 g of water, but carbon dioxide is nearly 40 times as soluble, sulfur dioxide is nearly 2500 times as soluble, and ammonia is a whopping 120,000 times as soluble in water as oxygen.

There are two reasons for this. First, the molecules of these gases have $\delta+$ and $\delta-$ sites that can attract water molecules and be attracted by them. Figure 7.11, for example, shows how ammonia molecules can form hydrogen bonds to water molecules. Second, there is a chemical fact; a fraction of these gases that dissolves actually reacts with water. When water contains these gases, the following chemical equilibria are involved in addition to the physical equilibria:

$$CO_2(aq) + H_2O \rightleftharpoons H_2CO_3(aq)$$
Carbonic acid

$$SO_2(aq) + H_2O \rightleftharpoons H_2SO_3(aq)$$
Sulfurous acid

$$NH_3(aq) + H_2O \rightleftharpoons NH_4^+(aq) + OH^-(aq)$$
Ammonium ion   Hydroxide ion

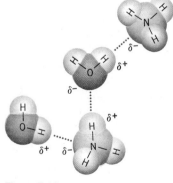

Figure 7.11
Hydrogen bonds ($\cdots\cdots$) between molecules of ammonia and water help to keep ammonia in solution

These are the first examples of *chemical* equilibria in our study. The forward reactions of these equilibria help draw the gases into solution and make them more soluble.

| SPECIAL TOPIC 7.1 | DECOMPRESSION SICKNESS (THE BENDS) |

People who work where the air pressure is high must return to normal atmospheric pressure slowly and carefully. Otherwise, they could experience the bends, or decompression sickness—severe pains in muscles and joints, fainting, and even deafness, paralysis, or death. At risk are deep-sea divers and those who work in deep tunnels where air pressures are increased to help keep out water.

Under high pressure, the blood dissolves more nitrogen and oxygen than at normal pressure, as Henry's law (and Figure 7.10) tells us. If blood thus enriched in nitrogen and oxygen is too quickly exposed to lower pressures, these gases suddenly come out of solution in blood. Their microbubbles block the tiny blood capillaries, close off the flow of blood, and lead to the symptoms we described.

If the return to normal pressure is made slowly, the gases leave the blood more slowly, and they can be removed as they emerge. The excess oxygen can be used by normal metabolism, and the excess nitrogen has a chance to be gathered by the lungs and removed by normal breathing. For each atmosphere of pressure above normal that the person was exposed to, about 20 minutes of careful decompression is usually recommended.

■ *Respiration* means all the activities that bring in *and use* oxygen and get rid of carbon dioxide.

■ Blood coming to the lungs is called venous blood and blood leaving the lungs is arterial blood.

Sometimes in discussions of human or animal respiration, the term *gas tension* is used to describe the availability of a gas from some body fluid. **Gas tension** is the partial pressure of a gas over a solution with which it is in equilibrium. It is an indirect measure of how much gas is in solution, because the more there is in solution the more there will be above the solution exerting a partial pressure. Thus, a high gas tension means a high availability of the gas from the solution.

In venous blood, the blood returning to the lungs in veins, the oxygen tension is about 40 mm Hg. In the air inside the lungs, it is about 100 mm Hg. Gases always tend to diffuse from a higher to a lower pressure, so oxygen naturally tends to move from the lungs into the returning blood. This, of course, is the direction it must move if we are to live. Carbon dioxide, on the other hand, has a gas tension in venous blood of about 46 mm Hg, but in the air inside the lungs its gas tension is about 40 mm Hg. Thus this gas, a waste product, naturally tends to migrate from venous blood to the lungs, as it must, where it can then be discharged in exhaled air.

7.5 OTHER CONCENTRATION EXPRESSIONS

The number of grams of solute in 100 g of solution is the percentage concentration of the solution.

In Section 5.6 we learned how to express a concentration in units of moles per liter—the molarity or molar concentration of a solution. These units are particularly important when we need to connect the quantities of solutions we use in the lab to the stoichiometries of the reactions being studied. However, this connection isn't always needed. Test tube tests, for example, often call for us to add a few drops of a solution to something. If a gas fizzes out, or there is a color change, or a precipitate forms, we judge that something was present.

The solution being added dropwise is often referred to as a **reagent,** and it isn't always crucial to know its molarity. Yet some information about its concentration is needed if only to be able to prepare more of it. Here is where a number of other expressions for concentrations have been developed. The most important of these are percentage concentrations.

Weight/Weight Percent   The **weight/weight percent (w/w%) concentration** of a solution is the number of grams of solute in 100 g of the solution. For example, a 10.0% (w/w) glucose solution has a concentration of 10.0 g of glucose in 100 g of solution. To make 100 g of this solution, you would mix 10.0 g of glucose with 90.0 g of the solvent for a total mass of 100 g.

EXAMPLE 7.2   **USING WEIGHT/WEIGHT PERCENTS**

Problem: How many grams of 0.900% (w/w) NaCl contain 0.250 g of NaCl?

Solution: The concentration term, 0.900% (w/w), gives us the following two conversion factors:

$$\frac{0.900 \text{ g NaCl}}{100 \text{ g NaCl soln}} \quad \text{and} \quad \frac{100 \text{ g NaCl soln}}{0.900 \text{ g NaCl}}$$

These two ratios are just equivalent ways of understanding the concentration, and we should remind ourselves that any expression of a concentration in any units can be expressed as either of two ratios, as we have done here. Next, we multiply the given, 0.250 g NaCl, by the second factor so that the final units will be g NaCl soln.

$$0.250 \text{ g NaCl} \times \frac{100 \text{ g NaCl soln}}{0.900 \text{ g NaCl}} = 27.8 \text{ g NaCl soln}$$

Thus 27.8 g of 0.900% (w/w) NaCl contains 0.250 g of NaCl.

EXAMPLE 7.3   **PREPARING WEIGHT/WEIGHT PERCENT SOLUTIONS**

Problem: A special kind of saline solution, called isotonic saline, is sometimes used in medicine. Its concentration is 0.90% NaCl (w/w). How would you prepare 750 g of such a solution?

Solution: Once again, we have to translate the label on the bottle, 0.90% (w/w) NaCl, into conversion factors.

$$\frac{0.90 \text{ g NaCl}}{100 \text{ g NaCl soln}} \quad \text{and} \quad \frac{100 \text{ g NaCl soln}}{0.90 \text{ g NaCl}}$$

What we basically have to determine is the number of grams of NaCl that we must weigh out and dissolve in water to make the final mass equal to 750 g. To find this number of grams of NaCl, we multiply the mass of the NaCl solution by the first conversion factor.

$$750 \text{ g NaCl soln} \times \frac{0.90 \text{ g NaCl}}{100 \text{ g NaCl soln}} = 6.8 \text{ g NaCl} \quad \text{(rounded from 6.75)}$$

Thus if we dissolve 6.8 g NaCl in water and add enough water to make the final mass equal to 750 g, we can write the label to read 0.90% (w/w) NaCl.

PRACTICE EXERCISE 2   Sulfuric acid can be purchased from a chemical supply house as a solution that is 96.0% (w/w) H_2SO_4. How many grams of this solution contain 9.80 g of H_2SO_4 (or 0.100 mol)?

PRACTICE EXERCISE 3   How many grams of glucose and how many grams of water are needed to prepare 500 g of 0.250% (w/w) glucose?

Sometimes weight/weight percent solutions are prepared by diluting a more concentrated solution. The equation used to make the necessary calculation is similar to the one we derived in Section 5.7 for dilutions involving molar concentrations. We will simply give the equation here.

$$g_{\text{concd soln}} \times \text{percent (w/w)}_{\text{concd soln}} = g_{\text{dil soln}} \times \text{percent (w/w)}_{\text{dil soln}}$$

Volume/Volume Percent   A concentration expressed as a **volume/volume percent (v/v%)** gives us the number of volumes of one substance dissolved in 100 volumes of the mixture. This is often used for solutions of gases or for solutions of liquids. For example, the concentration of oxygen in air is 21% (v/v), which means that there are 21 volumes of oxygen in 100 volumes of air. The unit used for volume can be any unit, as long as we use the same unit for the solute as for the solution. The units cancel when we deal with true percentages. Calculations involving volume/volume percents involve the same kinds of steps we used for problems of weight/weight percents.

Weight/Volume Percent Although this is a fairly common concentration expression, a weight/volume percent isn't a true percent because the units don't cancel. When a concentration is given as a **weight/volume percent (w/v%)**, it means the number of grams of solute in 100 mL of the solution. Thus a 0.90% (w/v) NaCl solution has 0.90 g of NaCl in every 100 mL of the solution.

Weight/volume percent problems are handled through conversion factors just as we did for weight/weight percent problems.

■ We now use *percent* instead of *percentage* to conform to common usage.

Milligram Percent, Parts per Million, and Parts per Billion You'll occasionally encounter some special concentration expressions that are handy when the solutions are very dilute. **Milligram percent** means the number of milligrams of solute in 100 mL of the solution.

For very dilute solutions, the concentration might be given in **parts per million (ppm),** which means the number of parts (in any unit) in a million parts (the same unit) of the solution. Parts per million might be interpreted as grams per million grams or pounds per million pounds. One ppm is analogous to one penny in a million pennies ($10,000) or 1 minute in a million minutes (about two years).

When water is the solvent, the volume in milliliters and the mass in grams of a dilute solution are numerically the same (at least to two significant figures), and it can be shown that 1 ppm is identical with 1 mg/L.

Parts per billion (ppb) similarly means parts per billion parts, such as grams per billion grams. This expression is used for *extremely* dilute systems. One ppb is like one penny in $10 million (a billion pennies), or like two drops of a liquid in a full, 33,000-gallon tank car.

Because of the many ways the term *percent* can be taken, there is a trend away from using it, which should be encouraged. Instead, the explicit units are given. Thus instead of referring to a concentration of, say, 10.0% (w/v) KCl, the label or the report should read 10.0 g KCl/100 mL. When no units are given, just a percent, and until you find out otherwise, you have to interpret the percent as weight/weight if the solute is a solid when pure and as a volume/volume percent if the solute is a liquid when pure. Usually, however, the labels are clear and, as always, *labels should be read carefully.*

■ Often the units of g/100 mL will be given as g/dL because 100 mL = 1 dL.

7.6 OSMOSIS AND DIALYSIS

The selective migrations of ions and molecules through cell membranes is an important mechanism for getting nutrients inside cells and waste products out.

Solutions generally have lower melting points and higher boiling points than their pure solvents. Aqueous solutions, for example, freeze not at 0 °C but at slightly lower temperatures. They also boil not at 100 °C but at slightly higher temperatures (both compared at 760 mm Hg). Interestingly, these effects of solutes depend not on what they are, but only on their concentrations. Properties of solutions or colloidal dispersions that depend only on the concentrations, not on the chemical identities of their solutes are called **colligative properties.** The depression of the freezing point and the elevation of the boiling point are two examples. The relative abilities of components of a solution to migrate through certain kinds of membranes — osmosis and dialysis — are also colligative properties.

The effects aren't very large unless the concentrations are very large. As we said, however, they are related to concentrations, not chemical identities. For example, if we

■ From the Greek *kolligativ,* depending on number and not on nature.

prepare two solutions, one that has 1.0 mole of NaCl in 1000 g of water and the other with 1.0 mole of KBr in 1000 g of water, each freezes at -3.4 °C (and not at 0 °C), and each boils at 101 °C (at 760 mm Hg). Both the freezing and the boiling points are the same, despite the difference in solutes, because the ratios of the moles of ions to the moles of water in both solutions are identical. Otherwise, the identities of the solutes are immaterial.

When the concentrations are very high, the effects can be quite large and important. The whole basis for the use of an antifreeze mixture in an automobile radiator is the large depression of the freezing point of the radiator fluid caused by the presence of the antifreeze. A 50–50 mixture (vol/vol) of antifreeze in water gives protection to about -40 °F.

■ The temperature of a mixture made from 33 g NaCl and 100 g ice is about -22 °C (-6 °F).

Osmosis Is the Diffusion of Solvent Molecules Through Membranes   Cells in living systems are enclosed by cell membranes. Generally, on both sides of them there are aqueous systems that contain substances both in solution and in colloidal dispersion. Materials and water have to be able to move through cell membranes in either direction so that nutrients can enter cells and wastes can leave. Two factors control these movements, *active transport* and *dialysis*.

■ The movements of Na$^+$ and K$^+$ ions into and out of cells is controlled by active transport mechanisms.

Active transport is the active involvement of specialized materials embedded in a cell membrane to propel ions and molecules through it. These substances accept and move ions and molecules by endothermic chemical reactions. We can do no more than mention active transport at this time.

Dialysis, the other mechanism for getting substances through cell membranes, depends on a property of the membrane that separates two solutions of unequal particle concentration. Membranes of cells, for example, are **semipermeable.** This means that they can let some but not all kinds of molecules and ions pass through. Cellophane, for example, is a synthetic, semipermeable membrane. When it is in contact with an aqueous solution, only water molecules and other small molecules and ions can migrate through it. Molecules of colloidal size are stopped. Evidently, there are ultrafine pores in cellophane just large enough to let small particles through but too small for larger particles.

Some membranes have pores so small that only water molecules can get through them. A semipermeable membrane that is so selective that only the solvent molecules can get through is called an **osmotic membrane.** Because ions are hydrated, their effective sizes are apparently too large for the pores. No other molecules can pass either.

■ Essentially no purely osmotic membranes occur naturally.

This situation gives us a special case that is enough different from dialysis to have its own name — osmosis. **Osmosis** is the net migration of just solvent from a solution with the lower concentration of solute into the solution with the higher concentration through an osmotic membrane.

Figure 7.12 shows why there is a net flow in one direction in osmosis. It shows the special case in which pure water is on one side of the membrane. Water molecules can move in *both*

Figure 7.12
Osmosis and osmotic pressure. (*a*) In the beaker, *A*, there is pure water and in the tube, *B*, there is a solution. An osmotic membrane closes the bottom of the tube. (*b*) A microscopic view at the osmotic membrane shows how solute particles interfere with the movements of water molecules from *B* to *A*, but not from *A* to *B*. (*c*) The level in *A* has fallen and that in *B* has risen because of osmosis. (*d*) A back pressure would be needed, to prevent osmosis, and the exact amount of pressure is the osmotic pressure of the solution in *B*.

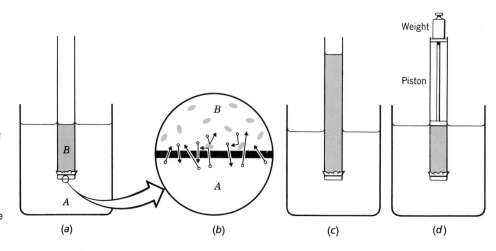

directions, but when solute particles are on one side, they get in the way. Water molecules, therefore, are prevented from leaving as frequently from that side as they are able to come in from the opposite side where no solute particles get in the way. Therefore more water molecules enter the concentrated solution than leave it, and this solution becomes increasingly diluted. Eventually, the column of water shown in Figure 7.12 will exert a high enough back pressure to prevent any further rise.

Sometimes students have a problem with remembering the direction of osmosis. Think of it this way. The net flow always makes the concentrated solution more dilute. If osmosis could continue long enough, the concentrated solution would become dilute enough and the other solution (by losing solvent) would become concentrated enough so that the two concentrations would become equal.

Osmotic Pressure Is a Measure of Concentration The exact back pressure necessary to prevent osmosis is called the **osmotic pressure** of the solution, and its symbol is Π.

■ Π is the Greek capital letter pi.

The value of osmotic pressure is directly proportional to the molar concentration of the particles in the solution (at least at relatively low molarities), and the equation for osmotic pressure is almost identical to the ideal gas equation, $PV = nRT$. For osmotic pressure, Π,

$$\Pi V = nRT$$

If we rearrange terms, and remember that $n/V =$ molarity (moles per liter), then

$$\Pi = \frac{n}{V} \times RT$$

Or

$$\Pi = MRT \tag{7.4}$$

This equation shows how osmotic pressure is directly proportional to the concentration.

The osmotic pressure of a solution has to be understood not as something that the solution is actually exerting, like some hand pushing on a surface. Instead, osmotic pressure is a potential, directly related to concentration, that can be realized only when an osmotic membrane separates the solution from pure water.

Even in relatively dilute solutions, the osmotic pressure can be very high, as the next worked example illustrates.

| EXAMPLE 7.4 | CALCULATING OSMOTIC PRESSURE |

Problem: A dilute solution, 0.100 M sugar in water, is separated from pure water by an osmotic membrane. What is its osmotic pressure at a temperature of 25 °C or 298 K?

Solution:

$$\Pi = \frac{nRT}{V} = \frac{0.100 \text{ mol}}{1000 \text{ mL}} \times 6.24 \times 10^4 \frac{\text{mm Hg mL}}{\text{mol K}} \times 298 \text{ K}$$
$$= 1.86 \times 10^3 \text{ mm Hg}$$

The solution has an osmotic pressure of 1.86×10^3 mm Hg. This means that a solution with this concentration can support a column of mercury 1.86×10^3 mm high, over 6 feet.

PRACTICE EXERCISE 4   What is the osmotic pressure of a 0.900 M glucose solution at 25 °C?

■ Water's density (1.00 g/mL) is much less than mercury's (13.6 g/mL), so the water column is 13.6 times higher.

If, instead of mercury, the column in Example 7.4 had been water (or the dilute solution), the column supported would have been 25.3 m (83.0 ft) high. Thus a relatively dilute solution, when separated from pure water, can be driven to a column height of several dozen feet. This phenomenon is one of the factors in the rise of sap in tall trees.

The Ions of an Ionic Compound Individually Affect Osmotic Pressure Solute particles that cause osmotic pressure can be ions, molecules, or macromolecules. Just remember that osmotic pressure is a *colligative* property, so it depends only on the concentrations of the particles. Thus when the solute is an ionic compound such as sodium chloride, the concentration of particles — ions in this situation — is twice the molar concentration of the salt given by the label on the bottle. For example, 0.10 M NaCl has a concentration of $2 \times (0.10) = 0.20$ mole of all ions per liter, because NaCl breaks up into two ions for each formula unit that goes into solution. The osmotic pressure of 0.10 M NaCl is therefore twice as large as that of 0.10 M glucose, which does not break up into ions.

For an ionic compound like Na_2SO_4, for which three ions are released for each formula unit that dissolves — two Na^+ and one SO_4^{2-} — the concentration of particles in a 0.10 M solution is $3 \times (0.10) = 0.30$ mole of all ions per liter.

The labeled molarity of a solution thus does not reveal enough about a solution when we think about its osmotic pressure. To express the concentration of all osmotically active particles in the solution, we sometimes use a related concentration expression, called the solution's **osmolarity,** the molar concentrations of all solute particles active in osmosis or dialysis. Thus 0.10 M NaCl has a molarity of 0.10 mol/L of NaCl but an osmolarity of 0.20 mol/L. The osmolarity of 0.10 M Na_2SO_4 is 0.30 mol/L. The concentration term in Equation 7.4, M, must refer to the osmolarity of the solution.

The abbreviation used in labeling osmolarities is **Osm.** Thus 0.0125 Osm means that the osmolarity of this solution is 0.0125 mol/L of all of the particles that contribute to the osmotic pressure.

PRACTICE EXERCISE 5   Assuming that any *ionic* solutes in this exercise break up completely into their constituent ions when they dissolve in water, what is the osmolarity of each solution?

(a) 0.010 M NH_4Cl (which ionizes as NH_4^+ and Cl^-)
(b) 0.005 M Na_2CO_3 (which ionizes as $2Na^+$ and CO_3^{2-})
(c) 0.100 M fructose (a sugar and a molecular substance)
(d) A solution that contains both fructose and NaCl with concentrations of 0.050 M fructose and 0.050 M NaCl

Small Solute Particles Pass Through Dialyzing Membranes   **Dialysis** is a phenomenon like osmosis except that in dialysis not only water molecules but also ordinary-sized ions and molecules can move through the membrane. A dialyzing membrane can be thought of as having larger pores than an osmotic membrane. Cell membranes are largely dialyzing membranes, but such membranes include substances that are able selectively to block the migration of even some small particles and to allow others to pass through.

Dialysis produces a net migration of water only if the fluid on one side of the dialyzing membrane has a higher concentration in colloidal substances than the other. Colloidal-sized particles are blocked by dialyzing membranes, so they get in the way of the movements of smaller particles through the membrane. The net flow of fluid in dialysis, as in osmosis, is from the side that has the lower concentration of colloidal substances to the side with the higher concentration. The effect is to make the concentrated solution more dilute.

The imbalance in concentration that is related to colloidally dispersed materials causes a **colloidal osmotic pressure,** which is similar to osmotic pressure in meaning. In the next section we present some situations involving life at the molecular level where osmotic pressure relationships are very critical and depend on the colloidal osmotic pressure of blood.

7.7 DIALYSIS AND THE BLOODSTREAM

When the osmotic pressure of blood varies too much, the result can be shock or damage to red blood cells.

The body tries to maintain the concentrations of all of the substances that circulate in blood within fairly narrow limits. Quite complicated mechanisms exist to excrete or retain solutes or to excrete or retain water. When they fail, the consequences can be life-threatening. In this section we will look briefly at two such situations that arise when the osmotic pressure of blood changes too much.

The Brain Loses Blood Flowage in Shock   One feature of the shock syndrome is a dramatic increase in the permeability of the blood capillaries to colloidal-sized particles, particularly protein molecules. When these leave the blood, the colloidal osmotic pressure of blood decreases, another way of saying that the concentration of colloidal substances in blood decreases. The blood, in effect, becomes less concentrated. It is less able, therefore, to take up water from the spaces that surround the blood capillaries.

A sufficient drop in the colloidal osmotic pressure of blood makes a net loss of water from blood possible. A loss of water means a loss of total blood volume. This makes it more difficult to bring nutrients to brain cells and carry wastes away. The brain functions much less well, and the result to the nervous system is called shock. When a person goes into shock, one of the many problems, but one that lies close to the central cause, is that blood capillaries become temporarily more permeable to the loss of macromolecules from blood.

Red Blood Cells Hemolyze in Water   Millions of red blood cells circulate in the bloodstream, and their membranes behave as dialyzing membranes. Within each red cell there is an aqueous fluid with dissolved and colloidally dispersed substances (Figure 7.13a). Although the colloidal particles are too large to dialyze, they contribute to the colloidal osmotic pressure. They help , therefore, to determine the direction of dialysis through the red cell membrane.

When red cells are placed in pure water, the fluid inside the red cell is more concentrated than the surrounding liquid. Dialysis now occurs to bring fluid *into the red cell.* Enough fluid moves in to make the cells burst open, as seen in Figure 7.13b. The rupturing of red cells is called **hemolysis,** and we say that the cells hemolyze.

On the other hand, when red cells are put into a solution with an osmolarity greater than their own fluid, dialysis occurs in the opposite direction — out of the cell and into the solution. Now the cells lose fluid volume, and shrivel and shrink. This process is called **crenation** (Figure 7.13c).

In some clinical situations, body fluids need replacement or nutrients have to be given by intravenous drip. It is important that the osmolarity of the solution being added matches that of the fluid inside the red cells. Otherwise, hemolysis or crenation will occur.

Two solutions of equal osmolarity are called **isotonic solutions.** If one has a lower osmotic pressure than the other, the first is said to be **hypotonic** with respect to the second. A **hypotonic solution** has a lower osmolarity than the one to which it is compared. Red cells hemolyze if placed in a hypotonic environment, including pure water.

A **hypertonic solution** is one with a higher osmotic pressure than another. Thus

Figure 7.13
Dialysis (a) The red cell is in an isotonic environment. (b) Hemolysis is about to occur because the red cell is swollen by extra fluids brought into it from its hypotonic environment. (c) The red cell experiences crenation when it is in a hypertonic environment.

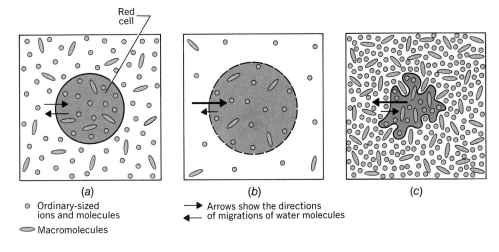

(a)   (b)   (c)

○ Ordinary-sized
     ions and molecules

⬭ Macromolecules

→ Arrows show the directions
← of migrations of water molecules

0.14 M NaCl is hypertonic with respect to 0.10 M NaCl. Red cells undergo crenation when they are in a hypertonic environment.

A 0.9% (w/w) NaCl solution, called **physiological saline solution,** is isotonic with respect to the fluid inside a red cell. Any solution to be added in any large quanitity into the bloodstream has to be isotonic in this way.

All the topics we have studied in this and the preceding section are important factors in the operation of artificial kidney machines, which are discussed in Special Topic 7.2.

SUMMARY

Water   The higher electronegativity of oxygen over hydrogen and the angularity of the water molecule make it very polar, so polar that hydrogen bonds exist between the molecules. They help to explain many of water's unusual thermal properties, such as its high heats of fusion and vaporization, its high surface tension, and its ability to dissolve ionic and polar molecular compounds.

Hydrogen bonds   When hydrogen is covalently bonded to atoms of any of the three most electronegative elements (O, N, or F), its partial positive charge is large enough to be attracted to the partial negative charge on an atom of O, N, or F on a nearby molecule. This force of attraction, although much weaker than a covalent bond, is large enough to have a special name, the hydrogen bond. (Never consider this bond to be a *covalent* bond within any molecule, neither the covalent bond in hydrogen itself, H_2, nor a covalent bond within any other molecule, like water.) The hydrogen bond is a (relatively weak) force of attraction between two dipoles, between the $\delta+$ on H in the polar bonds of the H—O, H—N, or H—F systems to the $\delta-$ of another O, N, or F.

Hydration   The attraction of water molecules to ions or to polar molecules leads to a loose solvent cage that shields the ions or molecules from each other. This phenomenon is called hydration, and it helps to explain why some substances dissolve in water. Sometimes water of hydration is present in a crystalline material in a definite proportion to the rest of the formula unit, and such a substance is a hydrate. Heat converts most hydrates to their anhydrous forms. And some anhydrous forms serve as drying agents—desiccants.

Solutions   Ions and molecules of ordinary size, if soluble in water at all, form solutions. These are homogeneous mixtures that neither gravity nor filtration can separate. The solubilities of most solids increase with temperature, because their dissolving is usually endothermic. (More energy is needed to break up the crystal than is recovered as the solvent cages form about the ions or molecules.)

Gas solubilities   Gases dissolve in water exothermically, so the addition of heat to an aqueous solution of a gas drives the gas out of solution. The solubility of a gas is directly proportional to its partial pressure in the space above the solution (Henry's law). Some gases do more than mechanically dissolve in water; part of what dissolves

forms hydrogen bonds with water and part reacts with water to form soluble species.

Colloidal dispersions   Large clusters of ions or molecules or macromolecules do not form true solutions but colloidal dispersions. These can reflect and scatter light (Tyndall effect), experience the Brownian movement, and (in time) succumb to the force of gravity (if the medium is fluid). Protective colloids, such as emulsifying agents, sometimes stabilize these systems. If the dispersed particles grow to an average diameter of about 1000 nm, they slip over into the category of suspended matter and such systems must be stirred to maintain the suspension.

Percent concentration   A variety of concentration expressions have been developed to provide ways to describe a concentration without going into molar concentrations. These include weight/weight percents, volume/volume percents, and hybrid descriptions that aren't true percentages—weight/volume percent, milligram percent, parts per million, and parts per billion.

Osmosis and dialysis   When a semipermeable membrane separates two solutions or dispersions of unequal osmolarities, a net flow occurs in the direction that, if continued, would produce solutions of identical osmolarities. When the membrane is osmotic, only the solvent can migrate, and the phenomenon is osmosis. The back pressure needed to prevent osmosis is called the osmotic pressure, and it's directly proportional to the concentration of all particles of solute that are osmotically active—ions, molecules, and macromolecules.

When macromolecules are present, their particular contribution to the osmotic pressure is called the colloidal osmotic pressure of a solution. It is this factor that operates when the membrane is a dialyzing membrane.

The permeability of blood capillaries changes temporarily when a person experiences shock, and macromolecules leave the blood. Their departure results in the loss of water, too, and the blood volume decreases.

Solutions of matched osmolarity are isotonic. Otherwise, one is hypertonic (more concentrated) with respect to the other, and the other is hypotonic (less concentrated). Only isotonic solutions, or those that are nearly so, should be administered in large quantities intravenously.

SPECIAL TOPIC 7.2   HEMODIALYSIS

The kidneys cleanse the bloodstream of nitrogen waste products such as urea and other wastes. If the kidneys stop working efficiently or are removed, these wastes build up in the blood and threaten the life of the patient. The artificial kidney is one remedy for this.

The overall procedure is called *hemodialysis* — the dialysis of blood — and the figure on the lower left shows how it works. The bloodstream is diverted from the body and pumped through a long, coiled cellophane tube that serves as the dialyzing membrane. (The blood is kept from clotting by an anticlotting agent such as heparin.) A solution called the *dialysate* circulates outside of the cellophane tube. This dialysate is very carefully prepared not only to be isotonic with blood but also to have the same concentrations of all the essential substances that should be left in solution in the blood. When these concentrations match, the rate at which such solutes migrate out of the blood equals the rate at which they return. In this way several key equilibria are maintained, and there is no net removal of essential components. The figure on the lower right shows how this works. The dialysate, however, is kept very low in the concentrations of the wastes, so the rate at which they leave the blood is greater than the rate at which they can get back in. In this manner, hemodialysis slowly removes the wastes from the blood.

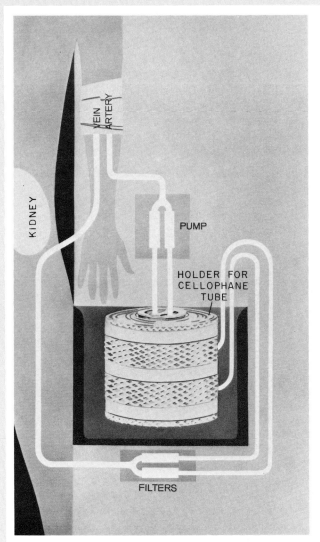

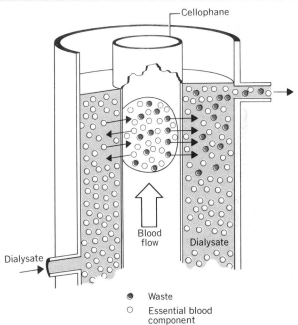

- ● Waste
- ○ Essential blood component

REVIEW EXERCISES

The answers to Review Questions that require a calculation and whose numbers are marked with an asterisk are given in Appendix D. The answers to the remaining Review Exercises are given in the *Study Guide* that accompanies this book.

Hydrogen Bond

7.1 The hydrogen molecule, H—H, does not become involved in hydrogen bonding.
(a) What kind of bond occurs in a hydrogen molecule?
(b) Why can't this molecule become involved in hydrogen bonding?

7.2 The methane molecule, CH_4, does not become involved in hydrogen bonding. Why not?

7.3 Solid sodium hydroxide, NaOH, includes two kinds of chemical bonds. Which ones are they, and how do they differ?

7.4 Draw the structures of two water molecules. Write in $\delta+$ and $\delta-$ symbols where they belong. Then draw a correctly positioned dotted line between two molecules to symbolize a hydrogen bond.

7.5 Hydrogen bonds exist between two molecules of ammonia, NH_3. Draw the structures of two ammonia molecules. (You don't have to try to duplicate their tetrahedral geometry.) Put $\delta+$ and $\delta-$ signs where they should be located. Then draw a dotted line that correctly connects two points to represent a hydrogen bond.

7.6 The hydrogen bond between two molecules of ammonia must be much weaker than the hydrogen bond between two molecules of water.
(a) How do boiling point data suggest this?
(b) What does this suggest about the relative sizes of the $\delta+$ and the $\delta-$ sites in molecules of water and ammonia?
(c) Why are the $\delta+$ and the $\delta-$ sites different in their relative amounts of fractional electric charge when we compare molecules of ammonia and water?

7.7 If it takes roughly 100 kcal/mol to break the covalent bond between O and H in H_2O, about how many kilocalories per mole are needed to break the hydrogen bonds in a sample of liquid water?

7.8 Explain in your own words how hydrogen bonding helps us understand each of the following.
(a) The high heats of fusion and vaporization of water
(b) The high surface tension of water

7.9 Explain in your own words why water forms tight beads on a waxy surface but spreads out on a clean glass surface.

7.10 What does a surfactant do to water's surface tension?

7.11 What common household materials are surfactants?

7.12 What surfactant is involved in digestion? What digestive juice supplies it? How does it aid digestion?

7.13 Bile comes from the gall bladder, and when someone has a gall bladder removed, he or she is put on a diet that is relatively low in fats and oils. Why?

Homogeneous Mixtures

7.14 What does it mean when we describe a solution or a colloidal dispersion as *homogeneous*?

7.15 What is the basis for distinguishing among solutions, colloidal dispersions, and suspensions?

7.16 Which of the three kinds of homogeneous mixtures
(a) Can be separated into its components by filtration?
(b) Exhibits the Tyndall effect?
(c) Shows observable Brownian movements?
(d) Has the smallest particles of all kinds?
(e) Is likeliest to be the least stable at rest over time?

7.17 What kinds of particles make the most stable colloidal dispersions? Explain.

7.18 The blood is simultaneously a solution, a colloidal dispersion, and a suspension. Explain.

7.19 Why won't a solution give the Tyndall effect?

7.20 What causes the Brownian movement?

7.21 What simple test could be used to tell if a clear, colorless solution contained substances in colloidal dispersion?

7.22 What is an emulsion? Give some examples.

7.23 What is a sol? Give some examples.

7.24 What is a gel? Give an example.

Aqueous Solutions

7.25 In a crystal of sodium chloride the sodium ions are surrounded by oppositely charged ions (Cl^-) as nearest neighbors. What replaces this kind of electrical environment for sodium ions when sodium chloride dissolves in water?

7.26 When we say that a chloride ion in water is *hydrated,* what does this mean? (Make a drawing as part of your answer.)

7.27 Carbon tetrachloride, CCl_4, is a liquid, and its molecules are tetrahedral, like those of methane, CH_4. This liquid does not dissolve in water. Why won't water let CCl_4 molecules in?

7.28 We have to distinguish between *how fast* something dissolves in water and *how much* can dissolve to make a saturated solution. The speed with which we can dissolve a solid in water increases if we (a) crush the solid to a powder, (b) stir the mixture, or (c) heat the mixture. Use the kinetic theory as well as the concept of forward and reverse processes to explain these facts.

7.29 Assuming that solid, undissolved sodium chloride is present, the rates of what two changes are equal in a saturated solution of sodium chloride in water? Write an equilibrium expression.

7.30 Suppose that you do not know and do not have access to a reference in which to look up the solubility of sodium nitrate, $NaNO_3$, in water at room temperature. Yet you need a solution that you know beyond doubt is saturated. How can you make such a saturated solution and know that it is saturated?

7.31 Explain why the solubility of a solid or a liquid in water generally increases with increasing temperature.

7.32 Ammonium chloride dissolves in water endothermically. Suppose that you have a saturated solution of this compound, that its temperature is 30 °C, and that undissolved solute is present. Write the equilibrium expression for this saturated solution, and use Le Chatelier's principle to predict what will happen if you cool the system to 20 °C.

Hydrates

7.33 Calcium sulfate dihydrate, $CaSO_4 \cdot 2H_2O$, loses all its water of hydration at a temperature of 163 °C. Write the equation for this reaction.

7.34 Why are hydrates classified as compounds and not as wet mixtures?

7.35 When water is added to anhydrous copper(II) sulfate, the pentahydrate of this compound forms. Write the equation.

7.36 Anhydrous sodium sulfate is hygroscopic. What does this mean? Does this property make it useful as a desiccant?

7.37 Sodium hydroxide is sold in the form of small pellets about the size and shape of split peas. It is a very deliquescent substance. What can happen if you leave the cover off of a bottle of sodium hydroxide pellets?

7.38 When 6.29 g of the hydrate of compound X was strongly heated to drive off all the water of hydration, the residue, the anhydrous form, X, had a mass of 4.97 y. What number should y be in the formula of the hydrate, $X \cdot yH_2O$? The formula weight of X is 136.

*7.39 When all the water of hydration was driven off of 4.25 g of a hydrate of compound Z, the residue, the anhydrous form, Z, had a mass of 2.24 g. What is the formula of the hydrate (using the symbol Z as part of it)? The formula weight of Z is 201.

Gas Solubilities

7.40 The solubility of methane, the chief component in bunsen burner gas, in water at 20 °C and 1.0 atm is 0.025 g/L. What will be its solubility at 1.5 atm?

*7.41 At 20 °C the solubility of nitrogen in water is 0.0150 g/L when the partial pressure of the nitrogen is 580 mm Hg. What is its solubility when the partial pressure is raised to 800 mm Hg?

7.42 Explain why carbon dioxide is more soluble in water than is oxygen.

7.43 Explain why ammonia is much more soluble in water than nitrogen.

7.44 Using Le Chatelier's principle, explain why the solubility of a gas in water should increase with increasing partial pressure of the gas.

7.45 If the gas tension of CO_2 in blood is described as 30 mm Hg, what specifically does this mean?

7.46 If in one region of the body the gas tension of oxygen over blood is 80 mm Hg and in a second region it is 50 mm Hg, which region (the first or the second) has a higher concentration of oxygen in the blood itself?

Percent Concentrations

7.47 If a solution has a concentration of 1.2% (w/w) NaOH, what two conversion factors can we write based on this value?

7.48 A solution bears the label 1.5% (w/v) NaCl. What two conversion factors can be written for this value?

7.49 The concentration of a pollutant in water is reported as 1.5 ppm. What is the concentration of this pollutant in units of mg/L?

7.50 A solution of wood alcohol in water is described as 12% (v/v). What two conversion factors are possible from this value?

7.51 How many grams of solute are needed to prepare each of the following solutions?
(a) 500 g of 0.900% (w/w) NaCl
(b) 250 g of 1.25% (w/w) $NaC_2H_3O_2$
(c) 100 g of 5.00% (w/w) NH_4Cl
(d) 500 g of 3.50% (w/w) Na_2CO_3

*7.52 Calculate the number of grams of solute needed to make each of the following solutions:
(a) 100 g of 0.500% (w/w) NaI
(b) 250 g of 0.500% (w/w) NaBr
(c) 500 g of 1.25% (w/w) $C_6H_{12}O_6$ (glucose)
(d) 750 g of 2.00% (w/w) H_2SO_4

7.53 How many grams of solute have to be weighed out to make each of the following solutions?
(a) 125 mL of 10.0% (w/v) NaCl
(b) 250 mL of 2.00% (w/v) KBr
(c) 500 mL of 1.50% (w/v) $CaCl_2$
(d) 750 mL of 0.900% (w/v) NaCl

*7.54 In order to prepare the following solutions, how many grams of solute are required?
(a) 250 mL of 5.00% (w/v) $Mg(NO_3)_2$
(b) 500 mL of 1.00% (w/v) NaBr
(c) 100 mL of 2.50% (w/v) KI
(d) 50.0 mL of 3.35% (w/v) $Ca(NO_3)_2$

7.55 How many milliliters of methyl alcohol have to be used to make 750 mL of 10.0% (v/v) aqueous methyl alcohol solution?

*7.56 A sample of 500 mL of 5.00% (v/v) aqueous ethyl alcohol contains how many milliliters of pure ethyl alcohol?

7.57 A chemical supply room has supplies of the following solutions: 5.00% (w/w) NaOH, 1.00% (w/w) Na_2CO_3, and 2.50% (w/v) glucose. If the densities of these solutions can be taken to be 1.00 g/mL, how many milliliters of the appropriate solution would you have to measure out to obtain the following quantities?
(a) 3.50 g of NaOH
(b) 0.250 g of Na_2CO_3
(c) 0.500 g of glucose
(d) 0.100 mol of NaOH
(e) 0.100 mol of glucose ($C_6H_{12}O_6$)

*7.58 The stockroom has the following solutions: 2.00% (w/w) KOH, 0.500% (w/w) HCl, and 0.900% (w/v) NaCl. Assuming that the densities of these solutions are all 1.00 g/mL, how many milliliters of the appropriate solution have to be measured out to obtain the following quantities of solutes?
(a) 0.220 g of KOH   (b) 0.150 g of HCl
(c) 0.100 mol of NaCl   (d) 0.100 mol of KOH

7.59 A student needed 50.0 mL of 10.0% (w/w) aqueous sodium acetate, $NaC_2H_3O_2$. (The density of this solution is 1.05 g/mL.) Only the trihydrate of this compound, $NaC_2H_3O_2 \cdot 3H_3O$, was available, and the student knew that the water of hydration would just become part of the solvent once the solution was made. How many grams of the trihydrate would have to be weighed out to prepare the needed solution?

*7.60 How many grams of $Na_2SO_4 \cdot 10H_2O$ have to be weighed out to prepare 100 mL of 10.0% (w/w) Na_2SO_4 in water? (The density of this solution is 1.09 g/mL.)

7.61 A student has to prepare 500 g of 1.25% (w/w) NaOH. The stock supply of NaOH is in the form of 5.00% (w/w) NaOH. How many grams of the stock solution have to be diluted to make the desired solution?

*7.62 A 10.0% (w/w) HCl solution is available from the stockroom. How many grams of this solution have to be weighed out to prepare, by dilution, 250 g of 0.500% (w/w) HCl? If the density of the 10.0% solution is 1.05 g/mL, how many milliliters would provide the grams of the concentrated solution that are called for?

7.63 Concentrated hydrochloric acid is available as 11.6 M HCl. The density of this solution is 1.18 g/mL.
(a) Calculate the percent (w/w) of HCl in this solution.
(b) How many milliliters of this concentrated acid have to be taken to prepare 500 g of a solution that is 10.0% (w/w) HCl?

*7.64 Commercial nitric acid comes in a concentration of 16.0 mol/L. The density of this solution is 1.42 g/mL.
(a) Calculate the percent (w/w) of nitric acid, HNO_3, in this solution.
(b) How many milliliters of the concentrated acid have to be taken to prepare 250 g of a solution that is 10.0% (w/w) HNO_3?

Osmosis and Dialysis

7.65 If a solution that contains 1.00 mol of glucose in 1000 g of water freezes at $-1.86\ °C$, what is the freezing point of a solution that contains 1.00 mol of glycerol in 1000 g of water? (Both are compounds that do not break up into ions when they dissolve.)

7.66 A solution that contains 1.00 mol of glucose in 1000 g of water has a normal boiling point of 100.5 °C. Another solution that contains 1.00 mol of an unknown compound in 1000 g of water has a normal boiling point of 101.0 °C. What is the likeliest explanation for the higher boiling point of the second solution?

7.67 Explain in your own words and drawings how osmosis gives a net flow of water from pure water into a solution on the other side of an osmotic membrane.

7.68 In general terms, how does an osmotic membrane differ from a dialyzing membrane?

7.69 Explain in your own words why the osmotic pressure of a solution should depend only on the concentration of its solute particles and not on their chemical properties.

7.70 The equation for osmotic pressure (Equation 7.4) shows that

this pressure is directly proportional to the Kelvin temperature. Use the kinetic model of molecules and ions in motion and other aspects of the general kinetic theory to explain why the osmotic pressure should increase with an increase in temperature.

7.71 Why is the osmolarity of 1 M NaCl not the same as its molarity?

7.72 Which has the higher osmolarity, 0.10 M NaCl or 0.080 M Na_2SO_4? Explain.

*7.73 Which solution has the higher osmotic pressure, 10% (w/w) NaCl or 10% (w/w) NaI? Both NaCl and NaI break up in water in the same way—two ions per formula unit.

7.74 Solution A consists of 0.5 mol of NaCl, 0.1 mol of $C_6H_{12}O_6$ (glucose, a molecular substance), and 0.05 mol of starch (a colloidal, macromolecular substance), all in 1000 g of water. Solution B is made of 0.5 mol of NaBr, 0.1 mol of $C_6H_{12}O_6$ (fructose, a molecular substance related to glucose), and 0.005 mol of starch all in 1000 g of water. Which solution, if either, has the higher osmotic pressure? Explain.

7.75 What is the osmotic pressure (in mm Hg) of a 0.0100 M solution in water of a molecular substance at 25 °C?

*7.76 Calculate the osmotic pressure in mm Hg of a 0.0100 M solution in water at 25 °C of a compound that breaks up into two ions per formula unit when it dissolves.

7.77 What happens to red blood cells in hemolysis?

7.78 Physiological saline solution has a concentration of 0.9% (w/w) NaCl.
(a) Is a solution that is 1.1% (w/w) NaCl described as hypertonic or hypotonic with respect to physiological saline solution?
(b) What would happen, crenation or hemolysis, if a red blood cell were placed in (1) 0.5% (w/w) NaCl? (2) In 1.5% (w/w) NaCl?

7.79 Explain how the loss of macromolecules from the blood can lead to the increased loss of water from blood and a reduction in blood volume.

Decompression Sickness (Special Topic 7.1)

7.80 The solubilities of which gases increase in blood to cause decompression sickness? Why do they increase?

7.81 How does an increased solubility of a gas in blood cause a problem when the individual comes back to normal pressure?

7.82 How does a slow decompression reduce the possibility of decompression sickness?

7.83 What is the "rule of thumb" about the rate of decompression needed to avoid decompression sickness?

Hemodialysis (Special Topic 7.2)

7.84 What does *hemodialysis* mean?

7.85 During hemodialysis, what is the *dialysate?*

7.86 With respect to the following solutes in blood, what should be the concentration of the dialysate for effective hemodialysis, more or less concentrated or the same concentration?
(a) Na^+ (b) Cl^- (c) urea

Acids, Bases, and Ionic Compounds

When this water hole in Canada dried up, its dissolved alkali formed a white border in which no plant life was possible. Early settlers and their livestock knew how life-threatening alkali water could be. We begin a study of the chemical properties of bases (alkalis), acids, and salts in this chapter.

8.1 ELECTROLYTES

Solutions of ionic compounds in water conduct electricity.

All aqueous fluids of living systems, plants or animals, contain dissolved ions and molecules. Blood, for example, contains sodium and chloride ions at low concentrations, even smaller concentrations of several other ions, as well as molecules of glucose and other molecular compounds. To understand these fluids at their molecular level, therefore, requires a study of the chemical properties of ions. This is chiefly what we will do in this and the next chapter.

■ Pure water does not conduct electricity.

One of the great differences made by the presence of ions in water is the ability of such solutions to conduct electricity. Any ions in aqueous solution enable this. This is one reason why being on moist ground near trees during electrical storms is so dangerous. The sap of trees has dissolved ions, and tree roots extend outward some distance. When lightening strikes a tree, it discharges some of its electricity through the roots, and if you are on the ground nearby you could be seriously injured or killed. Yet, on the other hand, the ability of solutions with ions to conduct electricity also makes life-helping procedures possible. If you ever need an electrocardiogram, you will value this property of blood and fluids in the skin.

Solutes Can Release Ions in Water by Dissociation or by Ionization When ionic compounds dissolve in water their ions dissociate. **Dissociation** is the separation of the ions already present in an ionic compound as its crystals break up during the dissolving process. Sodium chloride, for example, dissociates into its Na^+ ions and Cl^- ions as its crystals dissolve in water. We can write this as an equation:

■ (aq) = aqueous solution
(s) = solid

$$NaCl(s) \xrightarrow[\text{dissociation}]{H_2O} Na^+(aq) + Cl^-(aq)$$

Sodium hydroxide, NaOH, also dissolves by dissociation:

■ KOH dissociates in this manner, too.

$$NaOH(s) \xrightarrow[\text{dissociation}]{H_2O} Na^+(aq) + OH^-(aq)$$

PRACTICE EXERCISE 1

Write an equation to represent the dissociation that occurs when the following ionic compounds dissolve in water. Assume that they break up entirely into their ions.

(a) KBr   (b) Na_2SO_4 (c) $CaCl_2$

Molecular compounds can also generate ions in water. The process is not dissociation, but *ionization*. **Ionization** is the formation of ions by a chemical reaction of a molecular compound with the solvent. Hydrogen chloride, for example, undergoes ionization as it dissolves in water. We can describe this reaction using Lewis structures as follows:

■ HBr(g) and HI(g) react the same way with water to give hydrobromic acid and hydriodic acid, respectively.

$$H\!:\!\ddot{\underset{\displaystyle H}{O}}\!: + \;\widehat{H}\!:\!\ddot{\underset{..}{C}l}\!:(g) \xrightarrow{\text{ionization}} \left[H\!:\!\ddot{\underset{\displaystyle H}{O}}\!:\!H\right]^+ (aq) + \left[:\!\ddot{\underset{..}{C}l}\!:\right]^- (aq)$$

Hydrogen chloride   Hydrochloric acid

As a gaseous compound, hydrogen chloride contains no ions. The gas can be cooled and thereby condensed to its liquid state, but still it contains no ions. Yet when HCl(g) dissolves in water, essentially 100% of its molecules react by the foregoing equation. The resulting solution is called hydrochloric acid.

Ammonia is another compound that produces ions by reacting with water. The extent of its ionization is not 100%, but we can still write an equation for the reaction that does occur. We represent dissolved NH_3 as $NH_3(aq)$, not $NH_3(g)$, because most of its molecules remain as hydrated molecules involved in hydrogen bonding with water molecules (as we studied in Section 7.4). Lewis structures will again help us see what happens.

$$\underset{\text{Ammonia}}{\text{H}:\overset{\overset{\displaystyle H}{\cdot\cdot}}{\underset{\cdot\cdot}{N}}:\text{H}(aq)} + \text{(H)}:\overset{\cdot\cdot}{\underset{\cdot\cdot}{O}}: \xrightarrow[\text{ionization}]{\text{small percentage}} \left[\text{H}:\overset{\overset{\displaystyle H}{\cdot\cdot}}{\underset{\displaystyle H}{N}}:\text{H}\right]^{+}(aq) + \left[\text{H}:\overset{\cdot\cdot}{\underset{\cdot\cdot}{O}}:\right]^{-}(aq)$$

Ammonia   Ammonium ion   Hydroxide ion

Ions in Water Can Carry Electricity

Electricity in metals is a flow of electrons. A complete circuit includes a battery or generator that forces the electrons to move. (The energy of the flow is called electrical energy.) If the circuit is broken, the flow stops. The break might be just air at the gap of an open switch, or it might be a space filled with some inert insulating fluid, like sulfur hexafluoride or even pure water. If we add ions to the water, however, we close the gap again. Electricity flows through aqueous solutions of ions, as we said.

■ Electrical insulators prevent electricity from flowing even when the electrical pressure, the voltage, is very high.

The passage of electricity through a solution with dissolved ions is called **electrolysis.** A solute that enables a solution to conduct electricity is called an **electrolyte.** (Sometimes the solution itself is called the electrolyte.) The question now is, "How do electrolytes make electrolysis possible?"

Electrons do not move directly through a solution of electrolytes in the same way that they move through metals. Instead the dissolved ions move. Figure 8.1 shows a typical setup. The plates or wires that dip into the solution are called **electrodes.** The battery forces electrons to one electrode to make it electron-rich and negatively charged. In electrolysis, the negative electrode is called the **cathode.** Positive ions in solution naturally are attracted to the cathode, because opposite charges attract. Positive ions are called **cations** (pronounced cat-ions) after this behavior.

The electrons that make the cathode electron-rich are "pumped" from the other electrode, called the **anode,** which becomes electron-poor and positively charged. Negative ions are naturally attracted to the anode, and negative ions are called **anions.**

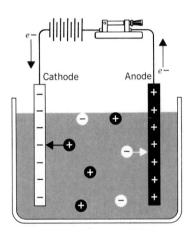

● Cation   ⊖ Anion

Figure 8.1
Electrolysis. Cations, positive ions, migrate to the cathode and remove electrons. Anions, negative ions, migrate to the anode and deposit electrons. The effect is a closed circuit.

Electrolysis Causes a Redox Reaction

We will take a simple example of an electrolysis, that of aqueous copper(II) bromide, to show how a cation can remove electrons at the cathode and an anion can deliver them to the anode. Copper(II) bromide dissociates in water as Cu^{2+} and $2Br^{-}$ ions. When Cu^{2+} cations arrive at the cathode, they pick electrons from the cathode's electron-rich surface and are reduced to Cu atoms. In other words, the oxidation number of copper changes from $+2$ to 0. We can represent this by an equation in which electrons are shown as actual reactants:

$$Cu^{2+}(aq) + 2e^{-} \xrightarrow[\text{reduction}]{} Cu(s)$$

Since the oxidation number becomes less positive, we know that reduction is what is happening to the Cu^{2+} ion. (In this example, *reduction* clearly is also a gain of electrons, the older definition of reduction.) Thus, in electrolysis, reduction occurs at a cathode.

When Br^{-} anions move to the anode, they deposit electrons at the anode's electron-poor surface. Two Br^{-} ions give up electrons at the anode, and one molecule of Br_2 forms. The oxidation number of bromine thus changes from -1 to 0, which means that oxidation is happening. (And, by the older definition, there is clearly a loss of electrons as two Br^{-} change to Br_2.) The reaction is

$$2Br^{-}(aq) \xrightarrow[\text{oxidation}]{} Br_2(l) + 2e^{-}$$

■ Some electrolytes, like KNO_3, give more complex electrode reactions. The electrolyte does not change but water breaks down to H_2 and O_2, instead.

Thus oxidation occurs at an anode during electrolysis.

During electrolysis we have something taking electrons from one electrode and something else putting them on the other electrode. The effect, therefore, is the same as if the

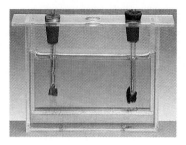

Figure 8.2
Electrolysis of $CuBr_2(aq)$. The solution is blue because of the copper(II) ion. The cathode, on the right, has a deposit of copper metal, and some has flaked off and fallen below it. The color around and below the anode, on the left, is brownish because Br_2 is forming.

electrons themselves were actually moving through the solution, but actually they move through the wire.

Notice how the sum of the two equations for the reactions at the electrodes gives the overall equation for the reaction caused by electrolysis.

■ Br_2 is somewhat soluble in water, so $Br_2(aq)$ could just as well be used in this equation as $Br_2(l)$.

At the cathode: $\qquad Cu^+(aq) + 2e^- \xrightarrow[\text{reduction}]{} Cu(s)$

At the anode: $\qquad\qquad 2Br^-(aq) \xrightarrow[\text{oxidation}]{} Br_2(l) + 2e^-$

Sum: $\qquad\quad \overline{Cu^{2+}(aq) + 2Br^-(aq) \xrightarrow[\text{electrolysis}]{} Cu(s) + Br_2(l)}$

The electrons cancel as this summation is made. They must cancel, of course, because we cannot have free electrons as actual reactants or products. But electrons can transfer. In electrolysis, they transfer from one dissolved species to the other through the wiring of the external circuit. Figure 8.2 shows how an aqueous solution of $CuBr_2$ appears some time after its electrolysis has been started. You can see that both copper metal and bromine form.

■ The electrolysis of anhydrous *molten* NaCl is the industrial synthesis of both sodium and chlorine.

$2NaCl(l) \xrightarrow{\text{electrolysis}} 2Na(l) + Cl_2(g)$

Molten Ionic Compounds Are Also Electrolytes For electrolysis to happen, ions must be mobile. When ions are immobilized in the solid state, no electrolysis occurs. If the solid, ionic compound is heated until it melts, however, then the ions become mobile, and molten salts conduct electricity. Thus the term *electrolyte* can refer either to a solution of ions or to the pure, solid ionic compound. (The term does not apply to metals. Metals that conduct electricity are simply called *conductors*.)

Strong Electrolytes Give High Concentrations of Ions in Water Electrolytes are not equally good at enabling the flow of electricity. A "good" electrolyte is a substance that even in low concentrations enables a strong electrical current to flow. It's a solute that can readily supply ions. Good electrolytes, in this sense, are called **strong electrolytes,** which means that in aqueous solutions essentially 100% of their formula units have dissociated or ionized. Sodium hydroxide, hydrochloric acid, and sodium chloride are all strong electrolytes.

■ In 1 *M* ammonia and 1 *M* acetic acid, the percentage ionization is less than 0.5%.

A **weak electrolyte** is a substance that generates ions in water only to a small percentage of its molar concentration. A typical example is aqueous ammonia. Although 1 *M* NaCl is 100% ionized and is thus an excellent conductor, 1 *M* aqueous ammonia is a poor conductor because a small percentage of dissolved NH_3 molecules react with water to give ions. Aqueous ammonia is thus a weak electrolyte. Acetic acid, the acid that gives vinegar its tart taste, is also a weak electrolyte.

Many substances are **nonelectrolytes,** whether they are in the liquid state or in solution. They do not conduct ordinary currents of electricity (e.g., household currents) at all. Pure water is an example of a nonelectrolyte, and alcohol and gasoline are others.

We can summarize the relationships we have just studied as follows. Be sure to notice the emphasis on *percentage* ionization as the feature dominating these definitions.

Strong electrolyte	One that is strongly dissociated or ionized in water—a high percentage ionization
Weak electrolyte	One that is weakly ionized in water—a low-percentage ionization
Nonelectrolyte	One that does not dissociate or ionize in water—essentially zero-percentage ionization

■ Weak electrolytes are generally molecular compounds that give ions by ionization, not dissociation.

8.2 ACIDS AND BASES AS ELECTROLYTES

Acids supply hydrogen ions, and bases neutralize hydrogen ions.

■ Even the most minute traces of acids or bases can switch enzymes on or off, and enzymes are essential to almost all reactions in living systems.

The three principal ion-producers in water are *acids*, *bases*, and *salts*. At the molecular level of life, the *acid–base balance* of body fluids, part of the overall *electrolyte balance,* is a matter of life and death. In this section we will learn about the major acids and bases and what it means for an aqueous solution to be acidic, basic, or neutral. We begin with another look at water, because some of our definitions are related to its self-ionization.

Traces of H_3O^+ and OH^- Ions Form from the Self-Ionization of Water We said in the previous section that pure water is a nonconductor, and this is true. Traces of ions, H_3O^+ and OH^-, are present, but not at concentrations high enough to conduct electricity. These ions come from the self-ionization of water.

■ The colliding molecules, of course, must be properly aligned in this collision for H^+ to transfer.

$$\left[H\!:\!\overset{\displaystyle ..}{\underset{\displaystyle H}{O}}\!:\!H \right]^+$$

Hydronium ion

$$[:\overset{\displaystyle ..}{\underset{\displaystyle ..}{O}}\!:\!H]^-$$

Hydroxide ion

Remember that liquid water has mobile molecules, and these bump into each other. The collisions vary from mere taps to those of great violence. When two water molecules collide powerfully enough, a transfer of H^+ occurs from one to the other, as visualized in Figure 8.3, to give two ions in a 1:1 mole ratio, the **hydronium ion,** H_3O^+, and the **hydroxide ion,** OH^-. This self-ionization of water is actually the forward reaction in a chemical equilibrium:

$$2H_2O \rightleftharpoons H_3O^+(aq) + OH^-(aq)$$

The forward reaction is definitely not favored; at 25 °C the concentration of each product ion is only 1.0×10^{-7} mol/L. Out of a little over 1 billion water molecules, only 2 have, at any one moment, changed into these ions.

It is customary to use brackets, [ ], around a formula of a solute when we mean its concentration in the specific units of moles per liter. Thus, in pure water at 25 °C,

$$[H_3O^+] = [OH^-] = 1.0 \times 10^{-7} \text{ mol/L}$$

Although concentrations this low may seem too unimportant to mention, life itself hinges on holding the molar concentrations of H_3O^+ and OH^- ions in body fluids at about this level.

We have already learned that equilibria can be shifted, and shifts in water's self-ionization equilibrium are life-threatening. Almost all of what we will be studying about acids and bases is

Figure 8.3
The self-ionization of water. Extremely violent collisions are necessary, and at equilibrium the fraction of all collisions occurring at any instant that are energetic enough is very small, so the forward reaction is not favored.

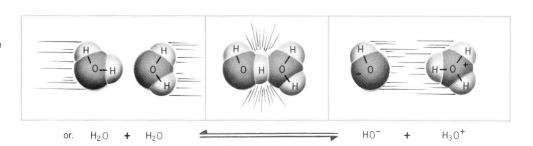

or: H_2O + H_2O $\rightleftharpoons$ HO^- + H_3O^+

essential to the study of how the body controls the equilibrium for the self-ionization of water and the acid–base balance of body fluids.

The Hydronium Ion Is Often Referred To As the Hydrogen Ion

The existence of ions in aqueous solutions of electrolytes was first proposed by Svante Arrhenius (1859–1927), a Swedish scientist. He said that all acids produce hydrogen ions in water. He actually spoke of *hydrogen* ions, H^+, not hydronium ions, H_3O^+, but he had no way then of knowing that bare protons, which H^+ really represents, are *always* piggybacked on something else in solution. Although protons can be *transferred* from one place to another, they have no independent existence as separate entities in solution any more than do electrons. H^+ is always held by an electron-pair bond to a water molecule or to something else. It is the ability of something to transfer H^+ that makes it an acid.

■ In 1884, Arrhenius nearly lost his bid for a doctorate degree for proposing ions, so rash was the idea considered. But in 1903, the idea earned him a Nobel prize.

In a practical sense, Arrhenius's supposition about H^+ wasn't too wide of the mark. H^+ is so easily available from H_3O^+ that scientists today commonly use the terms *proton, hydrogen ion,* and *hydronium ion* interchangeably. We will use *hydrogen ion* as a convenient nickname for *hydronium ion* ourselves, and we will often employ the symbol $H^+(aq)$ as a simpler way of writing $H_3O^+(aq)$.

Acids Make the H^+ Level Exceed the OH^- Level and Bases Do the Opposite

When the molar concentrations of aqueous hydrogen ions and hydroxide ions are exactly equal, as they are in pure water at any temperature, the solution is called a **neutral solution.**

Acids make the molar concentration of hydrogen ion higher than that of hydroxide ion. Because acidic solutions all have the hydrogen ion, they all have many common properties. Acidic solutions, for example, turn blue litmus to a red color. Litmus is an example of an **acid–base indicator,** a compound whose color is different in acid than in base, so it can be used to tell if an aqueous solution is acidic or basic. Acidic solutions also have tart tastes, like solutions of acetic acid, citric acid, lactic acid, oxalic acid, and hydrochloric acid. But don't make a taste test without great care. Even dilute acids can corrode teeth.

■ Paper impregnated with litmus dye is called *litmus paper.*

Acid	A Natural Source
acetic acid	vinegar
citric acid	lemons
lactic acid	sour milk
oxalic acid	rhubarb
hydrochloric acid	gastric juice

Bases make the molar concentration of hydroxide ion greater than that of hydronium ion. Such solutions usually have a bitter taste and a soapy "feel," and they turn red litmus blue.

We can summarize the important conditions that define acidic, basic, and neutral solutions as follows:

■ >, greater than
<, less than

Acidic solutions:	$[H^+] > [OH^-]$
Neutral solutions:	$[H^+] = [OH^-]$
Basic solutions:	$[H^+] < [OH^-]$

Acids and Bases According to Brønsted

We said earlier that it is the ability of something to transfer H^+ that makes it an acid. We can also say that it is the ability of something to accept H^+ that makes it a base. Johannes Brønsted (1879–1947), a Danish chemist, is generally credited with the development of these definitions.

■ Thomas Martin Lowry (1847–1936), an English chemist, proposed the same idea independently.

Brønsted Definitions of Acids and Bases

Acids are proton donors.
Bases are proton acceptors.

These definitions apply regardless of the solvent and even in the absence of any liquid solvent. Hydrogen chloride gas, for example, reacts with ammonia gas in a proton-transfer reaction.

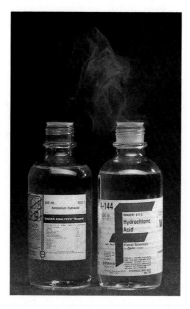

Figure 8.4
The reaction of $NH_3(g)$, from the bottle on the left, with $HCl(g)$, from the bottle on the right, produces a cloud of microcrystals of $NH_4Cl(s)$ by a neutralization reaction. These gaseous reactants are always present in the air spaces above concentrated solutions of aqueous ammonia and hydrochloric acid.

$$HCl(g) + NH_3(g) \longrightarrow NH_4Cl(s)$$

The product is a crystalline solid that forms in a cloud of microcrystals when fumes of ammonia and hydrogen chloride intermingle, as seen in Figure 8.4. The H—Cl molecules are proton-donors; NH_3 molecules are proton-acceptors. When H^+ transfers from the acid, H—Cl, to the base, NH_3, NH_4^+ ions and Cl^- ions form, and no solvent was involved.

Acids and Bases Vary Widely in Strength   Acids and bases are quite different in their abilities to function as proton-donors or proton-acceptors. Water, for example, is extremely weak as both a donor and an acceptor, as we have just learned. Hydrogen chloride, $HCl(g)$, on the other hand, so readily donates H^+ that even such a weak acceptor as H_2O is able to take H^+ from $HCl(g)$. Essentially 100% of all hydrogen chloride molecules that dissolve in water react as follows:

$$HCl(g) + H_2O \longrightarrow H_3O^+(aq) + Cl^-(aq)$$

Because water is the solvent nearly always used in acid–base chemistry, we normally define all strong acids with reference to their reactions with water. If we use the general symbol HA for any acid, whether it is a gas, liquid, or solid, then all strong acids react as follows essentially 100%:

■ Think of A in HA or A^- as standing for the anion of the acid.

$$HA + H_2O \longrightarrow H_3O^+(aq) + A^-(aq)$$

We define a **strong acid** as one that is 100% ionized in this proton-donating reaction. The hydronium ion, itself, so readily donates a proton that we also apply the term *strong acid* to any aqueous solution of a strong acid.

   A **weak acid** is one for which only a small percentage of its molecules react with water in this way. You may have already noticed that the terms *strong* and *weak* are used alike with both acids and electrolytes. They refer to percentage ionization. All strong acids are strong electrolytes. All weak acids are weak electrolytes. Let's now look at a few of the most common strong and weak acids.

Hydrochloric Acid and Nitric Acid Are Strong Monoprotic Acids   Hydrochloric acid is a **monoprotic acid** because the ratio of H_3O^+ ions to Cl^- ions in this aqueous solution of

Figure 8.5
The ionization of acetic acid in water. Only a small fraction of the collisions are energetic enough at equilibrium to make a proton transfer from O in acetic acid to O in H_2O. The forward reaction is thus not favored, and acetic acid is a weak acid.

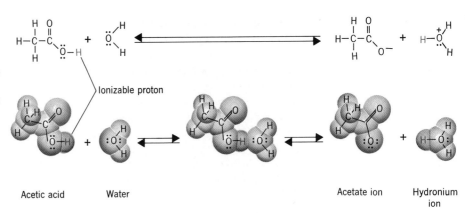

Acetic acid   Water   Acetate ion   Hydronium ion

HCl is 1 to 1. Other monoprotic acids are those that can be made by dissolving the other hydrogen halide gases in water — hydrofluoric acid, HF(*aq*), hydrobromic acid, HBr(*aq*), and hydriodic acid, HI(*aq*). All but hydrofluoric acid are strong acids.[1]

PRACTICE EXERCISE 2   Depict the ionization of HBr and HI in water using Lewis structures such as we did for HCl in the previous section.

Nitric acid, HNO_3(*aq*), is also a strong, monoprotic acid. We can represent its ionization as follows:

$$H_2O + HNO_3(aq) \longrightarrow H_3O^+(aq) + NO_3^-(aq)$$

Nitric acid (molecular formula)   Hydronium ion   Nitrate ion

Nitric acid in water

Acetic Acid Is a Weak Monoprotic Acid   Acetic acid is a typical organic acid, and like virtually all organic acids, it is a weak acid. **Organic compounds,** we should say here, are the compounds of carbon other than its oxides, the cyanides, or those related to earth-like substances like carbonate rocks and other carbonates. Compounds that are not organic compounds are called **inorganic compounds.**

The acetic acid molecule, $HC_2H_3O_2$, has four hydrogen atoms, but only one is attached to an oxygen atom. Only this one can transfer to a water molecule, and a powerful collision is needed. See Figure 8.5. The H—O bond in acetic acid is considerably stronger than the H—Cl bond in HCl(*g*), so acetic acid does not so readily transfer H^+ as H—Cl. A chemical equilibrium is present in aqueous acetic acid, which can be represented as follows.

$$H_2O + H\!-\!C_2H_3O_2 \rightleftharpoons H_3O^+(aq) + C_2H_3O_2^-(aq)$$

Acetic acid[2]   Acetate ion

In 0.1*M* acetic acid, only 0.5% of all acetic acid molecules are at any moment ionized. But there is the coming and going characteristic of all dynamic equilibria. The forward reaction here requires hard collisions, and they don't happen frequently. But the concentrations of water and molecular acetic acid are high, so such successful collisions still occur. The reverse reaction requires mild collisions, so they can happen readily. But the colliding species, the

Nitric acid

$HC_2H_3O_2$
Acetic acid

$C_2H_3O_2^-$
Acetate ion

---

[1] Hydrofluoric acid, HF(*aq*), is unusual because its ions, H_3O^+ and F^-, attract each other so strongly in solution that they behave as if they were not very free of each other. HF(*aq*) is thus classified as a *weak acid.*

[2] We will usually use $HC_2H_3O_2$ instead of the full structure as our symbol for acetic acid in this chapter and the next. Just remember that only one hydrogen is active in acid–base reactions, and that acetic acid is monoprotic.

hydronium ion and acetate ion, are at low concentrations, and this reduces the rate. At equilibrium, the two opposing rates are equal.

The C=O Group Makes Acetic Acid More Acidic Than Water

We might pause to ask here why acetic acid is an acid at all, why the proton of its H—O group more easily transfers than the proton of the H—O group in water. The difference is made by the group that directly holds H—O in the acetic acid molecule, the system of the carbon–oxygen double bond, C=O. This is an electronegative group. Its electronegative oxygen atom makes it so, and it pulls some electron density away from the oxygen atom of the H—O group in acetic acid. This weakens the H—O bond, so the hydrogen more easily transfers to a water molecule than the hydrogen of a water molecule itself.

■ Sulfuric acid is the most widely used acid in industrial applications. Over 70 billion pounds (over 250 billion moles) are annually used in the United States.

Sulfuric acid

Sulfuric Acid

Sulfuric acid, $H_2SO_4(aq)$, is the only common aqueous **diprotic acid,** one that gives two hydronium ions per formula unit in solution. The ionization of the first proton is so easy that sulfuric acid is a strong acid.

$$H_2O + \underset{\text{Sulfuric acid}}{H_2SO_4} \longrightarrow H_3O^+(aq) + \underset{\substack{\text{Hydrogen sulfate} \\ \text{ion}}}{HSO_4^-(aq)}$$

■ A "lone oxygen" is one joined only to one other atom.

The two extra "lone oxygens" on sulfur in sulfuric acid help to make sulfuric acid an acid in a way similar to the effect of the lone oxygen in acetic acid.

Hydrogen sulfate ion

The Hydrogen Sulfate Ion Is an Acid

The hydrogen sulfate ion is a monoprotic acid. The transfer of H^+ from it, however, requires a positively charged particle to leave one already oppositely charged. Although this is harder than the transfer of the first H^+ from H_2SO_4, it still happens. The following equilibrium exists, and the products are favored.

$$H_2O + \underset{\substack{\text{Hydrogen sulfate} \\ \text{ion}}}{HSO_4^-} \rightleftharpoons H_3O^+ + \underset{\text{Sulfate ion}}{SO_4^{2-}}$$

Sulfate ion

In later sections, when we consider the chemical properties of sulfuric acid, we will treat it as a fully ionized species. This means, in other words, that we treat a dilute solution of sulfuric acid as consisting of hydronium ions and sulfate ions, as if hydrogen sulfate ions were not involved. This will often simplify a discussion.

Phosphoric Acid Is a Moderately Strong, Triprotic Acid

A **triprotic acid** is one that can release three H^+ ions, but each separates with greater difficulty that the previous one. Phosphoric acid, H_3PO_4, is the only common example among the inorganic acids. Like the ionization of sulfuric acid, that of phosphoric acid occurs in steps, each one more difficult than the previous. Even the first step does not occur to 100% of the phosphoric acid molecules. In $1M\ H_3PO_4$, less than a third are ionized, so we have to write equilibrium expressions for all steps.

Phosphoric acid

$$H_2O + \underset{\substack{\text{Phosphoric} \\ \text{acid}}}{H_3PO_4(aq)} \rightleftharpoons H_3O^+(aq) + \underset{\substack{\text{Dihydrogen} \\ \text{phosphate ion}}}{H_2PO_4^-(aq)}$$

■ $H_2PO_4^-$ is a weak acid.

$$H_2O + H_2PO_4^-(aq) \rightleftharpoons H_3O^+(aq) + \underset{\substack{\text{Monohydrogen} \\ \text{phosphate ion}}}{HPO_4^{2-}(aq)}$$

■ HPO_4^{2-} is a *very* weak acid.

$$H_2O + HPO_4^{2-}(aq) \rightleftharpoons H_3O^+(aq) + \underset{\text{Phosphate ion}}{PO_4^{3-}(aq)}$$

Diphosphoric acid

Triphosphoric acid

Carbonic acid

Bicarbonate ion

Carbonate ion

The percentage ionization of H_3PO_4 is roughly 27% in a dilute solution of phosphoric acid. This is too low to be a strong acid but high enough to make it a good conductor of electricity in water. It's classified as a moderate acid. (In the next chapter we'll get some numbers that reveal relative strengths better than qualitative terms like strong, medium, and weak.)

It is important to learn the names and formulas of the three ions available from phosphoric acid, because the phosphate ion system occurs widely in the body. Close relatives of phosphoric acid — diphosphoric acid and triphosphoric acid — are particularly important systems in metabolism.

Carbonic Acid Is Involved in Respiration Carbonic acid, H_2CO_3, is a weak diprotic acid that is unusual because it is unstable. Its instability, however, is an important property when the body has to manage one of the respiratory gases, carbon dioxide. When carbon dioxide dissolves in water, some of it reacts with water to form carbonic acid in the following equilibrium (in which unchanged CO_2 is strongly favored):

$$CO_2(aq) + H_2O \rightleftharpoons H_2CO_3(aq)$$
$$\text{Carbonic acid}$$

Then a small fraction of the carbonic acid molecules ionizes, a fraction small enough to make carbonic acid a weak acid.

$$H_2CO_3(aq) + H_2O \rightleftharpoons H_3O^+ + HCO_3^-(aq)$$
$$\text{Bicarbonate ion}$$

The bicarbonate ion is itself a (very) weak acid. It ionizes to a very slight extent in water in the following equilibrium (which strongly favors unchanged bicarbonate ion):.

$$HCO_3^-(aq) + H_2O \rightleftharpoons H_3O^+ + CO_3^{2-}(aq)$$
$$\text{Carbonate ion}$$

The bicarbonate ion is the chief form in which waste carbon dioxide is carried from body tissues to the lungs. We'll give a brief overview of this process in Section 8.6, but we need to know something about the general reactions of acids and bases first.

PRACTICE EXERCISE 3

■ Sulfurous acid is actually $SO_2 \cdot H_2O(aq)$, not $H_2SO_3(aq)$, but the latter formula is the more commonly used.

■ You can know that lactic, acetic, oxalic, and citric acids are weak acids because they aren't on our list of strong acids.

Sulfurous acid, $H_2SO_3(aq)$, is a moderately strong, diprotic acid, but like carbonic acid it is also unstable. When sulfur dioxide dissolves in water, some of it reacts with the water to give a solution called sulfurous acid, traditionally written as H_2SO_3. Write the equilibrium equations for the successive ionizations of this weak acid.

Table 8.1 summarizes the common aqueous acids. You should memorize the names and formulas of all the strong and moderate acids on this list. We'll need this knowledge as we go along. There are very few of them, and once they are learned, you can be fairly certain that any unfamiliar acid you encounter will be a weak acid. It's easier to learn a few strong and moderate acids than several hundred weak acids.

Sodium Hydroxide Is the Most Common Strong Base Table 8.2 lists the common bases. The **strong bases** are those that dissociate nearly 100% in water, and they furnish a strong proton-binding or proton-accepting species, like the hydroxide ion. Sodium hydroxide, NaOH, and potassium hydroxide, KOH, are examples.

■ Solid NaOH is very hygroscopic, so its containers must be promptly and tightly reclosed each time some is taken.

$$NaOH(s) \xrightarrow{\text{water}} Na^+(aq) + OH^-(aq)$$
$$KOH(s) \xrightarrow{\text{water}} K^+(aq) + OH^-(aq)$$

TABLE 8.1 **Common Acids**[a]

Acid	Formula	Percentage Ionization
Strong Acids		
Hydrochloric acid	HCl	very high
Hydrobromic acid	HBr	very high
Hydriodic acid	HI	very high
Nitric acid	HNO_3	very high
Sulfuric acid[b]	H_2SO_4	very high
Moderate Acids		
Phosphoric acid	H_3PO_4	27
Sulfurous acid[c]	H_2SO_3	20
Weak Acids		
Nitrous acid[c]	HNO_2	1.5
Acetic acid	$HC_2H_3O_2$	1.3
Carbonic acid[c]	H_2CO_3	0.2

[a] Data are for 0.1 *M* solutions of the acids in water at room temperature.

[b] *Concentrated* sulfuric acid (99%) is particularly dangerous not only because it is a strong acid but also because it is a powerful dehydrating agent. This action generates considerable heat at the reaction site, and at higher temperatures sulfuric acid becomes even more dangerous. Moreover, concentrated sulfuric acid is a thick, viscous liquid that does not wash away from skin or fabric very quickly.

[c] An unstable acid.

TABLE 8.2 **Common Bases**

Base	Formula	Solubility[a]	Percentage Ionization
Strong Bases			
Sodium hydroxide	NaOH	109	>90 (0.1 *M* solution)
Potassium hydroxide	KOH	112	>90 (0.1 *M* solution)
Calcium hydroxide	$Ca(OH)_2$	0.165	100 (saturated solution)
Magnesium hydroxide	$Mg(OH)_2$	0.0009	100 (saturated solution)
Weak Base			
Aqueous ammonia	NH_3	89.9	1.3 (18 °C)[b]

[a] Solubilities are in grams of solute per 100 g of water at 20 °C except where otherwise noted.

[b] The ionization referred to here is the equilibrium:

$$NH_3(aq) + H_2O \rightleftharpoons NH_4^+(aq) + OH^-(aq)$$

Milk of magnesia, a slurry of $Mg(OH)_2(s)$ in water, is a common remedy for acid indigestion. Too heavy and frequent doses, however, can upset the levels of $Mg^{2+}(aq)$ in various body fluids.

Two other strong bases are the hydroxides of group IIA metals. These are magnesium hydroxide, $Mg(OH)_2$, and calcium hydroxide, $Ca(OH)_2$. They ionize essentially 100% in water, but as the data in Table 8.2 show, they are so insoluble in water that even saturated solutions provide only very dilute solutions of hydroxide ions.

$$Ca(OH)_2(s) \longrightarrow Ca^{2+}(aq) + 2OH^-(aq)$$
$$Mg(OH)_2(s) \longrightarrow Mg^{2+}(aq) + 2OH^-(aq)$$

In sufficient concentration, the hydroxide ion causes a severe chemical burn, certainly enough to be very hazardous to the eyes. Both sodium and potassium hydroxides can be prepared in solutions concentrated enough to be dangerous chemicals. Calcium and magnesium hydroxide, however, are so insoluble that they not only pose no grave danger to the skin, they are used internally in home remedies. Calcium hydroxide is a component of one commercial antacid tablet. A slurry of magnesium hydroxide in water, called "milk of magnesia," is used as an antacid and a laxative.

A **weak base** is a poor proton-acceptor, one that is unable to take protons from water molecules to any appreciable extent. Ammonia is the most common example. A solution of ammonia in water, called aqueous ammonia, does have some excess hydroxide ion, but only a small percentage of ammonia molecules react to produce it, as we earlier learned. The following equilibrium is present, and the reactants are strongly favored:

■ You'll sometimes see *aqueous ammonia* called "ammonium hydroxide," but this is misleading. NH$_4$OH is unknown as a pure compound.

$$NH_3(aq) + H_2O \rightleftharpoons NH_4{}^+(aq) \quad + OH^-(aq)$$
Ammonia $\qquad\qquad$ Ammonium ion

A dilute solution (about 5%) of ammonia in water is sold as household ammonia in supermarkets. It's a good cleaning agent, but watch out for its fumes.

The names and formulas of the bases in Table 8.2 should also be memorized.

All Salts Are Strong Electrolytes The third major family of ion-producing substances is the salts. We have to say something about them here — they'll be treated more fully in a later section — because salts are products of the reactions of acids and bases, which we'll study in the next section.

Salts are ionic compounds in which the positive ion is a metal ion or any other positive ion except H$^+$, and the negative ion is any except OH$^-$ or O^{2-}. All salts are crystalline ionic solids at room temperature. All are strong electrolytes. When salts dissolve in water, their ions dissociate essentially 100%. Even for very insoluble salts, what little of them that does dissolve becomes 100% dissociated, and many can be made in aqueous solution by the reaction of an acid with a base.

8.3 THE CHEMICAL PROPERTIES OF AQUEOUS ACIDS AND BASES

Acids react with hydroxides, bicarbonates, carbonates, ammonia, and active metals.

In this section we will principally study the reactions of the hydronium ion, H$_3$O$^+$. We will see how a variety of substances are able to accept H$^+$ from this ion in reactions that neutralize acidic solutions. They include the hydroxide ion, the bicarbonate ion, the carbonate ion, and the ammonia molecule. All are Brønsted bases, of course, because all accept H$^+$. We'll also see that many metals are able to reduce two H$^+$ ions to H$_2$ and themselves be oxidized to metal ions. Some metals are so active that they can even abstract protons directly from molecules of water.

As we mentioned before, we'll use the symbol H$^+$(aq) as a shorthand symbol for the hydronium ion in most of the equations. The anions of the acids have their own chemical reactions, of course, but we'll not be concerned about them here unless they are Brønsted bases whose reactions we have to study at this time.

There is a special kind of equation, the net ionic equation, that is particularly helpful when we concentrate on the chemical properties of ions, and we will learn how to write and interpret such equations first.

A Net Ionic Equation Omits "Spectator" Species The conventional equation for a reaction is called a **molecular equation** because it shows all of the substances in the molecular or empirical formulas that we would need to plan an actual experiment. The molecular equation for the reaction of sodium carbonate decahydrate with hydrochloric acid, for example, is

■ We say *molecular* equation even though some of the chemicals in the equation might be ionic.

$$Na_2CO_3 \cdot 10H_2O(s) + 2HCl(aq) \longrightarrow 2NaCl(aq) + CO_2(g) + 11H_2O$$

To take a simpler example, the molecular equation for the reaction of hydrochloric acid with aqueous sodium hydroxide is

$$HCl(aq) + NaOH(aq) \longrightarrow NaCl(aq) + H_2O$$

However, as we now know, $HCl(aq)$ is really $H^+(aq)$ and $Cl^-(aq)$; and $NaOH(aq)$ is actually $Na^+(aq)$ and $OH^-(aq)$. We know this because we know the acid is a *strong* acid and the base is a *strong* base, so both must be essentially fully ionized in solution. We don't have nonionized molecules of HCl or NaOH in the solution. We also know that $NaCl(aq)$ is fully ionized because all salts are strong electrolytes, and the (*aq*) by its formula tells us that the NaCl is in solution. [An insoluble salt would have had (*s*) after its formula.] The fourth formula in the equation is that of water, a nonelectrolyte. Its molecules aren't separated into ions. (We ignore, of course, the self-ionization of water, because it occurs to an exceedingly low percentage.) We'll always assume that H_2O means $H_2O(l)$.

Using these facts we can expand the molecular equation into what is called the **ionic equation,** one that shows all of the dissolved species, whether ionic or molecular. We do this by replacing anything that we know is present as ions by the actual formulas of these ions. Thus the ionic equation for our example is

$$\underbrace{H^+(aq) + Cl^-(aq)}_{\text{These came from } HCl(aq)} + \underbrace{Na^+(aq) + OH^-(aq)}_{\text{These came from } NaOH(aq)} \longrightarrow \underbrace{Na^+(aq) + Cl^-(aq)}_{\text{These came from } NaCl(aq)} + \underset{\text{Not ionized}}{H_2O}$$

An ionic equation is actually just a scratch paper operation, because we next cancel all of the formulas that appear identically on opposites sides of the arrow. The foregoing ionic equation shows us, for example, that nothing happens either to $Na^+(aq)$ or to $Cl^-(aq)$. There is no reason, therefore, to let them remain in the equation when we just want to give full attention to the species that react and form. $Na^+(aq)$ and $Cl^-(aq)$, of course, do serve one function; they give electrical neutrality to their respective compounds. Otherwise, they are nothing more than *spectator particles* in this reaction.

We can cancel the spectator particles, whether they are ions or molecules, from the ionic equation. This leaves the **net ionic equation,** one that shows only the reacting species and the products they form. As you can see, this equation is a simple description of what happens when hydrochloric acid, *or any strong acid,* neutralizes sodium hydroxide, *or any hydroxide base* in solution.

$$H^+(aq) + OH^-(aq) \longrightarrow H_2O$$

Net Ionic Equations Must Balance Both Electrically and Materially For a net ionic equation to be balanced, two conditions must be met: a material balance and an electrical balance. We have **material balance** when the numbers of atoms of each element, regardless of how they are chemically present, are the same on both sides of the arrow. We have **electrical balance** when the algebraic sum of the charges left of the arrow equals the sum of the charges to the right.

■ Sometimes we don't cancel but only reduce in number. If an ionic equation , for example, has

$$\ldots + 4H_2O \longrightarrow \ldots + 2H_2O$$

we can simplify it to

$$\ldots + 2H_2O \longrightarrow$$

■ The material balance is what we need in any kind of balanced equation.

| **EXAMPLE 8.1** | **WRITING A NET IONIC EQUATION** |

■ Sulfuric acid must be handled very carefully. See Table 8.1.

Problem: Sulfuric acid is the most important acid in industrial use, and sometimes it has to be neutralized by sodium hydroxide. The reaction can be carried out to produce sodium sulfate, $Na_2SO_4(aq)$, and water. Write the molecular, ionic, and net ionic equations.

Solution: We always start with a molecular equation, and to write it we put down the formulas of the reactants and products in the conventional manner, and then we balance. The molecular equation is

$$H_2SO_4(aq) + 2NaOH(aq) \longrightarrow Na_2SO_4(aq) + 2H_2O$$

Next, we have to recall the following facts.

$H_2SO_4(aq)$ means $2H^+(aq) + SO_4{}^{2-}(aq)$ (This is a strong, fully ionized acid.)

$2NaOH(aq)$ means $2Na^+(aq) + 2OH^-(aq)$ (This is a strong, fully ionized metal hydroxide.)

$Na_2SO_4(aq)$ means $2Na^+(aq) + SO_4{}^{2-}(aq)$ (This is a salt, and (*aq*) tells us that it is in solution; hence, it is fully ionized.)

$2H_2O$ means $2H_2O$ (No breaking up occurs with this nonelectrolyte.)

These facts let us transform the molecular equation into the following ionic equation:

$$2H^+(aq) + SO_4{}^{2-}(aq) + 2Na^+(aq) + 2OH^-(aq) \longrightarrow 2Na^+(aq) + SO_4{}^{2-}(aq) + 2H_2O$$

■ Formulas must be of the same physical state before they can be canceled. We could not, for example, cancel HCl(*g*) by HCl(*aq*), because their states are different.

Next we identify the particles that appear identically on opposite sides of the arrow, the spectators, and cancel them.

$$2H^+(aq) + \cancel{SO_4{}^{2-}(aq)} + \cancel{2Na^+(aq)} + 2OH^-(aq) \longrightarrow \cancel{2Na^+(aq)} + \cancel{SO_4{}^{2-}(aq)} + 2H_2O$$

This leaves us with

$$2H^+(aq) + 2OH^-(aq) \longrightarrow 2H_2O$$

We have both a material and an electrical balance, but we should note that we can divide all the coefficients by 2 and convert them to smaller whole numbers. Thus the final net ionic equation is

$$H^+(aq) + OH^-(aq) \longrightarrow H_2O$$

In other words, the only chemical event that occurs when we mix sodium hydroxide and sulfuric acid in the ratios of the molecular equation is the reaction of $H^+(aq)$ with $OH^-(aq)$. As we said earlier, this is the neutralization of any strong acid by a soluble metal hydroxide.

PRACTICE EXERCISE 4   Write the molecular, the ionic, and the net ionic equation for the neutralization of nitric acid by potassium hydroxide. A water-soluble salt, $KNO_3(aq)$, and water form.

Strong Acids React with Metal Hydroxides To Give Water and a Salt   Example 8.1 and Practice Exercise 4 illustrate reactions of strong acids with metal hydroxides, and we saw in the net ionic equations that they are the reaction of a Brønsted acid, H^+, with a Brønsted base, OH^-. If we let *M* stand for any group IA metal, we can write the reactions of aqueous solutions of their hydroxides with a strong acid such as hydrochloric acid by the following general equation:

■ The group IA hydroxides are LiOH, NaOH, KOH, RbOH, and CsOH.

$$MOH(aq) + HCl(aq) \longrightarrow MCl(aq) + H_2O$$

or, as the net ionic equation:

$$OH^-(aq) + H^+(aq) \longrightarrow H_2O$$

Only the group IA hydroxides are very soluble in water. Most of the others are relatively insoluble, but their solid forms can still neutralize strong acids. The net ionic equations for these reactions, therefore, reflect the insolubility of such hydroxides. If we now use M for any metal in group IIA (except beryllium), the equations are

$$M(OH)_2(s) + 2HCl(aq) \longrightarrow MCl_2(aq) + 2H_2O$$

or

$$M(OH)_2(s) + 2H^+(aq) \longrightarrow M^{2+}(aq) + 2H_2O$$

PRACTICE EXERCISE 5   When milk of magnesia is used to neutralize hydrochloric acid (stomach acid), solid magnesium hydroxide in the suspension reacts with the acid. Write the molecular and net ionic equations for this reaction.

NaHCO$_3$(aq) and HCl(aq) acid react to give NaCl(aq), H$_2$O, and CO$_2$(g), which can be seen bubbling out of this tube.

Strong Acids React with Metal Bicarbonates To Give CO$_2$, H$_2$O, and a Salt   All metal bicarbonates react the same way with strong, aqueous acids. They react to give carbon dioxide, water, and a salt. For example, sodium bicarbonate and hydrochloric acid react as follows:

$$HCl(aq) + NaHCO_3(aq) \longrightarrow CO_2(g) + H_2O + NaCl(aq)$$

Potassium bicarbonate and hydrobromic acid give a similar reaction.

$$HBr(aq) + KHCO_3(aq) \longrightarrow CO_2(g) + H_2O + KBr(aq)$$

What actually forms initially is not CO$_2$ and H$_2$O but H$_2$CO$_3$, carbonic acid. However, almost all of it promptly decomposes to CO$_2$ and H$_2$O, so the solution fizzes strongly as the reaction proceeds and CO$_2$ evolves.

Notice that the salt whose formula appears as a product in the molecular equation is always a combination of the cation of the bicarbonate (Na$^+$ or K$^+$ in our examples) and the anion of the acid (Cl$^-$ or Br$^-$ in our examples). Let's be sure we can write the formula of the salt that forms in these reactions before we continue.

EXAMPLE 8.2   **WRITING THE FORMULA OF THE SALT THAT FORMS WHEN A BICARBONATE REACTS WITH AN ACID**

Problem: What salt forms when lithium bicarbonate reacts with nitric acid?

Solution: Using the name, lithium bicarbonate, we can write its formula, LiHCO$_3$, so the cation has to be Li$^+$. The anion furnished by nitric acid, HNO$_3$(aq), is the nitrate ion, NO$_3^-$. Therefore we *must* combine one NO$_3^-$ ion with one Li$^+$ ion to figure out the formula of the salt. The 1 to 1 ratio is required by the necessity of electrical neutrality in the salt. Hence, the salt's formula is LiNO$_3$.

PRACTICE EXERCISE 6   What is the formula of the salt that forms when potassium bicarbonate reacts with sulfuric acid? Assume the salt is a sulfate and not a hydrogen sulfate.

■ Bicarbonates exist as *solid* salts with group IA metal ions and generally not with other metal ions.

In writing net ionic equations of reactions between strong acids and metal bicarbonates, we'll treat all metal bicarbonates as ionized in water to the metal ion and the bicarbonate ion.

As we will see, the reaction of bicarbonates with acids is one in which the bicarbonate ion is a base, a proton-acceptor.

WRITING EQUATIONS FOR THE REACTIONS OF BICARBONATES WITH STRONG ACIDS

| EXAMPLE 8.3 |

Problem: What are the molecular and the net ionic equations for the reaction of potassium bicarbonate with hydriodic acid?

Solution: Using what we learned in Example 8.2, the salt must be a combination of the potassium ion, K^+, and the iodide ion, I^-. The salt is KI. Now we can write the molecular equation:

$$KHCO_3(aq) + HI(aq) \longrightarrow CO_2(g) + H_2O + KI(aq)$$

To prepare the ionic equation, we analyze each of the formulas in the molecular equation.

$KHCO_3(aq)$ means $K^+(aq)$ and $HCO_3^-(aq)$	(As we were told.)
$HI(aq)$ means $H^+(aq) + I^-(aq)$	(Because this is a fully ionized acid.)
$KI(aq)$ means $K^+(aq) + I^-(aq)$	(Because we treat all water-soluble salts as fully ionized.)
$CO_2(g)$ and H_2O stay the same	(Neither is ionized.)

Using these facts, we expand the molecular equation into the ionic equation.

$$[\cancel{K^+(aq)} + HCO_3^-(aq)] + [H^+(aq) + \cancel{I^-(aq)}] \longrightarrow CO_2(g) + H_2O + [\cancel{K^+(aq)} + \cancel{I^-(aq)}]$$

The $K^+(aq)$ and the $I^-(aq)$ cancel from each side of the arrow. This leaves the following net ionic equation:

$$H^+(aq) + HCO_3^-(aq) \longrightarrow CO_2(g) + H_2O$$

It is balanced both materially and electrically.

The equation produced by Example 8.3 is the same net ionic equation for the reaction of all metal bicarbonates with all strong, aqueous acids. Had we wanted to be a bit more exact and used $H_3O^+(aq)$ instead of $H^+(aq)$, the net ionic equation would have been

$$H_3O^+(aq) + HCO_3^-(aq) \longrightarrow CO_2(g) + 2H_2O$$

The only difference is in how H_2O becomes balanced. The essential chemistry has not changed.

Because this reaction destroys the hydrogen ions of the acid, it must also be called an acid neutralization. In fact, the familiar "bicarb" used as a home remedy for acid stomach is nothing more than sodium bicarbonate. Stomach acid is roughly $0.1\ M$ HCl, and bicarbonate ion neutralizes this acid by the reaction we have just studied. An overdose of "bicarb" must be avoided because it can cause a medical emergency involving the respiratory gases. Another use of sodium bicarbonate is as an isotonic solution given intravenously to neutralize acid in the blood. For still another use, see Special Topic 8.1.

PRACTICE EXERCISE 7   Write the molecular, ionic, and net ionic equations for the reaction of sodium bicarbonate with sulfuric acid in which sodium sulfate, $Na_2SO_4(aq)$, is one of the products.

INSTANT CARBONATED BEVERAGES AND MEDICATIONS

As you no doubt know, you can buy fruit-flavored tablets that dissolve in water to give a fizzy drink. Alka-Seltzer and similar tablets contain a solid acid, citric acid, and solid sodium bicarbonate, besides aspirin. The way that these tablets respond when they're dropped into water illustrates the importance of water as a solvent in the reactions of ions. In the crystalline materials, ions are not free to move, but as soon as these tablets hit the water and the ions become mobile, the ions start to react.

Citric acid is a triprotic acid, and we can represent it as H_3Cit, where Cit stands for the citrate ion, an ion with a charge of 3−. The hydrogen ions liberated by citric acid when it is in solution react with the bicarbonate ions that become free to move around when sodium bicarbonate dissolves. This reaction gives the CO_2 that fizzes out of solution as it forms.

$$H^+(aq) + HCO_3^-(aq) \longrightarrow CO_2(g) + H_2O$$

Strong Acids React with Carbonates To Give CO_2, H_2O, and a Salt Carbonates react with hydrogen ions to give the same products as bicarbonates. Only the stoichiometry changes. The CO_3^{2-} ion is thus a base and, mole for mole, it neutralizes twice as much H^+ as the HCO_3^- ion, as we'll see in the next example.

EXAMPLE 8.4 **WRITING EQUATIONS FOR THE REACTIONS OF METAL CARBONATES WITH STRONG, AQUEOUS ACIDS**

Solid sodium carbonate is being pumped by a highway snow blower onto concentrated nitric acid spilling from a ruptured tank car. (This accident occurred in April 1983, in a Denver, Colorado railyard.)

Problem: Sodium carbonate, Na_2CO_3, neutralizes nitric acid and forms sodium nitrate, carbon dioxide, and water. Write the molecular, ionic, and net ionic equations for this reaction. Assume that the reaction occurs in an aqueous solution.

Solution: We first write the formulas into a conventional, molecular equation and balance it.

$$2HNO_3(aq) + Na_2CO_3(aq) \longrightarrow CO_2(g) + H_2O + 2NaNO_3(aq)$$

Then we analyze each of the formulas in this equation to see how to use them in the ionic equation.

$2HNO_3(aq)$ means $2H^+(aq) + 2NO_3^-(aq)$ — (The acid is strong and fully ionized.)

$Na_2CO_3(aq)$ means $2Na^+(aq) + CO_3^{2-}(aq)$ — (This is a salt and it is written with (aq). So, it is in solution and fully ionized.)

$2NaNO_3(aq)$ means $2Na^+(aq) + 2NO_3^-(aq)$ — (This soluble salt is treated, like all salts dissolved in water, as fully ionized.)

$CO_2(g)$ and H_2O remain unchanged

Now we can expand the molecular equation to the ionic equation.

$$[2H^+(aq) + 2NO_3^-(aq)] + [2Na^+(aq) + CO_3^{2-}(aq)] \longrightarrow$$
$$CO_2(g) + H_2O + [2Na^+(aq) + 2NO_3^-(aq)]$$

We can cancel the $2Na^+(aq)$ and the $2NO_3^-(aq)$ from both sides of the equation, which leaves the following net ionic equation:

$$2H^+(aq) + CO_3^{2-}(aq) \longrightarrow CO_2(g) + H_2O$$

Notice in Example 8.4 that one carbonate can neutralize two hydrogen ions, twice as many as are neutralized by a bicarbonate ion. The net ionic equation that we devised in Example 8.4,

$$2H^+(aq) + CO_3^{2-}(aq) \longrightarrow CO_2(g) + H_2O$$

is the same for the reactions of all of the carbonates of the group IA metals with all strong, aqueous acids.

PRACTICE EXERCISE 8 Write the molecular, ionic, and net ionic equations for the reaction of aqueous potassium carbonate, $K_2CO_3(aq)$, with sulfuric acid to give potassium sulfate, $K_2SO_4(aq)$, a water-soluble salt, and the other usual products.

■ Stalactites and stalagmites in limestone caverns are chiefly deposits of limestone.

Only the carbonates of group IA metal ions (as well as ammonium carbonate) are very soluble in water. Most other carbonates are water-insoluble compounds. Calcium carbonate, $CaCO_3$, for example, is the chief substance in limestone and marble. Despite its insolubility in water, calcium carbonate reacts readily with strong, aqueous acids (with their hydrogen ions, of course). The products are soluble in water, so the insoluble carbonates dissolve by this reaction.

■ The addition of a few drops of hydrochloric acid to a rock sample is a field test for carbonate rocks. A positive test is the fizzing of an odorless gas.

$$CaCO_3(s) + 2HCl(aq) \longrightarrow CO_2(g) + H_2O + CaCl_2(aq)$$

For water-insoluble carbonates, we have to write their entire formulas in net ionic equations, so the net ionic equation is

$$CaCO_3(s) + 2H^+(aq) \longrightarrow CO_2(g) + H_2O + Ca^{2+}(aq)$$

PRACTICE EXERCISE 9 Dolomite, a limestone-like rock, contains both calcium and magnesium carbonates. Magnesium carbonate is attacked by nitric acid. The salt that forms is water-soluble. Write the molecular, ionic, and net ionic equations for this reaction.

Ammonia Neutralizes Strong, Aqueous Acids An aqueous solution of ammonia is an excellent reagent for neutralizing acids. We learned in Section 4.5 how an unshared pair of electrons on nitrogen in ammonia can form a coordinate covalent bond to H^+ furnished by an acid. This makes the ammonium ion an effective Brønsted base. For example,

$$NH_3(aq) + HCl(aq) \longrightarrow NH_4Cl(aq)$$

or

$$NH_3(aq) + H^+(aq) \longrightarrow NH_4^+(aq)$$

All ammonium salts are soluble in water, so they liberate NH_4^+ ions in aqueous solutions. Many biochemicals have ammonia-like molecules that also neutralize hydrogen ions.

PRACTICE EXERCISE 10 Write the molecular and net ionic equations for the reaction of aqueous ammonia with (a) HBr(aq) and (b) $H_2SO_4(aq)$.

Active Metals React with Strong Acids to Give Hydrogen and a Salt Nearly all metals are attacked more or less readily by the hydrogen ion in solution. The products are generally hydrogen gas and a salt made of the cation from the metal and the anion from the acid. Zinc, for example, reacts with hydrochloric acid as follows:

$$Zn(s) + 2HCl(aq) \longrightarrow H_2(g) + ZnCl_2(aq)$$

The net ionic equation is

$$Zn(s) + 2H^+(aq) \longrightarrow H_2(g) + Zn^{2+}(aq)$$

Aluminum is also attacked by acids. Its reaction with nitric acid, for example, can be written as follows:

$$2Al(s) + 6HNO_3(aq) \longrightarrow 2Al(NO_3)_3(aq) + 3H_2(g)$$

The net ionic equation is

$$2Al(s) + 6H^+(aq) \longrightarrow 2Al^{3+}(aq) + 3H_2(g)$$

PRACTICE EXERCISE 11   *Write the molecular and the net ionic equations for the reaction of magnesium with hydrochloric acid.*

■ In oxidation, an oxidation number becomes more positive. The loss of electrons by transfer is a common cause.

■ In reduction, an oxidation number becomes more negative. The gain of electrons by transfer is a common cause.

Metals Form an Activity Series in Their Reactions with Acids   Metals differ greatly in their tendencies to react with aqueous hydrogen ions. When they do, atoms of the metal are oxidized because they lose electrons and become metal ions. The oxidizing agent is H^+. The electrons are transferred to H^+, taken from H_3O^+ ions (sometimes from H_2O), and these protons are reduced and made electrically neutral. Two H atoms combine and emerge as a molecule of hydrogen gas, H_2. Thus the metal is oxidized by H^+ to a cation and H^+ is reduced by the metal to H_2.

The group IA metals such as sodium and potassium include the most reactive metals of all. They not only reduce H^+ taken from hydronium ions, they also reduce H^+ taken from water molecules. No acid need be present. The following reaction of sodium metal with water is extremely violent, and it should never be attempted except by an experienced chemist working with safety equipment, including a fire extinguisher. See Figure 8.6.

$$2Na(s) + 2H_2O \longrightarrow 2NaOH(aq) + H_2(g)$$

This reaction, violent in water, is even more violent in aqueous acids.

Gold, silver, and platinum, in contrast, are stable not only toward water but also toward hydronium ions. Lead and tin react very slowly with acids. Figure 8.7 shows how the reactivities of iron, zinc, and magnesium differ toward 1 *M* HCl.

The vast differences in the reactivities of metals toward acids make it possible to arrange the metals in an order of reactivity. The result is the **activity series** of the metals, given in Table 8.3. Atoms of any metal above hydrogen in the series can transfer electrons to H^+, either from H_2O or from H_3O^+, to form hydrogen gas, and the metal atoms change to metal

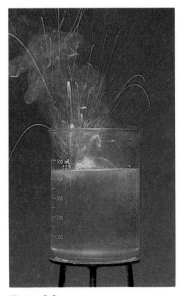

Figure 8.6
The reaction of metallic sodium with water is violent. It produces hydrogen gas and enough heat to ignite the sodium metal. You can see it burning at the surface and sending out a shower of sparks.

Figure 8.7
Metals vary widely in their ease of oxidation. Iron is in the first tube, zinc in the second, and magnesium in the third, and all are exposed to HCl(*aq*) at the same molarity. All these metals can be oxidized to their metal ion states by H^+, and H^+ is reduced to hydrogen gas. Iron, the least readily oxidized of these metals, produces hardly any visible fizzing of hydrogen gas. Zinc, the next most easily oxidized of the three, reacts rather well. Magnesium reacts very vigorously and is the most easily oxidized of the three.

TABLE 8.3 The Activity Series of the Common Metals

Greatest tendency to become ionic

Decreasing tendency to become ionic	Potassium Sodium	React violently with water
	Calcium	Reacts slowly with water
React with hydrogen ions to liberate H_2	Magnesium Aluminum Zinc Chromium	React very slowly with steam
	Iron Nickel Tin Lead	
	HYDROGEN	
Do not react with hydrogen ions	Copper Mercury Silver Platinum Gold	

Least tendency to become ionic

ions. The farther a metal is above hydrogen, the more reactive it is toward acids. The metals below hydrogen in the activity series do not transfer electrons to H^+.

Strong, Moderate, and Weak Acids React at Different Rates with the Same Metals   The rate of the reaction of an acid with a metal depends on the acid as well as the metal. When compared at the same molar concentrations, strong acids react far more rapidly than weak acids, as Figure 8.8 shows. These differences reflect the differences in percentage ionizations, because the actual reaction, as we have said, is with the hydrogen ion. When the concentration of hydrogen ion is high, as it can be when the acid is strong, the reaction is vigorous. In 1 M HCl, the concentration of $H^+(aq)$ is also 1 M, because for each HCl one $H^+(aq)$ is released. However, in 1 M $HC_2H_3O_2$, acetic acid (a weak acid), the actual concentration of $H^+(aq)$ is closer to 0.004 M, which is about 1/250 as much. No wonder the liveliness of the reaction pictured in Figure 8.8c, the reaction of zinc with 1 M acetic acid, is much less than in Figure 8.8a, the reaction with 1 M HCl. In Figure 8.8b, the reaction is with 1 M H_3PO_4, a moderate acid, and the vigor of the reaction is somewhere in between that of the other two.

8.4 STRENGTHS OF BRØNSTED ACIDS AND BASES—A QUALITATIVE VIEW

Acid–base equilibria involve two *acids and* two *bases.*

What we are leading up to is the study of Brønsted acid–base interactions in the fluids of interest at the molecular level of life. We want to be able to sense, at least in a qualitative way, if a particular species poses a threat to the acid–base balance of some fluid in a living system or to a similar balance in foods by being too strong a Brønsted acid or base. We also want to understand how other dissolved species are able to stand guard over such systems by keeping excesses of either acids or bases neutralized.

■ Some additives are put into food products solely to control their acidity and thereby prolong their shelf lives.

In this section we will develop a strategy to predict the relative strengths of weak bases using our knowledge of strong and weak acids. We'll thus make the list of strong acids serve

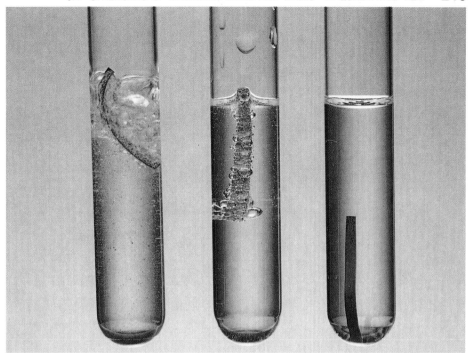

Figure 8.8
Relative hydrogen ion concentrations and the reactivity of zinc. Zinc reacts with hydrogen ion to give zinc ion and hydrogen gas, which fizzes out of the test tubes. Three different acids, ranging from strong to moderate to weak, are used here in identical molar concentrations. (a) The acid is HCl(aq), a strong, fully ionized acid. (b) The acid is $H_3PO_4(aq)$, a moderate, partly ionized acid. (c) The acid is acetic acid, $HC_2H_3O_2(aq)$, a weak, poorly ionized acid. Although the molarities of the acids are the same, the actual molar concentrations of their hydrogen ions are greatly different, being highest in part a, where the bubbles of hydrogen are evolving the most vigorously, next highest in part b, and lowest in part c.

double duty. To do this, we have to view the equilibria in weak acids the way Brønsted suggested.

Every Acid Has a Conjugate Base and Every Base Has a Conjugate Acid   We wrote the following equilibrium for the ionization of acetic acid:

$$HC_2H_3O_2(aq) + H_2O \rightleftharpoons H_3O^+(aq) + C_2H_3O_2^-(aq)$$

In the forward reaction, the acid (the proton donor) is the acetic acid molecule, and the base (the proton acceptor) is the water molecule. So the forward reaction is the reaction of a weak acid with a (very) weak base. But notice that the reverse reaction is also a proton transfer, also the reaction of an acid and a base. In the reaction from right to left, the acid is the hydronium ion, because it donates a proton. The base is the acetate ion, $C_2H_3O_2^-$, because it accepts a proton.

In other words, in this equilibrium we can identify *two* Brønsted acids and *two* Brønsted bases. Notice, now, that each base is related to one of the two acids in the equation. The acetate ion, a base, is related to and comes from acetic acid, an acid. The other base, H_2O, is related to the other acid, H_3O^+. We can, therefore, label the species in our equilibrium expression as follows:

$$HC_2H_3O_2(aq) + H_2O \rightleftharpoons H_3O^+(aq) + C_2H_3O_2^-(aq)$$

| Weaker acid | Weaker base | Stronger acid | Stronger base |

The favored species in this equilibrium

Pairs of particles like H_2O and H_3O^+ or $C_2H_3O_2^-$ and $HC_2H_3O_2$, whose formulas differ by just one H^+, are called **conjugate acid–base pairs.** Thus H_2O is the conjugate base of H_3O^+, and H_3O^+ is the conjugate acid of H_2O. Similarly, $C_2H_3O_2^-$ is the conjugate base of $HC_2H_3O_2$, and $HC_2H_3O_2$ is the conjugate acid of $C_2H_3O_2^-$.

Conjugate pair

$$HC_2H_3O_2(aq) + H_2O \rightleftharpoons H_3O^+(aq) + C_2H_3O_2^-(aq)$$

Conjugate pair

Before we go further, it will be useful, given the name or formula of one member of a conjugate acid–base pair, to be able to write the formula of the other, so let's study some examples.

EXAMPLE 8.5   **WRITING THE FORMULA OF A CONJUGATE ACID**

Problem: Ammonia, NH_3, accepts protons, H^+, when it neutralizes acids, as we learned in the previous section. What is the conjugate acid of NH_3?

Solution: All we have to do is change NH_3 by one H^+. When we do this we have to add not just the H but also the + charge. We add the charge algebraically. The conjugate acid is NH_4^+.

EXAMPLE 8.6   **WRITING THE FORMULA OF A CONJUGATE ACID**

Problem: The phosphate ion, PO_4^{3-}, is a Brønsted base. What is the formula of its conjugate acid?

Solution: When we add H^+ to PO_4^{3-} we get HPO_4^{2-}, the conjugate acid of PO_4^{3-}. The algebraic sum of 1+ and 3− is 2−, the charge on the conjugate acid.

EXAMPLE 8.7   **WRITING THE FORMULA OF A CONJUGATE BASE**

Problem: What is the conjugate base of nitrous acid, HNO_2, a weak acid?

Solution: When we take H^+ away from HNO_2, we're left with NO_2^-, the conjugate base. (When we take a charge of 1+ from a particle with a charge of 0, the remaining charge is 1−.)

EXAMPLE 8.8   **WRITING THE FORMULA OF A CONJUGATE BASE**

Problem: The anion, $H_2PO_4^-$, is a weak proton-donor—a weak Brønsted acid. What is its conjugate base?

Solution: We have to remove H^+ from $H_2PO_4^-$, both the H and a net of one + charge. This leaves us with HPO_4^{2-}. (When we take 1+ away from 1−, the result is 2−.)

| PRACTICE EXERCISE 12 | Write the formulas of the conjugate acids of the following particles: |
| | (a) NO_3^- (b) SO_3^{2-} (c) CO_3^{2-} (d) SO_4^{2-} (e) Cl^- (f) H_2O (g) OH^- |

| PRACTICE EXERCISE 13 | Write the formulas of the conjugate bases of the following particles: |
| | (a) HCO_3^- (b) HPO_4^{2-} (c) H_2SO_4 (d) HSO_4^- (e) HBr (f) H_3O^+ (g) H_2O |

Strong Acids Have Weak Conjugate Bases; Weak Acids Have Strong Conjugate Bases When an acid is *strong*, it readily gives up a proton. Some unit of its structure—the unit that becomes the conjugate base—is not holding the proton well. In other words, *every strong acid has a weak conjugate base*. H—Cl(g) is a very strong acid, for example, so Cl^-, its conjugate base, is a very weak base. Conversely, in a *weak* acid, the unit holding the proton—the unit that becomes the conjugate base—is a strong base. This unit is holding the proton very well within the structure of the acid. In other words, *every weak acid has a strong conjugate base*. H_2O, for example, is a very weak acid, so OH^-, its conjugate base, is a very strong base.

We can summarize these observations as rules of thumb for conjugate acid–base relationships. The last two are just "opposite sides of the same coin" of the first two.

Conjugate Acid–Base Relationships, Brønsted Concept

If an acid is strong, its conjugate base is weak.
If an acid is weak, its conjugate base is strong.
If a base is strong, its conjugate acid is weak.
If a base is weak, its conjugate acid is strong.

These rules will enable us to judge when to expect a base to be strong or weak just by using our knowledge of the list of strong acids. Let's work an example to show how this list enables us to figure out if a particular species is strong or weak. We'll first review how to tell if an acid not studied before is strong or weak.

EXAMPLE 8.9 **DEDUCING WHETHER AN ION OR MOLECULE IS A WEAK BRØNSTED ACID**

Problem: Lactic acid is the acid responsible for the tart taste of sour milk. Is lactic acid a strong or a weak acid?

Solution: The list of strong acids does not include lactic acid. Hence, it is a weak acid. It's as simple as that (and we'd err very seldom).

EXAMPLE 8.10 **DEDUCING WHETHER AN ION OR MOLECULE IS A STRONG OR A WEAK BRØNSTED BASE**

Problem: Is the bromide ion a strong or a weak Brønsted base?

Solution: When the question deals with a potential *base,* we have to find the answer in a round about fashion. We accept this because the alternative would be to memorize a rather extensive list of the stronger Brønsted bases. Here's how to go about it.

Pretend that the potential base actually functions as a base, so write the formula of its conjugate acid. If Br^- were to be a base, its conjugate acid would be HBr, which, in water, is hydrobromic acid. Now comes the crucial question. Is hydrobromic acid a strong acid? We have to know the list, and HBr is on the list of *strong* acids, so we know that it easily gives up a proton. Therefore we know that what remains when the proton so readily leaves HBr, Br^-, has to be a poor proton binder. So our answer is that Br^- is a weak Brønsted base.

| EXAMPLE 8.11 | **DEDUCING WHETHER AN ION OR A MOLECULE IS A STRONG OR A WEAK BRØNSTED BASE** |

Problem: Is the phosphate ion, PO_4^{3-}, a strong or a weak Brønsted base?

Solution: Using the strategy described in Example 8.10, we pretend that this ion actually is a base, a proton acceptor. So we give it a proton, and write the result, the conjugate acid. The conjugate acid of PO_4^{3-} is HPO_4^{2-}. This Brønsted acid isn't on our list of strong acids, so we conclude it's a weak acid. This means that PO_4^{3-} is a good proton binder (holding the proton as HPO_4^{2-}). A good proton binder is a strong base, so our answer to the question is that PO_4^{3-} is a strong base.

PRACTICE EXERCISE 14 Classify the following particles as strong or as weak Brønsted acids.

(a) HSO_3^- (b) HCO_3^- (c) $H_2PO_4^-$

PRACTICE EXERCISE 15 Classify the following ions as strong or as weak Brønsted bases.

(a) I^- (b) NO_3^- (c) CN^- (d) NH_2^-

■ OH^- is the conjugate acid of O^{2-}.

The Strongest Base We Can Have in Water Is OH^- If we try to dissolve a base stronger than the OH^- ion in water, it reacts with water, takes a proton, and changes to the conjugate acid. For example, the oxide ion, O^{2-}, which is the conjugate *base* of OH^-, is a much stronger base than OH^-. If we add it to water in the form of sodium oxide, the following reaction occurs (very exothermically), and none of the oxide ions supplied by Na_2O is in the solution. They have all changed to hydroxide ions by the following reaction:

■ Solid Na_2O or any other group IA oxides cannot be stored exposed to humid air.

$$Na_2O(s) \ + H_2O \longrightarrow 2NaOH(aq)$$
Sodium oxide   Sodium hydroxide

Thus, although sodium oxide is very soluble in water, its solution contains no oxide ions. It dissolves by reacting with water, and its oxide ions change to hydroxide ions. Most metal oxides that dissolve in water do so by reacting in this way. The ionic equation can be written:

$$O^{2-}(s) + H_2O \longrightarrow 2OH^-(aq)$$

The Strongest Acid We Can Have in Water Is H_3O^+ If we try to dissolve in water any acid stronger than H_3O^+, it reacts with water to give hydronium ion. Hydrogen chloride, for example, is a stronger proton-donor than H_3O^+. As we already know, when we bubble $H—Cl(g)$ into water, the following reaction occurs, a typical Brønsted acid–base reaction. We'll write it as an equilibrium, although the forward reaction occurs essentially 100%.

$$HCl(g) \ + H_2O \ \rightleftharpoons H_3O^+(aq) + Cl^-(aq)$$
Stronger   Stronger   Weaker   Weaker
acid   base   acid   base

Evidently, the hydronium ion holds the proton better than it is held by the Cl atom in $H—Cl(g)$.

In All Brønsted Acid–Base Equilibria, the Weaker Acid and Weaker Base Are Favored Now that we can make reasonable predictions of relative acid or base strengths, let's see how we can use this skill in predicting reactions. This will enable us to judge which side of an acid–base equilibrium is favored.

A logical consequence of our rules of thumb about acid–base strengths is that the stronger acid and the stronger base will always react to give the weaker acid and base in all proton-transfer equilibria. We can condense this to another rule of thumb: *The stronger always give way to the weaker in acid–base reactions.*

EXAMPLE 8.12

PREDICTING WHICH SUBSTANCES ARE FAVORED IN AN ACID–BASE EQUILIBRIUM

Problem: If we add hydrochloric acid to an aqueous solution of sodium cyanide, NaCN, will HCN and NaCl form to any significant extent? (If they do, the evolving HCN, hydrogen cyanide, might kill anyone who mixes these substances. Hydrogen cyanide is a very dangerous poison.)

Solution: Because we are dealing with $HCl(aq)$, the reagent actually consists of $H_3O^+(aq)$ and $Cl^-(aq)$. Because NaCN, a salt, is in solution, we are dealing with $Na^+(aq)$ and $CN^-(aq)$. Sodium ions and chloride ions would be spectator ions. The question, therefore, is, Does the following reaction occur?

$$H_3O^+(aq) + CN^-(aq) \xrightarrow{\ ?\ } H_2O + HCN(aq)$$

Remembering the rule that the "stronger give way to the weaker" in these proton-transfer reactions, we have to identify the acids and bases, and then infer what is stronger and what is weaker.

When we look for the conjugate pairs, we can see them as follows:

Conjugate acid–base pair

$$H_3O^+(aq) + CN^-(aq) \longrightarrow H_2O + HCN(aq)$$

Conjugate acid–base pair

Each pair must have an acid and each must have a base, so let's write in these labels (and, to reduce clutter, omit the lines that have served to connect conjugate pairs).

$$H_3O^+(aq) + CN^-(aq) \longrightarrow H_2O + HCN(aq)$$

Acid   Base   Base   Acid

Now we decide which of the two acids is stronger. We know that H_3O^+ is the strongest acid species we can have in water. (We also know that because HCN isn't on the list of strong acids, it must be weak.) So we modify our labels with this new information.

$$H_3O^+(aq) + CN^-(aq) \longrightarrow H_2O + HCN(aq)$$

Stronger   Base   Base   Weaker
acid   acid

Because the conjugate of a stronger acid must be a weaker base, and the conjugate of a weaker acid must be a stronger base, we can modify the remaining labels as follows:

$$H_3O^+(aq) + CN^-(aq) \longrightarrow H_2O + HCN(aq)$$

Stronger   Stronger   Weaker   Weaker
acid   base   base   acid

Finally, we can tell that the reaction, as written, must occur, because the stronger are always replaced by the weaker in acid–base reactions. What we actually would have is an equilibrium in which the products of the forward reaction (as we draw the equilibrium expression) are favored.

$$H_3O^+(aq) + CN^-(aq) \rightleftharpoons H_2O + HCN(aq)$$

Stronger   Stronger   Weaker   Weaker
acid   base   base   acid

TABLE 8.4 **Relative Strengths of Some Brønsted Acids and Bases**

Brønsted Acid		Brønsted Base	
Name	Formula	Name	Formula
Perchloric acid	$HClO_4$	Perchlorate ion	ClO_4^-
Hydrogen iodide	HI	Iodide ion	I^-
Hydrogen bromide	HBr	Bromide ion	Br^-
Sulfuric acid	H_2SO_4	Hydrogen sulfate ion	HSO_4^-
Hydrogen chloride	HCl	Chloride ion	Cl^-
Nitric acid	HNO_3	Nitrate ion	NO_3^-
HYDRONIUM ION	H_3O^+	WATER	H_2O
Hydrogen sulfate ion	HSO_4^-	Sulfate ion	SO_4^{2-}
Phosphoric acid	H_3PO_4	Dihydrogen phosphate ion	$H_2PO_4^-$
Acetic acid	$HC_2H_3O_2$	Acetate ion	$C_2H_3O_2^-$
Carbonic acid	H_2CO_3	Bicarbonate ion	HCO_3^-
Dihydrogen phosphate ion	$H_2PO_4^-$	Monohydrogen phosphate	HPO_4^{2-}
Ammonium ion	NH_4^+	Ammonia	NH_3
Bicarbonate ion	HCO_3^-	Carbonate ion	CO_3^{2-}
Monohydrogen phosphate ion	HPO_4^{2-}	Phosphate ion	PO_4^{3-}
WATER	H_2O	HYDROXIDE ION	OH^-
Methyl alcohol	CH_3OH	Methoxide ion	CH_3O^-
Ammonia	NH_3	Amide ion	NH_2^-
Hydroxide ion	OH^-	Oxide ion	O^{2-}
Hydrogen	H_2	Hydride ion	H^-

Increasing acid strength (arrow pointing up on left) / *Increasing base strength* (arrow pointing down on right)

PRACTICE EXERCISE 16

When the meat preservative sodium nitrite, $NaNO_2$, enters the stomach and encounters the hydrochloric acid in gastric juice, can nitrous acid, HNO_2, be produced? Write the equilibrium expression for any net ionic interactions. State which are favored, the reactants or the products. (Nitrous acid is suspected of being a cause of cancer, but no evidence presently exists that it actually causes cancer in humans.)

Acids and Bases Can Be Organized in Their Order of Strengths   Table 8.4 lists several Brønsted acids and bases in their orders of increasing strength. Carbonic acid, for example, is a weaker acid than acetic acid so it stands above acetic acid in the table.

All acids above H_3O^+ in the column of acids in the table — those that we have learned are the strong acids — are essentially 100% ionized into the hydronium ion and the conjugate base in aqueous solutions. We even treat $HSO_4^-(aq)$ as a strong acid. $H_3PO_4(aq)$ is a moderate acid.

■ Perchloric acid in Table 8.4 was not on our earlier list of strong acids because it is less common.

Moving down the column, the next acids — acetic acid, carbonic acid, the dihydrogen phosphate ion, the ammonium ion, the bicarbonate ion, and the monohydrogen phosphate ion — are all weak acids (becoming progressively weaker as we move down the column).

The acids from water and below in Table 8.4 ionize in water to such a low percentage that, except in discussions of the Brønsted concept, we almost never refer to them as proton-donors.

Moving over to the column of bases, the conjugate bases of all strong acids in Table 8.4 are such weak bases that we almost never refer to them as bases. Neither water nor the sulfate ion are routinely called bases either (except in discussions of the Brønsted concept). The dihydrogen phosphate ion is a weak base, and as we move down the list through the acetate ion, the bicarbonate ion, the mononhydrogen phosphate ion, ammonia, the carbonate ion, and the phosphate ion, the bases get stronger. This means that as we move down through this series, the products in the following equilibrium expression become more and more favored. (We let B^- represent any base except NH_3.)

$$B^-(aq) + H_2O \rightleftharpoons BH(aq) + OH^-(aq)$$

■ Sodium salts of all these strongly basic anions are known— $NaOCH_3$, $NaNH_2$, and NaH.

The ions below OH^- — CH_3O^-, NH_2^-, O^{2-}, and H^- — react quantitatively with water to give their conjugate acids. As we said, no base stronger than OH^- can exist in water. In the reactions, for example, of NH_2^- and H^- with water, we don't normally even use equilibrium arrows; they go to completion for all practical purposes.

$$NH_2^-(s) + H_2O \longrightarrow NH_3(aq) + OH^-(aq)$$
$$H^-(s) + H_2O \rightarrow H_2(g) + OH^-(aq)$$

Our discussion of relative strengths of acids and bases has been qualitative because that is all that is needed for many uses. Sometimes, however, it helps to have numbers to describe these relative strengths, and we will describe such numbers in the next chapter.

The Ammonium Ion Is a Brønsted Acid   The ammonium ion occupies a special place in our study because many biochemicals, like proteins, have a molecular part that is very much like this ion. Although the ammonium ion is a weak acid (Table 8.4), it still is a Brønsted acid, and it can neutralize the hydroxide ion. When we add sodium hydroxide to a solution of ammonium chloride, the following reaction occurs:

$$NaOH(aq) + NH_4Cl(aq) \longrightarrow NH_3(aq) + H_2O + NaCl(aq)$$

The net ionic equation is

$$OH^-(aq) + NH_4^+(aq) \longrightarrow NH_3(aq) + H_2O$$

This reaction neutralizes the hydroxide ion, and it leaves a solution of the weaker base, NH_3. (If the initial solution is concentrated enough, the final solution has a strong odor of ammonia.)

In some medical emergencies, when the blood has become too alkaline or too basic, an isotonic solution of ammonium chloride is administered by intravenous drip. Its ammonium ions can neutralize some of the base in the blood and bring the acid–base balance back to normal.

8.5 SALTS

A very large number of ionic reactions can be predicted from a knowledge of the solubility rules of salts.

Salts are ionic compounds whose cations are any except H^+ and whose anions are any except OH^- or O^{2-}. All are crystalline solids at room temperature, because forces of attraction between ions in crystals are very strong.

A **simple salt** is one that is made of just *two* kinds of oppositely charged ions. Examples are NaCl, $MgBr_2$, and $CuSO_4$. *Mixed salts* are those that have three or more different ions. Alum, used in water purification, is an example: $K_2SO_4 \cdot Al_2(SO_4)_3 \cdot 24H_2O$. As the formula of alum illustrates, the salt family includes hydrates. Some salts of practical value are given in Table 8.5.

Formation of Salts   In the laboratory, salts are obtained whenever an acid is used in any of the following ways. We summarize and review these methods here and show their similarities.

$$\text{Acid} + \text{metal hydroxide} \longrightarrow \text{a salt} + H_2O$$
$$\text{Acid} + \text{metal oxide} \longrightarrow \text{a salt} + H_2O$$
$$\text{Acid} + \text{metal bicarbonate} \longrightarrow \text{a salt} + H_2O + CO_2$$
$$\text{Acid} + \text{metal carbonate} \longrightarrow \text{a salt} + H_2O + CO_2$$
$$\text{Acid} + \text{metal} \longrightarrow \text{a salt} + H_2$$

If the salt is soluble in water, we have to evaporate the solution to dryness to isolate it.

TABLE 8.5 Some Salts and Their Uses

Formula and Name	Uses
$BaSO_4$ Barium sulfate	Used in the "barium cocktail" given prior to X-raying the gastrointestinal tract

$(CaSO_4)_2 \cdot H_2O$
   Calcium sulfate
   hemihydrate (plaster of
   paris)
	Plaster casts, wall stucco, wall plaster

$MgSO_4 \cdot 7H_2O$
   Magnesium sulfate
   heptahydrate (epsom salt)
	Purgative

$AgNO_3$ Silver nitrate	Antiseptic and germicide. Used in eyes of infants to prevent gonorrheal conjunctivitis. Photographic film sensitizer

$NaHCO_3$
   Sodium bicarbonate
   (baking soda)
	Baking powders, effervescent salts, stomach antacid, fire extinguishers

$Na_2CO_3 \cdot 10H_2O$
   Sodium carbonate
   decahydrate (soda ash,
   sal soda, washing soda)
	Water softener, soap and glass manufacture

$NaCl$ Sodium chloride	Manufacture of chlorine, sodium hydroxide, preparation of food
$NaNO_2$ Sodium nitrite	Meat preservative

Many Salts Are Insoluble in Water Sometimes a salt precipitates as it forms instead of remaining in solution. To predict when to expect this, we use a small number of solubility rules for ionic compounds. We say that a compound is *soluble* in water if it can form a solution with a concentration of at least 3 to 5% (w/w). When a *counter ion* is referred to in the following rules, it means the unnamed ion of the ionic compound. For example, in the lithium salt, LiCl, the counter ion is the chloride ion. In the hydroxide, $Ca(OH)_2$, the counter ion is Ca^{2+}.

Solubility Rules for Ionic Compounds in Water

1. All lithium, sodium, potassium, and ammonium salts are soluble regardless of the counter ion.

2. All nitrates and acetates are soluble, regardless of the counter ion.

3. All chlorides, bromides, and iodides are soluble, except when the counter ion is lead, silver, or mercury(I).

4. All sulfates are soluble except those of lead, calcium, strontium, mercury(I), and barium.

5. All hydroxides and metal oxides are insoluble except those of the group IA cations and those of calcium, strontium, and barium.

6. All phosphates, carbonates, sulfites, and sulfides are insoluble except those of the group IA cations and NH_4^+

There are exceptions to these rules, but we will seldom be wrong in applying them. One of the many applications of these rules is to predict possible reactions involving ionic compounds.

Salts Can Form by Double Replacement ("Exchange of Partners") Reactions In addition to the reactions we have already studied to make salts by acid–base

■ Some references use the term *metathesis reaction* for double replacement.

The precipitate in the beaker above is being separated by *filtration*. It is collected in a cone of filter paper in the funnel, and the *filtrate*—the clear solution—is collected in the beaker below.

neutralizations, we can also make salts by a "change of partners" reaction called **double replacement.** For example, sodium carbonate and calcium chloride are both soluble in water. But if we mix aqueous solutions of the two, the following reaction occurs because CO_3^{2-} ion and Ca^{2+} ions cannot remain in solution in each other's presence. Their combination, $CaCO_3$, is too insoluble.

$$Ba_2CO_3(aq) + CaCl_2(aq) \longrightarrow CaCO_3(s) + 2NaCl(aq)$$

An ion from each salt combines with an ion from the other salt, which gives the informal name, "exchange of partners," to the reaction or, more formally, *double replacement.* The ionic equation for this reaction more clearly shows this exchange.

$$[2Na^+(aq) + CO_3^{2-}(aq)] + [Ca^{2+}(aq) + 2Cl^-(aq)] \longrightarrow$$
$$CaCO_3(s) + [2Na^+(aq) + 2Cl^-(aq)]$$

The net ionic equation is

$$Ca^{2+}(aq) + CO_3^{2-}(aq) \longrightarrow CaCO_3(s)$$

The other product, NaCl, stays in solution in its dissociated form. You would have to filter off the precipitate of calcium carbonate and then evaporate the filtrate to dryness to obtain crystalline NaCl.

Not all combinations of solutes give double replacement reactions. If you mixed solutions of NaI and KCl, no combination of oppositely charged ions is insoluble, so the solution would just contain separated (and hydrated) ions of Na^+, K^+, I^-, and Cl^-.

| **EXAMPLE 8.13** | **PREDICTING DOUBLE REPLACEMENT REACTIONS OF SALTS** |

Problem: What happens if we mix aqueous solutions of sodium sulfate and barium nitrate?

Solution: By the solubility rules, we know that both sodium sulfate and barium nitrate are soluble in water, so their solutions contain their separated *ions.* When we pour the two solutions together, four ions experience attractions and repulsions. Hence, we have to examine each possible combination of oppositely charged ions to see which, if any, makes a water-insoluble salt. If we find one, then we can write an equation for the reaction that produces this salt. Here are the possible combinations when Ba^{2+}, NO_3^-, Na^+, and SO_4^{2-} ions intermingle in water.

■ $BaSO_4$ is the white, insoluble substance in a flavored slurry given to patients as a "barium cocktail" before an X ray is taken of the intestinal tract. The barium ion stops X rays, so the tract is outlined on the film.

$Ba^{2+} + 2NO_3^- \xrightarrow{?} Ba(NO_3)_2(s)$ This possibility is obviously out, because barium ions and nitrate ions do not precipitate together from water. ("All nitrates are soluble.")

$2Na^+ + SO_4^{2-} \xrightarrow{?} Na_2SO_4(s)$ This possibility is also out. ("All sodium salts are soluble.")

$Na^+ + NO_3^- \xrightarrow{?} NaNO_3(s)$ No. Again, "All sodium salts are soluble."

$Ba^{2+} + SO_4^{2-} \xrightarrow{?} BaSO_4(s)$ Yes. Barium sulfate, $BaSO_4$, is not in any of the categories of water-soluble salts. And it is among the insoluble salts (rule 4.)

Because we predicted that $BaSO_4$ can form a precipitate, we can write a molecular equation, and we'll use some connector lines to show how partners exchange—how *double* replacement occurs.

$$Ba(NO_3)_2(aq) + Na_2SO_4(aq) \longrightarrow 2NaNO_3(aq) + BaSO_4(s)$$

The net ionic equation, however, is a better way to describe what happens.

$$Ba^{2+}(aq) + SO_4^{2-}(aq) \longrightarrow BaSO_4(s)$$

The sodium and nitrate ions are only spectators. To obtain the solid barium sulfate, we would filter the mixture and collect this compound on the filter. If we also wanted the sodium nitrate, we would evaporate the clear filtrate to dryness.

PRACTICE EXERCISE 17   If solutions of sodium sulfide, Na_2S, and copper(II) nitrate, $Cu(NO_3)_2$, are mixed, what if anything will happen chemically? Write a molecular and a net ionic equation for any reaction.

One of the many uses of the solubility rules is to understand what it means for water to be called *hard water* and what it means to *soften* such water. See Special Topic 8.2.

To Summarize, the Chief Reactions of Ions Are Those That Form Gases, Molecules in Solution, or Precipitates   Our study of the reaction of sodium sulfate and barium nitrate in Example 8.13 illustrates the power of knowing just a few facts for the sake of predicting an enormous number of others with a high probability of success. The following facts summarize those that should now have become well learned.

1. The solubility rules of ionic compounds (because then we can assume that all the other ionic compounds are insoluble).

2. The five strong acids in Table 8.1 (because then we can assume that all the other acids, including organic acids, are weak).

3. The first two strong bases of Table 8.2 (because then we can assume that all the other bases are either weak or are too insoluble in water to matter much).

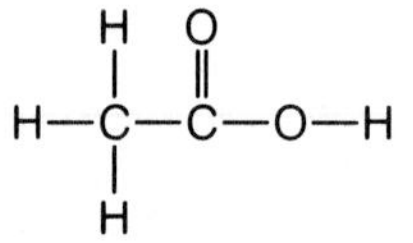

To summarize, we expect ions to react with each other if any one of the following possibilities is predicted.

1. A gas forms that (mostly) leaves the solution. It could be
   (a) Hydrogen — from the action of acids on metals, or
   (b) Carbon dioxide — from acids reacting with carbonates or bicarbonates

2. An un-ionized, molecular compound forms that remains in solution. It could be
   (a) Water — from acid–base neutralizations or
   (b) A weak acid — by the action of H^+ on a strong Brønsted base, the conjugate base of any weak acid, or
   (c) Ammonia — by the reaction of OH^- with NH_4^+.

3. A precipitate forms — some water-insoluble salt or one of the water-insoluble hydroxides.

■ The chief organic acids all have the group $-\overset{\overset{\displaystyle O}{\|}}{C}-O-H$ as in acetic acid,

$$H-\overset{\overset{\displaystyle H}{|}}{\underset{\underset{\displaystyle H}{|}}{C}}-\overset{\overset{\displaystyle O}{\|}}{C}-O-H$$

PRACTICE EXERCISE 18   When a solution of hydrochloric acid is mixed in the correct molar proportions with a solution of sodium acetate, $NaC_2H_3O_2$, essentially all the hydronium ion concentration vanishes. What happens and why? Write the net ionic equation.

PRACTICE EXERCISE 19   What, if anything, happens chemically when each pair of solutions is mixed? Write net ionic equations for any reactions that occur.

(a) $NaCl$ and $AgNO_3$
(b) $CaCO_3$ and HNO_3
(c) KBr and $NaCl$

SPECIAL TOPIC 8.2   HARD WATER

Groundwater that contains magnesium, calcium, or iron ions at a high enough level to interact with ordinary soap to form scum is called **hard water.** In **soft water** these "hardness ions" — Ca^{2+}, Mg^{2+}, Fe^{2+}, and Fe^{3+} — are either absent or are present in extremely low concentrations. (The anions that most frequently accompany the hardness ions are SO_4^{2-}, Cl^-, and HCO_3^-).

Hard water in which the principal anion is the bicarbonate ion is called **temporary hard water.** Hard water in which the chief negative ions are anything else is called **permanent hard water.** When temporary hard water is heated near its boiling point, as in hot boilers, steam pipes, and instrument sterilizers, the bicarbonate ion breaks down to the carbonate ion. And this ion forms insoluble precipitates with the hardness ions. Their carbonate salts form, come out of solution, and deposit as scaly material that can even clog the equipment, as the accompanying photograph illustrates. The equations for these changes are as follows.

The breakdown of the bicarbonate ion:

$$2HCO_3^-(aq) \longrightarrow CO_3^{2-}(aq) + CO_2(g) + H_2O$$

The formation of the scaly precipitate (using the calcium ion to illustrate):

$$CO_3^{2-}(aq) + Ca^{2+}(aq) \longrightarrow CaCO_3(s)$$

Water-Softening Removes the Hardness Ions Chemically   Hard water can be softened in various ways. Most commonly, excess soap is used. Some scum does form, but then the extra soap does the cleansing work. To avoid the scum altogether, softening agents are added before the soap is used. One common water-softening chemical is sodium carbonate decahydrate, known as washing soda. Its carbonate ions take out the hardness ions as insoluble carbonates by the kind of reaction for which we wrote the previous net ionic equation.

Another home water-softening agent is household ammonia — 5% (w/w) NH_3. We've already learned about the following equilibrium in such a solution:

$$NH_3(aq) + H_2O \rightleftharpoons NH_4^+(aq) + OH^-(aq)$$

In other words, aqueous ammonia has some OH^- ions, and the hydroxides of the hardness ions are not soluble in water. Therefore, when aqueous ammonia is added to hard water, the following kind of reaction occurs (illustrated using the magnesium ion this time):

$$Mg^{2+}(aq) + 2OH^-(aq) \longrightarrow Mg(OH)_2(s)$$

As hydroxide ions are removed by this reaction, more are made available from the ammonia–water equilibrium. (A loss of OH^- ion from this equilibrium is a stress, and the equilibrium shifts to the right in response, as we'd predict using Le Chatelier's principle.)

Still another water-softening technique is to let the hard water trickle through zeolite, a naturally-occurring porous substance that is rich in sodium ions. When the hard water is in contact with the zeolite, sodium ions go into the water and the hardness ions leave solution and attach themselves to the zeolite. Later, the hardness ions are flushed out by letting water that is very concentrated in sodium chloride trickle through the spent zeolite, and this restores the zeolite for reuse. Synthetic, ion-exchange materials are also used to soften water by roughly the same principle.

Perhaps the most common strategy in areas where the water is quite hard is to use synthetic detergents instead of soap. Synthetic detergents do not form scums and precipitates with the hardness ions.

A deposit of calcium carbonate has nearly closed this 2-in. hot-water pipe after just two years of service in northeastern New Jersey.

The Common Ion Effect Shifts Solubility Equilibria To Favor Insoluble or Un-ionized Species   The solubility rules predict the solubility of an individual salt when it is the lone solute in solution. In nature and in living systems, however, solutions this simple seldom occur. Usually, two or more electrolytes are present, so it is important to consider any changes in the solubility of one compound that might be caused by the presence of another.

If the other solutes provide *different* ions entirely, then the solubility rules work just by themselves, at least in solutions that are relatively dilute in all dissolved species. But if some other solute contributes one ion that is *common* to the salt whose solubility we are studying,

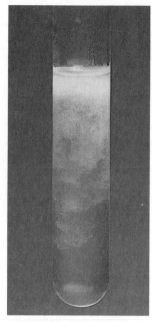

Figure 8.9
The common ion effect. At the start there is a saturated solution of sodium chloride (first frame). When concentrated hydrochloric acid is added (second frame), a white precipitate of sodium chloride appears, grows in quantity (third frame), and finally settles (last frame).

then the solubility of the latter is reduced. This reduction in solubility of one salt by the addition of a common ion is called the **common ion effect.** Let's see how it works.

Suppose that we have a *saturated* solution of sodium chloride. The following equilibrium exists:

$$NaCl(s) \rightleftharpoons Na^+(aq) + Cl^-(aq)$$

What happens if we now pour into this solution some concentrated hydrochloric acid, a fully ionized acid? By using *concentrated* HCl(*aq*) we can quickly increase the concentration of the chloride ion in the solution, and this ion is *common* to the original solute, NaCl. By increasing the concentration of Cl^-, we place a stress on the equilibrium. In accordance with Le Chatelier's principle, the equilibrium has to shift to absorb this stress, and it has to shift to the left. Only by running the *reverse* reaction of the equilibrium can the system reduce the concentration of dissolved Cl^- and so reduce the stress. But this has to cause the precipitation of some solid sodium chloride, and this is exactly what happens, as the photos of Figure 8.9 show. After the activity has quieted, we still have a saturated solution, but we also have more solid NaCl, and we have a lower concentration of dissolved Na^+ ions.

Special Topic 8.3 describes an interesting common ion effect that leads to some of the symptoms of urinary calculus disease (kidney stones).

Concentrations of Individual Ions in Solutions of Several Substances Are Often Given in Equivalents or Milliequivalents per Liter   Before we leave this introduction to salts, we must look at a concentration expression often used for their individual ions. It is based not on the moles of an ion per liter but on a quantity called an *equivalent* per liter. We'll see why soon.

One **equivalent** of an ion, abbreviated **eq,** is the number of grams of the ion that corresponds to Avogadro's number, one mole, of electrical charges. For example, when the charge is unity, either $1+$ or $1-$, it takes Avogadro's number of ions to have Avogadro's number of electrical charges. Thus 1 eq for ions such as Na^+, K^+, Cl^-, or Br^- is the same as the molar mass of each ion. The molar mass of Na^+ is 23.0 g Na^+/mol, so 1 eq of Na^+ = 23.0 g

URINARY CALCULUS DISEASE

In medicine a *calculus* is an abnormal nonliving aggregation of mineral salts in a framework or matrix of organic materials. Urinary calculi, commonly called kidney stones or bladder stones depending on location, include calcium and magnesium salts. Why they develop in some people and not in others is not known. However, something goes wrong in the way that the system manages its calcium and magnesium ions.

Body fluids contain some of the ions of phosphoric acid. They consist mostly of $H_2PO_4^-$ and HPO_4^{2-}, but some PO_4^{3-} is also present. The salts of calcium or magnesium with the phosphate ion, PO_4^{3-}, are insoluble in water. Thus if too high a level of either calcium or magnesium ion in body fluids develops, the excess Ca^{2+} or Mg^{2+} ions begin to form insoluble matter with phosphate ions. The following equilib-

rium is established in certain areas of the body:

$$Ca_3(PO_4)_2(s) \rightleftharpoons 3Ca^{2+}(aq) + 2PO_4^{3-}(aq)$$

Should the calcium or magnesium levels rise further, this equilibrium shifts more to the left, and this is an illustration of the common ion effect. The insoluble phosphates can develop into urinary calculi that become larger and larger over a period of time until they are so large that they become life-threatening.

Gallstones include different salts, but their formation follows the same general principle. Mineral deposits that form in some joints in the condition known as gout are explained in a similar fashion, except that the negative ions come from uric acid, a breakdown product of nitrogen compounds called the nucleic acids.

of Na^+. This much sodium ion, 23.0 g of Na^+, contributes Avogadro's number of positive charges. Thus the equivalent weight of the sodium ion is 23.0 g Na^+/eq.

When an ion has a double charge, either 2+ or 2−, then the mass of one equivalent equals the molar mass divided by 2. For example, 1 mol of CO_3^{2-} ion = 60.0 g of CO_3^{2-}, so 1 eq of CO_3^{2-} ion = 30.0 g of CO_3^{2-} ion. This much carbonate ion carries Avogadro's number of negative charge. The extension of this to ions of higher charges should now be obvious. **The equivalent weight of an ion is its formula weight divided by its charge.** You can see this in Table 8.6, which gives equivalent weights for a number of ions.

The advantage of the concept of the equivalent is the simplicity of a 1 to 1 ratio. Regardless of the amounts of charges on the individual ions, when cations and anions are present either in an ionic crystal or in a solution, we can always be sure that for every equivalent of positive charge there has to be one equivalent of negative charge. The condition of electrical neutrality in an ionic compound or a solution of ions is that

$$eq\ of\ cations = eq\ of\ anions$$

or

$$meq\ of\ cations = meq\ of\ anions$$

where the **milliequivalent,** or **meq,** is related to the equivalent by the relationship, 1000 meq = 1 eq.

The normal ranges of values of the concentrations of several components of blood are listed on the inside back cover where you will see that many are given in units of meq/L. There

TABLE 8.6 Equivalents of Ions

Ion	g/mol	g/eq
Na^+	23.0	23.0
K^+	39.1	39.1
Ca^{2+}	40.1	20.1
Mg^{2+}	24.3	12.2
Al^{3+}	27.0	9.0
Cl^-	35.5	35.5
HCO_3^-	61.0	61.0
CO_3^{2-}	60.0	30.0
SO_4^{2-}	96.1	48.1

SPECIAL TOPIC 8.4   **ESTIMATING UNMEASURED ANION CONCENTRATION BY THE ANION GAP**

The ions in blood that contribute the highest levels of concentration and charge are Na^+, Cl^-, and HCO_3^-. For example, the concentration of Na^+ normally is in the range of 135–145 meq/L; of Cl^-, 100–108 meq/L; and of HCO_3^-, 21–29 meq/L. In contrast, the levels of K^+, Ca^{2+}, and Mg^{2+} ions are on the order of only 2 to 5 meq/L each. The blood also carries varying concentrations of negatively charged ions of organic acids, such as the anions (the conjugate bases) of acetic acid, citric acid, and many others.

The levels of the organic anions tend to rise in several metabolic disturbances such as diabetes or kidney disease, but measuring these anions is difficult. The combined levels of the organic ions, however, can be estimated by calculating a quantity known as the **anion gap,** which can be defined by the following equation:

$$\text{Anion gap} = \frac{\text{meq of } Na^+}{L} - \left(\frac{\text{meq of } Cl^-}{L} + \frac{\text{meq of } HCO_3^-}{L} \right)$$

The anion gap in a patient's blood is determined by analyzing a sample for the concentrations in meq/L of Na^+, Cl^-, and HCO_3^-, which as we said are the most abundant ions and are also relatively easy to analyze. Then the concentration data are fed into this equation. For example, suppose that analyses found the following data: Na^+ = 137 meq/L; Cl^- = 100 meq/L; and HCO_3^- = 28 meq/L. Then the anion gap is found by

$$\text{Anion gap} = 137 \, \frac{\text{meq}}{L} - \left(100 \, \frac{\text{meq}}{L} + 28 \, \frac{\text{meq}}{L} \right)$$
$$= 9 \text{ meq/L}$$

The normal range for the anion gap is 5 to 14 meq/L, so in our example the anion gap of 9 meq/L falls within the normal range. This 9 meq/L is accounted for by the presence of unmeasured ions of low concentration.

If metabolic disturbances cause the levels of organic anions to rise, the body must retain cations in the blood and excrete some of the more common anions such as Cl^- and HCO_3^- to maintain the absolute requirement that the blood be electrically neutral. In other words, negative organic ions tend to expel other negative ions but retain whatever positive ions are available. This is how the anion gap widens in metabolic disturbances that generate organic anions. The anion gap routinely rises above 14 meq/L in untreated diabetes.

You can see that by using rather easily measured data on the meq/L concentrations of Na^+, Cl^-, and HCO_3^-, and calculating the anion gap from these data, the clinical chemist can inform the health care professionals of any unusual buildups in anions which indicate possible disease. In severe exercise, the anion gap rises above normal, too, but it goes back down again in time. Thus an above-normal anion gap has to be interpreted in the light of other facts.

is also an application, described in Special Topic 8.4, in which the concentrations of anions in blood that are hard to determine directly can be estimated. When the level of such anions increases sufficiently, it can indicate a malfunction somewhere in the body.

8.6   ## THE CARBONIC ACID SYSTEM AND ITS PLACE IN RESPIRATION AND METABOLISM—A PRELIMINARY LOOK

The body sends waste CO_2 to the lungs largely as HCO_3^- dissolved in the blood.

The acidity of carbonic acid and its instability are particularly important at the molecular level of life. In this chapter we take a first look at how carbonic acid participates in respiration. Later in this book we will study it again at a more quantitative level.

■ Breathing is done to expel CO_2 as much as to take in O_2. Chemical interference with either process affects the other.

H_2CO_3, CO_2, and HCO_3^- Are Intimately Involved in Respiration   Carbon dioxide is one of the major waste products of metabolism. But this gas cannot be directly expelled through the skin at a rate fast enough to be lost from the body in this way. Moreover, it is not soluble enough in water to be carried in the bloodstream as $CO_2(aq)$. Although $CO_2(aq)$ does react with water to give $H_2CO_3(aq)$,

$$CO_2(aq) + H_2O \rightleftharpoons H_2CO_3(aq)$$

the position of equilibrium in pure water does not favor $H_2CO_3(aq)$. The body could not use it to carry CO_2 away fast enough from the places where it is made by metabolism, if the fluid carrying it were not slightly basic.

The blood, however, is slightly basic, and carbon dioxide equilibrates in a slightly basic aqueous medium with the bicarbonate ion. Thus, to carry CO_2 back to the lungs, H_2CO_3 forms and then most of it is neutralized in the basic medium of the blood to the bicarbonate ion stage. (This neutralization is done largely by oxyhemoglobin, a Brønsted base that is a slightly stronger base than HCO_3^-. Oxyhemoglobin is an anion that carries oxygen, and as it neutralizes carbonic acid, it is forced to unload its oxygen. But this part of the chemistry of respiration will come later.) The bicarbonate ion is the principal form in which CO_2 is transported in the blood to the lungs.

Carbonic Anhydrase Handles the Rapid Equilibration of CO_2 and H_2CO_3   When the $HCO_3^-(aq)$ ion is circulated back to the lungs, reactions occur there to change it back to $H_2CO_3(aq)$. Then, virtually as fast as this forms, it is broken down to CO_2 and water. The $CO_2(aq)$ then leaves the blood, becomes $CO_2(g)$ in an air space in the lungs, and is expelled when the lungs exhale. This breakdown of H_2CO_3 in the lungs must be extremely rapid. Such speed is necessary despite the fact that the following equilibrium overwhelmingly favors $CO_2(aq)$ under the conditions in the lungs — body temperature, the acid–base balance of the blood, the partial pressure of $CO_2(g)$, and the presence of a catalyst (an enzyme).

$$H_2CO_3(aq) \rightleftharpoons H_2O + CO_2(aq)$$

Under these conditions, the mole ratio of $CO_2(aq)$ to $H_2CO_3(aq)$ at equilibrium is a huge 400 to 1. But $H_2CO_3(aq)$ is constantly being produced from $HCO_3^-(aq)$ and so must just as steadily be broken down as the blood moves through the lungs. A steady influx of $H_2CO_3(aq)$, of course, tends to shift the equilibrium to the right. But without the special catalyst, this shift would not occur rapidly enough.

To make the breakdown of H_2CO_3 happen rapidly enough, the body has a special catalyst, an enzyme called carbonic anhydrase. It is estimated that one molecule of this enzyme can catalyze the conversion of 600,000 molecules of CO_2 to H_2CO_3 *per second*(!), the fastest rate for any enzyme-catalyzed reaction, and 10 million times faster than the uncatalyzed reaction. This enzyme, like all enzymes — like all catalysts of any kind involved in chemical equilibria — *affects the rates of forward and reverse reactions identically.* **Enzymes do not affect positions of equilibria, only how rapidly equilibria are established.**

Wherever in the body carbonic anhydrase is present, no major buildup of $H_2CO_3(aq)$ is possible. $CO_2(aq)$ will exist mostly as $HCO_3^-(aq)$ in body fluids or, in the air spaces of the lungs prior to its removal, as $CO_2(g)$. You can begin to sense here how crucial is the acid–base balance of the blood. The blood must be basic enough so that most waste $CO_2(aq)$ gets changed into $HCO_3^-(aq)$, but not so basic that it cannot get changed back again.

SUMMARY

Ionization of water   Trace concentrations of hydronium ions, H_3O^+, and hydroxide ions, OH^-, are always present in water. In neutral water, their molar concentrations are equal (and very low). In writing equations, we usually write H_3O^+ as H^+, calling the latter either the hydrogen ion or the proton. In explaining these reactions, however, we usually find it necessary to use the correct formula, H_3O^+.

Aqueous solutions of ions form either by the dissociation of ionic compounds as they dissolve or by the ionization of molecular substances as they react with water.

Electrolytes   Solutes that are dissociated or ionized in water are electrolytes. Their solutions conduct electricity between a positively charged electrode, or anode, and a negatively charged electrode, or

cathode. Cations that accept electrons from cathodes are reduced. Anions that deliver electrons to anodes are oxidized.

Chief ion producers   Acids, bases, and salts are the common electrolytes. In the Brønsted concept, acids are chemical species that can donate hydrogen ions. Their aqueous solutions are also called acids. The five most common strong acids are hydrochloric, hydrobromic, hydriodic, sulfuric, and nitric acid. All are monoprotic except sulfuric acid, which is diprotic. The chief acid species in all is H_3O^+.

Bases are substances that accept hydrogen ions. Among the common bases are those that directly supply OH^- ion in water, like the hydroxides and oxides of sodium and potassium. Other common proton-acceptors that readily take H^+ from H_3O^+ (but not from H_2O)

are the carbonate and bicarbonate ions, the monohydrogen phosphate and phosphate ions, and ammonia.

Salts are ionic compounds that involve any other ions but H^+, OH^-, or O^{2-}.

Strong and weak electrolytes; strong and weak acids and bases A strong electrolyte is one fully ionized or dissociated in solution, and all strong acids and strong bases are strong electrolytes. Salts in their molten states or in aqueous solutions are fully dissociated and are therefore all strong electrolytes. Remember that *strong* refers to percentage dissociation or ionization. Many salts are quite insoluble in water and so cannot supply a high concentration of ions. But what does dissolve of such salts is 100% dissociated.

Many molecular acids and bases ionize to a small percentage in water and so are weak electrolytes. Acetic acid and ammonia are examples. Many other molecular substances can be present in an aqueous system without being ionized and so are called nonelectrolytes. Pure water is a nonelectrolyte.

H_3O^+ is the strongest acid that can be present in water, and OH^- is the strongest base.

Conjugate acids and bases in the Brønsted concept All proton-transfer reactions can be expressed in terms of equilibria in which two acids and two bases appear. An acid and a base whose formulas differ only by one H^+ are a conjugate acid–base pair.

In the Brønsted concept, the terms *strong* and *weak* are enlarged. A strong acid is one that is a good proton-donor. It readily gives up H^+. A strong acid has a weak conjugate base. A weak acid has a strong conjugate base. A strong base is one that strongly binds a proton, and a weak base is one that cannot hold H^+ very well. A strong base has a weak conjugate acid, and a weak base has a strong conjugate acid.

Reactions of aqueous acids The hydronium ions in strong aqueous acids react with

Metals hydroxides, to give a salt and water
Metal carbonates, to give a salt, carbon dioxide, and water
Metal bicarbonates, to give a salt, carbon dioxide, and water
Metals, to give the salt of the metal and hydrogen

A solution of an acid is neutralized when any sufficiently strong proton-binding species is added in the correct mole proportion to make the concentration of hydrogen ion and hydroxide ion equal (and very small).

Carbonic acid and carbonates Carbonic acid, H_2CO_3, is both a weak acid and an unstable acid. When it is generated in water by the reaction of any stronger acid with a bicarbonate or a carbonate salt, virtually all the carbonic acid decomposes to carbon dioxide and water, and most of the carbon dioxide fizzes out. The carbonate ion and the bicarbonate ion are both Brønsted bases, and the bicarbonate ion is involved in carrying waste carbon dioxide from cells, where it is made, to the lungs.

Ammonia and the ammonium ion Ammonia is a strong base toward H_3O^+ but a weak base toward H_2O. The ammonium ion is a strong acid toward OH^- but a weak acid toward H_2O. Ammonia can neutralize strong acids and the ammonium ion can neutralize strong bases.

Salts The chemical properties of salts in water are the properties of their individual ions. If the anion of the salt is the conjugate base of a weak acid, as HCO_3^- is the conjugate base of H_2CO_3, then the salt can neutralize strong acids. Thus bicarbonates, carbonates, acetates, and the salts of other organic acids supply Brønsted bases, their anions.

If the cation of the salt is the conjugate acid of a weak base, as NH_4^+ is the conjugate acid of NH_3, then the salt supplies a Brønsted acid in water.

Salts can be produced by any of the reactions of strong acids that were studied (and summarized, above) as well as by double replacement reactions. The solubility rules are guides for the prediction of their reactions. If a combination of oppositely charged ions can lead to an insoluble salt, an un-ionized species that stays in solution, or a gas, then the ions react.

If a different compound that can furnish an ion that is common to an ion of a salt already in solution is added to this solution, the solubility of the salt might be reduced enough to force it out of solution (common ion effect).

The carbonate system in respiration Several factors enable waste CO_2 to be carried largely as HCO_3^- from tissues making this waste to the lungs — the slight basicity of blood, the partial pressure of CO_2, the presence of the enzyme carbonic anhydrase, and the interconvertability of CO_2 in water to H_2CO_3. The enzyme extremely rapidly reestablishes equilibrium between CO_2 and H_2CO_3 when some stress shifts it. All catalysts involved in equilibria speed up both forward and reverse reactions. They do not affect the *position* of the equilibrium, only how rapidly it gets established.

Equivalents of ions An equivalent (eq) of an ion is the number of grams of the ion that carry Avogadro's number of positive or negative charges. It is calculated by dividing the molar mass of the ion by the size of the charge it carries. The concentration of an ion in a dilute solution is often given in meq/L, where 1000 meq = 1 eq, and meq means milliequivalent.

REVIEW EXERCISES

The answers to Review Exercises that require a calculation and that are marked with an asterisk are found in Appendix D. The answers to the other Review Exercises are found in the *Study Guide* that accompanies this book.

Electrolytes

8.1 What is the difference between *ionization* and *dissociation?*

8.2 Na_2SO_3 is a crystalline solid that dissolves in water to give a solution that conducts electricity. By what process does it form this solution? How can you tell?

8.3 SO_3 is a colorless gas that dissolves in water to give a solution that conducts electricity. By what process does it form this solution? How can you tell?

8.4 The word *electrolyte* can be understood in two ways. What are they? Give examples.

8.5 To which electrode do cations migrate?

8.6 The anode has what electrical charge, positive or negative?

8.7 The electrode that is negatively charged attracts what kinds of ions, cations or anions?

8.8 Explain in your own words how the presence of cations and anions in water enables the system to conduct electricity.

8.9 When NaOH(s) is dissolved in water, the solution is an excellent conductor of electricity, but when methyl alcohol is dissolved in water, the solution won't conduct electricity at all. What does this behavior suggest about the structural natures of NaOH and methyl alcohol, whose structure is given below? (Notice that both appear to have OH groups in their formulas.)

$$
\begin{array}{c}
H \\
| \\
H-C-O-H \\
| \\
H
\end{array}
$$

Methyl alcohol

8.10 If a water-soluble compound breaks up entirely into ions as it dissolves in water, do we call it a weak or a strong electrolyte?

8.11 In the liquid state, tin(IV) chloride, $SnCl_4$, is a nonconductor. What does this suggest about the structural nature of this compound?

8.12 Molten sodium chloride conducts electricity. At the cathode, one of its ions is reduced and at the anode the other ion is oxidized.
(a) Write an equation for the reaction at the cathode (using electrons as species in the reaction).
(b) Write an equation for the reaction at the anode (again, using electrons as species in the reaction).
(c) Write the overall reaction for the electrolysis.

8.13 What families of compounds are the principal sources of ions in aqueous solutions?

8.14 Review the differences between atoms and ions by answering the following questions.
(a) Are there any atoms that have more than one nucleus? If so, give an example.
(b) Are there any ions with more than one nucleus? If so, give an example.
(c) Are there any ions that are electrically neutral? If so, give an example.
(d) Are there any atoms that are electrically charged? If so, give an example.

Acids and Bases as Electrolytes

8.15 Write the equilibrium equation for the self-ionization of water, and label the ions that are present.

8.16 Tell whether each of the following solutions is acidic, basic, or neutral.
(a) $[H^+] = 6.2 \times 10^{-6}$ mol/L and $[OH^-] = 1.6 \times 10^{-9}$ mol/L
(b) $[H^+] = 1.0 \times 10^{-7}$ mol/L and $[OH^-] = 1.0 \times 10^{-7}$ mol/L
(c) $[H^+] = 1.36 \times 10^{-8}$ mol/L and $[OH^-] = 7.35 \times 10^{-7}$ mol/L

8.17 Salts are all crystalline solids at room temperature. Why do you suppose this is?

8.18 How did Arrhenius define an acid? A base?

8.19 What features do the common aqueous acids have in common?

8.20 In the context of acid–base discussion, what are two other names that we can use for *proton*?

8.21 Acids have a set of common reactions, and so do bases, but not salts. Explain.

8.22 How does litmus paper work to tell whether a solution is acidic, basic, or neutral?

8.23 How did Brønsted define an acid? A base?

8.24 What is the difference between hydrochloric acid and hydrogen chloride?

8.25 In which species is the covalent bond to hydrogen stronger, in HCl(g) or in $H_3O^+(aq)$? How do we know?

8.26 $HClO_4$ (perchloric acid) is a less common, strong acid. Represent its ionization in water by an equation.

8.27 Write the equation for the ionization of nitric acid in water.

8.28 Is $HC_2H_3O_2$ a mono-, di-, tri-, or tetraprotic acid? (What is its name?)

8.29 What are the names and the formulas of the aqueous solutions of the four hydrohalogen acids?

8.30 If we represent all diprotic acids by the symbol H_2A, write the equilibrium expressions for the two separate ionization steps.

8.31 Would the ionization of the second proton from a diprotic acid occur with greater ease or with greater difficulty than the ionization of the first proton? Explain.

8.32 Write the equations for the progressive ionizations of sulfuric acid. Include the names of the ions.

8.33 Write the equations for the progressive ionizations of phosphoric acid, including the names of the ions.

8.34 Compare the structures of nitrous acid, HNO_2, and nitric acid, HNO_3.

$$
H-\overset{..}{\underset{..}{O}}-\overset{..}{N}=\overset{..}{O}: \qquad H-\overset{..}{\underset{..}{O}}-N\overset{\displaystyle \overset{..}{O}:}{\underset{\displaystyle :\overset{..}{O}:}{\diagup}}
$$

Nitrous acid   Nitric acid

Nitrous acid is a much weaker acid than nitric acid. How does the extra oxygen in the structure of nitric acid help to explain this?

8.35 Which is the stronger acid in water, sulfurous acid or sulfuric acid? How can you tell?

Sulfurous acid   Sulfuric acid

8.36 Write the equilibrium expression for the solution of carbon dioxide in water that produces some carbonic acid.

8.37 Write the equilibrium expressions for the successive steps in the ionization of carbonic acid.

8.38 NaOH is a strong base and a strong electrolyte. What do these terms mean in connection with this compound?

8.39 Magnesium hydroxide is practically insoluble in water, and yet it is classified as a strong base. Explain.

8.40 Ammonia is very soluble in water, and yet it is called a weak base. Explain.

8.41 What are the names and formulas of two bases that are both strong and are capable of forming relatively concentrated solutions in water?

8.42 When carbon dioxide is bubbled into pure water to form a solution, it takes only time and the help of a little warming to drive essentially all of it out of solution again. When this gas is bubbled into aqueous sodium hydroxide, however, it is completely trapped by a chemical reaction. If we assume that the reaction involves CO_2 and NaOH in a mole ratio of one to one, what is the molecular equation for this trapping reaction?

8.43 What is meant by *aqueous ammonia?* Why don't we call it "ammonium hydroxide"?

8.44 Write the names and the formulas of the five strong acids that we have studied.

8.45 What are the four strong bases—both the names and formulas? Which are quite soluble in water?

Net Ionic Equations

8.46 Consider the following net ionic equation:

$$2H^+(aq) + Cu(s) + NO_3^-(aq) \longrightarrow$$
$$Cu^{2+}(aq) + NO_2(g) + H_2O$$

  (a) Does it have material balance?
  (b) Does it have electrical balance?

8.47 Complete and balance the following molecular equations, and then write the net ionic equations.
  (a) $HNO_3(aq) + NaOH(aq) \longrightarrow$
  (b) $HCl(aq) + K_2CO_3(aq) \longrightarrow$
  (c) $HBr(aq) + CaCO_3(s) \longrightarrow$
  (d) $HNO_3(aq) + NaHCO_3(aq) \longrightarrow$
  (e) $HI(aq) + NH_3(aq) \longrightarrow$
  (f) $HNO_3(aq) + Mg(OH)_2(s) \longrightarrow$
  (g) $HBr(aq) + Zn(s) \longrightarrow$

8.48 Complete and balance the following molecular equations, and then write the net ionic equation.
  (a) $KOH(aq) + H_2SO_4(aq) \longrightarrow$
  (b) $Na_2CO_3(aq) + HNO_3(aq) \longrightarrow$
  (c) $KHCO_3(aq) + HCl(aq) \longrightarrow$
  (d) $MgCO_3(s) + HI(aq) \longrightarrow$
  (e) $NH_3(aq) + HBr(aq) \longrightarrow$
  (f) $Ca(OH)_2(s) + HCl(aq) \longrightarrow$
  (g) $Al(s) + HCl(aq) \longrightarrow$

8.49 What are the net ionic equations for the following reactions of strong, aqueous acids? (Assume that all reactants and products are soluble in water.)
  (a) With metal hydroxides
  (b) With metal bicarbonates
  (c) With metal carbonates
  (d) With aqueous ammonia

8.50 Write net ionic equations for the reactions of all the water-insoluble group IIA carbonates, where you use $MCO_3(s)$ as their general formula, with hydrochloric acid (chosen so that all the products are soluble in water).

8.51 If we let $M(OH)_2(s)$ represent the water-insoluble group IIA metal hydroxides, what is the general net ionic equation for all their reactions with nitric acid (chosen so that all the products are soluble in water)?

8.52 If we let $M(s)$ represent either calcium or magnesium metal, what net ionic equation represents the reaction of either with hydrochloric acid?

8.53 Sodium and potassium in group IA are higher in the activity series than calcium and magnesium in group IIA.
  (a) What does it mean to be *higher* in the activity series?
  (b) If you check back to Figure 3.5*b*, on page 61, you will see that sodium and potassium have lower ionization energies than calcium and magnesium. In what way does this fact correlate with their higher position in the activity series of the metals?

8.54 Zinc metal reacts more rapidly with which acid, 1 *M* nitric acid or 1 *M* acetic acid?

•8.55 How many moles of sodium bicarbonate can react quantitatively with 0.250 mol of HCl?

8.56 How many moles of potassium hydroxide can react quantitatively with 0.400 mol of H_2SO_4 (assuming that both H^+ in H_2SO_4 are neutralized)?

•8.57 How many grams of sodium carbonate does it take to neutralize 4.60 g of HCl?

8.58 How many grams of calcium carbonate react quantitatively with 6.88 g of HNO_3?

•8.59 How many grams of sodium bicarbonate does it take to neutralize all the acid in 25.4 mL of 1.15 *M* H_2SO_4?

8.60 How many grams of potassium carbonate will neutralize all the acid in 36.8 mL of 0.550 *M* HCl?

•8.61 How many milliliters of 0.246 *M* NaOH are needed to neutralize the acid in 32.4 mL of 0.224 *M* HNO_3?

8.62 How many milliliters of 0.108 *M* KOH are needed to neutralize the acid in 16.4 mL of 0.116 *M* H_2SO_4?

8.63 For an experiment that required 12.0 L of dry CO_2 gas (as measured at 740 mm Hg and 25 °C), a student let 5.00 M HCl react with marble chips, $CaCO_3$.
(a) Write the molecular and net ionic equations for this reaction.
(b) How many grams of $CaCO_3$ and how many milliliters of the acid are needed?

8.64 How many liters of dry CO_2 gas are generated (at 750 mm Hg and 20 °C) by the reaction of $Na_2CO_3(s)$ with 250 mL of 6.00 M HCl? Write the molecular and the net ionic equations for the reaction, and calculate how many grams of Na_2CO_3 are needed.

Strengths of Conjugate Brønsted Acids and Bases

8.65 What is the reason that OH^- is the strongest base we can have in water?

8.66 Why is H_3O^+ the strongest acid we can have in water?

8.67 Write the formulas of the conjugate acids of the following:
(a) HSO_4^- (b) HCO_3^- (c) I^- (d) NO_2^-

8.68 What are the formulas of the conjugate acids of the following?
(a) HSO_3^- (b) Br^- (c) H_2O (d) $C_2H_3O_2^-$

8.69 What are the conjugate bases of the following? Write their formulas.
(a) H_2CO_3 (b) $H_2PO_4^-$ (c) NH_4^+ (d) OH^-

8.70 Write the formulas of the conjugate bases of the following:
(a) NH_3 (b) HNO_2 (c) HSO_3^- (d) H_2SO_3

8.71 Which member of each pair is the stronger Brønsted base?
(a) Br^- or HCO_3^- (b) $H_2PO_4^-$ or HSO_4^-
(c) NO_2^- or NO_3^-

8.72 Which member of each pair is the stronger Brønsted base?
(a) NH_3 or NH_2^- (b) OH^- or H_2O
(c) HS^- or S^{2-}

8.73 Study each pair and decide which is the stronger Brønsted acid.
(a) $H_2PO_4^-$ or HPO_4^{2-} (b) H_2SO_3 or HSO_3^-
(c) NH_4^+ or NH_3

8.74 Which member of each pair is the stronger Brønsted acid?
(a) H_2CO_3 or HCl   (b) H_2O or OH^-
(b) HSO_4^- or HSO_3^-

8.75 If sodium phosphate and sodium hydrogen sulfate solutions are mixed in equimolar amounts of their solutes, the following ionic equilibrium is established:

$$HPO_4^{2-}(aq) + SO_4^{2-} \rightleftharpoons PO_4^{3-}(aq) + HSO_4^-(aq)$$

Which side is favored, the reactants or products? How can you tell?

8.76 Aspirin is a weak acid. We can represent it as H(Asp), and it has a sodium salt that we can symbolize as Na(Asp). When the sodium salt of aspirin is given as a medication and it encounters gastric juice, which contains HCl(aq), the following ionic equilibrium is established (at least temporarily). Which side is favored, the reactants or products? How can you tell?

$$(Asp)^-(aq) + H_3O^+(aq) \rightleftharpoons H(Asp)(aq) + H_2O$$

8.77 Suppose you are handed a test tube and told that it contains a concentrated solution of either ammonium chloride or potassium chloride. An aqueous solution of one of the substances that we have studied in this chapter could be added to the unknown solution as a test for deciding which of the two solutes is present. What is this test reagent, and what would you observe as a result of the test if the unknown contained ammonium chloride?

8.78 Complete and balance the following molecular equations.
(a) $K_2O(s) + H_2O \longrightarrow$
(b) $NaNH_2(s) + H_2O \longrightarrow$
(c) $NaH(s) + H_2O \longrightarrow$

Salts

8.79 Write the names and formulas of three compounds that, by reacting with hydrochloric acid, give a solution of potassium chloride. Write the molecular equations for these reactions.

8.80 Write the names and formulas of three compounds that will give a solution of lithium bromide when they react with hydrobromic acid. Write the molecular equations for these reactions.

8.81 Which of the following compounds are insoluble in water (as we have defined solubility)?
(a) NaOH   (b) NH_4Br (c) Hg_2Cl_2
(d) $Ca_3(PO_4)_2$ (e) KBr   (f) Li_2SO_4

8.82 Which of the following compounds are insoluble in water?
(a) $(NH_4)_2SO_4$ (b) KNO_2 (c) LiCl
(d) AgCl   (e) $Mg_3(PO_4)_2$ (f) $NaNO_3$

8.83 Identify the compounds that do not dissolve in water.
(a) NH_4NO_3 (b) $BaCO_3$ (c) $PbCl_2$
(d) K_2CO_3 (e) $LiC_2H_3O_2$ (f) Na_2SO_4

8.84 Which of the following compounds do not dissolve in water?
(a) Li_2CO_3 (b) $Na_2Cr_2O_7$ (c) NH_4I
(d) AgBr   (e) K_2CrO_4 (f) $FeCO_3$

8.85 Assume you have separate solutions of each compound in the pairs below. Predict what happens chemically when the two solutions of a pair are poured together. If no reaction occurs, state so. If there is a reaction, write its net ionic equation.
(a) LiCl and $AgNO_3$ (b) $NaNO_3$ and $CaCl_2$
(c) KOH and H_2SO_4 (d) $Pb(NO_3)_2$ and KCl
(e) NH_4Br and K_2SO_4 (f) Na_2S and $CuSO_4$
(g) K_2SO_4 and $Ba(NO_3)_2$ (h) NaOH and HI
(i) K_2S and $NiCl_2$ (j) $AgNO_3$ and NaCl
(k) $LiHCO_3$ and HBr   (l) $CaCl_2$ and KOH

8.86 If you have separate solutions of each of the compounds given below and then mix the two of each pair together, what (if anything) happens chemically? If no reaction occurs, state so, but if there is a reaction write its net ionic equation.
(a) H_2S and $CdCl_2$
(b) KOH and HBr
(c) Na_2SO_4 and $BaCl_2$
(d) $Pb(C_2H_3O_2)_2$ and Li_2SO_4
(e) $Ba(NO_3)_2$ and KCl
(f) $NaHCO_3$ and H_2SO_4
(g) Na_2S and $Ni(NO_3)_2$
(h) NaOH and HBr

    (i) $Hg(NO_3)_2$ and KCl
    (j) $NaHCO_3$ and HI
    (k) KBr and $NaCl$
    (l) $Pb(NO_3)_2$ and Na_2CrO_4

8.87 Soap is a mixture of the sodium salts of certain organic acids. One is sodium stearate, which we can represent as Na(Ste).
    (a) Write the equilibrium expression for a saturated solution of this salt in water.
    (b) What would happen to this equilibrium if a concentrated solution of sodium chloride were added to it?
    (c) The NaCl solution need not be concentrated. Seawater is about 3% (w/w) NaCl, and soap doesn't work well when seawater is used. Suggest a reason.

Equivalents and Milliequivalents of Ions

8.88 The concentration of potassium ion in blood serum is normally in the range of 0.0035 to 0.0050 mol K^+/L. Express this range in units of milliequivalents of K^+ per liter.

8.89 The concentration of calcium ion in blood serum is normally in the range of 0.0042 to 0.0052 eq Ca^{2+}/L. Express this range in units of milliequivalents of Ca^{2+} per liter.

*8.90 The level of chloride ion in blood serum is normally quoted as 100 to 106 meq/L. How many grams and how many milligrams constitute 106 meq of Cl^-?

8.91 The sodium ion level in the blood is normally 135 to 145 meq/L. How many grams and how many milligrams of sodium ion constitute 135 meq of Na^+?

*8.92 The potassium ion level of blood serum normally does not exceed 0.196 g of K^+ per liter. How many milliequivalents of K^+ ion are in 0.196 g of K^+?

8.93 The magnesium ion level in plasma normally does not exceed 0.0243 g of Mg^{2+}/L. How many milliequivalents of Mg^{2+} are in 0.0243 g of Mg^{2+}?

Ion Mobility and Ionic Reactions
(Special Topic 8.1)

8.94 How can an acid, like citric acid, and a bicarbonate salt be stable in each other's presence since we know that acids and bicarbonates react to give an unstable acid?

8.95 What is the net ionic equation between citric acid and sodium bicarbonate when something like an Alka-Seltzer tablet is dropped into water?

Hard Water
(Special Topic 8.2)

8.96 What is *hard water*?

8.97 What are the formulas of the "hardness ions"?

8.98 What chemical property of these ions and of ordinary soap makes it hard to use such soap in hard water?

8.99 What is *temporary* hard water? Why is it designated *temporary?*

8.100 What is *permanent* hard water?

8.101 What is meant by *water softening*?

8.102 Concerning washing soda as a water-softening agent,
    (a) What is its molecular formula?
    (b) What part of its formula is the active softening agent?
    (c) What is the net ionic equation for its work in water where the hardness is caused by Ca^{2+}? By Mg^{2+}?

8.103 Concerning aqueous ammonia as a water-softening agent,
    (a) What is the composition of aqueous ammonia?
    (b) What is the specific species in aqueous ammonia that is the active softening agent?
    (c) How does this species arise in aqueous ammonia? (Write an equilibrium expression.)
    (d) What is the net ionic equation for its work in water where the hardness is caused by Ca^{2+}?

8.104 In general terms, what is a zeolite and how does it work in water softening?

Equilibria in Urinary Calculi
(Special Topic 8.3)

8.105 What is a *calculus* in medicine?

8.106 What inorganic anions (give their names and formulas) are commonly involved in the formation of urinary calculi?

8.107 Write the expression for the ionic equilibrium that involves these anions in the formation of urinary calculi.

The Anion Gap
(Special Topic 8.4)

*8.108 The analysis of the blood from a young man recovering from polio found 137 meq of Na^+/L, 34 meq of HCO_3^-/L, and 93 meq of Cl^-/L. Calculate the anion gap. Does it suggest a serious disturbance in his metabolism?

8.109 A patient on a self-prescribed diet consisting essentially only of protein was found to have the following blood analyses after two weeks of the diet: Na^+, 174 meq/L; Cl^-, 135 meq/L; and HCO_3^-, 20 meq/L. Calculate the anion gap. Does it suggest a disturbance in metabolism?

CHAPTER NINE

Acid–Base Equilibria

If the concentration of hydrogen ion in the water going over Niagara Falls were about 1×10^{-10} mol/L, we'd have to watch the falls about an hour before a mole of H^+ ions would go by. We'll learn how to describe very low H^+ concentrations in this chapter.

9.1 THE ION PRODUCT CONSTANT OF WATER

The product of the molar concentrations of the hydrogen ion and the hydroxide ion in water is a constant called the ion product constant, K_w.

■ The brackets in $[H^+]$ signify that the concentration is specifically moles per liter.

We have learned that the acid–base balance in an aqueous fluid, defined by $[H^+] = [OH^-]$, is upset by the presence of acids and bases, including such Brønsted bases as NH_3, HCO_3^-, $C_2H_3O_2^-$, CO_3^{2-}, and the anions of phosphoric acid. We went as far as we could go with a qualitative discussion of this in the previous chapter. We'll take the discussion to a quantitative level in this chapter as we shift to a deeper study of chemical equilibria. In all our discussions, we will always assume that solutions are *aqueous* solutions.

An Equilibrium Law Exists for Every Chemical Equilibrium In 1867, C. M. Guldberg and Peter Waage, two Norwegian scientists, discovered a relationship concerning the molar concentrations of the species in a chemical equilibrium that we now call the *equilibrium law* for the system. We first illustrate this with a general equation. If reactants A and B are in equilibrium with products C and D, according to the equilibrium equation (where a, b, c, and d are the coefficients),

$$aA + bB \rightleftharpoons cC + dD$$

then the **equilibrium law** for the system is

■ Equation 9.1 is often called the **law of mass action.**

$$\frac{[C]^c[D]^d}{[A]^a[B]^b} = K_{eq} \tag{9.1}$$

Thus the equilibrium law for a system is always an *equation* patterned after Equation 9.1, and there is a unique equation, a unique equilibrium law, for each and every chemical equilibrium. K_{eq}, called the **equilibrium constant** and calculated from measured molar concentrations, therefore has a different value for each chemical equilibrium.

Since equilibria can be shifted by increasing or decreasing the temperature, the value of K_{eq} depends on the temperature, and its value at 25 °C, for example, is not the same as at 30 °C.

■ Reference tables for K_{eq} values do not record the actual equilibrium law equations because they can always be written according to the convention.

The Size of K_{eq} Indicates the Position of Equilibrium Notice in Equation 9.1 that the products appear in the numerator and the reactants in the denominator. By universal convention, the value of the equilibrium constant is always meant to correspond to this arrangement. This lets us always associate the size of K_{eq}, regardless of the reference table, with the position of equilibrium.

The value of K_{eq} is small, less than 1, whenever the denominator in the equilibrium law is larger than the numerator. The denominator carries the reactant concentrations, so a larger denominator means that *reactants'* concentrations are greater than those of the products. Thus a small value of K_{eq} means that the reactants are favored at equilibrium.

Conversely, a value of K_{eq} greater than 1 means that the *products* are favored, because their molarities appear in the numerator of Equation 9.1. We can summarize these relationships of K_{eq} to positions of equilibrium as follows.

■ When K_{eq} is greater than 10^2, we almost never express the equation as an equilibrium but use just a single arrow.

$$K_{eq} < 1, \quad \text{reactants are favored at equilibrium}$$
$$K_{eq} > 1, \quad \text{products are favored at equilibrium}$$

In all the equilibria we will study, those of weak acids and bases or the self-ionization of water, K_{eq} will be less than 1. In aqueous acetic acid, for example, we have the following equlibrium,

$$HC_2H_3O_2(aq) + H_2O \rightleftharpoons H_3O^+ + C_2H_3O_2^-(aq)$$

Putting the molar concentrations of the products in the numerator (and noting that all chemical coefficients are 1), we find the equilibrium law with the known value of K_{eq} to be

$$\frac{[H_3O^+][C_2H_3O^-]}{[HC_2H_3O_2][H_2O]} = K_{eq} = 3.2 \times 10^{-7} \quad (25\ °C)$$

We now have a number, K_{eq}, that quantitatively indicates just how weak acetic acid is as an acid. K_{eq} is small, 3.2×10^{-7}, so the molarities of the product ions must be smaller than those of the un-ionized reactants. Thus far all we said was that acetic acid has a low percentage ionization, but percentage ionization changes with the overall concentration of the acid. K_{eq} does not, giving this term (or terms just like it) the advantage for comparing the relative strengths of acids.

K_{eq} Remains a Constant Even When the Equilibrium Shifts If we add sodium acetate to the equilibrium in aqueous acetic acid, we add the acetate ion. The common ion effect will now operate — a special case of Le Chatelier's principle — and the equilibrium will shift to the left in an effort to use up as much of the added acetate ion as possible. This shift changes the values of every term in the equilibrium law. But an increase in $[C_2H_3O_2^-]$ is offset by a decrease in $[H_3O^+]$ and comparable changes in the denominator as the equilibrium adjusts to the stress of added acetate ion. When the new equilibrium values of concentrations are measured and then inserted into the equilibrium law equation, the constant, K_{eq}, turns out to be the same as before.

K_{eq} is a constant in the midst of other changes. Guldburg and Waage were the first to realize this important fact about chemical equilibria, and scientists have always paid attention to anything in nature that is a constant in the midst of change. No matter how we try to change the concentrations of individual species in the equilibrium and thereby make the equilibrium shift, the value of K_{eq} remains a constant. This is why the word *law* is used in this connection; it is something nature does very consistently.

Certain kinds of ionic equilibria have equilibrium laws that can be simplified without any loss in meaning. The self-ionization of water is one example. We'll see next how this works out.

■ Other constants in the midst of change are the total energy of the universe and the masses of chemicals before and after a reaction. (Perhaps we might add death and taxes to the list.)

The Ion Product Constant of Water Is a Modified Equilibrium Law As we have indicated, the self-ionization of water is one of nature's most important chemical equilibria. Its equilibrium expression (using H^+ for H_3O^+) is

$$H_2O \rightleftharpoons H^+(aq) + OH^-(aq)$$

The equilibrium law for this system is

$$K_{eq} = \frac{[H^+][OH^-]}{[H_2O]} \qquad (9.2)$$

Although Equation 9.2 isn't very complex, it can be made simpler with no loss of precision. Remember that the values of $[H^+]$ and $[OH^-]$ in pure water are 1.0×10^{-7} mol/L each at 25 °C. This figure is so low that the formation of these ions from water molecules has no effect on the value of $[H_2O]$, even if we round to seven significant figures. Thus the value of $[H_2O]$ is really a constant, for all practical purposes, in Equation 9.2.

In mathematics we learn that if we multiply one constant by another, we just get a new constant. So if we multiply Equation 9.2 on both sides by the constant value of $[H_2O]$, then do an obvious cancellation, we obtain a new expression and a new constant.

■ $K_{eq} \times [H_2O]$ is one constant multiplied by another.

$$K_{eq} \times [H_2O] = \frac{[H^+][OH^-]}{[H_2O]} \times [H_2O] = \text{a new constant}$$

The new constant is called the **ion product constant of water,** and its symbol is K_w.

$$K_w = [H^+][OH^-] \qquad (9.3)$$

Equation 9.3 is not a true equilibrium law, because it omits the reactant's term in the denominator, but it still behaves exactly like such a law. In accordance with the equilibrium law, no matter how we change, say, $[H^+]$ by adding acid or base to a solution, the value of $[OH^-]$ in Equation 9.3 adjusts, and the *product* of the two terms remains equal to the constant, K_w. The only way to change K_w is to change the temperature, as data in the margin show.

■ If we add H^+, we shift

$$H_2O \rightleftharpoons H^+ + OH^-$$

to the left and so diminish $[OH^-]$

At 25 °C (and to two significant figures),

$$[H^+] = 1.0 \times 10^{-7} \text{ mol/L}$$

and

$$[OH^-] = 1.0 \times 10^{-7} \text{ mol/L}$$

Therefore at 25 °C,

$$K_w = (1.0 \times 10^{-7})(1.0 \times 10^{-7})$$
$$= 1.0 \times 10^{-14} \quad \text{(at 25 °C)}$$

■ K_w at Various Temperatures

Temperature (°C)	K_w
0	1.5×10^{-15}
10	3.0×10^{-15}
20	6.8×10^{-15}
30	1.5×10^{-14}
40	3.0×10^{-14}

■ Units are never included in quoted values for K_w or K_{eq}.

In all our work, we will assume a temperature of 25 °C.

Knowing that $K_w = 1.0 \times 10^{-14}$, we can calculate the value of one of the two concentration terms, $[H^+]$ or $[OH^-]$, if we know the other.

EXAMPLE 9.1   USING THE ION PRODUCT CONSTANT OF WATER

Problem: The value of $[H^+]$ of blood (when measured at 25 °C, not body temperature) is 4.5×10^{-8} mol/L. What is the value of $[OH^-]$, and is the blood acidic, basic, or neutral?

Solution: We simply use the value of $[H^+]$ in the equation for K_w.

$$K_w = 1.0 \times 10^{-14} = (4.5 \times 10^{-8}) \times [OH^-]$$

$$[OH^-] = \frac{1.0 \times 10^{-14}}{4.5 \times 10^{-8}}$$

$$= 2.2 \times 10^{-7} \text{ mol/L}$$

■ A review of exponents is in Appendix A.

Because the value of $[H^+]$ is less than the value of $[OH^-]$, the blood is (very slightly) basic.

PRACTICE EXERCISE 1   For each of the following values of $[H^+]$, calculate the value of $[OH^-]$ and state whether the solution is acidic, basic, or neutral.

(a) $[H^+] = 4.0 \times 10^{-9}$ mol/L
(b) $[H^+] = 1.1 \times 10^{-7}$ mol/L
(c) $[H^+] = 9.4 \times 10^{-8}$ mol/L

9.2   THE pH CONCEPT

Very low levels of H^+ are more easily described and compared in terms of pH values than as molar concentrations.

Our interest in acid–base balance at the molecular level of life is usually with *weak* acids and bases and with very small concentrations of H^+ or OH^-. We therefore encounter very small numbers quite frequently, numbers usually expressed as negative exponentials, like 10^{-7}. When we have to compare two such numbers very often to see which is larger, like those in Example 9.1, (4.5×10^{-8} versus 2.2×10^{-7}), we soon feel a small annoyance. We have to look in *two* places in each number. We have to compare the exponents of 10 and then the numbers before the 10s. To make the comparisons of very small quantities easier, a Danish biochemist, S.P.L. Sorenson (1868 – 1939), invented the concept of pH. His simplification, some argue, wasn't much (if any), but the concept is very deeply entrenched. (Even shampoo ads boast of their "pH balance.")

The pH of a Solution Is the Negative Logarithm of Its [H$^+$]   There are two equivalent ways of defining pH.

$$[H^+] = 1 \times 10^{-pH} \tag{9.4}$$
$$pH = -\log [H^+] \tag{9.5}$$

Equation 9.4 tells us that the **pH** of a solution is the negative power (the p in pH) to which the number 10 must be raised to express the molar concentration of a solution's hydrogen ions (hence, the H in pH). Equation 9.5 is simply the result of taking the logarithms of both sides of Equation 9.4 and relocating the minus sign.[1]

In pure water at 25 °C, $[H^+] = 1.0 \times 10^{-7}$ mol/L. This value has the same form as the pH-defining Equation 9.4, so we can tell at a glance that the pH of pure water at 25 °C is 7.00. Thus a pH of 7.00 corresponds to a neutral solution at 25 °C.[2]

There are analogous equations for expressing low concentrations of OH$^-$ in terms of the **pOH** of a solution.

$$[OH^-] = 1 \times 10^{-pOH} \tag{9.6}$$
$$pOH = -\log [OH^-] \tag{9.7}$$

Values of pOH are seldom used but when they are, a simple relationship between pH and pOH exists. Notice that if we insert the pH and the pOH expressions for [H$^+$] and [OH$^-$] into the equation for the ion product constant of water, Equation 9.3, we get

$$(1.0 \times 10^{-pH})(1.0 \times 10^{-pOH}) = 1.0 \times 10^{-14} \quad \text{(at 25 °C)}$$

Recall that when we multiply numbers that involve exponents we *add* the exponents, so this equation means that

$$-pH + (-pOH) = -14$$

If we multiply both sides of this by -1, we get the following relationship between pH and pOH at 25 °C.

$$pH + pOH = 14.00 \quad \text{(at 25 °C)} \tag{9.8}$$

---

[1] Appendix A has a unit on logarithms as well as directions for using a hand-held calculator to work with equations like either 9.4 or 9.5 in solving pH/[H$^+$] problems.

[2] A word about significant figures in logarithms. The 7 in 7.00 comes from the *exponent* in 1.0×10^{-7}, so it actually does nothing more than set off a decimal point when we rewrite the number as 0.00000010. Hence the 7 in the pH value of 7.00 can't be counted as a significant figure. A pH value of 7.00 therefore has just two significant figures, those that *follow* the decimal point, just as there are but two significant figures in the value of the molar concentration of H$^+$, 1.0×10^{-7} mol/L. To repeat, the number of significant figures in any value of pH is the number of figures that *follow* the decimal point.

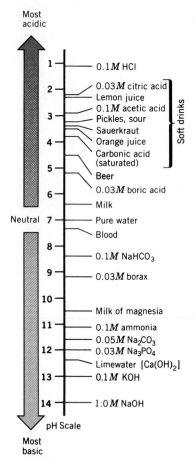

Most
acidic

1 —— 0.1M HCl

2 — 0.03M citric acid
— Lemon juice
— 0.1M acetic acid
3 — Pickles, sour
— Sauerkraut
4 — Orange juice
— Carbonic acid
(saturated)
5 — Beer
— 0.03M boric acid
6 —— Milk

Neutral 7 —— Pure water
— Blood
8 — 0.1M NaHCO₃
9 —— 0.03M borax

10 —
— Milk of magnesia
11 — 0.1M ammonia
— 0.05M Na₂CO₃
12 — 0.03M Na₃PO₄
— Limewater [Ca(OH)₂]
13 — 0.1M KOH

14 — 1:0M NaOH

pH Scale

Most
basic

Soft drinks

Figure 9.1
The pH scale and the pH values of
several common substances.

TABLE 9.1   pH, [H⁺], [OH⁻], and pOH

pH	[H⁺]	[OH⁻]	pOH	
0	1	1×10^{-14}	14	⎤
1	1×10^{-1}	1×10^{-13}	13	
2	1×10^{-2}	1×10^{-12}	12	
3	1×10^{-3}	1×10^{-11}	11	Acidic Solutions
4	1×10^{-4}	1×10^{-10}	10	
5	1×10^{-5}	1×10^{-9}	9	
6	1×10^{-6}	1×10^{-8}	8	⎦
7	1×10^{-7}	1×10^{-7}	7	⎱ Neutral Solution
8	1×10^{-8}	1×10^{-6}	6	⎤
9	1×10^{-9}	1×10^{-5}	5	
10	1×10^{-10}	1×10^{-4}	4	Basic Solutions
11	1×10^{-11}	1×10^{-3}	3	
12	1×10^{-12}	1×10^{-2}	2	
13	1×10^{-13}	1×10^{-1}	1	
14	1×10^{-14}	1×10^{-0}	0	⎦

Concentrations are in mol/L at 25 °C.

Acidic Solutions Have pHs Less Than 7   Because pH occurs as a *negative* exponent in Equation 9.4, it takes a pH value that is less than 7.00 for a solution to be acidic, and a value more than 7.00 for it to be basic. In pH terms, then, we have the following definitions of acidic, basic, and neutral solutions when their temperatures are 25 °C.

At 25 °C,

Acidic solution	pH < 7.00
Neutral solution	pH = 7.00
Basic solution	pH > 7.00

(9.9)

The pH values of several common substances are shown in Figure 9.1. Soft drinks, beer, and even milk are slightly acidic, as you can see, and sour pickles are sour for a now obvious reason.

Table 9.1 gives the correlations of pH, [H⁺], [OH⁻], and pOH values for the entire useful range of pH, 0 to 14. This is the useful range because when the value of [H⁺] is 1 mol/L or higher, the pH concept is almost never used. The exponents would no longer be negative, so there would be none of the confusion that Sorenson addressed when he invented pH.

Seemingly Small pH Changes Can Mean Large [H⁺] Changes   One of the very deceptive features of the pH concept is that the actual hydrogen ion concentration changes greatly — by a factor of 10 — for each change of only one unit of pH. For example, if the pH of a solution is zero (meaning that [H⁺] = 1×10^0 mol/L), only 1 L of water is needed to contain 1 mol of H⁺. When the pH is 1, however, then 10 L of water (about the size of an average wastebasket) is needed to hold 1 mol of H⁺. At a pH of 5, it takes a large railroad tank car full of water to include just 1 mol of H⁺. If the pH of the water flowing over Niagara Falls, New York, were 10 (which, of course, it isn't), an entire 1-hour flowage would be needed for 1 mol of H⁺ to pass by. And at a pH of 14, the volume that would hold 1 mol of H⁺ is about a quarter of the volume of Lake Erie, one of the Great Lakes. You can see that seemingly small changes in pH numbers signify enormous changes in real concentrations of hydrogen ions.

pH Refers to [H⁺], Not to Un-Ionized Acid Concentration   Another point about pH to be emphasized is that it refers to the molar concentration of *hydrogen ions,* not to the molar concentration of any particular solute that contributes these ions. When the solute is a weak

■ In mass, 1 mol of H⁺ has a mass of only 1.0 g, so 1×10^{-7} mol of H⁺ weighs 0.1 microgram (μg).

■ A solution at pH 4.56 has ten times the concentration of H⁺ as one at a pH of 5.56.

acid, just a small percentage of its molecules are ionized at equilibrium, so no simple correlation exists between the concentration of the weak acid and the pH of the solution. The pH of such a solution tells us about $[H^+]$, not necessarily about the molarity of the substance that gave H^+.

Only with dilute solutions of strong, 100% ionized acids is there a simple correlation between pH and the molarity of the acid. For example, each molecule of HCl that goes into solution ionizes to give one H^+ and one Cl^- ion, because HCl is a strong acid. Therefore, for example, in a 0.010 M HCl solution, $[H^+] = 0.010$ mol H^+/L $= 1.0 \times 10^{-2}$ mol H^+/L. Because $[H^+] = 1.0 \times 10^{-2}$ mol/L, the pH is simply 2.00. Similarly, a solution that is 0.00010 M HNO_3, another strong monoprotic acid, has $[H^+] = 0.00010$ mol/L $= 1.0 \times 10^{-4}$ mol/L. So the pH of this solution is 4.00.

The correlation between pOH and the concentration of a strong base, like NaOH, is also simple. In 0.0010 M NaOH, for example, $[OH^-] = 0.0010$ mol/L $= 1.0 \times 10^{-3}$ mol/L, so the pOH is simply 3.00. Because pH + pOH = 14.00 at 25 °C, a pOH of 3.00 means a pH of 11.00.

In all these simple correlations, the numbers were picked to let 1.0 stand before the 10 in the exponential expression. We will work one example involving a strong acid for which the numbers do not have this relation, just to get used to using a hand-held calculator for pH calculations.

EXAMPLE 9.2	CALCULATING pH FROM $[H^+]$

■ Rain made acidic by air pollutants is called **acid rain**.

Problem: Lakes in upper New York State and some New England areas, as well as in the Boundary Waters Canoe Area of northern Minnesota, are receiving rain-dissolved air pollutants, such as oxides of sulfur and nitrogen, that make the lake waters more acidic than normal. The water in one lake was found to have $[H^+] = 3.1 \times 10^{-5}$ mol/L. Calculate the pH and the pOH of the lake water.

Solution: We use Equation 9.5 because it gives us the most direct relationship between $[H^+]$ and pH.

$$pH = -\log [H^+]$$
$$= -\log(3.1 \times 10^{-5})$$

Enter 3.1×10^{-5} into your calculator. If your calculator has the function keys, $\boxed{10^x}$ and $\boxed{\log}$, it almost certainly also has the keys, $\boxed{EXP}$ and $\boxed{+/-}$. (Your EXP key might be labeled EE. Check your manual. If your calculator does not have these functions, you should think seriously about buying one that does). Remember, EXP means "times ten to the" as in "3.2 *times 10 to the* minus 5 power." And be doubly sure to remember that the $\boxed{+/-}$ key *must* be used to get a negative exponent from an entered positive number. To enter 3.1×10^{-5}, therefore, hit the following keys.

$$\boxed{3}\ \boxed{.}\ \boxed{1}\ \boxed{EXP}\ \boxed{+/-}\ \boxed{5}$$

The display screen should now look something like 3.1^{-05}. Now all you have to do is hit the $\boxed{\log}$ key. The display should now read -4.508638306. The pH is the negative of this, so just change the sign. And also round off, to two significant figures, the number allowed by the value of $[H^+]$, 3.1×10^{-5}. The answer, therefore, is that the pH = 4.51.

The pOH is found from Equation 9.8

$$pH + pOH = 14.00$$
$$4.51 + pOH = 14.00$$
$$pOH = 9.49$$

PRACTICE EXERCISE 2   Calculate the pH and the pOH in each of the following solutions. (a) 0.025 M HCl (b) 0.00025 M NaOH (*Hint:* Calculate pOH first, then the pH using Equation 9.8.) (c) 0.00025 M $Ba(OH)_2$. Consider this to be 100% dissociated.

PRACTICE EXERCISE 3   A blood specimen was found to have $[H^+] = 7.3 \times 10^{-8}$ mol/L. Calculate its pH. Is it acidic, basic, or neutral?

Another calculation that sometimes has to be made is to find $[H^+]$ from the pH. We'll work an example to show how your calculator can handle this.

EXAMPLE 9.3   **CALCULATING [H⁺] FROM pH**

■ Acid rain also harms forests and accelerates the corrosion of exposed objects made of metal, limestone, or marble.

Problem: Because of acid rain, thousands of lakes in southern Norway no longer have game fish. The pH of the lake waters is below 5.50. What $[H^+]$ corresponds to a pH of 5.50?

Solution: Equation 9.4 now becomes the best equation to use.

$$[H^+] = 1 \times 10^{-pH}$$

We have to get 5.50 into the exponent as a negative number, so enter 5.50 into your calculator *and then hit the* $\boxed{+/-}$ *key.* You now have actually entered *x* for the 10ˣ key, so now use this key and the display will read 3.16227766^{-06}. This means 3.2×10^{-6}, after we round to the two significant figures allowed in the pH value of 5.50. Thus a pH of 5.50 means $[H^+] = 3.2 \times 10^{-6}$ mol/L.

PRACTICE EXERCISE 4   Calculate the values of $[H^+]$ for solutions of the following pH and state if the solutions are acidic or basic. (a) 6.34 (b) 7.89

PRACTICE EXERCISE 5   A blood sample had a pH of 7.28. What is $[H^+]$ for this sample?

PRACTICE EXERCISE 6   The pOH of a solution was 4.56. Calculate $[H^+]$.

The question now arises, "How are very small values of $[H^+]$ or their associated pH values measured in the lab?"

Litmus Isn't the Only Acid–Base Indicator   The most common way to get a very rough idea of the pH of a solution is to use an acid–base indicator or a combination of them. A number of organic dyes are available for this purpose. Litmus, which we mentioned in the previous chapter, is just one example. Litmus is blue above a pH of about 8.5 and red below a pH of 4.5. Each indicator has its own pH range and set of colors, and Figure 9.2 gives just a few examples. The dye called phenolphthalein, for example, has a bright pink color at a pH above 10.0 and is colorless below a pH of 8.2. In the range of 8.2 to 10.0 phenolphthalein undergoes a gradual change from colorless to pale pink to deep pink. Bromothymol blue is pink above a pH of 7.6 and yellow below 6.0. Thus if you found that a solution turns phenolphthalein definitely colorless (so its pH is no higher than 8.2) but it makes bromothymol blue a definite blue in color (so its pH is above 7.6), you would know that the pH of the solution is between 7.6 and 8.2.

■ Phenolphthalein (fee-noll-THAY-lean).

There are commercial test papers, like Hydrion^R (Figure 9.3), impregnated with several indicator dyes. Their containers carry a pH-color code, so you can match the color produced by a drop of solution to this code and so learn the pH of the solution. (The precision is not high.)

When the solutions to be tested for pH are themselves highly colored, we can't use indicators. Moreover, we often need more than a rough idea of pH. For such situations a variety of commercial pH meters (Figure 9.4) come equipped with specially designed electrodes that can be dipped into the solution to be tested. With a good pH meter, pH values can be read to the second decimal place. In addition, pH meters with microelectrodes are commercially available. These enable operating room specialists, for example, to measure the pH of very tiny samples of some body fluid of interest.

Figure 9.2
The colors of some common
acid–base indicators.

pH 8.2 pH 10.0
Phenolphthalein

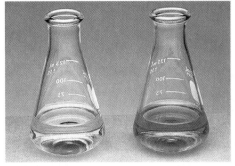

pH 6.0 pH 7.6
Bromothymol blue

pH 3.2 pH 4.4
Methyl orange

pH 9.4 pH 10.6
Thymolphthalein

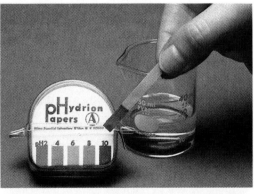

Figure 9.3
A pH test paper. A drop of the solution in
the beaker, when touched to the Hydrion
paper, caused the purple color. The pH of
the solution was therefore closer to 10 than
to 8, according to the color code.

Figure 9.4
A pH meter.

9.3 ACID IONIZATION CONSTANTS

The strengths of weak acids are described quantitatively by their acid ionization constants, K_a.

■ The weak acids of greatest importance to our study are acetic acid, carbonic acid, and the organic acids produced as intermediates in metabolism.

Weak acids vary widely in weakness. To compare them, we use a new kind of constant called an *acid ionization constant, K_a*, which we will study in this Section. It is obtained by a small simplification of the equilibrium law for the ionization of the weak acid in water. The prime objectives of this section are to learn what K_a means, how the K_a expression for any weak acid can be written, and how to use values of K_a to judge the relative weakness of an acid. Our longer-range objective is to use K_a in a study of systems called buffers that protect fluids at the molecular level of life from lethal changes in pH.

Acid Ionization Constants of Acids Are Smaller the Weaker the Acid Is We will represent any weak acid by the symbol HA, where A denotes the species that separates from H^+ when HA ionizes. The weak acid might be electrically neutral like acetic acid, positively charged like the ammonium ion, or negatively charged like the bicarbonate ion. All these are acids, but they differ in acid strengths. If the acid is diprotic or triprotic, we use HA to consider the ionization of just one of its protons. The equilibrium equation for the ionization of HA in water is as follows. Notice particularly that one product is always H_3O^+ (or, later, H^+), and the other is always the conjugate base of the acid.

$$HA \quad + H_2O \rightleftharpoons H_3O^+ + A^-$$

Weak
Brønsted
acid

Conjugate
base

To illustrate, the equilibria for the Brønsted acids already mentioned are

$$HC_2H_3O_2 + H_2O \rightleftharpoons H_3O^+ + C_2H_3O_2^-$$
$$NH_4^+ + H_2O \rightleftharpoons H_3O^+ + NH_3$$
$$HCO_3^- + H_2O \rightleftharpoons H_3O^+ + CO_3^{2-}$$

■ The concentrations in the brackets are the concentrations after equilibrium has been established.

The general form for the equilibrium law for these equilibria is

$$K_{eq} = \frac{[H_3O^+][A^-]}{[HA][H_2O]} \tag{9.10}$$

The Value of [H₂O] in Equation 9.10 Is Essentially a Constant We can now simplify Equation 9.10 exactly as we simplified Equation 9.2 for the self-ionization of water on our way to the ion product constant of water.

In dilute solutions of *weak* acids, the ionization equilibrium does not disturb the molar concentration of water even if we think in terms of several significant figures. Therefore the value of [H₂O] in Equation 9.10 is essentially a constant. Let us multiply both sides of Equation 9.10 by this constant and then do an obvious cancellation.

$$K_{eq} \times [H_2O] = \frac{[H_3O^+][A^-]}{[HA][\cancel{H_2O}]} \times [\cancel{H_2O}] = \text{a new constant}$$

■ Some references call it the *acid dissociation constant.*

The new constant is called the **acid ionization constant,** and its symbol is $\boldsymbol{K_a}$. If we switch from H_3O^+ to H^+, the equation for K_a is

$$K_a = \frac{[H^+][A^-]}{[HA]} \quad \text{(for } HA \rightleftharpoons H^+ + A^-\text{)} \tag{9.11}$$

Equation 9.11 is the equilibrium law for all Brønsted acids that ionize as monoprotic acids.

TABLE 9.2 K_a Values for Acids[a]

Name	Formula	K_a (25 °C)
Perchloric acid	$HClO_4$	Large
Hydriodic acid	HI	Large
Hydrobromic acid	HBr	Large
Sulfuric acid	H_2SO_4	Large
Hydrochloric acid	HCl	Large
Nitric acid	HNO_3	Large
HYDRONIUM ION	H_3O^+	55
Phosphoric acid	H_3PO_4	7.1×10^{-3}
Acetic acid	$HC_2H_3O_2$	1.8×10^{-5}
Carbonic acid	H_2CO_3	4.5×10^{-7}
Dihydrogen phosphate ion	$H_2PO_4^-$	6.3×10^{-8}
Ammonium ion	NH_4^+	5.7×10^{-10}
Bicarbonate ion	HCO_3^-	4.7×10^{-11}
Monohydrogen phosphate ion	HPO_4^{2-}	4.5×10^{-13}
WATER	H_2O	1.8×10^{-16}
Hydroxide ion	OH^- (est)	1×10^{-36}

[a] Data are rounded to two significant figures from the values given in E. H. Martell and R. M. Smith, *Critical Stability Constants,* Plenum Press, New York, 1974. For water, see R. Starkey, J. Norman, and M. Hintze, *J. Chem. Ed. 63* (1986), p. 473. For OH⁻ see R. J. Myers, *J. Chem. Ed. 63* (1986), p. 687, and references cited therein.

Weak, Moderate, and Strong Acids Can Be Defined by K_a Values   The K_a values of several acids are given in Table 9.2. The table does not provide the modified equilibrium law — the equation for K_a — for each acid. No such tables in any references do, because the equation for K_a can be figured out whenever it is needed. We will work an example to show how easy this is.

EXAMPLE 9.4	WRITING EQUATIONS FOR K_a FOR ACIDS

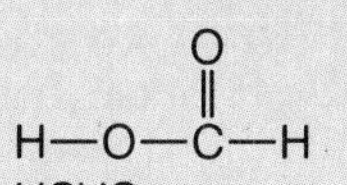

$$\begin{matrix} & & O \\ & & \| \\ H\!-\!O\!-\!C\!-\!H \end{matrix}$$

$HCHO_2$
Formic acid

Problem: What is the equation for K_a for formic acid, $HCHO_2$, the acid present in the stinging juices of ants?

Solution: First we have to write the equation for the equilibrium in aqueous formic acid (letting H^+ represent H_3O^+).

$$HCHO_2(aq) \rightleftharpoons H^+(aq) + CHO_2^-(aq)$$

Next, we write the equation for K_a. We have to remember that the products always appear in the numerator and the reactants in the denominator. The answer, therefore, is

$$K_a = \frac{[H^+][CHO_2^-]}{[HCHO_2]}$$

PRACTICE EXERCISE 7   Write the equilibrium equation and the K_a equation for acetic acid, $HC_2H_3O_2$.

PRACTICE EXERCISE 8   Write the equilibrium equation and the K_a equation for the bicarbonate ion.

PRACTICE EXERCISE 9   Write the equilibrium equation and the K_a equation for the ammonium ion.

Because the products, including H^+, are in the numerator of the general equation for K_a (Equation 9.11), when the products are not favored, the value of K_a is small. *The weaker the* *acid, the smaller its K_a.* A strong acid generates a high percentage of H^+, so the K_a values of strong acids are high. *The stronger the acid, the larger its K_a.*

PRACTICE EXERCISE 10   The K_a for HCN, hydrogen cyanide, is 6.2×10^{-10} and for ascorbic acid (vitamin C) it is 7.9×10^{-5}. Which is the stronger acid?

Acid ionization constants are used to classify acids as weak, moderate, or strong according to the following criteria.

$K_a < 10^{-3}$	**Weak acid**
$K_a = 1$ to 10^{-3}	**Moderate acid**
$K_a > 1$	**Strong acid**

K_a values are obtained by a calculation using the measured pH of a solution and the molarity of the acid. Special Topic 9.1 shows how to do such a calculation.

The pH of a solution, from which we can calculate $[H^+]$, can be measured directly with a pH meter. It's also possible to estimate $[H^+]$ and then calculate the pH by using the K_a of the acid and its molar concentration. Special Topic 9.2 shows how this is done.

Most Transition Metal Cations and the Ammonium Ion Hydrolyze to Generate H_3O^+ Ions and Lower the pH of the Solution   A solution of ammonium chloride, NH_4Cl, in water turns blue litmus red, so $[H^+] > [OH^-]$ in this solution. The extra hydrogen ions come from the forward reaction of the following equilibrium involving the NH_4^+ ion:

$$NH_4^+ + H_2O \rightleftharpoons NH_3(aq) + H_3O^+(aq)$$

This, of course, is nothing more than the ammonium ion acting as a weak acid. (Its K_a is 5.7×10^{-10}.) But NH_4^+ is not so weak that it cannot produce enough hydronium ions in water to turn blue litmus red.

■ "Hydrolysis" is from the Greek *hydro,* water, and *lysis,* loosening or breaking—breaking or loosening by water.

The reaction of a cation with water to generate hydronium ion is called the **hydrolysis of the cation.** The lesson here is that certain *salts,* like ammonium chloride, can make a solution acidic, even though their names do not have the word *acid* in them. It's a lesson we need to know, because of our interest in acid–base balances at the molecular level of life. We have to be aware of any solute that can make a solution have a pH other than 7.00. Ammonium salts are such solutes.

Even the hydrated cations of most metals can make a solution test acidic. The aluminum ion in water, for example, exists largely as $[Al(H_2O)_6]^{3+}$. The high positive charge on the central metal ion in this hydrated ion attracts electron density from the H—O bonds of the H_2O molecules it holds. These bonds are thus weakened, so $[Al(H_2O)_6]^{3+}$ can donate H^+ to H_2O as follows.

$$[Al(H_2O_6]^{3+}(aq) + H_2O \longrightarrow [Al(H_2O)_5(OH)]^{2+} + H_3O^+(aq)$$

We can see how this happens by means of modified Lewis structures.

■ The arrows signify a force of attraction between $\delta-$ on O and the central cation.

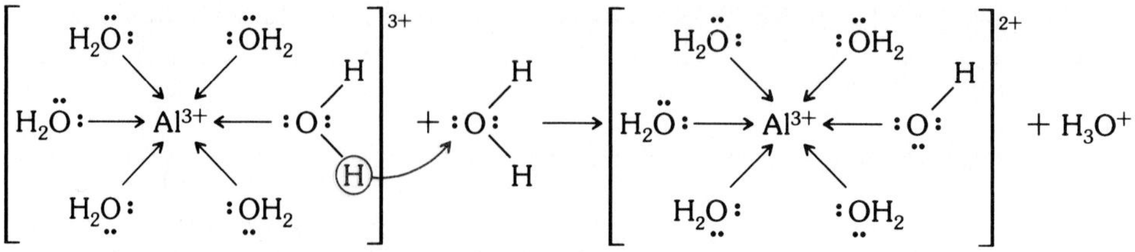

SPECIAL TOPIC 9.1   **CALCULATING K_a FROM pH**

We will show here how the K_a of an acid can be calculated from the pH of a solution of a known molar concentration.

Formic acid, $HCHO_2$, is a monoprotic acid. The pH of a 0.10 M solution of formic acid is 2.38 at 25 °C. Our assignment is to calculate K_a for formic acid at this temperature.

We begin any equilibrium problem by writing the equation for the equilibrium. We need this equation here so that we can set up the expression for K_a.

$$HCHO_2 \rightleftharpoons H^+ + CHO_2^- \qquad K_a = \frac{[H^+][CHO_2^-]}{[HCHO_2]}$$

Always remember that the terms in brackets all refer to concentrations at *equilibrium,* not to initial concentrations. We also note that the equilibrium concentration of CHO_2^- must be the same as that of H^+ because they form in a 1 : 1 ratio by the ionization. So when we find $[H^+]$ from the pH we also find $[CHO_2^-]$. To find $[H^+]$ (and $[CHO_2^-]$), we use one of the defining equations for pH:

$$[H^+] = 10^{-pH} \text{ mol/L} \qquad \text{(not neglecting the units)}$$
$$= 10^{-2.38} \text{ mol/L}$$
$$= 4.2 \times 10^{-3} \text{ mol/L}$$
$$= 0.0042 \text{ mol/L} \qquad \text{(the form most useful next)}$$

This result means that

$$[CHO_2^-] = 0.0042 \text{ mol/L}$$

So we have two of the three equilibrium concentrations. We next have to find the value of $[HCO_2H]$ *at equilibrium* (which is not the same as the molarity of the solution).

The best strategy to keep both our data and our thinking straight is to prepare a *concentration table.* The column headings are the formulas of the species in the equilibrium, so we rewrite the equilibrium equation at the top of our table. Then we will prepare three rows of data. The first row is for *initial concentrations.* For this row we imagine the solution immediately after the solute has been added and before any ionization has occurred. No H^+ or CHO_2^- have yet formed.

The second row will express all *changes* in concentration that are caused by the ionization. The concentration of H^+, for example, increases from 0 to 0.0042 mol/L, because we calculated this value from the pH, earlier.

The third row of data in the concentration table will have the final, equilibrium concentrations. We get these by a simple algebraic addition of the data in the respective columns, as we will show. The data in the third row, all equilibrium data, are then plugged into the equation for K_a.

(All concentrations in such a table, of course, are in moles per liter.) Here is how the table for this problem looks.

	$HCHO_2$	$\rightleftharpoons$	H^+	+	CHO_2^-
Initial concentration	0.100		0		0 (Note 1)
Change in concentration caused by the ionization	−0.0042		+0.0042		+0.0042 (Note 2)
Final concentration at equilibrium	(0.100 − 0.0042) = 0.096 (correctly rounded)		0.0042		0.0042

Note 1. The *initial* concentration of the acid is the molarity of the acid, 0.100 M. It ignores any ionization. This is why we then have to set the *initial* values of $[H^+]$ and $[CHO_2^-]$ equal to zero. (The H^+ from the self-ionization of water is ignored throughout our calculation. It is just too small.)

Note 2. These *changes* come from what we calculated from the pH. There is one less molecule of the initial acid for every H^+ ion that forms by ionization. We use a minus sign in −0.0042 for the change in concentration of $HCHO_2$ to indicate a *decrease.* The initial concentration of $HCHO_2$ decreases because of the ionization.

The last row of data gives us the equilibrium concentrations that we now use to calculate K_a. Each value here comes from the algebraic sums of the two data in the column just above it, as you can verify.

$$K_a = \frac{(4.2 \times 10^{-3})(4.2 \times 10^{-3})}{0.096}$$
$$= 1.8 \times 10^{-4}$$

Thus the acid ionization constant for formic acid is 1.8×10^{-4}.

PRACTICE EXERCISE A 0.0100 M solution of butyric acid has a pH of 3.40 at 20 °C. Calculate the K_a of butyric acid at 20 °C. (Use the symbols HBu and Bu^- for butyric acid and its conjugate base.) Butyric acid is the odorous compound in rancid butter.   Answer: $K_a = 1.7 \times 10^{-5}$.

A proton transfers from a water molecule of the hydrated ion to a molecule of the surrounding solvent; H_3O^+ forms and the solution thereby is made acidic. A solution that is 0.1 M $AlCl_3$ has a pH of about 3, for example, the same as that of 0.1 M acetic acid, but there is nothing about the formula $AlCl_3$ to suggest this property.

SPECIAL TOPIC 9.2   CALCULATING [H⁺] AND pH FROM K_a AND [ACID]

The molar concentration [H⁺] in a solution of a weak acid does not equal the molarity of the weak acid, because the weak acid is poorly ionized. If we want to know the value [H⁺] in such a solution, we have two choices. One is experimental. We measure the pH and convert it to [H⁺]. The other is to calculate the pH (estimate it might be a better term) from the K_a of the acid and its molarity. We will see how such a calculation can be done in this Special Topic.

A sample of vinegar was found to be 0.75 M acetic acid, $HC_2H_3O_2$. Our assignment is to calculate the values of [H⁺] and pH of this sample.

We can use the same general approach given in Special Topic 9.1 — writing the chemical equilibrium and then preparing a concentration table. Of course, we do not know [H⁺] (we are to find it), so we have to let x stand for it.

	$HC_2H_3O_2$ ⇌ H^+ +	$C_2H_3O_2^-$	
Initial concentration	0.75	0	0
Change in concentration caused by the ionization	$-x$	$+x$	$+x$ (Note 1)
Final concentration at equilibrium	$(0.75 - x)$ = 0.75 (Note 2)	x	x

Note 1. We let $+x$ stand for the increase in the concentration of both H^+ and $C_2H_3O_2^-$, and so the initial concentration of $HC_2H_3O_2$ is reduced by the same amount.

Note 2. Saying that $0.75 = (0.75 - x)$ is an important simplification. But we can do this with almost no loss in precision and it makes the calculation much easier. The problem we would otherwise have is as follows. If we use $(0.75 - x)$ for $[HC_2H_3O_2]$, we would soon have to solve for x in an equation with both an x^2 and an x term — a quadratic equation. The quadratic equation in this case would result from making the following substitutions from the table just given. (The value of K_a is taken from Table 9.2.)

$$K_a = \frac{[H^+][C_2H_3O_2^-]}{[HC_2H_3O_2]} = \frac{(x)(x)}{(0.75 - x)} = 1.8 \times 10^{-5}$$

We could solve this for x, but it can be simplified first. We can let $0.75 = (0.75 - x)$ because x itself will clearly turn out to be very small, too small to change 0.75 after we round to the correct significant figures. We know that x, which is [H⁺], will be very small because K_a is very small. (A small K_a means a low percentage ionization, so little H^+ forms.) Let's at least see whether this simplification works.

Letting $(0.75 - x) = 0.75$, and $x = [H^+] = [C_2H_3O_2^-]$, we have

$$K_a = \frac{[H^+][C_2H_3O_2^-]}{[HC_2H_3O_2]} = \frac{(x)(x)}{(0.75)} = 1.8 \times 10^{-5}$$

$$x^2 = (0.75)(1.8 \times 10^{-5})$$
$$= 1.35 \times 10^{-5}$$
$$x = 3.7 \times 10^{-3}$$

In other words, since $x = [H^+]$,

$$[H^+] = 3.7 \times 10^{-3} \text{ mol/L} = 0.0037 \text{ mol/L}$$

Was the simplification justified? Notice that $(0.75 - 0.0037) = 0.7463$, which rounds properly to 0.75. So the assumption was valid, the simplification worked, and it clearly made the calculation easier.

Having found that at equilibrium $[H^+] = 3.7 \times 10^{-3}$ mol/L, we next have to calculate the pH of this solution:

$$pH = -\log [H^+]$$
$$= -(\log 3.7 \times 10^{-3})$$
$$= -(-2.43)$$
$$pH = 2.43 \quad \text{(the answer to the second part)}$$

The simplifications permitted in K_a calculations involving *weak* acids are so useful that we will restate them. Whenever we calculate [H⁺] and pH for a dilute solution of a weak acid, given K_a,

1. We can ignore the contribution to [H⁺] from the self-ionization of water.

2. We can drop the term, $[HA]_{ionized}$, in the expression for $[HA]_{eq}$:

$$[HA]_{eq} = [HA]_{init} - [HA]_{ionized}$$
$$= [HA]_{init}$$

                    | very small and dropped |

These simplifications do not work in two situations, in *extremely dilute solutions* of weak acids, and when K_a increases and approaches 10^{-3} or larger.

PRACTICE EXERCISE   Nicotinic acid, $HC_2H_4NO_2$, a B vitamin, is a weak acid with $K_a = 1.4 \times 10^{-5}$. Calculate the [H⁺] and the pH of a 0.010 M solution.
Answers: $[H^+] = 3.7 \times 10^{-4}$ mol/L, pH = 3.43.

We don't have K_a values for hydrated metal cations, but all with charges of 3+ and most with charges of 2+ on the central metal ion can generate hydronium ions in water. Metal ions with such charges have relatively small ionic radii, so the *density* of charge, the charge per unit volume, is high, as in the hydrated aluminum ion. A high positive-charge density is able to act in a strongly electronegative way to weaken H—O bonds in the surrounding water molecules of their hydrated forms.

The only common metal ions that do *not* hydrolyze to give acidic solutions are those of groups IA and IIA (except Be^{2+} of IIA)—for example, Li^+, Na^+, and K^+, Mg^{2+}, Ca^{2+}, and Ba^{2+} do not hydrolyze. Evidently, except for Be^{2+}, the cations of groups IA and IIA do not have sufficiently high positive-charge densities.

9.4 BASE IONIZATION CONSTANTS

Base ionization constants let us compare the strengths of weak bases.

Strong bases, like sodium hydroxide, dissociate completely in water to release OH^- ions.

$$NaOH(s) \xrightarrow[\text{dissociation}]{} Na^+(aq) + OH^-(aq)$$

Other, even stronger bases, like the oxide ion in sodium oxide, react completely with water and generate OH^- ions.

$$Na_2O(s) + H_2O \longrightarrow 2Na^+(aq) + 2OH^-(aq)$$

■ The weak bases of greatest importance in our study are NH_3, HCO_3^-, CO_3^{2-}, HPO_4^{2-}, $H_2PO_4^-$, and any of the conjugate bases of the weak organic acids that we will encounter.

Weak bases, like ammonia or the bicarbonate ion, react incompletely with water, usually to a small percentage to make some OH^-. An equilibrium is established in which the unchanged base is favored. Ammonia and the carbonate ion, for example, generate OH^- ions in water in the following equilibria:

$$NH_3(aq) + H_2O \rightleftharpoons NH_4^+(aq) + OH^-(aq)$$
$$HCO_3^-(aq) + H_2O \rightleftharpoons H_2CO_3(aq) + OH^-(aq)$$

Enough forward reaction occurs to make $[OH^-] > [H^+]$ in the resulting solutions, so they test basic to litmus.

Weak bases vary considerably in their abilities to accept protons from water molecules and generate hydroxide ions. To compare these abilities, we use a special equilibrium constant called the *base ionization constant, K_b*. The equilibrium this refers to is always of the following type, where we represent any base by the symbol B, regardless of its electrical charge. In this equilibrium, one product is always OH^- and the other is always the conjugate acid of the base.

$$B(aq) + H_2O \rightleftharpoons BH^+(aq) + OH^-(aq)$$

Weak   Conjugate
base   acid

The **base ionization constant** for this equilibrium, K_b, is defined by the following equation. (You can see how closely it parallels the definition of the acid ionization constant, K_a.)

■ $[H_2O]$ is incorporated into K_b just as it was into K_a.

$$K_b = \frac{[BH^+][OH^-]}{[B]} \tag{9.12}$$

The K_b values for several bases are given in Table 9.3 on page 248.

The Smaller the K_b, the Weaker the Base   Equation 9.12 has the products of the base ionization equilibrium in the numerator. When their concentrations are small, therefore, the base is weak and so K_b has a small value. *The smaller the K_b, the weaker the base.* When the

TABLE 9.3 K_b **Values for Bases**[a]

Name	Formula	K_b (25 °C)
Oxide ion	O^{2-}	1×10^{22}
HYDROXIDE ION	OH^-	55
Phosphate ion	PO_4^{3-}	2.2×10^{-2}
Carbonate ion	CO_3^{2-}	2.1×10^{-4}
Ammonia	NH_3	1.8×10^{-5}
Monohydrogen phosphate ion	HPO_4^{2-}	1.6×10^{-7}
Bicarbonate ion	HCO_3^-	2.6×10^{-8}
Acetate ion	$C_2H_2O_3^-$	5.7×10^{-10}
Dihydrogen phosphate ion	$H_2PO_4^-$	1.4×10^{-12}
WATER	H_2O	1.8×10^{-16}
Nitrate ion	NO_3^-	Very small
Chloride ion	Cl^-	Very small
Hydrogen sulfate ion	HSO_4^-	Very small
Bromide ion	Br^-	Very small
Iodide ion	I^-	Very small
Perchlorate ion	ClO_4^-	Very small

[a] K_b values (except for ammonia) were calculated from the K_a values obtained from the references cited for Table 9.2 and then rounded to two significant figures.

base is strong, then the products are in relatively high concentration, the numerator in Equation 9.12 now is larger, and the K_b value is higher. *The larger the K_b, the stronger the base.*

PRACTICE EXERCISE 11   The base ionization constant for the CN^-, cyanide ion, is 1.6×10^{-5} and for the bicarbonate ion is 2.6×10^{-8}. Which is the stronger base?

The interpretation of K_b values depends always on the ability to translate just the formula of the base both into its chemical equilibrium in water and into the specific equation for its K_b. The next example shows how this is done.

EXAMPLE 9.5   **WRITING EXPRESSIONS FOR K_b FOR BRØNSTED BASES**

Problem: The monohydrogen phosphate ion is a base. Write the equilibrium expression on which its K_b is based and then write the equation for K_b.

Solution: To write the equilibrium expression for HPO_4^{2-} in water, we put HPO_4^{2-} and H_2O as the reactants, and OH^- and the conjugate acid of HPO_4^{2-} as the products. We figure out the formula of the conjugate acid of any base, you will recall, by adding one H^+ to the formula of the base (remembering to adjust the charge correctly). So the conjugate acid of HPO_4^{2-} is $H_2PO_4^-$. Our equilibrium equation, then, is

$$HPO_4^{2-}(aq) + H_2O \rightleftharpoons H_2PO_4^-(aq) + OH^-(aq)$$

Now we can write the equation for K_b, omitting H_2O and remembering that the products are always in the numerator. The answer, then, is

$$K_b = \frac{[H_2PO_4^-][OH^-]}{[HPO_4^{2-}]}$$

PRACTICE EXERCISE 12   Write the equilibrium equations and the equations for K_b for each of the following Brønsted bases:

(a) CO_3^{2-} (b) $C_2H_3O_2^-$ (acetate ion)   (c) NH_3

Two kinds of calculations are possible with what has been studied thus far in this section: the calculation of a value of K_b from $[OH^-]$ or pOH, and the calculation of equilibrium concentrations of $[H^+]$ or $[OH^-]$ from values of K_b and $[B]_{init}$. These calculations are very similar to those in Special Topics 9.1 and 9.2, and we'll not pursue them further.

The Reaction of an Anion with Water To Produce OH⁻ Is Called the Hydrolysis of the Anion Most of the Brønsted base anions with K_b values greater than 10^{-13} are available as their sodium salts, like Na_3PO_4, Na_2CO_3, $NaCN$, Na_2HPO_4, $NaHCO_3$, $NaC_2H_3O_2$, and NaH_2PO_4. Aqueous solutions of these salts test basic to litmus because their anions have reacted with water — it's called the **hydrolysis of anions** — to generate an excess of OH^- over H^+. The bicarbonate ion in aqueous $NaHCO_3$, for example, hydrolyzes to establish the following equilibrium in which OH^- ions are present in excess over H^+ ions.

■ One reason we are interested in any solute that can affect the pH of a solution is that enzyme action is very sensitive to pH.

$$HCO_3^-(aq) + H_2O \rightleftharpoons H_2CO_3(aq) + OH^-(aq)$$

Anions like Cl^-, Br^-, I^-, NO_3^-, and SO_4^{2-}, which are conjugate bases of strong acids, do not hydrolyze in this way. To summarize,

> Anions whose conjugate acids are weak acids hydrolyze in water and tend to make the solution basic.
> Anions of strong acids do not hydrolyze.

In the previous section we developed similar rules of thumb about cations, which we'll repeat here.

> Metals ions from group IA or IIA (except Be^{2+}) do not hydrolyze.
> Expect other metal ions as well as NH_4^+ to hydrolyze and generate H^+.

With these rules we can generally predict correctly whether a given salt will affect the pH of an aqueous solution. The exceptions would be salts where both cation and anion can hydrolyze, like $NH_4C_2H_3O_2$, ammonium acetate. These have to be taken on a case-by-case basis with the result hinging on the relative strengths of the cation as an proton-producer and the base as a proton-neutralizer. We will not work with such salts. But let's see how we can predict the hydrolysis of salts that respond to a simpler analysis.

EXAMPLE 9.6   **PREDICTING HOW A SALT AFFECTS THE pH OF ITS SOLUTION**

Problem: Sodium phosphate, Na_3PO_4 ("trisodium phosphate"), is a strong cleaning agent for walls and floors. Is its aqueous solution acidic or basic?

Solution: Na_3PO_4 involves Na^+ and PO_4^{3-}. Na^+ does not hydrolyze, but PO_4^{3-} does. Its conjugate acid, HPO_4^{2-}, is not on our list of strong acids, so we can infer that it is a weak acid. We therefore expect PO_4^{3-} to be a relatively strong base and we expect it to hydrolyze as follows.

$$PO_4^{3-}(aq) + H_2O \rightleftharpoons HPO_4^{2-}(aq) + OH^-(aq)$$

This equilibrium generates some OH^- ions, so the solution will be basic.

Notice that in Example 9.6 we did not need a table of Brønsted bases to predict that PO_4^{3-} would hydrolyze. We used our knowledge of just a few facts — which acids are strong acids in water and which cations do not hydrolyze — to figure out what we needed to know. We will work another example to practice using the list of strong aqueous acids to decide whether a given salt can affect the pH of its solution.

EXAMPLE 9.7   **PREDICTING WHETHER A SALT AFFECTS THE ACIDITY OF ITS SOLUTION**

Problem: Chromium(III) nitrate, $Cr(NO_3)_3$, is soluble in water. Does this salt make its aqueous solution acidic or basic?

Solution: This salt dissociates into $Cr^{3+}(aq)$ and three $NO_3^-(aq)$ ions. Since the nitrate ion is the conjugate base of a strong acid, HNO_3, we know that it is unable to react with water to generate hydroxide ions. The nitrate ion does not hydrolyze. The Cr^{3+} ion, however, is not from groups IA or IIA. Moreover, like the aluminum ion, it has a high positive charge. We therefore expect it to hydrolyze and generate some hydrogen ion, like the aluminum ion. This salt solution tests acidic.

PRACTICE EXERCISE 13   Determine without the use of tables whether each ion can hydrolyze. If so, state whether it tends to make the solution acidic or basic.

(a) CO_3^{2-} (b) S^{2-}
(c) HPO_4^{2-} (d) Fe^{3+}
(e) NO_2^- (f) F^-

PRACTICE EXERCISE 14   Is a solution of potassium acetate, $KC_2H_3O_2$, acidic, basic, or neutral to litmus?

PRACTICE EXERCISE 15   Is a solution of copper(II) nitrate, $Cu(NO_3)_2$, acidic, basic, or neutral?

PRACTICE EXERCISE 16   Ammonium sulfate, $(NH_4)_2SO_4$, is a nitrogen fertilizer. Could the application of an aqueous solution of this fertilizer affect the pH of the soil? If so, will it increase or decrease the pH?

9.5   THE pK_a AND pK_b CONCEPTS

The negative logarithms of K_a and K_b, pK_a and pK_b, are useful in the same way as pH.

For the same reason that the pH concept was invented, analogous **pK_a** and **pK_b** expressions, based on K_a and K_b, have been defined. The pK_a is the negative logarithm of K_a, and the pK_b is the negative logarithm of K_b.

$$pK_a = -\log K_a \qquad (9.13)$$
$$pK_b = -\log K_b \qquad (9.14)$$

Be sure to notice that pK_a and pK_b are defined as *negative* logarithms, like the definition of pH. Therefore the generalizations we want to carry forward from Equations 9.13 and 9.14 are the following.

The larger the pK_a, the weaker the acid.

The larger the pK_b, the weaker the base.

EXAMPLE 9.8   **CALCULATING pK_a FROM K_a**

Problem: The K_a for acetic acid is 1.8×10^{-5} (at 25 °C). What is its pK_a at this temperature?

Solution: We simply use the defining equation for pK_a,

$$pK_a = -\log K_a$$
$$= -\log (1.8 \times 10^{-5})$$
$$pK_a = 4.74 \quad \text{(rounded as per footnote 2, page 237)}$$

PRACTICE EXERCISE 17   What is the pK_a for the bicarbonate ion? (Consult Table 9.2 for its K_a value.)

EXAMPLE 9.9	USING pK_a VALUES TO COMPARE STRENGTHS OF ACIDS

Problem: Hypoiodous acid, HIO, has a pK_a of 10.6. The pK_a of the very similar hypobromous acid, HBrO, is 8.64. Which is the weaker acid?

Solution: Remember, the larger the pK_a is, the weaker the acid is. So HIO is the weaker acid.

PRACTICE EXERCISE 18   The pK_a of carbonic acid, H_2CO_3, is 6.35, and that of acetic acid is 4.76. Which is the stronger acid?

EXAMPLE 9.10	CALCULATING pK_b FROM K_b

Problem: The K_b of ammonia is 1.8×10^{-5} (at 25 °C). What is its pK_b?

Solution: For this we simply use the equation that defines pK_b.

$$pK_b = -\log K_b$$
$$= -\log (1.8 \times 10^{-5})$$
$$pK_b = 4.74 \quad \text{(rounded as per footnote 1)}$$

PRACTICE EXERCISE 19   The K_b for the monohydrogen phosphate ion is 1.6×10^{-7}. Calculate its pK_b.

For a Conjugate Acid–Base Pair, the Product of K_a and K_b is K_w   A very simple relationship exists between K_a and K_b when we work with a conjugate acid–base pair.

$$K_a K_b = K_w \quad \text{(for a conjugate acid–base pair)} \quad (9.15)$$

To prove this, all we have to do is substitute the expressions for K_a, K_b, and K_w into it and cancel what terms we can. We know, for example, that in the equilibrium in a solution of a weak acid we have

$$HA \rightleftharpoons H^+ + A^- \quad \text{and} \quad K_a = \frac{[H^+][A^-]}{[HA]}$$

A solution of the conjugate base of HA, which is A^- (put into solution as some salt, like NaA), we have

$$A^- + H_2O \rightleftharpoons HA + OH^- \quad \text{and} \quad K_b = \frac{[HA][OH^-]}{[A^-]}$$

We now multiply the expressions for K_a and K_b and cancel what we can.

$$K_a \times K_b = \frac{[H^-][\cancel{A^-}]}{[\cancel{HA}]} \times \frac{[\cancel{HA}][OH^-]}{[\cancel{A^-}]}$$
$$= [H^+][OH^-]$$
$$= K_w \qquad \text{(proving Equation 9.15)}$$

■ Because $K_a \times K_b = K_w$,

$$K_a = \frac{K_w}{K_b} \quad \text{and} \quad K_b = \frac{K_w}{K_a}$$

When We Know Either K_a or K_b for a Conjugate Acid–Base Pair, We Can Calculate the Other Equation 9.15 lets us calculate K_b when we know K_a for its conjugate acid or it lets us calculate K_a for an acid when we know K_b for its conjugate base. All the K_b values in Table 9.3, for example, were calculated from the values of K_a in Table 9.2.

| EXAMPLE 9.11 | CALCULATING K_b FROM K_a |

Problem: What is the value of K_b at 25 °C for the conjugate base of hypochlorous acid, HOCl, whose K_a is 3.0×10^{-8}?

Solution: At 25 °C, $K_w = 1.0 \times 10^{-14}$, so we simply substitute this value and the given value of K_a, 3.0×10^{-8}, into Equation 9.15.

$$(3.0 \times 10^{-8}) \times K_b = 1.0 \times 10^{-14}$$

Solving for K_b gives us

$$K_b = \frac{1.0 \times 10^{-14}}{3.0 \times 10^{-8}}$$
$$= 3.3 \times 10^{-7}$$

Thus the K_b for OCl^-, the conjugate base of HOCl, is 3.3×10^{-7}.

PRACTICE EXERCISE 20 For NH_4^+, $K_a = 5.7 \times 10^{-10}$. What is the conjugate base of this weak acid, and what is its K_b?

For a Conjugate Acid–Base Pair, $pK_a + pK_b = 14.00$ (25 °C) The relationship among K_a, K_b, and K_w leads to a simple relationship between pK_a and pK_b for a conjugate acid–base pair. If we take the logarithms of both sides of Equation 9.15, we obtain

$$\log(K_a \times K_b) = \log K_w$$

Or

■ One of the rules of logarithms is
$$\log(a \times b) = \log a + \log b$$

$$\log K_a + \log K_b = \log K_w$$

After multiplying both sides by -1, we get

$$(-\log K_a) + (-\log K_b) = (-\log K_w)$$

But the first two terms define pK_a and pK_b, respectively, so this equation is equivalent to writing

■ We could also say, $pK_w = -\log K_w$, so at 25 °C, $pK_w = 14.00$.

$$pK_a + pK_b = -(\log 1.0 \times 10^{-14}) \qquad \text{(at 25 °C)}$$

Since $\log 1.0 \times 10^{-14} = 14.00$, we have the following simple relationship between the pK_a and pK_b values for an acid and its conjugate base.

$$pK_a + pK_b = 14.00 \qquad (25 \text{ °C}) \tag{9.16}$$

| EXAMPLE 9.12 | FINDING pK_a FROM pK_b OR pK_b FROM pK_a FOR CONJUGATE ACID–BASE PAIRS |

Problem: The pK_a of acetic acid at 25 °C is 4.74. What is the pK_b of its conjugate base, the acetate ion, $C_2H_3O_2^-$?

Solution:

$$pK_a + pK_b = 14.00$$
$$4.74 + pK_b = 14.00$$
$$pK_b = 14.00 - 4.74$$
$$= 9.26$$

Thus the pK_b for the acetate ion is 9.26.

PRACTICE EXERCISE 21

■ Hydrocyanic acid, HCN(*aq*), is a solution of hydrogen cyanide, HCN(*g*), in water. Both are extremely poisonous.

Hydrocyanic acid, HCN, is a very weak acid with a pK_a of 9.2 at 25 °C. Calculate the pK_b of its conjugate base, CN^-. Write the equation for the chemical equilibrium in which CN^- acts as a Brønsted base in water, and then write the equation for K_b.

9.6 BUFFERS

The pH of a solution can be held relatively constant if it contains a buffer — a weak base and its conjugate acid.

It takes just a little strong acid or strong base to cause a large change in the pH of a solution. The addition of only one drop of concentrated hydrochloric acid to a liter of pure water drops the pH of the system from 7 to 4, a change of three units in pH but a 10^3 or 1000-fold change in acidity. If such a change occurred in the bloodstream, you would die. The pH of blood can't be allowed to change by more than 0.2 to 0.3 pH units from its normal pH of 7.35.

■ $\dfrac{10^{-4}}{10^{-7}} = 1000$

Acidosis and Alkalosis Are Life-Threatening So critical is the maintenance of the pH of the blood that a special vocabulary exists to describe small shifts away from it. If the pH becomes lower, which means that the acidity of the blood is increasing, the condition is called **acidosis.** Acidosis is characteristic of untreated diabetes and emphysema, and other conditions. If the pH of the blood increases, which means that the blood is tending to become more basic, the condition is called **alkalosis.** An overdose of bicarbonate, exposure to the low partial pressure of oxygen at high altitudes, or prolonged hysteria can cause alkalosis.

■ Emergency room personnel at hospitals must be extremely well versed in recognizing signs of acidosis or alkalosis.

In their more advanced stages, acidosis and alkalosis are medical emergencies because they interfere with the smooth working of respiration, the physical and chemical apparatus that brings oxygen in, uses it, and then removes waste carbon dioxide. We need much more background before we can really understand this complex subject, but important parts of the preparation are in this chapter. We will learn in general terms in this section, for example, how the body controls the pH of its fluids.

Buffers Prevent Serious Changes in pH Certain combinations of solutes, called **buffers,** keep changes in pH to a minimum when strong acids or bases are added to an aqueous solution. One part of the buffer system can neutralize H^+, and the other part can neutralize OH^-. Fluids that contain buffers are said to be *buffered* against the changes in pH that H^+ or OH^- ions otherwise cause. The blood and other body fluids include buffers, and much of the body's work in maintaining its acid–base balance depends on buffers. Both acidosis and alkalosis are greatly restrained and sometimes totally prevented by buffers. Let's first see what they are and how they work, and then we can study them quantitatively.

■ Every form of life is very sensitive to slight changes of pH in internal fluids.

The Phosphate Buffer Is Important Within Cells The principal buffer at work inside cells is called the **phosphate buffer.** It consists of the pair of ions, HPO_4^{2-} and $H_2PO_4^-$, the monohydrogen and the dihydrogen phosphate ions. Notice that $H_2PO_4^-$ is the conjugate acid of HPO_4^{2-}, so $H_2PO_4^-$ is the member of this pair that is better able to neutralize base. Any added OH^- is neutralized by $H_2PO_4^-$, and this keeps the pH from increasing.

$$H_2PO_4^-(aq) + OH^-(aq) \longrightarrow HPO_4^{2-}(aq) + H_2O$$

The proton-acceptor or base in the phosphate buffer is the conjugate base of $H_2PO_4^-$, the HPO_4^{2-} ion. It can neutralize H^+ and so keep the pH from decreasing.

$$HPO_4^{2-}(aq) + H^+(aq) \longrightarrow H_2PO_4^-(aq)$$

■ In blood, $[HCO_3^-]$ is normally about 24 mmol/L (about 1.5 g/L).

The Carbonate Buffer Is Important in the Blood   The principal buffer in blood is called the **carbonate buffer.** It consists of the conjugate pair, H_2CO_3 and HCO_3^-, carbonic acid and the bicarbonate ion. Actually, the carbonic acid in blood is almost entirely in the form of $CO_2(aq)$, as we learned in Section 8.6. But any demand for $H_2CO_3(aq)$ is almost instantly met by the equilibrium-shifting ability of carbonic anhydrase, the enzyme that catalyzes the forward and reverse reactions in the following equilibrium:

■ The concentration of CO_2 in blood is normally about 1.2 mmol/L (about 0.05 g/L).

$$CO_2(aq) + H_2O \underset{\text{anhydrase}}{\overset{\text{carbonic}}{\rightleftharpoons}} H_2CO_3(aq)$$

We'll continue to use H_2CO_3 as a stand-in for $CO_2(aq)$ until we have to make the discussion more quantitative.

The carbonic acid of the blood's carbonate buffer can neutralize OH^-, and thus prevent an increase in pH. If there should be some metabolic or respiratory problem that increases the blood's OH^- level, this OH^- is neutralized by H_2CO_3, and alkalosis is prevented:

$$H_2CO_3(aq) + OH^-(aq) \longrightarrow HCO_3^-(aq) + H_2O \tag{9.17}$$

■ The "total CO_2" concentration of blood is $[HCO_3^-] + [CO_2]$ and is normally about 26 mmol/L.

The bicarbonate ion is the base of the blood's carbonate buffer. If in a particular metabolic or respiratory situation the blood's level of H^+ ion increases, the H^+ is neutralized by HCO_3^- and acidosis is prevented:

$$HCO_3^-(aq) + H^+(aq) \longrightarrow H_2CO_3(aq) \tag{9.18}$$

The Ability To Breathe Out CO_2 Is Essential to the Control of Acidosis   When acid is neutralized by the carbonate buffer (Equation 9.18), the blood's level of carbonic acid increases. As we know, this is an unstable acid, and when its level increases, the following equilibrium shifts to the right to produce dissolved carbon dioxide and water.

$$H_2CO_3(aq) \rightleftharpoons CO_2(aq) + H_2O \tag{9.19}$$

We have to use the symbol $CO_2(aq)$ instead of $CO_2(g)$ in Equation 9.19 because the carbon dioxide as still in solution. When the blood moves through the capillaries in the lungs, however, gaseous CO_2 is released from dissolved CO_2 and breathed out. Because the gas leaves, we cannot write this change as an equilibrium:

$$CO_2(aq) \longrightarrow CO_2(g) \tag{9.20}$$

The loss of one molecule of $CO_2(g)$ by this change means that the H^+ ion neutralized by the buffer action (Equation 9.18) is now permanently neutralized. The H^+ ion is now in an H_2O molecule made by the breakdown of H_2CO_3 (Equation 9.19). This H^+ could not be regenerated from H_2CO_3, because the CO_2 needed to make H_2CO_3 is lost from the body. All these steps are summarized in Figure 9.5, where you can see that the H^+ to be neutralized ends up in a molecule of water. The ability of this water molecule to form finally depends on the loss of the CO_2 molecule from the body.

■ A third mechanism involves the kidneys, which remove H^+ from blood and resupply HCO_3^-. But this work takes hours to days.

The blood thus brings to bear *two* mechanisms that rapidly handle an influx of H^+. It neutralizes H^+ by the work of the carbonate buffer, and it uses a physical process, ventilation, to make this neutralization permanent.

Figure 9.5
The irreversible neutralization of H^+ through the loss of CO_2 is one way the carbonate buffer system handles acidosis. It is the last step, the change of dissolved CO_2 into gaseous CO_2, which is exhaled, that draws all the equilibria to the right and makes H^+ "disappear" into H_2O.

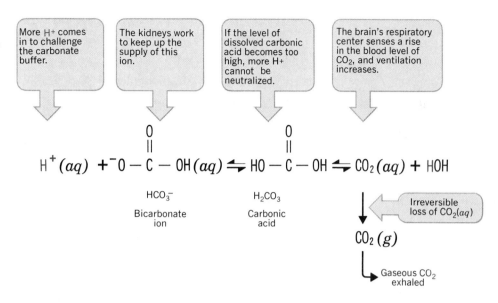

$$H^+(aq) + {}^-O - \underset{\substack{\| \\ O}}{C} - OH(aq) \rightleftharpoons HO - \underset{\substack{\| \\ O}}{C} - OH \rightleftharpoons CO_2(aq) + HOH$$

<table>
<tr><td>HCO_3^-
Bicarbonate
ion</td><td>H_2CO_3
Carbonic
acid</td></tr>
</table>

More H^+ comes in to challenge the carbonate buffer.

The kidneys work to keep up the supply of this ion.

If the level of dissolved carbonic acid becomes too high, more H^+ cannot be neutralized.

The brain's respiratory center senses a rise in the blood level of CO_2, and ventilation increases.

Irreversible loss of $CO_2(aq)$

$CO_2(g)$

Gaseous CO_2 exhaled

Ventilation is the circulation of air into and out of the lungs. The brain has a site called the *respiratory center* that monitors the level of $CO_2(aq)$ in the blood. When this level increases, the brain instructs the breathing apparatus to breathe more rapidly and deeply, a response called **hyperventilation.** This response increases the rate at which CO_2 can be exhaled, and the permanent loss of CO_2 shifts all the carbonate equilibria in their acid-neutralizing directions.

One of many lessons we can draw from this discussion is that anything that interferes with the loss of CO_2 inhibits the neutralization of the H^+ ion and causes acidosis. One such interference is involuntary **hypoventilation,** the slow and shallow breathing found in people with emphysema. They are unable to breathe deeply enough. They struggle with acidosis as well, because they are unable to get rid of CO_2 and so are unable to neutralize H^+ as well as they should. Any other cause of involuntary hypoventilation that renders the body unable to breathe out CO_2, like asthma, pneumonia, or overdoses of narcotics or barbiturates, also threatens the system with acidosis.

■ This retention of CO_2 because of hypoventilation is called "the retention of acid" because CO_2, one way or another, neutralizes OH^-.

There is much more to say about the various ways in which metabolism and respiration interact with the buffer systems in the blood, and we will return to this topic in considerable detail in a later chapter, after we have learned more about metabolism and about the chemistry of the blood.

9.7 SOME QUANTITATIVE ASPECTS OF BUFFERS

Buffers help to keep a pH constant, but not necessarily at pH 7.

In this section we move our study of buffers to a more quantitative level. We'll first explore the relationship between the pH of a buffered solution and the concentrations and relative acid–base strengths of its components.

The pH Values of Buffered Solutions Can Be Calculated from Ionization Constants and Buffer Concentrations
To make the discussion general, we assume that the buffer is made by dissolving some weak acid, HA, together with some of its sodium salt, NaA, in water. We use a group IA salt, like the sodium salt, because we generally want a fully soluble salt. Then it is very soluble, 100% ionized, and thus makes available the maximum amount of the conjugate base, A^-, of the weak acid.

The HA/A^- type of buffer system could involve any one of a number of weak acids of widely varying K_a values. So we cannot expect just one weak acid to work for the buffering of all ranges of pH. We therefore need an equation to tell us at what pH a specific HA/A^- buffer system will work.

Recall Equation 9.11, which defines K_a for a weak acid, HA:

$$K_a = \frac{[H^+][A^-]}{[HA]} \qquad \text{(This is Equation 9.11.)}$$

Because we want to know $[H^+]$ and then pH, let us rearrange this equation to give us an expression for $[H^+]$. (We can find pH after we find $[H^+]$.)

$$[H^+] = K_a \times \frac{[HA]}{[A^-]} \tag{9.21}$$

All molar concentrations in Equations 9.11 or 9.21, remember, are the concentrations *at equilibrium* after the solution has been prepared. The terms $[HA]$ and $[A^-]$ do not mean the *initial* concentrations of solutes used to prepare the solution. To keep this point before us in our discussion, we probably should write $[HA]$ and $[A^-]$ as $[HA]_{eq}$ and $[A^-]_{eq}$.

Yet when we deal with buffers, we can safely make some *very important simplifications.* We actually can use *initial* values of molarities of the weak acid, HA, and of the anion, A^- (as supplied by the salt), to be the same as the equilibrium values. Initial values are easier to use because we get them directly from the moles of solutes used to make the buffer solution. Here is why these simplifications work.

Because HA is a weak acid, little would be ionized at equilibrium, even if it were the only solute. But when its anion, A^-, is also present (supplied by the salt), the ionization of HA is suppressed even more. The presence of A^- from the salt, in other words, acts as a stress on the following equilibrium and keeps it shifted to the left, in favor of un-ionized HA:

$$HA(aq)_{eq} \rightleftharpoons H^+(aq)_{eq} + A^-(aq)_{eq}$$

The result is that the value of $[HA(aq)]_{eq}$ is essentially identical to that of $[HA(aq)]_{init}$, the value we know about from preparing the solution. Thus our first simplification is

$$[HA(aq)]_{eq} = [HA(aq)]_{\text{from initial}} = \underset{\substack{\text{concentration} \\ \text{of acid}}}{[\text{acid}]}$$

Thus we let [acid] be our symbol for the *initial* molar concentration of the weak acid in the buffer.

Now let us see what we can do about simplifying $[A^-(aq)]_{eq}$. Not much $A^-(aq)_{eq}$ is supplied by the ionization of the weak acid. ("Weak" implies this.) Nearly 100% of the $A^-(aq)_{eq}$ is supplied, instead, by the salt, because the ionization of the weak acid is suppressed. Thus not much of anything changes the value of $[A^-(aq)]$ *as initially supplied by the salt.* We conclude that the value of $[A^-(aq)]_{eq}$ is essentially the same as $[A^-(aq)]_{init}$. So our second simplification is

$$[A^-(aq)]_{eq} = [A^-(aq)]_{\text{from initial}} = \underset{\substack{\text{concentration} \\ \text{of the salt}}}{[\text{anion}]}$$

■ For all practical purposes, the *only* source of A^- is the salt, NaA, used to prepare the buffer.

So we let [anion] stand for the *initial* molar concentration of the other component of the buffer, the component supplied by the salt.

These relationships define new terms, [acid] and [anion], which we can now substitute into Equation 9.21 for $[HA]$ and $[A^-]$, respectively. Always remember that [acid] refers to the *initial* concentration of the weak acid and [anion] refers to the *initial* concentration of the anion directly provided by the salt in the buffer system. So for a buffer system made of the HA/A^- pair, we have the following equation for $[H^+]$.

For HA/A^- buffers:

$$[H^+] = K_a \times \frac{[\text{acid}]}{[\text{anion}]} \qquad (9.22)$$

Let's see how we can use what we have learned to find $[H^+]$ and, from it, the pH of a buffer solution.

EXAMPLE 9.13 **CALCULATING THE pH OF A BUFFERED SOLUTION**

Problem: To study the effect of a weakly acidic medium on the rate of growth of a species of bacteria, a biochemist prepared a buffer from the weak acid, acetic acid, and used sodium acetate as the source of the conjugate base, the acetate ion. The buffer was made with concentrations of 0.11 M $NaC_2H_3O_2$ (sodium acetate) and 0.090 M $HC_2H_3O_2$ (acetic acid). What is the pH of this solution?

Solution: We note first, from Table 9.2, that K_a for acetic acid is 1.8×10^{-5}. We'll work directly from Equation 9.11, which defines K_a (and which you should now know), instead of from its rearranged form, Equation 9.22, to emphasize how the simplifications work. In fact, Equation 9.11 is the only equation you really need to remember to work these kinds of buffer problems. We have

$$K_a = \frac{[H^+][A^-]}{[HA]} \quad \text{(This is Equation 9.11.)}$$

Here is where we remember the crucial substitutions allowed when we are working with a buffer system — [anion] for $[A^-]$ and [acid] for $[HA]$. Since [anion] = 0.11 mol/L, since [acid] = 0.090 mol/L, and since $K_a = 1.8 \times 10^{-5}$, we have

$$1.8 \times 10^{-5} = \frac{[H^+](0.11)}{(0.090)}$$

Solving this for $[H^+]$, we have

$$[H^+] = \frac{(1.8 \times 10^{-5})(0.090)}{(0.11)} \quad \text{(Notice how this parallels Equation 9.22.)}$$

$$= 1.5 \times 10^{-5} \text{ mol/L}$$

Since   pH $= -\log[H^+]$,

pH $= -\log(1.5 \times 10^{-5})$
$= 4.82$

Thus the pH of this buffer solution is 4.82.

PRACTICE EXERCISE 22   A buffer solution was prepared using 0.085 M formic acid, $HCHO_2$, and sodium formate, $NaCHO_2$, dissolved in the same solution at a concentration of 0.12 mol/L. Calculate the pH of this solution. For formic acid, $K_a = 1.8 \times 10^{-4}$.

The pH of a Buffer Solution Can Also Be Found by the Henderson–Hasselbalch Equation   We can convert Equation 9.22 into a form that includes pH instead of $[H^+]$. We'll use the result, called the Henderson–Hasselbalch equation, to continue our study of the carbonate buffer in blood.

If we take the logarithm of both sides of Equation 9.22, and then multiply every resulting term by -1, we get

■ $-\log[H^+] = pH$
$-\log K_a = pK_a$

$$-\log[H^+] = -\log K_a - \log \frac{[acid]}{[anion]}$$

We can recognize expressions for pH and pK_a in this, so we can write

$$pH = pK_a - \log \frac{[acid]}{[anion]}$$

If we note that

■ Another rule of logarithms:
$-\log a/b = +\log b/a$

$$-\log \frac{[acid]}{[anion]} = +\log \frac{[anion]}{[acid]}$$

we can write

$$pH = pK_a + \log \frac{[anion]}{[acid]} \qquad (9.23)$$

Equation 9.23 is the **Henderson–Hasselbalch equation.**[3] Let's rework Example 9.13 using it.

| EXAMPLE 9.14 | CALCULATING THE pH OF A BUFFERED SOLUTION |

Problem: Calculate the pH of the buffer solution described in Example 9.13.

Solution: We note first that for acetic acid $K_a = 1.8 \times 10^{-5}$, so pK_a = 4.74. (p$K_a = -\log K_a$) The buffer of Example 9.13 had [anion] = 0.11 mol/L and [acid] = 0.090 mol/L. Substituting these values into the Henderson–Hasselbalch equation, we get

$$pH = 4.74 + \log \frac{(0.11)}{(0.090)}$$

$$= 4.74 + \log 1.2$$
$$= 4.74 + 0.079$$
$$pH = 4.82$$

PRACTICE EXERCISE 23   Calculate the pH of a buffered solution made up to be 0.016 M sodium acetate and 0.12 M acetic acid.

Buffers Hold a pH Steady, But Not Necessarily at pH 7   One important point about buffers is the distinction between keeping a solution at a particular pH and keeping it neutral—at a pH of 7. Although it is certainly possible to prepare a buffer to work at pH 7, buffers can be made that will work at any pH value throughout the pH scale.

The Ratio [Anion]/[Acid] Dominates the pH Once a Buffer Pair Is Selected   The Henderson–Hasselbalch equation very clearly shows that two factors govern the pH of a buffered solution. The first is the pK_a of the weak acid in the buffer pair and the second is the ratio [anion]/[acid]. To decide what weak acid and salt to use in a buffer, we first decide the pH

[3] Some references give the Henderson–Hasselbalch equation as

$$pH = pK_a + \log \frac{[salt]}{[acid]}$$

In other words, [salt] is used instead of [anion], as though the two were always identical in value. They are identical only when the cation of the salt is of the form M^+ (e.g. Na^+ or K^+) so that each formula unit of the salt furnishes only *one* anion. But when the cation is of the form M^{2+} (e.g., Ca^{2+}), then *two* anions are released by the dissociation of only one formula unit of the salt. With such salts the value of [anion] is twice the value of [salt]. It is safest to stick with the form of Equation 9.23.

■ When [anion] = [acid],

$$\log \frac{[anion]}{[acid]} = \log \frac{1}{1} = 0$$

So then pH = pK_a + 0

that we want to protect. Then we look for a weak acid with a pK_a as close to it as possible. We can see from Equation 9.23 that if we prepare a buffer with the ratio of [anion] to [acid] made equal to 1, then the pH of the buffered solution equals the pK_a of the weak acid.

Of course, when we work with the buffered solutions found in a living system, we have to take what nature gives us. And nature gives us carbonic acid as the acid component of the chief blood buffer. This makes the second factor in the Henderson–Hasselbalch equation decisive for this buffer.

The second factor, as we said, is the *ratio* [anion]/[acid]. The pH of a buffer solution depends entirely on this once the acid component with its pK_a has been picked. Notice particularly that it isn't the absolute values of [anion] and of [acid] *but the ratio of these values* that determines the pH of the buffer. You could get a one to one ratio, for example, with [anion] and [acid] both equal to 0.50 mol/L or both equal to 0.25 mol/L or to 0.10 mol/L. The pH of the buffer would be the same as long as the acid has not been changed.

PRACTICE EXERCISE 24

How is the pH of a buffered solution related by an equation to the pK_a of the weak acid in the buffer when

(a) The ratio of [anion] to [acid] is 10 to 1?
(b) The ratio of [anion] to [acid] is 1 to 10?

Buffers Minimize But Do Not Completely Prevent pH Changes Let's compare what happens if we add a small amount of NaOH, a strong base, to pure water with what happens when we add the same amount to a buffer solution.

■ [OH⁻] = 1.0 × 10^{-pOH}

When we add 0.010 mol of NaOH to 1.0 L of pure water, the concentration of OH⁻ ion becomes 0.010 mol/L. Because 0.010 mol OH⁻/L is the same as 1.0×10^{-2} mol OH⁻/L, we can see that the pOH is 2 (pOH = −log [OH⁻]). This makes the pH 12 (pH + pOH = 14.00), so the addition of 0.010 mol of NaOH (only 0.40 g of NaOH) to a liter of pure water has changed the pH from 7 to 12. The concentration of OH⁻ ion has gone from 1.0×10^{-7} to 1.0×10^{-2} mol/L, a whopping 100,000-fold increase in [OH⁻].

Now let's add 0.010 mol of NaOH to 1.0 L of a hypothetical buffer in which the weak acid component has pK_a = 7.00 and in which [anion] = [acid] = 0.10 mol/L. (Because [anion] = [acid], the pH of the buffer equals the given pK_a or 7.00.) When we add 0.010 mol of OH⁻ to this solution, we neutralize 0.010 mol of the acid. This reduces the amount of acid by 0.010 mol, but it also increases the amount of anion by 0.010 mol. So after the addition of the sodium hydroxide, we have the following new concentrations of the buffer components:

$$[anion] = (0.10 \text{ mol} + 0.010 \text{ mol})/L = 0.11 \text{ mol/L}$$
$$[acid] = (0.10 \text{ mol} - 0.010 \text{ mol})/L = 0.090 \text{ mol/L}$$

By the Henderson–Hasselbalch equation, the new pH is

$$pH = 7.00 + \log \frac{(0.11)}{(0.090)}$$
$$= 7.09$$

When the buffer is present, in other words, the addition of 0.010 mol of NaOH causes a change in pH from 7.00 to 7.09, a change of only 0.090 unit. (It can be calculated that this amounts to a 1.25-fold increase in OH⁻ concentration, a vastly smaller change than the 100,000-fold increase.) Thus, although the buffer has not prevented some change in pH, it has surely kept the change very small.

PRACTICE EXERCISE 25

Suppose that in the illustration just concluded the hypothetical buffer had been more dilute, say, [anion] = [acid] = 0.050 mol/L. (The weak acid still has pK_a = 7.00.)

(a) What is the pH of this buffer?
(b) What is the pH of 1.0 L of this buffer after 0.010 mol of NaOH has been added?
(c) Compare the result in part (b) to the result of the previous illustration; there we began with 1.0 L in which [anion] = [acid] = 0.10 mol/L. One can conclude that the *capacity* of a buffer solution to

keep a pH change to a minimum depends on the absolute values of the concentrations of acid and anion even when the ratio of these concentrations is initially unchanged.

PRACTICE EXERCISE 26 Suppose that so much strong base is added to a buffer made of HA and A^-, initially at a ratio of one to one, so that the ratio of [anion] to [acid] changes to 1000 to 1. The pK_a of HA is 4.75. What is the new pH of the solution? Can one conclude from this result that buffers have an *unlimited* capacity to hold a pH fairly constant?

Dissolved CO_2, Not Just H_2CO_3, Must Be Factored into a Henderson–Hasselbalch Treatment of the Blood's Carbonate Buffer We have thus far described the principal buffer in blood, the "carbonate buffer," as consisting of the weak acid, H_2CO_3, and its conjugate base, HCO_3^-. But we also noted that at the temperature of the body, at the concentrations of all ions in the blood, and in the presence of carbonic anhydrase, not much H_2CO_3 is actually present. Most CO_2 is present not as $H_2CO_3(aq)$ but simply as $CO_2(aq)$; the ratio is roughly 1 molecule of $H_2CO_3(aq)$ to 400 molecules of $CO_2(aq)$. Indeed, it is entirely possible that $CO_2(aq)$ is the hydroxide-ion-neutralizing species, doing so by the reaction

$$CO_2(aq) + OH^-(aq) \longrightarrow HCO_3^-(aq)$$

instead of by the reaction

$$H_2CO_3(aq) + OH^-(aq) \longrightarrow HCO_3^-(aq) + H_2O$$

(In fact, some evidence exists that carbonic anhydrase catalyzes the direct reaction of OH^- with CO_2 instead of the equilibration of H_2O and CO_2 with H_2CO_3.) The Henderson–Hasselbalch equation should take the following form in the light of these facts. Here we make a small but significant change in one symbol: pK' for pK_a.

■ K_a values are usually assumed to be for 25 °C unless another temperature is specified, like body temperature.

$$pH = pK' + \log \frac{[HCO_3^-(aq)]}{[CO_2(aq)]} \tag{9.24}$$

We cannot employ the usual symbol, pK_a, because we are not working with a system at 25 °C but at 37 °C. Moreover, we're not working simply with H_2CO_3 for which pK_a is 4.5×10^{-7} and pK_a is 6.35 (at 25 °C for the ionization of the first proton). To handle these different conditions, we use what is called an *apparent acid ionization constant,* symbolized as K' and a corresponding apparent pK'. The accepted value of pK' for the carbonate buffer under body conditions is 6.1, so we can rewrite Equation 9.24 as follows when we are dealing with the carbonate buffer in the body:

$$pH = 6.1 + \log \frac{[HCO_3^-]}{[CO_2]} \tag{9.25}$$

Under normal pH conditions in human arterial blood, $[HCO_3^-] = 24$ mmol/L, and $[CO_2] = 1.2$ mmol/L. The pH of human arterial blood should then calculate to be 7.4:

$$pH = 6.1 + \log \frac{(24 \text{ mmol/L})}{(1.2 \text{ mmol/L})}$$

$$= 7.4$$

Statistically, the average human arterial blood in health is 7.35, so the calculated and the observed values agree well.

Normal Exhaling of CO_2, Hyperventilation, and Resupply of HCO_3^- by the Kidneys All Work to Combat Acidosis Let's suppose that the blood were challenged with a sudden influx of acid in the equivalent of 10 mmol of HCl per liter of blood. This would neutralize 10 mmol/L of HCO_3^- and so reduce its concentration from 24 mmol/L to 14 mmol/L. The HCO_3^-, of course, changes almost entirely to $CO_2(aq)$, so 10 mmol/L of new $CO_2(aq)$ appears in the blood. If this new CO_2 could not be removed by breathing, the level of $CO_2(aq)$ would increase by 10 mmol/L, from 1.2 mmol/L to 11.2 mmol/L. This would be fatal because, by Equation 9.25, the resulting pH of the blood would be 6.2, far, far too low to permit life to continue.

$$pH = 6.1 + \log \frac{(14 \text{ mmol/L})}{(11.2 \text{ mmol/L})}$$
$$= 6.2$$

However, essentially all the $CO_2(aq)$ leaves the blood in the lungs and is breathed out as $CO_2(g)$. Although the level of HCO_3^- stays the same, at 14 mmol/L, the level of $CO_2(aq)$ quickly drops back to 1.2 mmol/L. So the pH quickly bounces back up to 7.2.

$$pH = 6.1 + \log \frac{(14 \text{ mmol/L})}{(1.2 \text{ mmol/L})}$$
$$= 7.2$$

■ A pH of 7.2 corresponds to fairly severe acidosis.

Of course, a blood pH of 7.2 is still too low for health, but it doesn't cause death.

There is another mechanism to provide further upward readjustment of the blood pH. The body, when healthy, responds quickly to a lowering of the blood pH by increasing the rate of breathing, by causing *hyperventilation*. This works to force even more CO_2 out of the blood and into the exhaled air. It's quite common for hyperventilation to pull the level of $CO_2(aq)$ from 1.2 mmol/L down to 0.70 mmol/L, sometimes a bit lower. This would bring the pH of the blood in our example — the sudden influx of 10 mmol/L of acid — back to 7.4.

$$pH = 6.1 + \log \frac{(14 \text{ mmol/L})}{(0.70 \text{ mmol/L})}$$
$$= 7.4$$

Thus two mechanisms have protected the system against the otherwise lethal assault of an influx of 10 mmol/L of strong acid. The buffer system has neutralized the acid and the respiratory system has, by removing CO_2, readjusted the ratio of $[HCO_3^-]/[CO_2]$. Neither of these two mechanisms could save the situation alone.

The situation, however, is not back to normal in all respects. The system will continue to produce CO_2, which will increase the denominator in $[HCO_3^-]/[CO_2]$ and so the pH will gradually decline again. The system must, therefore, also increase the level of HCO_3^-, and this is done principally by the chemical work of the kidneys. The kidneys, as we have said, can manufacture "new" HCO_3^- to replenish the base of the blood's carbonate buffer, and as they do this the kidneys can also export H^+. We won't delve further into this here, but you can see that the management of the pH of the blood, so that respiration may proceed well, involves an intricate interplay of chemical and physiological events at the molecular level of life. The smooth, harmonious working of these events in the healthy body is one of the grandest, most beautiful aspects of nature.

■ When a person is battling severe acidosis, the pH of the urine can go as low as 4.

9.8 ACID–BASE TITRATIONS

At the end point of an acid–base titration, the number of moles of H^+ should match the number of moles of H^+ acceptor.

One of the very common kinds of chemical analysis is to determine the concentration of an acid or a base. The purpose is to find the molarity of some whole solute, like moles of acetic acid per liter of solution, not just to measure the pH of the solution. Thus we have to make some distinctions between the kinds of acid species present.

pH Refers to $[H^+]$, Not to $[HA]$ The pH of a solution tells us indirectly the *acidity* of a solution, what the concentration of its hydronium ions is. It does not, however, disclose the **neutralizing capacity** of the solution — its capacity to neutralize a strong base. The 1 mol

Figure 9.6
The apparatus for titration. By manipulating the stopcock, the analyst controls the rate at which the solution in the buret is added to the flask below.

of acetic acid in 1 L of 1 M $HC_2H_3O_2$ can neutralize 1 mol of NaOH, yet this solution has an actual quantity of H_3O^+ of only about 0.004 mol, the result of acetic acid being a weak acid.

Always remember that acids are classified as *weak* or *strong* according to their abilities to transfer a proton to one particular and very weak base, H_2O. When sodium hydroxide is added to an acid, however, we are adding a very strong base, OH^-. This base can take H^+ not only from H_3O^+ but also from $HC_2H_3O_2$. Thus the neutralizing capacity of 1 M acetic acid is considerably greater than its concentration of hydronium ions.

The Titration of an Acid with a Base Gives Data from Which Concentrations Can Be Calculated The procedure used to measure the total acid (or base) neutralizing capacity of a solution is called **titration.** It involves comparing the volume of a solution of unknown concentration to the volume of a *standard solution* that exactly neutralizes it. A **standard solution** is simply one whose concentration is accurately known.

■ The careful measurement of the concentration of a standard solution is called **standardization.** We say that we standardize the solution.

The apparatus for titration is shown in Figure 9.6. When a titration is used for an acid–base analysis, a carefully measured volume of the solution of unknown acidity (or basicity) is placed in a beaker or a flask. A very small amount of an acid–base indicator, like phenolphthalein, is added. Then a *standard solution* of the neutralizing reagent is added through a stopcock, portion by portion, from a special tube called a *buret,* marked in 1 mL and 0.1 mL divisions (Figure 9.6). This addition is continued until a change in color, caused by the acid–base indicator, signals that the unknown has been *exactly neutralized.*

End Points Ideally Occur at Equivalence Points With a carefully selected acid–base indicator, the color change in an acid–base titration occurs when all the available hydrogen ions have reacted with all the available proton-acceptors. This point in a titration is called the **equivalence point.**

■ To reach the equivalence point the moles of H^+ used must be the same as, must be *equivalent to,* the moles of proton-acceptor present.

A well-chosen indicator is one whose color at the equivalence point is the same as it would be in a solution made up of the *salt* that forms in the titration (and in the same concentration). When this salt has an ion that hydrolyzes, the equivalence point cannot be at pH 7.00. For example, when one mole of acetic acid has been exactly neutralized by one mole of sodium hydroxide, exactly one mole of sodium acetate has been made. Because the acetate ion hydrolyzes (but not the sodium ion), this salt gives a solution that is slightly basic to litmus, not a solution with a pH of 7.00. So it would be poor to pick an indicator that changes color

■ The pH of 1 M $NaC_2H_3O_2$ is about 9.4

over an acidic range. (Phenolphthalein works very well in this titration.) Whether or not the indicator has been well-chosen, the analyst has little choice but to stop the titration when the indicator's color changes. This stopping point is called the **end point** of the titration. In a well run titration, of course, the end point and the equivalence point coincide.

In Chapter 5 we studied how to do calculations involving volumes and concentrations of solutions with an emphasis on calculating volumes. Acid–base titrations, however, are usually done to determine concentrations, so we'll work through an example to see how it's done.

EXAMPLE 9.15　　　　　**CALCULATING MOLARITIES FROM CONCENTRATION DATA**

Problem: A student titrated 25.0 mL of sodium hydroxide solution with standard sulfuric acid. It took 13.4 mL of 0.0555 M H_2SO_4 to neutralize the sodium hydroxide in the solution. What was the molarity of the sodium hydroxide solution? The equation for the reaction is

$$2NaOH(aq) + H_2SO_4(aq) \longrightarrow Na_2SO_4(aq) + 2H_2O$$

Solution: Be sure to understand the goal first. We are to calculate the molarity of the NaOH, which means the ratio of the moles of NaOH to liters of NaOH solution. We were given (indirectly) the liters of the NaOH solution, 25.0 mL = 0.025 L. To find the moles of NaOH we need two conversion factors, one involving the molarity of the acid, and the other involving the coefficients in the equation.

The molarity of the H_2SO_4 solution, 0.0555 M, gives us the following conversion factors. We'll be using the first.

$$\frac{0.0555 \text{ mol } H_2SO_4}{1000 \text{ mL } H_2SO_4 \text{ soln}} \qquad \frac{1000 \text{ mL } H_2SO_4 \text{ soln}}{0.0555 \text{ mol } H_2SO_4}$$

The balanced equation gives us these conversion factors, and we'll be using the second.

$$\frac{1 \text{ mol } H_2SO_4}{2 \text{ mol NaOH}} \qquad \frac{2 \text{ mol NaOH}}{1 \text{ mol } H_2SO_4}$$

Now let's begin with the given volume of the acid and convert it into the number of moles of NaOH it neutralized.

■ You should draw the cancel lines yourself.

$$13.4 \text{ mL } H_2SO_4 \text{ soln} \times \underbrace{\frac{0.0555 \text{ mol } H_2SO_4}{1000 \text{ mL } H_2SO_4 \text{ soln}}}_{\text{To convert mL acid to mol of acid}} \times \underbrace{\frac{2 \text{ mol NaOH}}{1 \text{ mol } H_2SO_4}}_{\substack{\text{To find mol} \\ \text{of base from} \\ \text{mol of acid}}} = 0.00149 \text{ mol NaOH}$$

Thus 0.00149 mol of NaOH was present in 25.0 mL of 0.025 L of NaOH solution. To find the molarity of the NaOH solution, we take the following ratio of moles to liters:

$$\frac{0.00149 \text{ mol NaOH}}{0.025 \text{ L NaOH soln}} = 0.0596 \ M \text{ NaOH}$$

Thus the molarity of the NaOH solution is 0.0596 M.

PRACTICE EXERCISE 27　　If it takes 24.3 mL of 0.110 M HCl to neutralize 25.5 mL of freshly prepared sodium hydroxide solution, what is the molarity of the NaOH solution?

PRACTICE EXERCISE 28　　If 20.0 mL of 0.125 M solution of NaOH exactly neutralized the sulfuric acid in 10.0 mL of H_2SO_4 solution, what was the molarity of the H_2SO_4 solution?

SUMMARY

Equilibrium laws An equilibrium law exists for every chemical equilibrium. It is of the form

$$\frac{[C]^c[D]^d}{[A]^a[B]^b} = K_{eq}$$

when the equilibrium is of the type

$$aA + bB \rightleftharpoons cC + dD$$

The equilibrium constant, K_{eq}, which is different for each equilibrium, depends only on the temperature. If any stress other than a temperature change is placed on an equilibrium, such as the addition of a common ion, all concentrations adjust, but K_{eq} stays the same. A large value of K_{eq} means that the products are favored at equilibrium; a small value means that the reactants are favored.

Ion product constant of water, K_w The ion product constant of water, $K_w = [H^+][OH^-]$, although not a true equilibrium constant, has all the properties of one. At 25 °C, $K_w = 1.0 \times 10^{-14}$. If acids or bases are added, the value of K_w stays the same but individual values of $[H^+]$ and $[OH^-]$ adjust.

The pH concept A simple way to express very low values of $[H^+]$ is by pH, where $[H^+] = 1 \times 10^{-pH}$, or $pH = -\log [H^+]$. When pH < 7, the solution is acidic. When pH > 7, the solution is basic. An analogous pOH concept exists. $pOH = -\log [OH^-]$, and at 25 °C, $pH + pOH = 14.00$.

To measure the pH of a solution we use indicators, dyes whose colors change over a narrow range of pH, or we use a pH meter.

Acid ionization constants A modified equilibrium law called the acid ionization constant, K_a, exists for weak acids. Letting HA represent the acid,

$$K_a = \frac{[H^+][A^-]}{[HA]}$$

for the equilibrium,

$$HA \rightleftharpoons H^+ + A^-$$

For weak acids, $K_a < 10^{-3}$. For moderate acids K_a is roughly 1×10^{-3}, and for strong acids $K_a > 1$.

Besides weak acids, like HA, most metal ions in water generate hydrogen ions by the ionization of a water molecule attracted to the metal ion (e.g., in the hydrated metal ion). The exceptions that do not make a solution acidic are the group IA and IIA cations (below beryllium). Ammonium salts also give acidic solutions.

Base ionization constants Bases weaker than OH^- or O^{2-} occur mostly as anions, the conjugate bases of weak acids. Ammonia is also a base weaker than OH^-. A base, B, ionizes according to the equilibrium,

$$B + H_2O \rightleftharpoons BH^+ + OH^-$$

The base ionization constant is then

$$K_b = \frac{[BH^+][OH^-]}{[B]}$$

Strong bases have large values of K_b. Weak bases have small values of K_b.

The reaction of a basic anion with water is called the hydrolysis of the anion, and a salt of such an anion with any group IA or IIA metals (except beryllium) gives a basic solution in water. The anions that do not hydrolyze are the conjugate bases of strong acids, like Cl^-, Br^-, I^-, NO_3^-, and SO_4^{2-}.

The pK_a and pK_b concepts The negative logarithm of K_a is pK_a, and the negative logarithm of K_b is pK_b.

$$pK_a = -\log K_a$$
$$pK_b = -\log K_b$$

The weaker the acid the larger its pK_a. The weaker the base the larger its pK_b. $pK_a + pK_b = 14.00$ at 25 °C.

Buffers Solutions that contain something that can neutralize OH^- ion (such as a weak acid) and something else that can neutralize H^+ ion (such as the conjugate base of the same weak acid) are buffered against changes in pH when either additional base or acid is added.

The phosphate buffer, which is present in the fluids inside cells of the body, consists of HPO_4^{2-} (to neutralize H^+) and $H_2PO_4^-$ (to neutralize OH^-).

The normal pH of blood is 7.35. A decrease in the pH of blood is called acidosis and an increase is called alkalosis. Either condition interferes with respiration, and extreme cases (pH < 7 or pH > 8) are lethal.

The carbonate buffer, which is the chief buffer in blood, consists of HCO_3^- (to neutralize H^+) and H_2CO_3 (to neutralize OH^-). The supply of H_2CO_3 comes from the reaction of dissolved CO_2 with water. (It could be that this CO_2 reacts directly with OH^-, instead of through H_2CO_3.) Carbonic acid breaks down in the lungs where the CO_2 is expelled. The ability to exhale CO_2 is essential to the prevention of acidosis.

When metabolism or some deficiency in respiration produces or retains H^+ at a rate faster than the blood buffer can neutralize them, the lungs try to remove CO_2 at a faster rate (hyperventilation). Overall, for each molecule of CO_2 exhaled, one proton is neutralized.

The pH of a buffer solution consisting of a weak acid, HA and its conjugate base, A^-, can be calculated from the defining equation for K_a. In such a buffer at equilibrium, for all practical purposes, $[HA]_{eq} = [acid]_{init}$ and $[A^-]_{eq} = [anion]_{init}$. So the defining equation for K_a can be modified to express $[H^+]$ as

$$[H^+] = K_a \times \frac{[acid]}{[anion]}$$

The defining equation for pH lets us convert this equation to the Henderson–Hasselbalch equation:

$$pH = pK_a + \log \frac{[\text{anion}]}{[\text{acid}]}$$

The two factors that determine at what pH a buffer works are the pK_a of the weak acid component and the *ratio* [anion]/[acid]. As this ratio varies from 10/1 to 1/1 to 1/10, the pH varies as $pK_a \pm 1$.

A buffer thus does not keep a solution necessarily at a pH of 7, but it holds a fairly constant pH when extra acid or base enters.

At body temperature the Henderson–Hasselbalch equation takes the following working form, in which $[CO_2(aq)]$ appears instead of $[H_2CO_3]$.

$$pH = 6.1 + \log \frac{[\text{HCO}_3^-]}{[\text{CO}_2(aq)]}$$

If an acid neutralizes some HCO_3^-, the ratio in the log term decreases too much unless the lungs simultaneously breathe out the extra CO_2 produced. If the lungs are able to work, some hyperventilation helps this process, and the pH of the blood stays quite close to 7.35. Over a longer period, the supply of HCO_3^- is replenished by the work of the kidneys.

Acid–base titration The concentration of an acid or a base in water can be determined by titrating the unknown solution with a standard solution of what can neutralize it. The indicator is selected to have its color change occur at whatever pH the final solution would have were it made from the salt that forms by the neutralization. The unknown concentration can be calculated from the volumes of the acid and base used, the molarity of the standard solution, and the coefficients in the equation for the specific neutralization reaction.

REVIEW EXERCISES

The answers to Review Exercises that require a calculation and that are marked with an asterisk are found in Appendix D. The answers to the other Review Exercises are found in the *Study Guide* that accompanies this book.

Equilibrium Law

9.1 What did Guldburg and Waage discover about chemical equilibria?

9.2 In setting up an equilibrium law for a system,
(a) What concentration units are assumed?
(b) How are the coefficients of the chemical equation used?
(c) The terms for what substances, reactants or products, appear in the denominator?
(e) Why must the temperature be specified?

9.3 Write the equilibrium laws for the following.
(a) $NH_3(aq) + H_2O \rightleftharpoons NH_4^+(aq) + OH^-(aq)$
(b) $2H_2(g) + O_2(g) \rightleftharpoons 2H_2O(g)$
(c) $N_2(g) + 3H_2(g) \rightleftharpoons 2NH_3(g)$

9.4 For the equilibrium in which ethylene reacts with water to give ethyl alcohol,

$$C_2H_4(g) + H_2O(g) \rightleftharpoons C_2H_5OH(g)$$

$K_{eq} = 8.3 \times 10^3$. Is the product favored or are the reactants? How can you tell?

Ion Product Constant of Water

9.5 Write the equation that defines K_w. How does it differ from the equilibrium law for water (written using H^+ and OH^-)?

9.6 What is the value of K_w at 25 °C?

9.7 The higher the temperature, the higher the value of K_w. Why should there be this trend?

*9.8 At the temperature of the human body, 37 °C, the concentration of hydrogen ion in pure water is 1.56×10^{-7} mol/L. What is the value of K_w at 37 °C? Is this water acidic, basic, or neutral?

9.9 "Heavy water" or deuterium oxide, D_2O, is used in nuclear power plants. It self-ionizes like water, and at 20 °C there is a concentration of D^+ ion of 3.0×10^{-8} mol/L. What is the value of K_w for heavy water at 20 °C?

pH

9.10 What equation defines pH in exponential terms? In log terms?

9.11 The average pH of urine is about 6. Is this acidic, neutral, or basic?

9.12 The pH of gastric juice is in the range of 1.5 to 3.5. Is gastric juice acidic, basic, or neutral?

9.13 What is the pH of 0.01 M HCl(aq), assuming 100% ionization?

9.14 What is the pOH of 0.01 M NaOH(aq), assuming 100% ionization? What is the pH of this solution?

9.15 Explain why a pH of 7.00 corresponds to a neutral solution at 25 °C.

9.16 A certain brand of beer has a pH of 5.0. What is the concentration of hydrogen ion in moles per liter? Is the beer slightly acidic or basic?

9.17 The pH of a soft drink was found to be 4.5. What is $[H^+]$?

9.18 A solution of a monoprotic acid was prepared with a molar concentration of 0.10 M. Its pH was found to be 1.0. Is the acid a strong or a weak acid? Explain.

9.19 The pH of a solution of a monoprotic acid was found to be 4.56, whereas its molar concentration was 0.010 M. Is this acid a strong or a weak acid? Explain.

9.20 When a soil sample was stirred with pure water, the pOH of the water changed to 6.10. Did the soil produce an acidic or a basic reaction with the water?

*9.21 A solution was prepared by dissolving 0.426 g of Ba(OH)₂ in a final volume of solution of 100 mL. Calculate the pOH and the pH of this solution, assuming that the Ba(OH)₂ is fully dissociated.

Acid Ionization Constants

9.22 Write the equilibrium equation and the equation for K_a for the ionization of nitrous acid, HNO_2.

9.23 Write the equilibrium equation and the equation for K_a for the ionization of the hydrogen sulfite ion, HSO_3^-.

9.24 Write the equilibrium equation and the equation for K_a for the ionization of the ammonium ion.

9.25 The K_a for the hydrogen sulfite ion, HSO_3^-, is 6.6×10^{-8} and for barbituric acid is 9.9×10^{-5}. Which is the stronger acid?

9.26 The K_a for the ammonium ion is 5.7×10^{-10} and for the hydrogen sulfide ion, HS^-, is 1×10^{-19}. Which is the stronger acid?

Base Ionization Constants

9.27 Write the equilibrium equation and the equation for K_b for the bicarbonate ion acting as a base.

9.28 Write the equilibrium equation and the equation for K_b for the hydrogen sulfide ion, HS^-, acting as a base.

9.29 Write the equilibrium equation and the equation for K_b for the phosphate ion acting as a base.

9.30 Which is the stronger base, ammonia ($K_b = 1.8 \times 10^{-5}$) or the hypochlorite ion, OCl^- ($K_b = 3.3 \times 10^{-7}$)?

Hydrolysis of Ions

9.31 Explain why a solution of ammonium bromide tests slightly acidic.

9.32 Explain in your own words why a solution of sodium acetate, $NaC_2H_3O_2$, is slightly basic, not neutral.

9.33 Predict whether each of the following solutions is acidic, basic, or neutral:
(a) K_2SO_4 (b) NH_4NO_3 (c) $KHCO_3$
(d) $FeCl_3$ (e) Li_2CO_3

9.34 Predict whether each of the following solutions is acidic, neutral, or basic:
(a) KNO_3 (b) Na_2HPO_4 (c) K_3PO_4
(d) $Cr(NO_3)_3$ (e) $KC_2H_3O_2$

9.35 Aspirin is a weak, monoprotic acid for which $K_a = 3.3 \times 10^{-4}$. Does a solution of the sodium salt of aspirin test acidic, basic, or neutral?

9.36 The K_b of the hydrogen sulfide ion, SH^- is 1.1×10^{-7}. Does a solution of sodium hydrogen sulfide, $NaSH$, test acidic, basic, or neutral?

pK_a and pK_b

•9.37 Calculate the pK_a values of the following acids.
(a) HF ($K_a = 6.8 \times 10^{-4}$), hydrofluoric acid
(b) HOCl ($K_a = 3.0 \times 10^{-8}$), hypochlorous acid

9.38 Calculate the pK_b values of the following bases.
(a) NO_2^- ($K_b = 1.4 \times 10^{-11}$), nitrite ion
(b) CHO_2^- ($K_b = 5.6 \times 10^{-11}$), formate ion

•9.39 What are the pK_b and K_b values for the conjugate bases of the acids in Practice Exercise 9.37?

9.40 What are the pK_a and K_a values for the conjugate acids of the bases given in Practice Exercise 9.38?

•9.41 Acid X has a pK_a of 6.45 and acid Y has a pK_a of 4.72. Which is the stronger acid? Which has the stronger conjugate base?

9.42 Base M has a pK_b of 4.33 and base N has a pK_b of 7.66. Which is the stronger base? Which has the weaker conjugate acid?

Buffers

9.43 In the study of the molecular basis of life, why is the study of buffers important?

9.44 What is acidosis?

9.45 What is alkalosis?

9.46 In very general terms, why are both acidosis and alkalosis serious?

9.47 Following surgery, a patient experienced persistent vomiting and the pH of his blood became 7.56. (Normally it is 7.35.) Has the blood become more alkaline or more acidic? Is the patient experiencing acidosis or alkalosis?

9.48 A patient brought to the emergency room following an overdose of aspirin was found to have a pH of 7.20 for the blood. (Normally the pH of blood is 7.35.) Has the blood become more acidic or more basic? Is the condition acidosis or alkalosis?

9.49 A patient entered the emergency room of a hospital after three weeks on a self-prescribed low-carbohydrate, high-fat diet and the regular use of the diuretic, acetazolamide. (A diuretic promotes the formation of urine and thus causes the loss of body fluid.) The pOH of the patient's blood was 6.80. What was the pH, and was the condition acidosis or alkalosis?

9.50 What does it mean when we say that a solution of pH 7.40 is *buffered* at this pH?

9.51 What chemical species constitute the chief buffer inside cells?

9.52 Write the equation that shows how the phosphate buffer neutralizes OH^-.

9.53 How does the phosphate buffer neutralize acid? Write the equation.

9.54 What two chemical species make up the chief buffer in blood?

9.55 Write the equations that show how the chief buffer system in the blood works to neutralize hydroxide ion and hydrogen ion.

9.56 Explain in your own words, using equations as needed, how the loss of a molecule of CO_2 at the lungs permanently neutralizes a hydrogen ion.

9.57 What is meant by *ventilation* in connection with respiration? What is hyperventilation? Hypoventilation?

9.58 What does the respiratory center in the brain instruct the lungs to do when the level of CO_2 in blood rises? Why?

9.59 Why does the hypoventilation of someone with emphysema lead to acidosis?

9.60 In high-altitude sickness, the patient *involuntarily* overbreathes, and expels CO_2 from the body at a faster than normal rate. This results in an *increase* in the pH of the blood.
(a) Is this condition alkalosis or acidosis?

(b) Why should excessive loss of CO_2 result in an increase in the pH of the blood? (*Note:* Such a patient should be returned to lower elevations as soon as possible. It helps to rebreathe one's own air, as by breathing into a paper sack, because this helps the system retain CO_2.)

9.61 A patient with emphysema *involuntarily* hypoventilates. (In other words, the respiratory system is not working properly.) This leads to a decrease in the pH of the blood.

(a) Is this alkalosis or acidosis?

(b) Why should hypoventilation under these circumstances cause a decrease in the pH of the blood?

Buffer Calculations

9.62 When we use the defining equation for K_a, the concentrations in brackets refer to what condition, to the initial quantities of solutes used to prepare the solution or to the concentrations after equilibrium has been established?

9.63 Why is it, in using the defining equation for pK_a in working buffer problems, we can substitute initial concentrations of acid and conjugate base for equilibrium concentrations?

*9.64 Calculate the pH of a buffer solution consisting of $0.18\ M$ acetic acid and $0.22\ M$ sodium acetate.

9.65 What is the pH of a buffer solution made to be $0.15\ M$ in dihydrogen phosphate ion and $0.13\ M$ in its conjugate base, the monohydrogen phosphate ion?

*9.66 A 500-mL supply of a buffer solution is made of a weak acid, HA ($K_a = 5.0 \times 10^{-6}$) and its conjugate base, A^-, so that the solution contained 0.12 mol of the weak acid and 0.10 mol of the base.

(a) Calculate the pH of this solution.

(b) Calculate the pH of the solution after the addition of 0.020 mol of strong, monoprotic acid.

(c) Calculate the pH of a different sample of the original solution after the addition of 0.020 mol of NaOH.

(d) Calculate the pH that 500 mL of water would have had in parts (b) and (c) had no buffer been present.

9.67 Why is it better to use $[CO_2(aq)]$ instead of $[H_2CO_3(aq)]$ in the Henderson–Hasselbalch equation for the carbonate buffer in blood?

9.68 What is the apparent pK_a of the weak-acid component of the carbonate buffer in blood?

9.69 Under normal pH conditions in human arterial blood, what values are usually assigned to the following? Be sure to include the correct units.

(a) $[HCO_3^-]$ (b) $[CO_2]$

*9.70 Suppose that normal human arterial blood is suddenly made to accept 12 mmol of HCl(*aq*) per liter of blood.

(a) What is the resulting pH of the blood if no CO_2 is allowed to escape?

(b) What is the resulting pH of the blood if 12 mmol/L of CO_2 can be quickly exhaled by normal processes?

(c) What additional event will happen quickly to help bring the pH up still farther toward normal?

(d) How does the body normally replace HCO_3^- lost by a battle with developing acidosis?

Acid–Base Titrations[4]

9.71 What does it mean to have a *standard* solution of, say, HCl(*aq*)?

9.72 When doing a titration, how does one know when the end point is reached?

9.73 What steps does an analyst take to ensure that the end point and the equivalence point in an acid–base titration occur together?

9.74 Give an example of a titration in which the equivalence point has a pH that is equal to 7. (Give a specific example of an acid and a base that, when titrated together, produce such a solution.)

9.75 Give a specific example of an acid and a base that, when titrated together, produce a solution with a pH greater than 7.

9.76 At the equivalence point in a titration the pH is less than 7. Give a specific example of an acid and a base that, when titrated together, would produce this result.

9.77 Individual aqueous solutions were prepared that contained the following substances. Calculate the molarity of each solution.

(a) 7.292 g of HCl in 500.0 mL of solution

(b) 16.18 g of HBr in 500.0 mL of solution

9.78 What is the molarity of each of the following solutions?

(a) 25.58 g of HI in 500.0 mL of solution

(b) 9.808 g of H_2SO_4 in 500.0 mL of solution

*9.79 If 20.00 g of a monoprotic acid in 100.0 mL of solution gives a concentration of $0.5000\ M$, what is the formula weight of the acid?

9.80 A solution with a concentration of $0.2500\ M$ could be made by dissolving 4.000 g of a base in 250.0 mL of solution. What is the formula weight of this base?

*9.81 How many grams of each solute are needed to prepare the following solutions?

(a) 1000 mL of $0.2500\ M$ HCl

(b) 750.0 mL of $0.1150\ M$ HNO_3

(c) 500.0 mL of $0.01500\ M$ H_2SO_4

9.82 To prepare each of the following solutions would require how many grams of the solute in each case?

(a) 100.0 mL of $0.1000\ M$ HBr

(b) 250.0 mL of $0.1000\ M$ H_2SO_4

(c) 500.0 mL of $1.250\ M$ Na_2CO_3

*9.83 For standardizing a sodium carbonate solution, 21.45 mL of this solution was titrated to the end point with 18.78 mL of $0.1018\ M$ HCl.

(a) Calculate the molarity of the sodium carbonate solution.

(b) How many grams of sodium carbonate does it contain per liter?

9.84 A freshly prepared solution of sodium hydroxide was standardized with $0.1148\ M$ H_2SO_4.

(a) If 18.32 mL of the base was neutralized by 20.22 mL of the acid, what was the molarity of the base?

---

[4] For all the calculations in Review Exercises that follow, round atomic weights to their *second* decimal places before adding them to find formula weights.

(b) How many grams of NaOH were in each liter of this solution?

Finding K_a from pH (Special Topic 9.1)

9.85 The pH of 0.10 M chloroacetic acid, $HC_2H_2ClO_2$ is 1.96. Calculate the K_a and the pK_a of this acid.

9.86 At 60 °C, the pH of 0.010 butyric acid is 2.98. What are the K_a and pK_a of this acid at this temperature?

Finding the pH of a Solution of a Weak Acid (Special Topic 9.2)

9.87 Calculate the pH of a 0.030 M solution of *para*-amino benzoic acid (PABA) at 25 °C. Its pK_a is 4.92 (25 °C). (Use the symbol H-*Paba* for the acid.) PABA is used in powerful sunscreening ointments.

9.88 Calculate the pH of a 0.20 M solution of HF at 25 °C. Its K_a is 6.8×10^{-4} at this temperature.

CHAPTER TEN

Oxidation – Reduction Equilibria

Redox reactions in batteries send electrical currents through circuits to operate laptop computers anywhere that people can go. We'll learn in this chapter more about how such currents can be produced chemically.

10.1 OXIDATION NUMBERS

A redox reaction is one in which oxidation numbers change.

■ In metabolic oxidations, electrons are passed along a series of enzymes with Fe^{2+}/Fe^{3+} systems to an enzyme with the Cu^+/Cu^{2+} system, which is able to transfer the electrons to O_2. The final event is $4H^+ + O_2 + 4e^- \rightarrow 2H_2O$.

At the molecular level of life, redox reactions are at the heart of an organism's use of oxygen. In redox reactions, oxidation numbers change, and electrons transfer. In acid–base reactions, protons transfer. Thus the transfer of two of nature's tiniest particles, the electron and proton, dominate two of the most important kinds of chemical events in nature: acid–base and redox reactions.

Just as in acid–base chemistry, so in redox chemistry, chemical equilibria abound with products favored over reactants to a widely varying degree. In this chapter our major goal will be to learn how to assess the potential for a chemical species to stay in its reduced state, and how these relative potentials enable us to predict how much a redox equilibrium will favor the products. This study can help us to appreciate better what drives biological oxidations when we take up this topic in our study of metabolism.

Because we define **redox reactions** as those in which oxidation numbers change, let's first review and extend our knowledge of how to assign these numbers, a skill begun in Section 4.2.

■ Values of electronegativities are found on page 98.

Oxidation Numbers Are the Charges Atoms in a Compound Would Have If the Electrons of Each Bond Belonged to the More Electronegative Atoms The Lewis structure of a molecule of hydrogen fluoride is $H \overset{\times}{\underset{\cdot\cdot}{\overset{\cdot\cdot}{F}}}\cdot$, with the dots designating the outer-shell electrons of F (seven in all, because F is in group VIIA). One of these electrons has been shared with an electron from H, shown by the lone ×. If both shared electrons were given entirely to the more electronegative atom, F, the charge on F would be $1-$ and the charge on H would be $1+$.

■ All monatomic ions, recall, have oxidation numbers numerically equal to their ionic charges.

This is roughly how **oxidation numbers** are assigned. They're determined by the charge that results when both of the shared pair of electrons in each bond are given to the more electronegative atom. They are assigned as though every compound were made entirely of ions, which obviously isn't true. Thus oxidation numbers do not necessarily correspond to real electrical charges, although sometimes they do, as we learned in Section 4.2. Oxidation numbers are assigned by using a set of rules. There aren't many, they are logical, and they let us assign oxidation numbers without having to remember a large number of electronegativities.

To distinguish an oxidation number from a real charge, we will reverse the number and the charge sign. For example, the charge on the sodium ion is written as $1+$, but its oxidation number is given as $+1$.

The rules for assigning oxidation numbers are as follows.

1. Atoms of any element not combined with atoms from another element have oxidation numbers of zero.
   Examples: The oxidation numbers of the atoms in N_2, Br_2, Cl_2, P_4, and S_8 are zero.

2. The oxidation numbers of monatomic ions equal their ionic charge.
   Examples: The oxidation numbers of Na^+ and K^+ are $+1$, of Ca^{2+}, Cu^{2+}, and Mg^{2+} are $+2$, and of Cl^- and Br^- are -1.

3. *In their compounds,* the oxidation number of any atom of the
   —group IA elements is $+1$ (e.g., Na^+, K^+).
   —group IIA elements is $+2$ (e.g., Ca^{2+}, Mg^{2+}).
   The oxidation number of aluminum (group IIIA) is $+3$.

4. The oxidation number of any nonmetal *in its binary compounds with metals* equals the charge of the monatomic anion.
   Example: The oxidation number of Br in $CrBr_3$ is -1 because the monatomic ion of Br is the bromide ion, which has a charge of $1-$.

5. In compounds, the oxidation number of

    O is almost always -2.   (Exceptions occur only when the rules for H or F would be violated.)

    H is almost always $+1$.   (The exceptions are binary compounds with metals, like NaH, in which the H has the oxidation number -1.)

    F is always -1.   (No exceptions. Fluorine is the most electronegative of all elements.)

■ The oxidation number of O in OF_2 is $+2$, not -2. The oxidation number of H in NaH, KH, or CaH_2 is -1, not $+1$.

6. The sum of the oxidation numbers of all the atoms in the formula of the atom, ion, or molecule must equal the overall charge given for the formula—the *sum rule*.

Now let's work some examples to show how the oxidation numbers of the atoms in some molecules or polyatomic ions can be assigned.

EXAMPLE 10.1   ASSIGNING OXIDATION NUMBERS

■ Calomel has been used as a laxative, but if it's contaminated by $HgCl_2$ it contains a dangerous poison.

Problem: Calomel, long used in medicine, has the formula Hg_2Cl_2. What are the oxidation numbers of the atoms in this compound?

Solution: This is a binary compound of a nonmetal with a metal. The oxidation number of Cl must be -1 (rule 4). The sum rule, rule 6, tells us that the sum of oxidation numbers must be zero. Let x be the oxidation number of Hg.

For Hg_2Cl_2:   Cl   2 atoms $\times (-1) = -2$

                                Hg 2 atoms $\times (x)\quad = \quad 2x$

                                                sum $= \quad 0$

The value of x comes from the sum, $2x + (-2) = 0$

$$2x = +2$$
$$x = +1$$

The oxidation number of Hg in Hg_2Cl_2 is $+1$.

EXAMPLE 10.2   ASSIGNING OXIDATION NUMBERS

Problem: What is the oxidation number of carbon in ethane, C_2H_6?

Solution: Both carbon and hydrogen are nonmetals. Of the two, we assign a number, $+1$, to hydrogen first because of rule 5. Letting x be the oxidation number of carbon, we have

For C_2H_6:   H   6 atoms $\times (+1) = +6$

                                C   2 atoms $\times (x)\quad = \quad 2x$

                                           sum $= \quad 0$

So $2x + 6 = 0$

$$2x = -6$$
$$x = -3$$

The oxidation number of C in C_2H_6 is -3.

EXAMPLE 10.3   ASSIGNING OXIDATION NUMBERS

Problem: What are the oxidation numbers of the atoms in the nitrate ion, NO_3^-?

Solution: Of the two nonmetals, N and O, O takes priority because it always has a oxidation number of -2 (except where this would cause violations of the rules for H and F—rule 5).

We note that we have a charged ion, so the sum of oxidation numbers must equal this charge, -1. Letting x equal the oxidation number of N, we have

For $\qquad NO_3^-:$ $\quad$ O $\quad$ 3 atoms $\times (-2) = -6$
$\qquad\qquad\qquad\qquad$ N $\quad$ 1 atm $\times (x) \qquad = \quad x$
$\qquad\qquad\qquad\qquad\qquad\qquad\qquad\qquad$ sum $= -1$

So $\qquad\qquad\qquad\qquad\qquad\qquad x + (-6) = -1$
$\qquad\qquad\qquad\qquad\qquad\qquad\qquad\qquad x = +5$

The oxidation number of N in NO_3^- is $+5$.

■ The $+5$ state is the highest oxidation state of nitrogen, and it makes NO_3^- a good oxidizing agent, particularly in acid.

PRACTICE EXERCISE 1 $\qquad$ Assign the oxidation numbers to the atoms in the following.

(a) H_2S $\quad$ (b) SO_2 $\quad$ (c) H_2SO_3 $\quad$ (d) SO_3 $\quad$ (e) H_2SO_4 $\quad$ (f) SO_4^{2-}

PRACTICE EXERCISE 2 $\qquad$ Assign the oxidation numbers to the atoms in the following.

(a) CH_4 (methane) $\qquad$ (b) CH_3OH (methyl alcohol)
(c) CH_2O (formaldehyde) $\quad$ (d) $HCHO_2$ (formic acid)
(e) H_2CO_3 (carbonic acid)

By Noting Whether Oxidation Numbers Change, One Can Tell Whether a Redox Reaction Has Occurred $\quad$ The series of compounds, (a) through (e) in Practice Exercise 2, can be prepared by a series of redox reactions, each one from the preceding one. If you worked this exercise you found that the oxidation number of carbon steadily becomes more positive in going from methane to carbonic acid. Thus the series represents a steady oxidation because **oxidation** means that an oxidation number becomes more positive or less negative. The opposite, **reduction,** corresponds to an oxidation state becoming less positive or more negative.

PRACTICE EXERCISE 3 $\qquad$ Calculate the oxidation number of carbon in (a) C_2H_2 (acetylene), (b) C_2H_4 (ethylene), and (c) C_2H_6 (ethane). Does the series, from compounds (a) to (c), which can be carried out experimentally, represent oxidation or reduction (or neither)?

10.2 BALANCING REDOX REACTIONS

A redox reaction can be balanced by separately balancing its half-reactions and then adding them.

■ Another method, the "oxidation-number-change" method, is trickier, in the view of many teachers.
■ Electrical balance means that the net charge to the left of the arrow equals the net charge to the right.

The method that we will learn for balancing a redox reaction is called the *ion–electron method*. A redox reaction is viewed as consisting of two parts, called **half-reactions,** one an oxidation and the other a reduction. Each half-reaction is separately balanced, first by atoms (the material balance) and then, using electrons, by net charge (the electrical balance). Only when both half-reactions are balanced in both atoms and charges are they combined to give the final, balanced redox reaction.

$\qquad$ Using the ion–electron method sometimes causes a problem in balancing O or H atoms. However, whenever water is present, as it nearly always is, *molecules* of H_2O can be used either to obtain O atoms or as places to put them. This, of course, worsens the balance of H atoms, because we can't take O from H_2O without getting 2H. We solve this by using H^+ as either a reactant or a product, taking as many H^+ as needed to get them to balance. There is no logical (or chemical) problem in doing this when the medium is (or becomes) acidic. When the medium is basic, the ion–electron method has a way around the problem. But let's first see how to balance a redox reaction when the solution is acidic. Then we can build on that for situations in which the medium is basic.

We will first simply list the steps to balance a redox reaction in an acidic (or neutral) medium, and then go back and illustrate each one. The steps must be taken in the order given.

Balancing Redox Reactions by the Ion–Electron Method

1. Write a skeletal equation that shows only the ions or molecules involved in the reaction.

2. Divide the skeletal equation into two half-reactions.

3. Balance all atoms that are not H or O.

4. Balance O by adding H_2O.

5. Balance H by adding H^+ (not H or H_2 or H^-, but H^+).

6. Balance the net charge by adding e^-. (Remember its minus sign.)

7. Multiply entire half-reactions by simple whole numbers, as needed, to get the gain of e^- in one half-reaction to match the loss of e^- in the other. Then add the half-reactions.

8. Cancel whatever is the same on both sides of the arrow.

Now let's see how to apply these rules in balancing the equation for the oxidation of methyl alcohol, CH_3OH, to formic acid, $HCHO_2$, using the dichromate ion, $Cr_2O_7{}^{2-}$ in an acidic medium. As this reaction proceeds, the chromium in $Cr_2O_7{}^{2-}$ changes to Cr^{3+}.

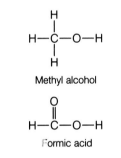

Methyl alcohol

Formic acid

$Cr_2O_7{}^{2-}$

Dichromate ion

Step 1. *Write a skeletal equation showing reactants and products as given.*

$$CH_3OH + Cr_2O_7{}^{2-} \longrightarrow HCHO_2 + Cr^{3+}$$

Step 2. *Divide the skeletal equation into two half-reactions.* Except for H and O, the same elements *must* appear on both sides of each half-reaction.

$$CH_3OH \longrightarrow HCHO_2$$
$$Cr_2O_7{}^{2-} \longrightarrow Cr^{3+}$$

Step 3. *Balance all atoms that are not H or O.*

$$CH_3OH \longrightarrow HCHO_2 \qquad \text{(No change, yet.)}$$
$$Cr_2O_7{}^{2-} \longrightarrow 2Cr^{3+} \qquad \text{(Balances Cr atoms.)}$$

Step 4. *Balance O by adding H_2O.*

$$CH_3OH + H_2O \longrightarrow HCHO_2 \qquad \text{(Cs and Os balance.)}$$
$$Cr_2O_7{}^{2-} \longrightarrow 2Cr^{3+} + 7H_2O \qquad \text{(Crs and Os balance.)}$$

Step 5. *Balance H by adding H^+.*

$$CH_3OH + H_2O \longrightarrow HCHO_2 + 4H^+ \qquad \text{(All atoms now balance.)}$$
$$Cr_2O_7{}^{2-} + 14H^+ \longrightarrow 2Cr^{3+} + 7H_2O \qquad \text{(All atoms now balance.)}$$

Step 6. *Balance the net charge by adding e^-.* The first half-reaction after Step 5 has 0 charge on the left and $+4$ on the right, so we have to add $4e^-$ to the right side to get electrical balance. The second half-reaction has a net of $+12$ on the left side $[(-2) + (+14)]$ and $+6$ on the right $[2 \times (+3)]$. There is a net excess of $+6$ charge on the left. We therefore have to add $6e^-$ to the left side to make the net charge on the left side of the arrow equal to the net charge on the right side. Our half-reactions are now fully balanced.

$$CH_3OH + H_2O \longrightarrow HCHO_2 + 4H^+ + 4e^-$$
$$Cr_2O_7{}^{2-} + 14H^+ + 6e^- \longrightarrow 2Cr^{3+} + 7H_2O$$

Step 7. *Multiply half-reactions by whole numbers so that the electrons will cancel when the half-reactions are added.* If we multiply every item in the first half-reaction by 3 and the second by 2, we will be able to cancel the electrons when we add the half-reactions.

■ The physical states, for example, (aq), are not included until the last step to reduce clutter, but remember that you can't cancel species that are not in the same state.

$$3 \times [CH_3OH + H_2O \longrightarrow HCHO_2 + 4H^+ + 4e^-]$$
$$2 \times [Cr_2O_7^{2-} + 14H^+ + 6e^- \longrightarrow 2Cr^{3+} + 7H_2O]$$

Sum: $3CH_3OH + 2Cr_2O_7^{2-} + 3H_2O + 28H^+ + 12e^- \longrightarrow$
$$3HCHO_2 + 4Cr^{3+} + 12H^+ + 14H_2O + 12e^-$$

Step 8. *Cancel everything that can be canceled.* The 12 electrons on each side obviously cancel. But we can also get rid of some water molecules. There are 3 on the left and 14 on the right, so we can strike those on the left and change those on the right to 11. Thus

$$\cdots + 3H_2O + \cdots \longrightarrow \cdots + 14H_2O + \cdots$$

becomes

$$\cdots \longrightarrow \cdots + 11H_2O + \cdots$$

We can also cancel some H^+.

$$\cdots + 28H^+ \cdots \longrightarrow \cdots + 12H^+ \cdots$$

becomes

$$\cdots + 16H^+ \cdots \longrightarrow \cdots$$

This leaves, putting in the physical states,

$$3CH_3OH(aq) + 2Cr_2O_7^{2-}(aq) + 16H^+(aq) \longrightarrow$$
$$3HCHO_2(aq) + 4Cr^{3+}(aq) + 11H_2O$$

Check to see that both material and electrical balance exist.

PRACTICE EXERCISE 4   Balance the following equation, which occurs in an acidic medium.

$$Cu(s) + NO_3^-(aq) \longrightarrow Cu^{2+}(aq) + NO_2(g)$$

To Balance a Redox Equation When the Medium Is Basic, First Balance It for an Acid Medium and Then Neutralize the Acid   We really should not employ H^+ to balance H atoms when the medium is basic, but it turns out to be much simpler if we begin this way. Then, after all the steps have been done, we neutralize the H^+ by adding enough OH^- to *both sides of the equation* to neutralize any H^+. Acid–base neutralization is not a redox process, so this approach does not upset any redox balance.

If, for example, you had been asked to balance the following equation for the reaction carried out in base.

$$MnO_4^-(aq) + SO_3^{2-}(aq) \longrightarrow MnO_2(s) + SO_4^{2-}(aq)$$

you would have obtained the following by using Steps 1 through 8 for acidic solutions (omitting physical states for the moment).

$$2MnO_4^- + 3SO_3^{2-} + 2H^+ \longrightarrow 2MnO_2 + 3SO_4^{2-} + H_2O$$

Step 9. *Add as many OH^- as there are H^+ to both sides of the equation.* There are $2H^+$ on the left so we add $2OH^-$ to both sides. (It must be done to both sides so that we do not upset either the material or the electrical balance.)

$$2OH^- + 2MnO_4^- + 3SO_3^{2-} + 2H^+ \longrightarrow 2MnO_2 + 3SO_4^{2-} + H_2O + 2OH^-$$

■ As this oxidation proceeds, the purple color of $MnO_4^-(aq)$ disappears and a brown, mud-like precipitate of $MnO_2(s)$ appears.

Step 10. *When they occur on the same side of the arrow, combine H^+ and OH^- into H_2O.* On the left side we have $2OH^-$ and $2H^+$, so we combine them into $2H_2O$.

$$2H_2O + 2MnO_4^- + 3SO_3^{2-} \longrightarrow 2MnO_2 + 3SO_4^{2-} + H_2O + 2OH^-$$

Step 11. *Cancel H₂O molecules as possible.* We can cancel one H₂O molecule from each side, which leaves the final equation, with all physical states again in place, as

$$H_2O + 2MnO_4^-(aq) + 3SO_3^{2-}(aq) \longrightarrow 2MnO_2(s) + 3SO_4^{2-}(aq) + 2OH^-(aq)$$

PRACTICE EXERCISE 5

Ethyl alcohol

Balance the following equation for the oxidation of ethyl alcohol to the acetate ion by the permanganate ion in base.

$$C_2H_6O(aq) + MnO_4^-(aq) \longrightarrow C_2H_3O_2^-(aq) + MnO_2(s)$$

Notice that the half-reactions we produced in the preceding discussion clearly showed which part of the redox reaction represented an electron loss and so an oxidation and which was an electron gain and so a reduction.

Half-reactions written as reductions, those in which electrons appear as reactants, can be assigned numbers whose signs and magnitudes measure the potential for the reaction to occur. We'll study this in the next section.

10.3 REDUCTION POTENTIALS

The more positive (or less negative) the reduction potential of a half-reaction, the greater its tendency to operate as a reduction.

As we saw in the previous chapter, every weak acid can donate H^+ but each has its own potential for doing so, and we used K_a values to compare these potentials. Redox reactions also involve the donation of something, electrons, but these are not *chemical* species like H^+ that can be described by an equilibrium concentration. Yet, like acid–base equilibria, redox equilibria have varying potentials for going to completion. So it would be nice to have a table of numbers, like the K_a values of weak acids, that indicate this potential. The dilemma is that no term like [electrons], the molar concentration of electrons, can appear in any equilibrium law. The one "species" common to all redox equilibria, electrons, cannot be measured as we can measure $[H^+]$.

Half-Reactions, Written as Reductions, Have Different Potentials for Proceeding To solve the dilemma just described, we use a feature of redox equilibria that we have already found useful, the half-reaction. Every redox reaction has two. Each involves electrons either as a reactant or as a product. It should be possible, therefore, to assign a number to each half-reaction that describes its relative potential to manage electrons. Then we could make a table of half-reactions, each with its own number (potential), and thereby know the relative potentials of all half-reactions to proceed to completion.

This strategy is a bit tricky, because we cannot run a half-reaction by itself. We cannot, therefore, *directly* measure anything that we could call a "potential for going to completion" for any half-reaction. To get around the problem, we pick one particular half-reaction to be the standard of comparison. Its potential for proceeding is arbitrarily assigned a value of zero. *The potentials of all other half-reactions are then made relative to this reference half-reaction.* We will not be able to study the experimental details of how to get these data, but let's see how the results work out.

To make comparisons as easy as possible when we finally construct a table, we write all half-reactions in the same pattern, just as we wrote acid equilibria in the same pattern. This pattern shows electrons as *reactants* in the *forward* reaction. Thus the forward reactions in the table will all be reductions. Each such half-reaction has a **reduction potential,** the potential, relative to the reference, for one of its chemical species to be reduced. A *high* reduction potential will thus mean a half-reaction with some chemical that readily consumes electrons, because it is prone to being reduced. A half-reaction like this will have one of the more *positive* numbers in the table. Half-reactions with chemicals that easily give up electrons (because they are easily oxidized) will have low reduction potentials and the more negative numbers in the table.

■ We can always write a reduction half-reaction in reverse when we want an oxidation half-reaction.

The reference half-reaction against which all others are rated is the following equilibrium:

$$2H^+(aq) + 2e^- \rightleftharpoons H_2(g) \tag{10.1}$$

Notice that it conforms to the pattern; the forward reaction is a reduction and electrons are shown as *reactants*. When the solution is *exactly* 1 *M* in H^+, the temperature is 25 °C, and the pressure of the H_2 is *exactly* 1 atm, the reduction potential for equilibrium 10.1 is *defined* as 0.00 volt. Any reduction potential that corresponds to these arbitrary but standard conditions — concentrations of all chemical species of 1 *M*, a temperature of 25 °C, and pressures of any gaseous species at 1 atm — is called a **standard reduction potential.**

As we indicated, the unit for a reduction potential is the **volt,** V, the SI unit for electrical potential. The symbol for reduction potential is *E* except when it refers to a standard reduction potential, when $E°$ is used. The volt is to the flow of electrons in a conductor roughly what pressure is to the flow of water in a conduit. We can think of the volt as the force that pushes an electrical current through a wire. This force, to distinguish it from other forces, is called the *electromotive force,* or the *emf* of the electrical system.

■ Notice that Au^{3+}, the gold(III) cation, has the most powerful tendency of all metals to stay in its reduced form, Au.

Table 10.1 gives the standard reduction potentials for *several* common half-reactions. Those with positive $E°$ values all have greater tendencies to run as reductions than does the reference $2H^+/H_2$ half-reaction. We already know, for example, that Cl_2, has a strong tendency to change to Cl^- ions, which is a reduction. The half-reaction is

$$Cl_2(g) + 2e^- \rightleftharpoons 2Cl^-(aq) \qquad E° = +1.36 \text{ V}$$

TABLE 10.1 Standard Reduction Potentials (at 25 °C)

Half-Reaction	$E°$(volts)
$F_2(g) + 2e^- \rightleftharpoons 2F^-(aq)$	+2.87
$PbO_2(s) + SO_4^{2-}(aq) + 4H^+(aq) + 2e^- \rightleftharpoons PbSO_4(s) + 2H_2O$	+1.69
$MnO_4^-(aq) + 8H^+(aq) + 5e^- \rightleftharpoons Mn^{2+}(aq) + 4H_2O$	+1.49
$PbO_2(s) + 4H^+(aq) + 2e^- \rightleftharpoons Pb^{2+}(aq) + 2H_2O$	+1.46
$Au^{3+}(aq) + 3e^- \rightleftharpoons Au(s)$	+1.42
$Cl_2(g) + 2e^- \rightleftharpoons 2Cl^-(aq)$	+1.36
$O_2(g) + 4H^+(aq) + 4e^- \rightleftharpoons 2H_2O$	+1.23
$Br_2(aq) + 2e^- \rightleftharpoons 2Br^-(aq)$	+1.07
$NO_3^-(aq) + 4H^+(aq) + 3e^- \rightleftharpoons NO(g) + 2H_2O$	+0.96
$Ag^+(aq) + e^- \rightleftharpoons Ag(s)$	+0.80
$Fe^{3+}(aq) + e^- \rightleftharpoons Fe^{2+}(aq)$	+0.77
$I_2(s) + 2e^- \rightleftharpoons 2I^-(aq)$	+0.54
$Cu^{2+}(aq) + 2e^- \rightleftharpoons Cu(s)$	+0.34
$SO_4^{2-}(aq) + 4H^+(aq) + 2e^- \rightleftharpoons H_2SO_3(aq) + H_2O$	+0.17
$2H^+(aq) + 2e^- \rightleftharpoons H_2(g)$	0.00
$Pb^{2+}(aq) + 2e^- \rightleftharpoons Pb(s)$	−0.13
$Sn^{2+}(aq) + 2e^- \rightleftharpoons Sn(s)$	−0.14
$Ni^{2+}(aq) + 2e^- \rightleftharpoons Ni(s)$	−0.25
$Co^{2+}(aq) + 2e^- \rightleftharpoons Co(s)$	−0.28
$Cd^{2+}(aq) + 2e^- \rightleftharpoons Cd(s)$	−0.40
$Fe^{2+}(aq) + 2e^- \rightleftharpoons Fe(s)$	−0.44
$Cr^{3+}(aq) + 3e^- \rightleftharpoons Cr(s)$	−0.74
$Zn^{2+}(aq) + 2e^- \rightleftharpoons Zn(s)$	−0.76
$2H_2O + 2e^- \rightleftharpoons H_2(g) + 2OH^-(aq)$	−0.83
$Al^{3+}(aq) + 3e^- \rightleftharpoons Al(s)$	−1.66
$Mg^{2+}(aq) + 2e^- \rightleftharpoons Mg(s)$	−2.37
$Na^+(aq) + e^- \rightleftharpoons Na(s)$	−2.71
$Ca^{2+}(aq) + 2e^- \rightleftharpoons Ca(s)$	−2.76
$K^+(aq) + e^- \rightleftharpoons K(s)$	−2.92
$Li^+(aq) + e^- \rightleftharpoons Li(s)$	−3.05

For this half-reaction, $E° = +1.36$ V. Fluorine, like chlorine in group VIIA, has an even more powerful tendency to change to its negative ion, F^-, and be reduced.

$$F_2(g) + 2e^- \rightleftharpoons 2F^-(aq) \qquad E° = +2.87 \text{ V}$$

We know this from chemical knowledge. F_2 is the most reactive of all elements and always gets an oxidation number of -1. It is also the most electronegative element. No wonder, therefore, that the reduction half-reaction for F_2 has the highest, most positive reduction potential of all, $E° = +2.87$ V. Thus the reduction potentials parallel, as they must, our knowledge of which systems are relatively easily reduced.

The half-reactions in Table 10.1 with negative $E°$ values are less able to run as reductions than the $2H^+/H_2$ half-reaction. They are, in fact, more prone to run as oxidations — that is, as the *reverse* of the half-reactions shown in the table. For example, we already know that sodium metal, like all group IA elements, has a powerful tendency to lose electrons — an oxidation — and change to sodium ions. The half-reaction representing this tendency is

$$Na(s) \longrightarrow Na^+(aq) + e^-$$

■ Notice in Table 10.1 how the group IA and IIA elements are clustered at the bottom, which indicates how powerfully they tend to be in their oxidized forms.

This half-reaction is opposite to the way the half-reaction is given in Table 10.1, so the $E°$ value for the one in the table has a negative sign, -2.71 V.

Standard Reduction Potentials Enable Us To Predict Redox Reactions We can now use the tabulated half-reactions to predict whether a given combination, one a reduction as written and one an oxidation and written in reverse, can make up a full redox reaction that proceeds spontaneously. There is a pattern to the way half-reactions cooperate in all spontaneous redox reactions. Let's first summarize it and then show how it works.

> **Rule for Combining Reduction Half-Reactions.**   When two reduction half-reactions are combined into a full redox reaction the one with the more positive $E°$ always runs as written, as a reduction, and it forces the other, with the less positive $E°$, to run in reverse, as an oxidation.

To illustrate, suppose we came for the first time to the question, "Will sodium react with chlorine?" Standard reduction potentials of half-reactions can be used to answer a question like this. Let's take the relevant data from Table 10.1. The product, NaCl, will be shown not as a solid, NaCl(s), but in solution as separated, hydrated ions, because the data are presented this way.

$$Na^+(aq) + e^- \rightleftharpoons Na(s) \qquad E° = -2.71 \text{ V}$$
$$Cl_2(g) + 2e^- \rightleftharpoons 2Cl^-(aq) \qquad E° = +1.36 \text{ V}$$

The $E°$ for the reaction of chlorine is more positive than the $E°$ for the reaction of sodium. This tells us that the reaction involving chlorine will proceed as written, as a reduction, and that the reaction involving sodium is forced to proceed in the opposite direction, as an oxidation. So let's rewrite the two half-reactions to reflect these facts. We have to reverse the reaction for sodium. (We will now use only a forward arrow. We have already learned how powerfully this reaction proceeds.)

$$Na(s) \longrightarrow Na^+(aq) + e^- \qquad \text{(oxidation)}$$
$$Cl_2(g) + 2e^- \longrightarrow 2Cl^-(aq) \qquad \text{(reduction)}$$

To get the net reaction, we multiply the coefficients of the first half-reaction by 2. Then the electrons can cancel as we add the two.

$$2Na(s) \longrightarrow 2Na^+(aq) + 2e^-$$
$$\underline{Cl_2(g) + 2e^- \longrightarrow 2Cl^-(aq)}$$
$$\text{Sum:} \quad 2Na(s) + Cl_2(g) \longrightarrow 2Na^+(aq) + 2Cl^-(aq)$$

Thus sodium and chlorine spontaneously react but sodium ions and chloride ions do not.

Before we turn to a less obvious example, we must issue a caution. Just because we can prepare a redox reaction, like this one, with a powerful tendency to take place doesn't mean that we can go into the lab and set up the reaction exactly as the equation is written. If we tried to mix sodium and chlorine so as to get *aqueous* sodium ions and chloride ions *directly,* we'd be in great trouble. We have already learned that sodium reacts powerfully with water, too, to give hydrogen and NaOH,

$$2Na(s) + 2H_2O \longrightarrow H_2(g) + 2NaOH(aq)$$

The earlier reaction of sodium with chlorine to give *aqueous* sodium and chloride ions would require two experimental steps. The first would let sodium and chlorine react in the absence of water to give crystalline NaCl. Then this would be dissolved in water. Thus, although the data in Table 10.1 can be used to indicate how powerful the driving force for a postulated redox reaction might be, we have to think about water itself as a possible reactant before we try the reaction.

Now let's study another illustration of the use of reduction potentials to predict a redox reaction.

EXAMPLE 10.4   **PREDICTING SPONTANEOUS REDOX REACTIONS**

Problem: If both Cl_2 and I_2 are present in a solution that contains Cl^- and I^- ions, what spontaneous reaction will occur? (The chlorine would have to be bubbled into the solution.)

Solution: We notice that the conditions provide both the oxidized and reduced forms of chlorine and of iodine. This tells us we have a redox situation. There are two possible half-reactions (and both are in Table 10.1.).

$$Cl_2(g) + 2e^- \rightleftharpoons 2Cl^-(aq) \qquad E° = +1.36 \text{ V}$$
$$I_2(s) + 2e^- \rightleftharpoons 2I^-(aq) \qquad E° = +0.54 \text{ V}$$

Thus the $Cl_2/2Cl^-$ system has the more positive reduction potential than the $I_2/2I^-$ system. This tells us that the $Cl_2/2Cl^-$ system must run as a reduction, which forces the $I_2/2I^-$ system to run in reverse, as an oxidation. When a reaction occurs in the mixture, the half-reactions will be

$$Cl_2(g) + 2e^- \longrightarrow 2Cl^-(aq) \qquad \text{(reduction)}$$
$$2I^-(aq) \longrightarrow I_2(s) + 2e^- \qquad \text{(oxidation)}$$

The net redox reaction, therefore, is

$$Cl_2(g) + 2I^-(aq) \longrightarrow 2Cl^-(aq) + I_2(s) \qquad \text{(net reaction)}$$

This reaction is actually one method for preparing iodine. Chlorine gas is bubbled through a solution of sodium iodide, where it reacts by the equation we just figured out. The reverse reaction, which can be attempted by mixing iodine with aqueous sodium chloride, does not happen. Chlorine can oxidize iodide ion to iodine, but iodine cannot oxidize chloride ion to chlorine.

EXAMPLE 10.5   **PREDICTING SPONTANEOUS REDOX REACTIONS**

Problem: Predict what will happen if both lead and silver are placed in contact with a solution that contains both Cu^{2+} and Ag^+ ions.

Solution: If anything happens, it will be a redox reaction because we are obviously seeing these two elements in two different oxidation states. So we can go to Table 10.1 for help. The relevant half-reactions from the table are

Figure 10.1
The redox reaction of copper with silver ion to give copper ion and silver metal. A coil of copper is ready to be put into a solution of silver nitrate, a source of $Ag^+(aq)$ — first frame. Crystals of silver metal begin to deposit on the coil — second frame — and the solution starts to turn blue because of the $Cu^{2+}(aq)$ ions that form. In the last frame, the deposit of silver is heavy and the solution has become quite blue.

$$Cu^{2+}(aq) + 2e^- \rightleftharpoons Cu(s) \qquad E° = +0.34 \text{ V}$$
$$Ag^+(aq) + e^- \rightleftharpoons Ag(s) \qquad E° = +0.80 \text{ V}$$

The Ag^+/Ag system has the more positive reduction potential, so it will run as written, as a reduction. It will force the Cu^{2+}/Cu system to run in reverse, as an oxidation. Of course, to balance the two (to cancel the electrons) we have to multiply the Ag^+/Ag half-reaction by 2. When the redox reaction occurs, the two half-reactions will be

$$2Ag^+(aq) + 2e^- \longrightarrow 2Ag(s) \qquad \text{(reduction)}$$
$$\underline{Cu(s) \longrightarrow Cu^{2+}(aq) + 2e^-} \qquad \text{(oxidation)}$$
$$2Ag^+(aq) + Cu(s) \longrightarrow 2Ag(s) + Cu^{2+}(aq) \qquad \text{(net reaction)}$$

This is a pretty reaction (Figure 10.1). A coil of copper wire metal is immersed into a solution of silver nitrate, and crystals of silver metal begin to deposit on the coil as copper atoms change to ions and go into solution. Given time, the solution acquires the blue color of the newly formed $Cu^{2+}(aq)$ ion.

PRACTICE EXERCISE 6   Using the data in Table 10.1, predict the net ionic equation for what can happen if zinc and iron metal strips are placed in contact with a solution that contains $Fe^{2+}(aq)$ and $Zn^{2+}(aq)$ ions.

Often the question is not "What can happen?" but "Will a given reaction occur as written?" We'll show an example.

EXAMPLE 10.6   **PREDICTING WHETHER A REDOX REACTION IS SPONTANEOUS**

Problem: The following is a balanced equation of a redox reaction between copper metal and nitric acid. But does it occur?

$$3Cu(s) + 8H^+(aq) + 2NO_3^-(aq) \longrightarrow 3Cu^{2+}(aq) + 2NO(g) + 4H_2O$$

■ Depending on the concentration of the nitric acid, either NO or NO_2 forms.

Solution: We must first separate the half-reactions from this equation. Remember that except for H and O, other elements *must* appear on both sides of the arrows in their respective half-reactions. So one half-reaction involves copper, and the other involves nitrogen.

$$Cu(s) \longrightarrow Cu^{2+}(aq) + 2e^- \quad \text{(an oxidation)}$$
$$NO_3^-(aq) + 4H^+(aq) + 3e^- \longrightarrow NO(g) + 2H_2O \quad \text{(a reduction)}$$

In Table 10.1, the $E°$ for the reduction half-reaction, which here involves NO_3^-, is $+0.96$ V. The oxidation half-reaction, which involves Cu, when reversed and written as a reduction is

$$Cu^{2+}(aq) + 2e^- \longrightarrow Cu(s) \quad \text{(a reduction)}$$

It has a reduction potential of $+0.34$ V. The more positive of the reduction potentials, therefore, is for the NO_3^-/NO system, so its half-reaction must run as a reduction. This is just what it does in the given redox reaction. It forces the Cu^{2+}/Cu system to run as an oxidation, and that is what it actually does in the given redox reaction. So these two half-reactions proceed as they must when put together.

The given redox reaction does, in fact, occur. Copper metal dissolves in nitric acid. The oxidizing agent provided by nitric acid is the nitrate ion, not the hydrogen ion.

PRACTICE EXERCISE 7

We saw in the previous example that copper metal should dissolve in nitric acid. Will it dissolve in hydrochloric acid? Will the following reaction occur? Since $Cl^-(aq)$ cannot accept electrons from Cu (or anything), we have to suppose that $H^+(aq)$ would.

$$Cu(s) + 2H^+(aq) \longrightarrow Cu^{2+}(aq) + H_2(g)$$

10.4 REDOX EQUILIBRIA

The equilibrium constant for a redox equilibrium can be calculated from the standard reduction potentials of its half-reactions.

In the previous section we learned that the half-reaction with the more positive reduction potential in a redox system forces the other half-reaction to run as an oxidation. Our task in this section is to use the standard reduction potentials to calculate a number that can be related to an equilibrium constant for a redox reaction. When K_{eq} is high, you will recall, the products are strongly favored, which is another way of saying that the forward reaction goes well toward completion.

The Spread Between $E°$ for the Substance Reduced and the $E°$ for the Substance Oxidized Is a Measure of the Potential for a Redox Reaction If we can think of a *driving force* for a reaction, it would be some characteristic of the reactants and products that impels the former to change into the latter. With redox reactions, this characteristic might logically reside in the relative potentials for the oxidation and reduction half-reactions to proceed. It would seem logical that the more dissimilar two half-reactions are in their $E°$ values, the greater is the driving force for the redox reaction. Figure 10.2 illustrates what this means. The redox reaction of Figure 10.2a is

■ Another powerful driving force for reactions is to make stronger covalent bonds from weaker bonds.

$$Zn(s) + Cl_2(g) \longrightarrow Zn^{2+}(aq) + 2Cl^-(aq)$$

This is a combination of the following half-reactions

$$Zn(s) \longrightarrow Zn^{2+}(aq) + 2e^- \quad \text{(oxidation)}$$
$$Cl_2(g) + 2e^- \longrightarrow 2Cl^-(aq) \quad \text{(reduction)}$$

To compare these in terms of their reduction potentials, we have to reverse the oxidation half-reaction. Then we have, together with $E°$ values:

$$Zn^{2+}(aq) + 2e^- \rightleftharpoons Zn(s) \qquad E° = -0.76 \text{ V}$$
$$Cl_2(g) + 2e^- \rightleftharpoons 2Cl^-(aq) \qquad E° = +1.36 \text{ V}$$

Obviously, the reduction of Cl_2 to $2Cl^-$ is able to force the other half-reaction to run in reverse;

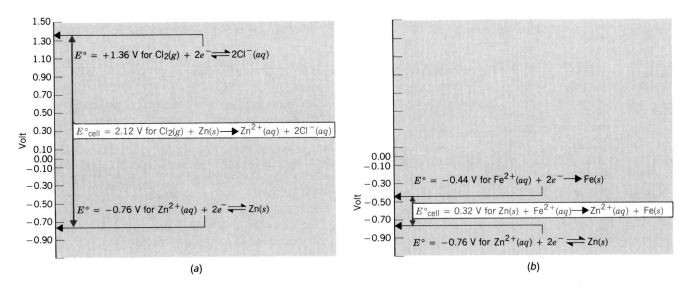

Figure 10.2
Standard cell potentials as the difference between E°_{cell} for the substance reduced and the E°_{cell} for the substance oxidized. (a) For the reaction $Zn(s) + Cl_2(g) \rightarrow Zn^{2+}(aq) + 2Cl^-(aq)$. (b) For the reaction $Zn(s) + Fe^{2+}(aq) \rightarrow Zn^{2+}(aq) + Fe(s)$.

the $Cl_2/2Cl^-$ system has the more positive reduction potential. The spread between the two values of E° is $(+1.36\ V) - (-0.76\ V) = 2.12\ V$, as Figure 10.2a also shows.

Now let's consider a redox reaction with a smaller spread. If we take another reaction of zinc,

$$Zn(s) + Fe^{2+}(aq) \longrightarrow Zn^{2+}(aq) + Fe(s)$$

and break it down into its two half-reactions, we get

$$Zn(s) \longrightarrow Zn^{2+}(aq) + 2e^- \quad \text{(an oxidation)}$$
$$Fe^{2+}(aq) + 2e^- \longrightarrow Fe(s) \quad \text{(a reduction)}$$

For comparisons, and to illustrate the spread in E° values, we rewrite the oxidation as a reduction and, after inserting the E° values, we have

$$Zn^{2+}(aq) + 2e^- \rightleftharpoons Zn(s) \quad E^\circ = -0.76\ V$$
$$Fe^{2+}(aq) + 2e^- \rightleftharpoons Fe(s) \quad E^\circ = -0.44\ V$$

The Fe/Fe^{2+} system has the more positive (less negative) E°, so it runs as the reduction, forcing the Zn/Zn^{2+} system to again run as the oxidation. The spread between the E° values is $(-0.44\ V) - (-0.76\ V) = 0.32\ V$, shown in Figure 10.2b, which is much smaller than the 2.12 V spread when zinc reacts with chlorine.

The "spread" we have been talking about has the technical name of standard cell potential. (Why the word *cell* is used will be explained shortly.) The **standard cell potential, E°_{cell}**, is the magnitude of the difference between the reduction potentials of the two half-cells of a redox reaction. The difference is always taken as follows.

$$E^\circ_{cell} = \begin{pmatrix} \text{standard reduction} \\ \text{potential of} \\ \text{substance reduced} \end{pmatrix} - \begin{pmatrix} \text{standard reduction} \\ \text{potential of} \\ \text{substance oxidized} \end{pmatrix} \quad (10.2)$$

Thus we can rewrite the two redox reactions of Figure 10.2 so as to include their standard cell potentials.

$$\text{Zn}(s) + \text{Cl}_2(g) \longrightarrow \text{Zn}^{2+}(aq) + 2\text{Cl}^-(aq) \qquad E^\circ_{cell} = 2.12 \text{ V}$$
$$\text{Zn}(s) + \text{Fe}^{2+}(aq) \longrightarrow \text{Zn}^{2+}(aq) + \text{Fe}(s) \qquad E^\circ_{cell} = 0.32 \text{ V}$$

The first reaction, you can see, has a substantially greater standard cell potential, implying that it has a far greater tendency to go to completion as shown than the second reaction. Before we see how much greater it is, let's clear up the use of the word *cell* here.

■ Scientists call devices that use redox reactions to generate electricity *galvanic cells* after Luigi Galvani (1737–1798), an Italian scientist.

A standard cell potential is actually a measure of the voltage of a battery made up to correspond to the redox reaction and its half-reactions. All that a battery does is arrange to have the electron transfer of a redox reaction occur through an external circuit. The electrons given up by the reducing agent do not go directly to the atoms or ions of the oxidizing agent but through the circuit instead. As the electrons move in the external circuit, they do some work for us, like start a car, or trip a camera shutter. Special Topic 10.1 describes how the reaction of Cu with Ag^+ of Example 10.5 (and Figure 10.1) can be set up to make electricity flow in an external circuit.

Unfortunately, we cannot delve more deeply into the applications of redox reactions to batteries, but we now can see why the term *cell* and the unit of *volt* came into use in this field of chemistry. Special Topic 10.2 describes the chemistry of the standard lead storage battery used in vehicles and the silver oxide battery used in cameras, wrist watches, and hand-held calculators.

■ The first battery was invented by Alessandro Volta (1745–1827), an Italian scientist.

The connection between a standard cell potential and a real battery explains why the difference in Equation 10.2 is always taken this way, as the E° of the reduced substance minus the E° of the oxidized substance. The result of this calculation must always be a positive number (or zero). No battery has a negative voltage, and thus no E°_{cell} can be negative. If you make a mistake and obtain a negative value, the redox reaction you are studying would actually run the opposite way from what you have written.

The Standard Cell Potential Is Proportional to the Log of the Equilibrium Constant for a Redox Equilibrium   We can now get back to the question "How far toward completion do redox equilibria go?" We have a hint in terms of the relative E°_{cell} values, which we just learned to calculate. But these are not K_{eq} values.

The relationship between E°_{cell} and K_{eq} is one that we will have to state without explaining how it was derived. (We would have to go much farther into the electricity of these reactions as well as into the laws of thermodynamics than we can.) Ultimately, we want only to demonstrate how even extremely small values of E°_{cell} correspond to large values of K_{eq}. The equation relating E°_{cell} to K_{eq} is

$$E^\circ_{cell} = \frac{0.0592}{n} \log K_{eq} \tag{10.3}$$

where n is the number of moles of electrons that transfer in the balanced redox equation. Let's use Equation 10.3 to calculate values of K_{eq} for the two redox reactions involving zinc that we studied earlier.

EXAMPLE 10.7   **CALCULATING K_{eq} FROM E°_{cell}**

Problem: What are the K_{eq} values for the following redox reactions?
(a) $\text{Zn}(s) + \text{Cl}_2(g) \longrightarrow \text{Zn}^{2+}(aq) + 2\text{Cl}^-(aq)$ $E^\circ_{cell} = 2.12 \text{ V}$
(b) $\text{Zn}(s) + \text{Fe}^{2+}(aq) \longrightarrow \text{Zn}^{2+}(aq) + \text{Fe}(s)$ $E^\circ_{cell} = 0.32 \text{ V}$

Solution: (a) There is a two-electron transfer from a zinc atom to make two chloride ions, so on a mole level, $n = 2$. Substituting this, together with E°_{cell} (2.12 V), into Equation 10.3 gives

$$2.12 = \frac{0.0592}{2} \log K_{eq}$$

Or

$$\log K_{eq} = \frac{2.12 \times 2}{0.0592}$$
$$= 71.6$$

Therefore

$$K_{eq} = 10^{71.6}$$
$$= 4 \times 10^{71} \text{ (!)}$$

(b) Again $n = 2$, but now $E_{cell}^{\circ} = 0.32$ V. So

$$0.32 = \frac{0.0592}{2} \log K_{eq}$$

Or

$$\log K_{eq} = \frac{0.32 \times 2}{0.0592}$$
$$= 10.81$$
$$K_{eq} = 10^{10.81}$$
$$= 6.5 \times 10^{10} \text{ (Also !)}$$

Even this reaction with a small E_{cell}° proceeds entirely to completion, for all practical purposes, as equilibrium becomes established. (We normally would not even write the double arrows, just a single forward arrow for the redox reaction.)

You can see by the examples just worked that it would take extremely small values of E_{cell}° to have a redox equilibrium with K_{eq} between 1 and 10. Even then, we would say that the products are favored. Even if you found a value of E_{cell}° equal to 0, K_{eq} would equal 1, since $10^0 = 1$. And we do not have values of E_{cell}° less than 0 (i.e., negative numbers). Later, when we study some redox reactions that occur during the body's use of oxygen in cells, we'll better appreciate how powerfully these tend to go to completion.

In summary, when $E_{cell}^{\circ} > 0$ for a redox reaction, the forward reaction has a good to exceptionally strong tendency to proceed to completion.

PRACTICE EXERCISE 8   Calculate E_{cell}° and K_{eq} for the following redox reaction, which is a commercial preparation of bromine from sodium bromide and chlorine gas.

$$Cl_2(g) + 2Br^-(aq) \longrightarrow 2Cl^-(aq) + Br_2$$

We have two cautions to issue before we continue. The first is a reminder that a "tendency to go to completion" is no more than that. It carries no indication of *how rapidly* the reaction goes. The rate depends on the energy of activation, and nothing in E°, E_{cell}°, or K_{eq} carries the slightest clue about *energy of activation*.

The second caution is that the actual cell potential of a redox reaction depends not just on the calculated value of E_{cell}°, the *standard* cell potential, but also on the concentrations of the chemicals in solution. We'll look very briefly at this next.

The Relationship Between E_{cell}, E_{cell}°, and Concentrations Is Given by the Nernst Equation   We again must simply state an equation without justifying it as fully as might be desired. But our goals are very limited in this area. We want to point out that E_{cell} depends on concentration and that this fact is behind the way pH meters and similar devices work.

| SPECIAL TOPIC 10.1 | A GALVANIC CELL |

If silver and copper electrodes as well as an aqueous solution of silver nitrate and copper(II) nitrate were all present in the same vessel, a spontaneous redox reaction would occur:

$$Cu(s) + 2Ag^+(aq) \longrightarrow Cu^{2+}(aq) + 2Ag(s)$$

It would not give electricity, however, because the electrons would transfer directly from copper atoms to silver ions. For the transfer to go through wires, the chemicals involved in each of the two half-reactions of the redox system have to be in separate places and be kept from mixing. Figure 10.3 shows a simple way in which this could be done.

In the left beaker is a solution of $AgNO_3$ with a silver electrode, the cathode. In the right beaker is a solution of $Cu(NO_3)_2$ with a copper electrode, the anode. The electrons that copper atoms leave behind at the anode cannot get to the silver ions that are able to accept them except by going through the external circuit (and the switch is closed). As these electrons reach the cathode, they attract silver ions and reduce them to silver atoms, which deposit on the cathode as silver metal.

The *salt bridge* shown in Figure 10.3 has an essential function. It is made of open-ended bent glass tubing and is filled with a solution of a neutral electrolyte, such as $KNO_3(aq)$. Tufts of glass wool or cotton stuck into the open ends keep the solution from spilling out. But, being soaked with the electrolyte, they do not prevent its K^+ ions or NO_3^- ions from moving in whichever directions events elsewhere in the system force them to move. And move they must. When a copper atom gives up two electrons at the anode and moves into the solution, the solution would, if nothing else happened, have an excess of positive charge. This is not permitted in nature. But two nitrate ions are attracted into the solution to balance the charge. Similarly, at the cathode, when two silver ions pick up the two electrons and become silver atoms, they would, should nothing else happen, leave the solution in the left beaker with an excess of negative charge. However, two K^+ ions are attracted from the salt bridge into the beaker and so keep the solution electrically neutral. The salt bridge thus allows for a closed circuit. If it were not present, no current could flow. It would be like opening the switch, which would also stop the redox reaction.

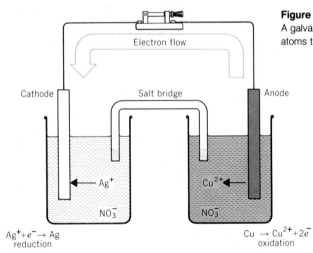

Figure 10.3
A galvanic cell. The "driving force" is the natural tendency for copper atoms to give electrons to silver ions, as shown in Figure 10.1.

| SPECIAL TOPIC 10.2 | THE LEAD STORAGE BATTERY AND THE SILVER OXIDE BATTERY |

Portable sources of electricity are popularly called batteries. They are packages of chemicals that can react, when the external electrical circuit is closed (the switch is "on"), and cause a flow of electrons through some conducting system. We describe two common batteries here.

The Lead Storage Battery We use the lead storage battery to start vehicles. The most common come in a 12-V size, but they are available in 6-, 24-, and 32-V sizes, too. To

develop such relatively high voltages by *chemical* reactions requires that several individual cells, each with a cell potential of about 2 V, be combined.

Figure 10.4 sketches the working parts of a 6-V lead storage battery, which has three individual cells. The anode, where oxidation occurs, is made of several plates of lead metal. The cathode, where reduction happens, is made of slabs of compressed lead dioxide, PbO_2. The solution is aqueous sulfuric acid. When we draw electricity from the battery, the following half-cell reactions are allowed to happen spontaneously inside each cell.

(cathode) $PbO_2(s) + 4H^+(aq) + SO_4^{2-}(aq) + 2e^- \longrightarrow$
$$PbSO_4(s) \quad E° = +1.69 \text{ V}$$

(anode) $Pb(s) + SO_4^{2-}(aq) \longrightarrow PbSO_4(s) + 2e^-$
$$E° = -0.36 \text{ V}$$

The net reaction within each cell is thus

$$PbO_2(s) + Pb(s) + 4H^+(aq) + SO_4^{2-}(aq) \longrightarrow$$
$$2PbSO_4(s) + 2H_2O \quad E°_{cell} = +2.05 \text{ V}$$

When three such cells are combined—wired *in series* is the technical description—the total voltage is about three times the individual cell potential, or about 6 V.

As electricity is drawn, the net reaction proceeds from left to right. This reaction consumes sulfuric acid, because its sulfate ion ends up in solid lead sulfate and its hydrogen ions in molecules of water. As sulfuric acid is used up, the density of the aqueous phase in the battery diminishes. It's easy to measure this change in density by a battery hydrometer, Figure 10.5; service stations perform this routine operation to check on the status of a car's battery.

One property of the lead storage battery that continues to make it popular for vehicles is the ability to reverse the net discharge reaction. This more or less restores the cells to their original conditions, and after such a ''recharge'' the battery is ready to go again. The recharge is done by passing direct electrical current backward through the system. If done slowly, it works well.

The Silver Oxide Battery Figure 10.6 shows the inner parts of the silver oxide battery, which is very popular for use with calculators and automatic cameras. The half-reactions are the following:

(cathode) $Ag_2O(s) + H_2O + 2e^- \longrightarrow 2Ag(s) + 2OH^-(aq)$
(anode) $Zn(s) + 2OH^-(aq) \longrightarrow Zn(OH)_2(s) + 2e^-$

An alkaline, moist paste makes up the electrolyte medium. This cell is able to generate about 1.5 V.

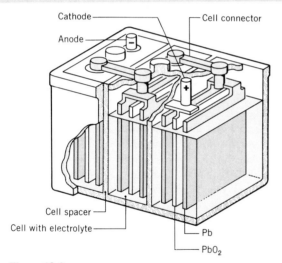

Figure 10.4
The 6-V lead storage battery consists of three cells, each able to produce about 2 V.

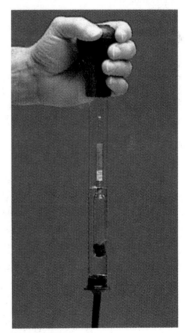

Figure 10.5
This battery hydrometer is used to monitor the charge of a lead storage battery. Battery acid is drawn up into the glass cylinder, which contains a float. The float will sink farther the more dilute the acid is and, therefore, the more run-down the battery is.

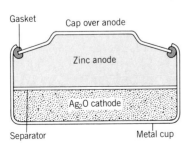

Figure 10.6
The silver oxide battery is a miniature cell capable of delivering 1.5 V.

The effect of the concentrations of reactants and products on the cell potential of a redox reaction, E_{cell}, is given by an equation developed by Walter Nernst and, appropriately, now called the *Nernst equation*.

$$E_{cell} = E_{cell}^\circ - \frac{0.0592}{n} \log Q \qquad (10.4)$$

The symbol Q stands for the expression that K_{eq} equals in the equilibrium law, with the difference that the concentrations in brackets need not be *equilibrium* concentrations. When an equilibrium can be written as

$$aA + bB \rightleftharpoons cC + dD$$

$$Q = \frac{[C]^c[D]^d}{[A]^a[B]^b}$$

■ Q stands for *reaction quotient.*

Only when the bracket concentrations are equilibrium concentrations does $Q = K_{eq}$.

Now notice in Equation 10.4 the condition needed for E_{cell} to equal E_{cell}°, the standard cell potential. For this to be true, the value of $\log Q$ must be zero. This can happen only when Q itself equals 1, and this is possible only when all concentrations, of both reactants and products, are exactly 1 mol/L. When the concentrations have other values, the cell potential, E_{cell}, generally does not equal E_{cell}°.

Notice also that when $Q = K_{eq}$, the last term in Equation 10.4 equals E_{cell}°, as we learned from Equation 10.3. Thus at equilibrium, $E_{cell} = E_{cell}^\circ - E_{cell}^\circ = 0$ V. In other words, a redox system that has reached equilibrium has no more potential left to do anything by itself. It's a battery run down, literally so when the redox system has been used to construct a real battery. This, of course, is what we mean by a chemical equilibrium — no further net change.

Finally, the Nernst equation suggests a way to measure the concentration of some species in a redox equilibrium. Actual cell potentials are easily measured by devices called voltmeters. If for a particular system there is a difference between the measured E_{cell} and the known value of E_{cell}°, such data can be plugged into the Nernst equation for the system to calculate a molarity of some species present and in the expression of Q. The pH meter works roughly this way. The meter is able to use its special electrode, sensitive to $[H^+]$, to measure E_{cell} for its special cell, to compare it to E_{cell}°, and to translate the data directly into a pH reading. A large number of similar meters, ones that are able to relate values of E_{cell} to the molarity of a particular species, even when many other solutes are in solution, have been invented. Many are used in the analysis of body fluids, like blood or urine, particularly in an emergency when very rapid results are critical.

SUMMARY

Oxidation numbers A reaction in which oxidation numbers change is a redox reaction — oxidation–reduction. An atom whose oxidation number becomes more positive is said to be oxidized. One whose number is made less positive (more negative) is reduced. One event cannot occur without the other in a reaction.

With monatomic ions, oxidation numbers are the same as the real electrical charges on the ions. Thus the ions of all group IA elements have oxidation numbers of $+1$; those of group IIA, $+2$, and aluminum (group IIIA), $+3$. The monatomic ions of group VIIA elements have oxidation numbers of -1; those in group VIA, -2.

With molecules and polyatomic ions, oxidation numbers are the hypothetical charges that their atoms would have if both electrons in electron-pair bonds were assigned to the more electronegative atom. Fluorine, the most electronegative element, always has an oxidation number of -1. That of hydrogen is always $+1$ except in metal hydrides. That of oxygen is always -2 except when this would lead

to a violation of the rules for F or H. When an atom is not combined with an atom from a different element, its oxidation number is zero. The sum of all oxidation numbers in a formula unit must equal the charge on the unit.

Balancing redox reactions The ion–electron method breaks the skeletal equation of a redox reaction into two half-reactions, one an oxidation and the other a reduction. Atoms that are not H or O are balanced first, then O is balanced using H_2O. H is next balanced using H^+. The necessary electrical balance is obtained by using or releasing electrons. After each half-reaction has been balanced, small whole-number multipliers may be needed for one or both so that when the half-reactions are added the electrons will cancel. (A final trimming of excess H^+ or H_2O may be needed.)

If the medium is basic, the redox reaction is first balanced pretending that the medium isn't basic. Then OH^- ions are added to both sides of the balanced equation in enough numbers to enable neutralization of any H^+.

Reduction potentials The tendency for a half-reaction to proceed as a reduction, relative to the reduction of H^+, is described by the standard reduction potential, $E°$. Its value corresponds to concentrations of dissolved species at $1\ M$. A half-reaction with a positive reduction potential represents a system more easily reduced than H^+. Those with negative reduction potentials are less easily reduced than H^+. The $H_2/2H^+$ system is assigned a reduction potential of 0.00 V when $[H^+]$ is exactly $1\ M$, the temperature is $25°C$, and the pressure of H_2 is 1 atm.

The most easily reduced species have the most positive reduction potentials. They are the strongest oxidizing agents. Fluorine, F_2, is an example. The most easily oxidized species have the most negative reduction potentials. The metals in groups IA and IIA are examples.

When two half-reactions are combined into a full redox reaction, the half-reaction with the more positive $E°$ always runs as a reduction and forces the other to run as an oxidation.

Redox equilibria The spread between $E°$ for the substance reduced and $E°$ for the substance oxidized in a redox reaction is called the standard cell potential, $E°_{cell}$ for the reaction. It is always a positive number (or zero), and is calculated by the algebraic subtraction of $E°$ for the oxidized species from $E°$ for the reduced species.

$E°_{cell}$ is proportional to the log of the equilibrium constant for the redox reaction. $E°_{cell} = (0.0592/n)\log K_{eq}$. Even very small values of $E°_{cell}$ correspond to sizable values of K_{eq}, so just about all redox reactions go entirely to completion for all practical purposes.

$E°_{cell}$ is for all concentrations at $1\ M$, the temperature at $25\ °C$, and any gases in the redox reaction at 1 atm of pressure. E_{cell}, the cell potential under any other conditions, is related to $E°_{cell}$ and concentrations by the Nernst equation. When all concentrations are the *equilibrium* concentrations, E_{cell} is zero, and no potential remains for further change. (It's like a run-down battery.)

REVIEW EXERCISES

The answers to Review Exercises that require a calculation and that are marked with an asterisk are found in Appendix D. The answers to the other Review Exercises are found in the *Study Guide* that accompanies this book.

Oxidation Numbers

10.1 Define the following terms. (These also review parts of Section 4.2.)
  (a) oxidation
  (b) reduction
  (c) oxidizing agent
  (d) reducing agent
  (e) redox reaction

*10.2 What are the oxidation numbers of the atoms in the following species?
  (a) N_2O (laughing gas)
  (b) NO (in hot auto exhaust)
  (c) NO_2 (another air pollutant that forms from NO in air)
  (d) N_2O_4
  (e) N_2O_5

10.3 What are the oxidation numbers of the atoms in the following?
  (a) HClO   (b) $HClO_2$ (c) $HClO_3$ (d) $HClO_4$

*10.4 Calculate the oxidation numbers of the atoms in the following.
  (a) HS^- (b) HSO_3^- (c) HSO_4^-

10.5 What are the oxidation numbers of the atoms in each?
  (a) MnO_4^- (a common oxidizing agent)
  (b) $Cr_2O_7^{2-}$ (also a common oxidizing agent)

Balancing Redox Reactions

10.6 How can you tell from a balanced half-reaction whether it represents oxidation or reduction without resorting to the use of oxidation numbers?

*10.7 Balance the following half-reactions occurring in aqueous acid and tell whether it represents oxidation or reduction.
  (a) $MnO_4^- \rightarrow Mn^{2+}$
  (b) $Fe^{2+} \rightarrow Fe_2O_3$
  (c) $H_2C_2O_4 \rightarrow CO_2$
  (d) $NO_2 \rightarrow N_2$

10.8 Balance the following half-reactions occurring in aqueous acid. Tell whether they represent oxidation or reduction:
  (a) $HCHO_2 \rightarrow CO_2$
  (b) $CH_2O \rightarrow CO_2$
  (c) $CH_3OH \rightarrow CO_2$
  (d) $CH_2O \rightarrow CH_3OH$

*10.9 Balance the following redox reactions occurring in aqueous acid.
  (a) $Cu + NO_3^- \rightarrow Cu^{2+} + NO$
  (b) $Zn + SO_4^{2-} \rightarrow Zn^{2+} + SO_2$
  (c) $BiO_3^- + Cr^{3+} \rightarrow Bi^{3+} + Cr_2O_7^{2-}$
  (d) $OCl^- + I_2 \rightarrow Cl^- + IO_3^-$

10.10 Balance the following redox reactions, which take place in acid.
  (a) $Zn + NO_3^- \rightarrow Zn^{2+} + NH_4^+$
  (b) $I^- + HNO_2 \rightarrow I_2 + NO$
  (c) $MnO_4^- + HNO_2 \rightarrow Mn^{2+} + NO_3^-$
  (d) $Sn + NO_3^- \rightarrow SnO_2 + NO$

*10.11 Balance the following redox reactions occuring in a basic solution.

(a) $MnO_4^- + CH_3OH \rightarrow CO_2 + MnO_2$

(b) $CrO_4^{2-} + S^{2-} \rightarrow CrO_2^- + S$

10.12 Balance the following redox reactions that occur in aqueous base.

(a) $MnO_4^- + SO_3^{2-} \rightarrow MnO_2 + SO_4^{2-}$

(b) $C_6H_5CH_3 + CrO_4^{2-} \rightarrow C_6H_5CO_2^- + CrO_2^-$

Reduction Potentials

10.13 Describe the reference half-reaction to which other standard reduction potentials are related. Use the appropriate chemical equation and describe the experimental conditions that must exist if a value of E_{cell} can be called E_{cell}°.

•10.14 The Ca/Ca^{2+} system has a standard reduction potential of -2.76 V. To show what this means,

(a) Write the half-cell reaction for this system.

(b) Does this half-cell reaction have a greater or lesser tendency to occur under the standard conditions than the $H_2/2H^+$ system?

(c) Which is the stronger oxidizing agent under the standard conditions, Ca^{2+} or H^+?

10.15 The $I_2/2I^-$ system has a standard reduction potential of $+0.54$ V.

(a) Write the half-cell reaction for this system.

(b) Which has the greater tendency to occur as a reduction under the standard conditions, this system or the Cu/Cu^{2+} system, whose $E^\circ = +0.34$ V?

(c) Which is the stronger reducing agent under the standard conditions, I_2 or H_2?

10.16 Find the standard half-reactions for the halogens listed in Table 10.1.

(a) Arrange the elements in their order of increasing ability to function as oxidizing agents. Place the formula of the halogen with the weakest oxidizing power on the left in the series.

(b) Arrange the elements in the order in which their monatomic anions are able to function as reducing agents. Place the formula of the halide ion with the weakest reducing power on the left in the series.

10.17 Given the large negative standard reduction potentials of the group IA and IIA metals, should one expect them to have low or high ionization energies? Explain.

10.18 Find the symbol of the metal with the highest standard reduction potential in Table 10.1. How does its position in the table correlate with a well-known chemical fact about it?

10.19 Compare Table 10.1 with Table 8.3. What is the basis for the activity series of the metals?

•10.20 If O_2, I_2, I^-, H^+, and water are together, what spontaneous

reaction will occur? Write the equation for the redox reaction.

10.21 If Cl_2, Cl^-, Fe^{3+}, and Fe^{2+} are brought together, what spontaneous chemical reaction can occur? Write the equation.

•10.22 Using data in Table 10.1, could the following reaction occur spontaneously?

$$Cu + 2Ag^+ \longrightarrow Cu^{2+} + 2Ag$$

10.23 Could the following reaction occur spontaneously? Use data in Table 10.1.

$$PbO_2(s) + 4H^+(aq) + 2F^-(aq) \longrightarrow$$
$$Pb^{2+}(aq) + F_2(g) + 2H_2O$$

Redox Equilibria

•10.24 Calculate the standard cell potential for the following reaction.

$$Fe(s) + Br_2(aq) \longrightarrow Fe^{2+}(aq) + 2Br^-(aq)$$

10.25 What is the standard cell potential for the reaction:

$$Sn^{2+}(aq) + Ni(s) \longrightarrow Sn(s) + Ni^{2+}(aq)$$

•10.26 Consider the redox reaction of Review Exercise 10.24 as an equilibrium and calculate its equilibrium constant.

10.27 Calculate the equilibrium constant for the reaction of Practice Exercise 10.25. Are the products favored at equilibrium?

10.28 Under what conditions does $E_{cell} = E_{cell}^\circ$?

10.29 Under what conditions does $E_{cell} = 0$?

Galvanic Cells (Special Topic 10.1)

10.30 Prepare a drawing of a galvanic cell that could use the following redox reaction to generate electricity.

$$Fe^{2+}(aq) + Mg(s) \longrightarrow Fe(s) + Mg^{2+}(aq)$$

Label the parts and show which half-reactions occur in each chamber. (The salt bridge could contain aqueous KNO_3.)

10.31 Explain why a salt bridge is necessary in the cell of Review Exercise 10.30.

10.32 What would the standard cell potential for the cell of Practice Exercise 10.30 be?

Batteries (Special Topic 10.2)

10.33 What are the half-reactions in a cell of a lead storage battery?

10.34 What is the net reaction in the lead storage battery?

10.35 What happens as a lead storage battery runs down that enables the use of a battery hydrometer to measure the battery's condition?

10.36 What are the half-reactions and the net equation for the silver oxide battery?

CHAPTER ELEVEN

Radioactivity and Nuclear Chemistry

Atomic radiations and X rays have long been used in medicine, but on occasion they can cause harm. Magnetic resonance imaging, the MRI scan, seems to pose no such problem. One of the Special Topics in this chapter describes how the doctor in this photograph is able to see the inside of the patient's head.

11.1 ATOMIC RADIATIONS

Unstable atomic nuclei eject high-energy radiations as they change to more stable nuclei.

Some atomic nuclei are unstable and the isotopes with such nuclei are **radioactive,** meaning that they emit streams of high-energy radiations. Each radioactive isotope is called a **radio-nuclide,** and its radiations can cause grave harm to human life. When carefully used, however, their potential benefits outweigh their possible harm. In this chapter we will study what these radiations are, how they can be dangerous, how they can be used wisely, and how they are measured.

Unstable Nuclei Undergo Radioactive Decay, Emit Radiations, and Transmute to Nuclei of Different Elements   Radioactivity was discovered in 1896 when a French physicist, A. H. Becquerel (1852–1908), happened to store some well-wrapped photographic plates in a drawer that contained samples of uranium ore. The film became fogged, meaning that when developed the picture was like a photograph of fog.

Becquerel might have blamed the accident on faulty film or careless handling, but a mysterious radiation called X rays had recently been discovered by a German scientist, Wilhelm Roentgen (1845–1923). X rays were known to be able to penetrate the packaging of unexposed film and ruin it. What fogged Becquerel's film was a natural radiation that resembled X rays. It was soon found to be emitted by any compound of uranium as well as by uranium metal itself.

Several years later, two British scientists, Ernest Rutherford (1871–1937) and Frederick Soddy (1877–1956), explained radioactivity in terms of events inside unstable atomic nuclei. Such nuclei undergo small disintegrations called **radioactive decay,** and they hurl tiny particles into space or emit a powerful radiation, one which is like X rays but is called gamma radiation.

The nuclei that remain after decay almost always are those of an entirely different element, so decay is usually accompanied by the **transmutation** of one element or isotope into another. The natural sources of radiation on our planet emit one or more of three kinds: alpha radiation, beta radiation, and gamma radiation. We receive another kind called **cosmic radiation,** from the sun and outer space (see Special Topic 11.1).

Alpha Particles Are the Nuclei of Helium Atoms   One natural atomic radiation is called **alpha radiation.** It consists of particles called **alpha particles** that move with a velocity almost one-tenth the velocity of light as they leave the atom. Alpha particles are clusters of two protons and two neutrons, so they are actually the nuclei of helium atoms (Figure 11.1). They are the largest of the decay particles and they have the greatest charge, so when alpha particles travel in air, they soon collide with air molecules and lose their energy (and charge). Alpha particles cannot penetrate even thin cardboard or the outer layer of dead cells on the skin. Exposure to an intense dose of alpha radiation, however, causes a severe burn.

The most common isotope of uranium, uranium-238 or $^{238}_{92}U$, is an alpha-emitter. When its nucleus ejects an alpha particle, it loses two protons, so the atomic number changes from 92 to 90. It also loses four units of mass number (two protons + two neutrons), so its mass number changes from 238 to 234. The result is that uranium-238 transmutes into an isotope of thorium, $^{234}_{90}Th$.

Beta Radiation Is a Stream of Electrons   Another natural radiation, **beta radiation,** consists of a stream of particles called **beta particles,** which are actually electrons. They are produced *within* the nucleus (Figure 11.2) and then emitted. With less charge and a much smaller size, beta particles can penetrate matter, including air, more easily than alpha particles. Different sources emit beta particles with different energies, and those of lower energy

■ Becquerel shared the 1903 Nobel prize in physics with Pierre and Marie Curie.

■ Roentgen won the 1901 Nobel prize in physics, the first to be awarded.

■ Nobel prizes in chemistry were awarded to both Rutherford (1908) and Soddy (1921).

■ The special symbols for isotopes were introduced in Section 3.1. Thus in $^{238}_{92}U$, 238 is the mass number and 92 is the atomic number.

COSMIC RAYS

Cosmic rays are streams of particles that enter our outer atmosphere from the sun and outer space. They consist mostly of high-energy protons plus some alpha and beta particles and the nuclei of the lower-formula-weight elements (up through number 26, iron).

Cosmic-ray particles do not travel far when they enter the atmosphere because they quickly collide with the air's molecules and atoms. These collisions, however, generate all the subatomic particles, including neutrons and some others we haven't studied in this chapter. These secondary cosmic rays are what we are exposed to on the earth's surface.

Figure 11.1
Emission of an alpha particle.

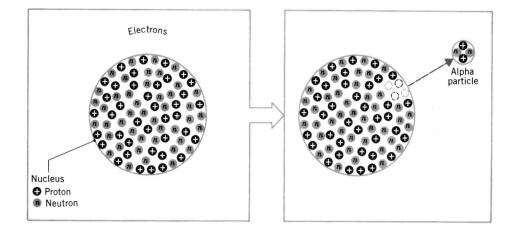

Nucleus
⊕ Proton
ⓝ Neutron

are unable to penetrate the skin. Those of the highest energy can reach internal organs from outside the body.

As a nucleus emits a beta particle, a neutron changes into a proton (Figure 11.2). Thus there is no loss in mass number, but the atomic number *increases* by 1 unit because of the new proton. For example, thorium-234, $^{234}_{90}$Th, is a beta-emitter, and when it ejects a beta particle it changes to an isotope of protactinium, $^{234}_{91}$Pa.

■ Losing one electron from the nucleus is like adding one proton without changing the mass number.

Gamma Radiation Often Accompanies Other Radiation   A radionuclide achieves greater stability by emitting alpha or beta radiation. There are nuclear energy states just as there are electron energy states in atoms. By ejecting small particles, unstable nuclei acquire a lower, more stable nuclear state. The energy lost by the nucleus is carried away by the moving particles, but often some photons of high-energy electromagnetic radiation also stream out. This is called **gamma radiation,** and it is like X rays or ultraviolet rays, but with more energy. Like X rays, gamma radiation is quite penetrating and very dangerous. It easily travels through the entire body.

Figure 11.2
Emission of a beta particle.

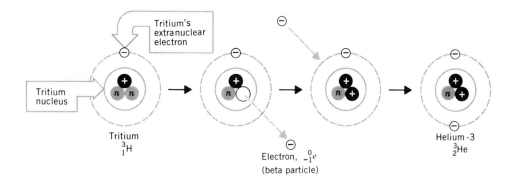

Tritium's extranuclear electron

Tritium nucleus

Tritium
$^{3}_{1}$H

Electron, $^{0}_{-1}e$
(beta particle)

Helium-3
$^{3}_{2}$He

TABLE 11.1 Radiations from Naturally Occurring Radionuclides

Radiation	Composition	Mass Number	Electrical Charge	Symbols
Alpha radiation	Helium nuclei	4	2+	$_2^4$He or α
Beta radiation	Electrons	0	1−	$_{-1}^0e$ or β
Gamma radiation	X-ray type of energy	0	0	$_0^0\gamma$ or γ

The composition and symbols of the three radiations studied thus far are summarized in Table 11.1.

Nuclear Equations In *chemical* reactions no changes in atomic nuclei occur. But nuclear reactions are nearly always accompanied by transmutations. Therefore **nuclear equations** are different from chemical equations in important ways. They must, in particular, describe the changes in atomic numbers, mass numbers, and identities of radionuclides.

In nuclear equations the alpha particle is symbolized as $_2^4$He, and although it is positively charged, the charge is omitted from the symbol. The particle soon picks up electrons, anyway, from the matter through which it is passing, and it becomes a neutral atom of helium. The beta particle has the symbol $_{-1}^0e$ because its mass number is 0 and its charge is 1−. Gamma radiation is symbolized simply by γ (or, sometimes, by $_0^0\gamma$). Both its mass number and charge are 0.

■ It's proper to think of the electron as having an atomic number of −1.

A nuclear equation is balanced when the sums of the mass numbers on either side of the arrow are equal and when the sums of the atomic numbers are equal. The alpha decay of uranium-238, for example, is represented by the following equation:

$$_{92}^{238}\text{U} \longrightarrow {}_{90}^{234}\text{Th} + {}_2^4\text{He}$$

Notice that the sums of the atomic numbers agree: $92 = 90 + 2$. And the sums of the mass numbers agree: $238 = 234 + 4$.

The beta decay of thorium-234, which also emits gamma radiation, is represented by the following nuclear equation:

$$_{90}^{234}\text{Th} \longrightarrow {}_{91}^{234}\text{Pa} + {}_{-1}^0e + \gamma$$

The sums of the atomic numbers agree: $90 = 91 + (-1)$.

EXAMPLE 11.1

BALANCING NUCLEAR EQUATIONS

Problem: Cesium-137, $_{55}^{137}$Cs, is one of the radioactive wastes that form during fission in a nuclear power plant or an atomic bomb explosion. This radionuclide decays by emitting both beta and gamma radiation. Write the nuclear equation for this decay.

Solution: First we set up as much of the nuclear equation as we can and leave blanks for any information we have to figure out. Thus our partial nuclear equation is

$$_{55}^{137}\text{Cs} \longrightarrow {}_{-1}^0e + {}_0^0\gamma + \underset{\text{Atomic number needed}}{\overset{\substack{\text{Mass number needed} \\ \text{Atomic symbol needed}}}{\rule{1cm}{0.4pt}}}$$

The first thing to do is to figure out the atomic symbol for the isotope that forms. For this we need the atomic number, because then we can look up the symbol in a table. We will find the atomic number by using a step-by-step process, but with just a little experience, you will be able to do this by inspection. We find the atomic number by using the fact that the sum of the atomic numbers on one side of the nuclear equation must equal the sum on the other side. Therefore letting x be the atomic number,

$$55 = -1 + 0 + x$$
$$x = 56$$

Now we can use the periodic table to find that the atomic symbol that goes with element 56 is Ba (barium). Next, to find out which particular isotope of barium forms, we use the fact that the sum of the mass numbers on one side of the nuclear equation must equal the sum on the other side. Letting y equal the mass number of the barium isotope,

$$137 = 0 + 0 + y$$
$$y = 137$$

The balanced nuclear equation therefore is

$$^{137}_{55}\text{Cs} \longrightarrow ^{0}_{-1}e + ^{0}_{0}\gamma + ^{137}_{56}\text{Ba}$$

EXAMPLE 11.2 | **BALANCING NUCLEAR EQUATIONS**

Problem: Until the 1950s, radium-226 was widely used as a source of radiation for cancer treatment. It is an alpha-emitter and a gamma-emitter. Write the equation for its decay.

■ The radium used in cancer therapy was held in a thin, hollow gold or platinum needle to retain the alpha particles and all the decay products.

Solution: We have to look up the atomic number of radium, which turns out to be 88, so the symbol we'll use for this radionuclide is $^{226}_{88}\text{Ra}$. When one of its atoms loses an alpha particle, $^{4}_{2}\text{He}$, it loses 4 units in mass number—from 226 to 222. And it loses 2 units in atomic number—from 88 to 86. Thus the new radionuclide has a mass number of 222 and an atomic number of 86. We have to look up the atomic symbol for element number 86, which turns out to be Rn, for radon. Now we can assemble the nuclear equation.

$$^{226}_{88}\text{Ra} \longrightarrow ^{222}_{86}\text{Rn} + ^{4}_{2}\text{He} + \gamma$$

PRACTICE EXERCISE 1 | Iodine-131 has long been used in treating cancer of the thyroid. This radionuclide emits beta and gamma rays. Write the nuclear equation for this decay.

PRACTICE EXERCISE 2 | Plutonium-239 is a by-product of the operation of nuclear power plants. It can be isolated from used uranium fuel and made into fuel itself or into atomic bombs. A powerful alpha- and gamma-emitter, it is one of the most dangerous of all known substances. Write the equation for its decay.

A Short Half-Life Means a Rapid Decay and a More Dangerous Radionuclide

Some radionuclides are much more stable than others, and we use the concept of a half-life to describe the differences. The **half-life** of a radionuclide, symbolized as $t_{1/2}$, is the time it takes for half of the atoms in a sample of a single, pure isotope to decay. (The atoms that decay don't just vanish, of course. They change into different isotopes.) Table 11.2 gives several half-lives.

The half-life of uranium-238 is 4.51×10^9 years, which means that an initial 100 g of this radionuclide would have only 50.0 g of uranium-238 left after 4.51×10^9 years. Strontium-90, a by-product of nuclear power plants, is a beta-emitter with a half-life of 28.1 years. Figure 11.3 shows graphically how an initial supply of 40 g is reduced successively by units of one-half for each half-life period. At the end of eight half-life periods (224.8 years, from 8×28.1), only 0.3 g of strontium-90 remains in the sample.

The shorter the half-life, the larger the number of decay events per mole per second occurring in the isotope. Mole for mole, it's generally much safer to be near a sample that has a long half-life and thus decays very slowly than to be near one that has a short half-life and decays very rapidly.

TABLE 11.2 Typical Half-Life Periods

Element	Isotope	Half-Life Period	Radiations
Naturally Occurring Radionuclides			
Potassium	$^{40}_{19}K$	1.3×10^9 years	Beta, gamma
Neodymium	$^{144}_{60}Nd$	5×10^{15} years	Alpha
Radon[a]	$^{222}_{86}Rn$	3.832 days	Alpha
Radium[a]	$^{226}_{88}Ra$	1590 years	Alpha, gamma
Thorium	$^{230}_{90}Th$	8×10^4 years	Alpha, gamma
Uranium	$^{238}_{92}U$	4.51×10^9 years	Alpha
Synthetic Radionuclides			
Hydrogen (tritium)	^3_1H	12.26 years	Beta
Oxygen	$^{15}_8O$	124 seconds	Positron[b]
Phosphorus	$^{32}_{15}P$	14.3 days	Beta
Technetium	$^{99m}_{43}Tc$	6.02 hours	Gamma
Iodine	$^{131}_{53}I$	8.07 days	Beta
Cesium	$^{137}_{55}Cs$	30 years	Beta
Strontium	$^{90}_{38}Sr$	28.1 years	Beta
Americium	$^{243}_{95}Am$	7.37×10^3 years	Alpha

[a] Although short-lived, radon-222 and radium-226 are found in nature because the uranium-238 disintegration series continuously produces them.

[b] The positron has a mass number of 0 and a charge of 1+. (It is sometimes called a positive electron.)

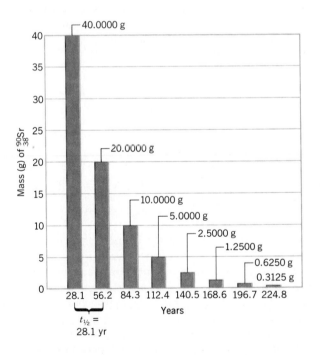

Figure 11.3
Each half-life period reduces the quantity of a radionuclide by a factor of two. Shown here is the pattern for strontium-90, a radioactive pollutant with a half-life of 28.1 years.

A Succession of Decays Occurs in a Radioactive Disintegration Series   The decay of one radionuclide sometimes produces not a stable isotope but just another radionuclide. This might, in turn, decay to still another radionuclide, with the process repeating until a stable nuclide is finally reached. There are four such series in nature, called **radioactive disintegration series,** and uranium-238 is at the head of one. (See Figure 11.4.) This series ends in a stable isotope of lead.

■ An extremely long half-life is typical of the radionuclides that head a radioactive disintegration series.

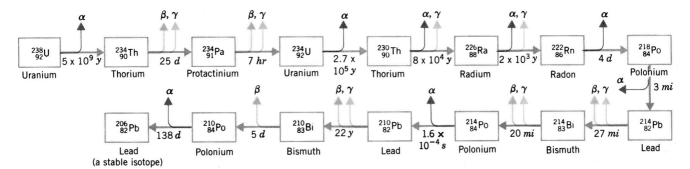

Figure 11.4
The uranium-238 radioactive disintegration series. The time given beneath the arrow is the half-life of the preceding isotope (y = year; m = month; d = day; mi = minute; and s = second).

11.2 IONIZING RADIATIONS—DANGERS AND PRECAUTIONS

Atomic radiations create unstable ions and radicals in tissue, which can lead to cancer, mutations, tumors, or birth defects.

Atomic radiations are dangerous because they can generate strange, unstable, highly reactive particles as they travel through living tissues. In this section we will study how radiations do this and some steps for self-protection.

Unstable Ions and Radicals Are Produced in Tissue by Radiations Alpha and beta particles, as well as X rays and gamma rays, are called **ionizing radiations** because they can nick electrons from molecules as they strike them and so produce unstable polyatomic ions. Alpha particles, for example, can make ions from water molecules by the following reaction:

$$H—\overset{..}{\underset{..}{O}}—H + \text{high-energy alpha particle} \longrightarrow$$

$$[H—\overset{.}{\underset{..}{O}}—H]^+ + e^- + \text{lower-energy alpha particle}$$

The ion, $[H—\overset{.}{\underset{..}{O}}—H]^+$, is an uncommon, unstable system. Its oxygen atom no longer has an outer octet. Moreover, the collision has left this strange ion with sufficient energy to break up spontaneously as follows.

$$[H—\overset{.}{\underset{..}{O}}—H]^+ \longrightarrow H^+ + :\overset{.}{\underset{..}{O}}—H$$

Hydroxyl radical

A proton forms plus a hydroxyl radical, a kind of particle new to our study. It's a *neutral* particle with an unpaired electron and without an octet for its oxygen atom. Any particle with an unpaired electron is called a **radical** and, with few exceptions, radicals are very reactive species.

■ Sometimes the term used is *free* radical.

The new ions and radicals produced by ionizing radiations cause chemical reactions in the more stable substances around them, altering them in ways foreign to metabolism. If such chemical reactions happen in genes and chromosomes, the cell's genetic substances, subsequent reactions could lead to cancer, tumor growth, or a genetic mutation. If they happen in a sperm cell, an ovum, or a fetus, the result might be a birth defect. Prolonged and repeated exposures to *low* levels of radiation are more likely to induce these problems than bursts of high-level radiation. It depends on whether the injured cell is still able to duplicate itself by cell division. High-energy radiation bursts usually kill a cell outright, or at least render it reproductively dead. For this reason high doses of radiations are used in cancer treatment. But low-level

■ Technical terms are
Carcinogen, a cancer causer
Tumorogen, a tumor causer
Mutagen, a mutation causer
Teratogen, a birth defect causer

radiations that leave a cell reproductively viable can alter the cell contents in ways that are actually reproduced.

There Is No Safe Threshold Exposure to Radiations All radiations that penetrate the skin or enter the body on food or through the lungs are considered harmful, and *the damage can accumulate* over a working lifetime. Even the ultraviolet radiation in strong sunlight, which barely penetrates the skin, can alter the genetic molecules in skin cells so as to lead to skin cancer. No "tiny bit of exposure," no **threshold exposure** exists for radiations below which no harm is possible. In well-run establishments, medical personnel who work with radionuclides, X rays, or emitters of gamma rays are expected to wear devices that automatically record the exposure. The exposure data are periodically logged into a permanent record book, and when the maximum permissible dose has been attained, the worker has to be transferred.

■ No technology in any medical field is entirely risk-free. We take risks when we believe that the benefits outweigh them.

Cells do have a capacity for self-repair, and some exposures carry very low risks. But no exposure is entirely risk-free. The widespread and routine use of X rays for public health screenings has long been curtailed.

The Collection of Symptoms Caused by Radiations Is Called Radiation Sickness Molecules of hereditary materials in the cell's chromosomes are the primary site of radiation damage. Damage to these leads to all other problems. The first symptoms of exposure to radiation therefore occur in tissues whose cells divide most frequently, for example, the cells in bone marrow. These make white blood cells, so an early sign of radiation damage is a sharp decrease in the blood's white cell count. Cells in the intestinal tract also divide frequently, and even moderate exposure to X rays or gamma rays (as in cobalt-ray therapy for cancer) produces intestinal disorders.

The set of symptoms caused by nonlethal exposures to atomic radiations or X rays is called **radiation sickness.** The symptoms include nausea, vomiting, a drop in the white cell count, diarrhea, dehydration, prostration, hemorrhaging, and the loss of hair. They often appear when sharp bursts of radiations are used to halt the spread of cancer.

Protection from Radiation Is Achieved by Shields, Fast X-Ray Film, and Distance Shields have long been used for protection against radiations. (No doubt on a visit to the dentist you have had a lead apron placed over your chest before a dental X ray.) Alpha and beta rays are the easiest to stop as the data in Table 11.3 show. Gamma radiations and X rays are stopped effectively only by particularly dense substances. Lead, a very dense metal but still fairly inexpensive, is the most common material used to shield against gamma or X rays. But notice in the data in Table 11.3 that even 30 mm (3.0 cm, a little over an inch) of lead reduces the intensity of gamma radiation by only 10%. A vacuum is least effective, of course, and air isn't much better. Low-density materials such as cardboard, plastic, and aluminum are poor shielders, but concrete works well if it is thick (and it's much cheaper than lead). Thus by a careful choice of a shielding material, protection can be obtained.

Another strategy to minimize exposure when radiations are used in medical diagnosis, such as in taking X rays, is to use fast film. With fast film, the *time* of exposure is kept as low as possible.

The least expensive self-protection step is to get as far from the radiation source as you can. Radiations, like light from a bulb, move in straight lines, spreading out in all the directions open to them from their sources. From any point on the surface of the source, the radiations form a cone of rays, so fewer rays can strike a unit of surface the more distant the surface is from the source. The area of the base of such a cone increases with the square of the distance. Hence the radiation intensity I on a unit area diminishes with the square of the distance d from the source. This is the **inverse square law** of radiation intensity.

TABLE 11.3 Penetrating Abilities of Some Common Radiations

Type of Radiation	Common Sources	Approximate Depth of Penetration of Radiation into		
		Dry Air	Tissue	Lead
Alpha rays	Radium-226 Radon-222 Polonium-210	4 cm	0.05 mm[b]	0
Beta rays	Tritium Strontium-90 Iodine-131 Carbon-14	6 to 300 cm[a]	0.06 to 4 mm[b]	0.005 to 0.3 mm
		Thickness to Reduce Initial Intensity by 10%		
Gamma rays	Cobalt-60 Cesium-137 Decay products of radium-226	400 m	50 cm	30 mm
X rays Diagnostic Therapeutic		120 m 240 m	15 cm 30 cm	0.3 mm 1.5 mm

Data from J. B. Little. *The New England Journal of Medicine*, Vol. 275, 1966, pages 929–938, 1966.

[a] The range of beta particles in air is about 12 ft/MeV. Thus a 2-MeV beta ray has a range of about 24 ft in air.

[b] The approximate energy needed to penetrate the protective layer of skin (0.07 mm thick), is 7.5 MeV for alpha particles and 70 keV for beta particles.

Inverse Square Law. The intensity of radiation is inversely proportional to the square of the distance from the source.

$$I \propto \frac{1}{d^2} \tag{11.1}$$

This law holds strictly only in a vacuum, but it holds closely enough when the medium is air to make good estimates. If we move from one location, a, to another location, b, the variation of Equation 11.1 that we can use to compare the intensities at the two different places, I_a and I_b, is given by the following equation:

$$\frac{I_a}{I_b} = \frac{d_b^2}{d_a^2} \tag{11.2}$$

EXAMPLE 11.3   **USING THE INVERSE-SQUARE LAW OF RADIATION INTENSITY**

Problem: At 1.0 m from a radioactive source the radiation intensity was measured as 30 units. If the operator moves away to a distance of 3.0 m, what will the radiation intensity be?

Solution: As usual, it's a good idea to assemble the data.

$$I_a = 30 \text{ units} \qquad d_a = 1.0 \text{ m}$$
$$I_b = ? \qquad d_b = 3.0 \text{ m}$$

Now we can use Equation 11.2:

$$\frac{30 \text{ units}}{I_b} = \frac{(3.0 \text{ m})^2}{(1.0 \text{ m})^2}$$

Solving for I_b, we get

$$I_b = 30 \text{ units} \times \frac{1.0 \text{ m}^2}{9.0 \text{ m}^2}$$

$$= 3.3 \text{ units}$$

Thus tripling the distance cut the intensity almost by a factor of 10.

PRACTICE EXERCISE 3　　If the intensity of radiation is 25 units at a distance of 10 m, what does the intensity become if you move to a distance of 0.50 m?

PRACTICE EXERCISE 4　　If you are receiving an intensity of 80 units of radiation at a distance of 6.0 m, to what distance would you have to move to reduce this intensity by half, to a value of 40 units?

No Escape from the Natural Background Radiation Is Possible　　Shielding materials and distance can never completely reduce our exposure to radiations. We are constantly exposed to **background radiation,** the radiations given off, for example, by the naturally occurring radionuclides, by radioactive pollutants, cosmic rays, and medical X rays. About 50 of the roughly 350 isotopes of all elements in nature are radioactive. Natural radiations are in the food we eat, the water we drink, and the air we breathe. Radiations enter our bodies with every X ray taken of us. They come in cosmic-ray showers. On the average, the top 15 cm of soil on our planet has 1 g of radium per square mile. Thus radioactive materials are in the soils and rocks on which we walk and which we use to make building materials.

■ People became aware of the radon problem only in the early 1980s.

Radon, a *chemically* inert but radioactive gas and a product of the uranium-238 disintegration series, makes the largest contribution to our background radiation. See Special Topic 11.2. (We will discuss the problems of radioactive pollutants from the operation of nuclear reactors in Section 11.6.)

The background radiation varies widely from place to place, and only estimates (which vary widely with the estimator) are possible. Table 11.4 gives the averages of radiations from various sources for the U.S. population. We will discuss the millirem (mrem), the unit of *dose equivalent* used in this table, shortly. For comparison purposes, a dose of 500 rem (500,000 mrem) given to the individuals in a large population would cause the deaths of half of them in 30 days. In relation to this, the intensity of natural background radiation is very small. At higher altitudes the intensity of background radiation is greater because incoming cosmic rays, which contribute to the background, have had less opportunity to be absorbed and destroyed by the earth's atmosphere.

11.3　UNITS TO DESCRIBE AND MEASURE RADIATIONS

Units have been devised to describe the activity of a radioactive sample, the energies of its radiations, and the energies they can deliver to tissue.

A number of units exist for a variety of measurements of radiations, and each has been invented to serve in the answer to a particular question. Note carefully what these questions are and the units will be easier to learn.

■ Marie Curie is one of two scientists to win two Nobel prizes in a field of science, a share of the physics prize in 1903 and the chemistry prize in 1911.

The Curie (Ci) Describes How Active a Sample Is　　The curie, the unit of activity most commonly used by U.S. radiologists, was devised to answer the question, "How *active* is a sample of a radionuclide?" It was named after Marie Sklodowska Curie (1867–1934), a Polish scientist, who discovered radium. One **curie, Ci,** is the number of radioactive disinte-

SPECIAL TOPIC 11.2   RADON IN THE ENVIRONMENT

Radon-222 is a naturally occurring radionuclide in the family of noble gases produced by the U-238 disintegration series. Chemically, it is as inert as the other noble gases, but radiologically it is a dangerous air pollutant. It is an alpha-emitter and a gamma-emitter with a half-life of only four days. Produced in rocks and soil wherever uranium-238 is found, it migrates as a gas into the surrounding air. Basements not fully sealed act like fireplace chimneys to draw radon-222 into homes.

The first indication of how serious radon-222 pollution might be came when an engineer at a nuclear power plant in Pennsylvania set off radiation alarms just by his presence. The problem was traced to his home, where the radiation level in the basement was 2700 picocuries per liter of air. In the average home basement, the level is just 1 picocurie/L. (The picocurie is 10^{-12} curie.) The engineer had carried radon-222 and its radioactive decay products on his clothing into his workplace.

As a result of the incident, geologist went looking for unusual concentrations of uranium-238 nearby. They found that the Reading Prong, a formation of bedrock that cuts across Pennsylvania, New Jersey, New York State, and up into the New England states, is relatively rich in U-238.

Radon-222 enters the lungs with breathing, and some decays within the lungs. Several decay products in the series after radon-222 are not gases, like polonium-218 ($t_{1/2}$ 3 min, alpha-emitter), lead-214 ($t_{1/2}$ 27 min, beta- and gamma-emitter) and polonium-214 ($t_{1/2}$ 1.6×10^{-4} sec, alpha- and gamma-emitter). Left in the lungs, these can cause cancer; U.S. officials estimate that 7% to 8% of the country's annual deaths from lung cancer are caused by indoor radiation from radon-222.

The recommended upper limit on radon-222 concentration in home air is 4 picocuries/L. A conservative estimate puts the percentage of homes in the United States with levels above this at 1%.

---

grations that occur per second in a 1.0 g sample of radium, 3.7×10^{10} disintegrations/second:

$$1 \text{ Ci} = 3.7 \times 10^{10} \text{ disintegrations/sec}$$

This is an intensely active rate, so fractions of the Ci, such as the millicurie (mCi, 10^{-3} Ci), the microcurie (μCi, 10^{-6} Ci), and the picocurie (pCi, 10^{-12} Ci), are often used.

The **becquerel, Bq,** is the SI unit of activity, but it has achieved essentially no popularity among U.S. scientists (a situation that might change, of course).

$$1 \text{ Bq} = 1 \text{ disintegration/sec}$$

Therefore

$$1 \text{ Ci} = 3.7 \times 10^{10} \text{ Bq}$$

TABLE 11.4   Average Radiation Doses Received Annually by the U.S. Population[a]

Source	Mrem Dose	Percent of Total
Natural radiation — 295 mrem, 82%		
Radon[b]	200	55
Cosmic rays	27	8
Rocks and soil	28	8
From inside the body	40	11
Artificial radiation — 65 mrem, 18%		
Medical X rays[c]	39	11
Nuclear medicine	14	4
Consumer products	10	3
Others	2	<1
Total[d]	360	

[a] Data from "Ionizing Radiation Exposure of the Population of the United States." Report 93, 1987, National Council on Radiation Protection. These are averages. Individual exposures can vary widely.

[b] See Special Topic 11.2.

[c] A normal chest X ray gives 10- to 20-mrem exposure.

[d] The federal standard for maximum safe occupational exposure in the United States is roughly 5000 mrem/yr.

The Roentgen (R) Describes Exposure to X-Ray or Gamma-Ray Radiation   The roentgen serves to answer the question, "How *intense* is the exposure to X-ray or gamma-ray radiation?" One **roentgen** of either of these radiations, in passing through 1 cm^3 of dry air at normal temperature and pressure, generates ions with a total charge of 2.1 × 10^9 units. If members of a large population were exposed to 650 roentgens, half would die in one to four weeks. (The rest would have radiation sickness.)

The Rad (D) Describes the Energy Absorbed by Tissue   The *rad* is commonly used to answer the question, "How much *energy* is *absorbed* by a unit mass of tissue or other materials?" We will define it in terms of the less commonly used SI unit for the same purpose, the gray, Gy, named after a British radiologist, Harold Gray. The **gray, Gy,** corresponds to the absorption of 1 joule (J) of energy per kilogram of tissue. (The joule is the SI unit of energy; 1 J = 4.184 cal.)

$$1 \text{ Gy} = 1 \text{ J/kg}$$

■ *Rad* comes from *radiation absorbed dose.*

The **rad, D,** is 1/100th of a gray.

$$1 \text{ D} = 10^{-2} \text{ Gy}$$

Because the joule is an extremely small amount of energy, both the gray and the rad are also very small quantities. Nevertheless, only 600 rad of gamma radiation would be lethal to most people. We have to remember that it is not the quantity of energy that matters so much as the formation of unstable radicals and ions caused by this energy. A 600-rad dose delivered to water ionizes only one molecule in every 36 million, but the ions or radicals thus produced can begin a cascade of harmful reactions inside a cell.

The roentgen and the rad are close enough in magnitude that they are nearly equivalent from a health standpoint. Thus one roentgen of gamma radiation from a cobalt-60 source, often used in cancer treatment, equals 0.96 rad in muscle tissue and 0.92 rad in compact bone.

The Rem Adjusts Rad Doses for Different Effects in Different Tissues   The rem is a unit that satisfies the need for a unit of absorbed dose that is additive for different radiations and different target tissues. A dose of one rad of gamma radiation is not *biologically* the same as a dose of one rad of beta radiation or of neutrons. Thus the rad does not serve as a good basis for comparison when working with biological effects. The rem fits this need.

■ *Rem* comes from *roentgen equivalent for man.*

The **rem** is the unit of *dose equivalent*. To convert rads to rems, we multiply the dose in rads from some radiation by a factor that takes into account biologically significant properties of the radiation. One rem of any given radiation is the dose that has, in a human being, the effect of one roentgen.

The rem, like the rad, is a quantity small in terms of energy but significant in terms of danger. Even millirem quantities of radiation should be avoided, and when this isn't possible the workers must wear monitoring devices that allow the day-to-day exposures to be calculated.

■ The higher is their energy, the more penetrating are X rays and gamma rays.

The Electron-Volt Describes the Energy of X Rays or Gamma Rays   Those who work with X rays or gamma radiation use an old unit of energy to describe the energies of these radiations. This unit is the **electron-volt, eV,** defined as follows:

$$1 \text{ eV} = 1.602 \times 10^{-19} \text{ J}$$

(Originally, the electron-volt was viewed as the energy an electron receives when it is accelerated by a voltage of 1 V.)

With an exponent of −19 in the equation defining the electron-volt, you might guess that it is an extremely small amount of energy. Multiples of the electron-volt are therefore very common, such as the kiloelectron-volt (1 keV = 10^3 eV) and the megaelectron-volt (MeV = 10^6 eV). X rays used for diagnosis are typically 100 keV or less. The gamma radiations from cobalt-60 used in cancer treatment have energies of 1.2 and 1.3 MeV. Beta radiation of

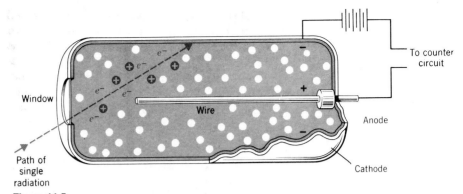

Figure 11.5
The basic features of a gas-ionization radiation detection tube such as used in a Geiger-Müller counter.

70 keV or more can penetrate the skin, but alpha particles (which are much larger than beta particles) need energies of more than 7 MeV to do this. Alpha radiation from radium-226 has an energy of 5 MeV. The cosmic radiation that enters our outer atmosphere has energies ranging from 200 MeV to 200 GeV (1 GeV = 1 gigaelectron-volt = 10^9 eV).

Film Dosimeters, Scintillation Counters, and Geiger Counters Measure Radiations   People who work around radioactive sources cannot avoid receiving some exposure, and it's important that they keep a log of how much exposure they accumulate. A device for measuring exposure is called a *dosimeter;* one common type is a film badge that contains photographic film, which becomes fogged by radiations. The degree of fogging, which is related to the exposure, can be measured.

Ionizing radiations also affect substances called phosphors, salts with traces of rare earth metal ions that scintillate when struck by radiation. These scintillations — brief, spark-like flashes of light — can be translated into doses of radiation received. Devices based on this technology are called *scintillation counters.*

Evacuated tubes that are fitted with two electrodes and hold a gas at very low pressure are used in devices such as the Geiger counter. This is a type of *ionization counter,* and Figure 11.5 shows how the tube itself is constructed. The tube, called a Geiger-Müller tube, is especially useful in measuring the beta and gamma radiation that has enough energy to penetrate the window. When a pulse of this radiation enters the rarified gaseous atmosphere in the tube, it creates ions that conduct a brief pulse of electricity. The pulse shoots from one electrode to the other, signaling the apparatus to record a "count."

11.4   SYNTHETIC RADIONUCLIDES

Most radionuclides used in medicine are made by bombarding other atoms with high-energy particles.

Radioactive decay is nature's way of causing transmutations. They can also be caused artificially by bombarding atoms with high-energy particles. Several hundred isotopes that do not occur naturally have been made this way. Several have been used successfully in medicine, both in diagnosis and in treatment.

Various bombarding particles can be used, including alpha particles, neutrons, and gaseous protons. The first artificial transmutation, observed by Rutherford, was the conversion of nitrogen-14 into oxygen-17 by alpha-particle bombardment. Rutherford let alpha particles from a naturally radioactive source travel through a tube that contained nitrogen-14. He soon detected that another radiation was being generated, one far more penetrating than the alpha radiation he used. He showed that it consisted of high-energy protons and that atoms of oxygen-17 now existed in the tube.

■ Linear accelerators produce radiation for cancer treatment in the range of 6 to 12 MeV.

■ Inside the screen of a color TV tube is a coating that includes various phosphors; these glow with different colors when struck by the focused electron beam in the tube.

■ These are gaseous protons, true subatomic particles, and not hydronium ions.

To explain his observations, Rutherford reasoned that alpha particles had plowed right through the electron clouds of nitrogen-14 atoms and buried themselves in their nuclei. The strange new nuclei, called *compound nuclei,* evidently had too much energy to exist for long. They were excited nuclei of fluorine-18, and to rid themselves of excess energy each ejected a proton, which left behind an atom of oxygen-17. The equation is

$$\underset{\substack{\text{Alpha}\\\text{particle}}}{^{4}_{2}\text{He}} + \underset{\substack{\text{Nitrogen}\\\text{nucleus}}}{^{14}_{7}\text{N}} \longrightarrow \underset{\substack{\text{Fluorine}\\\text{nucleus}}}{^{18}_{9}\text{F}^{*}} \longrightarrow \underset{\substack{\text{Oxygen}\\\text{nucleus}}}{^{17}_{8}\text{O}} + \underset{\text{Proton}}{^{1}_{1}p}$$

(The asterisk by the symbol for fluorine-18 signifies that the particle is a high-energy, compound nucleus.) Oxygen-17 is a rare but nonradioactive isotope of oxygen. Usually, transmutations caused by bombardments produce *radioactive* isotopes of other elements.

Electrically charged bombarding particles, like the alpha particle and the proton, can be given greater velocity and therefore greater energy when attracted by opposite charge. Particle accelerators, devices that do this, include some of the multimillion dollar hardware of atomic research — cyclotrons, betatrons, synchrotrons, and many others. The interactions of their ultrahigh-energy beams with selected targets have made possible the synthesis of dozens of new radionuclides.

Certain isotopes of uranium in atomic reactors eject neutrons, and although neutrons cannot be accelerated (they are electrically neutral), they have sufficient energy to serve as bombarding particles. Being neutral is an advantage, because the neutrons aren't repelled either by the electrons that surround an atom or by the nucleus. One of the very important applications of neutron bombardment is the synthesis of molybdenum-99 from molybdenum-98. With $^{1}_{0}n$ the symbol for the neutron, the equation is

$$^{98}_{42}\text{Mo} + {}^{1}_{0}n \longrightarrow {}^{99}_{42}\text{Mo} + \gamma$$

As we will learn in the Section 11.6, the decay of molybdenum-99 leads to one of the radionuclides most commonly used in medicine.

■ Remember that the energy of a moving object increases with the *square* of its velocity.

$$KE = \tfrac{1}{2}mv^2$$

11.5 RADIATION TECHNOLOGY IN THE FOOD INDUSTRY

Food irradiated with controlled doses of X rays, gamma rays, or electron beams is less likely to spoil.

X rays, gamma rays, and particle radiations have long been used in medicine as technologies for diagnosis and for cancer treatments. In treatments for cancer the aim is to kill the cells in cancer tissue. This same kind of aim, to kill cells that can subdivide, such as those of disease-causing microorganisms, is behind food irradiation technology, as we will study in this section.

Food Irradiation Inhibits, Inactivates, or Kills Molds and Bacteria When food products are passed through a beam of gamma rays, X rays, or accelerated electrons, the effects depend on the energy of the beam. A low-dose beam — up to 100 kilorads — renders reproductively dead any insects that remain after harvest and inhibits the sprouting of potatoes and onions during storage. Such beams also inactivate trichinae (*Trichinella spiralis,* a nematode worm) in pork, the parasite that causes trichinosis.

Medium-dosage beams of radiation — 100 to 1000 kilorads — significantly reduce the populations of salmonella bacteria in poultry, fish, and other meats. Such radiation also greatly extends the shelf lives of strawberries (see Figure 11.6) and certain other fruits, which otherwise form molds quickly.

High-dosage beams — 1000 to 10,000 kilorads — sterilize poultry, fish, and other meats. They also kill microorganisms and insects on seasonings and spices.

■ The occurrence of trichinosis in the pork supply of the United States is small, and thorough cooking destroys it. (Pork is never served ''rare.'')

Figure 11.6
After 15 days of storage at 4 °C (38 °F), the unirradiated strawberries on the left became heavily covered with mold. Those on the right, however, had been protected by 200 kilorads of radiation.

Food Irradiation Does Not Appear To Produce Any Unique Radiolytic Products Radiations cause chemical reactions in foods or any insects or microorganisms in them. Since water is generally the most abundant substance present, the primary products result from the splitting of water into radicals and ions. Some recombine to form water and others combine to give hydrogen peroxide. Otherwise, the primary products of irradiation react with food molecules to give secondary products. Generally, however, these are the same as will be produced by cooking or baking, or by the subsequent digestion of foods.

■ Hydrogen peroxide, H_2O_2, quickly breaks down to water and oxygen.

The irradiation of wheat and potatoes to control insects has been permitted in the United States for over twenty years, but no commercial operator is doing so. Some herbs and spices are now marketed after irradiation to reduce insects, bacteria, molds, and yeasts. The U.S. Food and Drug Administration (FDA) has approved the use of low-dosage radiation to control trichinae in pork and to inhibit the spoilage of fruit and vegetables. None of these operations is as yet widespread, mostly because they are expensive.

Besides cost, customer confidence is another barrier to further use of irradiation. Any technology with the word *nuclear* or *radiation* in it makes people nervous. The legitimate question is, "Does radiation produce substances — radiolytic products — that would not be present once foods have been otherwise processed, cooked, and digested?" If so, "Are the radiolytic products harmful at the levels at which they are present?"

Specialists in food irradiation claim that their research has yet to turn up any unique radiolytic products. Even benzene, for example, is not uniquely a product of radiation. Repeated environmental exposure to benzene is known to increase a person's likelihood of contacting leukemia, and *high-level* irradiation of certain foods gives traces of benzene. But small traces of this substance are naturally present in some nonirradiated foods, like boiled eggs, at much higher levels than produced by irradiation.

■ A half a pound of the botulinus toxin would be enough to kill all the people on earth.

Still another safety issue concerns botulism, a particularly dangerous form of food poisoning caused by an odorless chemical, a toxin, produced by *Clostridium botulinum*. This bacterium is more resistant to radiation than the microorganisms that cause food spoilage. Organisms that spoil foods give them dreadful odors which warn people, but the botulinus toxin cannot be detected in this way. High-dose food irradiation could thus prevent the kind of food spoilage associated with odors, without necessarily destroying all the botulinus bacillus. (Low-dose radiation kills too few of any kind of bacteria to pose this problem.)

Food irradiation technology has its strong proponents and opponents, and it is not yet clear how widely it will be used and accepted in the United States. Customers will in any event see labels to the effect that the food has been treated with radiation or that it has been made from such substances. This will give customers the choice of buying or not buying such food.

11.6 RADIATION TECHNOLOGY IN MEDICINE

Both in diagnosis and in cancer treatment, ionizing radiations are used when their benefits are judged to outweigh their harm.

■ *Radiology:* the science of radioactive substances and of X rays.
Radiologist: a specialist in radiology who also usually has a medical degree.
Radiobiology: the science of the effects of radiations on living things.

For medical uses, radiations either are supplied as X rays or electron beams generated by machinery or are emitted by selected radionuclides. In diagnostic work, radiations are used to locate a cancer or tumor or to assess the function of some organ, like the thyroid gland. In therapeutic work, radiations are used to kill cancerous cells or to inhibit their growth. Generally, therapeutic doses are of much higher energy than those used for diagnostic purposes. We look here at the radioactive chemicals used in diagnosis, and discuss beam radiation technologies in Special Topics.

Both Chemical and Radiological Properties Are Important in the Selection of Radionuclides in Medicine The *chemical* properties of radionuclides are identical to those of the stable isotopes of the same element. When radionuclides are selected for use in medicine, their chemistry, therefore, has to be considered. They must be *chemically* compatible with the living system when used for their radiations. Moreover, their *chemistry* is what guides them naturally to desired tissues. Iodine-127, for example, the only stable isotope of this element, is used chemically in the body by the thyroid gland to make the hormone thyroxin. This chemical property also will guide iodine-131, a beta-emitter, to the thyroid gland, where its radiations can be used to assess thyroid function or to treat cancer of the thyroid gland, as we will see.

Minimizing Harm and Maximizing Benefit Guide the Selection of Radionuclides in Medicine Exposing anyone to any radiation entails some risks, because prolonged exposure can produce cancer. No such exposure is permitted unless the expected benefit from finding and treating a dangerous disease is thought to be greater than the risk. To minimize the risks, the radiologist uses radionuclides that, as much as possible, have the following properties.

1. The radionuclide should have a half-life that is short. (Then it will decay *during* the diagnosis when the decay gives some benefit, and as little as possible of the radionuclide will decay later, when the radiations are of no benefit.)

2. The product of the decay of the radionuclide should have little if any radiation of its own. (Either the product should be a stable isotope or it should have a very long half-life.) It should also be quickly eliminated.

3. The half-life of the radionuclide must be long enough for it to be prepared and administered to the patient.

4. If the radionuclide is to be used for diagnosis, it should decay by penetrating radiation entirely, which means gamma radiation. (Nonpenetrating radiations, such as alpha and beta radiation, add to the risk by causing internal damage without contributing to the detection of the radiation externally. For uses in *therapy,* as in cancer therapy, nonpenetrating radiation is preferred because a radionuclide well placed in cancerous tissue *should* cause damage to such tissue.)

5. The diseased tissue should concentrate the radionuclide, giving a "hot spot" where the diseased area exists, or it should do the opposite and reject the radionuclide, making the diseased area a "cold spot" insofar as external detectors are concerned.

Let us now look briefly at a few of the more important radionuclides employed in medicine.

Technetium-99*m* Is the Radionuclide Most Widely Used in Medicine Technetium-99*m* is a radionuclide produced by the decay of molybdenum-99. (The synthesis of molybdenum-99 was described at the end of Section 11.4.) See also Special Topic 11.3. You

TECHNETIUM-99*m* IN MEDICINE

To make a dilute solution of technetium-99*m* (in the form of TcO_4^-) a radiologist "milks a molybdenum cow." See the accompanying figure. This device contains molybdenum-99 (in the form of MoO_4^{2-}) mixed with granules of alumina. (Alumina is one of the crystalline forms of Al_2O_3, and it is used here as a support for the molybdenate ion.) The device is charged at a nuclear reactor facility by the neutron bombardment of the molybdenum-98 present (as MoO_4^{2-}) on the alumina granules, as described in Section 11.6. After neutron bombardment, the device is shipped to the hospital, and all the while the molybdenum-99 is decaying to technetium-99*m*.

Each morning, a member of the radiology staff lets a predetermined volume of isotonic salt solution trickle through the bed of granules. Some of the pertechnetate ions dissolve and are leached out. Then the solution so obtained is used for the day's work. After several days, too little molybdenum-99 remains, so the device is shipped back to the reactor for recharging.

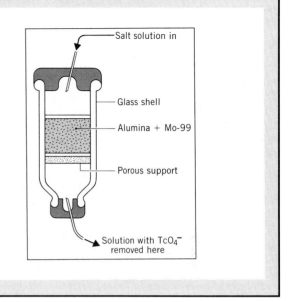

already know that gamma radiation often accompanies the emission of other radiations, but with molybdenum-99 the gamma radiation comes after a pause. Molybdenum-99 first emits a beta particle:

$$\ce{^{99}_{42}Mo} \longrightarrow \ce{^{99m}_{43}Tc} + \ce{^{0}_{-1}e}$$

The other decay product is a metastable form of technetium-99, hence the *m* in 99*m*. Metastable means poised to move toward greater stability. Technetium-99*m* decays by emitting gamma radiation with an energy of 143 keV:

$$\ce{^{99m}_{43}Tc} \longrightarrow \ce{^{99}_{43}Tc} + \gamma$$

Technetium-99*m* almost ideally fits the criteria for a radionuclide intended for diagnostic work. Its half-life is short, 6.02 hr. Its decay product, technetium-99, has a very long half-life, 212,000 years, so it has too little activity to be of much concern. (Technetium-99 decays to a stable isotope of ruthenium, $\ce{^{99}_{44}Ru}$.) The half-life of technetium-99*m*, although short, is still long enough to allow time to prepare it and administer it. It decays entirely by gamma radiation, which means that *all* the radiation gets to a detector to signal where the radionuclide is in the body. Finally, a variety of chemically combined forms of technetium-99*m* have been developed that permit either hot spots or cold spots to form.

One form of technetium-99*m* is the pertechnetate ion, TcO_4^-. It behaves in the body very much like a halide ion, so it tends to go where chloride ions, for example, go. It is eliminated by the kidneys, so it is used to assess kidney function. Other organs whose functions are also studied by technetium-99*m* are the liver, spleen, lungs, heart, brain, bones, and the thyroid gland.

Technetium-99*m* technology has received competition from the CT scan (Special Topic 11.4), the PET scan (Special Topic 11.5), and MRI imaging (Special Topic 11.6). But they are much more expensive, so technetium-99*m* will continue to be used for some time.

Iodine-131 and Iodine-123   The thyroid gland, the only user of iodine in the body, takes iodide ion and, as we said, makes the hormone thyroxin. When an underactive or an overactive thyroid is suspected, one technique is to let the patient drink a glass of flavored water that contains some radioactive iodine as I^-. By placing radiation detection equipment

SPECIAL TOPIC 11.4 — X RAYS AND CT SCANS

X rays are generated by bombarding a metal surface with high-energy electrons. These can penetrate the metal atom far enough to knock out one of its low-level orbital electrons, such as a 1s electron. This creates a "hole" in the electron configuration, and orbital electrons at higher levels begin to drop down. In other words, the creation of this "hole" leads to electrons changing their energy levels. The difference between two of the lower levels corresponds to the energy of an X ray, which is emitted.

The refinement of X-ray techniques and the development of powerful computers made possible the generation of a diagnostic technology called computerized tomography, or CT for short. A. M. Cormack (United States) and G. N. Hounsfield (England) shared the 1979 Nobel prize in medicine for their work in the development of this technology. The instrument includes a large array of carefully positioned and focused X-ray generators. In the procedure called a CT scan, this array is rotated as a unit around the body or the head of the patient. Extremely brief pulses of X rays are sent in from all angles across one cross section of the patient. (See the accompanying photo.)

The changes in the X rays that are caused by internal organs or by tumors are sent to a computer, which then processes the data and delivers a picture of the cross section. It's like getting a picture of the inside of a cherry pit without cutting open the cherry. The CT scan is widely used for locating tumors and cancers (see the other accompanying figure).

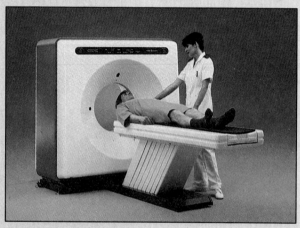

Instrument for the CT scan. Shown here is General Electric's CT/T Total Body Scanner which can complete an entire scan of the head or body in as short a period as 4.8 seconds.

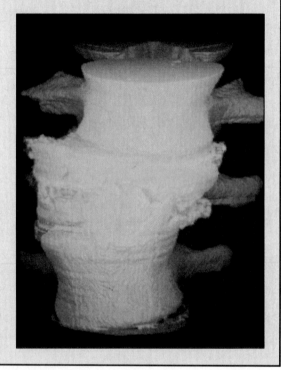

A three-dimensional image, based on 63 CT scans, of a section of the vertebrae of a man injured in a motorcycle accident. Both the compression and the twisting are clearly evident.

near the thyroid gland, the radiologist can tell how well this gland takes up iodide ion from circulation. For diagnostic purposes, iodine-123 is popular because it has a short half-life (13.3 h) and it emits only gamma radiation (159 keV). Iodine-131 also has a short half-life (8 days), but it emits both beta particles (600 keV) and gamma radiation (mostly 360 keV). Certain types of thyroid cancer have been treated with this radionuclide. The ability of this gland to concentrate iodide ion is so good that if a small whole-body dose of iodine-131 is given, nearly 1000 times this much dose concentrates in the thyroid.

Technetium-99m as the hydrated pertechnetate ion, TcO_4^-, has about the same radius and charge density as the hydrated iodide ion. Cells of the thyroid gland, therefore, do not distinguish between these two ions at the point where they move inside the cells. When the purpose is to get any kind of detectable radiation inside the thyroid gland in order to detect a tumor or cancer, then Tc-99m, because of its short half-life (6.02 hr), is preferred over any radionuclide of iodine.

SPECIAL TOPIC 11.5   POSITRON EMISSION TOMOGRAPHY — THE PET SCAN

A number of synthetic radionuclides emit positrons. These are particles that have the same small mass as an electron but carry one unit of *positive* charge. (They're sometimes called a positive electron.) A positron forms by the conversion of a proton into a neutron:

$$\,_{1}^{1}p \longrightarrow \,_{0}^{1}n \;+\; \,_{1}^{0}e$$

Proton   Neutron   Positron
(in atom's   (stays in   (is emitted)
nucleus)   nucleus)

Positrons, when emitted, last for only a brief interval before they collide with an electron. The two particles annihilate each other, and in so doing their masses convert entirely into energy in the form of two tiny bursts of gamma radiation (511 keV). The gamma radiation formed in this way is called annihilation radiation.

$$\,_{-1}^{0}e \;+\; \,_{1}^{0}e \longrightarrow 2\,_{0}^{0}\gamma$$

Electron   Positron   Gamma
radiation

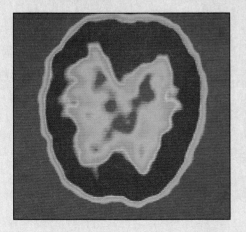

The patient is shown undergoing a brain scan performed by means of the PET technology.

The two bursts leave the collision site in almost exactly opposite directions.

For a medically useful technology to be based on this property of the positron, a positron-emitting nuclide must be part of a molecule with a chemistry that will carry it into the particular tissue to be studied. Once the molecule gets in, the tissue now has a gamma-radiator *on the inside.* Thus instead of X rays being sent through the body, as in a CT scan (Special Topic 11.4), the radiation originates right within the site being monitored. The overall procedure is called positron emission tomography, or PET for short.

Three positron-emitters are often used: oxygen-15, nitrogen-13, and carbon-11. Glucose, for example, can be made in which one carbon atom is carbon-11 instead of the usual carbon-12. Glucose can cross the blood–brain barrier and get inside brain cells. If some part of the brain is experiencing abnormal glucose metabolism, this will be reflected in the way in which positron-emitting glucose is handled, and gamma-radiation detectors on the outside can pick up the differences. The use of the PET scan has led to the discovery that glucose metabolism in the brain is altered in schizophrenia and manic depression. PET scanning technology is able to identify extremely small regions in the brain that are in early stages of breakdown and that CT and MRI techniques miss. The PET scan is particularly useful in detecting abnormal brain function in infants, as in early stages of epilepsy.

PET technology is being used to study a number of neuropsychiatric disorders, including Parkinson's disease. When a drug labeled with carbon-11 is used, its molecules go to the parts of the brain with nerve endings that release dopamine. A PET scan then discloses the dopamine-releasing potential of the patient. This potential becomes impaired in Parkinson's disease.

By labeling blood platelets with a positron-emitter, scientists can follow the development of atherosclerosis in even the tiniest of human blood vessels. Blood flow in the heart can be monitored without having to insert a catheter.

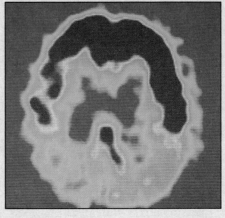

Left: Normal brain scan using PET technology. Right: PET scan of the brain of a patient with Alzheimer's disease.

SPECIAL TOPIC 11.6   MAGNETIC RESONANCE IMAGING—THE MRI SCAN

The CT scan subjects a patient to large numbers of short bursts of X rays. The PET scan exposes the patient to gamma radiation that is generated on the inside. Thus both technologies carry the usual risks that attend ionizing radiations, and they are used when the potential benefits from correct diagnoses far outweigh such risks. The MRI imaging technology operates without these dangers. At least, none has been discovered thus far. The principal developer of the first hardware for MRI imaging was Raymond Damadian.

MRI stands for magnetic resonance imaging. Atomic nuclei that have odd numbers of protons and neutrons behave as though they were tiny magnets, hence the *magnetic* part of MRI. The nucleus of ordinary hydrogen (which has no neutrons and one proton) constitutes the most abundant nuclear magnet in living systems, because hydrogen atoms are parts of water molecules, and all biochemicals. Nuclear magnets spin about an axis much as the electron spins about its axis.

When molecules with spinning nuclear magnets are in a strong magnetic field and are simultaneously bathed with properly tuned radio-frequency radiation (which is of very low energy), the nuclear magnets flip their spins. (This is the *resonance* part of MRI.) As they resonate, they emit electromagnetic energy that is biologically harmless, being of very low energy, and this energy is picked up by detectors. The data are fed into computers, which produce an image much like that of a CT or a PET scan, but without having subjected the patient to ultrahigh-energy electromagnetic radiation such as X rays or gamma rays. The MRI images are actually sophisticated plots of the distributions of the spinning nuclear magnets, of hydrogen atoms, for example.

MRI imaging has proved to be especially useful for studying soft tissue, the sort of tissue least well studied by X rays. Different soft tissues have different population densities of water molecules or of fat molecules (which are loaded with hydrogen atoms). And tumors and cancerous tissue have their own water inventories. Calcium ions do not produce any signals to confuse MRI imaging, so bone,

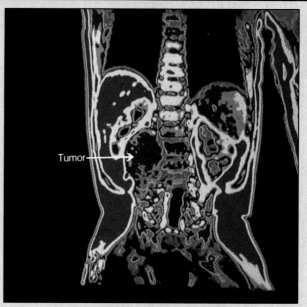

An MRI scan of a seven-month-old child revealed a malignant tumor pushing its way into the spinal canal. (The tumor was treated in time.)

which is rich in calcium, is transparent to MRI.

MRI technology has developed during the 1980s as a method superior to the CT scan for diagnosing tumors at the rear and base of the skull and equal to the CT scan for finding other brain tumors. MRI is now the preferred technology for assessing problems in joints (particularly the knees) and in the spinal cord, such as ruptured (herniated, "slipped") disks. Patients with heart pacemakers or embedded shrapnel or surgical clips present problems to the use of MRI because of the powerful magnets used.

CT scans are still better than MRI for the early detection of hemorrhages in the brain, so CT is the method of choice for finding them in potential stroke victims. CT scans are also still preferred for detecting tumors in the kidneys, lungs, pancreas, and the spleen.

Cobalt-60 Provides Gamma Radiation above the Megaelectron-Volt Level

Cobalt-60 emits beta radiation (315 keV) and gamma radiation (2.819 MeV), and it has a half-life of 5.3 years. Gram for gram, cobalt-60 has an activity more than 200 times that of pure radium, which until the 1950s had been widely used in treating cancer. The sample of cobalt-60 is placed in a lead container that is many centimeters thick and has an opening pointed toward the cancerous site. All beta radiations are shielded by a thin piece of aluminum.

■ Cobalt-60 therapy is being replaced by the radiations from linear accelerators.

Linear Accelerators Make Ultrahigh-Energy X Rays

Betatrons are linear accelerators that are tending to supplant cobalt-60 therapy for several reasons. These devices generate X rays for therapeutic uses with energies in the range of 6 to 12 MeV, which are much more powerful and so more penetrating than the gamma rays from cobalt-60. The output of the machines is stable; the output of cobalt-60 declines over time. The edges of the beams are sharply defined; those from cobalt-60 are less so. This means that X-ray pictures obtained as the therapy is applied are of higher quality. Linear accelerator machines are easily mounted so that they can rotate about a central point, which makes it easier to position the patient and plan the treatment.

Other Medically Useful Radionuclides Are Available for Special Purposes Indium-111 ($t_{1/2}$ = 2.8 days; gamma-emitter, 173 and 247 keV) has been found to be a good labeler of blood platelets.

Gallium-67 ($t_{1/2}$ = 78 hr; gamma-emitter, 1.003 MeV) is used in the diagnosis of Hodgkin's disease, lymphomas, and bronchogenic carcinoma.

Phosphorus-32 ($t_{1/2}$ = 14.3 days; beta-emitter, 1.71 MeV) in the form of the phosphate ion has been used to treat a form of leukemia, a cancer of the bone that affects white cells in the blood. Because the phosphate ion is part of the hydroxyapatite mineral in bone, this ion is a bone-seeker.

11.7 ATOMIC ENERGY AND RADIONUCLIDES

Nuclear power plants generate atomic wastes that must be kept from human contact for several centuries.

All operating nuclear power plants in the United States today use fission to generate heat. **Fission** is the disintegration of a large atomic nucleus into small fragments following neutron capture. It releases additional neutrons, radioactive isotopes, and enormous yields of heat. Unless the reactor is continuously cooled by a flowing coolant, usually water, the whole system will melt very quickly. The heat converts the coolant into a hot gas under high pressure, such as steam, which drives electric turbines. See Figure 11.7. Thus some of the fission energy becomes electrical energy, and what isn't used for this is vented as heat to the atmosphere or into a moving stream of cooler water from a river or lake.

■ Neutrons moving too rapidly are poorly captured.

The uranium-235 isotope is the only naturally occurring radionuclide that spontaneously undergoes fission when it captures a slow-moving and relatively low-energy neutron. After

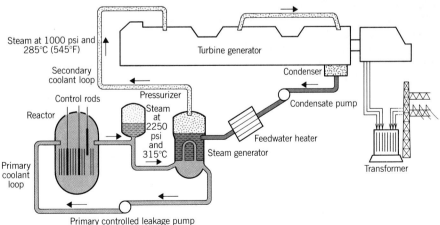

Figure 11.7

Pressurized-water nuclear power station. Water in the primary coolant loop circulates around the reactor core and carries away the heat of fission. This water is sealed under pressure, so its temperature can rise well above its normal boiling point. The water delivers its heat to the water in the secondary loop, which then turns to high-pressure steam and drives the electrical turbines. Maximum efficiency is reached by having as large a drop as possible between the inlet steam temperature in this loop and the outlet water temperature. (Drawing from WASH 1261, U.S. Atomic Energy Commission, 1973.)

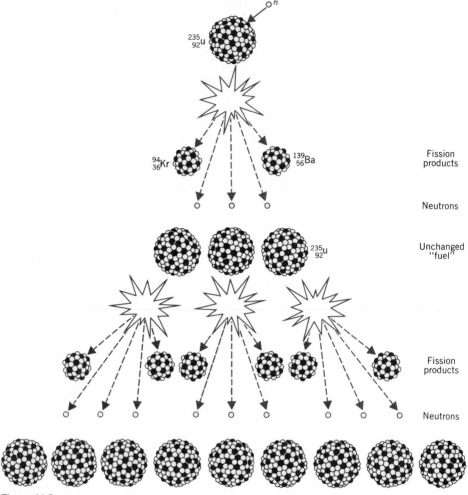

Figure 11.8
Fission is initiated when a nucleus of uranium-235 captures a neutron. The new nucleus splits apart, and more neutrons are released. These can initiate subsequent fission events, and unless this is prevented or at least tightly controlled, the whole mass of uranium-235 will detonate—as in the explosion of an atomic bomb. One method of control is to keep the mass of uranium-235 low, below what is called the critical mass. Now, enough neutrons escape before being captured by neighboring nuclei.

capturing such a neutron, the nucleus spontaneously splits apart. It can split in a number of ways that give different products. We'll give the equation for just one mode of splitting.

$$^{235}_{92}\text{U} + ^{1}_{0}n \xrightarrow[\text{capture}]{\text{neutron}} ^{236}_{92}\text{U} \xrightarrow{\text{fission}} ^{139}_{56}\text{Ba} + ^{94}_{36}\text{Kr} + 3^{1}_{0}n + \gamma + \text{heat}$$

■ Plutonium-239, made in reactors, also can fission, and it is used as a nuclear fuel and in making atomic bombs.

More neutrons are released than are used up. Hence, one fission event produces particles that can initiate more than one new fission. In other words, a **nuclear chain reaction** takes place (Figure 11.8) that would almost instantly envelop all U-235 atoms present were the system not designed to hold the ratio of neutrons produced to neutrons captured at 1 : 1, the *critical* ratio. When this ratio goes higher, becomes *supercritical,* and the concentration of U-235 is very high, an atomic explosion will occur. If the U-235 concentration is low, no *atomic* explosion occurs, but the heat generated cannot be removed rapidly enough to prevent the whole system from melting.

A nuclear *reactor* is a device to enable the control of nuclear fission at the critical ratio so that heat is generated without running any risk of an atomic explosion and is removed rapidly

■ The fuel is a mixture of powdered oxides of U-235 and U-238 baked into ceramic-like pellets.

■ The circulating water is also a good neutron moderator.

enough to prevent a meltdown. The nuclear "fuel" is U-235 at a concentration of 3% to 5%. It is distributed among a large number of small-radius tubes (called cladding tubes) so that a significant fraction of neutrons can escape without causing fission. Control rods can be moved into or out of the spaces between these tubes. They are made of materials that can capture neutrons harmlessly. Circulating around and among the tubes is the coolant (water in nearly all reactors), which is heated by the atomic fission taking place.

In *pressurized water reactors,* the water is kept under pressure so that it can be heated above its normal boiling point. As seen in Figure 11.7, this water is in a closed, primary loop engineered to heat the water in a secondary loop. The steam thus generated in the secondary loop drives the turbines, and this operation cools the fluid back to liquid water for recirculation.

Fission Products Are Potential Pollutants   The new isotopes produced by fission are radioactive, and their decay leads to radioactive pollutants, which must be contained by the reactor and, later, by safe storage. They include strontium-90 (a bone-seeking element in the calcium family), iodine-131 (a thyroid-gland-seeker), and cesium-137 (a group IA radionuclide that goes wherever Na^+ or K^+ can go). The U.S. government has set limits to the release of each radioactive isotope into the air and into the cooling water of nuclear power plants. Plants that operate in compliance with these standards expose people living near them to an extra dose of no more than 5% of the dose they normally receive from background radiations.

Two Steam Explosions Ruptured a Large Atomic Reactor at Chernobyl
Nuclear reactors are encased in huge chambers called containment vessels with thick walls made of steel-reinforced concrete. If a rupture occurs in the coolant lines that lead into and out of the reactor's core, and there is suddenly a loss of coolant around the core, an emergency backup coolant system is activated, and the reactor is shut down by means of the control rods. Between the time of the first loss of coolant and the successful operation of the backup and shutdown activities, the containment vessel is meant to retain any radioactivity.

A loss-of-coolant emergency occurred in 1979 at a nuclear power plant at Three-Mile Island in Pennsylvania. The emergency systems worked, but it took nearly seven years of cleanup just to get the *undamaged* reactor back into reaction. There was widespread public alarm over the accident.

The nightmare scenario of nuclear power, a breach in the reactor vessel, occurred on April 26, 1986, at the great atomic energy park at Chernobyl, Russia. The reactors at Chernobyl were not encased in massive containment structures such as are used in other countries. Through operator error, the emergency cooling system was not operational when a loss of coolant occurred in one reactor. Within 5 seconds the reactor's power increased 1400-fold, and steam developed with enough pressure to blow off a cover plate weighing 1000 tons. The tops of all the some 1600 cladding tubes were also torn off. Each erupted like a shotgun, and 8 tons of radioactive, incandescent fuel and wastes were hurled into the night sky. A radioactive plume rose 3200 feet into the atmosphere and started to drift on the prevailing winds. The human exposure to radioactive cesium-137 in the northern hemisphere from this accident is estimated to be 60% of the human exposure to this radionuclide from all previous atmospheric nuclear tests.

The explosions that occurred were *not* atom-bomb-like explosions. The concentration of fissionable U-235 in the fuel of atomic reactors is, as we said, far to low for this to happen under any circumstances. In an atomic bomb, essentially pure U-235 is used, and when a sufficient mass is suddenly brought together, fission multiplies much more rapidly than neutrons can escape. The explosions at Chernobyl were those of steam suddenly raised to ultrahigh pressure, which the reactor could not contain.

■ If the reactor core starts to melt, it cannot be shut down and will melt its way through the containment vessel.

■ At Chernobyl the graphite used as a moderator ignited and burned like any charcoal fire. Some extremely brave fire fighters managed to extinguish this fire.

Wastes from Nuclear Power Plants Must Be Kept Apart from Human Contact for a Thousand Years   One of the most vexing problems of nuclear energy has been the permanent storage of long-lived radioactive wastes. Most are now in temporary storage at nuclear power plants. Because several waste radionuclides have very long half-lives, the

■ The entire reactor becomes a radioactive waste once the power plant's working lifetime is over.

wastes must be sequestered from all human contact for at least a thousand years, and scientists are seeking deep geologic formations out of all contact with mining operations or underground water supplies into which these wastes can be placed. The sites must be marked and continuously maintained so that archeologists several centuries hence will not unknowingly venture into them.

Wastes Can Enter Food Chains Atomic wastes that do escape, like I-131 from Chernobyl, enter food chains wherever they deposit. Milk from cows that have grazed on pastures contaminated by I-131 fallout carries this isotope into the human diet. We indicated earlier how effectively the human thyroid gland concentrates iodine, so those parts of Europe where the Chernobyl plume drifted were suddenly faced with hard decisions. One strategy was to distribute sodium iodide to the populations with instructions about taking it in drinking water. By thus raising the level of nonradioactive iodide ion, the fraction of radioactive iodide ion taken up by the thyroid gland would be reduced. Another strategy was to forbid the consumption of meat products from animals testing at unnaturally high radiation levels. (Two years after Chernobyl, for example, this affected roughly 300,000 sheep in northern Great Britain.)

■ Workers at Chernobyl received at least 400 rem of radiation dose, and 31 died. In a town nearby, 135,000 people were evacuated; they were receiving 1 rem/hr the day after the explosion.

The Chernobyl accident, according to one study, will probably be responsible for 1000 extra cancer deaths among the 12 countries of the European Community over the next 50 years. Compared to the roughly 30 million cancers from other causes during the same period, this number is statistically negligible. The same study also estimated that in the same community the average individual's dose of radiation from Chernobyl over the next 50 years would be less than that received from one year's worth of natural background radiation. Despite such estimates, a breach-of-containment accident is still a nightmare, and Chernobyl dramatically dampened public support for nuclear power, particularly in Europe, where most countries have canceled plans for future nuclear power plants.

SUMMARY

Atomic radiations Radionuclides in nature emit alpha radiation (helium nuclei), beta radiation (electrons), and gamma radiation (high-energy X-ray-like radiation). This radioactive decay causes transmutation. The penetrating abilities of the radiations are a function of the sizes of the particles, their charges, and the energies with which they are emitted. Gamma radiations, which have no associated mass or charge, are the most penetrating.

Each decay can be described by a nuclear equation in which mass numbers and atomic numbers on either side of the arrow must balance. To describe how stable a radionuclide is we use its half-life, and the shorter this is, the more radioactive is the radionuclide.

The decay of one radionuclide doesn't always produce a stable nuclide. Uranium-238 is at the head of a radioactive disintegration series that involves several intermediate radionuclides until a stable isotope of lead forms.

Ionizing radiations — dangers and precautions When radiations travel in matter, they create unstable ions and radicals that have chemical properties dangerous to health. Intermittent exposure can lead to cancer, tumors, mutations, or birth defects. Intense exposures cause radiation sickness and death. Intense exposures focused on cancer tissue are used in cancer therapy. The use of distance, fast film, and dense shielding material are the best strategies to guard against the hazards of ionizing radiations. According to the inverse-square law, the intensity of radiation falls off with the square of the distance from the source. Complete protection, however, is not possible because of the natural background radiation that now includes traces of radioactive pollutants.

Units of radiation measurement To describe activity we use the curie, Ci, or the becquerel, Bq. To describe the intensity of exposure to X rays or gamma radiation, we use the roentgen. The gray (Gy) or the rad (D) is used to indicate how much energy has been absorbed by a unit mass of tissue (or other matter). To put the damage that different radiations can cause when they have the same values of rads (or grays) on a comparable and additive basis, we use the rem. Finally, to describe the energy possessed by a radiation, we use the electron-volt. Diagnostic X rays are on the order of 100 keV. Radiations used in cancer treatment are in the low MeV range. To measure radiations there are devices such as film badges, scintillation counters, and ionization counters (Geiger-Müller tubes).

Synthetic radionuclides A number of synthetic radionuclides have been made by bombarding various isotopes with alpha radiation, neutrons, or accelerated protons. The target nucleus first accepts the mass, charge, and energy of the bombarding particle, and then it ejects something else to give the new nuclide.

Radiation technology in the food industry X rays, gamma rays, and accelerated electrons can be used to inhibit or to kill insects, molds, and bacteria on seeds, potatoes, fruit, and meats. High doses fully sterilize the products. Low doses inhibit bacterial or mold growth. Radiolytic products, those formed by the chemical reactions induced by the radiation, are generally the same as the substances found naturally in food either before cooking and digestion or after. The resistance of the botulinus bacillus to radiations is one problem with the technology.

Radionuclides in medicine For diagnostic uses, the radionuclide should have a short half-life (but not so short that it decays before any benefit can be obtained). It should decay by gamma radiation only, and it should be chemically compatible with the organ or tissue so that either a hot spot or a cold spot appears. Its decay products should be as stable as possible, and capable of being eliminated from the body.

Technetium-99m is almost ideal for diagnostic work, particularly for assessing the ability of an organ or a tissue to function. Radionuclides of iodine (I-123 and I-131) are used in diagnosing or treating thyroid conditions. Gallium-67, indium-111, and phosphorus-32 are a few of the many other radionuclides used in diagnosis. Cobalt-60 has powerful gamma radiation, and is used in cancer treatment. Linear accelerators also provide high-energy (6 to 12 MeV) radiation for cancer therapy.

REVIEW EXERCISES

The answers to the Review Exercises that require a calculation or the balancing of an equation and that are marked with an asterisk are found in Appendix D. The answers to the other Review Exercises are found in the *Study Guide* that accompanies this book.

Radioactivity and Radiations

11.1 If a sample is described as *radioactive,* what specifically do we know about it?

11.2 The forerunners of chemists were called alchemists, and in ancient times one of their quests was for a way to change a base metal such as lead into gold. Today what technical word would be used to describe such a change if it were successful?

11.3 The film that Becquerel put in his desk drawer was wrapped in fairly heavy paper. In view of what we know today, his discovery of radioactivity depended on the emission of which radiation from the uranium ore sample?

11.4 When we write nuclear equations, which symbols are used for each of the following?
(a) the alpha particle
(b) the beta particle
(c) a gamma ray

11.5 The energy of an alpha particle is often higher than that of beta or gamma rays. Why is it, then, the least penetrating of the radiations?

11.6 The loss of an alpha particle changes the radionuclide's mass number by how many units? Its atomic number by how many units?

11.7 Why does the loss of a beta particle not change the radionuclide's mass number but *increase* its atomic number?

11.8 What happens to the mass number and to the atomic number of a radionuclide if it is only a gamma emitter?

11.9 Are *all* radioactive decays also transmutations?

11.10 If electrons do not exist in the nucleus, how can one originate in a nucleus in beta decay?

Atomic energy and radioactive pollutants The reactors of most nuclear power plants use U-235 as a fuel. When its atoms capture neutrons, they fission into smaller, usually radioactive atoms as neutrons are released that can cause additional fissions. The concentration of U-235 atoms is kept too small (3% to 5%) to make an atomic bomb type of explosion possible at a nuclear reactor. Circulating water keeps the reactor cool enough not to melt. The heat generated by fission converts water into high-pressure steam that drives electrical turbines. A containment vessel surrounding the reactor is intended to prevent the escape of radioactive materials should a loss-of-coolant emergency arise. (The containment system worked at Three-Mile Island.)

Radioactive by-products of fission, such as I-131, Sr-80, and Cs-137, cannot be allowed to enter the food supply and must be contained. Some fission products have such long half-lives that radioactive wastes must be kept from human contact for a thousand years.

Nuclear Equations

*11.11 Write the symbols of the missing particles in the following nuclear equations.
(a) $^{245}_{96}Cm \rightarrow {}^{4}_{2}He +$ _____
(b) $^{22}_{9}F \rightarrow {}_{-1}^{0}e +$ _____

11.12 Complete the following nuclear equations by writing the symbols of the missing particles.
(a) $^{220}_{86}Rn \rightarrow {}^{4}_{2}He +$ _____
(b) $^{140}_{56}Ba \rightarrow {}_{-1}^{0}e +$ _____

*11.13 Write a balanced nuclear equation for each of the following changes.
(a) Alpha emission from einsteinium-252
(b) Beta emission from magnesium-28
(c) Beta emission from oxygen-20
(d) Alpha and gamma emission from californium-251

11.14 Give the nuclear equation for each of the following radioactive decays.
(a) Beta emission from bismuth-211
(b) Alpha and gamma emission from plutonium-242
(c) Beta emission from aluminum-30
(d) Alpha emission from curium-243

Half-Lives

11.15 Lead-214 is in the uranium-238 disintegration series. Its half-life is 19.7 min. Explain in your own words what being in this series means and what *half-life* means.

11.16 Which would be more dangerous to be near, a radionuclide that has a short half-life and decays by alpha emission only, or a radionuclide that has the same half-life but decays by beta and gamma emissions? Explain.

*11.17 A 12.00-ng sample of technetium-99m will still have how many nanograms of this radionuclide left after four half-life periods? (This is about a day.)

11.18 If a patient is given 9.00 ng of iodine-123 (half-life 13.3 hr), how many nanograms of this radionuclide remain after 12 half-life periods (about a week)?

Dangers of Ionizing Radiations

11.19 We have ions in every fluid of the body. Why, then, are ionizing radiations dangerous?

11.20 What is a chemical *radical,* and why is it chemically reactive?

11.21 Radiations are teratogenic agents. What does this mean?

11.22 Plutonium-239 is a carcinogen. What does this mean?

11.23 What two properties of ionizing radiations are exploited in strategies for providing radiation protection?

11.24 Atomic radiations are said to have no threshold exposure. What does this mean?

11.25 How is it that the same agent—radiations from a radionuclide—can be used both to cause cancer and to cure it?

11.26 The inverse-square law tells us that if we double the distance from a radioactive source, we will reduce the radiation intensity received by a factor of what number?

11.27 What general property of radiations is behind the inverse-square law?

11.28 List as many factors as you can that contribute to the background radiation.

11.29 Why does a trip in a high-altitude jet plane increase a person's exposure to background radiation?

•11.30 A radiologist discovered that at a distance of 1.80 m from a radioactive source, the intensity of radiation was 140 millirad. How far should the radiologist move away to reduce the exposure to 2 millirad?

11.31 Using a Geiger-Müller counter, a radiologist found that in a 20-min period the dose from a radioactive source would measure 40 millirad at a distance of 10.0 m. How much dose would be received in the same time by moving to a distance of 1.00 m?

Units of Radiation Measurement

11.32 What SI unit is used to describe the activity of a radioactive sample?

11.33 A hospital purchased a sample of a radionuclide rated at 1.5 mCi. What does this rating mean?

11.34 Give the name of the unit that describes the intensity of an exposure to X rays.

11.35 What are the name and symbol of the SI unit used in describing how much energy a given mass of tissue receives from exposure to radiation? What are the name and symbol of the older, common unit?

11.36 Approximately how many rads would kill half of a large population within four weeks, assuming that each individual received this much?

11.37 From a health protection standpoint, how do the roentgen and the rad compare in their potential danger?

11.38 We cannot add a 1-rad dose of gamma radiation to some organ to a 1-rad dose of neutron radiation to the same organ and say that the total biologically effective dose is 2 rads. Why not?

11.39 How is the problem implied by the previous review exercise resolved?

11.40 In units of mrem, what is the average natural background radiation received by the U.S. population, exclusive of medical sources, radioactive pollutants, and fallout?

11.41 What is the name of the energy unit used to describe the energy associated with an X ray or a gamma ray?

11.42 In the unit traditionally used (Review Exercise 11.41), how much energy is associated with diagnostic X rays?

11.43 Why should diagnostic radiations ideally be of much lower energy than radiations used in therapy, in cancer treatment, for example?

11.44 In general terms, how does a film badge dosimeter work?

11.45 In your own words, how does a Geiger-Müller counter work? Why doesn't it detect alpha radiation?

Synthetic Radionuclides

•11.46 When manganese-55 is bombarded by protons, the neutron is one product. What else is produced? Write a nuclear equation.

11.47 To make indium-111 for diagnostic work, silver-109 is bombarded with alpha particles. What forms if the nucleus of silver-109 captures one alpha particle? Write the nuclear equation for this capture.

•11.48 The compound nucleus that forms when silver-109 captures an alpha particle (previous review exercise) decays directly to indium-111, plus *two* other identical particles. What are they? Write the nuclear equation for this decay.

11.49 To make gallium-67 for diagnostic work, zinc-66 is bombarded with accelerated protons. When a nucleus of zinc-66 captures a proton, the nucleus of what isotope forms? Write the nuclear equation.

•11.50 The isotope that forms when zinc-66 captures a proton (previous review exercise) is unstable in a novel way (novel at least to our study). This nucleus is able to capture one of its own electrons. When it does, what new nucleus forms? Write the equation for this kind of nuclear event—called electron capture.

11.51 When fluorine-19 is bombarded by alpha particles, both a neutron and a nucleus of sodium-22 form. Write the nuclear equation, including the compound nucleus that is the intermediate.

•11.52 When boron-10 is bombarded by alpha particles, nitrogen-13 forms and a neutron is released. Write the equation for this reaction.

11.53 When nitrogen-14 is bombarded with deuterons, $_1^2H$, oxygen-15 and a neutron form. Write the equation for this reaction.

'11.54 What bombarding particle could change aluminum-27 into phosphorus-32 and a proton? Write the equation.

11.55 What bombarding particle can change sulfur-32 into phosphorus-32 and a proton? Write the equation.

Radiation Technology and the Food Industry

'11.56 The unit commonly used to describe how much radiation has been given to a food product is the *kilorad,* krad. Using conversion factors supplied in Section 11.3, calculate how much energy is in 1.00 krad in units of J/kg.

11.57 What is meant by the term *radiolytic product?*

11.58 What is meant by the term *unique* radiolytic product?

11.59 Are any radiolytic products known cancer-causing substances? Are they also found in nonirradiated foods? Give an example.

11.60 What nonradiation processes produce the same compounds as food irradiation?

11.61 What potential hazard in food is the most difficult to remove by radiation?

11.62 In kilorads, what is regarded as a high dose of radiation? What beneficial effects does this have for meat products?

11.63 In what way does a low dose of radiation affect the wholesomeness and purity of a food product?

11.64 Describe the benefits of medium doses of radiation to food products.

Medical Applications of Radiations

11.65 Why is it desirable to use a radionuclide of short half-life in diagnostic work, when we know that even small samples of such isotopes can be very active?

11.66 The possible dangers related to the high activity of a sample of a radionuclide of short half-life can be minimized by taking advantage of this activity. What can be done with such a radionuclide that could not be done as easily with one of very long half-life?

11.67 We know that gamma radiation is the most penetrating of all natural radiations. Why, then, is a diagnostic radionuclide that emits only gamma radiation preferable to one that gives, say, only alpha radiation?

11.68 Why is iodine-123 better for diagnostic work than iodine-131?

11.69 Why did cobalt-60 replace radium for cancer treatment?

11.70 In what chemical form should phosphorus-32 be used to facilitate its seeking bone tissue? Explain.

Atomic Energy and Radionuclides

11.71 What is *fission?*

11.72 In general terms, how does fission differ from radioactive decay?

11.73 What fundamental aspect of fission makes it possible for it to proceed as a chain reaction?

11.74 Which naturally occurring radionuclide is able to undergo fission?

11.75 What concentration is the fissionable isotope in atomic reactors? What concentration is it in an atomic bomb?

11.76 The heat generated by fission in a power plant reactor is carried away in what way? And for what purpose?

11.77 What makes a loss of coolant an emergency?

11.78 What events are supposed to happen in a loss of coolant emergency?

11.79 What is a "containment vessel" at a nuclear power plant and what is its purpose?

11.80 The reactors of nuclear power plants are fitted with many movable rods. (Some are made of carbon, for example.) These rods are effective in capturing neutrons. They are pushed into the regions where fission occurs to turn down a reactor or to turn it off. How can their presence control the rate of fissioning?

11.81 Name three isotopes made in nuclear power plants that are particularly hazardous to health, and explain in what specific ways they endanger various parts of the body.

11.82 How can extra amounts of nonradioactive iodide ion in the diet provide some protection against radioactive iodide ion?

11.83 What fact about certain atomic wastes necessitates very long waste storage times?

Cosmic Rays (Special Topic 11.1)

11.84 Where do cosmic rays originate?

11.85 What is the chief particle found in primary cosmic rays?

11.86 What happens to cosmic rays as they enter the earth's atmosphere?

Radon in the Environment (Special Topic 11.2)

11.87 How is radon-222 produced in the environment?

11.88 What radiations does it emit?

11.89 Besides its own radiation, what other factors make radon-222 in the lungs particularly hazardous?

11.90 What upper limit on the level of radon-222 in the home is recommended?

Technetium-99*m* in Medicine (Special Topic 11.3)

11.91 What is done at a nuclear reactor facility to charge a molybdenum "cow"?

11.92 From what radionuclide does Tc-99*m* form?

11.93 In what chemical form is Tc-99*m* prepared?

X Rays and CT Scans (Special Topic 11.4)

11.94 In general terms, how are X rays prepared?

11.95 How does the CT scanner differ from an ordinary X-ray machine?

Positron Emission Tomography—The Pet Scan
(Special Topic 11.5)

11.96 Compare the positron and electron in terms of mass and charge.

11.97 Describe how a positron forms in a positron-emitting radionuclide.

11.98 What property makes the lifetime of a positron extremely short?

11.99 When a radiologist uses the PET scan, what radiation is converted into an X-ray-like picture?

11.100 In general terms, how can a positron-emitting radionuclide be gotten inside a tissue, like the brain?

11.101 Describe an advantage of the PET scan over the CT scan in studying the brain.

Magnetic Resonance Imaging—the MRI Scan
(Special Topic 11.6)

11.102 Why is the MRI less harmful a technique than the CT or PET scan?

11.103 How does MRI complement the use of X rays?

11.104 Why is bone transparent to the MRI?

CHAPTER TWELVE

Organic Chemistry. Saturated Hydrocarbons

The enduring wonder is that all these people and a few billion others can be viewed as unique packages of electrons, protons, and atomic nuclei; as, in fact, the nuclei of just a handful of nonmetal elements. In this chapter we start a new foundation for our study of the molecular basis of life.

12.1 ORGANIC AND INORGANIC COMPOUNDS

The major differences between organic and inorganic compounds stem from variations in composition, bond types, and molecular polarities.

Organic compounds are compounds made of atoms of carbon combined covalently with each other and with atoms of hydrogen and usually with atoms of other nonmetal elements, like oxygen, nitrogen, sulfur, and the halogens. **Inorganic compounds** are all the rest, and they do include a few that contain carbon, like the carbonates, bicarbonates, cyanides, and the oxides of carbon.

Organic chemistry is the study of the structures, properties, and syntheses of organic compounds. In this and the next few chapters we will study just the parts of organic chemistry that are most essential to the study of the molecular basis of life.

Wöhler's Experiment Opened the Doors to the Laboratory Synthesis of Organic Compounds The word *organic* arose from an association with organisms, because in the early days of organic chemistry all organic compounds were isolated from living systems or their remains. Up until 1828, all efforts to synthesize organic from inorganic compounds had failed. Out of such repeated failures the **vital force theory** emerged. It stated that it is actually impossible to make organic compounds in glass vessels, that a special *vital force* said to be found only in living systems was essential.

- *Vita*- is from a Latin root meaning "life."

In 1828, while trying to make a sample of crystalline ammonium cyanate, NH_4NCO, Friedrich Wöhler (1800–1882) boiled the water from an aqueous solution containing the ammonium ion and the cyanate ion, NCO^-. The white solid he obtained, however, was a different compound, urea. Ammonium cyanate, then as now, is regarded as an inorganic compound, but urea is clearly a product of metabolism. Wöhler had succeeded in making the first organic compound in a glass vessel. The heat used for boiling evidently caused the following reaction:

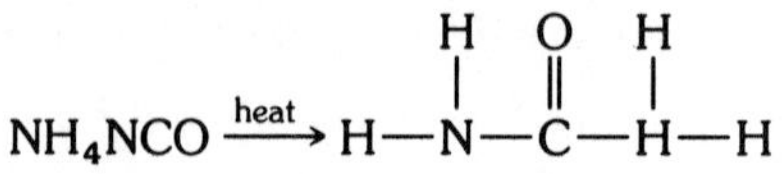

- Urea is the chief nitrogen waste from the body. It is also manufactured from ammonia and used as a commercial fertilizer.

$$NH_4NCO \xrightarrow{heat} \underset{\text{Urea}}{H-\underset{|}{\overset{H}{N}}-\underset{\|}{\overset{O}{C}}-\underset{|}{\overset{H}{H}}-H}$$

Ammonium cyanate

Following this discovery, other organic compounds were made from inorganic substances, and the vital force theory was dead. Today, about six million organic compounds are known, and all have been or could in principle be made from inorganic substances.

Covalent Bonds, Not Ionic Bonds, Dominate Organic Molecules The overwhelming prevalence of nonmetal atoms in organic compounds means that their molecular structures are dominated by covalent bonds. In contrast, most inorganic compounds are ionic. As we will see, the greatest parts of most organic molecules involve carbon–carbon bonds and carbon–hydrogen bonds. These are essentially nonpolar bonds, so except when atoms of such electronegative elements as oxygen and nitrogen are present, organic compounds tend to be quite nonpolar. These structural facts are behind several major properties of organic compounds.

Relatively nonpolar molecules are unable to attract each other very strongly, as oppositely charged ions can. This affects melting and boiling points. Most organic compounds have melting points and boiling points well below 400 °C, whereas most ionic compounds melt or boil well above this temperature.

- Organic *ions* tend to be very soluble in water.

Relatively nonpolar molecules are less soluble in water than ions. Thus most organic compounds are relatively insoluble in water, but many ionic compounds are soluble. This fact is particularly revelant at the molecular level of life where the central fluid is water. As we study organic chemistry we'll be alert to any molecular factors that improve the solubility in water of organic compounds. We'll also be interested in any chemical reactions that can make ions out of organic molecules.

12.2 SOME STRUCTURAL FEATURES OF ORGANIC COMPOUNDS

Organic molecules can have straight or branched chains and be open-chained or cyclic, saturated or unsaturated, and be carbocyclic or heterocyclic.

The uniqueness of carbon among the elements is that its atoms can bond to each other successively many times and still form equally strong bonds to atoms of other nonmetals. A typical molecule in the familiar plastic polyethylene has hundreds of carbon atoms covalently joined in succession, and each carbon binds enough hydrogen atoms to fill out its full complement of four bonds.

■ Only a short segment of a typical molecule of polyethylene is shown here.

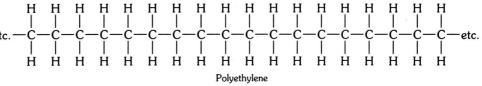

Polyethylene

The sequence of the heavier atoms, the carbon atoms, is called the *skeleton* of the molecule, and it holds the hydrogen atoms. Many variations of heavier-atom skeletons occur, and we will look at them next.

Carbon Skeletons Can Be in Straight Chains or Branched Chains   The carbon skeleton in the polyethylene molecule is described as a **straight chain.** *Straight* has a very limited and technical meaning here: the absence of carbon branches. This means that one carbon follows another, like the pearls in a single-strand necklace, with no additional carbons joined to the skeleton at intermediate points. Such chains can be very long, like that of polyethylene, but most in nature are much shorter. Pentane illustrates a straight chain of only five carbons. A molecule of 2-methylpentane has a **branched chain,** a chain with at least one carbon atom joined to the skeleton *between* the ends of the main chain, like a charm hung on a bracelet.

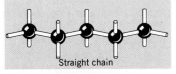

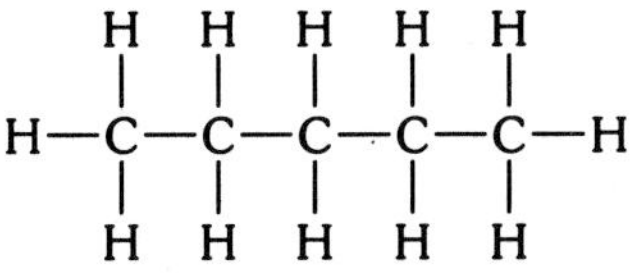

Straight chain

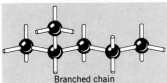

Branched chain

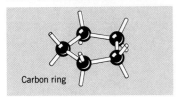

Carbon ring

Pentane
(straight chain)

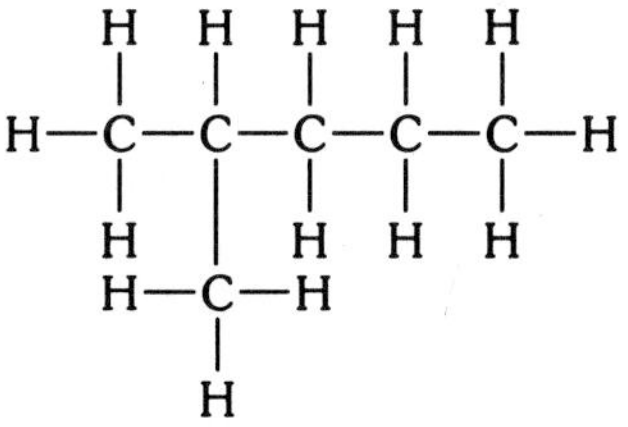

2-Methylpentane
(branched chain)

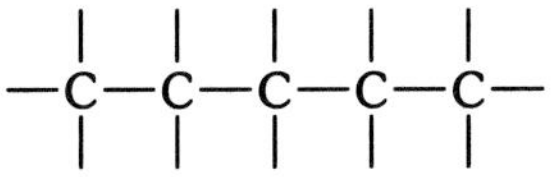

Pentane skeleton

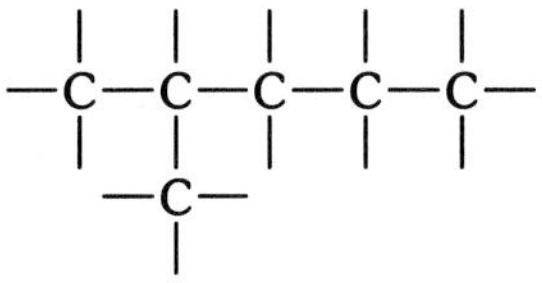

2-Methylpentane skeleton

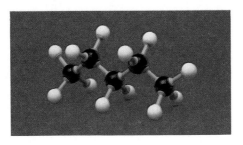

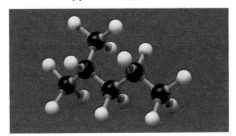

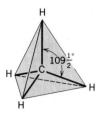

Some Features of Molecular Geometry Are Often "Understood" When Writing Structural Formulas

When you compare the ball-and-stick models of pentane and 2-methylpentane with their structural formulas, be sure to notice that the written (or printed) structures disregard the correct bond angles at carbon. A carbon that has four single bonds has a tetrahedral geometry with bond angles of 109.5°. The ball-and-stick models faithfully show the correct angles at each carbon, but the printed symbols do not. The point here is that it is perfectly all right to let bond angles be "understood" unless there is some important reason to the contrary.

Free Rotation at Single Bonds Is Also "Understood"

The molecules of pentane and 2-methylpentane are quite flexible. Figure 12.1 gives photographs of models of just a few of the many ways the pentane molecule can be flexed. These twistings actually occur as pentane molecules collide with each other in the liquid or gaseous states, and they illustrate an important property of at least large segments of organic molecules, a property called **free rotation** about single bonds. Two clusters of atoms held by a single bond can rotate with respect to each other about that bond.

Free rotation is possible because the single bond is a *sigma bond* as described in Figure 12.2. Its strength lies in the degree of overlap of the hybrid orbitals that make up the molecular orbital. As long as the degree of such overlap is not affected too much while one group rotates about the bond, the rotation not only is allowed but happens.

The differently twisted forms of pentane in Figure 12.1 are called *conformations,* and they cannot be physically separated from one another. The physical and chemical properties of pentane, therefore, are the net results of the effects that the whole collection of conforma-

■ Because of free rotation, we have to be able to interpret zig-zags. For example,

$$CH_3$$
$$|$$
$$CH_2CH_2CH_2$$
$$|$$
$$CH_3$$

is the same molecule as
$CH_3CH_2CH_2CH_2CH_3$

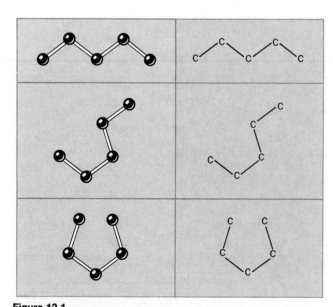

Figure 12.1
Free rotation at single bonds. Three of the innumerable conformations of the skeleton of the pentane molecule are shown here. (The hydrogens have been omitted.) Free rotation about single bonds easily converts one conformation into another.

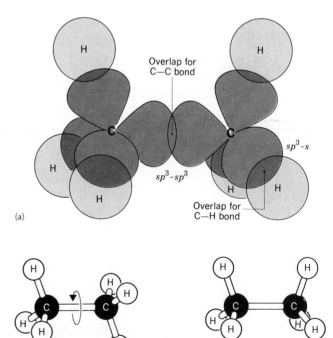

Figure 12.2
The sigma bonds in ethane. (*a*) Here are all the orbital overlappings that create the C—C and C—H bonds. (*b*) The sp^3 to sp^3 overlap that forms the C—C single bond, a sigma bond, is affected very little by a rotation of one CH_3 group relative to the other. Since such a rotation costs essentially no energy, it occurs easily.

tions has on whatever physical agent or chemical reactant has been used to observe the property.

Having said this, it would therefore seem that we could forget about free rotation and conformations. When we study how enzymes work, however, we will have to recall that organic molecules have unique geometries and possible conformations, that about single bonds there is free rotation, and that molecules have flexibility. We will see that molecular *shape* is as important to understanding events at the molecular level of life as anything else.

Condensed Structural Formulas Reduce Clutter with Little Sacrifice in Information Just as we can leave some aspects of molecular geometry to the informed imagination, we can leave most of the bonds in a structural formula to it as well. Remembering that any carbon in a structural formula must have four bonds (or else carry some charge), we can group beside its symbol, C, all the hydrogen atoms held by it. If it holds three hydrogens, we can write CH_3 (or H_3C, but you don't see this as often.) Just remember that these three hydrogen atoms are individually joined to the carbon. The structure of ethane illustrates this.

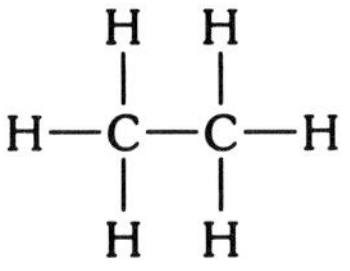

$$
\begin{array}{ccc}
H & H \\
| & | \\
H-C-C-H & \text{becomes} & CH_3-CH_3 \quad \text{or} \quad H_3C-CH_3 \\
| & | \\
H & H
\end{array}
$$

Full or expanded   Condensed structures
structure

Ethane

A carbon holding two hydrogen atoms can be represented as CH_2 or (less often seen) as H_2C. When a carbon holds just one hydrogen, we can write it as CH or (less commonly seen) as HC.

The result of these simplifications is called a **condensed structure,** or simply the **structure.** Condensed structures are used almost exclusively.

EXAMPLE 12.1   **CONDENSING A FULL STRUCTURAL FORMULA**

Problem: Condense the structural formula for 2-methylpentane.

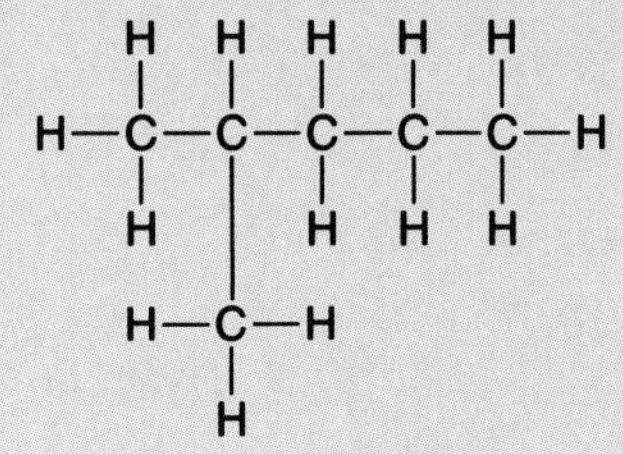

$$
\begin{array}{ccccc}
H & H & H & H & H \\
| & | & | & | & | \\
H-C-C-C-C-C-H & & & & \quad \text{2-Methylpentane} \\
| & | & | & | & \\
H & & H & H & H \\
& | & & & \\
& H-C-H & & & \\
& | & & & \\
& H & & &
\end{array}
$$

Solution: $CH_3-CH-CH_2-CH_2-CH_3$
                                      |
                                   CH_3

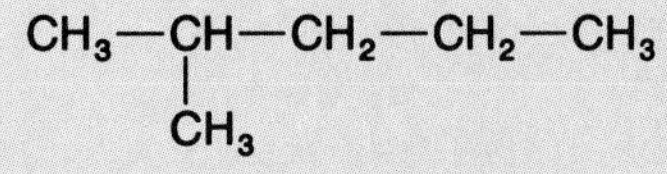

PRACTICE EXERCISE 1   Condense the following expanded structural formulas:

$$
\text{(a)} \quad
\begin{array}{ccc}
H & H & H \\
| & | & | \\
H-C-C-C-H \\
| & | & | \\
H & H & H
\end{array}
\qquad
\text{(b)} \quad
\begin{array}{ccc}
H & H & H \\
| & | & | \\
H-C-C-C-H \\
| & | & | \\
H & | & H \\
& H-C-H & \\
& | & \\
& H &
\end{array}
$$

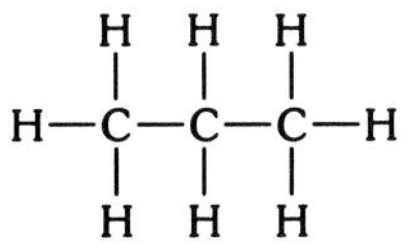

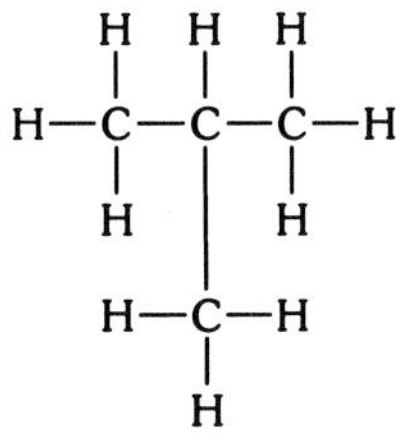

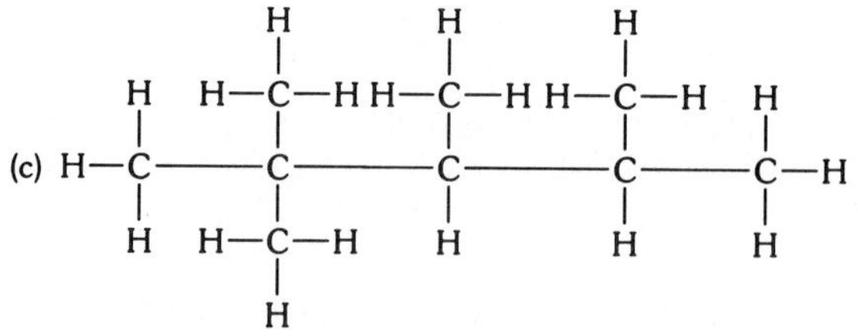

(c) Structure shown:

$$\begin{array}{c}
\text{H} \quad \text{H} \quad \text{H} \\
| \quad\quad | \quad\quad | \\
\text{H} \quad \text{H—C—H} \quad \text{H—C—H} \quad \text{H—C—H} \quad \text{H} \\
| \quad\quad\quad\quad\quad\quad\quad\quad\quad\quad\quad\quad\quad\quad | \\
\text{(c) H—C———C———C———C———C—H} \\
| \quad\quad | \quad\quad\quad | \quad\quad | \quad\quad | \\
\text{H} \quad \text{H—C—H} \quad \text{H} \quad \text{H} \quad \text{H} \\
\quad\quad | \\
\quad\quad \text{H}
\end{array}$$

Even Most Single Bonds Can Be "Understood"

When a *single* bond appears on a *horizontal* line, we need not write a straight line to represent it; we can leave such single bonds to the imagination. We do not do this, however, for bonds that are not on a horizontal line. Thus we can write the structure of 2-methylpentane, Example 12.1, as follows. Notice that the vertically oriented bond is shown by a line but that all other single bonds are understood.

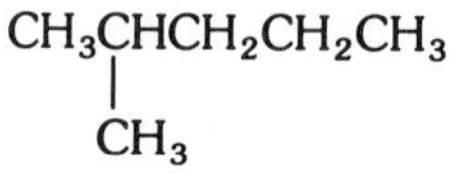

$$\begin{array}{c}
\text{CH}_3\text{CHCH}_2\text{CH}_2\text{CH}_3 \qquad \text{2-Methylpentane} \\
| \\
\text{CH}_3
\end{array}$$

PRACTICE EXERCISE 2 Rewrite the condensed structures that you drew for the answers to Practice Exercise 1 and let the appropriate carbon–carbon single bonds be left to the imagination.

PRACTICE EXERCISE 3 Just to be certain that you are comfortable with condensed structures, expand each of the following to make them full, expanded structures with no bonds left to the imagination.

(a) CH_3CH_3 　(b) 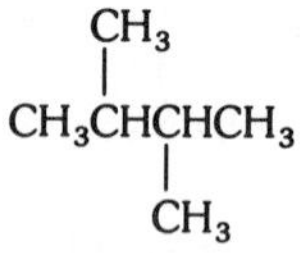
$$\begin{array}{c}
\text{CH}_3 \\
| \\
\text{CH}_3\text{CHCHCH}_3 \\
| \\
\text{CH}_3
\end{array}$$
(c)
$$\begin{array}{c}
\text{CH}_2\text{CH}_3 \\
| \\
\text{CH}_3\text{CH}_2\text{CCH}_2\text{CH}_2\text{CH}_3 \\
| \\
\text{CH}_3
\end{array}$$

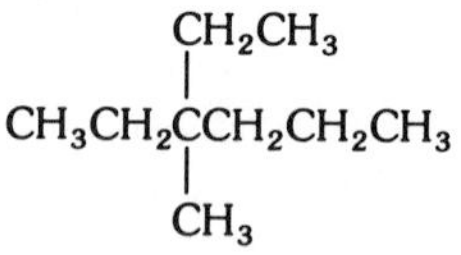

One important skill in using condensed structures is the ability to recognize errors. The most common is a violation of the rule that any carbon atom in a structure that carries no electrical charge must have exactly four bonds, no more and no fewer. Do the next practice exercise to test your skill in recognizing an error in structure.

PRACTICE EXERCISE 4 Which of the following structures cannot represent real compounds?

(a) 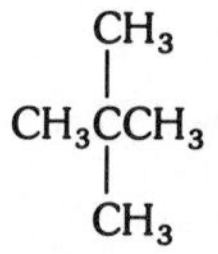
$$\begin{array}{c}
\text{CH}_3 \\
| \\
\text{CH}_3\text{CCH}_3 \\
| \\
\text{CH}_3
\end{array}$$
(b)
$$\begin{array}{c}
\text{CH}_3 \\
| \\
\text{CH}_3\text{CH}_2\text{CHCH}_3
\end{array}$$
(c)
$$\begin{array}{c}
\text{CH}_3 \quad\quad \text{CH}_3 \\
| \quad\quad\quad\quad | \\
\text{CH}_3\text{CHCH}_2\text{CHCH}_2\text{CH}_3 \\
| \\
\text{CH}_3
\end{array}$$

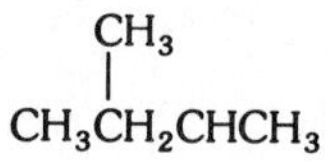

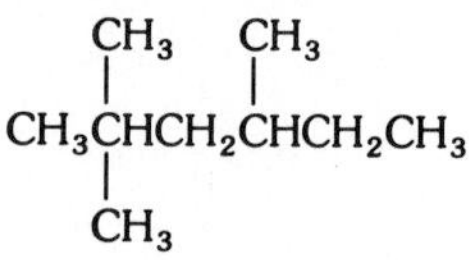

When atoms other than carbon and hydrogen are present in a molecule, there is no major new problem in writing condensed structures. Remember that every oxygen or sulfur atom carrying no electrical charge must have two bonds, every nitrogen must have three, and every halogen atom must have just one.

Double and Triple Bonds Are Seldom Condensed

Another rule about condensed structures is that carbon–carbon double and triple bonds are never left to the imagination. Carbon–oxygen double bonds are sometimes condensed, as some of the following examples illustrate. Study them as illustrations of how to condense structures.

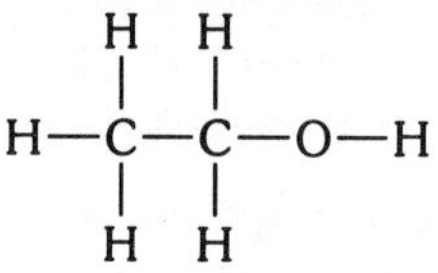

$$\begin{array}{c}
\text{H} \quad \text{H} \\
| \quad\quad | \\
\text{H—C—C—O—H} \quad \text{condenses to} \quad \text{CH}_3\text{—CH}_2\text{—O—H} \quad \text{or to} \quad \text{CH}_3\text{CH}_2\text{OH} \\
| \quad\quad | \\
\text{H} \quad \text{H}
\end{array}$$

Ethyl alcohol (in alcoholic drinks)

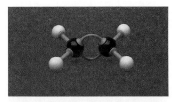

$$H-\overset{\overset{\displaystyle H}{|}}{C}=\overset{\overset{\displaystyle H}{|}}{C}-H \quad \text{condenses to} \quad CH_2=CH_2 \quad \text{or to} \quad H_2C=CH_2$$

Ethylene (the raw material for making polyethylene)

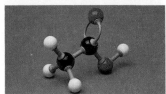

$$H-\overset{\overset{\displaystyle H}{|}}{\underset{\underset{\displaystyle H}{|}}{C}}-\overset{\overset{\displaystyle O}{\parallel}}{C}-O-H \quad \text{condenses to} \quad CH_3-\overset{\overset{\displaystyle O}{\parallel}}{C}-O-H \quad \text{or to} \quad CH_3COH$$

$$\text{and often to} \quad CH_3CO_2H \quad \text{or to} \quad CH_3COOH$$

Acetic acid (in vinegar)

$$H-\overset{\overset{\displaystyle H}{|}}{\underset{\underset{\displaystyle H}{|}}{C}}-\overset{\overset{\displaystyle O}{\parallel}}{C}-\overset{\overset{\displaystyle H}{|}}{\underset{\underset{\displaystyle H}{|}}{C}}-H \quad \text{condenses to} \quad CH_3-\overset{\overset{\displaystyle O}{\parallel}}{C}-CH_3 \quad \text{or to} \quad CH_3CCH_3$$

Acetone (nail polish remover)

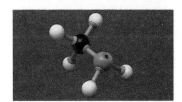

$$H-\overset{\overset{\displaystyle H}{|}}{\underset{\underset{\displaystyle H}{|}}{C}}-\overset{\overset{\displaystyle H}{|}}{N}-H \quad \text{condenses to} \quad CH_3-NH_2 \quad \text{or to} \quad CH_3NH_2$$

Methylamine (in decaying fish)

Parentheses Are Sometimes Used to Condense Structures Further Sometimes two or three identical groups that are attached to the same carbon are grouped inside a set of parentheses. For example,

$$\overset{\overset{\displaystyle CH_3}{|}}{CH_3CHCH_2CH_3} \quad \text{can be written as} \quad (CH_3)_2CHCH_2CH_3$$

$$\overset{\overset{\displaystyle CH_3 \quad CH_3}{|\qquad|}}{\underset{\underset{\displaystyle CH_3}{|}}{CH_3CCH_2CHCH_3}} \quad \text{can be written as} \quad (CH_3)_3CCH_2CH(CH_3)_2$$

We will not do this very often, but you will see it in many references and you should be aware of it.

Unsaturated Compounds Have Double or Triple Bonds If its molecules have only single bonds, the compound is called a **saturated compound.** When one or more double or triple bonds are present, the substance is said to be an **unsaturated compound.** Thus ethylene, acetic acid, and acetone, just shown, are all unsaturated compounds, but ethyl alcohol and methylamine are saturated.

Saturated describes any molecule whose atoms are making the fullest possible use of directly holding as many other atoms as they can. Each carbon in ethylene, for example, is holding just three atoms, but in ethyl alcohol each is directly holding four. *Unsaturated* implies that something can be added, and we will see that unsaturated compounds can add certain substances, like hydrogen, to their double or triple bonds.

Many Organic Molecules Contain Rings of Carbon Atoms A carbon **ring** is an arrangement of three or more carbon atoms into a closed cycle. Molecules with this feature are called ring compounds or cyclic compounds. (Sometimes an all-carbon ring is described as

■ Molecules of edible oils, like olive oil or corn oil, have many double bonds and are described as polyunsaturated.

carbocyclic.) Cyclohexane molecules, for example, have a ring of six carbon atoms. Cyclopropane, once an important anesthetic, is also a cyclic compound.

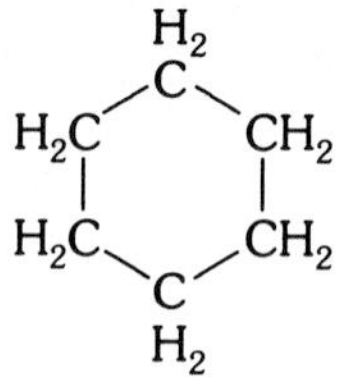

Cyclohexane

Cyclopropane

■ More than 2 billion pounds of cyclohexane are made annually in the United States, with over 90% being used to make nylon.

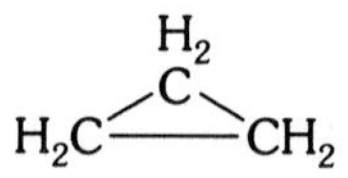

Cyclic compounds can have double bonds as in cyclohexene, but always remember that carbon–carbon double bonds are never left to the imagination. Rings, of course, can carry substituents, as in ethylcyclohexane. Not all the ring atoms have to be carbon atoms. They can be oxygen, nitrogen, or sulfur, too, and cyclic compounds with ring atoms other than carbon are called **heterocyclic compounds.** A simple example is tetrahydropyran, which has the basic ring system widely present among molecules of carbohydrates.

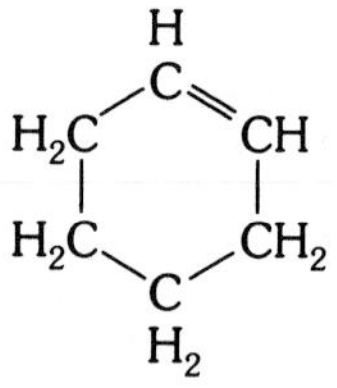

Cyclohexane 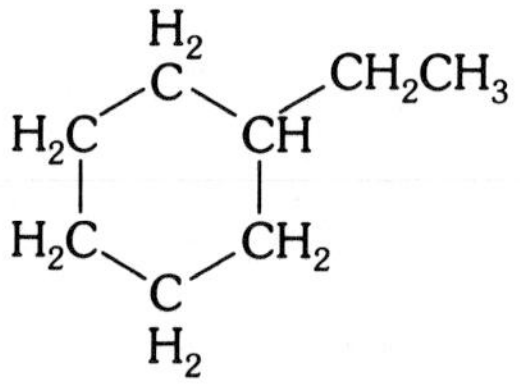   Ethylcyclohexane 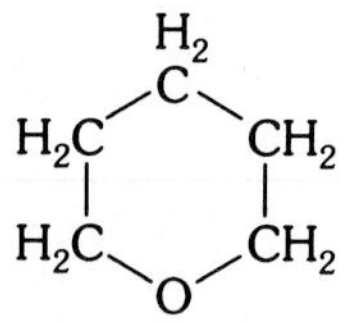   Tetrahydropyran

The Rings of Cyclic Compounds Can Be Condensed to Simple Polygons   Since we can leave to our imaginations so many structural features, a polygon, a many-sided figure, becomes a handy way to condense rings. A square, for example, can represent cyclobutane. The photograph of the ball-and-stick model of cyclobutane and its progressively more condensed structures show what is left to the imagination when just a square is used. At each corner, we have to understand that there is a CH_2 group. Each line in the square is a carbon–carbon single bond.

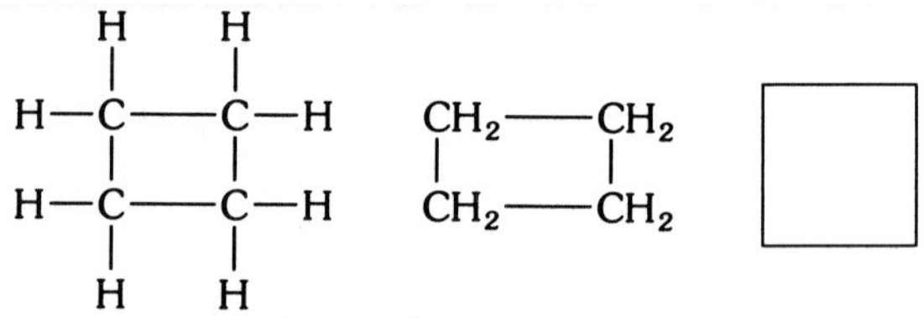

Three ways to represent the structure of cyclobutane

The model of methylcyclopentane and its progressively more condensed structures further show how a polygon can represent a ring.

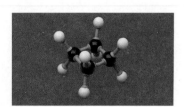

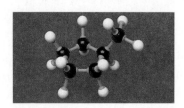

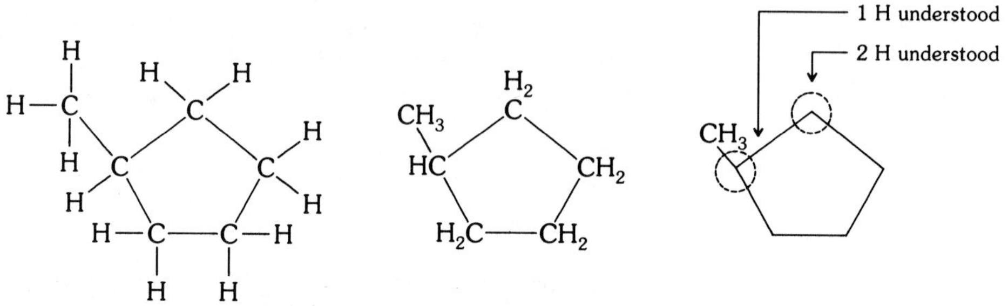

1 H understood

2 H understood

Three ways to represent the structure of methylcyclopentane

| EXAMPLE 12.2 | UNDERSTANDING CONDENSED STRUCTURES OF RING COMPOUNDS |

Problem: To make sure that you can read a condensed structure when it includes a polygon for a ring system, expand this structure, including its side chains.

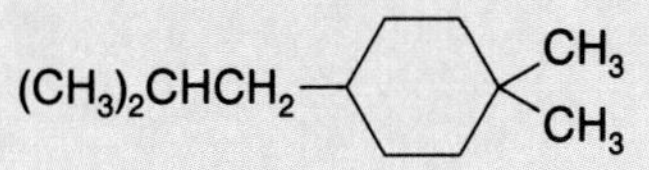

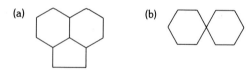

Solution:

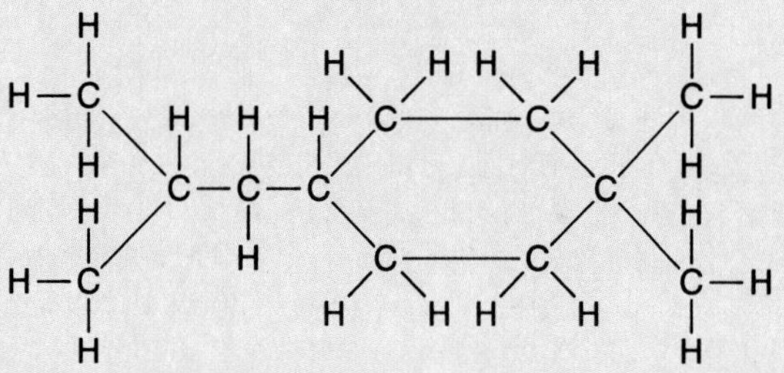

Note especially how we can tell the number of hydrogens that must be attached to a ring atom. We need as many as required to fill our a set of four bonds from each carbon. This example also shows a situation (on the right side of the ring) in which no bonding room is left for holding an H atom.

PRACTICE EXERCISE 5   Expand each of these two structures.

(a)   (b)

PRACTICE EXERCISE 6   Condense the following structure.

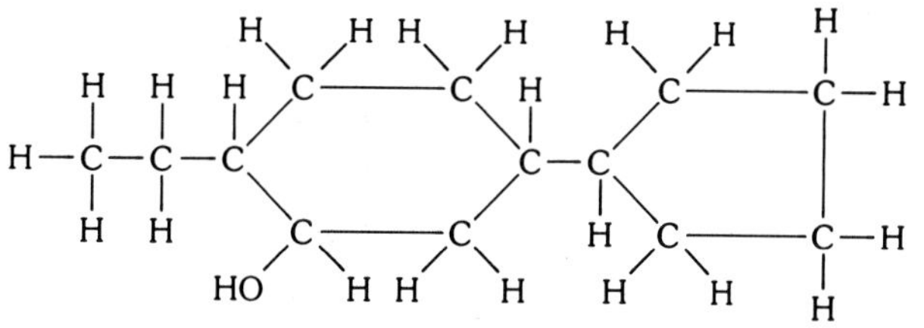

As you might expect, free rotation about the single bonds in a ring is not possible. Although there is a small amount of "flex" in rings, you'd have to break single bonds to get the kind of free rotation we observed with pentane (Figure 12.1).

When we use polygons to represent saturated rings that have six or more ring atoms, we gloss over one feature of such molecules. The ring atoms that make up the rings of this size do not all lie in the same plane. We will postpone a study of what this fact implies.

12.3 ISOMERISM

Compounds can have identical molecular formulas but different structures.

Ammonium cyanate and urea, the chemicals of Wöhler's important experiment, both have the molecular formula CH_4N_2O. The atoms are just organized differently:

TABLE 12.1 Properties of Two Isomers, Ethyl Alcohol, and Dimethyl Ether

Property	Ethyl Alcohol	Dimethyl Ether
Structure	CH_3CH_2OH	CH_3OCH_3
Boiling point	78.5 °C	−24 °C
Melting point	−117 °C	−138.5 °C
Density (25 °C)	0.79 g/mL (a liquid)	2.0 g/L (a gas)
Solubility in water	Soluble in all proportions	Slightly soluble

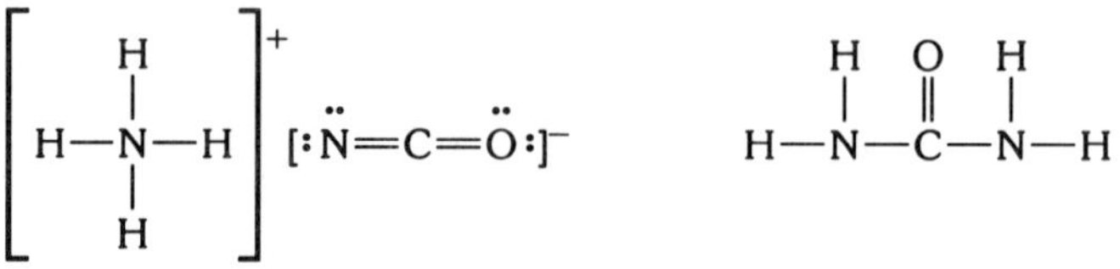

$$
\left[\begin{array}{c} H \\ | \\ H-N-H \\ | \\ H \end{array} \right]^+ \quad [:N=C=O:]^-
$$

Ammonium cyanate
CH_4N_2O

$$
\begin{array}{c} H \quad O \quad H \\ | \quad || \quad | \\ H-N-C-N-H \end{array}
$$

Urea
CH_4N_2O

■ "Isomer" has Greek roots — *isos*, the same, and *meros*, parts; that is, "the same parts" (but put together differently).

■ The names in parentheses are the common names of these compounds. The letter *n* stands for *normal*, meaning the straight-chain isomer. *Neo* signifies *new*, as in a new isomer.

Compounds that have identical molecular formulas but different structures are called **isomers** of each other, and the existence of isomers is a phenomenon called **isomerism.** Isomerism is one reason why there are so many organic compounds.

The three isomers of pentane all share the formula C_5H_{12}:

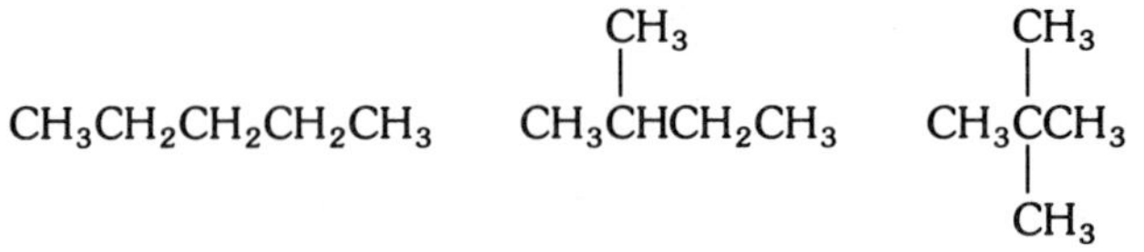

$$CH_3CH_2CH_2CH_2CH_3 \qquad \begin{array}{c} CH_3 \\ | \\ CH_3CHCH_2CH_3 \end{array} \qquad \begin{array}{c} CH_3 \\ | \\ CH_3CCH_3 \\ | \\ CH_3 \end{array}$$

Pentane   2-Methylbutane   2,2-Dimethylpropane
(*n*-pentane)   (isopentane)   (neopentane)

The larger the number of carbon atoms per molecule, the larger the number of isomers. For example, someone has figured out that roughly 6.25×10^{13} isomers are possible for $C_{40}H_{82}$. (Very few have actually been prepared. It would take nearly 200 billion years to make each one at the rate of one per day.)

The isomers of pentane or of $C_{40}H_{82}$ have quite similar chemical properties because their molecules all have only C—C and C—H single bonds. Often, however, isomers have very different properties. There are two ways, for example, to organize the atoms in C_2H_6O, as seen near the top of Table 12.1. One isomer is ethyl alcohol and the other is dimethyl ether. They are radically different, as the data in Table 12.1 show. At room temperature, the former is a liquid and the latter is a gas. Ethyl alcohol reacts with sodium; dimethyl ether does not. As we will see in the next section, these two isomers are members of entirely different families of compounds.

It is quite common for isomers to vary this much, which is one major reason why we use structural rather than molecular formulas for organic compounds. Only structures let us see at a glance how molecules are organized. Being able to recognize two structures as identical, isomers, or something else is, therefore, very necessary.

EXAMPLE 12.3   **RECOGNIZING ISOMERS**

Problem: Which pair of structures represents a pair of isomers?

$$1. \quad \begin{array}{cc} CH_3 & CH_3 \\ | & | \\ CH_3CH & CHCH_2CH_2CH_2CH_3 \end{array} \quad \text{and} \quad \begin{array}{cc} CH_3 & CH_3 \\ | & | \\ CH_3CH_2CH_2CH_2CH & CHCH_3 \end{array}$$

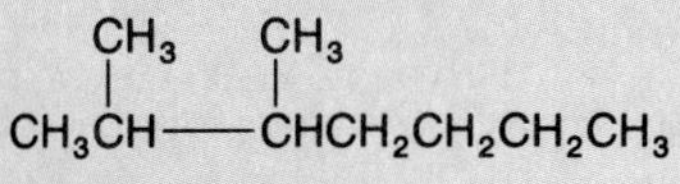

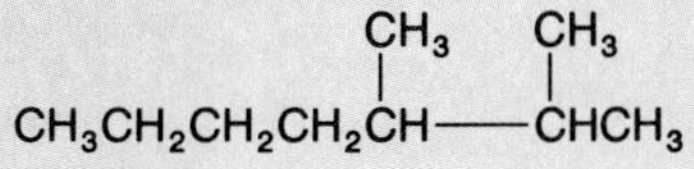

2. $CH_3-O-CH_2CH_3$ and $CH_3CH_2-O-CH_3$

3. $CH_3\overset{\displaystyle CH_3}{\overset{|}{C}}HCH_2CH_2CH_3$ and $CH_3CH_2\overset{\displaystyle CH_3}{\overset{|}{C}}HCH_2CH_3$

4. $\overset{\displaystyle CH_3}{\overset{|}{C}}H_2CH_3$ and $CH_3CH_2CH_3$

Solution: Unless you spot a difference that rules out isomerism immediately, the first step is to see whether the molecular formulas are the same. If they aren't, the two structures are not isomers; and if they are, the two might be identical or they might be isomers. In this problem, the members of each pair share the same molecular formula.

Pair 1: C_9H_{20} Pair 2: C_3H_8O Pair 3: C_6H_{14} Pair 4: C_3H_8

Next, to see whether a particular pair represents isomers, we try to find at least one structural difference. If we can't, the two structures are identical; they are just oriented differently on the page, or their chains are twisted into different conformations. Don't be fooled by an "east-to-west" versus a "west-to-east" type of difference. The difference must be *internal* within the structure. (Whether you face east or west, you're the same person!)

Pair 1 is an example of this east versus west difference in orientation. These two structures are identical. Their internal sequences are the same.

Pair 2 are similarly identical; they're just oriented differently on the page.

Pair 3 are isomers. In the first, a CH_3 group joins a five-carbon chain at the second carbon of the chain, and in the second, this group is attached at the third carbon.

Pair 4 are identical. The two structures differ only in the conformations of their chains.

PRACTICE EXERCISE 7   Examine each pair to see whether the members are identical, are isomers, or are different in some other way.

(a) $H-O-CH_3$ and CH_3-O-H

(b) $CH_3-NH-CH_3$ and $CH_3-CH_2-NH_2$

(c) $\overset{\displaystyle CH_2CH_3}{\overset{|}{C}}H_2CH_2CHCH_3$ and $CH_3CH_2CH_2CH_2\overset{\displaystyle CH_3}{\overset{|}{C}}HCH_3$

(d) $CH_2{=}CHCH_2CH_3$ and $CH_3CH{=}CHCH_3$

(e) $CH_3CH_2\overset{\displaystyle O}{\overset{\|}{C}}OH$ and $HO\overset{\displaystyle O}{\overset{\|}{C}}CH_3$

12.4 FUNCTIONAL GROUPS

The study of organic chemistry is organized around functional groups.

Pieces of molecules that include nonmetal atoms other than C and H or that have double or triple bonds are the specific sites in organic molecules that chemicals most often attack. These small structural units are called **functional groups,** because they are the chemically functioning locations. Sections of molecules consisting only of carbon and hydrogen and only single bonds are called the **nonfunctional groups.**

Each Functional Group Defines an Organic Family   Although over six million organic compounds are known, there are only a handful of functional groups, and each one serves to define a family of organic compounds. Our study of organic chemistry will be organized around just a few of these families, those outlined in Table 12.2. Let's see how the idea of a family will greatly simplify our study.

The alcohols make up a major organic family of compounds. We have learned, for example, that ethyl alcohol is CH_3CH_2OH. Its molecules have the —OH group attached to a chain of two carbons. But *chain length* is not what determines what family a compound is in; it only determines the name of the specific family member, as we will see later. The chain can be any length imaginable, and the substance will be in the alcohol family provided that somewhere on the chain there is an —OH group attached to a carbon from which only single bonds extend. This functional group, the alcohol group, is common to all carbohydrates and most proteins. Some examples of simple alcohols are

■ Isopropyl alcohol is commonly used as a rubbing alcohol.

$$-\underset{|}{\overset{|}{C}}-O-H \qquad CH_3-OH \qquad CH_3CH_2-OH \qquad CH_3CH_2CH_2-OH \qquad CH_3\underset{\underset{OH}{|}}{C}HCH_3$$

| Alcohol group | Methyl alcohol | Ethyl alcohol | Propyl alcohol | Isopropyl alcohol |

Because all these alcohols have the same functional group, they exhibit the same kinds of chemical reactions. When just one of these reactions is learned, it applies to all members of the family, literally to thousands of compounds. In fact, we will often summarize a particular reaction for an organic family by using a general family symbol. All alcohols, for example, can be symbolized by R—OH, where R— stands for a carbon chain, one of whatever length or branchings. All alcohols, for instance, react with sodium metal as follows:

■ R is from the German word *Radikal,* which we translate here to mean *group* as in a group of atoms.

$$2R-O-H + 2Na \longrightarrow 2R-ONa + H_2$$

If we wanted to write the specific example of this reaction that involves, say, ethyl alcohol, all we have to do is replace R— by CH_3CH_2—:

$$2CH_3CH_2-OH + 2Na \longrightarrow 2CH_3CH_2-ONa + H_2$$

Notice that this reaction changes only the —OH group of the alcohol. (Dimethyl ether, Table 12.1, which does not have the —OH group, cannot give this reaction with sodium, as we learned in the previous section.)

Another organic family is that of the *carboxylic acids.* All their molecules have the *carboxyl group,* and this group makes all its compounds weak acids. We've often illustrated this with acetic acid.

■ The carboxyl group is present in all fatty acids, products of the digestion of the fats and oils in our diets.

$$-\overset{\overset{\displaystyle O}{\|}}{C}-O-H, \text{ or } -CO_2H \qquad CH_3-\overset{\overset{\displaystyle O}{\|}}{C}-O-H \text{ or } CH_3CO_2H$$

Carboxyl group   Acetic acid

$$R-\overset{\overset{\displaystyle O}{\|}}{C}-O-H \text{ or } RCO_2H$$

Carboxylic acids

We know that acetic acid neutralizes the hydroxide ion:

$$CH_3-\overset{\overset{\displaystyle O}{\|}}{C}-O-H + OH^- \longrightarrow CH_3-\overset{\overset{\displaystyle O}{\|}}{C}-O^- + H-OH$$

Acetate ion

All molecules with the carboxyl group give the same reaction, so we can represent literally thousands of such reactions by just one simple equation:

TABLE 12.2 Some Important Families of Organic Compounds

Family	Molecular Features	Example
Hydrocarbons	Only C and H present Subfamilies: 　Alkanes: only single bonds 　Alkenes: some double bonds 　Alkynes: some triple bonds	CH_3CH_3, ethane $CH_2{=}CH_2$, ethene $HC{\equiv}CH$, ethyne
	Aromatic: benzene ring present	benzene
Alcohols	$-\overset{\displaystyle \mid}{\underset{\displaystyle \mid}{C}}-OH$ as in $R-O-H$	CH_3CH_2OH ethyl alcohol
Ethers	$-\overset{\displaystyle \mid}{\underset{\displaystyle \mid}{C}}-O-\overset{\displaystyle \mid}{\underset{\displaystyle \mid}{C}}-$ as in $R-O-R'$	$CH_3CH_2OCH_2CH_3$ diethyl ether
Thioalcohols (mercaptans)	$-\overset{\displaystyle \mid}{\underset{\displaystyle \mid}{C}}-S-H$ as in $R-S-H$	CH_3SH methyl mercaptan
Disulfides	$-\overset{\displaystyle \mid}{\underset{\displaystyle \mid}{C}}-S-S-\overset{\displaystyle \mid}{\underset{\displaystyle \mid}{C}}-$ as in $R-S-S-R'$	CH_3SSCH_3 dimethyl disulfide
Aldehydes	$-\overset{\displaystyle O}{\overset{\displaystyle \|}{C}}-H$ as in $R-\overset{\displaystyle O}{\overset{\displaystyle \|}{C}}-H$	$CH_3\overset{\displaystyle O}{\overset{\displaystyle \|}{C}}H$ acetaldehyde
Ketones	$-\overset{\displaystyle \mid}{\underset{\displaystyle \mid}{C}}-\overset{\displaystyle O}{\overset{\displaystyle \|}{C}}-\overset{\displaystyle \mid}{\underset{\displaystyle \mid}{C}}-$ as in $R-\overset{\displaystyle O}{\overset{\displaystyle \|}{C}}-R'$	$CH_3\overset{\displaystyle O}{\overset{\displaystyle \|}{C}}CH_3$ acetone
Carboxylic acids	$-\overset{\displaystyle O}{\overset{\displaystyle \|}{C}}-O-H$ as in $R-\overset{\displaystyle O}{\overset{\displaystyle \|}{C}}-O-H$	$CH_3\overset{\displaystyle O}{\overset{\displaystyle \|}{C}}OH$ acetic acid
Esters	$-\overset{\displaystyle O}{\overset{\displaystyle \|}{C}}-O-\overset{\displaystyle \mid}{\underset{\displaystyle \mid}{C}}-$ as in $R-\overset{\displaystyle O}{\overset{\displaystyle \|}{C}}-O-R'$	$CH_3\overset{\displaystyle O}{\overset{\displaystyle \|}{C}}OCH_2CH_3$ ethyl acetate
Phosphate esters	$-\overset{\displaystyle \mid}{\underset{\displaystyle \mid}{C}}-O-\overset{\displaystyle O}{\underset{\displaystyle OH}{\overset{\displaystyle \|}{P}}}-O-H$ as in $R-O-\overset{\displaystyle O}{\underset{\displaystyle OH}{\overset{\displaystyle \|}{P}}}-O-H$	$CH_3O\overset{\displaystyle O}{\underset{\displaystyle OH}{\overset{\displaystyle \|}{P}}}OH$ methyl phosphate
Diphosphate esters	$R-O-\overset{\displaystyle O}{\underset{\displaystyle OH}{\overset{\displaystyle \|}{P}}}-O-\overset{\displaystyle O}{\underset{\displaystyle OH}{\overset{\displaystyle \|}{P}}}-O-H$	$CH_3O\overset{\displaystyle O}{\underset{\displaystyle OH}{\overset{\displaystyle \|}{P}}}-O-\overset{\displaystyle O}{\underset{\displaystyle OH}{\overset{\displaystyle \|}{P}}}OH$ methyl diphosphate
Triphosphate esters	$R-O-\overset{\displaystyle O}{\underset{\displaystyle OH}{\overset{\displaystyle \|}{P}}}-O-\overset{\displaystyle O}{\underset{\displaystyle OH}{\overset{\displaystyle \|}{P}}}-O-\overset{\displaystyle O}{\underset{\displaystyle OH}{\overset{\displaystyle \|}{P}}}-O-H$	$CH_3O\overset{\displaystyle O}{\underset{\displaystyle OH}{\overset{\displaystyle \|}{P}}}-O-\overset{\displaystyle O}{\underset{\displaystyle OH}{\overset{\displaystyle \|}{P}}}-O-\overset{\displaystyle O}{\underset{\displaystyle OH}{\overset{\displaystyle \|}{P}}}-OH$ methyl triphosphate
Amines	$-NH_2$ as in $R-NH_2$ $-NH-$ as in $R-NH-R'$ $-\overset{\displaystyle \mid}{\underset{\displaystyle R}{N}}-$ as in $R-\overset{\displaystyle \mid}{N}-R'$	CH_3NH_2 methylamine $CH_3NHCH_2CH_3$ methylethylamine $CH_3\overset{\displaystyle \mid}{\underset{\displaystyle CH_3}{N}}CH_3$ trimethylamine
Amides	$-\overset{\displaystyle O}{\overset{\displaystyle \|}{C}}-NH_2$ as in $R-\overset{\displaystyle O}{\overset{\displaystyle \|}{C}}-NH_2$ [Amides can also be of the types: $R-\overset{\displaystyle O}{\overset{\displaystyle \|}{C}}-NH-R'$ and $R-\overset{\displaystyle O}{\overset{\displaystyle \|}{C}}-N(R)_2$]	$CH_3\overset{\displaystyle O}{\overset{\displaystyle \|}{C}}NH_2$ acetamide

$$R{-}\overset{\overset{\displaystyle O}{\|}}{C}{-}O{-}H + OH^- \longrightarrow R{-}\overset{\overset{\displaystyle O}{\|}}{C}{-}O^- + H{-}OH$$

Carboxylate ion

The groups characteristic of both carboxylic acids and the carboxylate ions are present in all proteins and their building blocks, the amino acids.

The amino acids are examples of substances with more than one functional group in the same molecule. They have the carboxyl group as well as a group that defines still another simple family, the amines.

■ The amino group is a proton-acceptor, like ammonia.

$-NH_2$	CH_3NH_2	$R{-}NH_2$	$NH_2{-}CH_2{-}CO_2H$
Amino group	Methyl-amine	Simple amines	Glycine, the simplest amino acid (one form)

Glycine, like all carboxylic acids, can neutralize hydroxide ion, too.

You can see how powerful a learning tool the functional group is. In the next few chapters, we will study just a few of the reactions of the most important functional groups found at the molecular level of life. Learning these reactions will be like mastering a set of map signs. You can read thousands of maps intelligently once you know their common signs and symbols. Similarly, we'll be able to "read" the chemical and physical properties of astonishingly complex molecules with the knowledge of the properties of a few functional groups.

Functional groups always occur in a setting of alkane-like, nonfunctional groups. To be able to contrast the properties of functional groups with those of the alkane-like groups we turn our attention next to the alkanes, the least reactive of the organic systems.

12.5 ALKANES AND CYCLOALKANES

Alkanes and cycloalkanes are saturated hydrocarbons.

Petroleum and natural gas are substances that consist almost entirely of a complex mixture of molecular compounds called hydrocarbons. **Hydrocarbons** are made from the atoms of just two elements, carbon and hydrogen, and the covalent bonds between the carbon atoms can be single, double, or triple. The carbon skeletons can be chains or rings. These possibilities define the various kinds of hydrocarbons, which are outlined in Figure 12.3.

■ Because the bond angle at a triple bond is 180°, a ring has to be quite large to have a triple bond, and cycloalkynes are rare.

The **alkanes,** whether open-chain or cyclic, are saturated hydrocarbons, those with only single bonds. Table 12.3 gives the first ten straight-chain members of this family. The

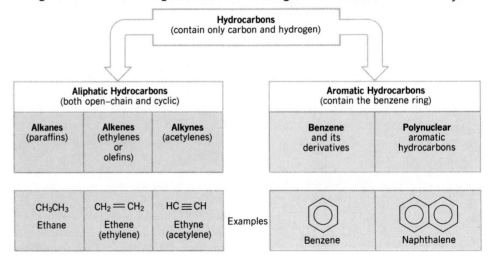

TABLE 12.3 Straight-Chain Alkanes

IUPAC Name	Number of Carbon Atoms	Molecular Formula[a]	Structure	Boiling Point (°C)	Melting Point (°C)	Density (g/mL, 20 °C)
Methane	1	CH_4	CH_4	−161.5	−182.5	
Ethane	2	C_2H_6	CH_3CH_3	−88.6	−183.3	
Propane	3	C_3H_8	$CH_3CH_2CH_3$	−42.1	−189.7	
Butane	4	C_4H_{10}	$CH_3CH_2CH_2CH_3$	−0.5	−138.4	
Pentane	5	C_5H_{12}	$CH_3CH_2CH_2CH_2CH_3$	36.1	−129.7	0.626
Hexane	6	C_6H_{14}	$CH_3CH_2CH_2CH_2CH_2CH_3$	68.7	−95.3	0.659
Heptane	7	C_7H_{16}	$CH_3CH_2CH_2CH_2CH_2CH_2CH_3$	98.4	−90.6	0.684
Octane	8	C_8H_{18}	$CH_3CH_2CH_2CH_2CH_2CH_2CH_2CH_3$	125.7	−56.8	0.703
Noname	9	C_9H_{20}	$CH_3CH_2CH_2CH_2CH_2CH_2CH_2CH_3$	150.8	−53.5	0.718
Decane	10	$C_{10}H_{22}$	$CH_3CH_2CH_2CH_2CH_2CH_2CH_2CH_2CH_3$	174.1	−29.7	0.730

[a] The molecular formulas of the open-chain alkanes fit the general formula C_nH_{2n+2}, where n = the number of carbon atoms per molecule.

alkenes are hydrocarbons with one or more carbon–carbon double bonds, whether the skeletons are chains or rings. Hydrocarbons with one or more carbon–carbon triple bonds are **alkynes.** We'll study the alkenes (and a little about the alkynes) in the next chapter. It is possible for one molecule to have both double and triple bonds, of course.

One important distinction in Figure 12.3 is between aliphatic and aromatic hydrocarbons. **Aliphatic compounds** of whatever family are any that have no benzene ring (or a similar system), and **aromatic compounds** are those with such rings. (We'll postpone the implications of the benzene ring to the next chapter.)

■ The first compounds found with benzene rings had pleasant odors. *Aliphatic* is from the Greek *aliphatos,* fat-like.

Hydrocarbons of All Types, Saturated or Not, Have Common Physical Properties

Both the carbon–carbon and the carbon–hydrogen bonds are almost entirely nonpolar, so hydrocarbon molecules have very little if any overall polarity. Hydrocarbons of all types, for this reason, are insoluble in water, but they dissolve well in nonpolar solvents. Indeed, many special mixtures of alkanes are themselves used as nonpolar solvents. Some people have used gasoline, a mixture of alkanes, to remove tar spots or grease, for example. (If you do, be sure to keep all flames away and work outside, never in a garage or other room.)

■ Petroleum "ether" is a mixture of alkanes with a boiling range of about 30 °C to 60 °C. (It is *not* anesthetic ether, which is $CH_3H_2OCH_2CH_3$, a true ether.)

Hydrocarbons are generally insoluble in water. Moreover, they are generally less dense than water so they will float on water. Thus using water to put out a hydrocarbon fire, like flaming gasoline, will only float the flames over a wider area. Nonflammable foams or CO_2 extinguishers must be used instead.

■ In the right proportion in air, hydrocarbon vapors explode when ignited.

Hydrocarbon Solvents Illustrate the Like-Dissolves-Like Rule

Grease and tar are relatively nonpolar materials, and their solubility in gasoline illustrates a very useful rule of thumb for predicting whether a solvent can dissolve some substance. It's called the **like-dissolves-like** rule, where "like" refers to a likeness in polarity. Polar solvents, such as water, are good for dissolving polar or ionic substances such as sugar or salt. Polar molecules or ions can attract water molecules around themselves, form solvent cages, and thus intermingle with water molecules. Nonpolar solvents such as gasoline do not dissolve sugar or salt. Nonpolar solvent molecules cannot be attracted to polar molecules or ions and form solvent cages.

Because of their low polarity, the hydrocarbons that have one to four carbons per molecule are generally gases at or near room temperature. Notice in Table 12.3, however, how the boiling points of the straight-chain alkanes increase with chain length. Hydrocarbons that have from 5 to about 16 carbon atoms per molecule are usually liquids at room temperature. When alkanes have approximately 18 or more carbon atoms per molecule, the substances are waxy solids at room temperature. Paraffin wax, for example, is a mixture of alkanes whose molecules have 20 and more carbon atoms.

■ Most candles are made from paraffin.

Our First Molecular "Map Sign," Hydrocarbon-Like Portions of Molecules Before moving on, let's pause to reflect on what we have done in relating physical properties to structural features. We have introduced the first molecular "map sign" in our study: substances whose molecules are entirely *or even mostly* hydrocarbon-like are likely to be insoluble in water but soluble in nonpolar solvents. When we see an unfamiliar structure, we can tell at a glance whether it is mostly hydrocarbon-like. If it is, we can predict with considerable confidence that the compound is not soluble in water. The structure of cholesterol illustrates our point:

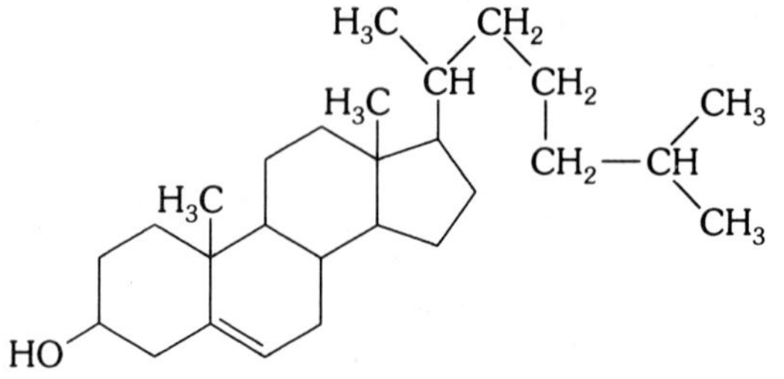

Cholesterol

You probably know that cholesterol can form solid deposits in blood capillaries, and even close them. The heart has to work harder, and a heart attack can occur. Notice, now, that virtually the entire cholesterol molecule is hydrocarbon-like. It has only one polar group, the —OH or alcohol group, and this isn't enough to make cholesterol sufficiently polar to dissolve either in water or in blood (which is mostly water).

What cholesterol illustrates is that by learning one very general fact, one "map sign," we don't have to memorize a long list of separate (but similar) facts about an equally long list of separate compounds that occur at the molecular level of life. With what we have just learned, we can look at the structures of hundreds of complicated compounds and confidently predict particular properties such as the likelihood of their being soluble in water.

EXAMPLE 12.4　　　　**PREDICTING PHYSICAL PROPERTIES FROM STRUCTURES**

Problem: Study the following two structures and tell which is the structure of the more water-soluble compound.

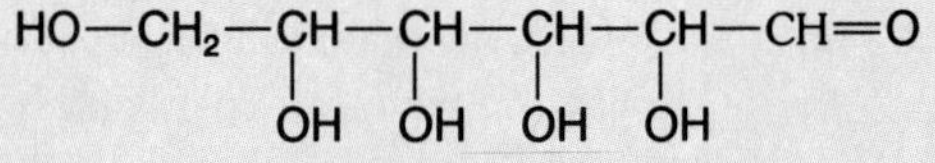

$$HO-CH_2-CH-CH-CH-CH-CH=O$$
$$\qquad\qquad |\quad\ |\quad\ |\quad\ |$$
$$\qquad\qquad OH\ \ OH\ \ OH\ \ OH$$

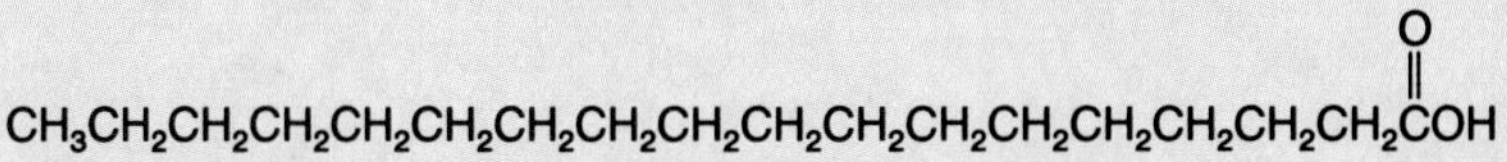

$$CH_3CH_2CH_2CH_2CH_2CH_2CH_2CH_2CH_2CH_2CH_2CH_2CH_2CH_2CH_2CH_2CH_2\overset{\displaystyle O}{\overset{\|}{C}}OH$$

Solution: The first structure has several polar —OH groups, but the second is almost entirely hydrocarbon-like. Hence, the first should be (and is) much more soluble in water. The first compound is glucose (in one of its forms), the chief sugar in the bloodstream. The second is stearic acid, which forms when we digest fats in the diet, and which does not dissolve in water.

PRACTICE EXERCISE 8　　Which of the following is more soluble in gasoline?

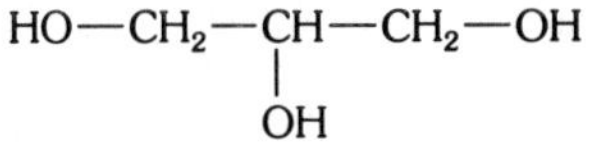

$$HO-CH_2-CH-CH_2-OH \qquad\qquad CH_3-CH_2-CH-CH_2-OH$$
$$\qquad\qquad |\qquad\qquad\qquad\qquad\qquad\qquad\qquad |$$
$$\qquad\qquad OH \qquad\qquad\qquad\qquad\qquad\qquad\qquad CH_3$$

　　　　　　　Glycerol 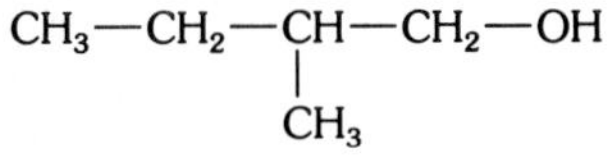　　　　　　　　　　　　　　2-Methyl-1-butanol

12.6 NAMING THE ALKANES AND CYCLOALKANES

An IUPAC name discloses the compound's family, the number of carbons in the parent chain, and the kinds and locations of substituents.

■ "Nomenclature" is from the Latin *nomen*, name, + *calare*, to call. Wealthy Romans had slaves called *nomenclators*, whose duty it was to remind their owners of the names of important people who approached them on the street.

In chemistry, **nomenclature** refers to the rules used to name compounds. The International Union of Pure and Applied Chemistry (IUPAC) is the organization that now develops the rules of chemical nomenclature, and all scientific societies in the world belong to it. Its rules are known as the **IUPAC rules.** They are so carefully drawn that only one name could be written for each compound, and only one structure could be drawn for each name.

The IUPAC names, unfortunately, are sometimes very long and difficult to write or pronounce. It's much easier to call table sugar *sucrose* than α-D-glucopyranosyl β-D-fructofuranoside. This illustrates why shorter names, referred to as *common names*, are still widely used. We will want to learn some common names, too, and you will see that even they usually have some system to them.

IUPAC Rules for Naming Alkanes and Cycloalkanes In the IUPAC rules, the last syllable in the name designates the family to which the compound belongs. The names of all the saturated hydrocarbons, for example, end in *-ane.* The names of hydrocarbons with double bonds end in *-ene,* and those with triple bonds end in *-yne.* The rules for the alkanes are as follows.

1. Use the ending *-ane* for all alkanes (and cycloalkanes).

2. Determine what is the longest continuous chain of carbons in the structure, and let this be the *parent chain* for naming purposes.
    For example, view the branched-chain alkane,

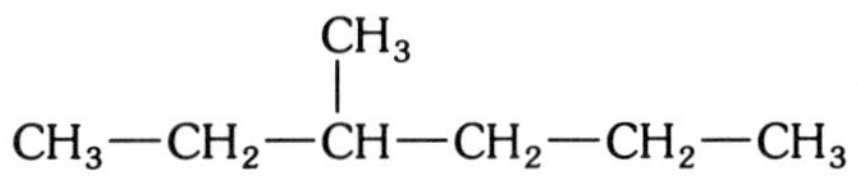

$$CH_3-CH_2-\underset{\underset{CH_3}{|}}{CH}-CH_2-CH_2-CH_3$$

as coming from

$$CH_3-CH_2-CH_2-CH_2-CH_2-CH_3$$

by replacing a hydrogen atom on the third carbon from the left with a CH_3 group.

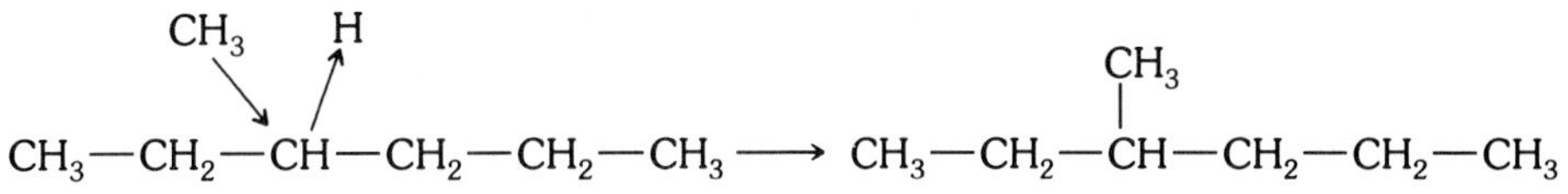

$$CH_3-CH_2-\underset{\underset{CH_3\ \ \ \ H}{\nearrow\ \ \nwarrow}}{CH}-CH_2-CH_2-CH_3 \longrightarrow CH_3-CH_2-\underset{\underset{CH_3}{|}}{CH}-CH_2-CH_2-CH_3$$

3. Attach a prefix to *-ane* that specifies the number of carbon atoms *in the parent chain.* The prefixes through C-10 are as follows (and these must be memorized). The names in Table 12.3 illustrate their use. You can see them used for the cycloalkanes, Table 12.4, too.

meth-	1 C	hex-	6 C
eth-	2 C	hept-	7 C
prop-	3 C	oct-	8 C
but-	4 C	non-	9 C
pent-	5 C	dec-	10 C

■ We won't need to know the prefixes for the higher alkanes.

For example, the parent chain of our example has six carbons, so the corresponding alkane is called hexane, *hex* for six carbons and *-ane* for being in the alkane family. The branched-chain compound whose name we are devising is regarded as a derivative of this parent, hexane.

TABLE 12.4 Some Cycloalkanes

IUPAC Name	Structure	Boiling Point (°C)	Melting Point (°C)	Density (20 °C)
Cyclopropane	△	−33	−127	1.809 g/L (0 °C)
Cyclobutane	□	−13.1	−80	0.7038 g/L (0 °C)
Cyclopentane	⬠	49.3	−94.4	0.7460 g/mL
Cyclohexane	⬡	80.7	6.47	0.7781 g/mL
Cycloheptane	⬡	118.5	−12	0.8098 g/mL

4. Assign numbers to each carbon of the parent chain starting from whichever of its ends gives the location of the first branch the lower of two possible numbers.

For example, the correct direction for numbering our example is from left to right.

$$\underset{1}{CH_3}-\underset{2}{CH_2}-\underset{3}{\overset{\overset{\displaystyle CH_3}{|}}{CH}}-\underset{4}{CH_2}-\underset{5}{CH_2}-\underset{6}{CH_3} \qquad \text{(Correct direction of numbering)}$$

Had we numbered from right to left, the carbon holding the branch would have had a higher number.

$$\underset{6}{CH_3}-\underset{5}{CH_2}-\underset{4}{\overset{\overset{\displaystyle CH_3}{|}}{CH}}-\underset{3}{CH_2}-\underset{2}{CH_2}-\underset{1}{CH_3} \qquad \text{(Incorrect direction of numbering)}$$

5. Determine the correct name for each branch (or for any other atom or group). We must now pause and learn the names of a few such groups.

Any branch that consists only of carbon and hydrogen and has only single bonds is called an **alkyl group,** and the names of all alkyl groups end in -*yl*. Think of an alkyl group as an alkane minus one of its hydrogen atoms. For example,

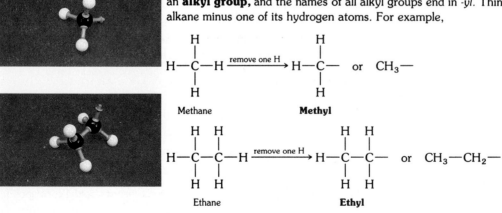

Two alkyl groups can be obtained from propane because the middle position is not equivalent to either of the end positions.

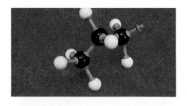

$$\underset{\text{Propane}}{H-\overset{\overset{\displaystyle H}{|}}{\underset{\underset{\displaystyle H}{|}}{C}}-\overset{\overset{\displaystyle H}{|}}{\underset{\underset{\displaystyle H}{|}}{C}}-\overset{\overset{\displaystyle H}{|}}{\underset{\underset{\displaystyle H}{|}}{C}}-H} \xrightarrow[\text{from either end}]{\text{remove one H}} \underset{\textbf{Propyl}}{H-\overset{\overset{\displaystyle H}{|}}{\underset{\underset{\displaystyle H}{|}}{C}}-\overset{\overset{\displaystyle H}{|}}{\underset{\underset{\displaystyle H}{|}}{C}}-\overset{\overset{\displaystyle H}{|}}{\underset{\underset{\displaystyle H}{|}}{C}}-} \quad \text{or} \quad CH_3-CH_2-CH_2-$$

$$\underset{\text{Propane}}{H-\overset{\overset{\displaystyle H}{|}}{\underset{\underset{\displaystyle H}{|}}{C}}-\overset{\overset{\displaystyle H}{|}}{\underset{\underset{\displaystyle H}{|}}{C}}-\overset{\overset{\displaystyle H}{|}}{\underset{\underset{\displaystyle H}{|}}{C}}-H} \xrightarrow[\text{from the middle}]{\text{remove one H}} \underset{\textbf{Isopropyl}}{H-\overset{\overset{\displaystyle H}{|}}{\underset{\underset{\displaystyle H}{|}}{C}}-\overset{|}{\underset{}{C}}-\overset{\overset{\displaystyle H}{|}}{\underset{\underset{\displaystyle H}{|}}{C}}-} \quad \text{or} \quad CH_3-\overset{|}{C}H-CH_3$$

Two alkyl groups can similarly be obtained from butane.

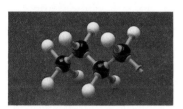

$$\underset{\text{Butane}}{H-\overset{\overset{\displaystyle H}{|}}{\underset{\underset{\displaystyle H}{|}}{C}}-\overset{\overset{\displaystyle H}{|}}{\underset{\underset{\displaystyle H}{|}}{C}}-\overset{\overset{\displaystyle H}{|}}{\underset{\underset{\displaystyle H}{|}}{C}}-\overset{\overset{\displaystyle H}{|}}{\underset{\underset{\displaystyle H}{|}}{C}}-H} \xrightarrow[\text{from either end}]{\text{remove one H}} \underset{\textbf{Butyl}}{H-\overset{\overset{\displaystyle H}{|}}{\underset{\underset{\displaystyle H}{|}}{C}}-\overset{\overset{\displaystyle H}{|}}{\underset{\underset{\displaystyle H}{|}}{C}}-\overset{\overset{\displaystyle H}{|}}{\underset{\underset{\displaystyle H}{|}}{C}}-\overset{\overset{\displaystyle H}{|}}{\underset{\underset{\displaystyle H}{|}}{C}}-}$$

or $CH_3-CH_2-CH_2-CH_2-$

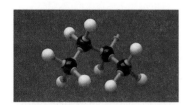

$$\underset{\text{Butane}}{H-\overset{\overset{\displaystyle H}{|}}{\underset{\underset{\displaystyle H}{|}}{C}}-\overset{\overset{\displaystyle H}{|}}{\underset{\underset{\displaystyle H}{|}}{C}}-\overset{\overset{\displaystyle H}{|}}{\underset{\underset{\displaystyle H}{|}}{C}}-\overset{\overset{\displaystyle H}{|}}{\underset{\underset{\displaystyle H}{|}}{C}}-H} \xrightarrow[\substack{\text{the second carbon}\\\text{in from either end}}]{\text{remove one H from}} \underset{\substack{\textit{sec}\textbf{-Butyl}\\(sec = secondary)}}{H-\overset{\overset{\displaystyle H}{|}}{\underset{\underset{\displaystyle H}{|}}{C}}-\overset{\overset{\displaystyle H}{|}}{\underset{\underset{\displaystyle H}{|}}{C}}-\overset{|}{\underset{}{C}}-\overset{\overset{\displaystyle H}{|}}{\underset{\underset{\displaystyle H}{|}}{C}}-}$$

or $CH_3-CH_2-\overset{|}{C}H-CH_3$

Primary carbons

$$CH_3-\overset{\overset{\displaystyle CH_3}{|}}{C}H-CH_2-CH_3$$

Tertiary carbon   Secondary carbon

This is called the *secondary* butyl group (abbreviated *sec*-butyl) because the open bonding site is at a **secondary carbon,** a carbon that is directly attached to just two other carbons. A **primary carbon** is one to which one other carbon is directly attached. The open bonding site in the butyl group, for example, is at a primary carbon atom. A **tertiary carbon** is one that holds directly three other carbons. We will encounter a tertiary carbon in a group that we will soon study.

Butane is the first alkane to have an isomer. Its common name is isobutane, and we can derive two more alkyl groups from it.

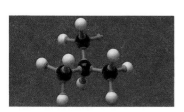

$$\underset{\text{Isobutane}}{\overset{\displaystyle H-\overset{\overset{\displaystyle H}{|}}{C}-H}{\overset{\displaystyle |}{H-\overset{\overset{\displaystyle H}{|}}{\underset{\underset{\displaystyle H}{|}}{C}}-\overset{\overset{\displaystyle H}{|}}{\underset{\underset{\displaystyle H}{|}}{C}}-\overset{\overset{\displaystyle H}{|}}{\underset{\underset{\displaystyle H}{|}}{C}}-H}}} \xrightarrow[\text{one of the }CH_3\text{ groups}]{\text{remove one H from any}} \underset{\textbf{Isobutyl}}{\overset{\displaystyle H-\overset{\overset{\displaystyle H}{|}}{C}-H}{\overset{\displaystyle |}{H-\overset{\overset{\displaystyle H}{|}}{\underset{\underset{\displaystyle H}{|}}{C}}-\overset{\overset{\displaystyle H}{|}}{\underset{\underset{\displaystyle H}{|}}{C}}-\overset{\overset{\displaystyle H}{|}}{\underset{\underset{\displaystyle H}{|}}{C}}-}}} \quad \text{or} \quad \overset{\overset{\displaystyle CH_3}{|}}{CH_3CHCH_2-}$$

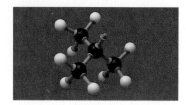

Isobutane → remove the lone H from the tertiary atom → **t-Butyl** *(t = tertiary)* or CH_3CCH_3 with CH_3

Notice that the open bonding site in the *tertiary*-butyl group (abbreviated *t*-butyl) occurs at a tertiary carbon.

The names and structures of these alkyl groups must now be learned. If you have access to ball-and-stick models, make models of each of the parent alkanes and then remove hydrogen atoms to generate the open bonding sites and the alkyl groups. The *Study Guide* accompanying this book has exercises that provide drills in recognizing alkyl groups when they are positioned in different ways on the page.

The prefix *iso-* in the name of an alkyl group, such as in isopropyl or isobutyl, has a special meaning. It can be used to name any alkyl group that has the following general features:

$$H_3C \diagdown CH-(CH_2)_n- \quad (n = 0, 1, 2, 3, \text{ etc.})$$
$$H_3C \diagup \qquad\qquad n = 0, \text{ isopropyl} \qquad n = 1, \text{ isobutyl}$$

Notice that in each of these names there is a word fragment (for example, *-prop-*, *-but-*, and so forth) associated with a number of carbon atoms. Here, it specifies the *total* number of carbons in the alkyl group. Thus the isopropyl group has three carbons and the isobutyl has four.

■ Here is another way to condense a structure. Thus $CH_3(CH_2)_3CH_3$ represents $CH_3CH_2CH_2CH_2CH_3$.

$$H_3C \diagdown CH(CH_2)_2-$$
$$H_3C \diagup$$
Isopentyl

$$H_3C \diagdown CH(CH_2)_3-$$
$$H_3C \diagup$$
Isohexyl

6. Attach the name of the alkyl group or other substituent to the name of the parent as a prefix. Place the location number of the group in front of the resulting name and separate the number from the name by a hyphen.

Returning to our original example, we find its name is 3-methylhexane:

$$CH_3-CH_2-\overset{\overset{\displaystyle CH_3}{|}}{CH}-CH_2-CH_2-CH_3$$
3-Methylhexane

7. When two or more groups are attached to the parent, name each and locate each with a number. Always use *hyphens* to separate numbers from words in the IUPAC names of compounds, and arrange the names of the alkyl groups alphabetically in the final name. For example,

$$CH_3-CH_2-CH_2-\overset{\overset{\displaystyle CH_2-CH_3}{|}}{CH}-CH_2-\overset{\overset{\displaystyle CH_3}{|}}{CH}-CH_3 \quad \text{4-ethyl-2-methylheptane}$$
$$\quad 7 \qquad 6 \qquad 5 \qquad 4 \qquad 3 \qquad 2 \qquad 1$$

8. When two or more substituents are identical, use such prefixes as di- (for 2), tri- (for 3), tetra- (for 4), and so forth; and specify the location number of *every* group. Always separate a number from another number in a name by a *comma*. For example,

$$CH_3-\overset{\overset{\displaystyle CH_3}{|}}{CH}-CH_2-\overset{\overset{\displaystyle CH_3}{|}}{CH}-CH_2-CH_3$$

Correct name: 2,4-dimethylhexane
Incorrect names: 2,4-methylhexane
                 3,5-dimethylhexane
                 2-methyl-4-methylhexane

9. When identical groups are on the *same* carbon, repeat the number of this carbon in the name. For example,

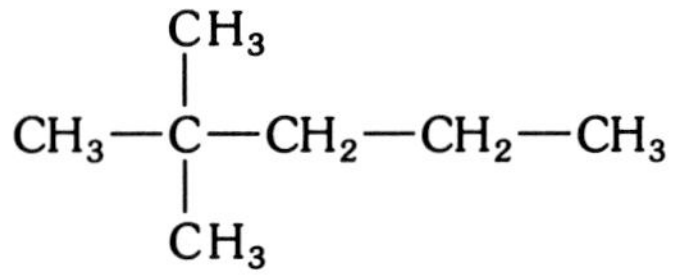

$$CH_3-\underset{\underset{CH_3}{|}}{\overset{\overset{CH_3}{|}}{C}}-CH_2-CH_2-CH_3$$

Correct name: 2,2-dimethylpentane
Incorrect names: 2-dimethylpentane
2,2-methylpentane
4,4-dimethylpentane

Another example:

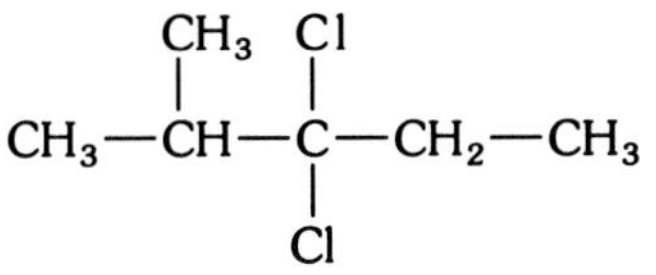

$$CH_3-\underset{}{CH}-\underset{\underset{Cl}{|}}{\overset{\overset{CH_3\;\;Cl}{|\;\;\;|}}{C}}-CH_2-CH_3$$

Correct name: 3,3-dichloro-2-methylpentane

Notice that the names of nonalkyl substituents are assembled first in the final name, so a compound such as in our previous example is viewed as a derivative of the hydrocarbon, 2-methylpentane.

10. To name a cycloalkane, place the prefix *cyclo* before the name of the straight-chain alkane that has the same number of carbon atoms as the ring. This was illustrated in Table 12.4.

11. When necessary, give numbers to the ring atoms by giving location 1 to a ring position that holds a substituent and numbering around the ring in whichever direction reaches the nearest substituent first. For example,

■ No number is needed when the ring has only one group. Thus,

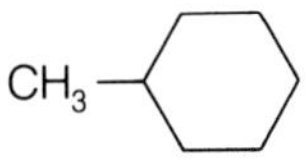

CH_3-⬡

is named methylcyclohexane, not 1-methylcyclohexane.

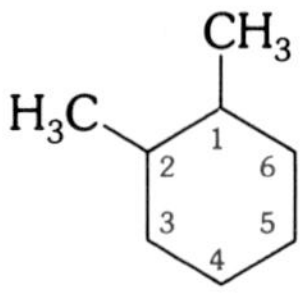

1,2-Dimethylcyclohexane 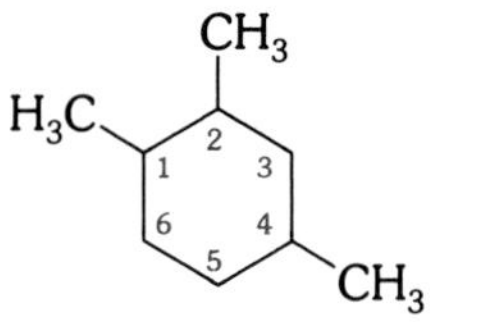   1,2,4-Trimethylcyclohexane

These are not all the IUPAC rules for alkanes, but they will cover all of our needs. Before we give more examples of the rules for alkanes, we will introduce the names that are used for several substituents that can be attached to alkane chains:

$-F$ fluoro $-I$ iodo
$-Cl$ chloro $-NO_2$ nitro
$-Br$ bromo $-NH_2$ amino

Now study the following examples of correctly named compounds. Be sure to notice that in choosing the parent chain we sometimes have to go around a corner as the chain zigzags on the page.

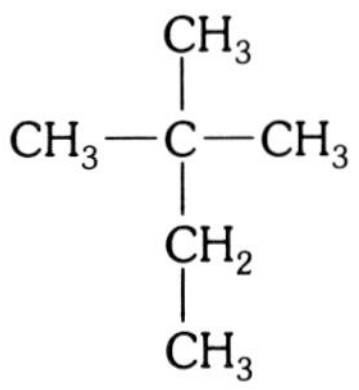

2,2-Dimethylbutane
Not 2-methyl-2-ethylpropane

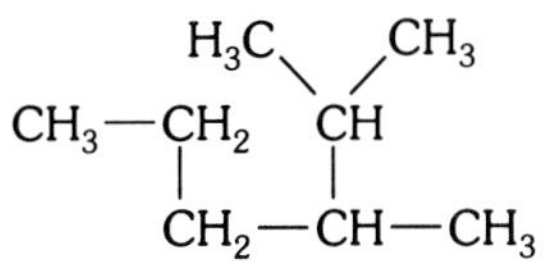

2,3-Dimethylhexane
Not 2-isopropylpentane

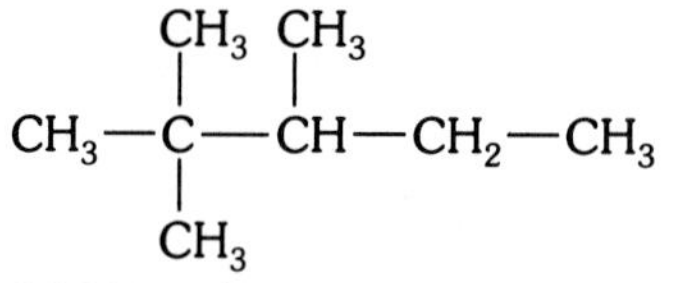

$$CH_3 - \underset{\underset{CH_3}{|}}{\overset{\overset{CH_3}{|}}{C}} - \underset{\overset{CH_3}{|}}{CH} - CH_2 - CH_3$$

2,2,3-Trimethylpentane
Not 2,3-trimethylpentane
Not 2-*t*-butylbutane

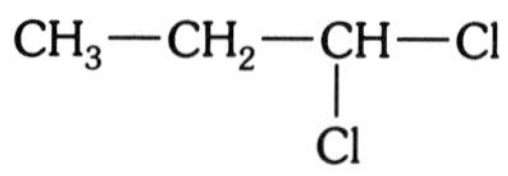

$$CH_3 - CH_2 - \underset{\underset{Cl}{|}}{CH} - Cl$$

1,1-Dichloropropane
Not 3,3-dichloropropane
Not 3,3-chloropropane
Not 1-dichloropropane
Not 1,1-chloropropane

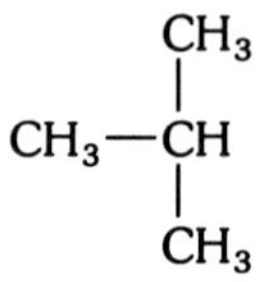

$$CH_3 - \underset{\overset{CH_3}{|}}{\overset{\overset{CH_3}{|}}{CH}}$$

2-Methylpropane
Not 1,1-dimethylethane
Not isobutane (which is its common name)

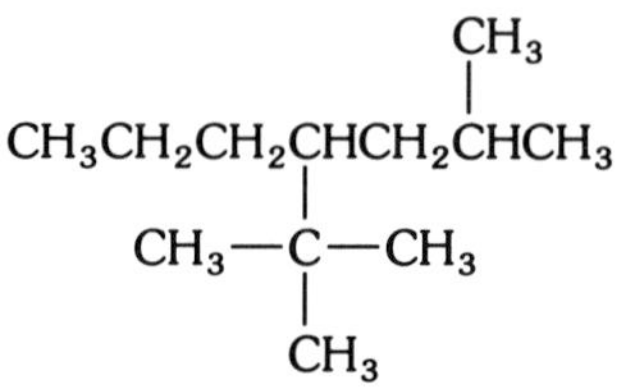

$$CH_3CH_2CH_2\underset{\underset{CH_3}{|}}{\overset{}{CH}}CH_2\underset{\overset{CH_3}{|}}{CH}CH_3$$

$$CH_3 - \underset{\overset{CH_3}{|}}{\overset{\overset{CH_3}{|}}{C}} - CH_3$$

4-*t*-butyl-2-methylheptane
Not 4-*t*-butyl-6-methylheptane

EXAMPLE 12.5   **USING THE IUPAC RULES TO NAME AN ALKANE**

Problem: What is the IUPAC name for the following compound?

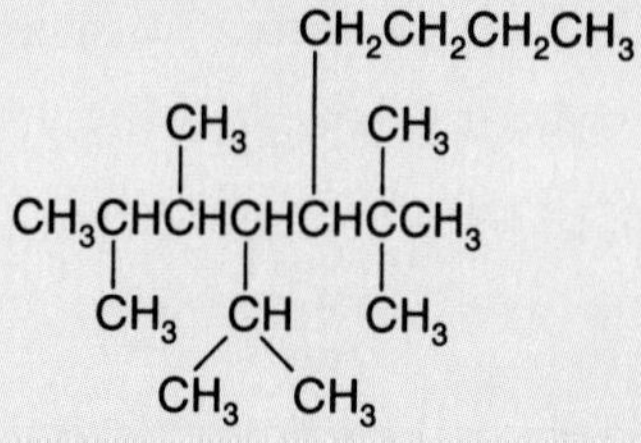

$$CH_2CH_2CH_2CH_3$$

$$CH_3\underset{\underset{CH_3}{|}}{\overset{\overset{CH_3}{|}}{CH}}\underset{\underset{CH_3}{|}}{\overset{}{CH}}CH\underset{\underset{CH_3}{|}}{\overset{}{CH}}\underset{\overset{CH_3}{|}}{C}CH_3$$

Solution: The compound is an alkane because it is a hydrocarbon with only single bonds, so the ending to the name is -ane. The next step is to find the longest chain even if we have to go around corners. This chain is nine carbons long, so the name of the parent alkane is *nonane*. We have to number the chain from left to right, as follows, in order to reach the first branch with the lower number.

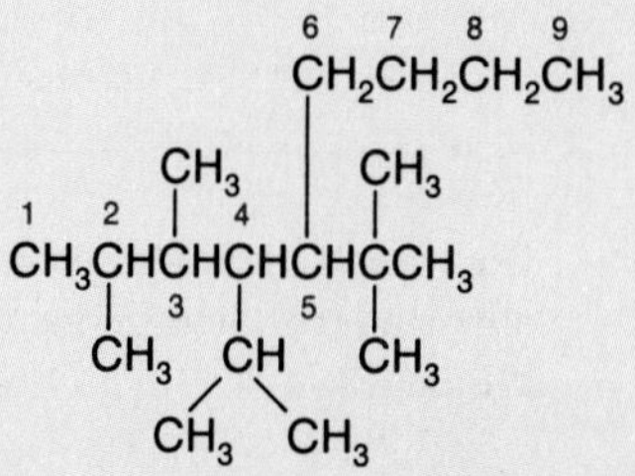

$$\overset{6 \quad 7 \quad 8 \quad 9}{CH_2CH_2CH_2CH_3}$$

$$\underset{1}{CH_3}\underset{2}{CH}\underset{3}{CH}\underset{4}{CH}\underset{5}{CH}C CH_3$$

At carbons 2 and 3 there are the one-carbon methyl groups. At carbon 4 there is a three-carbon isopropyl group (not the propyl group, because the bonding site is at the middle carbon of the three-carbon chain). At carbon 5 there is a four-carbon *t*-butyl group. (It has to be this particular butyl group because the bonding site is at a tertiary carbon.) In alphabetizing these alkyl groups, ignore Greek numerical prefixes like di- and tri-, and ignore designations of kinds of carbons, like *sec*- or *t*-. (The *iso*- prefix, however, is alphabetized among the "i"s.)

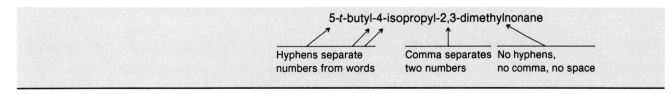

5-*t*-butyl-4-isopropyl-2,3-dimethylnonane

Hyphens separate | Comma separates | No hyphens,
numbers from words | two numbers | no comma, no space

PRACTICE EXERCISE 9

Write the IUPAC names of the following compounds.

(a)
$$CH_3{-}CH_2$$
$$\quad\quad\quad CH{-}CH_3$$
$$CH_2{-}CH_2$$
$$\quad\ \ |$$
$$\quad\ \ CH_3$$

(b)
$$\quad\quad\quad\quad\quad\quad CH_3$$
$$\quad\quad\quad\quad\quad\quad\ |$$
$$\quad\quad\quad\ \ CH_3{-}C{-}CH_3$$
$$H_3C\quad\ \ \ |$$
$$\quad\quad CH{-}CH{-}CH_2{-}CH_2{-}CH_3$$
$$CH_3{-}CH$$
$$\quad\quad |$$
$$\quad\quad CH_3$$

(c)
$$\quad\quad\quad\quad\ CH_3\quad\quad CH_3\quad\quad CH_3$$
$$\quad\quad\quad\quad\ |\quad\quad\quad |\quad\quad\quad |$$
$$CH_3{-}CH_2{-}CH{-}CH{-}CH{-}CH_2{-}CH{-}CH_3$$
$$\quad\quad\quad\quad\quad\quad |$$
$$\quad\quad\quad\quad\quad CH_2{-}CH_2{-}CH_2{-}CH_3$$

(d)
$$\quad\quad\quad\quad\quad\ Br$$
$$\quad\quad\quad\quad\quad\ |$$
$$Cl{-}CH_2{-}CH{-}CH_2{-}I$$

(e)
$$\quad\quad\quad\quad\quad\quad\quad CH_3{-}CH{-}CH_3$$
$$\quad\quad\quad\quad\quad\quad\quad\quad\quad\ |$$
$$CH_3{-}CH_2{-}CH_2{-}CH{-}CH{-}CH_2{-}CH_2{-}CH_3$$
$$\quad\quad\quad\quad\quad\quad |$$
$$\quad\quad\quad\ CH_3{-}C{-}CH_3$$
$$\quad\quad\quad\quad\quad\quad |$$
$$\quad\quad\quad\quad\quad\ CH_3$$

(f)
$$\quad\quad\quad\quad\quad CH_3$$
$$\quad\quad\quad\quad\quad\ |$$
$$NO_2{-}CH_2{-}C{-}CH_2{-}NO_2$$
$$\quad\quad\quad\quad\quad |$$
$$\quad\quad\quad\quad\quad CH_3$$

(g)
$$\quad\quad\quad\quad\quad\ CH_2{-}Cl$$
$$\quad\quad\quad\quad\quad\ |$$
$$CH_3{-}CH_2{-}CH{-}CH{-}CH_3$$
$$\quad\quad\quad\quad |$$
$$\quad\quad\quad\ CH_3$$

(h)
$$\quad\quad CH_3\quad\quad\quad\quad\quad CH_2{-}CH_3$$
$$\quad\quad\ |\quad\quad\quad\quad\quad\quad\ |$$
$$CH_3{-}CH{-}CH_2{-}CH_2{-}CH{-}CH{-}CH_3$$
$$\quad\quad\quad\quad\quad\quad\quad\quad |$$
$$\quad\quad\quad\quad\quad\quad\quad\ CH_3$$

PRACTICE EXERCISE 10

Write the condensed structures of the following compounds.

(a) 1-Bromo-2-nitropentane
(b) 5-Isopropyl-2,2,3,3,4,4-hexamethyloctane
(c) 2,2-Diiodo-5-*sec*-butyl-6-*t*-butyl-4-isopropyl-3-methylnonane
(d) 1-Bromo-1-chloro-2-methylpropane
(e) 5,5-Di-*sec*-butyldecane

PRACTICE EXERCISE 11

Examine the structure of part (e) of Practice Exercise 10. Underline each primary carbon, draw an arrow to each secondary carbon, and circle each tertiary carbon.

Butane   Isobutane

Common Names   In some references you might see the names of straight-chain alkanes with the prefix *n*-, as in *n*-butane, the common name of butane. It stands for *normal,* which is a way of designating that the straight-chain isomer is regarded as the *normal* isomer, as in the common names, *n*-pentane, *n*-hexane, and so forth. It is used only when isomers are possible. (You would never see *n*-propane printed as a name, for example, because there are no isomers of propane.)

Common Names of Alcohols, Amines, and Haloalkanes Employ the Names of the Alkyl Groups   The following examples of some halogen derivatives of the alkanes, called *haloalkanes,* illustrate how common names are easily constructed. The IUPAC names are given for comparison.

Structure	Common Name	IUPAC Name
CH_3Cl	methyl chloride	chloromethane
CH_3CH_2Br	ethyl bromide	bromoethane
$CH_3CH_2CH_2Br$	propyl bromide	1-bromopropane
$CH_3\overset{\displaystyle |}{\underset{\displaystyle Cl}{C}}HCH_3$	isopropyl chloride	2-chloropropane
$CH_3CH_2CH_2CH_2Cl$	butyl chloride	1-chlorobutane
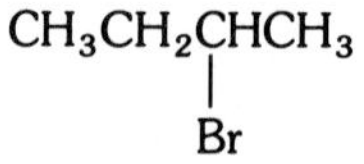 $CH_3CH_2\underset{\displaystyle Br}{C}HCH_3$	*sec*-butyl bromide	2-bromobutane
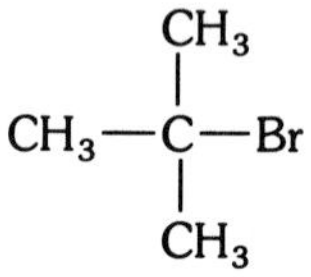 $CH_3-\overset{\displaystyle CH_3}{\underset{\displaystyle CH_3}{C}}-Br$	*t*-butyl bromide	2-bromo-2-methylpropane
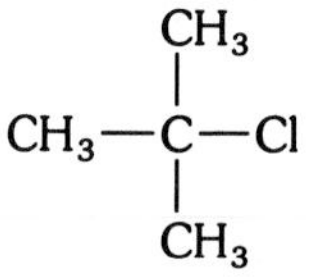 $CH_3-\overset{\displaystyle CH_3}{\underset{\displaystyle CH_3}{C}}-Cl$	*t*-butyl chloride	2-chloro-2-methylpropane

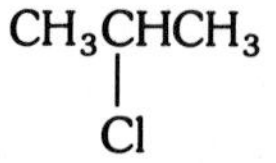

PRACTICE EXERCISE 12   Give the common names of the following compounds.

(a) $ClCH_2CH_3$ (b) $BrCH_2CH_2CH_2CH_3$ (c) 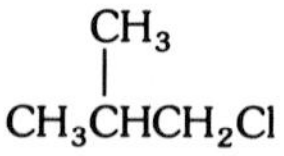 $CH_3\overset{\displaystyle CH_3}{\underset{\displaystyle |}{C}}HCH_2Cl$ (d) 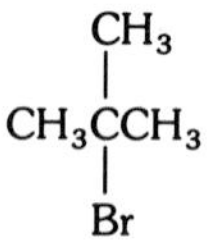 $CH_3\overset{\displaystyle CH_3}{\underset{\displaystyle Br}{C}}CH_3$

12.7   CHEMICAL PROPERTIES OF ALKANES

Alkanes can burn and can give substitution reactions with the halogens, but they undergo almost no other reaction.

■ Mineral oil is a safe laxative (when used with care) because it is a mixture of high-formula-weight alkanes that undergo no chemical reactions in the intestinal tract.

The chemistry of the alkanes and cycloalkanes is quite simple. Very few chemicals react with them. This is why they are nicknamed the *paraffins* or the paraffinic hydrocarbons, after the Latin *parum affinis,* meaning "little affinity" or "little reactivity." The alkanes are not chemically attacked by water, by strong acids such as sulfuric or hydrochloric acid, by strong bases such as sodium hydroxide, by active metals such as sodium, by strong oxidizing agents such as the permanganate ion or the dichromate ion, or by any of the reducing agents. Even when molecules have functional groups, most of their alkane-like parts ride unchanged through reactions involving the functional groups (which, of course, is why alkyl groups are called nonfunctional groups).

Among the few reactions of alkanes are combustion and chlorination. We will look briefly at them next.

The Combustion of Alkanes or Any Hydrocarbon Gives CO_2 and H_2O   Virtually all organic compounds burn, and the hydrocarbons are no exception. We burn mixtures of alkanes, for example, as fuel to obtain energy. Bunsen burner gas is mostly methane. Liquified propane is used as fuel in areas where gas lines have not been built. Gasoline, diesel fuel, jet fuel, and heating oil are all mixtures of hydrocarbons, mostly alkanes.

If enough oxygen is available, the sole products of the complete combustion of *any hydrocarbon,* not just alkanes, are carbon dioxide and water plus heat. To illustrate, using propane,

$$CH_3CH_2CH_3 + 5O_2 \longrightarrow 3CO_2 + 4H_2O + 531 \text{ kcal/mol propane}$$

WHY EQUATIONS FOR ORGANIC REACTIONS CANNOT ALWAYS BE BALANCED

SPECIAL TOPIC 12.1

Chemical reactions involve the breaking and reforming of bonds. Because organic molecules have several bonds of similar strengths, several products can sometimes form, even when we are trying to make just one of them. The substances we don't want are called the **by-products**, and the reactions that produce by-products are called **side reactions.** The reaction that produces the largest relative quantity of product is called the **main reaction.** Naturally, the chemist hopes this is the reaction that produces the desired product. In any case, most organic reactions produce a set of products, a mixture that must then be separated into the constituents. This often takes more time and effort than any other aspect of the synthesis.

As an example of a reaction that produces a mixture, we can use the chlorination of ethane. If we were to mix 1 mol of chlorine with 1 mol of ethane, naively trying to prepare 1 mole of ethyl chloride, we would obtain a mixture of mono-, di-, tri- and possibly still more highly chlorinated molecules (plus HCl).

$$CH_3CH_3 + Cl_2 \xrightarrow{\text{ultraviolet light}} CH_3CH_2Cl + CH_3CHCl_2 + ClCH_2CH_2Cl + CH_3CCl_3 + ClCH_2.CHCl_2 + \text{etc.} + HCl$$

It would be foolish to write coefficients in front of any of the products or to change the coefficients in front of the reactants — which, as they stand, say that a 1 : 1 molar ratio was taken — in an effort to balance the equation. If the mixture were to be completely separated, then the molar percentages of the various products could be reported, but seldom is such a thorough separation performed when just one product is sought.

Most organic reactions pose this kind of balancing problem, so the equation written is the equation for the main reaction only. Often it is balanced, but for just one reason — to provide a basis for the selection of the relative numbers of moles of the reactants to be mixed at the start. In nearly all the reactions that we will study, side reactions occur, which we generally will ignore.

If insufficient oxygen is present, some carbon monoxide forms. The same products, carbon dioxide and water, are also obtained by the complete combustion of any organic compound that consists only of carbon, hydrogen, and oxygen (for example, the alcohols).

The Chlorination of Alkanes Is a Substitution Reaction In the presence of ultraviolet radiation or at a high temperature, alkanes react with chlorine to give organochlorine compounds and hydrogen chloride. An atom of hydrogen in the alkane is replaced by an atom of chlorine, and this kind of replacement of one atom or group by another is called a **substitution reaction.** For example,

$$CH_4 + Cl_2 \xrightarrow[\text{or heat}]{\text{ultraviolet light}} CH_3Cl + HCl$$
$$\text{Methyl chloride}$$

The hydrogen atoms in methyl chloride can also be replaced by chlorine, so as methyl chloride starts to form it competes with the methane that hasn't reacted yet. This is how some methylene chloride forms when the above reaction is carried out. In fact, when 1 mol of CH_4 and 1 mol of Cl_2 are mixed and made to react, several reactions eventually occur, and a mixture of four chlorinated methanes, hydrogen chloride, plus some unreacted methane is the result. It isn't possible to write a balanced equation, but what we can do is represent it by a flow of symbols.

■ The numbers in parentheses are the boiling points of the compounds. Notice how they increase with formula weight.

$$CH_4 + Cl_2 \xrightarrow[HCl]{} CH_3Cl \xrightarrow[HCl]{Cl_2} CH_2Cl_2 \xrightarrow[HCl]{Cl_2} CHCl_3 \xrightarrow[HCl]{Cl_2} CCl_4$$

Methane	Methyl chloride	Methylene chloride	Chloroform	Carbon tetrachloride
(−162 °C)	(−24 °C)	(40 °C)	(61 °C)	(77 °C)

For a discussion of the use of unbalanced reaction sequences to represent organic reactions, see Special Topic 12.1.

Methylene chloride, chloroform, and carbon tetrachloride are examples of *organochlorine compounds,* and all are used as nonpolar solvents. Chloroform has been used as an anesthetic. Chlorinated solvents must be handled in well-ventilated areas, and they should not be allowed to spill on the skin. They are rapidly absorbed through the skin, and both

■ Chloroform (b.p. 61 °C) was an anesthetic better suited for use in the tropics than diethyl ether (b.p. 35 °C) because of its higher boiling point.

chloroform and carbon tetrachloride can cause liver damage. They should never be poured down the sink. Many organohalogen compounds are carcinogenic.

■ The reaction with bromine is much slower than with chlorine.

Bromine reacts with methane by the same kind of substitution as chlorine. Iodine does not react. Fluorine combines explosively with most organic compounds at room temperature, and complex mixtures form.

The higher alkanes can also be chlorinated. Ethyl chloride, plus more highly chlorinated products, form by the chlorination of ethane, and ethyl chloride (b.p. 12.5 °C) is used as a local anesthetic. When it is sprayed on the skin, it evaporates very rapidly, and this cools the area enough to prevent the transmission of pain signals during minor surgery at the site.

When propane is chlorinated, both propyl chloride and isopropyl chloride form in roughly equal amounts.

$$CH_3CH_2CH_3 + Cl_2 \xrightarrow{\text{ultraviolet light}} CH_3CH_2CH_2Cl + CH_3\overset{\displaystyle Cl}{\underset{\displaystyle |}{C}}HCH_3 + HCl$$

Propane   Propyl chloride   Isopropyl chloride

Besides these products, some higher chlorinated compounds also form.

PRACTICE EXERCISE 13   (a) How many monochloro compounds of butane are possible? Give both their common and IUPAC names. (Consider only the monochloro compounds with the formula C_4H_9Cl.) (b) How many monochloro derivatives of isobutane are possible? Write both their common and IUPAC names.

SUMMARY

Organic and inorganic compounds Most organic compounds are molecular and the majority of inorganic compounds are ionic. Molecular and ionic compounds differ in composition, in types of bonds, and in several physical properties.

Structural features of organic molecules The ability of carbon atoms to join to each other many times in succession—in straight chains, in branched chains, as well as in rings—accounts in large measure for the existence of several million organic compounds. The skeletons of the rings can be made entirely of carbon atoms or there may be one or more other nonmetal atoms (heterocyclic compounds).

Full structural formulas of organic compounds are usually condensed by grouping the hydrogens attached to a carbon immediately next to this carbon; by letting single bonds on a horizontal line be understood; and by leaving bond angles and conformational possibilities to the informed imagination. Skeletons of rings are usually represented by simple polygons. Free rotation about single bonds is possible in open-chain compounds but not in rings.

Compounds without multiple bonds are saturated. Those with double or triple bonds are unsaturated. Carbon–carbon double or triple bonds are never "understood" in structures.

The families of organic compounds are organized around functional groups, parts of molecules at which most of the chemical reactions occur. Nonfunctional units can sometimes be given the general symbol R—, as in R—O—H, the general symbol for all alcohols. These R— groups are hydrocarbon-like groups.

Isomerism Differences in the conformations of carbon chains do not create new compounds, but differences in the organizations of parts do. Isomers are compounds with identical molecular formulas but different structures. Sometimes isomers are in the same family,

like butane and isobutane. Often they are not, like ethyl alcohol and dimethyl ether.

Hydrocarbons Hydrocarbons are compounds in which the only elements are carbon and hydrogen. The alkanes are saturated hydrocarbons; the alkenes and alkynes are unsaturated. The alkenes have at least one double bond. The alkynes have at least one triple bond. The aromatic hydrocarbons have a benzene ring, and the aliphatic hydrocarbons do not. Being nonpolar compounds, the hydrocarbons are all insoluble in water, and many mixtures of alkanes are common, nonpolar solvents. The rule *like dissolves like* lets us predict solubilities.

Nomenclature of alkanes In the IUPAC system, a compound's family is always indicated by a name ending, like -ane for the alkanes. The number of carbons in the parent chain is indicated by a unique prefix for each number, like *but-* for four carbons in butane. The locations of side chains or groups are specified in the final name by numbers assigned to the carbons of the parent chain in the direction that locates the first branch at the lower of two possible numbers.

Alkane-like substituents are called alkyl groups, and the names and formulas of those having from one to four carbon atoms must be learned. Common names are still popular, particularly when the IUPAC names are long and cumbersome.

Chemical properties of alkanes Alkanes and cycloalkanes are generally unreactive at room temperature toward concentrated acids and bases, toward oxidizing and reducing agents, toward even the most reactive metals, and toward water. They burn, giving off carbon dioxide and water, and in the presence of ultraviolet light (or at a high temperature) they are attacked by chlorine.

REVIEW EXERCISES

The answers to these Review Exercises are in the *Study Guide* that accompanies this text.

Organic and Inorganic Compounds

12.1 Why are the compounds of carbon generally called *organic* compounds?

12.2 State the vital force theory in your own words.

12.3 What led scientists to adopt the vital force theory (prior to 1828)?

12.4 Describe what Wöhler did that made the vital force theory highly questionable.

12.5 What kind of bond between atoms predominates among organic compounds?

12.6 Which of the following compounds are inorganic?
(a) CH_3OH (b) CO   (c) CCl_4
(d) $NaHCO_3$ (e) K_2CO_3

12.7 Are the majority of all compounds that dissolve in water ionic or molecular? Inorganic or organic?

12.8 Explain why very few organic compounds can conduct electricity either in an aqueous solution or as molten materials.

12.9 Each compound described below is either ionic or molecular. State which it most likely is, and give one reason.
(a) The compound is a colorless gas at room temperature.
(b) This compound dissolves in water. When hydrochloric acid is added, the solution fizzes and an odorless, colorless gas is released, which can extinguish a burning flame.
(c) This compound melts at 300 °C, and it burns in air.
(d) This compound melts at 675 °C, and it becomes white when heated.
(e) This compound is a liquid that does not dissolve in water.

Structural Features of Organic Molecules

12.10 One can write the structure of butane, lighter fluid, as follows.

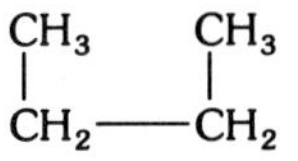

$$\begin{array}{cc} CH_3 & CH_3 \\ | & | \\ CH_2 \!-\!\!-\!\!-\! CH_2 & \end{array} \quad \text{Butane}$$

Are butane molecules properly described as straight chain or as branched chain, in the sense in which we use these terms? Explain.

12.11 Which of the following structures are possible, given the numbers of bonds that various atoms can form?
(a) $CH_2CH_2CH_3$
(b) $CH_3{=}CHCH_2CH_3$
(c) $CH_3CH{=}CH_2CH_2CH_3$

12.12 Write full (expanded) structures for each of the following *molecular* formulas. Remember how many covalent bonds that nonmetal atoms have in molecules: C, four; N, three; O, two; H, Cl, and Br, one each. In some structures you will have to use double or triple bonds. (*Hint:* A trial-and-error approach will have to be used.)

(a) CH_5N (b) CH_2Br_2
(c) $CHCl_3$ (d) C_2H_6
(e) CH_2O_2 (f) CH_2O
(g) NH_3O (h) C_2H_2
(i) N_2H_4 (j) HCN
(k) C_2H_3N (l) CH_4O

12.13 Expand the following structure of nicotinamide, one of the B-vitamins.

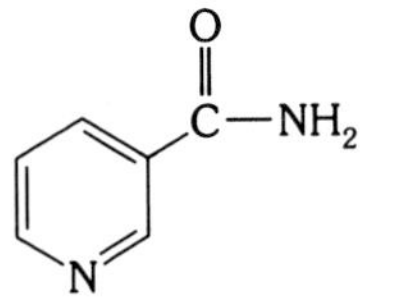

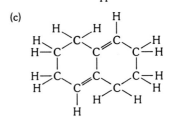

Nicotinamide

12.14 Expand the structure of thiamine, vitamin B_1. Notice that one nitrogen has four bonds, so it has a positive charge.

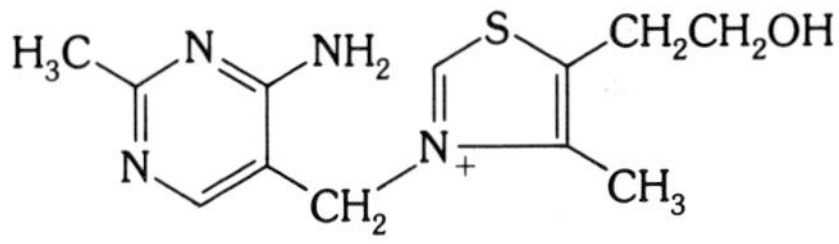

Thiamine

12.15 Write neat, condensed structures of the following.

(a)

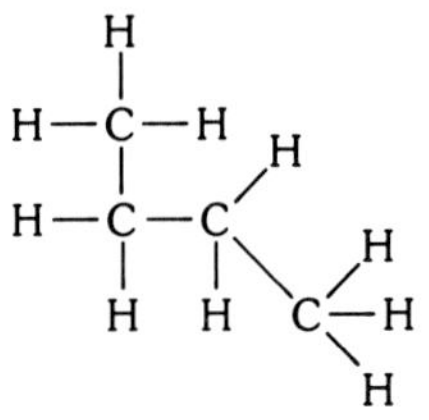

(b)

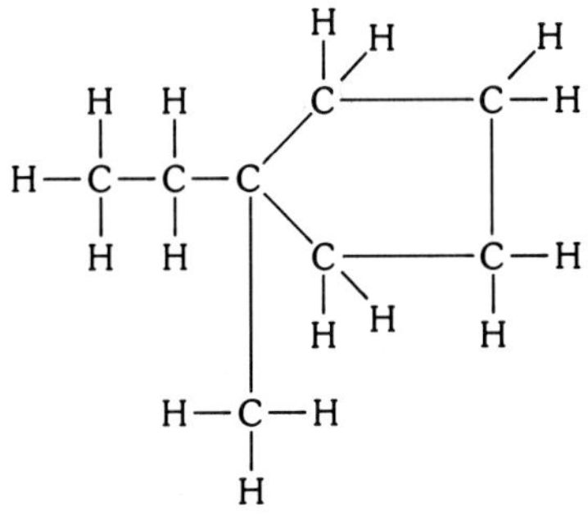

(c)

12.16 Why is the topic of molecular shape important at the molecular level of life?

12.17 What kinds of orbitals overlap when the C—C bond forms in ethane?

12.18 Free rotation can occur about single bonds (in open-chain structures) without breaking or weakening the bonds. Why is this possible?

12.19 Which of the following structures represent unsaturated compounds?

(a) 
Furan

(b) 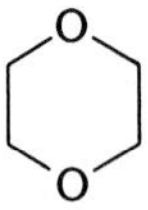
Dioxane

(c) 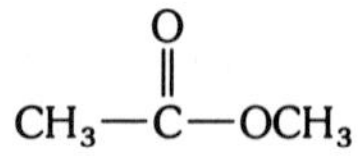
$CH_3-\overset{\overset{O}{\|}}{C}-OCH_3$
Methyl acetate

(d) 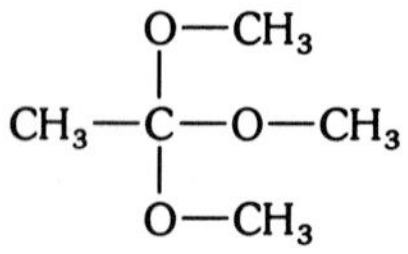
$CH_3-\overset{\overset{O-CH_3}{|}}{\underset{O-CH_3}{C}}-O-CH_3$
Methyl orthoacetate

12.20 Which compounds are saturated?

(a) 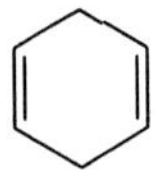
1,4-Cyclohexadiene

(b) $CH_3-C\equiv N$
Acetonitrile

(c) 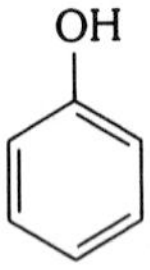
OH
Phenol

(d) 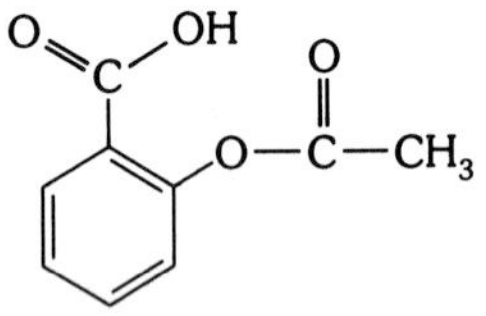
Aspirin

Isomers

12.21 Decide whether the members of each pair are identical, are isomers, or are unrelated.

(a) 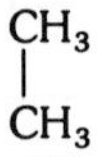 $\underset{\overset{|}{CH_3}}{CH_3}$ and CH_3-CH_3

(b) 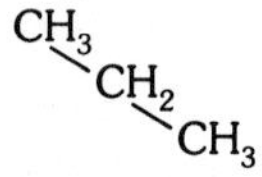 $CH_3\overset{}{\underset{CH_2}{\diagdown}}\underset{CH_3}{}$ and $CH_2\overset{CH_2}{\diagup}\diagdown CH_3$

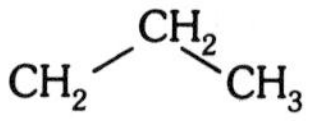

(c) CH_3CH_2-OH and $CH_3CH_2CH_2-OH$

(d) $CH_3CH=CH_2$ and $CH_2\overset{}{\underset{CH_2}{-}}CH_2$

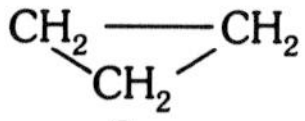

(e) 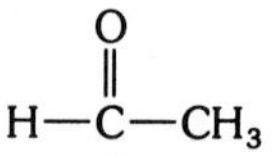 $H-\overset{\overset{O}{\|}}{C}-CH_3$ and $CH_3-\overset{\overset{O}{\|}}{C}-H$

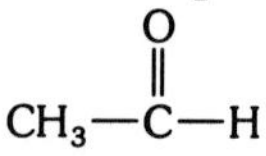

(f) 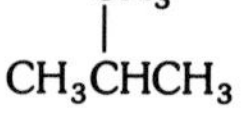 $CH_3\overset{\overset{CH_3}{|}}{CH}CH_3$ and $CH_3\overset{\overset{CH_3}{|}}{CH}\underset{CH_3}{}$

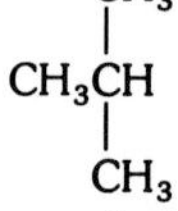

(g) $CH_3CH_2CH_2-NH_2$ and $CH_3CH_2-NH-CH_3$

(h) 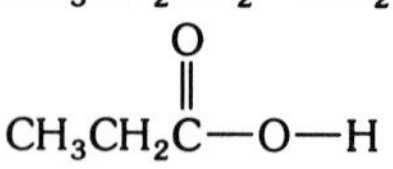 $CH_3CH_2\overset{\overset{O}{\|}}{C}-O-H$ and $H-O-\overset{\overset{O}{\|}}{C}CH_2CH_3$

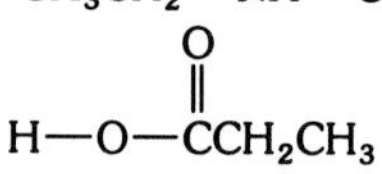

(i) 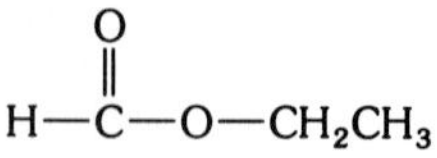 $H-\overset{\overset{O}{\|}}{C}-O-CH_2CH_3$ and $CH_3CH_2-\overset{\overset{O}{\|}}{C}-O-H$

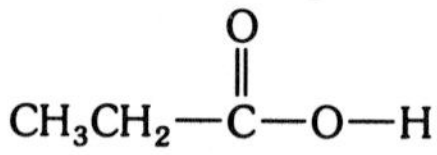

(j) 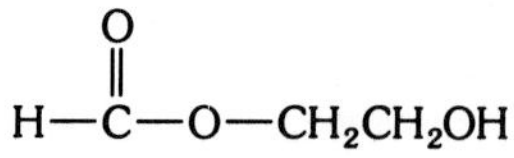 $H-\overset{\overset{O}{\|}}{C}-O-CH_2CH_2OH$ and $HOCH_2CH_2-\overset{\overset{O}{\|}}{C}-O-H$

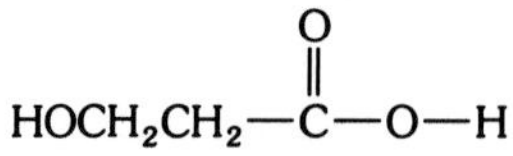

(k) 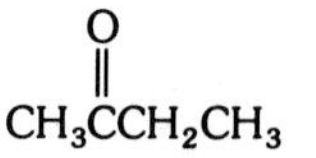 $CH_3\overset{\overset{O}{\|}}{C}CH_2CH_3$ and $CH_3CH_2\overset{\overset{O}{\|}}{C}CH_3$

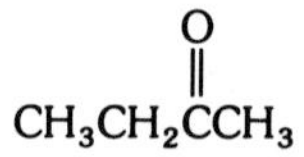

(l) 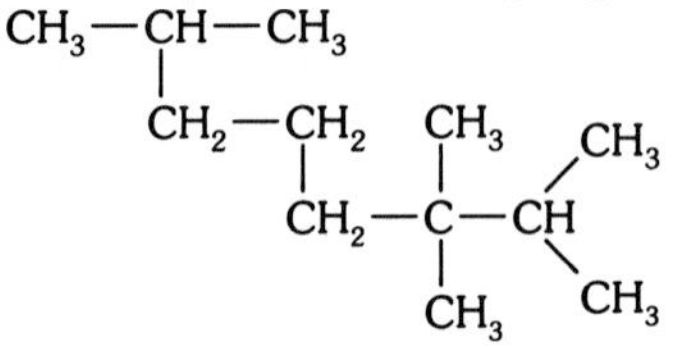 $CH_3-\overset{\overset{}{|}}{CH}-CH_3$ ... and

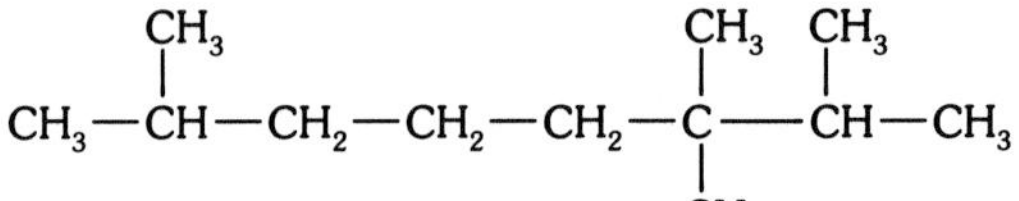

(m) 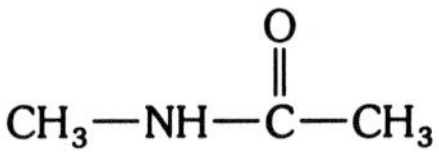 $CH_3-NH-\overset{\overset{O}{\|}}{C}-CH_3$ and $CH_3CH_2\overset{\overset{O}{\|}}{C}NH_2$

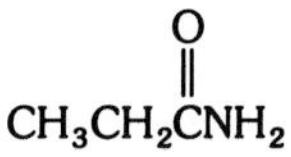

(n) $H-O-O-H$ and $H-O-H$

Families of Organic Compounds

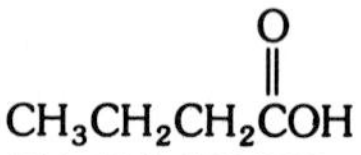

12.22 Name the family to which each compound belongs.
(a) $CH_3CH=CH_2$ (b) $HOCH_2CH_2CH_3$
(c) CH_3CH_2SH (d) $CH_3C\equiv CH$
(e) 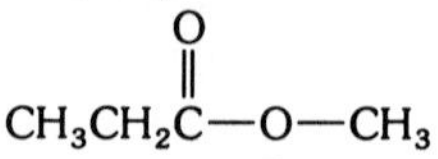 $CH_3CH_2\overset{\overset{O}{\|}}{C}-O-CH_3$ (f) 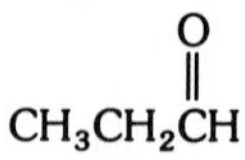 $CH_3CH_2\overset{\overset{O}{\|}}{C}H$
(g) $CH_3CH_2CH_2\overset{\overset{O}{\|}}{C}OH$ (h) $CH_3\overset{\overset{O}{\|}}{C}CH_2CH_2CH_3$
(i) $CH_3CH_2CH_2NH_2$ (j) $CH_3-O-CH_2CH_3$

12.23 Name the families to which the compounds in Practice Exercise 12.21 belong. (A few belong to more than one family.)

Physical Properties and Structure

12.24 Which compound must have the higher boiling point? Explain.
$CH_3CH_2CH_3$ $CH_3CH_2CH_2CH_2CH_3$
A   **B**

12.25 Which compound must be less soluble in gasoline? Explain.
$ClCH_2CH_2CH_2CH_2CH_2Cl$ $HOCH_2CH_2CH_2CH_2CH_2OH$
A   **B**

12.26 Suppose that you are handed two test tubes containing colorless liquids, and you are told that one contains pentane and the other holds hydrochloric acid. How can you use just water to tell which tube contains which compound without carrying out any chemical reaction?

12.27 Suppose that you are given two test tubes and are told that one holds methyl alcohol, CH_3OH, and the other hexane.

How can water be used to tell these substances apart without carrying out any chemical reaction?

Nomenclature

12.28 There are five isomers of C_6H_{14}. Write their condensed structures and their IUPAC names.

12.29 Which of the isomers of hexane (Review Exercise 12.28) has the common name *n*-hexane? Write its structure.

12.30 Which of the hexane isomers (Review Exercise 12.28) has the common name isohexane? Write its structure.

12.31 There are nine isomers of C_7H_{16}. Write their condensed structures and their IUPAC names.

12.32 Write the condensed structures of the isomers of heptane (Review Exercise 12.31) that have the following names:
(a) *n*-heptane   (b) isoheptane

12.33 Write the IUPAC names of the following compounds.

(a)

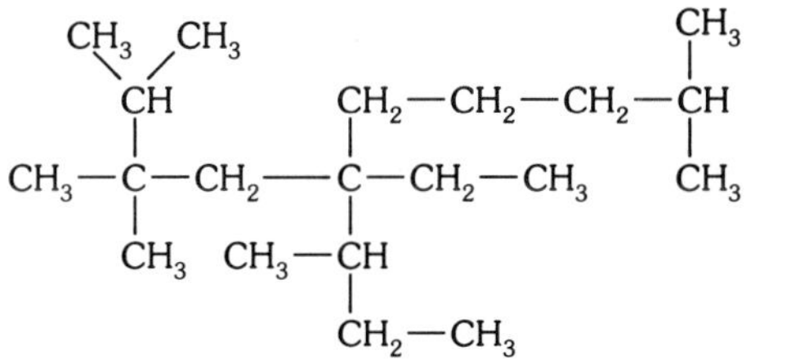

(b)

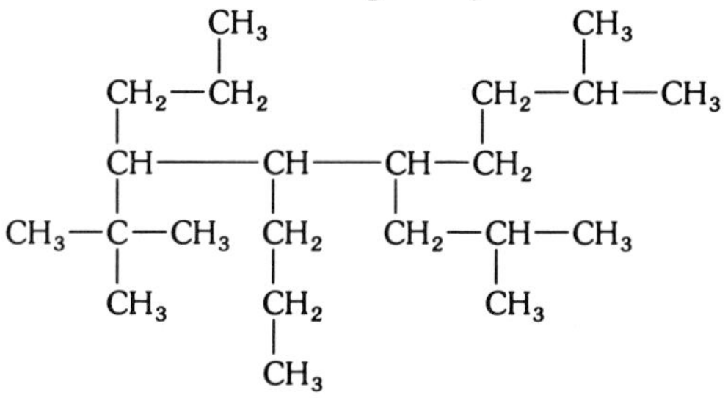

12.34 Write condensed structures for the following compounds.
(a) isobutyl bromide   (b) ethyl iodide
(c) propyl chloride   (d) *t*-butylcyclohexane

12.35 Write condensed structures for the following compounds.
(a) *sec*-butyl chloride   (b) *n*-butyl iodide
(c) isopropyl bromide   (d) isohexyl bromide

12.36 The following are incorrect efforts at naming certain compounds. What are the most likely condensed structures and correct IUPAC names?
(a) 1,6-dimethylcyclohexane
(b) 2,4,5-trimethylhexane
(c) 1-chloro-*n*-butane
(d) isopropane

12.37 The following names cannot be the correct names, but it is still possible to write structures from them. What are the correct IUPAC names and the condensed structures?
(a) 1-chloroisobutane
(b) 2,4-dichlorocyclopentane
(c) 2-ethylbutane
(d) 1,3-6-trimethylcyclohexane

Reactions of Alkanes

12.38 Write the balanced equation for the complete combustion of octane, a component of gasoline.

12.39 Gasohol is a mixture of ethyl alcohol, CH_3CH_2OH, in gasoline. Write the equation for the complete combustion of ethyl alcohol.

12.40 What are the formulas and common names of all the compounds that can be made from methane and chlorine?

12.41 There are two isomers of $C_2H_4Cl_2$. What are their structures and IUPAC names?

12.42 When propane reacts with chlorine, in addition to the two isomeric monochloropropanes, some dichloropropanes also form. Write the structures and the IUPAC names for all these possible dichloropropanes.

On Balancing Organic Reactions (Special Topic 12.1)

12.43 Explain in your own words why it is impossible to write a balanced equation for what actually happens when methane is chlorinated.

CHAPTER THIRTEEN

Unsaturated Hydrocarbons

- GEOMETRIC ISOMERS
- NAMING THE ALKENES
- ADDITION REACTIONS OF THE DOUBLE BOND
- HOW ADDITION REACTIONS OCCUR
- ADDITION POLYMERS
- THE BENZENE RING AND AROMATIC PROPERTIES
- NAMING COMPOUNDS OF BENZENE

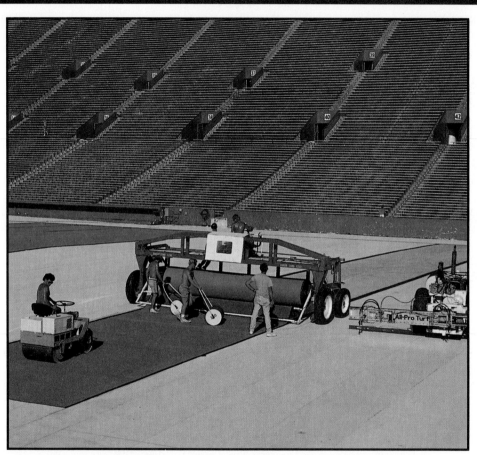

The material in artificial turf, shown here being installed at the University of Florida, is a synthetic polymer. In this chapter we learn what polymers are to prepare us for a later study of the great natural polymers, proteins and nucleic acids.

13.1 GEOMETRIC ISOMERS

The alkenes and cycloalkanes can exhibit geometric isomerism because there is no free rotation at the double bond or in a ring.

Unsaturation in hydrocarbons occurs as double bonds, as triple bonds, or as benzene rings. The hydrocarbons with double bonds are *alkenes*. This bond is very common at the molecular level of life, particularly in fats and oils or lipids.

The triple bond occurs in the *alkynes,* but is very uncommon in nature; we will use Special Topic 13.3 later in the chapter to discuss it very briefly. We will see that it gives many of the same kinds of reactions as alkenes.

The benzene ring and rings similar to it occur in proteins and nucleic acids, and it is widely present in compounds used as pharmaceuticals. This chapter is mostly about the alkene system and the properties of the carbon–carbon double bond, sometimes called the *-ene* function.

Table 13.1 shows the structures and some physical properties of several alkenes. As with the alkanes, the first four are gases at room temperature, and all are much less dense than water. Like all hydrocarbons, alkenes are insoluble in water and soluble in nonpolar solvents.

The six atoms at a double bond, the two carbons and the four atoms attached to them, all lie in the same plane, as illustrated in Figure 13.1, which shows the simplest alkene. The bond angles are 120°.

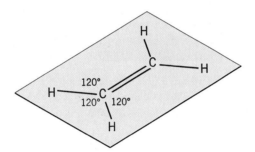

Figure 13.1
The geometry at a carbon–carbon double bond.

TABLE 13.1 Properties of Some 1-Alkenes

Name (IUPAC)	Structure	Boiling Point (°C)	Melting Point (°C)	Density (in g/mL at 10 °C)
Ethene	$CH_2{=}CH_2$	−104	−169	—
Propene	$CH_2{=}CHCH_3$	−48	−185	—
1-Butene	$CH_2{=}CHCH_2CH_3$	−6	−185	—
1-Pentene	$CH_2{=}CHCH_2CH_2CH_3$	30	−165	0.641
1-Hexene	$CH_2{=}CHCH_2CH_2CH_2CH_3$	64	−140	0.673
1-Heptene	$CH_2{=}CHCH_2CH_2CH_2CH_2CH_3$	94	−119	0.697
1-Octene	$CH_2{=}CHCH_2CH_2CH_2CH_2CH_2CH_3$	121	−102	0.715
1-Nonene	$CH_2{=}CHCH_2CH_2CH_2CH_2CH_2CH_2CH_3$	147	−81	0.729
1-Decene	$CH_2{=}CHCH_2CH_2CH_2CH_2CH_2CH_2CH_2CH_3$	171	−66	0.741
Cyclopentene		44	−135	0.722
Cyclohexene		83	−104	0.811

Some Alkene Isomers Have Identical Skeletons But Different Geometries   Alkenes can exist as isomers in three ways. They can have different carbon skeletons, as shown by 1-butene and 2-methylpropene. They can have the same skeletons but differ in the locations of their double bonds, as in 1-butene and 2-butene.

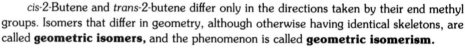

$$CH_2{=}CHCH_2CH_3 \qquad \underset{\displaystyle CH_3}{CH_2{=}\overset{|}{C}{-}CH_3} \qquad CH_3{-}CH{=}CH{-}CH_3$$

1-Butene	2-Methylpropene	2-Butene

Finally, some alkenes have identical skeletons, *including the location of the double bond*, but differ in geometry, as seen in the two isomers with the skeleton of 2-butene.

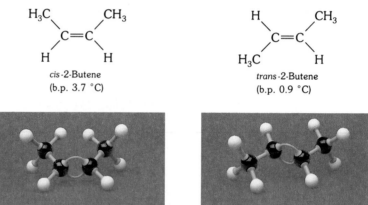

cis-2-Butene
(b.p. 3.7 °C)

trans-2-Butene
(b.p. 0.9 °C)

cis-2-Butene and *trans*-2-butene differ only in the directions taken by their end methyl groups. Isomers that differ in geometry, although otherwise having identical skeletons, are called **geometric isomers,** and the phenomenon is called **geometric isomerism.**

Geometric Isomers Are Possible Because There Is No Free Rotation at the Double Bond   Recall (Section 4.9) that one of the bonds at a double bond is a pi bond. It results from the side-to-side overlap of two unhybridized $2p$ orbitals, one on each carbon. The rotation of two groups joined by a double bond could happen only if the pi bond breaks. This costs too much energy under ordinary circumstances, so geometric isomers are possible.

When two atoms or groups are on the same side of the double bond, they are said to be *cis* to each other. When they are on opposite sides, they are said to be *trans* to each other. (Sometimes geometric isomerism is called *cis–trans isomerism*.) These cis or trans designations can be made parts of the names of the isomers, as the examples of *cis*- and *trans*-2-butene show.

When There Are Two Identical Groups at One End of a Double Bond, Geometric Isomers Are Not Possible   If one end of a double bond has two *identical* groups, like two Hs or two methyls, there is nothing for a group at the other end to be cis or trans to. 1-Butene, for example, has two H atoms at one end of its double bond, so the ethyl group at the other end cannot be positioned to give geometric isomers. We can *write* structures that might appear to be isomers:

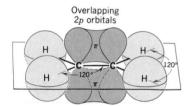

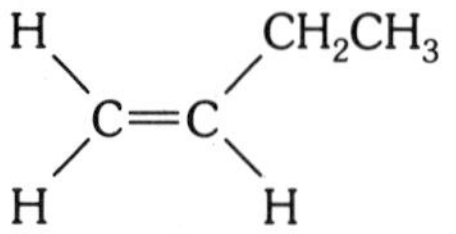

Overlapping
2p orbitals

Overlapping 2p orbitals form the pi bond at a double bond.

■ The *side* of a double bond is not the same as the *end* of a double bond.

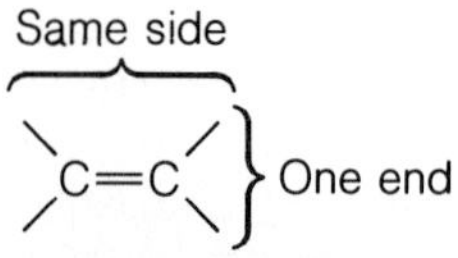

Same side

One end

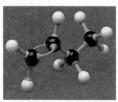

1-Butene

is the same as

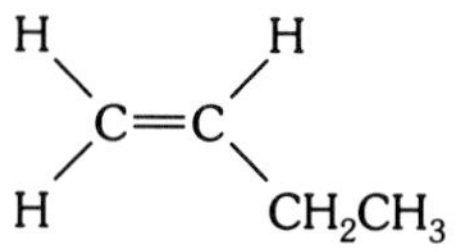

1-Butene   1-Butene

But they are actually identical. Simply flop the *whole* first structure over, top to bottom, and we get the second. Whole-molecule flopping, of course, does not reorganize bonds into any new structure. Thus there are no geometric isomers of 1-butene.

Geometric isomerism also occurs when the atoms involved at the ends of the double bond are halogen atoms or other groups, for example,

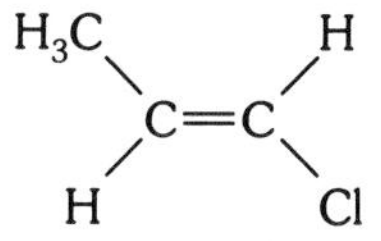

trans-1-Chloro-1-propene 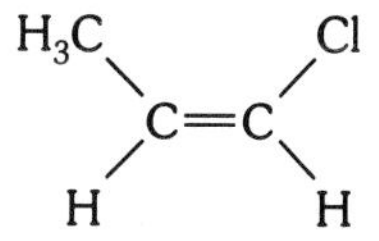   *cis*-1-Chloro-1-propene

---

EXAMPLE 13.1   **WRITING THE STRUCTURES OF CIS AND TRANS ISOMERS**

Problem: Write the structures of the cis and trans isomers, if any, of the following alkene.

$$CH_3CH{=}CHCH_2CH_3$$
2-Pentene

Solution: First, write a carbon–carbon double bond without any attached groups. Spread the single bonds at the carbon atoms at angles of roughly 120°. Draw two of these partial structures.

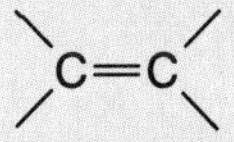

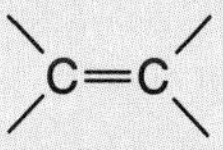

Then attach the two groups that are at one of the ends of the double bond. Attach them *identically* to make identical partial structures.

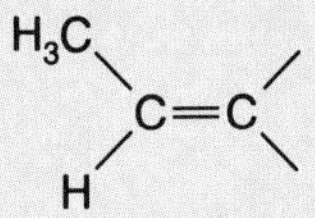

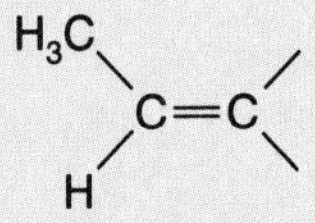

Finally, at the other end of the double bond, draw the other two groups, only this time be sure that they are switched in their relative positions.

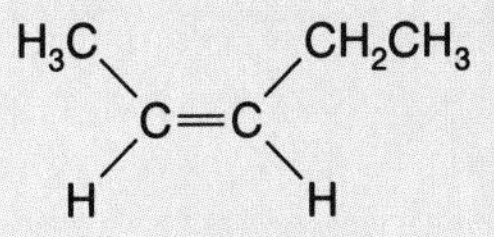

cis-2-Pentene 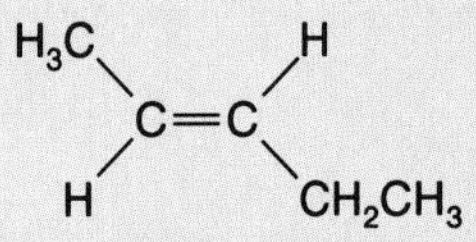   *trans*-2-Pentene

Be sure to check whether the two structures are geometric *isomers* and not two identical structures that are merely flip-flopped on the page.

PRACTICE EXERCISE 1   Write the structures of the cis and trans isomers, if any, of the following compounds.

(a) $CH_3CH_2C{=}CHCH_3$ with CH_3 below   (b) $ClCH{=}CHCl$ (c) $CH_3C{=}CH_2$ with CH_3 below   (d) $ClC{=}CHBr$ with Cl below

Cyclic Compounds Can Also Have Geometric Isomers   The double bond is not the only source of restricted rotation, the ring is another. For example, two geometric isomers of 1,2-dimethylcyclopropane are known, and neither can be twisted into the other without breaking the ring open. This costs too much energy to occur spontaneously even at quite high temperatures.

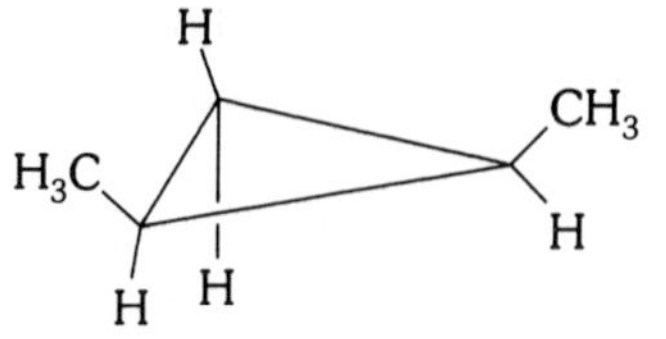

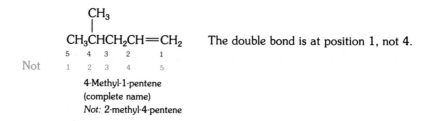

cis-1,2-Dimethyl
cyclopropane
(b.p. 37 °C)

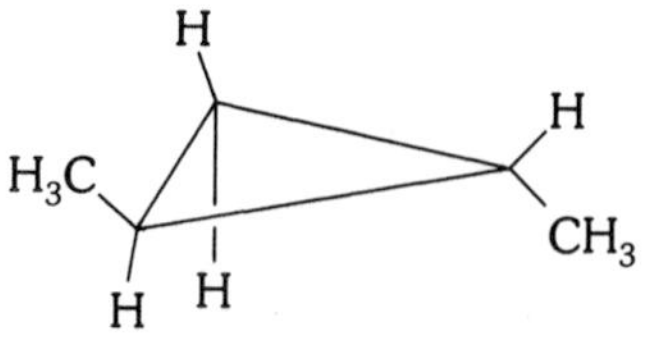

trans-1,2-Dimethyl
cyclopropane
(b.p. 28 °C)

We'll see this kind of cis–trans isomerism in the many cyclic structures of carbohydrates; their *geometric* differences alone make most carbohydrates unusable in human nutrition. As we have said before, molecular geometry is as important in living processes as functional groups.

13.2 NAMING THE ALKENES

The IUPAC names of alkenes end in *-ene*, and the double bond takes precedence over side chains in numbering the parent chain.

The IUPAC rules for naming alkenes and cycloalkenes are as follows.

1. Use the ending *-ene* for all alkenes and cycloalkenes.

2. As a prefix to this ending, count the number of carbon atoms in the longest sequence *that includes the double bond.* Then use the same prefix that would be used if the compound were saturated.

For example:

$$\overset{1}{C}H_2$$
$$\|$$
$$CH_3CH_2\underset{2\ 3}{C}CH_2\underset{4}{CH_2}\underset{5}{CH_2}\underset{6}{CH_3}$$

The parent chain has
six carbons, not seven.

Cyclopentene
(complete name)

3. For open-chain alkenes, number the parent chain from whichever end gives the lower number to the first carbon of the double bond to be reached.

This rule gives precedence to the numbering of the double bond over the location of the first substituent on the parent chain. For example,

$$\overset{CH_3}{\underset{|}{}}$$
$$\underset{5\ \ \ \ 4\ \ \ 3\ \ \ \ 2\ \ \ \ \ 1}{CH_3CHCH_2CH=CH_2}$$

The double bond is at position 1, not 4.

Not $\underset{1\ \ \ \ 2\ \ \ 3\ \ \ \ 4\ \ \ \ \ 5}{}$

4-Methyl-1-pentene
(complete name)
Not: 2-methyl-4-pentene

4. For cycloalkenes, always give position 1 to one of the two carbons at the double bond. To decide which carbon gets this number, number the ring atoms from carbon 1 *through the double bond* in whichever direction reaches a substituent first.

For example, the numbers inside the ring represent the correct numbering, not the numbers outside the ring.

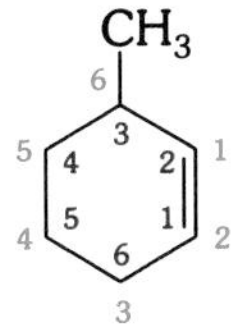

$$\text{CH}_3$$

3-Methylcyclohexene (complete name)
Not: 6-Methylcyclohexene

5. To the name begun with rules 1 and 2, place the number that locates the first carbon of the double bond as a prefix, and separate this number from the name by a hyphen.

6. If substituents are on the parent chain or ring, complete the name obtained by rule 5 by placing the names and location numbers of the substituents as prefixes.

    Remember to separate numbers from numbers by commas, but use hyphens to connect a number to a word.

    A few correctly named examples follow. Some have the common names that are given in parentheses. The ending -*ylene* characterizes the common names of open-chain alkenes.

■ The common name, ethylene, is also allowed by the IUPAC as the name for ethene.

$$CH_2{=}CH_2 \qquad CH_3CH{=}CH_2 \qquad CH_3{-}\underset{\underset{CH_3}{|}}{C}{=}CH_2$$

Ethene   Propene[1]   2-Methylpropene[2]
(Ethylene)   (Propylene)   (Isobutylene)

$$\underset{\underset{CH_3}{|}}{CH_3CH_2CHCH_2CH}{=}\underset{\underset{CH_3}{|}}{CCH_3}$$

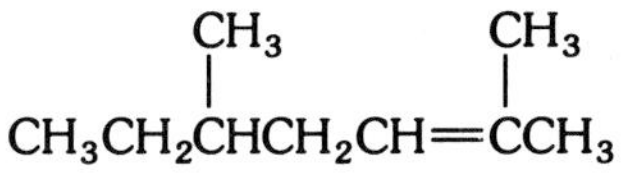

2,5-Dimethyl-2-heptene

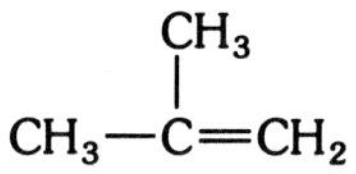

$$CH_3CH_2CH_2\underset{\underset{CHCH_2CH_2CH_3}{|}}{C}{=}CH_2$$

with CH_3 above

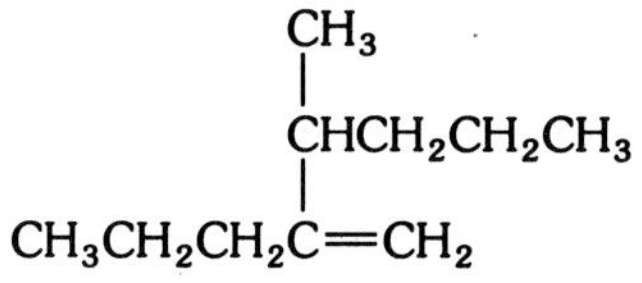

3-Methyl-2-propyl-1-hexene

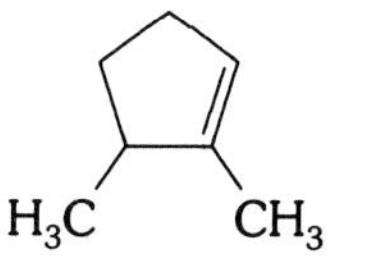

2,3-Dimethylcyclopentene[3]

$$Cl(CH_2)_6CH{=}CH_2$$

8-Chloro-1-octene

[1] Propene, not 1-propene, because by rule 3 there is no 2-propene.
[2] 2-Methylpropene, not 2-methyl-1-propene, because the 1 isn't needed.
[3] We don't include a number for the double bond's location, because by rule 4 it can only be at position 1.

EXAMPLE 13.2   **NAMING AN ALKENE**

Problem: Write the name of the following alkene.

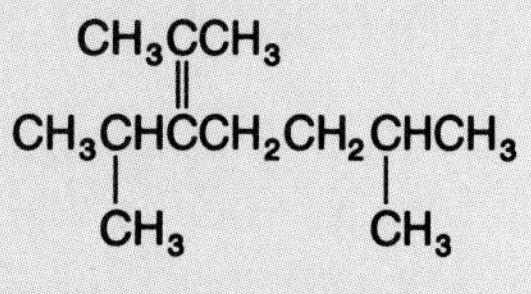

$$CH_3CHCCH_2CH_2CHCH_3$$
with CH_3CCH_3 (double bond) above, and CH_3 substituents below

Solution: First, identify the longest chain *that includes the double bond,* and number it to let one of the carbons of the double bond have the lower number.

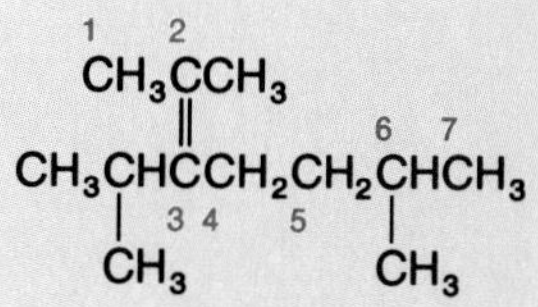

$$\begin{array}{c} \overset{1}{C}H_3\overset{2}{C}CH_3 \\ \| \\ CH_3\underset{3}{C}H\underset{4}{C}CH_2\underset{5}{C}H_2\underset{6}{C}H\underset{7}{C}H_3 \\ | \qquad\qquad | \\ CH_3 \qquad\quad CH_3 \end{array}$$

We can see that the parent alkene is 2-heptene. It holds two methyl groups (positions 2 and 6) and one isopropyl group (position 3). The names and location numbers are assembled as follows.

3-Isopropyl-2,6-dimethyl-2-heptene

A comma separates two numbers.

Hyphens separate numbers from names.

PRACTICE EXERCISE 2 Write the IUPAC names for the following compounds. (Ignore cis or trans designations.)

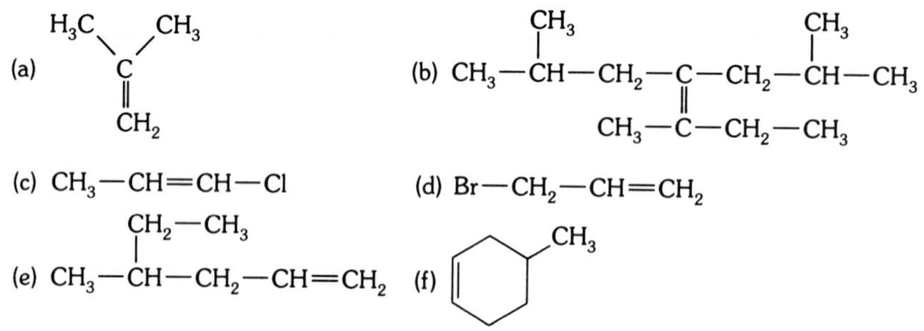

(a)
$$\begin{array}{c} H_3C \qquad CH_3 \\ \diagdown \quad \diagup \\ C \\ \| \\ CH_2 \end{array}$$

(b)
$$\begin{array}{c} \qquad\quad CH_3 \qquad\qquad\qquad CH_3 \\ \qquad\quad | \qquad\qquad\qquad\quad | \\ CH_3-CH-CH_2-C-CH_2-CH-CH_3 \\ \qquad\qquad\qquad \| \\ \qquad\qquad CH_3-C-CH_2-CH_3 \end{array}$$

(c) $CH_3-CH{=}CH-Cl$

(d) $Br-CH_2-CH{=}CH_2$

(e)
$$\begin{array}{c} \qquad CH_2-CH_3 \\ \qquad | \\ CH_3-CH-CH_2-CH{=}CH_2 \end{array}$$

(f)
$$\begin{array}{c} CH_3 \\ | \end{array}$$

PRACTICE EXERCISE 3 Write condensed structures for each of the following:

(a) 4-Methyl-2-pentene
(b) 3-Propyl-1-heptene
(c) 4-Chloro-3,3-dimethyl-1-butene
(d) 2,3-Dimethyl-2-butene

When a compound has two double bonds, it is named as a *diene* with two numbers in the name to specify the locations of the double bonds. For example,

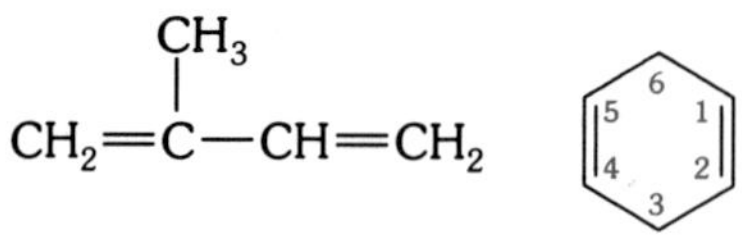

$$\begin{array}{c} CH_3 \\ | \\ CH_2{=}C-CH{=}CH_2 \end{array}$$

2-Methyl-1,3-butadiene

1,4-Cyclohexadiene

This pattern can be easily extended to *trienes, tetraenes,* and so forth.

13.3 ADDITION REACTIONS OF THE DOUBLE BOND

The carbon–carbon double bond adds H_2, Cl_2, Br_2, HX, H_2SO_4, and H_2O, and it is attacked by strong oxidizing agents, including ozone.

In an **addition reaction,** pieces of an adding molecule become attached to opposite ends of the double bond, which then becomes a single bond. All additions to an alkene double bond thus have the following features, where $X{-}Y$ is the adding molecule:

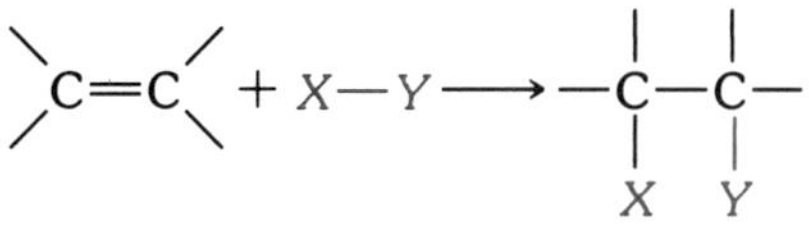

$$\begin{array}{c}\diagup\\ \diagdown\end{array}C=C\begin{array}{c}\diagup\\ \diagdown\end{array} + X—Y \longrightarrow \begin{array}{cc}|&|\\ —C—C—\\ |&|\\ X&Y\end{array}$$

We'll study a few examples and then see how they take place.

■ The addition of hydrogen is often called the *reduction* of the double bond.

Hydrogen Adds to a Double Bond and Saturates It   In the presence of a powdered metal catalyst, and under both pressure and heat, hydrogen adds to double bonds. The reaction, sometimes called *hydrogenation,* converts an alkene to an alkane as follows.

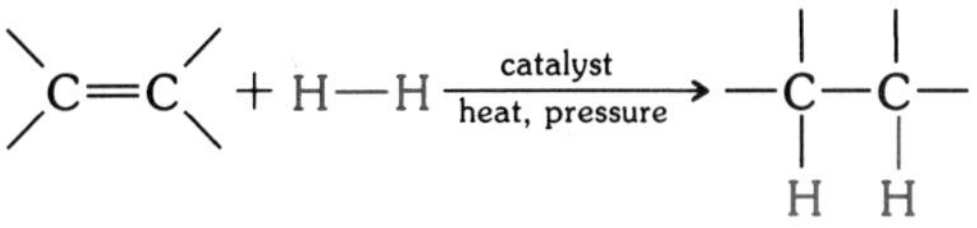

$$\begin{array}{c}\diagup\\ \diagdown\end{array}C=C\begin{array}{c}\diagup\\ \diagdown\end{array} + H—H \xrightarrow[\text{heat, pressure}]{\text{catalyst}} \begin{array}{cc}|&|\\ —C—C—\\ |&|\\ H&H\end{array}$$

Specific examples are

$$CH_2{=}CH_2 + H_2 \xrightarrow[\text{heat, pressure}]{\text{catalyst}} \begin{array}{cc}CH_2{-}CH_2\\ |\quad\ |\\ H\quad H\end{array} \text{ or } CH_3CH_3$$

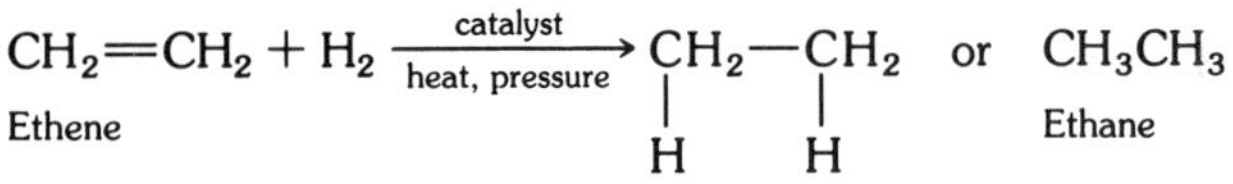

Ethene   Ethane

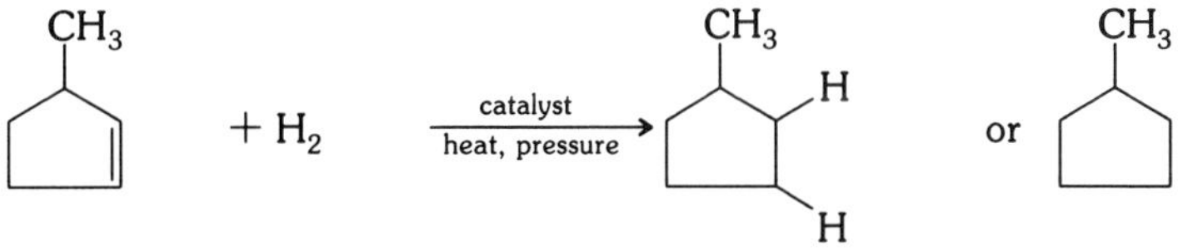

3-Methylcyclopentene   Methylcyclopentane

The Net Effect of Hydrogenation Occurs at the Molecular Level of Life   Molecules of H_2, high pressure, and powdered metal catalysts are, of course, unavailable in the body. Cells, however, have carrier systems that deliver the pieces of H—H to carbon–carbon double bonds. One piece is $H\!:^-$, donated by a carrier enzyme to one end of the double bond. The other piece is H^+, plucked from a proton-donor (which sometimes is just part of the surrounding buffer) and given to the other end. Together, $H\!:^-$ and H^+ add up to one $H\!:\!H$ molecule.

■ $H\!:^-$ must be donated by the carrier *directly* to the acceptor and not through the solution. $H\!:^-$ reacts vigorously with water:
$H\!:^- + H—OH \rightarrow H—H + OH^-$

EXAMPLE 13.3

WRITING THE STRUCTURE OF THE PRODUCT OF THE ADDITION OF HYDROGEN TO A DOUBLE BOND

Problem: Write the structure of the product of the following reaction:

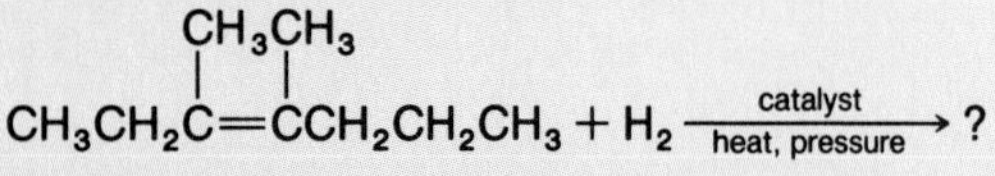

$$\begin{array}{c}CH_3\,CH_3\\ |\quad\ |\\ CH_3CH_2C{=}CCH_2CH_2CH_3 + H_2 \xrightarrow[\text{heat, pressure}]{\text{catalyst}} ?\end{array}$$

Solution: The only change occurs at the double bond, and all the rest of the structure goes through the reaction unchanged. *This is true of all the addition reactions we will study.* Therefore copy the structure of the alkene just as it is, except leave only a single bond where the double bond was. Then increase by one the number of hydrogens at each carbon of the original double bond. The structure of the product can be written as

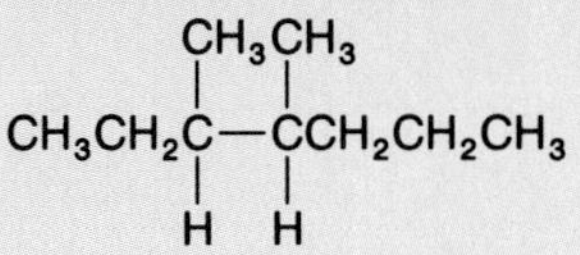

$$\begin{array}{c}CH_3\,CH_3\\ |\quad\ |\\ CH_3CH_2C{-}CCH_2CH_2CH_3\\ |\quad\ |\\ H\quad H\end{array} \quad \text{or, more condensed,} \quad \begin{array}{c}CH_3\ \ CH_3\\ |\qquad|\\ CH_3CH_2CH{-}CHCH_2CH_2CH_3\end{array}$$

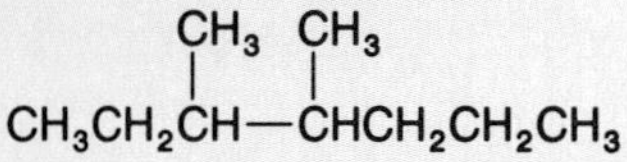

One major goal in these chapters is to learn some chemical properties of functional groups. We have just learned a chemical "map sign" for the carbon–carbon double bond, one of its important chemical properties. It can be made to add hydrogen, and when it does, it changes to a single bond as each of its carbon atoms picks up one hydrogen atom. This sentence states a chemical fact about the double bond that has to be learned. Learn it, however, by working illustrations involving specific alkenes. There are too many individual reactions to memorize, so use your memory work to learn the *kinds* of reactions and what they do *in general* to change a molecule. As you work each part of the following practice exercise, say to yourself the *general* fact, the chemical map sign about hydrogenation, each time you apply it to a specific case.

PRACTICE EXERCISE 4   Write the structures of the products, if any, of the following.

(a) $CH_3CH{=}CH_2 + H_2 \xrightarrow[\text{heat, pressure}]{\text{catalyst}}$

(b) $CH_3CH_2CH_3 + H_2 \xrightarrow[\text{heat, pressure}]{\text{catalyst}}$

(c) 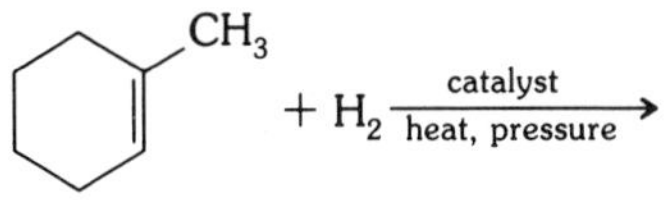 $+ H_2 \xrightarrow[\text{heat, pressure}]{\text{catalyst}}$

(d) $CH_3(CH_2)_7CH{=}CH(CH_2)_7CO_2H + H_2 \xrightarrow[\text{heat, pressure}]{\text{catalyst}}$

■ Use a good fume hood and protective gloves when dispensing bromine.

Chlorine and Bromine Also Add to Double Bonds   Without any need for a special catalyst or high pressures and temperatures, both Cl—Cl and Br—Br rapidly add to the carbon–carbon double bond. Iodine does not add, and fluorine reacts explosively with almost any organic compound to give a mixture of products.

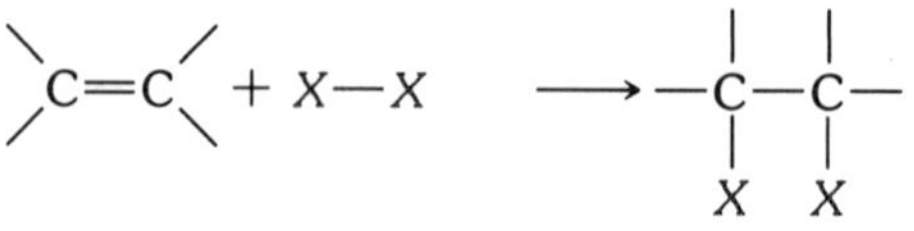

$X = $ Cl or Br

Specific examples are

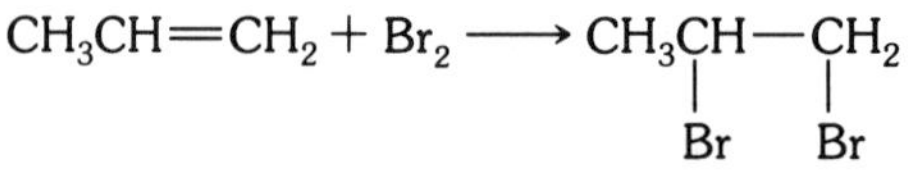

Propene   1,2-Dibromopropane

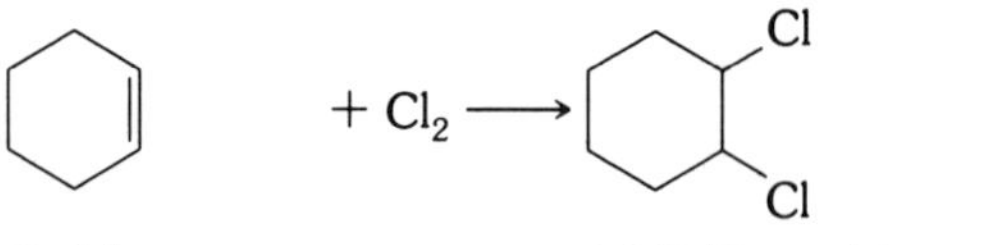

Cyclohexene   1,2-Dichlorocyclohexane

EXAMPLE 13.4

WRITING THE STRUCTURE OF THE PRODUCT OF THE ADDITION OF CHLORINE OR BROMINE TO A CARBON–CARBON DOUBLE BOND

Problem: What compound forms in the following situation?

$$CH_3{-}CH{=}CH{-}CH_3 + Br_2 \longrightarrow ?$$

Solution: This problem is very similar to that of the addition of hydrogen. We rewrite the alkene except that a single bond is left where the double bond was.

$$CH_3-CH-CH-CH_3 \quad \text{(Incomplete)}$$

Now we attach a bromine atom by a single bond to each carbon of the original double bond, and we have the answer.

$$CH_3-\underset{\underset{Br}{|}}{CH}-\underset{\underset{Br}{|}}{CH}-CH_3 \quad \text{2,3-Dibromobutane}$$

PRACTICE EXERCISE 5

Complete the following equations by writing the structures of the products. If no reaction occurs under the conditions shown, write "no reaction."

(a) $CH_3-\underset{\underset{CH_3}{|}}{C}=CH_2 + Br_2 \longrightarrow$

(b) $CH_3CH_2CH_2CH_3 + Cl_2 \longrightarrow$

(c) $CH_2=CHCH_2CH_3 + Cl_2 \longrightarrow$

(d) $CH_3-CH=CH-CH_3 + H_2 \xrightarrow[\text{heat, pressure}]{\text{catalyst}}$

A Change in Color Occurs as Bromine Adds to a Double Bond Bromine is dark brown, but the dibromoalkanes are virtually colorless. Therefore an unknown organic compound that rapidly decolorizes bromine quite likely has a carbon–carbon double bond.

The bromine color must disappear rapidly *without being accompanied by the evolution of hydrogen bromide gas*. If this happens, the decolorization was caused by a substitution, not an addition reaction. Remember that alkanes react (when heated or exposed to ultraviolet light) with chlorine and bromine, too, but this reaction generates HX.

■ HBr(g) also generates whitish fumes when it contacts humid air.

It's easy to see whether HBr evolves; hold a strip of moist blue litmus paper in the mouth of the test tube, and any HBr(g) evolving will turn it red. HBr(g) is not produced unless sunlight is absorbed by the mixture of the alkane and the bromine, so in the lab, if the reaction occurs at all, it doesn't happen at once. In contrast, the *addition* of Br_2 to a double bond is almost instantaneous, so the color of Br_2 very rapidly disappears in an addition reaction.

Hydrogen Chloride, Hydrogen Bromide, and Sulfuric Acid Add Easily to Double Bonds If gaseous hydrogen chloride or hydrogen bromide is bubbled into an alkene or if concentrated sulfuric acid is mixed with it, the following kind of reaction takes place. The pattern is the same in all these additions. We'll let H—G represent any of these reactants, where G stands for some electron-rich group, like Cl.

$$\underset{/}{\overset{\backslash}{}}C=C\underset{\backslash}{\overset{/}{}} + H-G \longrightarrow -\underset{\underset{H}{|}}{C}-\underset{\underset{G}{|}}{C}- \quad (G = \text{Cl, Br, or } OSO_3H)$$

An example.

$$CH_2=CH_2 + H-Cl \longrightarrow \underset{\underset{H}{|}}{CH_2}-\underset{\underset{Cl}{|}}{CH_2} \quad \text{or} \quad CH_3-CH_2-Cl$$

Unsymmetrical Reactants Add Selectively to Unsymmetrical Double Bonds We now have a small complication. H—G is not a symmetrical molecule, like H—H, Br—Br, or Cl—Cl. When the latter add to a double bond, it doesn't matter which end of the double bond gets which half of the adding molecule. But it matters when H—G adds, *if the double bond is itself unsymmetrical*. By *unsymmetrical double bond* we mean one whose two carbon atoms hold unequal numbers of hydrogen atoms. For example, 1-butene, $CH_2=CHCH_2CH_3$, and propene, $CH_3CH=CH_2$, both have unsymmetrical double bonds. Each has one carbon at the double bond with two Hs and the other has one, an unequal number. The double bond in 2-butene, $CH_3CH=CHCH_3$, however, is symmetrical; one H is at each carbon.

When $H—Cl(g)$ adds to propene we could imagine obtaining 1-chloropropane, 2-chloropropane, or a mixture of the two, perhaps $50:50$. Let's see what actually happens. We have

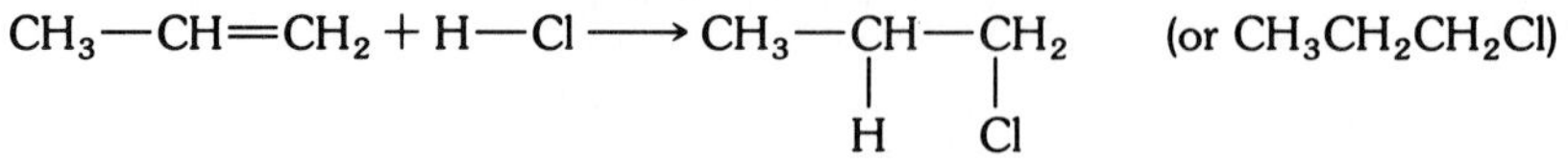

$$CH_3—CH=CH_2 + H—Cl \longrightarrow CH_3—\underset{\underset{H}{|}}{CH}—\underset{\underset{Cl}{|}}{CH_2} \qquad (\text{or } CH_3CH_2CH_2Cl)$$

Propene   1-Chloropropane
Very little forms.

or

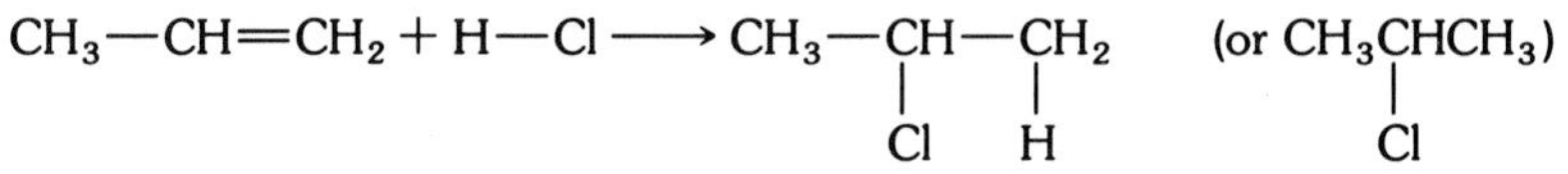

$$CH_3—CH=CH_2 + H—Cl \longrightarrow CH_3—\underset{\underset{Cl}{|}}{CH}—\underset{\underset{H}{|}}{CH_2} \qquad (\text{or } CH_3CHCH_3)$$

Propene   2-Chloropropane
The major product.

The actual product is largely 2-chloropropane, and very little of its isomer, 1-chloropropane, forms. In other words, the reactant, H—Cl, adds to the unsymmetrical double bond selectively.

Markovnikov's Rule Predicts Directions in Unsymmetrical Additions

Vladimer Markovnikov (1838–1904), a Russian chemist, was the first to notice that unsymmetrical alkenes add unsymmetrical reactants in one direction. Which direction can be predicted by **Markovnikov's Rule.**[4]

■ "Them that has, gits" applies here, too.

> **Markovnikov's Rule.** When an unsymmetrical reactant of the type H—G adds to an unsymmetrical alkene, the carbon with the greater number of hydrogens gets one more hydrogen.

The following examples illustrate Markovnikov's rule in action.

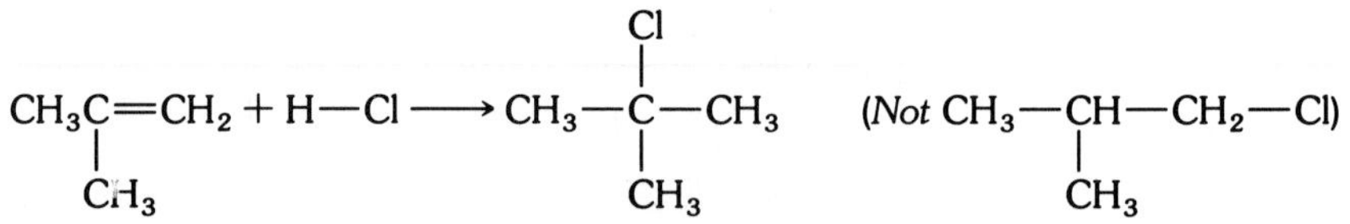

$$CH_3\underset{\underset{CH_3}{|}}{C}=CH_2 + H—Cl \longrightarrow CH_3—\underset{\underset{CH_3}{|}}{\overset{\overset{Cl}{|}}{C}}—CH_3 \qquad (Not\ CH_3—\underset{\underset{CH_3}{|}}{CH}—CH_2—Cl)$$

2-Methylpropene   *t*-Butyl chloride

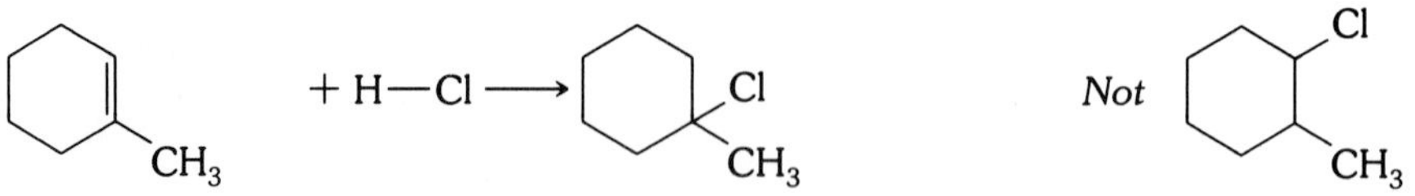

1-Methylcyclohexene   1-Chloro-1-methylcyclohexane

Concentrated Sulfuric Acid Actually Dissolves Alkenes

When an alkene is mixed with concentrated sulfuric acid, which is a very polar solvent, the hydrocarbon dissolves and heat evolves. How can two substances of such radically different polarities dissolve together? An alkane does not behave this way at all but merely forms a separate layer that floats on the sulfuric acid. (See Figure 13.2.)

---

[4] When hydrogen bromide is used, it is important that no peroxides, compounds of the type R—O—O—H or R—O—O—R, be present. Traces of peroxides commonly form in organic liquids that are stored in contact with air for long periods. When peroxides are present, the addition of H—Br occurs in the direction opposite to that predicted by Markovnikov's rule. Peroxides catalyze this anti-Markovnikov addition only of H—Br, not of H—Cl or $H—OSO_3H$.

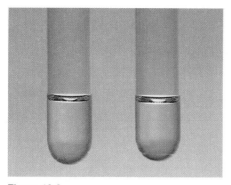 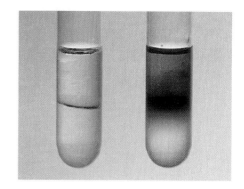

Figure 13.2
The effect of concentrated sulfuric acid on an alkane and an alkene. In the photograph on the left, the alkane (first tube) and the alkene (second tube) are seen as clear, colorless liquids. The photograph on the right shows the two systems soon after concentrated sulfuric acid has been added to each. The alkane floats unaffected on the acid (first tube), but the alkene (second tube) has already begun to react and form an alkyl hydrogen sulfate (together with darkly colored matter produced by side reactions). The alkyl hydrogen sulfate is soluble in the remaining concentrated sulfuric acid, and so all the alkene will appear to dissolve. (The alkane is cyclohexane and the alkene is cyclohexene.)

The alkene dissolves because it reacts by an addition reaction to form an alkyl hydrogen sulfate, which is very polar. For example,

■ The sodium salts of long-chain alkyl hydrogen sulfates are detergents, for example, $CH_3(CH_2)_{11}OSO_3Na$.

$$CH_3-CH=CH_2 + H-O-\underset{\underset{O}{\overset{O}{\|}}}{\overset{O}{\|}}{S}-O-H \xrightarrow{0\,°C} CH_3-\underset{\overset{CH_3}{|}}{CH}-O-\underset{\underset{O}{\overset{O}{\|}}}{\overset{O}{\|}}{S}-O-H$$

| Propene | Sulfuric acid | Isopropyl hydrogen sulfate |

As soon as the polar molecules of the alkyl hydrogen sulfates form, they move smoothly into the polar sulfuric acid layer and out of the nonpolar alkene layer. The heat generated by the reaction and the strongly acidic nature of the mixture causes side reactions that generate black by-products.

These properties make concentrated sulfuric acid another test reagent to distinguish between an alkene and an alkane. As the photographs in Figure 13.2 show, the alkene turns black but the alkane is unaffected by the presence of concentrated sulfuric acid.

Symmetrical Double Bonds Do Not Add H—G Reactants Selectively   Markovnikov's rule does not apply when the double bond is symmetrical. Reactants like H—G add in both of the two possible directions, and a mixture of isomers forms. For example,

$$CH_3CH_2CH=CHCH_3 + H-Br \longrightarrow CH_3CH_2\underset{\overset{|}{Br}}{CH}CH_2CH_3 + CH_3CH_2CH_2\underset{\overset{|}{Br}}{CH}CH_3$$

| 2-Pentene | 3-Bromopentane | 2-Bromopentane |

(For a reminder of why we don't try to balance an equation such as this, check back to Special Topic 12.1.)

Water Adds to Double Bonds To Give Alcohols   Water adds to the carbon–carbon double bond provided that an acid catalyst (or the appropriate enzyme) is present. The product is an alcohol. Water alone, or aqueous bases, have no effect on alkenes whatsoever.

$$\underset{\text{Alkene}}{>C=C<} + H-OH \xrightarrow[\text{heat}]{H^+} \underset{\text{Alcohol}}{-\underset{\overset{|}{H}}{C}-\underset{\overset{|}{OH}}{C}-}$$

Specific examples are:

$$CH_2{=}CH_2 + H{-}OH \xrightarrow[\substack{240\ ^\circ C \\ \text{(closed vessel)}}]{10\%\ H_2SO_4} CH_3{-}CH_2{-}OH$$

Ethene   Ethyl alcohol

$$CH_3{-}\underset{\overset{|}{CH_3}}{C}{=}CH_2 + H{-}OH \xrightarrow[25\ ^\circ C]{10\%\ H_2SO_4} CH_3{-}\underset{\overset{|}{OH}}{\overset{\overset{CH_3}{|}}{C}}{-}CH_3 \quad \textit{Not } CH_3{-}\underset{}{\overset{\overset{CH_3}{|}}{CH}}{-}CH_2{-}OH$$

2-Methyl   *t*-Butyl alcohol   (very little forms)
propene   (major product)

As you can see, Markovnikov's rule applies to this reaction, too. One H in H—OH goes to the carbon with the greater number of hydrogens, and the —OH goes to the other carbon of the double bond.

Notice in the last example, and in all previous examples of addition reactions, that the carbon skeleton does not change. Although this is not always true, it will be in all the examples we will use as well as in all the Practice and Review Exercises.

EXAMPLE 13.5 **USING MARKOVNIKOV'S RULE**

Problem: What product forms in the following situation?

$$CH_3{-}CH{=}CH_2 + H_2O \xrightarrow[\text{heat}]{H^+} ?$$

Solution: As in all the addition reactions we are studying, the carbon skeleton can be copied over intact, except that a single bond is shown where the double bond was.

$$CH_3{-}CH{-}CH_2 \quad \text{(Incomplete)}$$

To decide which carbon of the original double bond gets the H atom from H—OH, we use Markovnikov's rule. The H atom has to go to the CH_2 end. The —OH unit from H—OH goes to the other carbon. The product is

$$CH_3{-}\underset{\overset{|}{OH}}{CH}{-}\underset{\overset{|}{H}}{CH_2} \quad \text{or, more condensed,} \quad CH_3\underset{\overset{|}{OH}}{CHCH_3}$$

Isopropyl alcohol

Be sure at this stage to see whether each carbon in the product has four bonds. If not, you can be certain that some mistake has been made. This is always a useful way to avoid at least some of the common mistakes made in solving a problem such as this.

PRACTICE EXERCISE 6   Write structures for the product(s), if any, that would form under the conditions shown. If no reaction occurs, write "no reaction."

(a) $CH_2{=}CHCH_2CH_3 + HCl \rightarrow$

(b) $CH_2{=}\underset{\overset{|}{CH_3}}{C}{-}CH_3 + HBr \rightarrow$

(c) 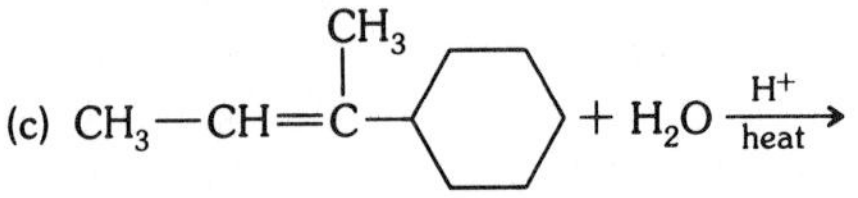 $CH_3{-}CH{=}\underset{\overset{|}{CH_3}}{C}{-}\bigcirc\ \ + H_2O \xrightarrow[\text{heat}]{H^+}$

(d) H$_3$C + H$_2$O $\xrightarrow[\text{heat}]{\text{H}^+}$ (What *mixture* forms?)

(e) + H$_2$O $\xrightarrow[\text{heat}]{\text{H}^+}$

Ketones

Carboxylic acids

Double Bonds Are Attacked by Many Oxidizing Agents   With two pairs of electrons, the double bond is more electron-rich than a single bond, so electron-seeking reagents attack it. These include oxidizing agents. Hot solutions of potassium permanganate (KMnO$_4$) and potassium dichromate (K$_2$Cr$_2$O$_7$), for example, vigorously oxidize molecules at carbon–carbon double bonds. The reaction begins as an addition reaction, but continues beyond to the point where the molecule is split apart. We will not study any of the details or learn how to predict products. We just have to take note of the fact that the carbon–carbon double bond makes a molecule susceptible to attack by strong oxidizing agents. The products can be ketones, carboxylic acids, carbon dioxide, or mixtures of these. Alkanes are utterly inert toward these oxidizing agents.

Aqueous Permanganate Changes Color in Reacting with Alkenes   The permanganate ion is intensely purple in water, and as it oxidizes double bonds it changes to manganese dioxide, MnO$_2$, a brownish, sludge-like, insoluble solid. In other words, an easily observed change makes a potassium permanganate solution still another reagent for distinguishing between an alkane and an alkene. An alkane gives no reaction with permanganate ion, but when an alkene is stirred with aqueous permanganate, the purple color gives way to the brownish precipitate.

The Dichromate Ion Also Changes Color in Oxidizing an Alkene   The dichromate ion is bright orange in water, and when it acts as an oxidizing agent, it changes to the bright green, hydrated chromium(III) ion, Cr^{3+}(*aq*). Hence, aqueous potassium (or sodium) dichromate also can be used as a test reagent to find out whether a substance has an easily oxidized group, like the alkene group.

So far we have studied four tests for distinguishing an alkane and an alkene: the bromine test, the concentrated sulfuric acid test, and the use of aqueous permanganate or aqueous dichromate.

■ Ozone destroys any vegetation that has the green pigment, chlorophyll, because chlorophyll contains double bonds.

Ozone Is One of the Most Powerful Oxidizing Agents   Ozone, O$_3$, a pollutant in smog, is dangerous because it is a very powerful oxidizing agent that attacks biochemicals wherever they have carbon–carbon double bonds. Because such bonds occur in the molecules of all cell membranes, you can see that exposure to ozone must be kept very low. Even a concentration in air of only one part per million parts (1 ppm) warrants the declaration of a smog emergency condition. Special Topic 13.1 describes how ozone gets into smog.

Although ozone is dangerous to us where we live and breath, it is vital to our well-being that ozone be in the stratosphere, the zone of the atmosphere in a band 10 to 25 miles above us. How stratospheric ozone benefits us and how its work is being threatened by air pollution are discussed in Special Topic 13.2.

13.4   HOW ADDITION REACTIONS OCCUR

The carbon–carbon double bond can accept a proton from an acid and change into a carbocation.

Because the double bond is somewhat electron-rich, it should be no surprise that it can behave like a base, a proton-acceptor. Evidently it does, because the double bond attracts and takes protons from many donors, for example HCl, HBr, HOSO$_3$H. Even with the addition of water, the initial attack is by the acid catalyst, not the water molecule.

Ozone is produced in smog because of the reactions of other air pollutants. The process starts with nitric oxide, NO, which forms inside vehicle engine cylinders by the direct, high-temperature combination of nitrogen and oxygen. As soon as nitric oxide hits the cooler outside air, it reacts further with oxygen to give nitrogen dioxide, NO_2, which gives smog its reddish-brown color.

$$2NO(g) + O_2(g) \longrightarrow 2NO_2(g)$$

Ultraviolet radiation in sunlight interacts with NO_2 and splits it to nitric oxide, NO, and *atomic* oxygen.

$$NO_2(g) \xrightarrow{\text{UV radiation}} NO(g) + O(g)$$
$$\text{Atomic oxygen}$$

Atomic oxygen is a rogue substance. When it collides with a molecule of oxygen at the surface of some particle in air (M), ozone forms.

$$O + O_2 + M \longrightarrow O_3 + M$$

(The M serves to absorb some of the energy. Otherwise, the ozone molecule would have enough energy itself to break up at once.)

The ozone level in the smog of an urban area builds up daily along a fairly consistent pattern that parallels the buildup of NO and NO_2. During the morning rush hour, the level of NO rises as vehicle traffic increases. Soon the level of NO_2 increases, reaching its peak at the end of the rush hour. By now the sun is high, and the rest of the ozone-producing reactions take place. The ozone level reaches its maximum about two hours after the NO_2 level peaks. Slowly, other components in smog provide reactions that bring the levels of NO, NO_2, and O_3 back down.

An ozone level of 1 ppm (one part per million parts of air) is considered dangerous enough to warrant issuing area-wide alerts to warn people with lung problems that they should reduce activities requiring deep breathing. Children are urged not to engage in strenuous activities.

To reduce ozone in urban smog, we need vehicle engines that can operate efficiently at lower temperatures so that less NO forms. We should also use mass transit systems more.

The stratosphere is the zone of the atmosphere lying just above the troposphere (where we live) and between 16 and 40 km (10 and 25 miles) in altitude. One of its trace gases is ozone. The synthesis and destruction of ozone in the stratosphere converts the ultraviolet energy in solar radiation into heat. This removes a form of energy that would greatly harm plants and animals. In humans, skin cancer is the chief result of overexposure to ultraviolet radiation.

High-energy ultraviolet radiation can break the bonds in oxygen molecules and generate oxygen atoms:

$$O_2 \xrightarrow{\text{UV radiation}} 2O$$

This reaction of oxygen, not of ozone, removes some of the UV radiation coming toward us from the sun. But considerable UV radiation remains. The oxygen atoms now participate in a two-step cyclic process, the **ozone cycle,** which removes nearly all the rest.

The oxygen atoms formed by the cracking of O_2 molecules can react with oxygen molecules at the surface of a neutral particle, as we saw in Special Topic 13.1:

$$O + O_2 + M \longrightarrow O_3 + M$$

The neutral particle M absorbs some of the collision energy

and thus leaves the new O_3 molecule less able to split apart immediately. What is desirable instead is that the splitting of O_3 be left to UV radiation. This is the chief means by which such UV radiation is removed from incoming sunlight:

$$O_3 \xrightarrow{\text{UV radiation}} O_2 + O*$$

Then, in a later collision at another M, ozone is remade:

$$O_2 + O* + M \longrightarrow O_3 + M$$

O* is an electronically excited oxygen atom able to react with oxygen to remake ozone.

The generation of O* from O_3 thus launches a chemical chain reaction, a two-step process in which the first step makes products needed by the second as reactants, and the second step regenerates a reactant needed to run the first step again. The cracking of one O_2 molecule to give two O atoms sets off two such chains. In each, atoms of O and molecules of O_2 first combine to give ozone and then are recovered when UV radiation splits the ozone. Each chain, in other words, constitutes a natural cycle in the stratosphere. See the accompanying figure. We depend on the

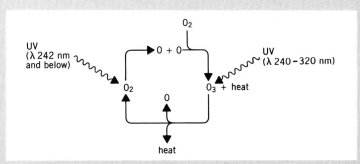

The stratospheric ozone cycle.

continuous operation of the ozone cycle to shield us from virtually all the UV radiation of incoming sunlight. Anything that interfers with this cycle and reduces the stratospheric ozone level, therefore, poses a threat to human health and to agriculture.

Several mechanisms can potentially affect the ozone cycle, some natural and some caused by industrial and commercial activities. One of these concerns a family of remarkable compounds called the chlorofluorocarbons, or CFCs.

Chlorofluorocarbons and the Ozone Cycle   The chlorofluorocarbons are a family of volatile, nonflammable, chemically stable, and essentially odorless and tasteless compounds. CFC-11, for example, is $CFCl_3$. It boils at 24 °C and was once the propellant in 50% to 60% of all aerosol cans. CFC-12 is CCl_2F_2, which boils at -30 °C. Their physical properties and chemical inertness make the CFCs ideal as refrigerants for air conditioners, freezers, and refrigerators as well as blowing agents for foam plastics. They have been superior solvents for cleaning computer parts. The CFCs were also the most commonly used aerosol propellants in the United States until their use in nearly all consumer products was banned in 1978.

When released, the CFCs enter the atmosphere where their inertness allows them to persist for a century. Their concentrations in the atmosphere have doubled in the last decade. They become globally distributed and migrate into the stratosphere where, according to mounting evidence, they likely have become an additional stress on the ozone cycle.

Ultraviolet energy can break chlorine atoms out of CFC molecules:

$$CCl_3F \xrightarrow{\text{UV radiation}} CCl_2F + Cl$$

$$CCl_2F_2 \xrightarrow{\text{UV radiation}} CClF_2 + Cl$$

Atomic chlorine destroys ozone and disrupts the ozone cycle by the following chain reaction.

$$Cl + O_3 \longrightarrow ClO + O_2$$
$$ClO + O \longrightarrow Cl + O_2$$

Net: $O_3 + O \longrightarrow 2O_2$

You can see that, once formed, a chlorine atom merely "carries" this cycle. It is not destroyed by the cycle. Thus the breakup of one CFC molecule can initiate the subsequent removal of thousands of ozone molecules. (Eventually Cl atoms find one another and combine.)

Getting definitive data directly from the stratosphere is very difficult, but most scientists consider that between 1978 and 1984 the total global ozone declined 3%. If so, roughly 7% more UV radiation now reaches the earth's surface than did ten years ago. The CFCs have contributed almost certainly to this change.

The Antarctic Ozone Hole   Over the Antarctic continent, the ozone level has declined much more than 3%, and since the late 1970s the decline and rise of the ozone level has followed a particularly intriguing seasonal trend. During the Antarctic winter, the ozone level over most of this continent has declined so much that scientists call it the "Antarctic ozone hole." (The ozone level over the Antarctic declined 50% in the winter of 1987.) Then the level rebounds in the Antarctic summer. What causes this phenomenon, whether it will continue annually, and whether it is spreading globally are questions that have prodded several nations to initiate actions at the diplomatic level to try to stabilize the ozone layer.

In late 1986, negotiations sponsored by the United Nations Environmental Program led to an agreement among member nations to freeze the production of CFC-11 and CFC-12. The intent was to roll back their production by 50% by the year 2000. By 1989, however, this was seen as too weak an action, and 80 countries agreed to eliminate the production and use of the CFCo by 2000. The potential harm to life on earth from the loss of stratospheric ozone was thought to be too great to wait for further proofs that the CFCs are indeed the culprits. By that time, the damage might be too great and incapable of correction.

When an Alkene Accepts a Proton, a Reactive Carbocation Forms We'll use the symbol H—G to represent any proton-donor. (In H—Cl, G is Cl. In H_2SO_4, G is OSO_3H. In dilute acid, the proton-donating species is H_3O^+, so G here is H_2O.) We can write the first step in an addition reaction as follows:

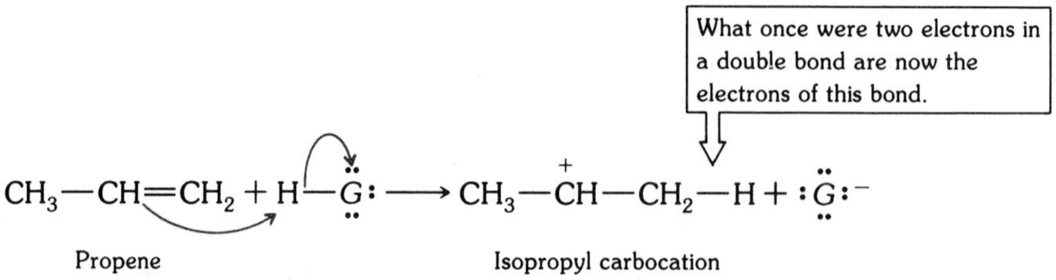

> What once were two electrons in a double bond are now the electrons of this bond.

$$CH_3-CH=CH_2 + H-\overset{\cdot\cdot}{\underset{\cdot\cdot}{G}}: \longrightarrow CH_3-\overset{+}{CH}-CH_2-H + :\overset{\cdot\cdot}{\underset{\cdot\cdot}{G}}:^-$$

Propene   Isopropyl carbocation

The curved arrows show how one of the two electron pairs of the double bond swings away from one carbon to form a bond to the proton during a collision with H—G.

One Carbon in a Carbocation Lacks an Octet The isopropyl cation that formed in the reaction is an example of a **carbocation,** a positive ion in which carbon has a sextet not an octet of electrons. But notice that it is the isopropyl carbocation that forms, not the propyl carbocation, $CH_3CH_2CH_2^+$. We'll see why shortly, and when we do we'll understand Markovnikov's rule.

Carbocations are particularly unstable cations. All their reactions are geared to the recovery of an outer octet of electrons for carbon. The instant a carbocation forms, it strongly attracts any handy electron-rich species, and just such particles emerge when H—Cl, H—Br, or H—OSO_3H attack a double bond. When these acids give up protons, their conjugate bases, $:\overset{\cdot\cdot}{\underset{\cdot\cdot}{Cl}}:^-$, $:\overset{\cdot\cdot}{\underset{\cdot\cdot}{Br}}:^-$, or $^-:\overset{\cdot\cdot}{\underset{\cdot\cdot}{O}}SO_3H$ remain, which we symbolize as $:\overset{\cdot\cdot}{\underset{\cdot\cdot}{G}}:^-$.

The newly formed carbocation reacts with $:\overset{\cdot\cdot}{\underset{\cdot\cdot}{G}}:^-$ in the next step of the addition.

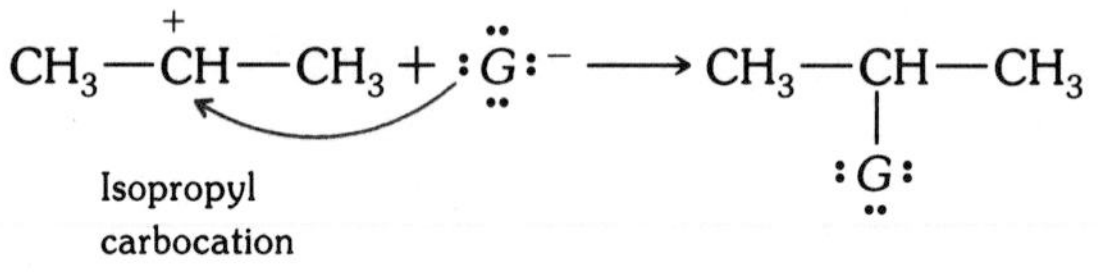

$$CH_3-\overset{+}{CH}-CH_3 + :\overset{\cdot\cdot}{\underset{\cdot\cdot}{G}}:^- \longrightarrow CH_3-\underset{\underset{\textstyle :\overset{\cdot\cdot}{\underset{\cdot\cdot}{G}}:}{|}}{CH}-CH_3$$

Isopropyl
carbocation

This restores the octet to carbon as it gives the product.

The More Stable Carbocation Preferentially Forms The stability of a carbocation, although always very low, varies with how many neighboring electron clouds surround its positively charged center. Alkyl groups provide larger overall electron clouds than H atoms. Packing alkyl groups around the carbon with the positive charge, instead of just H atoms, therefore helps to stabilize the carbocation. Thus when the positive charge is on a secondary carbon, as in the isopropyl carbocation, the electron clouds of *two* alkyl groups crowd around it. When the charge is on the end carbon of the propyl carbocation, the electron cloud of only one alkyl group is nearby.

$$CH_3-\overset{+}{CH}-CH_3 \qquad CH_3-CH_2-CH_2^+$$

Isopropyl   Propyl
carbocation   carbocation

As a result, the isopropyl carbocation is more stable than the propyl. Or, to generalize, a secondary carbocation is more stable than a primary. By extension, a tertiary carbocation is more stable than a secondary. The order of stability of carbocations is

■ The R groups are alkyl groups, and they need not be identical.

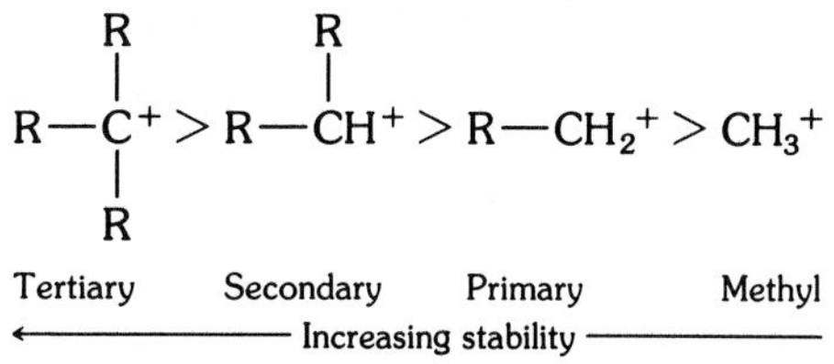

$$R-\overset{\overset{\displaystyle R}{|}}{\underset{\underset{\displaystyle R}{|}}{C}}{}^+ > R-\overset{\overset{\displaystyle R}{|}}{C}H^+ > R-CH_2{}^+ > CH_3{}^+$$

Tertiary   Secondary   Primary   Methyl

◄─────── Increasing stability ───────

This order of stability explains Markovnikov's rule. When there is an option, as in the addition of H—G to propene, the most stable carbocation always preferentially forms. H^+ is taken from H—G by the double bond at whichever of its ends leaves the positive charge in the best location.

When the two possible carbocations are of the same type, both secondary, for example, there is no preference. Both can form, and a mixture of isomers is produced. (We leave an example to a practice exercise.)

The Water Molecule Is Too Weak a Proton-Donor To Make a Carbocation from an Alkene

When water adds to an alkene under acid catalysis, the first step is a proton transfer *from the acid catalyst,* not from a water molecule. The water molecule has to wait for this to happen because it holds its protons much too strongly. The acid catalyst converts the double bond temporarily into an electron-poor site, a carbocation, which then attacks H_2O at its O atom, not at an H atom.

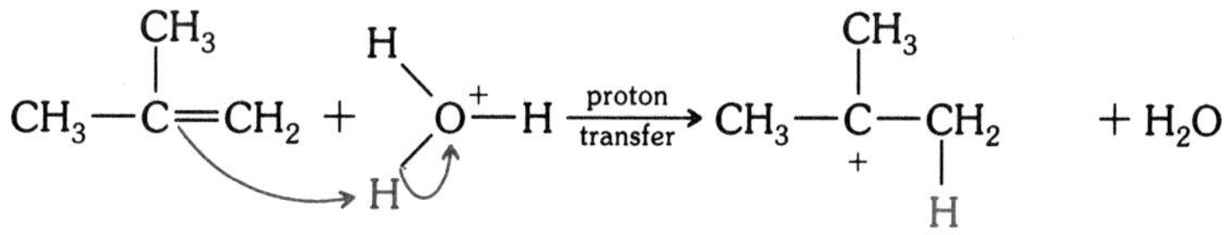

$$CH_3-\overset{\overset{\displaystyle CH_3}{|}}{C}=CH_2 + \overset{\displaystyle H}{\underset{\displaystyle H}{O}}{}^+-H \xrightarrow[\text{transfer}]{\text{proton}} CH_3-\overset{\overset{\displaystyle CH_3}{|}}{\underset{\underset{\displaystyle H}{|}}{C}}-\overset{+}{C}H_2 + H_2O$$

t-Butyl carbocation
(three alkyl groups on C^+)

The other possible but less stable carbocation, which does *not* form, is

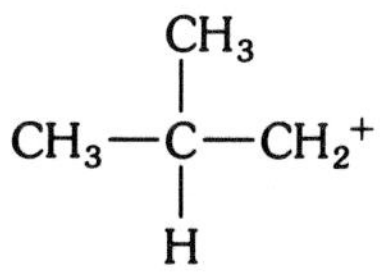

$$CH_3-\overset{\overset{\displaystyle CH_3}{|}}{\underset{\underset{\displaystyle H}{|}}{C}}-CH_2{}^+$$

Isobutyl carbocation
(one alkyl group on C^+)

The *t*-butyl carbocation now quickly is attracted to the most abundant, most concentrated electron-rich species around, a water molecule, specifically being attracted to an unshared pair of electrons on oxygen. This pair now becomes shared as a bond forms to carbon. The product is a hydronium ion in which one H has been replaced by an alkyl group:

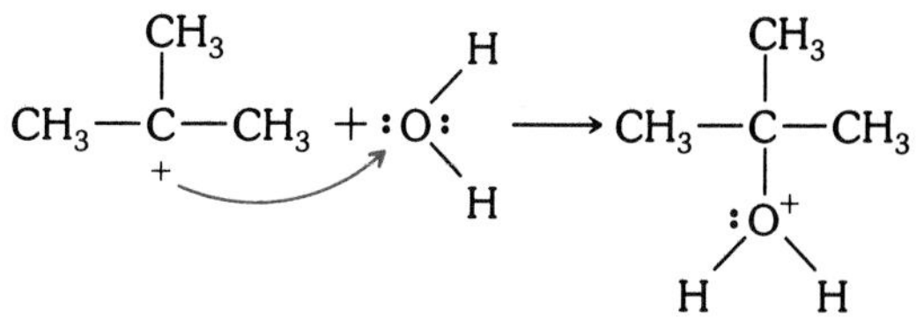

$$CH_3-\overset{\overset{\displaystyle CH_3}{|}}{\underset{+}{C}}-CH_3 + :\overset{\displaystyle H}{\underset{\displaystyle H}{O}}: \longrightarrow CH_3-\overset{\overset{\displaystyle CH_3}{|}}{\underset{\underset{\displaystyle \overset{+}{O}}{|}}{C}}-CH_3$$

Now the positive charge is on oxygen, which is acceptable because oxygen has an octet.

In the last step, the catalyst, H_3O^+, is recovered by another proton transfer, this time from the alkyl-substituted hydronium ion:

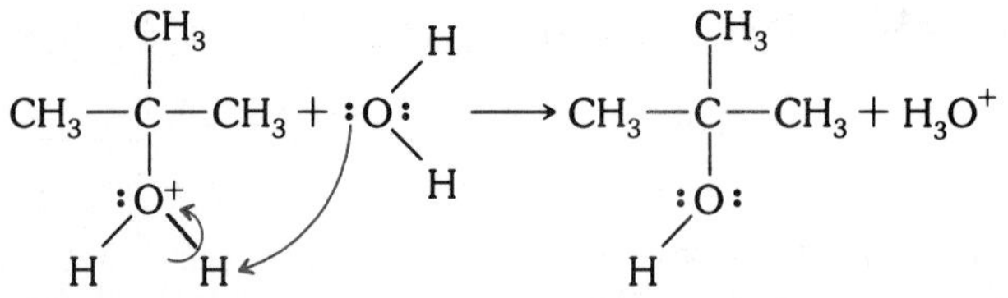

$$CH_3-\underset{\underset{H}{\overset{+}{O}}-\overset{CH_3}{\underset{|}{C}}-CH_3 + :\overset{H}{\underset{H}{O}}: \longrightarrow CH_3-\overset{CH_3}{\underset{|}{C}}-CH_3 + H_3O^+$$

An alkyl substituted   *t*-Butyl   Recovered
hydronium ion   alcohol   catalyst

PRACTICE EXERCISE 7   Write the condensed structures for the two carbocations that could conceivably form if a proton became attached to each of the following alkenes. Circle the carbocation that is preferred. If both are reasonable, state that they are. Then write the structures of the alkyl chlorides that would form by the addition of hydrogen chloride to each alkene.

(a) $CH_3-CH_2-CH=CH_2$ (b) $CH_3-\overset{CH_3}{\underset{|}{C}}=CH_2$ (c)

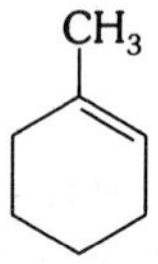

(d) $CH_3-CH=CH-CH_3$ (e) $CH_3-CH=CH-CH_2-CH_3$

(f) The addition of water to 2-pentene (part e) gives a mixture of alcohols. What are their structures? Why is the formation of a mixture to be expected here but not when water adds to propene?

13.5 ADDITION POLYMERS

Hundreds to thousands of alkene molecules can join together to make one large molecule of a polymer.

Under a variety of conditions, many hundreds of ethene molecules can reorganize their bonds, join together, and change into one large molecule:

$$nCH_2=CH_2 \xrightarrow[\text{trace of } O_2]{\text{heat, pressure}} \text{(}CH_2-CH_2\text{)}_n \qquad (n = \text{a large number})$$

Ethylene   Polyethylene
(ethene)   (repeating unit)

■ ''Polymer'' has Greek roots: *poly*, many, and *meros*, parts.

The product is an example of a **polymer,** a substance of very high formula weight whose molecules have repeating structural units. The idea of a polymer is important in our study because many biochemicals are polymers, like the proteins, some carbohydrates, and the nucleic acids (the chemicals of heredity).

The *repeating unit* in polyethylene is CH_2-CH_2, and one of these after another is joined together into an extremely long chain. Chain-branching reactions also occur during the formation of the polymer, so the final product includes both straight and branched chain molecules. The starting material for making a polymer is called a **monomer,** and the reaction is called **polymerization.** Since alkenes have long been nicknamed *olefins,* the polymers of alkenes are usually called the *polyolefins* in industry.

Carbocations Are Intermediates in Some Polymerizations   The catalysts used industrially to cause polymers to form vary widely. Some, for example, work by generating carbocation intermediates. When the catalyst is a proton-donor, it can convert ethylene into the ethyl carbocation:

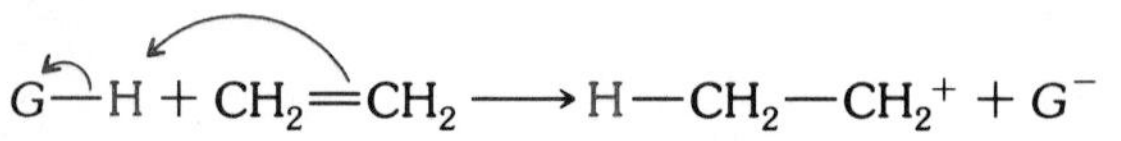

$$G-H + CH_2=CH_2 \longrightarrow H-CH_2-CH_2^+ + G^-$$
Acid   Ethylene   Ethyl
catalyst   carbocation

If, when the carbocation forms, the only *abundant* electron-rich species present is unreacted alkene, it has little choice but to attack an electron pair of such an alkene to recover its octet. For example,

$$CH_3-CH_2^+ + CH_2=CH_2 \longrightarrow CH_3-CH_2-CH_2-CH_2^+$$

But this just creates a new and longer carbocation still surrounded mostly by unreacted molecules of the alkene. So it attacks another molecule of the alkene:

$$CH_3-CH_2-CH_2-CH_2^+ + CH_2=CH_2 \longrightarrow CH_3-CH_2-CH_2-CH_2-CH_2-CH_2^+$$

■ Polymerization is an example of a *chemical chain reaction* because the product of one step initiates the next step.

You can begin to see how this works. Still another carbocation has been produced, and it can attack still another molecule of the alkene. Thus the chain grows at each step by one repeating unit, $-CH_2-CH_2-$, until it picks up some stray anion, like an anion left over from the catalyst, and the chain stops growing.

Actually, the catalyst should not be called this, because it is consumed. The term *promoter* is better. Some chains grow longer than others, and chain-branching reactions also occur, so the final polymer is a mixture of molecules. All are very large, however, and they all have the same general feature. This is why we can write the structure of a polymer simply by writing its repeating unit, as we did for polyethylene.

The Methyl Side Chains Occur Regularly in Polypropylene

When propene (common name, propylene) polymerizes, methyl groups appear on alternate carbons of the main chain.

$$-CH_2-\underset{\underset{CH_3}{|}}{CH}-CH_2-\underset{\underset{CH_3}{|}}{CH}-CH_2-\underset{\underset{CH_3}{|}}{CH}-CH_2-\underset{\underset{CH_3}{|}}{CH}-CH_2-\underset{\underset{CH_3}{|}}{CH}-etc \quad or, \quad \left(CH_2-\underset{\underset{CH_3}{|}}{CH} \right)_n$$

Polypropylene

Polymerizations generally take place in orderly fashions such as this because the reactive intermediates are governed by the same "rules" of stability that apply to carbocations.

The Polyolefins Are Chemically Very Stable

Because polyolefins, like polypropylene and polyethylene, are fundamentally alkanes, they have all the chemical inertness of this family. These polymers, therefore, are popular raw materials for making containers that must be inert to food juices and to fluids used in medicine. Refrigerator boxes and bottles, containers for chemicals, sutures, catheters, various drains, and wrappings for aneurysms are commonly made of polyolefins.

Substituted Alkenes Are Monomers for Important Polymers

Monomers with carbon–carbon double bonds often carry other functional groups or halogen atoms. The resulting polymers are extremely important commercial substances, ones we encounter continually in our daily lives. Table 13.2 contains a list of just a few examples.

Many dienes are used as monomers, too. Natural rubber is a polymer of a diene called isoprene (Table 13.2), and it can now be made industrially. The body uses the polymerization of certain isoprene-like monomers as some of the steps in the synthesis of larger molecules it needs. The chains do not become long, like those in polyethylene, however. Yet they include some very important substances, like cholesterol, and several sex hormones.

■ The carbon skeleton of isoprene becomes cyclized as these substances form.

13.6 THE BENZENE RING AND AROMATIC PROPERTIES

The benzene ring undergoes substitution reactions instead of addition reactions despite a high degree of unsaturation.

The molecular formula of benzene is C_6H_6, which indicates considerable unsaturation. Its ratio of hydrogens to carbon is much lower than in two simple, saturated hydrocarbons with six carbons, hexane (C_6H_{14}) and cyclohexane (C_6H_{12}). We should expect benzene, therefore, to be some kind of alkene, or alkyne, or a combination. Alkynes give addition reactions very

TABLE 3.2 Some Polymers of Substituted Alkenes

Polymer	Monomer	Uses
Polyvinyl chloride (PVC)	$CH_2{=}CHCl$	Bottles and other containers, insulation, plastic pipe
Saran	$CH_2{=}CCl_2$ and $CH_2{=}CHCl$	Packaging film, fibers, tubing
Teflon	$F_2C{=}CF_2$	Nonsticking surfaces for pots and pans
Orlon	$CH_2{=}CH{-}C{\equiv}N$	Fabrics
Polystyrene	$C_6H_5{-}CH{=}CH_2$	Foam plastics and molded items
Lucite	$\underset{\displaystyle CH_2{=}C{-}CO_2CH_3}{\overset{CH_3}{\overset{\mid}{}}}$	Coatings, windows, molded items
Natural Polymer Natural rubber	$\underset{\displaystyle \underset{(Isoprene)}{CH_2{=}C{-}CH{=}CH_2}}{\overset{CH_3}{\overset{\mid}{}}}$	Tires, hoses, boots

similar to those of alkenes (Special Topic 13.3), and we might expect benzene to give addition reactions just as readily. There is one that benzene does give; it adds hydrogen, and the product is cyclohexane. Unusually rigorous conditions of pressure and temperature are necessary, however.

$$C_6H_6 + 3H_2 \xrightarrow[\substack{\text{high pressure and}\\ \text{temperature}}]{\text{catalyst}} C_6H_{12}$$
$$\underset{\text{Benzene}}{} \qquad\qquad\qquad \underset{\text{Cyclohexane}}{}$$

Benzene's Typical Reactions Are Substitutions, Not Additions Alkenes (and alkynes) readily *add* chlorine and bromine without a catalyst, but benzene needs a catalyst, and the reaction is not simple addition but substitution. The catalyst is generally an iron halide (or iron itself).

$$C_6H_6 + Cl_2 \xrightarrow[\text{FeCl}_3]{\text{Fe or}} C_6H_5{-}Cl + H{-}Cl$$
$$\underset{\text{Benzene}}{} \qquad\qquad \underset{\text{Chlorobenzene}}{}$$

$$C_6H_6 + Br_2 \xrightarrow[\text{FeBr}_3]{\text{Fe or}} C_6H_5{-}Br + H{-}Br$$
$$\qquad\qquad\qquad \underset{\text{Bromobenzene}}{}$$

Benzene also reacts, by substitution, with sulfur trioxide dissolved in concentrated sulfuric acid. (Recall that alkenes react exothermically with concentrated sulfuric acid by *addition*.)

$$C_6H_6 + SO_3 \xrightarrow[\text{room temperature}]{\text{H}_2\text{SO}_4\ (\text{concd.})} C_6H_5{-}\overset{\displaystyle O}{\underset{\displaystyle O}{\overset{\displaystyle \|}{\underset{\|}{S}}}}{-}O{-}H$$
$$\qquad\qquad\qquad\qquad\qquad \underset{\text{Benzenesulfonic acid}}{}$$

(Benzenesulfonic acid is about as strong an acid as hydrochloric acid, and it is a raw material for the synthesis of aspirin.)

| SPECIAL TOPIC 13.3 | REACTIONS OF ALKYNES |

Because the triple bond has pi bonds like the double bond, alkynes give the same kinds of addition reactions as alkenes. Some examples are the following. Notice that the triple bond can add *two* molecules of a reactant. Usually, it is possible to control the reaction so that only one molecule adds.

$$CH_3C{\equiv}CH + H_2 \xrightarrow[\text{heat, pressure}]{\text{special catalyst}} CH_3CH{=}CH_2 \xrightarrow{\text{more } H_2} CH_3CH_2CH_3$$

Propyne   Propene   Propane

$$CH_3C{\equiv}CH + HCl \longrightarrow CH_3\overset{\overset{\displaystyle Cl}{|}}{C}{=}CH_2 \xrightarrow{+HCl} CH_3\overset{\overset{\displaystyle Cl}{|}}{\underset{\underset{\displaystyle Cl}{|}}{C}}CH_3$$

2-Chloropropene   2,2-Dichloropropane

Benzene reacts with warm, concentrated nitric acid when it is dissolved in concentrated sulfuric acid. We will represent nitric acid as $HO{-}NO_2$, instead of HNO_3, because it loses the HO group during the reaction.

$$C_6H_6 + HO{-}NO_2 \xrightarrow[50-55\ °C]{H_2SO_4\ \text{(concd.)}} C_6H_5{-}NO_2 + H{-}OH$$

Nitrobenzene

We have learned that alkenes (and alkynes) are readily oxidized by permanganate or dichromate ion, but benzene is utterly unaffected by these strong oxidizing agents even when boiled with them. (Ozone does attack benzene.)

In the light of all these chemical properties, whatever benzene is, it isn't an alkene or alkyne. Yet it surely is unsaturated. The problem of what benzene is wasn't satisfactorily solved in organic chemistry until the early 1930s, roughly a century after its molecular formula was known and half a century after its skeleton had been determined. Many of the reactions referred to helped to disclose the benzene skeleton. Let's see how.

The Six H Atoms in C_6H_6 Are Chemically Equivalent to Each Other

When benzene is used to make chlorobenzene (or any of the other products shown above), only one isomeric monosubstituted compound forms. Only one $C_6H_5{-}Cl$ exists. This reminds us of what happens when ethane, CH_3CH_3, is chlorinated. Only one *mono*-substituted compound forms: only one CH_3CH_2Cl exists. It doesn't matter which H in CH_3CH_3 is replaced by Cl. The same is true for benzene. All six H atoms in C_6H_6 are equivalent to each other.

The Benzene Skeleton Has a Six-Membered Ring with a Hydrogen on Each Carbon

Because cyclohexane forms when benzene is hydrogenated, the six carbons of a benzene molecule must also form a six-membered ring. Because benzene's six Hs are chemically equivalent, it seems reasonable to put one H on each of the ring carbons. This gives a very symmetrical structure.

■ The older structure, **2**, is still widely used to represent benzene, although it is usually abbreviated further:

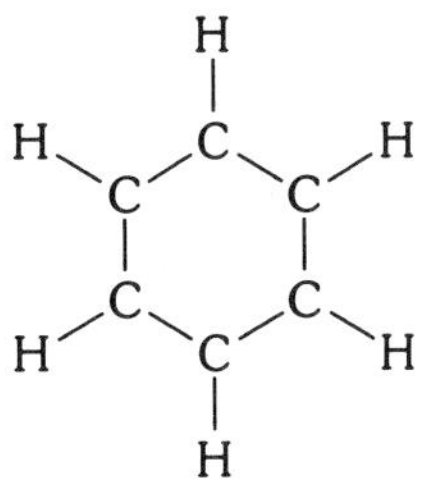

1
(Incomplete)

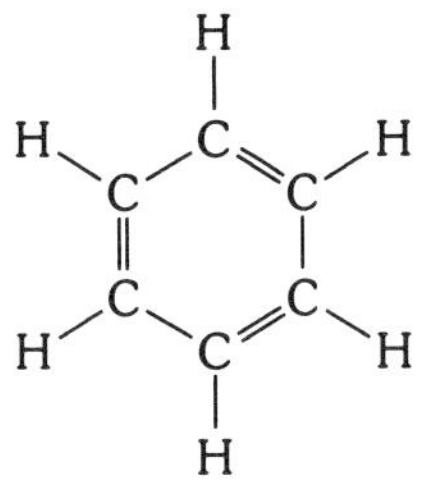

2
(Older structure for benzene)

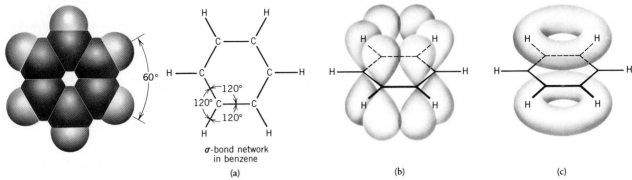

Figure 13.3
Scale model of a molecule of benzene. It shows the relative volumes of space occupied by the electron clouds of the atoms.

Figure 13.4
The molecular orbital model of benzene. (*a*) The sigma-bond framework. (*b*) The six 2*p* orbitals of the ring carbon atoms. (*c*) The double-doughnut-shaped region formed by the side-by-side overlapping of the six 2*p* orbitals.

The trouble with the incomplete structure identified as **1** is that each carbon has only three bonds, not four. To solve this, chemists for several decades simply wrote in three double bonds, as seen in structure **2**. As they well knew, the difficulty with **2** is that it says that benzene is a triene, a substance with three alkene groups per molecule.

Because the three double bonds indicated in structure **2** are misleading in a chemical sense, scientists often represent benzene simply by a hexagon with a circle inside, structure **3**.

3
Benzene

The ring system in **3**, the *benzene ring,* is planar. All its atoms lie in the same plane, and all the bond angles are 120°, as seen in the scale model of Figure 13.3.

Three Electron-Pairs Are Delocalized in the Benzene Ring   The development of the chemical bonding theory of molecular orbitals finally provided a satisfactory model for the structure of benzene. See Figure 13.4 Part (*a*) of the figure shows the sigma-bond network. Each carbon atom holds three other atoms, not four, so each carbon is *sp*²-hybridized and each has an unhybridized 2*p* orbital. The ring thus has six 2*p* orbitals, and their axes are co-parallel, as seen in part (*b*) of Figure 13.4.

The novel and important feature of benzene is that these six 2*p* orbitals overlap side to side *all around the ring.* They don't just pair off as in ethene and form three isolated double bonds. The result is a large, circular, double-doughnut-shaped space above and below the plane, as seen in part (*c*) of the figure. Six electrons are in this space, and we can refer to them as the pi electrons of the benzene ring.

A molecular orbital, like an atomic orbital, can hold no more than two electrons. The six pi electrons, therefore, are in three molecular orbitals within the double-doughnut-shaped space, and they enjoy considerably more room and freedom of movement than if they were in isolated double bonds. The electrons are said to be *delocalized.* When electrons have more room, the system is more stable. The delocalization of the pi electrons, in fact, explains much of the unusual stability of benzene and its resistance to addition reactions. When a hydrogen atom held by a ring carbon is replaced by another group, the closed-circuit pi-electron network is not broken up. But if an addition were to occur, the ring system would no longer be that of benzene but, instead, that of a cyclic diene. For example,

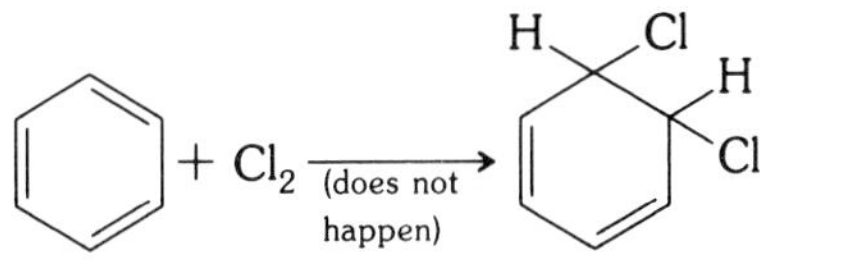

Benzene → 5,6-Dichloro-1,3-cyclohexadiene

It costs the system far more energy to react this way than to react by a substitution reaction, so the benzene ring strongly resists addition reactions.

Aromatic Compounds Have Unsaturated Rings That Give Substitution Reactions, Like Benzene Any substances whose molecules have benzene rings and whose rings give substitution reactions instead of addition reactions are called **aromatic compounds.** The term is a holdover from the days when most of the known compounds of benzene actually had aromatic fragrances, but now the term does not mean odor. Although oil of wintergreen and vanillin do have pleasant fragrances, aspirin does not. Yet all three have the benzene ring and all are classified as aromatic compounds.

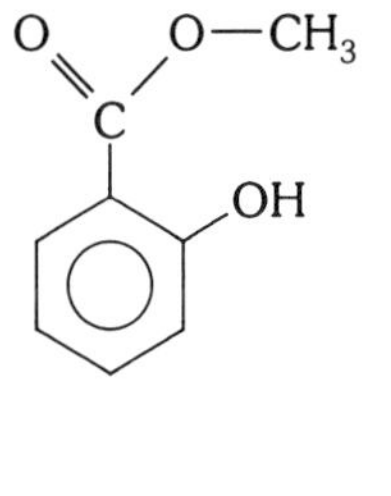

Oil of wintergreen 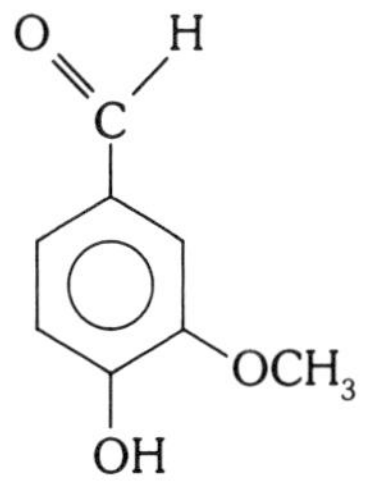   Vanillin 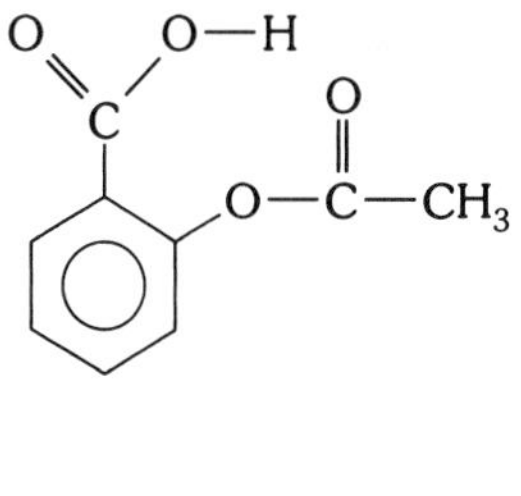   Aspirin

1-Phenylpropane is an example of an aromatic compound with an aliphatic side chain. (In the IUPAC, the group C_6H_5, derived from benzene by removing one H atom, is called the **phenyl** group.) So stable is the benzene ring toward oxidizing agents that alkylbenzenes like 1-phenylpropane are attacked by hot permanganate at *the side chain* and not at the ring. Benzoic acid can be made as follows:

$$C_6H_5{-}CH_2CH_2CH_3 \xrightarrow{\text{hot KMnO}_4} C_6H_5{-}\overset{\displaystyle O}{\overset{\|}{C}}{-}OH \quad (+ CO_2 + H_2O + MnO_2)$$

1-Phenylpropane   Benzoic acid

Most of the side chain is destroyed, but the ring is not attacked.

Not all benzene derivatives have rings that resist oxidation as strongly as this. Rings that hold the OH or the NH_2 groups, for example, are *very* readily oxidized. The unshared electrons on O and N in these groups are also somewhat delocalized into the ring network, which gives the rings more electron density than in benzene. Oxidizing agents, which seek electrons, are therefore able to react with C_6H_5OH and $C_6H_5NH_2$. We can't take this any further, but our goal has been to learn about the benzene ring and its unusual properties. This ring is present in proteins, and aromatic systems occur in all nucleic acids.

13.7 NAMING COMPOUNDS OF BENZENE

Common names dominate the nomenclature of simple derivatives of benzene.

The names of several monosubstituted benzenes are straightforward. The substituent is indicated by a prefix to the word *benzene*. For example,

■ All these compounds are oily liquids.

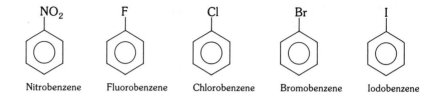

Nitrobenzene   Fluorobenzene   Chlorobenzene   Bromobenzene   Iodobenzene

Other derivatives of benzene have common names that are always used.

■ Phenol was the first antiseptic used by British surgeon Joseph Lister (1827–1912), the discoverer of antiseptic surgery.

Toluene   Phenol   Aniline   Benzoic acid   Benzaldehyde   Benzene-sulfonic acid

***Ortho, Meta,* and *Para* Are Terms for 1,2-, 1,3-, and 1,4- Relationships**   When two or more groups are attached to the benzene ring, both what they are and where they are must be specified. One common way to indicate the relative locations of two groups is by the prefixes *ortho, meta-,* and *para-,* which usually are abbreviated *o-, m-.* and *p-,* respectively. Two groups that are in a 1,2- relationship are said to be *ortho* to each other, as in 1,2-dichlorobenzene, commonly called *o*-dichlorobenzene. A 1,3-relationship is designated *meta,* as in *m*-dichlorobenzene. In *p*-dichlorobenzene, the substituents are 1,4- or *para* relative to each other.

Ortho or 1,2   Meta or 1,3   Para or 1,4
o-Dichlorobenzene   *m*-Dichlorobenzene   *p*-Dichlorobenzene

A disubstituted benzene is often named as a derivative of a monosubstituted benzene when the latter has a common name such as toluene or aniline, and *o-, m-,* or *p-* is used to specify the relative positions. For example,

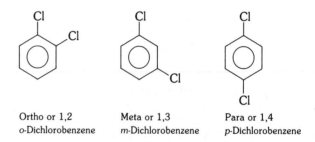

p-Nitrotoluene   *o*-Bromoaniline   *m*-Chlorobenzoic acid   *o*-Nitrophenol

When three or more groups are on a benzene ring, we can no longer use the *ortho, meta,* or *para* designations; we have to use numbers assigned to ring positions. For example,

■ TNT is an important explosive. TNB is an even better explosive than TNT, but it is more expensive to make.

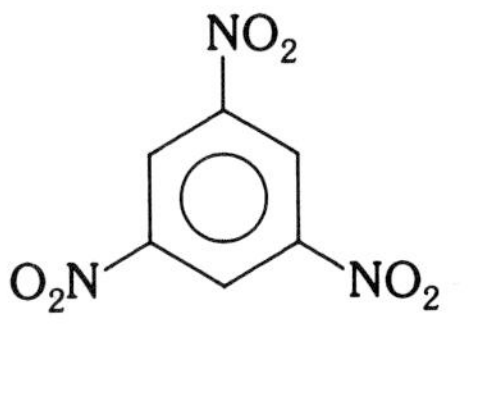

1,3,5-Trinitrobenzene (TNB)

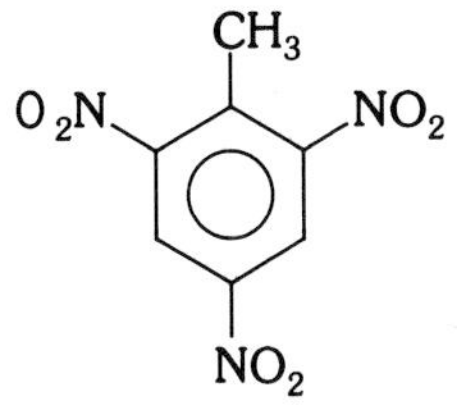

2,4,6-Trinitrotoluene (TNT)

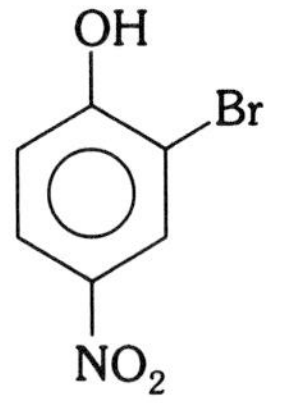

2-Bromo-4-nitrophenol

SUMMARY

Alkenes   The lack of free rotation at a double bond makes geometric (cis–trans) isomers possible, but they exist only when the two groups are not identical at *either* end of the double bond. Cyclic compounds also exhibit cis–trans isomerism.

Alkenes and cycloalkenes are given IUPAC names by a set of rules very similar to those used to name their corresponding saturated forms. However, the double bond takes precedence both in selecting and in numbering the main chain (or ring). The first unsaturated carbon encountered in moving down the chain or around the ring through the double bond must have the lower number.

Addition reactions   Several compounds add to the carbon–carbon double bond — H_2, Cl_2, Br_2, HCl, HBr, $HOSO_3H$, and H_2O (when an acid catalyst is present). The kinds of products that can be made are outlined in the accompanying chart of the reactions of alkenes. When both the alkene and the reactant are unsymmetrical, the addition proceeds according to Markovnikov's rule — the end of the double bond that already has the greater number of hydrogens gets one more. The double bond is vigorously attacked by strong oxidizing agents such as the permanganate ion, the dichromate ion, and ozone.

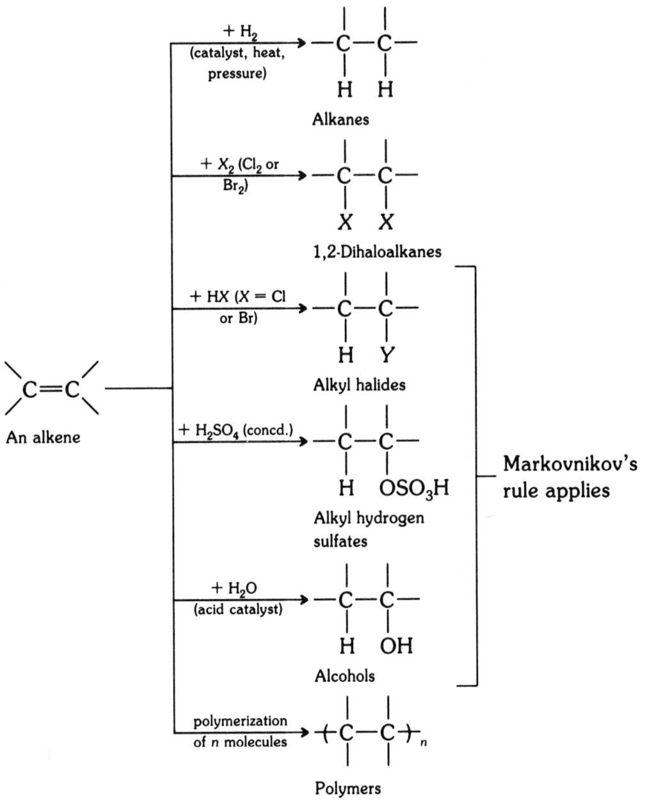

How additions occur   The carbon–carbon double bond serves as a proton-acceptor toward strong proton-donors. The proton becomes attached to one carbon at the double bond, using the pair of electrons in the pi bond to make the sigma bond to this hydrogen, and the other carbon becomes positively charged. This carbocation then accepts an electron-rich particle to complete the formation of the product.

Polymerization of alkenes   The polymerization of an alkene is like an addition reaction. The alkene serves as the monomer, and one alkene molecule adds to another, and so on until a long chain with a repeating unit forms — the polymer molecule.

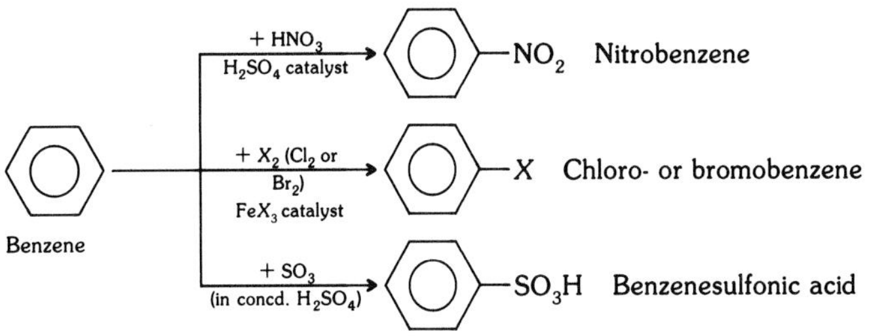

Aromatic properties   When aromatic compounds undergo reactions at the benzene ring, substitutions rather than additions occur. In this way, the close-circuit pi-electron network of the ring remains unbroken. This network forms when six unhybridized $2p$ orbitals of the ring carbon atoms overlap side-by-side to form a double-doughnut-shaped space found above and below the plane of the ring. There are three sublevels in this space, and the pi electrons enjoy considerable room and freedom of motion. Except when the ring holds OH or NH_2 groups, it is very resistant to oxidation.

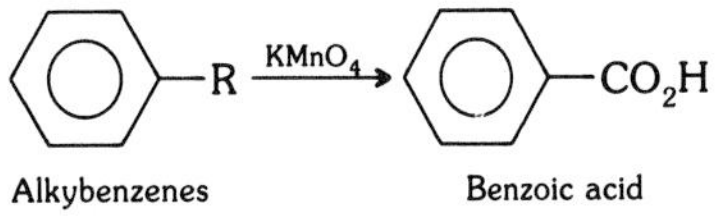

REVIEW EXERCISES

The answers to these Review Exercises are in the *Study Guide* that accompanies this book.

Cis–Trans Isomerism

13.1 Which of the following pairs of structures represent identical compounds or isomers?

(a) $CH_2=CH$ —— CH_3 and $CH=CH_2$ —— CH_3

(b) [cyclohexene with CH_3] and [cyclohexene with CH_3]

(c) [cyclopentene with CH_3] and [cyclopentene with CH_3]

(d) $CH_3-CH=C-CH_2-CH_3$ (with CH_3 substituent)

and $CH_3-CH_2-C=CH-CH_3$ (with CH_3 substituent)

(e) $CH_3-C=CH$ (with Cl) and $CH_3-C=CH$ (with Cl), with Br

13.2 Write the structures of the cis and trans isomers, if any, of each compound.

(a) $CH_3-C=CHCH_3$ (with CH_3)

(b) CH_3—[cyclohexane]—CH_3

(c) $CH_3CH=CCl_2$

(d) $CH_3C=CCH_3$ (with Cl, Cl)

13.3 Identify which of the following compounds can exist as cis and trans isomers and write the structures of these isomers.

(a) [cyclohexane with two CH_3 groups]

(b) [cyclohexane with two CH_3 groups]

(c) Cl—[cyclohexene]—Cl

Nomenclature

13.4 Write the condensed structures of the following compounds.
(a) propylene
(b) isobutylene

(c) *cis*-2-hexene
(d) 3-chloro-2-pentene
(e) 1,2-diethylcyclohexene
(f) 2,4-dimethylcyclohexene

13.5 Write the IUPAC names of the following compounds.
(a) $CH_3(CH_2)_7CH=CH_2$

(b) $Cl-CH=CHCHCH_3$ (with CH_3)

(c) $CH_3CH_2CH_2CCH_2CHCH_2CH_3$ (with CH_2, CH_3)

(d) $CH_3CCH=CH$ (with CH_3, CH_3)

13.6 Write the condensed structures and the IUPAC names for all the isomeric pentenes, C_5H_{10}. Include cis and trans isomers.

13.7 Write the condensed structures and the IUPAC names for all the isomeric methylcyclopentenes.

13.8 Write the condensed structures and IUPAC names for all the isomeric pentynes. The IUPAC rules for naming alkynes are identical with the rules for naming alkenes, except that the name ending is -*yne*, not -*ene*.

13.9 Write the condensed structures and the IUPAC names for all the isomeric dimethylcyclohexenes. Include the cis and trans isomers.

13.10 Write the condensed structures and the names for all the open-chain dienes with the molecular formula C_5H_8. (Note that there can be two double bonds from the same carbon.)

Reactions of the Carbon–Carbon Double Bond

13.11 Write equations for the reactions of 2-methylpropene with the following reactants:
(a) cold, concentrated H_2SO_4
(b) H_2 (Ni, heat, pressure)
(c) H_2O, (H^+ catalyst)
(d) H—Cl
(e) H—Br
(f) Br_2

13.12 Write equations for the reactions of 1-methylcyclopentene with the reactants listed in Review Exercise 13.11.

13.13 Write equations for the reactions of 2-methyl-2-butene with the compounds given in Review Exercise 13.11.

13.14 Write equations for the reactions of 1-methylcyclohexene with the reactants listed in Review Exercise 13.11. (Do not attempt to predict whether cis or trans isomers form.)

13.15 Ethane is insoluble in concentrated sulfuric acid, but ethene dissolves readily. Write an equation to show how ethene is changed into a substance polar enough to dissolve in concentrated sulfuric acid, which, of course, is highly polar.

13.16 1-Hexene, C_6H_{12}, has several isomers, and most but not all of them decolorize bromine, dissolve in concentrated sulfuric acid, and react with potassium permanganate. Give the structures of at least two isomers of C_6H_{12} that give *none* of these reactions.

13.17 One of the raw materials for the synthesis of nylon, adipic acid, can be made from cyclohexene by oxidation using potassium permanganate. The balanced equation for the first step in which the potassium salt of adipic acid forms is as follows:

$$3C_6H_{10} + 8KMnO_4 \longrightarrow$$
$$3K_2C_6H_8O_4 + 8MnO_2 + 2KOH + 2H_2O$$

How many grams of potassium permanganate are needed for the oxidation of 10.0 g of cyclohexene, assuming that the reaction occurs exactly and entirely as written?

13.18 Referring to Review Exercise 13.17, how many grams of the potassium salt of adipic acid can be made if 24.0 g of $KMnO_4$ are used in accordance with the equation given?

How Addition Reactions Occur

13.19 When 1-butene reacts with hydrogen chloride, the product is 2-chlorobutane, not 1-chlorobutane. Explain.

13.20 When 4-methylcyclohexene reacts with hydrogen chloride, the product consists of a mixture of roughly equal quantities of 3-chloro-1-methylcyclohexane and 4-chloro-1-methylcyclohexane. Explain why substantial proportions of *both* isomers form.

Polymerization

13.21 Rubber cement can be made by mixing some polymerized 2-methylpropene with a solvent such as toluene. When the solvent evaporates, a very tacky and sticky residue of the polymer remains, which soon hardens and becomes the glue. Write the structure of the polymer of 2-methylpropene (called polyisobutylene) in two ways. (The structure is quite regular, like polypropylene.)
(a) One that shows four repeating units, one after the other.
(b) The condensed structure.

13.22 Safety glass is made by sealing a thin film of polyvinyl acetate between two pieces of glass. If the glass shatters, its pieces remain glued to the film and cannot fly about. Using four vinyl acetate units, write part of the structure of a molecule of polyvinyl acetate. Also write its condensed structure. The structure of vinyl acetate is as follows:

Vinyl acetate

When it polymerizes, its units line up in a regular way, as in the polymerization of propene.

13.23 Gasoline is mostly a mixture of alkanes. However, when a sample of gasoline was shaken with aqueous potassium permanganate, a brown precipitate of MnO_2 appeared and the purple color of the permanganate ion disappeared. What kind of hydrocarbon was evidently also in this sample?

13.24 If gasoline rests for months in the fuel line of some engine, the line slowly accumulates some sticky material. This can clog the line and also make the carburetor work poorly or not at all. In view of your answer to Review Exercise 13.23, what is likely to be happening, chemically?

Aromatic Properties

13.25 Dipentene has a very pleasant, lemon-like fragrance, but it is not classified as an aromatic compound. Why?

Dipentene

13.26 Sulfanilamide, the structurally simplest of the sulfa drugs, has no odor at all, but it is still classified as an aromatic compound. Explain.

Sulfanilamide

13.27 Write equations for the reactions, if any, of benzene with the following compounds.
(a) Sulfur trioxide (in concentrated sulfuric acid)
(b) Concentrated nitric acid (in concentrated sulfuric acid)
(c) Hot sodium hydroxide solution
(d) Hydrochloric acid
(e) Chlorine (alone)
(f) Hot potassium permanganate
(g) Bromine in the presence of $FeBr_3$

13.28 Write the structure of any compound that would react with hot potassium permanganate to give benzoic acid.

13.29 Terephthalic acid is one of the raw materials for making Dacron, a polymer that is popular for making synthetic fabrics.

Terephthalic acid

What hydrocarbon with the formula C_8H_{10} could be changed to terephthalic acid by the action of hot potassium permanganate? (Write its structure.)

The Bonds in Benzene

13.30 Describe in your own words, making your own drawings, the ways in which the bonds in benzene form.

13.31 What is it about the delocalization of benzene's pi electrons that makes the benzene ring relatively stable?

13.32 Explain why benzene strongly resists addition reactions and gives substitution reactions instead.

Names of Aromatic Compounds

13.33 Write the condensed structure of each compound.
  (a) toluene   (b) aniline
  (c) phenol   (d) benzoic acid
  (e) benzaldehyde   (f) nitrobenzene

13.34 Give the condensed structures of the following compounds.
  (a) *o*-nitrobenzenesulfonic acid
  (b) *p*-chlorotoluene
  (c) *m*-bromonitrobenzene
  (d) 2,4-dinitrophenol

Predicting Reactions

13.35 Write the structures of the products to be expected in the following situations. If no reaction is to be expected, write "no reaction." To work this kind of exercise, you have to be able to do three things.
  (a) *Classify* a specific organic reactant into its proper family.
  (b) *Recall* the short list of chemical facts about the family. (If there is no matchup between this list and the reactants and conditions specified by a given problem, assume that there is no reaction.)
  (c) *Apply* the recalled chemical fact, which might be some "map sign" associated with a functional group, to the specific situation.

Study the next two examples before continuing.

EXAMPLE 13.6 PREDICTING REACTIONS

Problem: What is the product, if any, of the following?

$$CH_3CH_2CH_2CH_3 + H_2SO_4 \longrightarrow$$

Solution: We note first that the organic reactant is an alkane, so we next turn to the list of chemical properties about all alkanes that we learned. With this family, of course, the list is very short. Except for combustion and halogenation, we have learned no reactions for alkanes, and we assume, therefore, that there aren't any others, not even with sulfuric acid. Hence, the answer is "no reaction."

EXAMPLE 13.7 PREDICTING REACTIONS

Problem: What is the product, if any, in the following situation?

$$CH_3CH{=}CHCH_3 + H_2O \xrightarrow{\text{acid catalyst}} ?$$

Solution: We first note that the organic reactant is an alkene, so we review our mental "file" of reactions of the carbon–carbon double bond.

1. Alkenes add hydrogen (in the presence of a metal catalyst and under heat and pressure) to form alkanes.
2. They add chlorine and bromine to give 1,2-dihaloalkanes.
3. They add hydrogen chloride and hydrogen bromide to give alkyl halides.
4. They add sulfuric acid to give alkyl hydrogen sulfates.
5. They add water in the presence of an acid catalyst to give alcohols.

6. They are attacked by strong oxidizing agents.
7. They polymerize.

These are the chief chemical facts about the carbon–carbon double bond that we have studied, and we see that the list includes a reaction with water in the presence of an acid catalyst. We remember that in all addition reactions the double bond changes to a single bond and the pieces of the molecule that adds end up on the carbons at this bond. We also have to remember Markovnikov's rule to tell us which pieces of the water molecule go to which carbon. However, in this specific example, Markovnikov's rule does not apply (the alkene is symmetrical).

Answer:

$$\begin{array}{c} CH_3CH_2CHCH_3 \\ | \\ OH \end{array}$$

Now work the following parts. (Remember that C_6H_6 stands for benzene and that $C_6H_5{-}$ is the phenyl group.)

  (a) $CH_3CH_2CH{=}CH_2 + H_2 \xrightarrow[\text{pressure}]{\text{Ni, heat,}}$
  (b) $CH_3CH{=}CHCH_3 + H_2O \xrightarrow{H^+}$
  (c) $C_6H_6 + Br_2 \xrightarrow{FeBr_3}$
  (d) $CH_3CH_2CH_3 + \text{concd } H_2SO_4 \longrightarrow$

  (e) $\hexagon + H_2O \xrightarrow{H^+}$

  (f) $CH_3CH{=}CHCH_2CH_3 + H_2 \xrightarrow[\text{pressure}]{\text{Ni, heat,}}$

  (g) $\hexagon + \text{concd. } H_2SO_4 \longrightarrow$

  (h) $C_6H_5{-}CH{=}CH{-}C_6H_5 + H_2O \xrightarrow{H^+}$

  (i) $\hexagon + H_2 \xrightarrow[\text{pressure}]{\text{Ni, heat,}}$

  (j) $CH_3CH_2CH_2CH_3 + O_2 \xrightarrow[\text{combustion}]{\text{complete}}$
  (Balance the equation.)

  (k) $C_6H_6 + H_2O \xrightarrow{H^+}$

13.36 Write the structures of the products in the following situations. If no reaction is to be expected, write "no reaction."
  (a) $CH_3CH{=}CH_2 + H_2O \xrightarrow{H^+}$
  (b) $CH_2{=}CH{-}CH_2{-}CH{=}CH_2 + 2H_2 \xrightarrow[\text{pressure}]{\text{Ni, heat}}$
  (c) $({-}CH_2{-}CH_2{-})_n + H_2SO_4 \text{ (concd)} \longrightarrow$
  (d) $\begin{array}{c} \quad\;\; CH_3 \quad CH_3 \\ \quad\;\; | \qquad\; | \\ CH_3{-}C{=}C{-}CH_3 + HCl \longrightarrow \end{array}$

  (e) $\hexagon{=}CH_2 + HBr \longrightarrow$

  (f) $\hexagon + Br_2 \longrightarrow$

(g) $C_6H_6 + Cl_2 \xrightarrow{FeCl_3}$

(h) $C_6H_6 + NaOH(aq) \longrightarrow$

(i) $C_6H_5-CH_3 + O_2 \xrightarrow[\text{combustion}]{\text{complete}}$ (Balance the equation.)

(j) 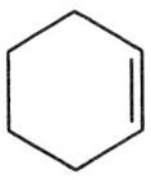 ⬡ $+ NaOH(aq) \longrightarrow$

(k) $CH_2{=}CH-CH{=}CH_2 + 2Cl_2 \longrightarrow$

(l) $C_6H_5-CH{=}CH_2 + Br_2 \longrightarrow$

Ozone in Smog (Special Topic 13.1)

13.37 What event in a vehicle engine launches the production of ozone in smog? (Write an equation.)

13.38 How is NO_2 formed in smog? (Write an equation.)

13.39 How is NO_2 involved in the production of ozone in smog? Write equations.

13.40 Why is ozone dangerous?

Ozone in the Stratosphere (Special Topic 13.2)

13.41 Write the equation for the stratospheric reaction of O_2 that removes some UV radiation from incoming solar energy.

13.42 Write the equations that explain how the reaction of Review Exercise 13.41 sets up two ozone cycles. Explain how such cycles convert UV radiation into heat.

13.43 What particular harm does solar UV radiation do to humans?

13.44 What are the CFCs?

13.45 Using equations, explain how CFC-11 can reduce the stratospheric ozone level.

Reactions of Alkynes (Special Topic 13.3)

13.46 Write the structures of the products that form when one mole of $CH_3-C{\equiv}C-CH_3$ reacts with one mole of each of the following.
(a) H_2 (b) Cl_2 (c) Br_2

13.47 Write the structures of the products that form when one mole of $CH_3-C{\equiv}C-CH_3$ reacts with two moles of each of the following.
(a) H_2 (b) Cl_2 (c) Br_2

Alcohols, Thioalcohols, Phenols, and Ethers

The skunk's weapon is a mixture of oily, clinging thioalcohols, compounds with SH groups, which we study in this chapter. Thioalcohols are sulfur analogs of alcohols, compounds with OH groups, and this simple substitution of S or O causes great differences in odor. (A question we can't answer is whether the skunk enjoys the fragrance of these desert dandelions.)

14.1 OCCURRENCE, TYPES, AND NAMES OF ALCOHOLS

In the alcohol family, molecules have the OH group attached to a saturated carbon.

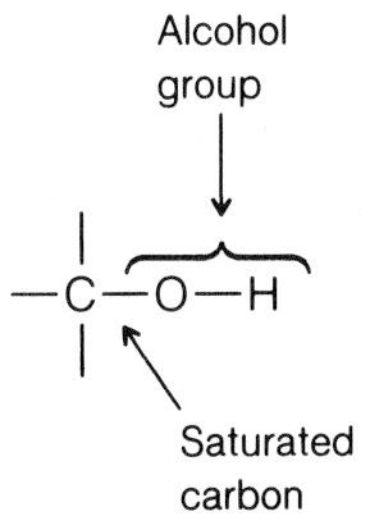

Alcohol
group

$$\downarrow$$

$$-\overset{|}{\underset{|}{C}}-O-H$$

Saturated
carbon

Alcohol
system

■ Pronounce 1° as *primary*, 2° as *secondary*, and 3° as *tertiary*.

The alcohol system is one of the most widely occurring in nature, being present in most of the major kinds of organic substances found in living things, for example, in carbohydrates, proteins, and nucleic acids. Members of the alcohol family include many common commercial products — wood alcohol (methanol), rubbing alcohol (2-propanol), beverage alcohol (ethanol), and compounds in antifreezes. See also Special Topic 14.1.

In **alcohols,** the OH group is covalently held by a *saturated* carbon atom, one from which only single bonds extend. When this condition is met, the OH group is called the **alcohol group.** Table 14.1 includes a number of simple alcohols, those with just one OH group.

The Alcohol Group Occurs As a 1°, 2°, and 3° System An alcohol is classified as primary (1°), secondary (2°), or tertiary (3°) according to the kind of carbon that holds the OH group. When the OH group is held by a 1° carbon, one that has only one carbon atom directly joined to it, the alcohol is a **primary alcohol.** In a **secondary alcohol,** the OH group is held

TABLE 14.1 Some Common Alcohols

Name[a]	Structure	Boiling Point (°C)
Methanol	CH_3OH	65
Ethanol	CH_3CH_2OH	78.5
1-Propanol	$CH_3CH_2CH_2OH$	97
2-Propanol	$CH_3\underset{\underset{OH}{\|}}{C}HCH_3$	82
1-Butanol	$CH_3CH_2CH_2CH_2OH$	117
2-Butanol (*sec*-butyl alcohol)	$CH_3CH_2\underset{\underset{OH}{\|}}{C}HCH_3$	100
2-Methyl-1-propanol (isobutyl alcohol)	$CH_3\underset{\underset{CH_3}{\overset{\|}{\underset{}{}}}}{C}HCH_2OH$	108
2-Methyl-2-propanol (*t*-butyl alcohol)	$CH_3\underset{\underset{CH_3}{\|}}{\overset{\overset{CH_3}{\|}}{C}}OH$	83
1,2-Ethanediol (ethylene glycol)	$\underset{\underset{OH}{\|}}{C}H_2-\underset{\underset{OH}{\|}}{C}H_2$	197
1,2-Propanediol (propylene glycol)	$CH_3\underset{\underset{OH}{\|}}{C}H-\underset{\underset{OH}{\|}}{C}H_2$	189
1,2,3-Propanetriol (glycerol)	$\underset{\underset{OH}{\|}}{C}H_2-\underset{\underset{OH}{\|}}{C}H-\underset{\underset{OH}{\|}}{C}H_2$	290

[a] The IUPAC names with the common names in parentheses.

SPECIAL TOPIC 14.1 | IMPORTANT INDIVIDUAL ALCOHOLS

Methanol (methyl alcohol, wood alcohol). When taken internally in enough quantity, methanol causes either blindness or death. In industry, it is used as the raw material for making formaldehyde (which is used to make polymers), as a solvent, and as a denaturant (poison) for ethanol. It is also used as the fuel in Sterno, as well as in burners for fondue pots.

Most methanol is made by the reaction of carbon monoxide with hydrogen under high pressure and temperature:

$$2H_2 + CO \xrightarrow[\substack{\text{temp.} = 350-400\ °C \\ \text{catalyst} = ZnO-Cr_2O_3}]{3000\ \text{lb/in.}^2} CH_3-OH$$

Ethanol (ethyl alcohol, grain alcohol). Some ethanol is made by the fermentation of sugars, but most is synthesized by the addition of water to ethene in the presence of a catalyst. A 70% (v/v) solution of ethanol in water is used as a disinfectant.

In industry, ethanol is used as a solvent and to prepare pharmaceuticals, perfumes, lotions, and rubbing compounds. For these purposes, the ethanol is adulterated by poisons that are very difficult to remove so that the alcohol cannot be sold or used as a beverage. (Nearly all countries derive revenue by taxing potable, i.e., drinkable, alcohol.)

2-Propanol (isopropyl alcohol). 2-Propanol is a common substitute for ethanol for giving back rubs. It is twice as toxic as ethanol, and in solutions with concentrations from 50% to 99% (v/v) it is used as a disinfectant.

1,2-Ethanediol (ethylene glycol), and **1,2-Propanediol** (propylene glycol). Ethylene and propylene glycol are the chief components in permanent-type antifreezes. Their great solubility in water and their very high boiling points make them ideal for this purpose. An aqueous solution that is roughly 50% (v/v) in either glycol does not freeze until about −40 °C (−40 °F).

1,2,3-Propanetriol (glycerol, glycerin). Glycerol, a colorless, syrupy liquid with a sweet taste, is freely soluble in water and insoluble in nonpolar solvents. It is one product of the digestion of the fats and oils in our diets. Because it has three OH groups per molecule, each capable of hydrogen-bonding to water molecules, glycerol can draw moisture from humid air. It is sometimes used as a food additive to help keep foods moist.

Sugars. All carbohydrates consist of polyhydroxy compounds, and we will study them in a later chapter.

---

by a 2° carbon. When the OH group is joined to a 3° carbon, the alcohol is a **tertiary alcohol.** We will see the usefulness of these subclasses when we learn that not all alcohols respond in the same way to oxidizing agents.

■ The R— groups in 2° and 3° alcohols don't have to be the same.

$$R-CH_2-OH \qquad R-\overset{\overset{\displaystyle R'}{|}}{C}H-OH \qquad R-\overset{\overset{\displaystyle R'}{|}}{\underset{\underset{\displaystyle R''}{|}}{C}}-OH$$

Primary alcohol · Secondary alcohol · Tertiary alcohol

Many substances classified as alcohols have more than one OH group per molecule. When only one is present, the alcohol is a **monohydric alcohol.** When two OH groups occur, as in 1,2-ethanediol (ethylene glycol), the substance is a **dihydric alcohol** or a **glycol.** A **trihydric alcohol** is one whose molecules have three alcohol groups, such as 1,2,3-propanetriol (glycerol).

Many substances, particularly among the various sugars, have several OH groups per molecule. One important structural restriction is that almost no stable system is known in which one carbon holds more than one OH group. If such should form during a reaction, it breaks up. (More will be said about this in the next chapter).

■ The following system, the 1,1-diol, is unstable; only rare examples are known.

$$R-\overset{\overset{\displaystyle OH}{|}}{\underset{\underset{\displaystyle R}{|}}{C}}-OH$$

1,1-Diols

$$\underset{\underset{\displaystyle OH}{|}}{CH_2}-\underset{\underset{\displaystyle OH}{|}}{CH_2}$$

1,2-Ethanediol (ethylene glycol)

$$\underset{\underset{\displaystyle OH}{|}}{CH_2}-\underset{\underset{\displaystyle OH}{|}}{CH}-\underset{\underset{\displaystyle OH}{|}}{CH_2}$$

1,2,3-Propanetriol (glycerol)

$$\underset{\underset{\displaystyle OH}{|}}{CH_2}-\underset{\underset{\displaystyle OH}{|}}{CH}-\underset{\underset{\displaystyle OH}{|}}{CH}-\underset{\underset{\displaystyle OH}{|}}{CH}-\underset{\underset{\displaystyle OH}{|}}{CH}-\overset{\overset{\displaystyle O}{\|}}{C}-H$$

Glucose — a sugar (open form of molecule)

PRACTICE EXERCISE 1 Classify each of the following as monohydric or dihydric. For each found to be monohydric, classify it further as 1°, 2°, or 3°. If the structure is too unstable to exist, state so.

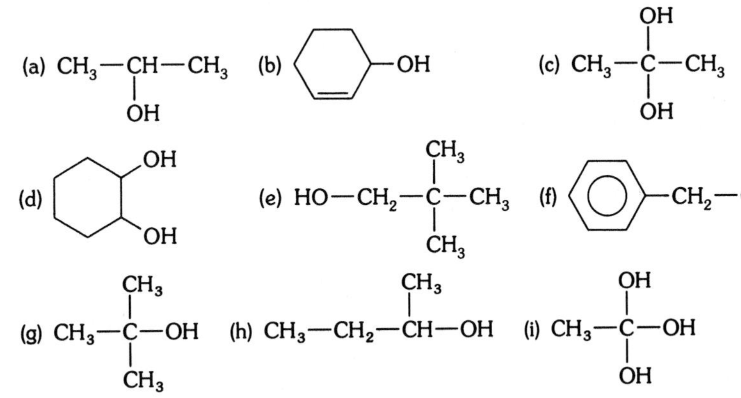

(a) CH_3—CH—CH_3
       |
       OH

(b) [cyclohexene ring]—OH

(c) OH
    |
    CH_3—C—CH_3
    |
    OH

(d) [cyclohexane ring with two OH groups]

(e) CH_3
          |
    HO—CH_2—C—CH_3
          |
          CH_3

(f) [benzene ring]—CH_2—OH

(g) CH_3
        |
    CH_3—C—OH
        |
        CH_3

(h) CH_3
              |
    CH_3—CH_2—CH—OH

(i) OH
    |
    CH_3—C—OH
    |
    OH

Not All Compounds with the OH Group Are Alcohols As you can see by the following structures, the OH group also occurs in the family of the phenols, where it is attached to a benzene ring, and in the family of the carboxylic acids, where it is attached to a carbon that has a double bond to oxygen.

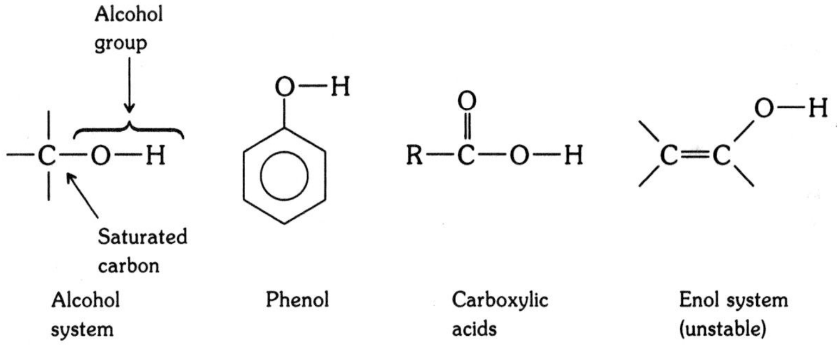

Alcohol group

        |
    —C—O—H
        |

Saturated carbon

Alcohol system

[benzene ring] O—H

Phenol

       O
       ‖
    R—C—O—H

Carboxylic acids

          O—H
          |
    C=C

Enol system (unstable)

When the OH is attached to an alkene group, the system — called the *enol* system (ene + ol) — is unstable. Most of our attention will be given to alcohols in this chapter, with some study of phenols. We will study the carboxylic acids in a later chapter.

PRACTICE EXERCISE 2 Classify the following as alcohols, phenols, or carboxylic acids.

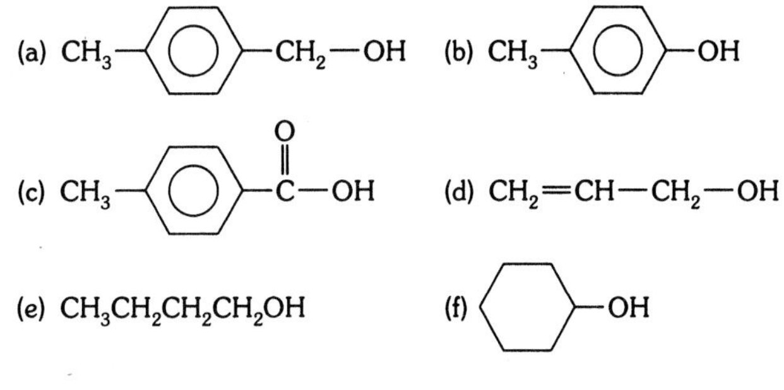

(a) CH_3—[benzene ring]—CH_2—OH

(b) CH_3—[benzene ring]—OH

(c) CH_3—[benzene ring]—
          O
          ‖
          C—OH

(d) CH_2=CH—CH_2—OH

(e) $CH_3CH_2CH_2CH_2OH$

(f) [cyclohexane ring]—OH

Common Names of Alcohols Are Popular Where the Alkyl Groups Are Easily Named Simple alcohols have common names devised by writing the word *alcohol* after the name of the alkyl group holding the OH group. For example,

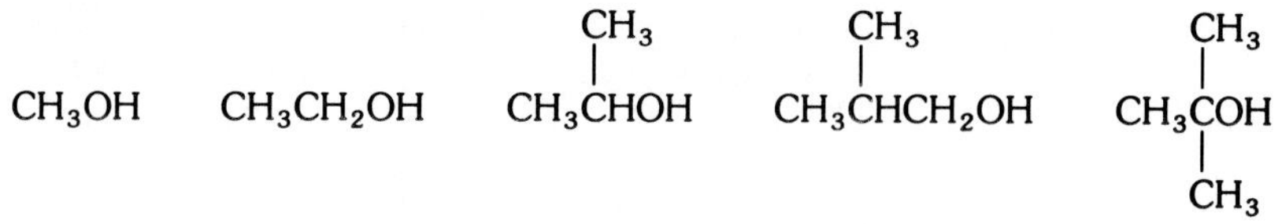

$$
\begin{array}{ccccc}
& & \overset{\displaystyle CH_3}{\underset{\displaystyle |}{}} & \overset{\displaystyle CH_3}{\underset{\displaystyle |}{}} & \overset{\displaystyle CH_3}{\underset{\displaystyle |}{}} \\
CH_3OH & CH_3CH_2OH & CH_3CHOH & CH_3CHCH_2OH & CH_3COH \\
& & & & \overset{\displaystyle |}{CH_3}
\end{array}
$$

| Methyl alcohol | Ethyl alcohol | Isopropyl alcohol | Isobutyl alcohol | *t*-Butyl alcohol |

IUPAC Names of Alcohols End in -ol The IUPAC rules for naming alcohols are similar to those for naming alkanes. The full name of the alcohol is based on the idea of a *parent alcohol* that has substituents on its carbon chain. The rules are as follows.

1. Determine the parent alcohol by selecting the longest chain of carbons *that includes the carbon atom to which the OH group is attached.* Name the parent alcohol by changing the name ending of the alkane that corresponds to this chain from *-e* to *-ol*. Examples are

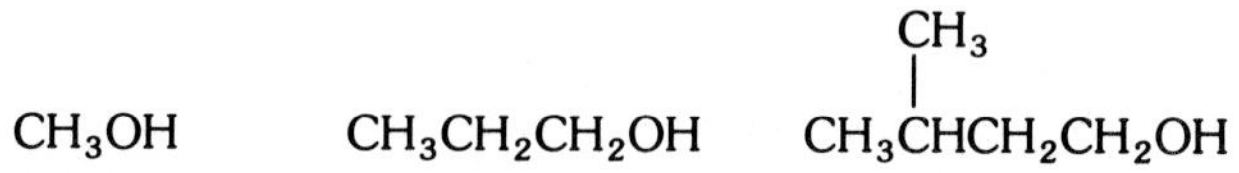

$$
\begin{array}{ccc}
& & \overset{\displaystyle CH_3}{\underset{\displaystyle |}{}} \\
CH_3OH & CH_3CH_2CH_2OH & CH_3CHCH_2CH_2OH
\end{array}
$$

| Methanol (parent alkane is methane) | Propanol (parent alkane is propane) | A substituted butanol (parent alkane is butane) |

2. Number the parent chain from whichever end gives the carbon that holds the OH group the lower number. Be sure to notice this departure from the IUPAC rules for numbering chains for alkanes; in the rules for alkanes, the location of the first branch determines the direction of numbering. With alcohols, *the location of the OH group takes precedence over alkyl groups or halogen atoms in deciding the direction of numbering.*

Examples are:

■ No number is needed to specify the location of the OH group in the names methanol and ethanol.

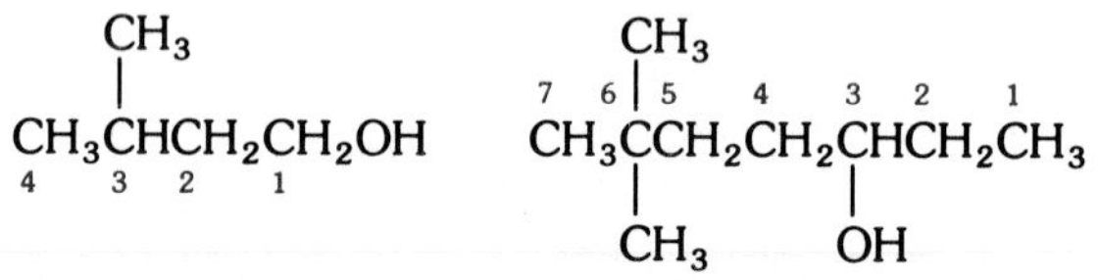

$$
\overset{\displaystyle CH_3}{\underset{\displaystyle |}{}}
\quad CH_3CHCH_2CH_2OH
$$
$$
\underset{\displaystyle 4\quad 3\quad 2\quad 1}{}
$$

3-Methyl-1-butanol
Not 2-methyl-4-butanol

$$
\overset{\displaystyle CH_3}{\underset{\displaystyle |}{}}
\quad \overset{7\ \ 6\ \ |\ 5\ \ \ 4\quad 3\ \ 2\ \ 1}{CH_3CCH_2CH_2CHCH_2CH_3}
$$
$$
\overset{\displaystyle |\qquad\qquad |}{CH_3\qquad OH}
$$

6,6-Dimethyl-3-heptanol
Not 2,2-dimethyl-5-heptanol

3. Write the number that locates the OH group in front of the name of the parent, and separate this number from the name of the parent by a hyphen. Then, as prefixes to what you have just written, assemble the names of the substituents and their location numbers. Use commas and hyphens in the usual way. See the examples following rule 2 for illustrations. If a halogen atom is present, place its part in the final name first. For example,

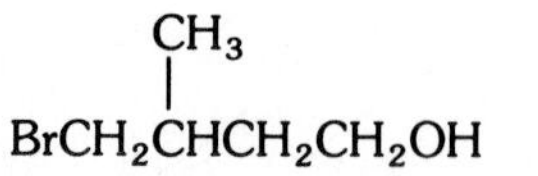

$$
\overset{\displaystyle CH_3}{\underset{\displaystyle |}{}}
\quad BrCH_2CHCH_2CH_2OH
$$

4-Bromo-3-methyl-1-butanol
Not 3-methyl-4-bromo-1-butanol

4. When two or more OH groups are present, use name endings such as *-diol* (for two OH groups), *-triol*, and so forth. Then place the two, three, or more location numbers immediately in front of the name of the parent alcohol. For example,

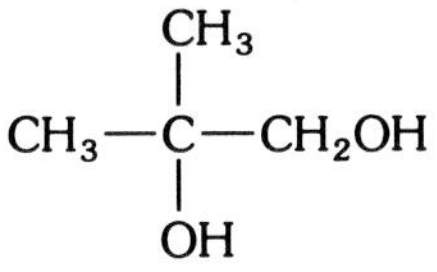

$$CH_3-\underset{\underset{\displaystyle OH}{|}}{\overset{\overset{\displaystyle CH_3}{|}}{C}}-CH_2OH \qquad CH_3-\underset{\underset{\displaystyle OH}{|}}{CH}-\underset{\underset{\displaystyle OH}{|}}{CH}-CH_2OH$$

2-Methyl-1,2-propanediol 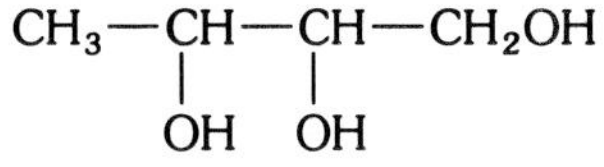   1,2,3-Butanetriol

5. If no parent alcohol name is possible or convenient, the OH group can be treated as another substituent, and it is named *hydroxy*. For example,

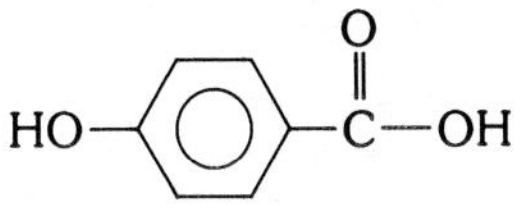

$$HO-\underset{}{\bigcirc}-\overset{\overset{\displaystyle O}{\|}}{C}-OH$$

4-Hydroxybenzoic acid

EXAMPLE 14.1   **USING THE IUPAC RULES TO NAME AN ALCOHOL**

Problem: What is the name of the following compound?

$$CH_3-CH_2-CH_2-\underset{}{CH}-\underset{\underset{\displaystyle CH_2-CH_2-CH_3}{|}}{\overset{\overset{\displaystyle CH_3}{|}}{C}}-CH_2-OH$$
$$\overset{\displaystyle CH_3-CH_2}{}\quad \overset{\displaystyle CH_3}{}$$

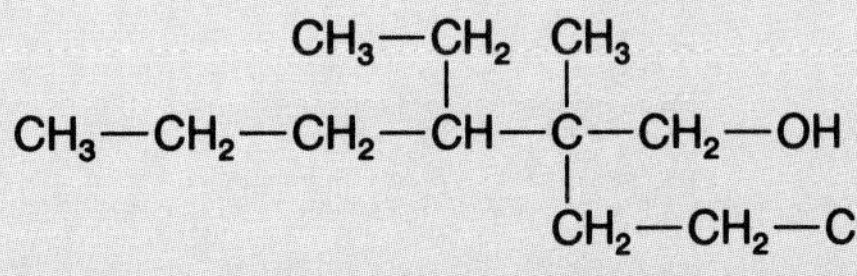

Solution: The longest chain *that includes the carbon atom to which the OH group is attached* has six carbons in it, so the name of the parent alcohol is hexanol. (We can't use the longest chain of all, a chain of eight, because it doesn't include the OH group.) We have to number the chain from right to left because this gives the carbon that holds the OH group the lower number.

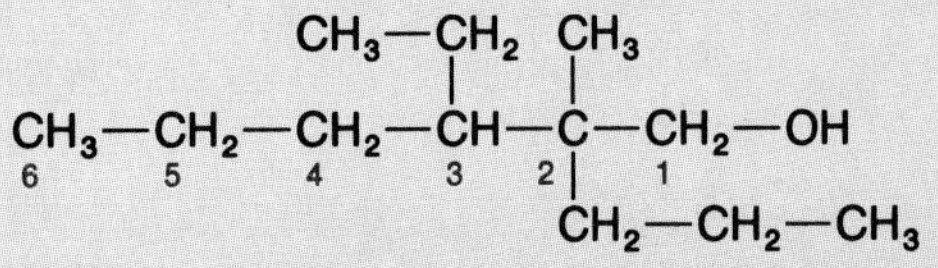

$$\underset{6}{CH_3}-\underset{5}{CH_2}-\underset{4}{CH_2}-\underset{3}{CH}-\underset{2}{C}-\underset{1}{CH_2}-OH$$

Thus the final name must end in -1-hexanol. Carbon 2 holds both a methyl and a propyl group, and carbon 3 has an ethyl group, so the final name, arranging the alkyl groups alphabetically, is

3-Ethyl-2-methyl-2-propyl-1-hexanol

PRACTICE EXERCISE 3   Name the following compounds by the IUPAC system.

(a) 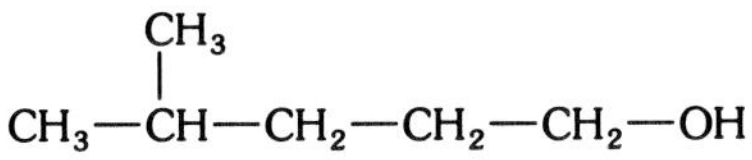 $CH_3-\underset{\underset{\displaystyle }{}}{\overset{\overset{\displaystyle CH_3}{|}}{CH}}-CH_2-CH_2-CH_2-OH$ (b) 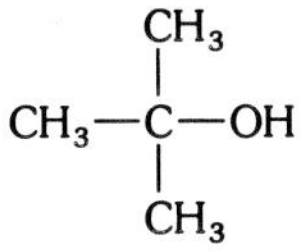 $CH_3-\underset{\underset{\displaystyle CH_3}{|}}{\overset{\overset{\displaystyle CH_3}{|}}{C}}-OH$

(c) $CH_3-CH_2-\underset{\underset{\displaystyle CH_2-CH_2-CH_3}{|}}{\overset{\overset{\displaystyle CH_3}{|}}{C}}-CH_2-OH$ (d) 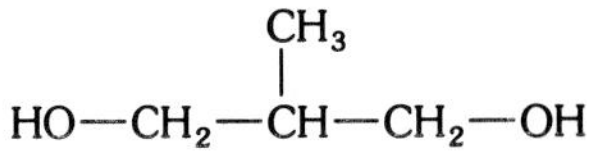 $HO-CH_2-\underset{\underset{\displaystyle }{}}{\overset{\overset{\displaystyle CH_3}{|}}{CH}}-CH_2-OH$

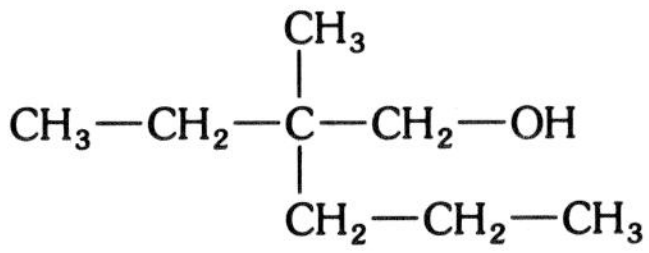

14.2 PHYSICAL PROPERTIES OF ALCOHOLS

Hydrogen bonding dominates the physical properties of alcohols.

The OH group is quite polar, and it can both donate and accept hydrogen bonds. This gives alcohols much higher boiling points and much greater solubilities in water than hydrocarbons of the same size.

The effect of the OH group on water solubility is particularly important at the molecular level of life, because some substances in cells must be in solution and others must not. Moreover, the body handles many toxic substances by using special liver enzymes to attach OH groups to their molecules so that they are more easily carried in the blood to the kidneys for elimination in the urine. The major factors that determine both relative solubilities and boiling points are OH groups and sizes of hydrocarbon groups.

Hydrogen Bonds Between Molecules Raise Boiling Points   Table 14.2 compares the boiling points of some alcohols to those of alkanes with comparable formula weights. The differences are caused by hydrogen bonding, which alcohol molecules can do and those of alkanes cannot. As seen in Figure 14.1a, each alcohol molecule can be attracted to two neighboring molecules by two hydrogen bonds. Water, despite its lower formula weight, has

TABLE 14.2   The Influence of the Alcohol Group on Boiling Points

Name	Structure	Formula Weight	Boiling Point (°C)	Difference in Boiling Point
Ethane	CH_3CH_3	30	−89	
Methyl alcohol	CH_3OH	32	65	154
Propane	$CH_3CH_2CH_3$	44	−42	
Ethyl alcohol	CH_3CH_2OH	46	78	120
Butane	$CH_3CH_2CH_2CH_3$	58	0	
Ethylene glycol	$HOCH_2CH_2OH$	62	197	197

Figure 14.1
Hydrogen bonding (*a*) in alcohols, and (*b*) in water.

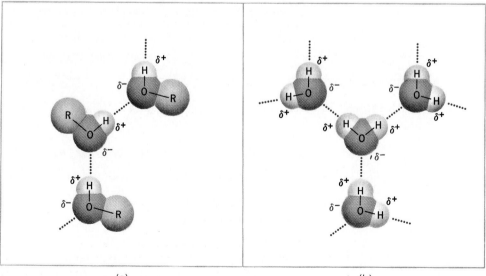

(a)   (b)

Figure 14.2
How a short-chain alcohol dissolves in water. (*a*) The alcohol molecule can take the place of a water molecule in the hydrogen-bonding network of water. (*b*) An alkane molecule cannot break into the hydrogen-bonding network in water, so the alkane cannot dissolve.

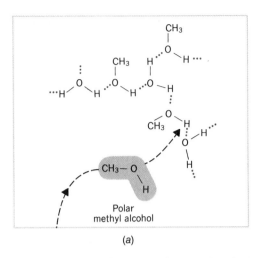

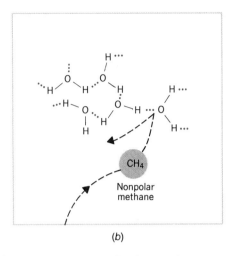

(*a*)   (*b*)

an even higher boiling point than methyl alcohol does, because its molecules can have an additional hydrogen bond between them, as seen in Figure 14.1*b*.

Ethylene glycol (Table 14.2), a typical dihydric alcohol, can have four hydrogen bonds between molecules, and it boils nearly 200 °C higher than butane. You can see by these data how significant the OH group is to forces of attraction between molecules.

The OH Group Makes Compounds More Soluble in Water   Methane, like all hydrocarbons, is insoluble in water, but methyl alcohol dissolves in all proportions because hydrogen bonds can be donated and accepted between its molecules and those of water. This enables methyl alcohol molecules to slip into the hydrogen-bonding network in water, as seen in Figure 14.2. The CH_3 group in CH_3OH is too small to interfere with this.

As the size of the R group in a monohydric alcohol molecule increases, its molecules become more and more alkane-like, and the R group increasingly interferes with the alcohol's dissolving in water. In 1-decanol, for example,

■ Only three elements, F, O, and N, have atoms that are electronegative enough to participate significantly in hydrogen bonds.

$$CH_3CH_2CH_2CH_2CH_2CH_2CH_2CH_2CH_2CH_2OH$$
1-Decanol

the small, water-like OH group is overwhelmed by the long hydrocarbon chain. Water molecules have no attraction for this part of the molecule, and the flexings and twistings of its long chain interfere too much with the hydrogen-bonding networks in water for water to let these molecules into solution. This alcohol, and most with five or more carbons, are insoluble in water. However, they do dissolve in such nonpolar solvents as diethyl ether, gasoline, and petroleum ether.

PRACTICE EXERCISE 4   1,2-Propanediol (propylene glycol) and 1-butanol have similar formula weights. In which of these two compounds is hydrogen bonding between molecules more extensive and stronger? How do the data in Table 14.1 support the answer? Which would be more soluble in water?

14.3   CHEMICAL PROPERTIES OF ALCOHOLS

The loss of water (dehydration) and the loss of hydrogen (oxidation) are two very important reactions of alcohols.

Alcohols react with both inorganic and organic compounds, but we will study only the inorganic reactants in this chapter. Before continuing, however, we need to point out some properties that the alcohols do not have but might be assumed because of their OH groups.

■ When an alcohol dissolves in water, it doesn't raise or lower the pH.

Despite the OH Group, Alcohols Are Not Strong Bases We can think of alcohols as mono-alkyl derivatives of water and, like water, they are extremely weak proton-donors and proton-acceptors. Alcohol molecules do not ionize to give either OH^- ions or H^+ ions. Water, as you know, does not ionize, at least not more than roughly 0.0000001% of its molecules are ionized at equilibrium. The same is true of alcohols. A solution of methyl alcohol (or any alcohol) in water has a neutral pH.

Alcohols Can Be Dehydrated to Alkenes In laboratory vessels, the action of heat and a strong acid catalyst causes the dehydration of an alcohol to an alkene. Water molecules split out and a carbon–carbon double bond emerges. The pieces of the water molecule, one H and one OH, come from *adjacent* carbons.

In general,

$$-\overset{|}{\underset{|}{C}}-\overset{|}{\underset{|}{C}}- \xrightarrow[\text{heat}]{H^+ \text{ catalyst}} \ \diagdown C = C \diagup + H-OH$$

Carbon that is adjacent to the carbon that holds the —OH group

H OH

Alcohol

Alkene

Specific examples are as follows.

$$CH_3CH_2OH \xrightarrow[170-180\ °C]{concd\ H_2SO_4} CH_2{=}CH_2 + H_2O$$

Ethanol

Ethene

$$\underset{\text{2-Butanol}}{CH_3CH_2\overset{\overset{\displaystyle OH}{|}}{C}HCH_3} \xrightarrow[100\ °C]{60\%\ H_2SO_4} \underset{\substack{\text{2-Butene}\\ \text{(chief product)}}}{CH_3CH{=}CHCH_3} + \underset{\substack{\text{1-Butene}\\ \text{(by-product)}}}{CH_3CH_2CH{=}CH_2} + H_2O$$

Special Topic 14.2 explains how the acid works as the catalyst for these reactions.

When Two Alkenes Are Possible, The More Highly Branched Alkene Forms Water can split out in two directions from 2-butanol, (foregoing equation) because its molecules have H atoms on *two* carbons adjacent to the carbon with the OH group. Two alkenes are therefore possible, 2-butene and 1-butene, and some of each forms. When options like this exist, however, one alkene predominates, generally the more highly branched alkene. This is the alkene with the greatest number of alkyl groups attached to the double bond. 2-Butene is more branched than 1-butene because it has two alkyl groups at the double bond (two methyl groups) and 1-butene has only one (an ethyl group). In acid-catalyzed dehydrations, the more-branched alkene predominates because it is the more stable.

Information about the relative stabilities of isomeric alkenes comes from combustion experiments. For example, the combustion of either 1- or 2-butene goes as follows.

$CH_3-CH{=}CH-CH_3$

2-Butene
(two alkyl groups)

$CH_2{=}CH-CH_2CH_3$

1-Butene
(one alkyl group)

$$C_4H_8(g) + 6O_2(g) \longrightarrow 4CO_2(g) + 4H_2O + \text{heat of combustion}$$

But slightly less heat per mole is obtained when 2-butene is used, despite the fact that it has the same number of carbons and hydrogens as 1-butene.

The only way by which 2-butene can release less energy is to have less energy initially. Having less energy always means being more stable, so 2-butene must be slightly more stable than 1-butene. None of this explains *why* 2-butene is more stable. The explanation is very complex. The release of less energy when 2-butene burns, as compared to the energy given off when 1-butene burns, is only one piece of experimental support for the generalization we made: that the more-branched alkene is the more stable.

■ When some alcohols undergo dehydration, their carbon skeletons rearrange, but we won't study any examples.

| SPECIAL TOPIC 14.2 | HOW ACIDS CATALYZE THE DEHYDRATION OF ALCOHOLS |

When a strong acid is added to an alcohol, the first chemical event is the ionization of the acid. The reaction is exactly analogous to the ionization of a strong acid when it is added to water; a proton transfers from the acid to the oxygen atom of a solvent molecule. Because sulfuric acid is often used as the catalyst in the dehydration of an alcohol, we will use it to illustrate these reactions. Its ionization in water establishes the following equilibrium, with the products very strongly favored.

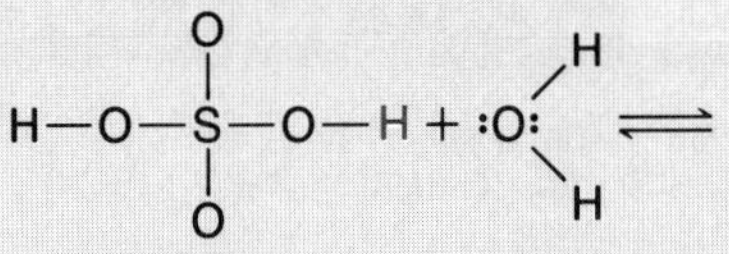

All the covalent bonds to the oxygen atoms in either the hydronium ion or the protonated form of the alcohol are weak, including, in the latter, *the covalent bond to carbon.* This bond is weakened through the work of the catalyst. As ions and molecules bump into one another, some of the ions of the protonated form of the alcohol break up, as we can illustrate using the protonated form of ethyl alcohol.

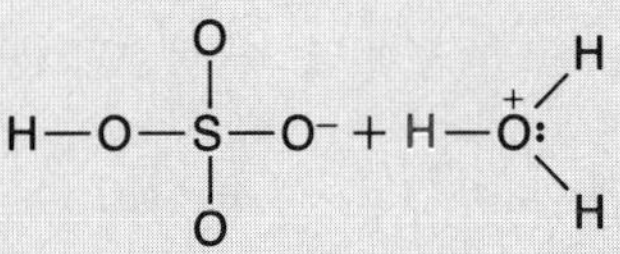

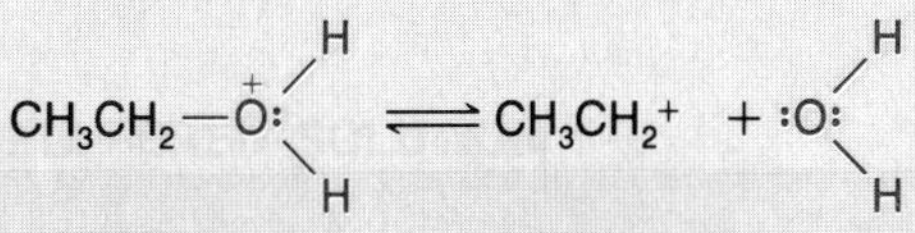

Sulfuric acid   Water

$$CH_3CH_2-\overset{+}{\underset{H}{O}}:H \rightleftharpoons CH_3CH_2^+ + :\overset{H}{\underset{H}{O}}$$

Protonated form   Ethyl
of ethyl alcohol   carbocation

Hydrogen   Hydronium
sulfate ion   ion

The same ionization happens in ethyl alcohol. (Be sure to notice the similarity of this reaction to the previous one.)

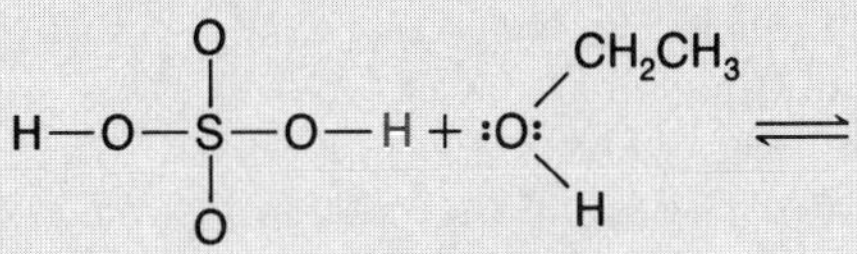

All carbocations are unstable, because a carbon atom does not handle anything less than an octet very well. The octet for carbon in the ethyl carbocation is restored when a proton from the carbon adjacent to the site of the positive charge transfers to a proton acceptor. As this proton transfers, the electron pair of its covalent bond to carbon pivots in to form the second bond of the emerging double bond. It is a smooth, synchronous operation. One acceptor for the proton is the hydrogen sulfate ion, and its acceptance of a proton restores the catalyst, as follows.

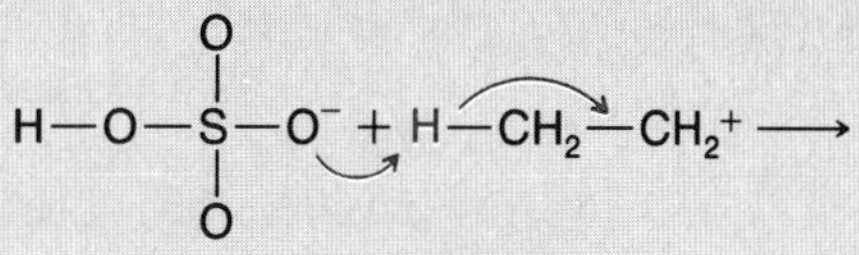

Sulfuric acid   Ethyl
                     alcohol

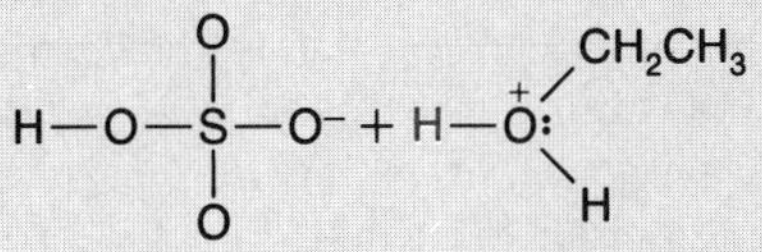

Hydrogen   Ethyl
sulfate ion   carbocation

Hydrogen   Protonated form
sulfate ion   of ethyl alcohol

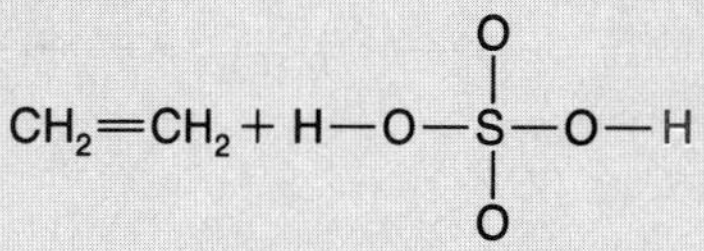

Ethene   Recovered
              catalyst

■ Enzymes are exceedingly selective in what they do and how they control reactions.

This complication of two possible products of dehydration is not a problem when the reaction happens to an alcohol system in the body. Such dehydrations are enzyme-catalyzed, not acid-catalyzed, and enzymes direct reactions in very specific ways. It is even possible for the less stable double bond to be produced when enzymes act.

| EXAMPLE 14.2 | WRITING THE STRUCTURE OF THE ALKENE THAT FORMS WHEN AN ALCOHOL UNDERGOES DEHYDRATION |

Problem: What is the product of the dehydration of isobutyl alcohol?

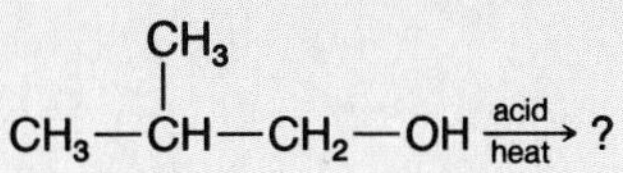

$$CH_3-\overset{CH_3}{\underset{|}{CH}}-CH_2-OH \xrightarrow[\text{heat}]{\text{acid}} ?$$

Solution: All we have to do is rewrite the given structure of the alcohol, except that we leave out the OH group from its carbon, and we omit one H from a carbon that is adjacent to the carbon holding the OH group. Doing this to isobutyl alcohol leaves

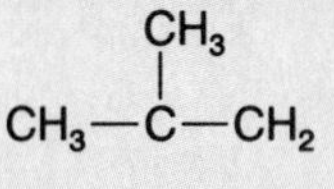

$$\underset{\displaystyle CH_3}{\overset{\displaystyle CH_3}{\underset{|}{C}}}\!\!-\!CH_2 \qquad \text{(Incomplete answer)}$$

Between the two adjacent carbons that lost the H and the OH groups we now have to write in another bond to make a double bond:

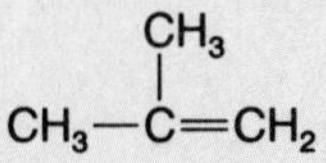

$$\underset{\displaystyle CH_3}{\overset{\displaystyle CH_3}{\underset{|}{C}}}\!\!=\!CH_2 \qquad \text{2-Methylpropene (the answer)}$$

Each carbon now has four bonds, unlike the situation in the incomplete answer.

PRACTICE EXERCISE 5   Write the structures of the alkenes that can be made by the dehydration of the following alcohols.

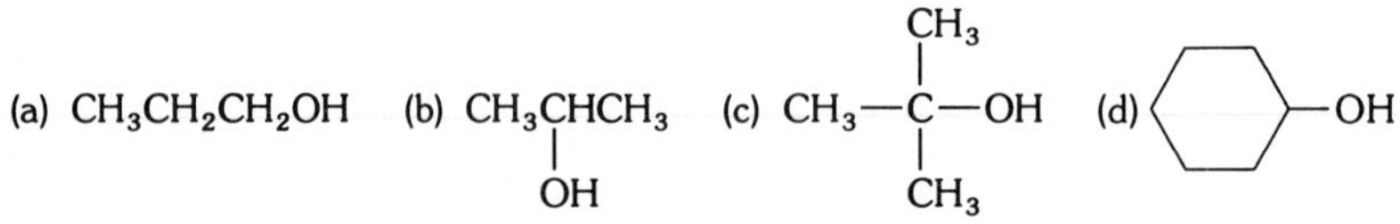

(a) $CH_3CH_2CH_2OH$ (b) $CH_3\underset{|}{\overset{}{C}}HCH_3$ (c) $CH_3\!-\!\underset{\underset{\displaystyle CH_3}{|}}{\overset{\overset{\displaystyle CH_3}{|}}{C}}\!-\!OH$ (d) ⬡—OH

                            OH

1° and 2° Alcohols Are Dehydrogenated by Strong Oxidizing Agents   We learned in an earlier chapter that an oxidation number becomes more positive for a species being oxidized. To use this definition to recognize whether something has been oxidized, however, requires the calculation of oxidation numbers. Organic chemists often use a shortcut, which the following two rules of thumb summarize. With organic compounds

    1 An *oxidation* is the loss of H or the gain of O by a molecule,
    2 A *reduction* is the loss of O or the gain of H by a molecule.

The oxidation of an alcohol is an example of the loss of H. Sometimes, therefore, the reaction is called *dehydrogenation.* Enzymes that catalyze such reactions in living systems are called *dehydrogenases.*

    In studying this reaction, we are particularly interested in the fate of the organic molecule being oxidized. What does it change into? To serve this limited interest, we make two further simplifications. We largely use unbalanced "reaction sequences," not balanced equations, and we use the symbol (O) for any oxidizing agent that can bring about the reaction. Strong oxidizing agents, such as the permanganate ion, MnO_4^-, or the dichromate ion, $Cr_2O_7^{2-}$, are generally needed. In the body, other substances remove hydrogen from alcohols, and we will learn about them later.

    When an oxidizing agent causes an alcohol molecule to lose hydrogen, molecular hydrogen, H_2, does not itself form. Instead, the hydrogen atoms end up in a water molecule whose oxygen atom comes from the oxidizing agent. One H comes from the OH group of the alcohol, and the other H comes from the carbon that has been holding the OH group. Left behind in the organic molecule is a carbon–oxygen double bond. This paragraph and the following sequence describe a new chemical "map sign" concerning alcohols. Study it very carefully.

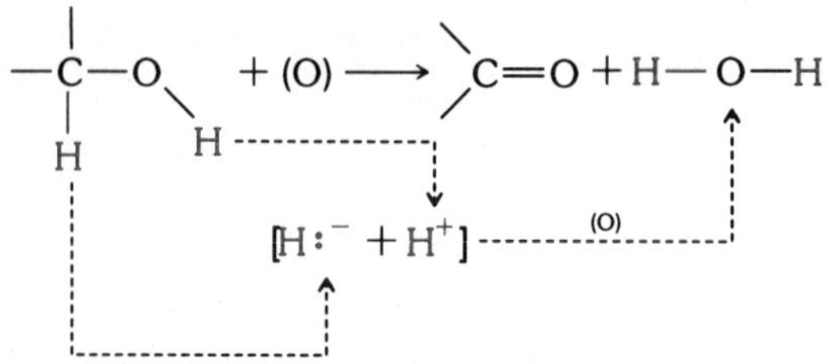

$$-\!\underset{\underset{\displaystyle H}{|}}{\overset{|}{C}}\!-\!O\underset{\displaystyle H}{\diagdown} \;+\;(O)\;\longrightarrow\; \overset{\diagup}{\underset{\diagdown}{C}}\!=\!O \;+\; H\!-\!O\!-\!H$$

$$[H\!:^- + H^+] \cdots\!\!\xrightarrow{\;(O)\;}$$

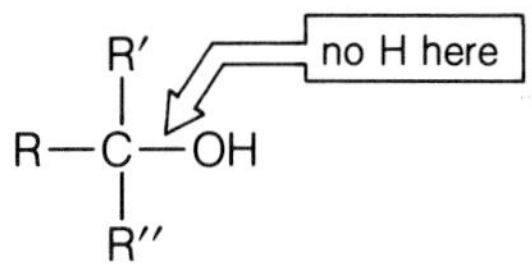

R—C—OH

no H here

3° alcohol system

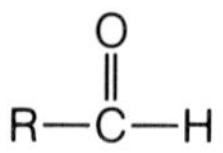

O
‖
R—C—H

Aldehyde

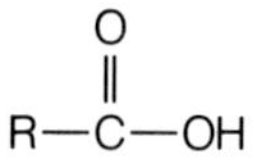

O
‖
R—C—OH

Carboxylic acid

O
‖
R—C—R'

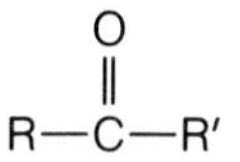

Ketone

3° Alcohols Cannot Be Dehydrogenated
Only 1° and 2° alcohols can be oxidized by this kind of loss of hydrogen. Molecules of 3° alcohols do not have an H atom on the carbon that holds the OH group, so 3° alcohols cannot be oxidized in this way.

1° Alcohols Are Oxidized to Aldehydes or to Carboxylic Acids
The organic product of the oxidation of either a 1° or a 2° alcohol has a carbon–oxygen double bond. Each subclass, however, gives a different organic family as the product. For example, 1° alcohols are oxidized first to aldehydes and then to carboxylic acids. It is difficult to stop the oxidation of a 1° alcohol at the aldehyde stage, because *aldehydes oxidize more easily than alcohols.* In body cells, of course, this is not a problem, because different enzymes are needed for each step. However, in experiments that employ strong oxidizing agents, the oxidation of a 1° alcohol is usually carried out with enough reactant to take the oxidation all the way to the carboxylic acid. These compounds strongly resist further oxidation.

In general,

$$RCH_2OH \xrightarrow[\text{(enzyme-catalyzed)}]{(O)} R-\overset{O}{\underset{\|}{C}}-H + H_2O$$

1° Alcohol   Aldehyde

$$RCH_2OH \xrightarrow[\substack{\text{(by } MnO_4^- \\ \text{in base,} \\ \text{for example)}}]{(O)} (R-\overset{O}{\underset{\|}{C}}-H) \xrightarrow{\text{more (O)}} R-\overset{O}{\underset{\|}{C}}-O^- + MnO_2 + KOH$$

Aldehyde   Anion of a carboxylic acid   Manganese dioxide

Add H⁺

$$R-\overset{O}{\underset{\|}{C}}-OH$$

Carboxylic acid

As the oxidation proceeds, the deep purple color of the permanganate ion gives way as a brown precipitate of manganese dioxide appears. When (O) is the dichromate ion, its bright orange color is replaced by the bright green color of the Cr^{3+} (aq) ion as it oxidizes the alcohol.

$$RCH_2OH + Na_2Cr_2O_7 \xrightarrow{H^+} (R-\overset{O}{\underset{\|}{C}}-H) \xrightarrow{\text{more } Cr_2O_7^{2-}} R-\overset{O}{\underset{\|}{C}}-OH + Cr^{3+}$$

The following are some specific examples of making aldehydes from 1° alcohols.

$$CH_3CH_2CH_2OH \xrightarrow{Cr_2O_7^{2-},\ H^+} CH_3CH_2\overset{O}{\underset{\|}{C}}H$$

1-Propanol (b.p. 97 °C)   Propanal (b.p. 55 °C)

■ The balanced general equation is

$3RCH_2OH + Cr_2O_7^{2-} + 8H^+ \longrightarrow$
$3RCH{=}O + 2Cr^{3+} + 7H_2O$

$$CH_3CH_2CH_2CH_2OH \xrightarrow{Cr_2O_7^{2-},\ H^+} CH_3CH_2CH_2\overset{O}{\underset{\|}{C}}H$$

1-Butanol (b.p. 118 °C)   Butanal (b.p. 82 °C)

These oxidations can be stopped at the aldehyde stage because an aldehyde boils so much lower than its parent alcohol that it can be boiled out of the reaction mixture as soon as it forms. This removes the aldehyde from the oxidizing agent, so it is not further oxidized.

However, it is *easy* to make the oxidation of a 1° alcohol go to the carboxylic acid stage, as in the next example. All it takes is enough oxidizing agent, as you can see by comparing the balanced equations shown in the margin.

■ The balanced general equation is

$$3RCH_2OH + 2Cr_2O_7^{2-} + 16H^+ \longrightarrow$$
$$3RCO_2H + 4Cr^{3+} + 11H_2O$$

$$CH_3CH_2CH_2OH \xrightarrow{Cr_2O_7^{2-},\ H^+} CH_3CH_2\overset{\displaystyle O}{\overset{\|}{C}}OH$$

1-Propanol   Propanoic acid

| **EXAMPLE 14.3** | **WRITING THE STRUCTURE OF THE PRODUCT OF THE OXIDATION OF A PRIMARY ALCOHOL** |

Problem: What aldehyde and what carboxylic acid could be made by the oxidation of ethyl alcohol?

Solution: First, write the structure of the given alcohol:

$$CH_3-CH_2-OH$$

Then either cross out or erase the H on the OH group, and reduce by one the number of H atoms on the carbon that holds the OH group. When we do this to ethyl alcohol, we have

$$CH_3-CH-O \qquad \text{(Incomplete structure)}$$

Finally, we make the carbon–oxygen bond a double bond. Thus the aldehyde that forms is

$$CH_3-CH{=}O \quad \text{or} \quad CH_3-\overset{\displaystyle O}{\overset{\|}{C}}-H \qquad \text{(Ethanal)}$$

The second way of writing the structure of the product might make it easier to solve the second part of the problem: write the structure of the carboxylic acid that can be made from ethyl alcohol. This structure is most easily written by inserting an oxygen atom between the carbon atom of the C=O group in ethanal and the H atom attached to it:

$$CH_3-\overset{\displaystyle O}{\overset{\|}{C}}\overset{\curvearrowleft O}{-H} \longrightarrow CH_3-\overset{\displaystyle O}{\overset{\|}{C}}-O-H \quad \text{(Acetic acid)}$$

PRACTICE EXERCISE 6   Write the structures of the aldehydes and carboxylic acids that can be made by the oxidation of the following alcohols.

(a) $CH_3-\overset{\displaystyle CH_3}{\overset{|}{CH}}-CH_2-OH$ (b) 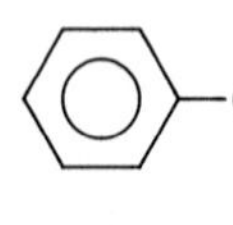 $\langle\bigcirc\rangle{-}CH_2-OH$ (c) CH_3-OH

Secondary Alcohols Are Oxidized to Ketones.   Ketones strongly resist further oxidation, so they are easily made by the oxidation of 2° alcohols using strong oxidizing agents like MnO_4^- or $Cr_2O_7^{2-}$.

In general, for 2° alcohols,

$$R-\overset{\displaystyle OH}{\overset{|}{C}H}-R' + (O) \longrightarrow R-\overset{\displaystyle O}{\overset{\|}{C}}-R' + H_2O$$

2° alcohol   Ketone

Specific examples are

$$\underset{\text{2-Butanol}}{\text{CH}_3\overset{\text{OH}}{\underset{|}{\text{CH}}}\text{CH}_2\text{CH}_3} \xrightarrow{\text{Cr}_2\text{O}_7{}^{2-},\ \text{H}^+} \underset{\text{Butanone}}{\text{CH}_3\overset{\text{O}}{\overset{||}{\text{C}}}\text{CH}_2\text{CH}_3}$$

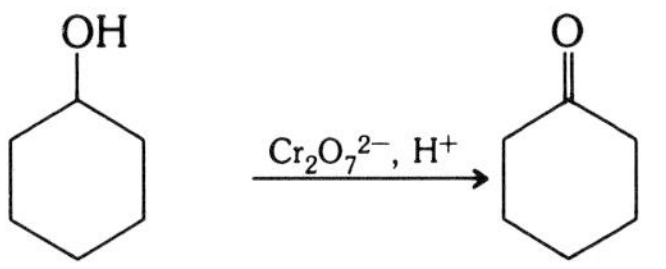

Cyclohexanol → Cyclohexanone ($\text{Cr}_2\text{O}_7{}^{2-}$, H^+)

| EXAMPLE 14.4 | **WRITING THE STRUCTURE OF THE PRODUCT OF THE OXIDATION OF A SECONDARY ALCOHOL** |

Problem: What ketone forms when 2-propanol is oxidized?

Solution: We work this essentially as we worked Example 14.3. We start with the structure of the given alcohol, and then we cross out or erase the H on the —OH group and the H on the carbon that is holding this —OH group.

$$\text{CH}_3-\overset{\text{OH}}{\underset{|}{\text{CH}}}-\text{CH}_3 \longrightarrow \text{CH}_3-\overset{\text{O}}{\underset{|}{\text{C}}}-\text{CH}_3 \quad \text{(Incomplete answer)}$$

Then we make the bond to oxygen a double bond.

■ The name chemists always use for propanone is *acetone*.

$$\text{CH}_3-\overset{\text{O}}{\overset{||}{\text{C}}}-\text{CH}_3 \quad \text{(Acetone, or propanone)}$$

PRACTICE EXERCISE 7

Write the structures of the ketones that can be made by the oxidation of the following alcohols.

(a) $\text{CH}_3-\overset{\text{OH}}{\underset{|}{\text{CH}}}-\text{CH}_2\text{CH}_3$ (b) [benzene ring]$-\overset{\text{OH}}{\underset{|}{\text{CH}}}-\text{CH}_3$ (c) [cyclopentane ring]$-\text{OH}$

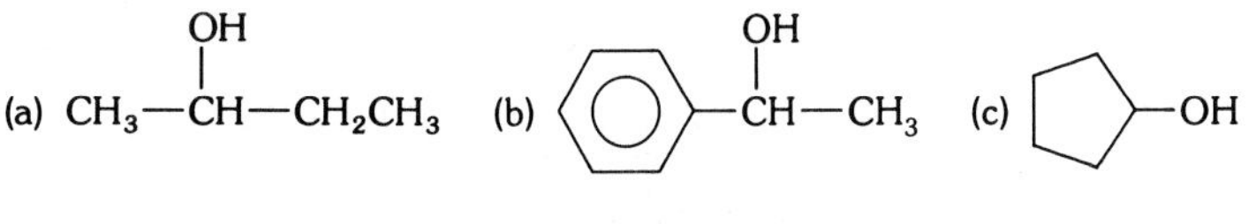

PRACTICE EXERCISE 8

What are the products of the oxidation of the following alcohols? If the alcohol is a 1° alcohol, show the structures of both the aldehyde and the carboxylic acid that could be made, depending on the conditions. If the alcohol cannot be oxidized, write "no reaction."

(a) $\text{CH}_3\overset{\text{CH}_3}{\underset{|}{\text{CH}}}\text{CH}_2\text{CH}_2\text{OH}$ (b) $\text{HO}-\overset{\text{CH}_3}{\underset{\underset{\text{CH}_3}{|}}{\overset{|}{\text{C}}}}-\text{CH}_3$

(c) $\text{CH}_3\overset{\text{CH}_3}{\underset{\underset{\text{CH}_3}{|}}{\overset{|}{\text{C}}}}\text{CH}_2\text{OH}$ (d) $\text{CH}_3\overset{\text{CH}_3}{\underset{|}{\text{CH}}}-\overset{\text{OH}}{\underset{|}{\text{CH}}}-\text{CH}_3$

Hydrogen-Acceptors, Not Suppliers of Oxygen, Oxidize 1° and 2° Alcohols in Living Systems Oxidations (dehydrogenations) of 1° and 2° alcohol groups and the oxidation of an aldehyde group are very common kinds of reactions in *intermediary metabolism,* the kinds of reactions that happen to the products of digestion. As far as the *organic* species is concerned, there is no difference between these oxidations and those carried out using MnO_4^- or $Cr_2O_7^{2-}$. What we have just learned works to predict the *organic* products. There is a difference otherwise, of course, because cells cannot tolerate species like MnO_4^- or $Cr_2O_7^{2-}$. They are just too indiscriminate and difficult to control (as well as being poisonous).

Hydrogen is removed from an alcohol inside living cells in an exquisitely controlled way, by the transfer of the *pieces* of $H:H$. An oxidizing enzyme, a dehydrogenase, accepts $H:^-$ from the CH unit that holds the OH group in the alcohol, and this gives the reduced form of the enzyme. The H^+ piece slips away from the OH group. Sometimes it simply enters the buffer system. Sometimes the oxidizing enzyme accepts it, too. We'll leave details to later chapters. Our point here is to help you get started in seeing similarities and differences in the kinds of reactions run in glass vessels and those taking place in living systems, and to begin to see reasons for the differences.

14.4 THIOALCOHOLS AND DISULFIDES

Both the SH group, an easily oxidized group, and the S—S system, an easily reduced group, are present in molecules of proteins.

■ *Mercaptan* is a contraction of *mercury-capturer*. Compounds with SH groups form precipitates with mercury ions.

Alcohols, R—O—H, can be viewed as alkyl derivatives of water, H—O—H. Similar derivatives of hydrogen sulfide, H—S—H, are also known, and are in the family called the **thioalcohols** or the **mercaptans.**

$$R—S—H \qquad R—S—R' \qquad R—S—S—R'$$

Thioalcohols Thioethers Disulfides
(mercaptans)

The SH group is variously called the thiol group, the mercaptan group, or the sulfhydryl group.

Table 14.3 gives the IUPAC names and structures of a few thioalcohols. (We will not study the IUPAC nomenclature as a separate topic because it is straightforward, and because our interest in thioalcohols is limited just to one reaction.) Some very important properties of proteins depend on the presence of the SH group, which is contributed to protein structure by one of the building blocks of proteins, the amino acid called cysteine (Table 14.3).

■ Lower-formula-weight thioalcohols are present in and are responsible for the considerable respect usually given to skunks.

Dialkyl derivatives of water, the ethers (R—O—R'), have their sulfur counterparts, too, the thioethers. (You can see that the prefix *thio-* indicates the replacement of an oxygen atom by a sulfur atom.) Although proteins also have the thioether system, our studies will not require that we learn anything of the chemistry of this group, and we will say no more about it.

TABLE 14.3 Some Common Thioalcohols

Name	Structure	Boiling Point (°C)
Methanethiol	CH_3SH	6
Ethanethiol	CH_3CH_2SH	36
1-Propanethiol	$CH_3CH_2CH_2SH$	68
1-Butanethiol	$CH_3CH_2CH_2CH_2SH$	98
Cysteine (a monomer for proteins)	$^+NH_3—CH—\overset{\overset{O}{\|\|}}{C}—O^-$ $\|$ $CH_2—SH$	(Solid)

Thioalcohols Are Oxidized to Disulfides   The one reaction of thioalcohols that will be important in our study of proteins is oxidation. Thioalcohols can be oxidized to **disulfides,** compounds whose molecules have two sulfur atoms joined by a covalent bond, R—S—S—R′.

In general,

$$R—S—H \quad H—S—R + (O) \longrightarrow R—S—S—R + H_2O$$

Two molecules of   One molecule
a thioalcohol   of a disulfide

A specific example is

$$2CH_3SH + (O) \longrightarrow CH_3—S—S—CH_3 + H_2O$$

Methanethiol   Dimethyl disulfide

EXAMPLE 14.5   **WRITING THE PRODUCT OF THE OXIDATION OF A THIOALCOHOL**

Problem: What is the product of the oxidation of ethanethiol?

Solution: Because the oxidation of the SH group generates the S—S group, begin simply by writing this group down.

$$S—S$$

Then attach the alkyl group from the thioalcohol, one on each sulfur atom. Ethanethiol furnishes ethyl groups, so the answer is

$$CH_3CH_2—S—S—CH_2CH_3 \quad \text{(Diethyl disulfide)}$$

If the problem had called for an equation, we would have had to use the coefficient of 2 for the ethanethiol.

$$2CH_3CH_2SH + (O) \longrightarrow CH_3CH_2—S—S—CH_2CH_3 + H_2O$$

However, this coefficient isn't necessary when all we are asked to do is to write the structure of the disulfide that can be made by the oxidation of ethanethiol. Always remember that balancing an equation comes *after* you have written the correct formulas for the reactants and products.

Disulfides Are Reduced to Thioalcohols   The sulfur–sulfur bond in disulfides is very easily reduced, and the products are molecules of the thioalcohols from which the disulfide could be made. We will use the symbol (H) to represent any reducing agent that can do the task, just as we used (O) for an oxidizing agent.

In general,

$$R—S—S—R + 2(H) \longrightarrow R—S—H + H—S—R$$

One molecule   Two molecules of
of disulfide   a thioalcohol

A specific example is

$$CH_3CH_2—S—S—CH_2CH_2CH_3 + 2(H) \longrightarrow$$
$$CH_3CH_2—S—H + H—S—CH_2CH_2CH_3$$

EXAMPLE 14.6   **WRITING THE PRODUCT OF THE REDUCTION OF A DISULFIDE**

Problem: What forms when the following disulfide reacts with a reducing agent?

$$CH_3—S—S—CH_2CH_3$$

Solution: The easiest approach is simply to split the disulfide molecule between the two sulfur atoms:

$$CH_3—S—S—CH_2CH_3 \longrightarrow CH_3—S + S—CH_2CH_3 \quad \text{(Incomplete)}$$

Then attach one H to each sulfur to make the SH groups.

$$CH_3—S—H + H—S—CH_2CH_3 \quad \text{(The answers)}$$
$$\text{Methanethiol} \qquad \text{Ethanethiol}$$

PRACTICE EXERCISE 9   Complete the following equations by writing the structures of the products that form. If no reaction occurs (insofar as we have studied organic chemistry), write "no reaction."

(a) $CH_3—S—S—CH_3 + (H) \longrightarrow ?$ (b) $CH_3—CH—CH_3 + (O) \longrightarrow ?$
$$\qquad\qquad\qquad\qquad\qquad\qquad\qquad\qquad | $$
$$\qquad\qquad\qquad\qquad\qquad\qquad\qquad SH$$

(c) 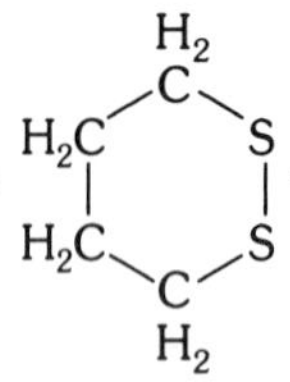 $+ (H) \longrightarrow ?$ (d) 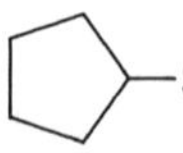 —SH $+ (O) \longrightarrow ?$

14.5 PHENOLS

Phenols are weak acids that can neutralize sodium hydroxide, and their benzene rings are easily oxidized.

In **phenols,** the OH group is attached to a benzene ring, and phenols are widespread in nature and in commerce. The simplest member of this family is called phenol, and it is a raw material for making aspirin. Vanillin, a flavoring agent, is both an aldehyde and a phenol. Tyrosine, one of the amino acids the body uses to make proteins, is also a phenol. Special Topic 14.3 describes some other phenols.

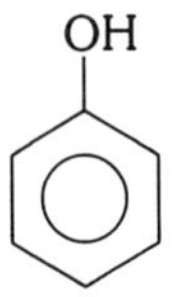

Phenol 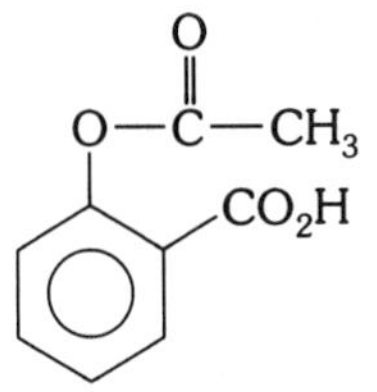   Aspirin 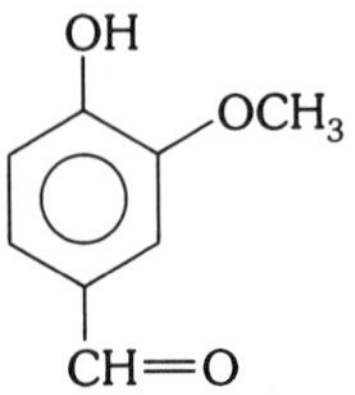   Vanillin 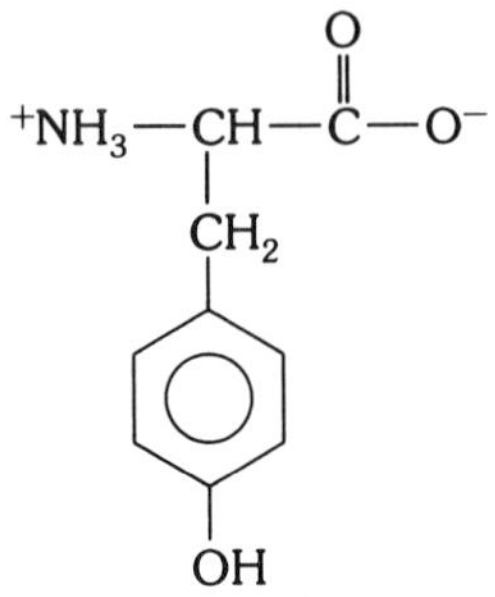   Tyrosine

Phenols Are Weak Acids   In sharp contrast to alcohols, phenols are acidic. They are *weak* acids, but they can still neutralize the hydroxide ion. For example,

Phenol (carbolic acid). Phenol, as we have already noted, was the first antiseptic to be used by Joseph Lister, an English surgeon. It kills bacteria by denaturing their proteins — that is, by destroying the abilities of their proteins to function normally. (Interestingly, phenol does not denature nucleic acids, the chemicals of heredity.) Phenol, however, is dangerous to healthy tissue, because it is a general protoplasmic poison, so other antiseptics have been developed since Lister's time.

BHA and **BHT.** BHA and BHT are widely used as antioxidants in gasoline, lubricating oils, rubber, edible fats and oils, and materials used for packaging foods that might

turn rancid. Being phenols and therefore easily oxidized themselves, they act by interfering with oxidations of the materials they are designed to protect.

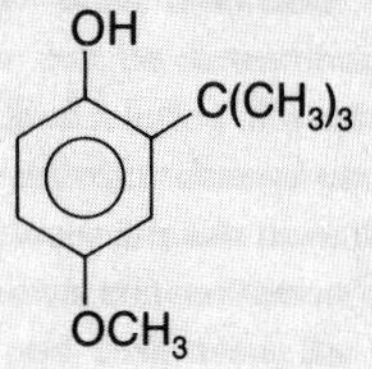

BHA (butylated hydroxy anisole)

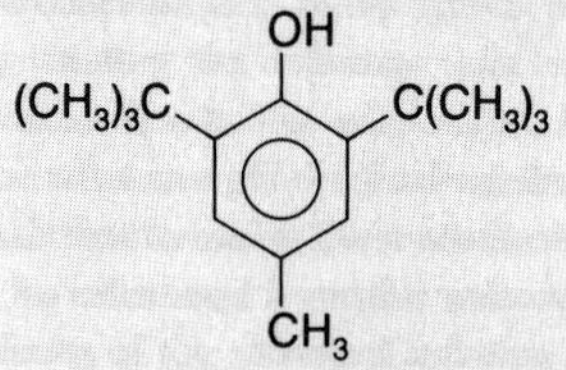

BHT (butylated hydroxy toluene)

■ For phenol itself, $K_a = 1.0 \times 10^{-10}$ (25 °C), which can be compared to $K_a = 1.8 \times 10^{-5}$ for acetic acid.

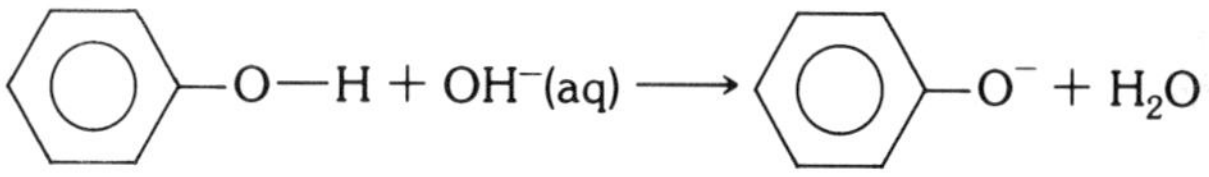

Phenol

Phenoxide ion

Understanding why OH^- can take H^+ from phenol but not from an alcohol comes down to considering what makes the phenoxide ion more stable than the corresponding anion of an alcohol, RO^-. Both anions appear to have one negative charge on oxygen. What the structures do not reveal, however, is that the negative charge on the phenoxide ion is somewhat spread out into the pi-electron network of the benzene ring. The surest way to stabilize negative charge is to spread it out, and the negative charge on neither HO^- nor RO^- can be spread out as it is in the phenoxide ion. HO^- and RO^-, therefore, are less stable and form to a lesser extent than the phenoxide ion, so $HO-H$ and $RO-H$ are extremely poor proton-donors compared to phenol.

The Ring in Phenols Is Easily Oxidized   Some of the electron density on the oxygen in phenol also spreads out over the pi-electron network of the ring. Oxidizing agents are electron-seekers, so this makes the benzene ring in a phenol more easily oxidized than the ring in benzene. Oxidations of phenols, however, produce complex mixtures that include some highly colored compounds. Even phenol crystals left exposed to air slowly turn dark because the oxygen in the air can attack phenol. In the body, special hydroxylating enzymes steer the oxidations of the benzene ring in phenols to specific products. We will encounter such reactions later.

Phenols Are Not Dehydrated   Unlike alcohols, phenols cannot be dehydrated. Dehydration would put a *triple* bond into a six-membered ring, and such a ring is too small to accommodate the linear geometry at a triple bond with its bond angles of 180°.

14.6   ETHERS

The ethers are almost as chemically unreactive as the alkanes.

Ethers are compounds in whose molecules two organic groups are joined to the same oxygen atom, and their family structure is $R-O-R'$. The two groups can be almost anything except that the carbon joined to the central oxygen atom cannot be the one in $C=O$. The first three compounds given below are ethers, but methyl acetate is in the ester family, not the ether family. (We will study esters in a later chapter.)

| SPECIAL TOPIC 14.4 | SOME IMPORTANT ETHERS |

Diethyl Ether ("ether"). Diethyl ether is a colorless, volatile liquid with a pungent, somewhat irritating odor, and it was once widely used as an anesthetic. It acts as a depressant for the central nervous system and as somewhat of a stimulant for the sympathetic system. It exerts an effect on nearly all tissues of the body.

Because mixtures of ether and air in the right proportions can explode, anesthesiologists avoid using it as an anesthetic whenever possible.

Divinyl Ether (vinethene). Divinyl ether is another anesthetic, but it also forms an explosive mixture in air. Its anesthetic action is more rapid than that of diethyl ether.

Methyl t-Butyl Ether. The standard treatment for stones in the gallbladder or the gallbladder duct has been surgical

removal of the gallbladder. Medical scientists have long sought a safe way to dissolve the stones where they are, and they have known that a chief constituent of these stones is cholesterol. Cholesterol, as we have already learned, is mostly hydrocarbon-like, so the search has been for a relatively nonpolar solvent for cholesterol that could therefore dissolve the stones without causing serious side effects, and that would be at least as safe as the surgical treatment. In the mid-1980s, medical scientists at the Mayo Clinic found that methyl t-butyl ether worked rapidly and well for this purpose. This ether is less toxic than diethyl ether, it can be inserted into the gallbladder by a catheter, it remains a liquid at body temperature, and it works in just a few hours with no evidence of disagreeable side effects.

$CH_3CH_2-O-CH_2CH_3$ $CH_3-O-\bigcirc$ $\bigcirc-O-\bigcirc$ $CH_3-\overset{\overset{\displaystyle O}{\|}}{C}-O-CH_3$

Diethyl ether   Methyl phenyl ether 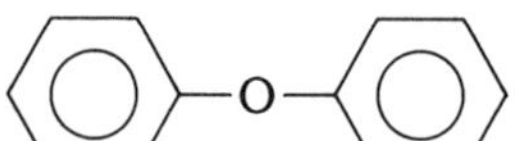   Diphenyl ether 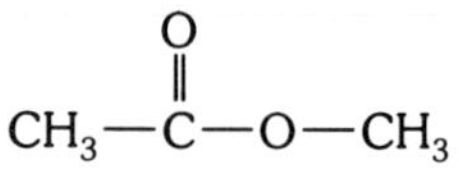   Methyl acetate (an ester, not an ether)

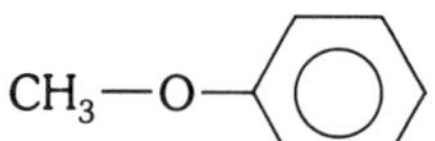

Table 14.4 gives some examples of ethers, and three are described in Special Topic 14.4, including methyl t-butyl ether, which has been used in an interesting way to remove gallstones.

The common names of ethers are made by naming the groups attached to the oxygen and adding the word *ether*, as illustrated in Table 14.4.

Ethers Cannot Donate Hydrogen Bonds   Because the ether group cannot donate hydrogen bonds, the boiling points of simple ethers are more like those of the alkanes of

TABLE 14.4 Some Ethers

Common Name	Structure	Boiling Point (°C)
Dimethyl ether	CH_3OCH_3	−23
Methyl ethyl ether	$CH_3OCH_2CH_3$	11
Methyl t-butyl ether	$CH_3OC(CH_3)_3$	55.2
Diethyl ether	$CH_3CH_2OCH_2CH_3$	34.5
Dipropyl ether	$CH_3CH_2CH_2OCH_2CH_2CH_3$	91
Methyl phenyl ether	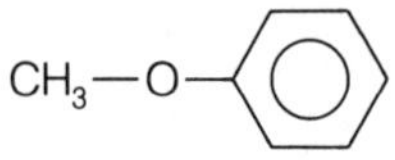 $CH_3-O-\bigcirc$	155
Diphenyl ether	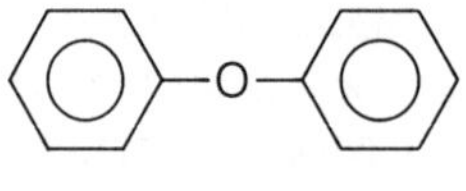 $\bigcirc-O-\bigcirc$	259
Divinyl ether	$CH_2{=}CHOCH{=}CH_2$	29

Compound	Boiling Point (°C)
Pentane	36
Diethyl ether	35
1-Butanol	118

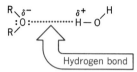

Figure 14.3
An ether molecule can accept a hydrogen bond from a water molecule. (The δ^- end of a hydrogen bond is the acceptor end.)

comparable formula weights than those of the alcohols. The oxygen of the ether group can accept hydrogen bonds (Figure 14.3), however, so ethers are more soluble in water than alkanes. For example, both 1-butanol and its isomer, diethyl ether, dissolve in water to the extent of about 8 g/100 mL, but pentane is completely insoluble in water.

Ethers Resemble Alkanes, Chemically   At room temperature, ethers do not react with strong acids, bases, or oxidizing or reducing agents. Like all organic compounds, they burn. We will learn no reactions of ethers, but we must be able to recognize this group and remember that it is not very reactive, particularly in the environment within the body.

Ethers Can Be Made from Alcohols   We learned earlier in this chapter that alcohols can be dehydrated by the action of heat and an acid catalyst to give alkenes. The precise temperature that works best has to be discovered experimentally for each alcohol, because if the temperature is not set correctly, a different pathway for dehydration can occur. Water can split out *between* two alcohol molecules rather than from within one molecule, and the product is an ether.
      In general,

$$R\!-\!O\!-\!H + H\!-\!O\!-\!R \xrightarrow{\text{acid catalyst}} R\!-\!O\!-\!R + H_2O$$

Two alcohol molecules   Ether

A specific example is

$$2CH_3CH_2OH \xrightarrow[\text{140 °C}]{H_2SO_4} CH_3CH_2\!-\!O\!-\!CH_2CH_3 + H_2O$$

Ethyl alcohol   Diethyl ether

■ Earlier we learned that concentrated H_2SO_4 acts on ethanol to give ethene when the temperature is 170 °C.

The dehydration that produces an ether usually requires a lower temperature than that which gives an alkene, but we won't need the details. Our interest is simply in the *possibility* of making an ether from an alcohol as well as the structure of the ether that can be made.

EXAMPLE 14.7

WRITING THE STRUCTURE OF AN ETHER THAT CAN FORM FROM AN ALCOHOL

Problem: If the conditions are right, 1-butanol can be converted to an ether. What is the structure of this ether?

Solution: What this questions asks is to complete the following reaction:

$$CH_3CH_2CH_2CH_2OH \xrightarrow[\text{heat}]{\text{acid catalyst}} \text{?}$$

As usual, the structure of the starting material gives us most of the answer. We know that the ether must get its organic groups from the alcohol, so to write the structure of the ether we write one O atom with two bonds from it:

$$-\text{O}-$$

Then we attach the alkyl group of the alcohol, one to each of the bonds:

$$CH_3CH_2CH_2CH_2\!-\!O\!-\!CH_2CH_2CH_2CH_3$$

Of course, we need *two* molecules of the alcohol to make one molecule of this ether, but always remember, *we balance an equation after we have written the correct formulas for reactants and products.* Remembering that water is the other product, we have as the balanced equation

$$2CH_3CH_2CH_2CH_2OH \xrightarrow[\text{heat}]{\text{acid catalyst}} CH_3CH_2CH_2CH_2-O-CH_2CH_2CH_2CH_3 + H_2O$$

1-Butanol   Dibutyl ether

PRACTICE EXERCISE 10   Write the structures of the ethers to which the following alcohols can be converted.

(a) CH_3OH (b) $CH_3CH_2CH_2OH$ (c) 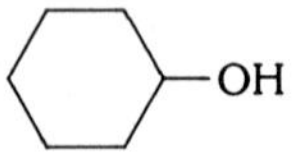 ⬡—OH

SUMMARY

Alcohols The alcohol system has an OH group attached to a saturated carbon. The IUPAC names of simple alcohols end in *-ol*, and their chains are numbered to give precedence to the location of the OH group. The common names have the word *alcohol* following the name of the alkyl group.

Alcohol molecules hydrogen-bond to each other and to water molecules. By the action of heat and an acid catalyst they can be dehydrated internally to give carbon–carbon double bonds or externally to give ethers. Primary alcohols can be oxidized to aldehydes and to carboxylic acids. Secondary alcohols can be oxidized to ketones. Tertiary alcohols cannot be oxidized (without breaking up the carbon chain). The OH group in alcohols does not function as either an acid or a base in the ordinary sense.

Thioalcohols The thioalcohols or mercaptans, R—S—H, are

easily oxidized to disulfides, R—S—S—R, and these are easily reduced back to the original thioalcohols.

Phenols When the OH group is attached to a benzene ring, the system is the phenol system, and it is now acidic enough to neutralize strong bases. The ring is vulnerable to oxidizing agents.

Ethers The ether system, R—O—R′, does not react at room temperature or body temperature with strong acids, bases, oxidizing agents, or reducing agents. It can accept hydrogen bonds but cannot donate them.

Reactions studied Without attempting to present balanced equations, or even all of the inorganic products, we can summarize the reactions studied in this chapter as follows.

Alcohols

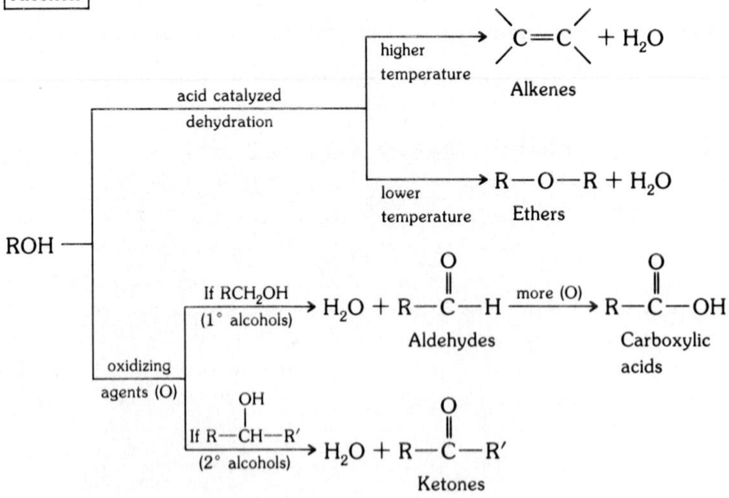

Thioalcohols and Disulfides

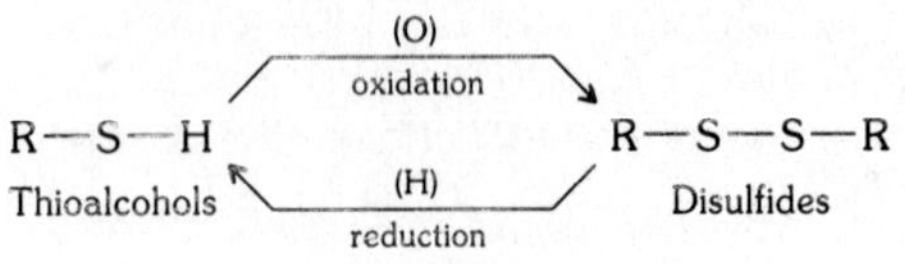

Phenols

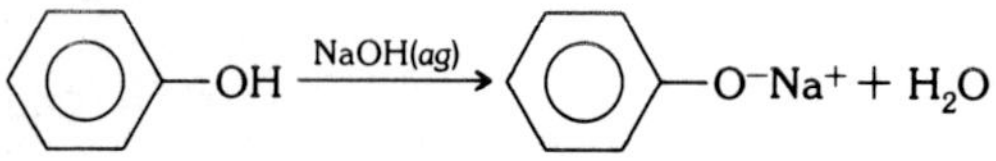

REVIEW EXERCISES

The answers to all Review Exercises are in the *Study Guide* that accompanies this book.

Functional Groups

14.1 Name the functional groups to which the arrows point in the structure of eugenol, an oily liquid sometimes used as a substitute for oil of cloves in formulating fragrances and perfumes.

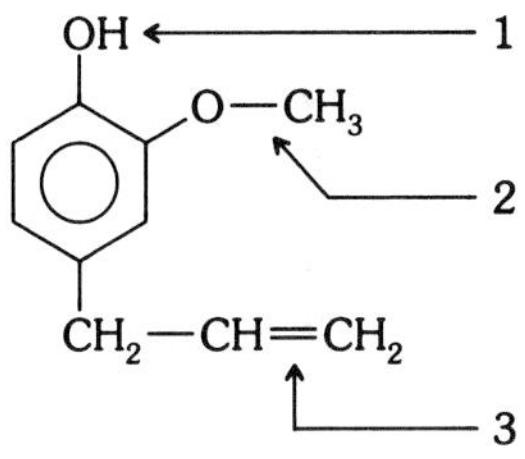

Eugenol

14.2 What are the functional groups to which the arrows point in the structure of geranial, a constituent of oil of lemon grass?

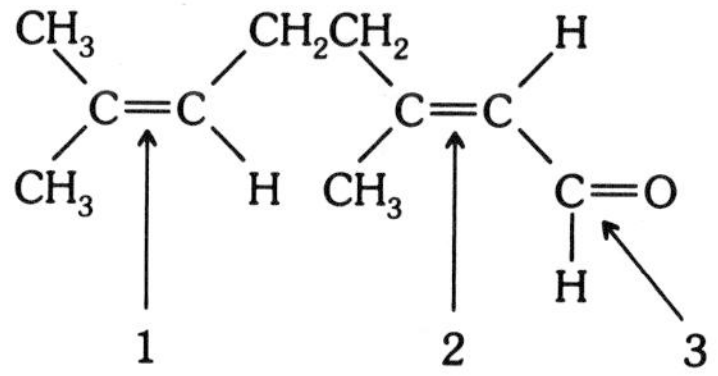

Geranial

14.3 Name the functional groups to which the arrows point in the structure of cortisone, a drug used in treating certain forms of arthritis. If a group is an alcohol, state if it is a 1°, 2°, or 3° alcohol.

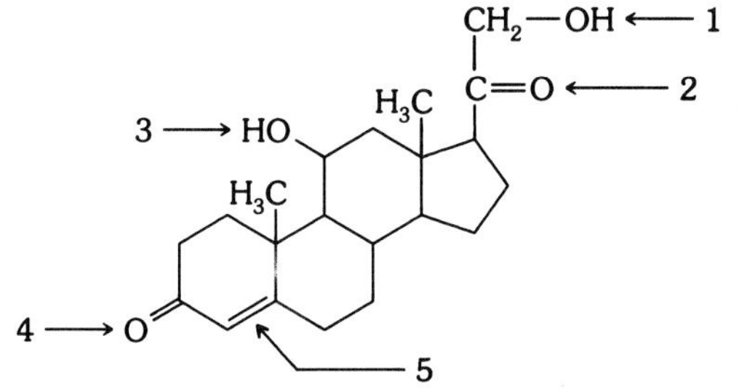

Cortisone

14.4 Give the names of the functional groups to which the arrows point in prostaglandin E_1, one of a family of compounds that are smooth muscle stimulants.

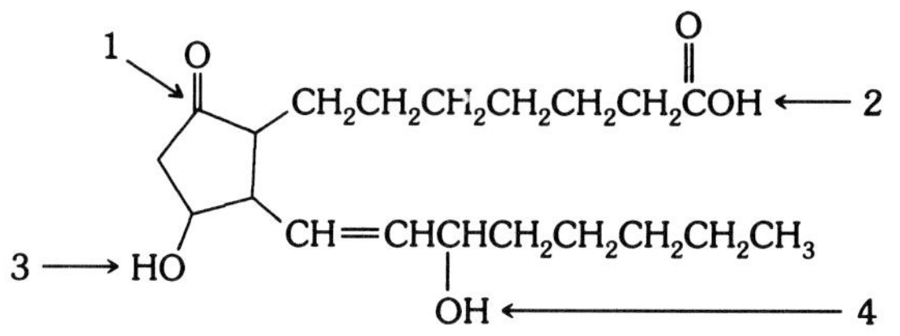

Prostaglandin E_1

Structures and Names

14.5 Write the structure of each compound.
(a) isobutyl alcohol (b) isopropyl alcohol
(c) propyl alcohol   (d) glycerol

14.6 Write the structures of the following compounds.
(a) methyl alcohol (b) *t*-butyl alcohol
(c) ethyl alcohol   (d) butyl alcohol

14.7 Give the common names of the following compounds.

(a) CH_3CHCH_3 (b) $HOCH_2CH_2OH$
       |
       OH

(c) $CH_3-\overset{\overset{CH_3}{|}}{\underset{\underset{CH_3}{|}}{C}}-OH$ (d) $HOCH_2CHCH_2OH$
                                                          |
                                                          OH

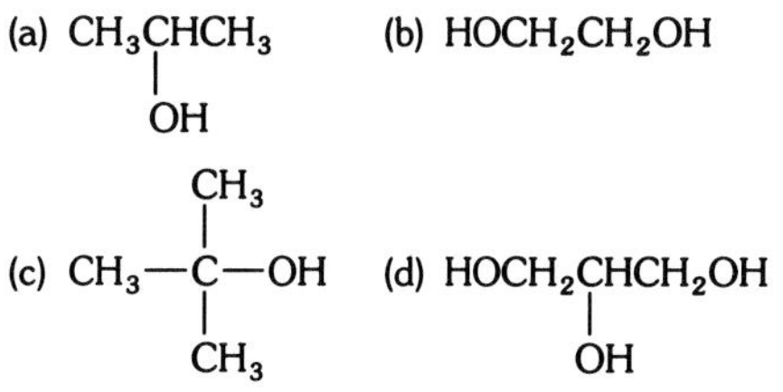

14.8 What are the common names of the following compounds?

(a) CH_3CH_2OH (b) $CH_3CH_2CH_2OH$
(c) $HOCH_2CHCH_3$ (d) $HOCH_2CH_2CH_2CH_3$
           |
           CH_3

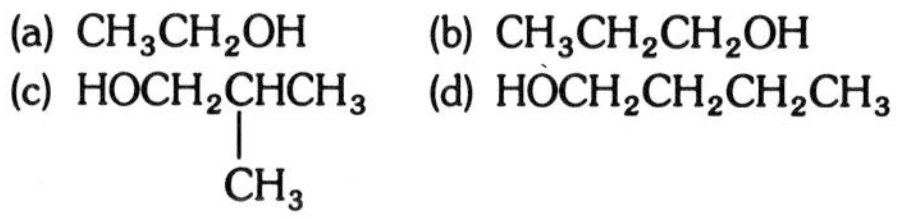

14.9 What is the structure and the IUPAC name of the simplest, stable dihydric alcohol?

14.10 Give the structure and the IUPAC name of the simplest, stable trihydric alcohol.

14.11 Give the IUPAC names for the compounds listed in Review Exercise 14.5.

14.12 What are the IUPAC names for the compounds given in Review Exercise 14.6?

14.13 Provide the IUPAC names for the compounds in Review Exercise 14.7.

14.14 What are the IUPAC names for the structures given in Review Exercise 14.8?

14.15 Write the IUPAC name of the following compound.

$$CH_3CH_2\overset{\overset{CH_3}{|}}{CH}CH-\overset{\overset{CH_3}{|}}{CH}CH_3$$
$$\underset{|}{}$$
$$CH_2OH$$

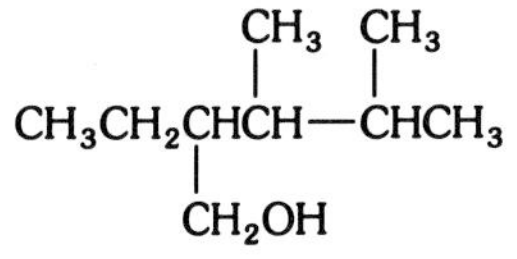

14.16 Write the IUPAC name of the following compound.

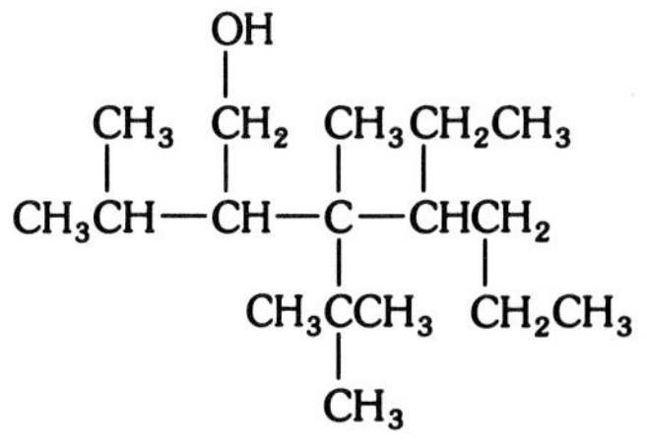

Physical Properties

14.17 Draw a figure that illustrates a hydrogen bond between two molecules of ethyl alcohol. Use a dotted line to represent this bond, and write in the $\delta-$ and $\delta+$ symbols where they belong.

14.18 When ethyl alcohol dissolves in water, its molecules slip into the hydrogen-bonding network in water. Draw a figure that illustrates this. Use dotted lines for hydrogen bonds, and place $\delta-$ and $\delta+$ symbols where they belong.

14.19 Arrange the following compounds in their order of increasing boiling points. Place the letter symbol of the compound that has the lowest boiling point on the left end of the series, and arrange the remaining letters in the correct order.

$$\underset{\text{A}}{CH_3\overset{\underset{|}{OH}}{C}HCH_2CH_3} \qquad \underset{\text{B}}{CH_3CH_2CH_2CH_2CH_2CH_3}$$

$$\underset{\text{C}}{CH_3\overset{\underset{|}{HO}}{C}H-\overset{\underset{|}{OH}}{C}H_2} \qquad \underset{\text{D}}{CH_3-O-CH_3}$$

$$\underline{\qquad < \qquad < \qquad < \qquad}$$

Lowest   Highest
b.p.   b.p.

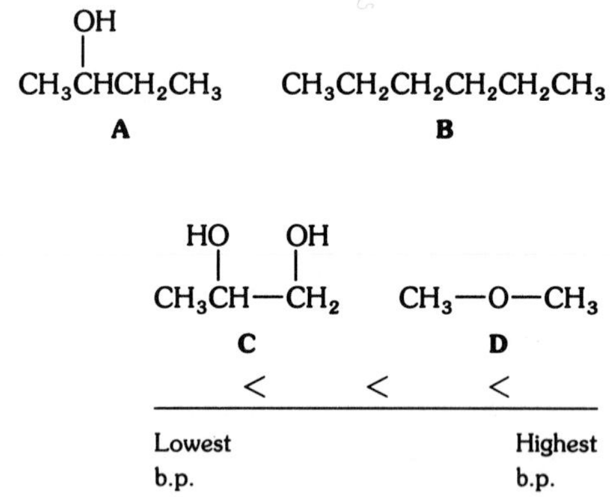

14.20 Arrange the following compounds in their order of increasing solubility in water. Place the letter symbol of the compound with the least solubility on the left end of the series, and arrange the remaining letters in the correct order.

$$\underset{\text{A}}{CH_3\overset{\underset{|}{HO}}{C}H\overset{\underset{|}{OH}}{C}HCHCH_3}\,\underset{|}{OH} \qquad \underset{\text{B}}{CH_3CH_2\overset{\underset{|}{OH}}{C}HCH_2CH_3} \qquad \underset{\text{C}}{CH_3CH_2CH_2CH_2CH_3}$$

$$\underline{\qquad < \qquad\qquad < \qquad}$$

Least   Most
soluble   soluble

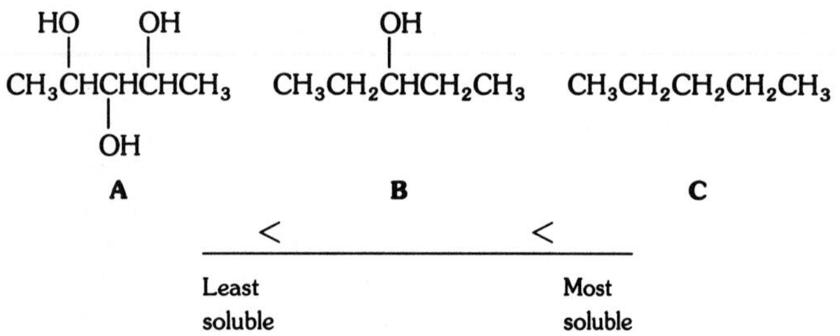

Chemical Properties of Alcohols

14.21 Write the structures of the alkenes that form when the following alcohols undergo acid-catalyzed dehydration.

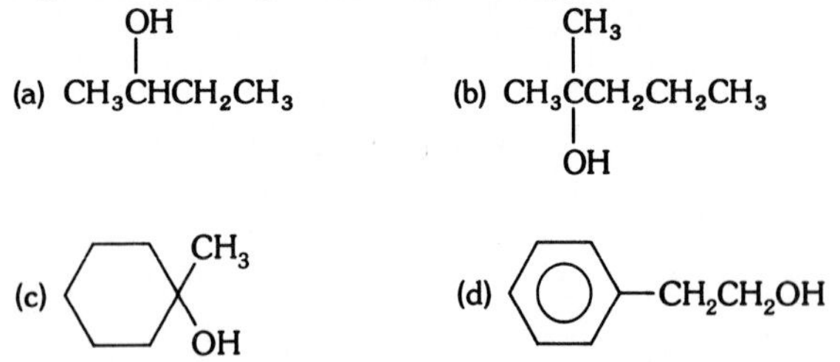

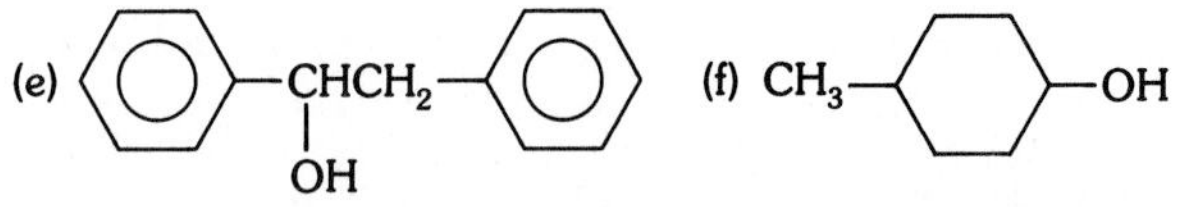

(a) $CH_3\overset{\underset{|}{OH}}{C}HCH_2CH_3$

(b) $CH_3\overset{\underset{|}{CH_3}}{\underset{\underset{|}{OH}}{C}}CH_2CH_2CH_3$

(c) [cyclohexane ring with CH3 and OH on same carbon]

(d) [benzene ring]—CH_2CH_2OH

(e) [benzene ring]—$\overset{\underset{|}{OH}}{C}HCH_2$—[benzene ring]

(f) CH_3—[cyclohexane ring]—OH

14.22 Write the structures of the products of the oxidation of the alcohols listed in Review Exercise 14.21. If the alcohol is a 1° alcohol, give the structures of both the aldehyde and the carboxylic acid that could be made by varying the quantities of the oxidizing agent.

14.23 Write the structure of any alcohol that could be dehydrated to give each alkene. In some cases, more than one alcohol would work.

(a) $CH_2{=}CH_2$

(b) $CH_3CH{=}CH_2$

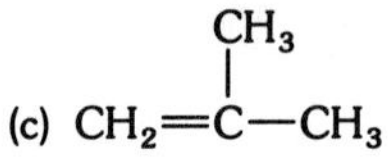

(c) $CH_2{=}\overset{\underset{|}{CH_3}}{C}-CH_3$

(d) $CH_3CH{=}CHCH_3$

14.24 Write the structures of any alcohols that could be used to prepare the following compounds by an oxidation.

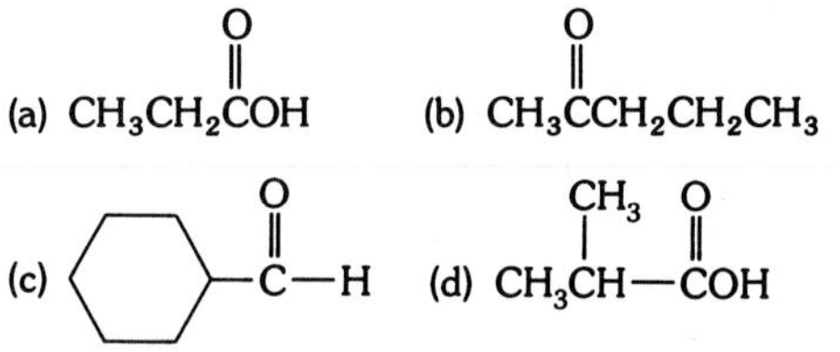

(a) $CH_3CH_2\overset{\overset{\displaystyle O}{\|}}{C}OH$

(b) $CH_3\overset{\overset{\displaystyle O}{\|}}{C}CH_2CH_2CH_3$

(c) [cyclohexane ring]—$\overset{\overset{\displaystyle O}{\|}}{C}-H$

(d) $CH_3\overset{\underset{|}{CH_3}}{C}H-\overset{\overset{\displaystyle O}{\|}}{C}OH$

14.25 Suppose you were given an unknown liquid and told that it is either t-butyl alcohol or butyl alcohol. You're also told that when a few drops of the unknown are shaken with dilute potassium permanganate, the purple color of the MnO_4^- ion disappears and a brown precipitate forms. Which alcohol is it? Explain, and include a reaction sequence for the reaction that occurs.

14.26 An unknown is either pentane or 2-butanol. When it is shaken with $Na_2Cr_2O_7$ and some acid, the orange color of the dichromate ion disappears and the solution becomes green. What is the unknown? Explain, including an equation.

Thioalcohols and Disulfides

14.27 Although we did not systematically develop the rules for naming thioalcohols, the patterns in Table 14.3 make these rules fairly obvious. Write the structures of the following compounds.
(a) isopropyl mercaptan   (b) 1-butanethiol
(c) dimethyl disulfide   (d) 1,2-ethanedithiol

14.28 Complete the following reaction sequences by writing the structures of the organic products that form.
(a) $CH_3SH + (O) \longrightarrow$

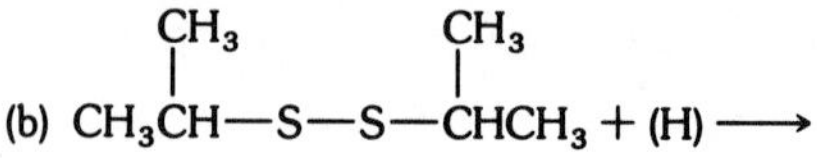

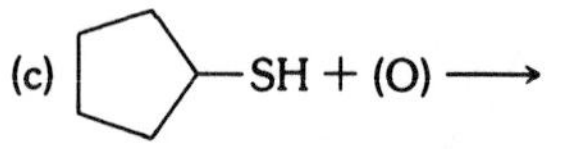

(b) $CH_3\overset{\underset{|}{CH_3}}{C}H-S-S-\overset{\underset{|}{CH_3}}{C}HCH_3 + (H) \longrightarrow$

(c) [cyclopentane ring]—$SH + (O) \longrightarrow$

(d) $CH_3-S-S-CH_2CH_2CH_3 + (H) \longrightarrow$

14.29 Propane, methanethiol, and ethanol have similar formula weights, but propane boils at $-42\ ^\circ C$, methanethiol at $6\ ^\circ C$, and ethanol at $78\ ^\circ C$. What do these data suggest about hydrogen bonding in the thioalcohol family? Does it occur at all? Are the hydrogen bonds as strong as those in the alcohol family?

Phenols

14.30 What is one chemical difference between phenol and cyclohexanol? Write an equation.

14.31 The cresols are three members of the phenol family, and they are isomers. In each structure there is a —OH group attached to the benzene ring in toluene. Write the structures of these isomers, and give each a common name (using the designations *o*, *m*, and *p*). (Disinfectants sometimes use a mixture of these cresols as germ killers.)

14.32 An unknown was either **A** or **B**.

$$CH_3CH_2CH_2CH_2\text{—}\langle\bigcirc\rangle\text{—}OH$$

A

$$CH_3CH_2CH_2\text{—}\langle\bigcirc\rangle\text{—}CH_2OH$$

B

The unknown dissolved in aqueous sodium hydroxide, but not in water. Which compound was it? How can you tell? (Write an equation.)

14.33 An unknown was either **I** or **II**.

When it was shaken with aqueous KOH, no reaction occurred. Which was the unknown? How can you tell?

I   **II**

Ethers

14.34 Which of the following compounds have the ether function and which do not?
(a) $CH_3\text{—}O\text{—}CH_2CH_2\text{—}O\text{—}CH_3$
(b) $CH_3\text{—}O\text{—}\overset{\overset{\displaystyle O}{\|}}{C}\text{—}CH_3$
(c) $CH_3\text{—}O\text{—}\overset{\overset{\displaystyle O}{\|}}{C}\text{—}O\text{—}CH_3$
(d) $\langle\bigcirc\rangle\text{—}O\text{—}CH_3$

(e)

(f) $CH_3\text{—}O\text{—}O\text{—}CH_3$
(g) $CH_2\text{=}CH\text{—}O\text{—}CH_2CH_3$

(h)

14.35 What are the structures of the ethers into which the following alcohols can be changed?
(a) $CH_3\overset{\overset{\displaystyle OH}{|}}{C}HCH_3$
(b) $CH_3\overset{\overset{\displaystyle CH_3}{|}}{C}HCH_2OH$
(c) $\langle\bigcirc\rangle\text{—}OH$
(d) $\langle\bigcirc\rangle\text{—}CH_2OH$

14.36 What alcohols would be needed to prepare the following ethers? Write their structures.
(a) $CH_3\text{—}O\text{—}CH_3$
(b) $CH_3CH_2CH_2CH_2\text{—}O\text{—}CH_2CH_2CH_3$

14.37 If an equimolar mixture of methanol and ethanol is heated with concentrated sulfuric acid under conditions suitable for making the ether system, what organic products will be isolated from this mixture after the reaction is over?

14.38 What happens, chemically, when the following compound is heated with aqueous sodium hydroxide?

$$CH_3CH_2\text{—}O\text{—}CH_2CH_3$$

Organic Reactions

14.39 Write the structure of the principal organic product that would be expected to form in each of the following situations. If no reaction occurs, state so.

If the reaction is the oxidation of a primary alcohol, give the structure of the *aldehyde* only. If the conditions are sulfuric acid and heat and the reactant is an alcohol, write the structure of the *alkene* when the coefficient of the alcohol is given as "1." If it is given as "2," write the structure of the *ether*. (This violates our rule that balancing an equation is the *last* step in writing a reaction, but we need a signal to tell what kind of a reaction is meant.)

(a) $(CH_3)_2CHOH \xrightarrow{\overset{Cr_2O_7^{2-}}{H^+}}$
(b) $CH_3CH_2CH_2CH_3 + H_2SO_4 \longrightarrow$
(c) $CH_3CH_2CH_2\overset{\overset{\displaystyle}{\underset{\underset{\displaystyle OH}{|}}{C}}}{}(CH_3)_2 \xrightarrow{MnO_4^-}$
(d) $CH_3CH_2CH_2OH + NaOH(aq) \longrightarrow$
(e) $2CH_3OH \xrightarrow[\text{heat}]{H_2SO_4}$
(f) $CH_3CH_2\overset{\overset{\displaystyle OH}{|}}{C}HCH_2CH_3 + (O) \longrightarrow$

(g) $CH_3—O—CH_3 + (O) \longrightarrow$

(h) $CH_3CH{=}CHCH_3 + H_2O \xrightarrow[\text{heat}]{H^+}$

(i) $CH_3CH_2CH_2OH \xrightarrow[\text{heat}]{H_2SO_4}$

(j) $CH_3\overset{\overset{\displaystyle OH}{|}}{C}HCH_2CH_3 + (O) \longrightarrow$

14.40 Following the same directions as given in Review Exercise 14.39, write the structure of the principal organic product that would be expected to form in each situation. If no reaction occurs, write "no reaction."

(a) $CH_3CH{=}CH_2 + H_2 \xrightarrow[\text{pressure}]{Ni, \text{ heat}}$

(b) $CH_3\overset{\overset{\displaystyle OH}{|}}{\underset{\underset{\displaystyle CH_3}{|}}{C}}CH_2CH_3 + (O) \longrightarrow$

(c) ⬠—OH $\xrightarrow[\text{heat}]{H_2SO_4}$

(d) $CH_3CH_2OCH_3 + HCl\ (aq) \longrightarrow$

(e) ⬡—$\overset{\overset{\displaystyle OH}{|}}{C}HCH_3 \xrightarrow[\text{heat}]{\text{dil } H_2SO_4}$

(f) ⬡ with OH and CH₃ $+ (O) \longrightarrow$

(g) $CH_3—O—CH_2CH{=}CH_2 + H_2 \xrightarrow[\text{pressure}]{Ni, \text{ heat}}$

(h) ⬡—$CH_2CH_3 + H_2O \longrightarrow$

(i) $CH_3\overset{\overset{\displaystyle CH_3}{|}}{\underset{\underset{\displaystyle OH}{|}}{C}}CH_3 \xrightarrow[\text{heat}]{H_2SO_4}$

(j) $CH_3CH_2CH_2OH + (O) \longrightarrow$

(k) $CH_3—O—CH_2\overset{\overset{\displaystyle OH}{|}}{C}HCH_3 + (O) \longrightarrow$

Stoichiometry of Alcohol Oxidations

14.41 The reactants and products for the oxidation of 1-butanol by aqueous dichromate ion in an acidic medium are

$CH_3CH_2CH_2CH_2OH + Cr_2O_7{}^{2-} \longrightarrow$
    1-Butanol

        $CH_3CH_2CH_2CO_2H + Cr^{3+}$
         Butanoic acid

(a) Balance this equation by the ion–electron method (Section 10.2). Show the half-reactions. Remember that the reaction occurs in aqueous acid.

(b) Transform the balanced net ionic equation of part (a) into a molecular equation assuming that the sodium salt of the dichromate ion is used and that the aqueous acid is hydrochloric acid.

(c) For each mole of 1-butanol used, how many moles (in theory) of sodium dichromate are needed according to the molecular equation?

(d) Suppose that the only form of sodium dichromate available from the stockroom is the dihydrate, $Na_2Cr_2O_7 \cdot 2H_2O$. How many moles of this compound are needed for each mole of 1-butanol?

(e) Suppose you had to carry out this reaction starting with 10.0 g of 1-butanol. What is the maximum number of grams of butanoic acid that you could obtain?

(f) What is the minimum number of grams of sodium dichromate dihydrate that would be needed to oxidize 10.0 g of 1-butanol according to the balanced equation?

Important Alcohols (Special Topic 14.1)

14.42 Name the alcohol used in each of the following ways.
    (a) As a rubbing alcohol (Name two.)
    (b) As a permanent-type antifreeze (Name two.)
    (c) As a fuel in "canned heat"
    (d) As a moisturizer in some foods
    (e) As the beverage alcohol

14.43 Name the alcohol made by
    (a) The fermentation of sugars
    (b) The digestion of dietary fats and oils
    (c) The hydrogenation of carbon monoxide

Acid-Catalyzed Dehydration of Alcohols (Special Topic 14.2)

14.44 Write an equation for the equilibrium that forms when sulfuric acid is dissolved in 2-propanol but before any further steps in the dehydration of the alcohol take place.

14.45 What is the structure of the carbocation that next forms?

14.46 Explain briefly why carbocations are unstable.

14.47 What inorganic species is a likely proton-acceptor when the isopropyl carbocation changes into propene?

14.48 What organic species might also serve as a proton-acceptor? If this species, which is quite abundant in the early phase of the dehydration, does act as the proton-acceptor, will such an event further the overall reaction or hinder it? Explain.

14.49 Propene can be made to *add* a water molecule in the presence of *dilute* sulfuric acid to give 2-propanol. The steps in the mechanism for this addition reaction are exactly the opposite of those for the dehydration of 2-propanol using concentrated sulfuric acid. Write the steps in this addition of water.

Important Phenols (Special Topic 14.3)

14.50 What compound was Lister's first antiseptic, and why is it no longer used?

14.51 What chemical property of BHA or BHT helps them interfere with the oxidation (by air) of the materials these additives are meant to protect?

Important Ethers (Special Topic 14.4)

14.52 What is the structure of the ether once widely used as an anesthetic?

14.53 Why is this ether no longer used so much?

14.54 What structural feature of methyl *t*-butyl ether accounts for its ability to dissolve cholesterol? (The structure of cholesterol can be looked up using the Index.)

14.55 Why is it important that the boiling point of methyl *t*-butyl ether be comfortably above 37 °C?

CHAPTER FIFTEEN

Aldehydes and Ketones

Many modern skyscrapers are sheathed in reflecting glass and so become giant mirrors, as illustrated here by the reflection of a cathedral in Los Angeles. One of the reactions studied in this chapter can be used to make mirrors.

15.1 STRUCTURES AND PHYSICAL PROPERTIES OF ALDEHYDES AND KETONES

Molecules of both aldehydes and ketones contain the carbonyl group, C=O, and when it holds at least one hydrogen atom, it becomes the aldehyde group.

A knowledge of some of the properties of aldehydes and ketones is essential to an understanding of the carbohydrates. All simple sugars are either polyhydroxy aldehydes or polyhydroxy ketones, and many intermediates in metabolism are aldehydes or ketones. Special Topic 15.1 describes just a few of them.

Aldehydes and Ketones Have the Carbonyl Group   Both aldehydes and ketones contain the carbon–oxygen double bond, which is called the **carbonyl group** (pronounced carbon-EEL). The nature of its double bond is discussed in Special Topic 15.2.

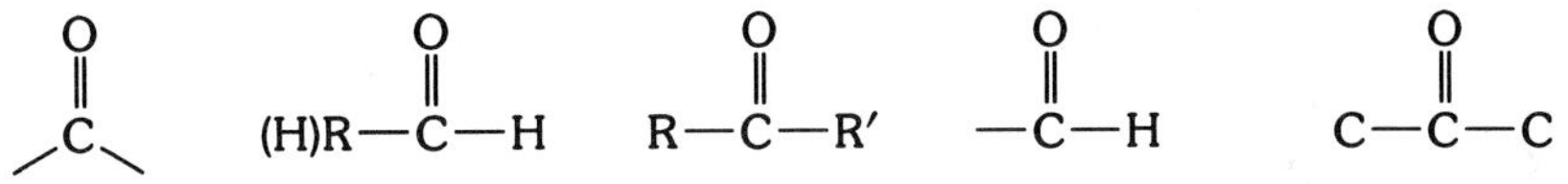

| Carbonyl group | Aldehydes | Ketones | Aldehyde group | Ketone system |

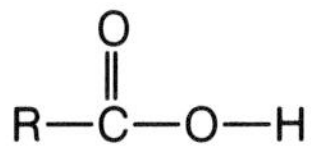

The carbonyl group also occurs in carboxylic acids, and we will study their salts, esters, anhydrides, and amides in the two chapters following this one.

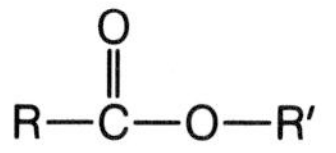

Aldehydes Have the CH=O Group   To be an **aldehyde,** the carbonyl group must have at least one H atom attached as well as a hydrocarbon group (or another H). Thus all aldehydes have the CH=O group, called the **aldehyde group.** (You will sometimes see CH=O condensed and written as CHO as in the general formula for aldehydes, RCHO.) The simplest aldehyde, H_2C=O, methanal (formaldehyde), has two hydrogens on the carbonyl carbon atom and no alkyl chain. Table 15.1 shows some other relatively simple aldehydes.

In Ketones, the Carbonyl Carbon Is Joined Directly to Two Carbons   The carbonyl group in a ketone is called the **keto group.** To have this special name, the carbonyl carbon atom must be flanked on both sides by other carbons. Several ketones are listed in Table 15.2. Sometimes the keto group is condensed in structures as —CO—.

Carboxylic acids

Esters

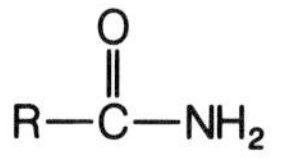

Amides

TABLE 15.1 Aldehydes

Name	Structure	Boiling Point (°C)	Solubility in Water
Methanal	CH_2=O	−21	Very soluble
Ethanal	CH_3CH=O	21	Very soluble
Propanal	CH_3CH_2CH=O	49	16 g/dL (25 °C)
Butanal	$CH_3CH_2CH_2CH$=O	76	4 g/dL
Benzaldehyde	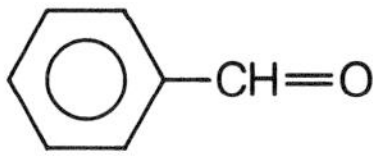 ⬡—CH=O	178	0.3 g/dL
Vanillin	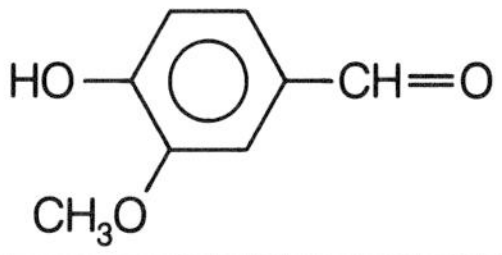 HO—⬡—CH=O, CH_3O	285	1 g/dL

SPECIAL TOPIC 15.1   SOME IMPORTANT ALDEHYDES AND KETONES

Formaldehyde Pure formaldehyde is a gas at room temperature, and it has a very irritating and distinctive odor. It is quite soluble in water, so it is commonly marketed as a solution called formalin (37% w/w) to which some methanol has been added. In this and more dilute forms, formaldehyde was once commonly used as a disinfectant and as a preservative for biological specimens. (Concern over formaldehyde's potential hazard to health has caused these uses to decline.) Most formaldehyde today is used to make various plastics such as Bakelite.

Acetone Acetone is valued as a solvent. Not only does it dissolve a wide variety of organic compounds, but it is also miscible with water in all proportions. Nail polish remover is generally acetone. Should you ever use "superglue," it would be a good idea to have some acetone (nail polish remover) handy because superglue can stick your fingers together so tightly that it takes a solvent such as acetone to get them unstuck.

    Acetone is a minor by-product of metabolism, but in some situations (e.g., untreated diabetes) enough is produced to give breath the odor of acetone.

Some Aldehydes and Ketones in Metabolism The aldehyde group and the keto group occur in many compounds at the molecular level of life. The following are just a few examples of substances with the aldehyde group.

$$HOCH_2-CH-CH-CH-CH-\overset{\displaystyle O}{\overset{\displaystyle \|}{C}}-H$$
$$\qquad\quad\ |\quad\ |\quad\ |\quad\ |$$
$$\qquad\quad OH\ \ OH\ \ OH\ \ OH$$

Glucose, a product of
the digestion of
sugars and starch

$$H-\overset{\displaystyle O}{\overset{\displaystyle \|}{C}}-CH-CH_2-OPO_3{}^{2-}$$
$$\qquad\quad\ |$$
$$\qquad\quad OH$$

Glyceraldehyde 3-phosphate,
an intermediate in glucose
metabolism

Pyridoxal, one of
the vitamins (B$_6$)

Just a few of the many substances at the molecular level of life that contain the keto group are the following.

$$CH_3-\overset{\displaystyle O}{\overset{\displaystyle \|}{C}}-CO_2{}^-$$

Pyruvate ion, a
product of the
metabolism of
glucose and fructose

$$CH_3-\overset{\displaystyle O}{\overset{\displaystyle \|}{C}}-CH_2-CO_2{}^-$$

Acetoacetate ion, a product
of the metabolism of long-
chain carboxylic acids, and
present in blood at elevated
levels in diabetes

$$HO-CH_2-\overset{\displaystyle O}{\overset{\displaystyle \|}{C}}-CH_2-O-PO_3{}^{2-}$$

Dihydroxyacetone phosphate,
an intermediate in the
metabolism of glucose
and fructose

Estrone, a female sex hormone

The Carbonyl Group Is a Moderately Polar Group Because oxygen is much more electronegative than carbon, there is a permanent $\delta-$ on the carbonyl group's oxygen atom and a permanent $\delta+$ charge on its carbon atom. The carbonyl group is permanently polarized, in other words, and aldehydes and ketones are moderately polar compounds. Their molecules are attracted to each other, but not as strongly as they would be if they had OH groups.

Polarization
of the carbonyl
group

SPECIAL TOPIC 15.2   THE NATURE OF THE CARBON–OXYGEN DOUBLE BOND

We have learned that the carbon–carbon double bond consists of one sigma bond and one pi bond. The carbon–oxygen double bond is exactly like this, except that an oxygen atom has replaced a carbon atom. Both the carbon atom and the oxygen atom of the carbonyl group are sp^2-hydridized, and the accompanying figure shows how, in methanal, the carbon–oxygen sigma bond forms by the overlap of two such hybrid orbitals. The figure also shows how the pi bond results from the side-to-side overlap of two unhybridized p orbitals.

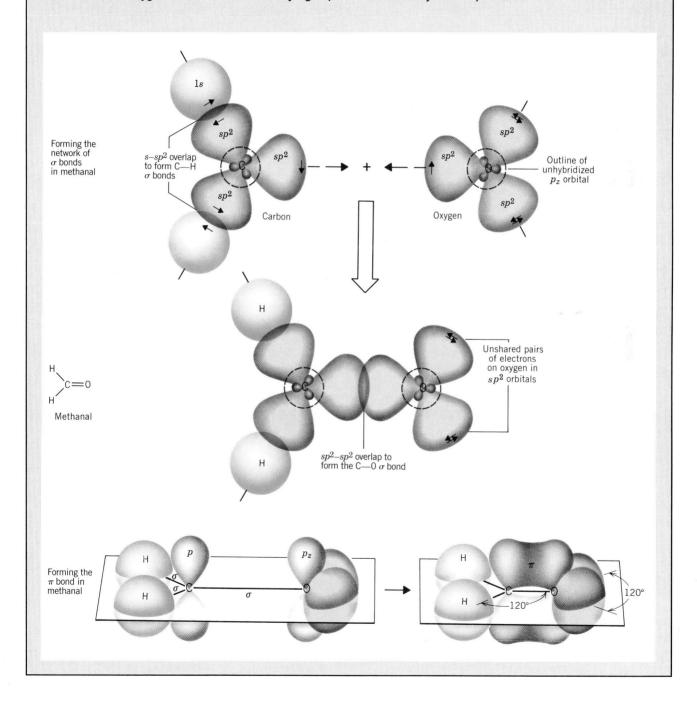

TABLE 15.2 Ketones

Name	Structure	Boiling Point (°C)	Solubility in Water
Propanone (acetone)	CH_3CCH_3 (C=O)	56	Very soluble
Butanone	$CH_3CCH_2CH_3$ (C=O)	80	33 g/dL (25 °C)
2-Pentanone	$CH_3CCH_2CH_2CH_3$ (C=O)	102	6 g/dL
3-Pentanone	$CH_3CH_2CCH_2CH_3$ (C=O)	102	5 g/dL
Cyclopentanone	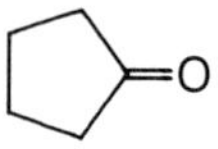 (cyclopentane ring)=O	129	Slightly soluble
Cyclohexanone	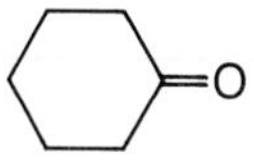 (cyclohexane ring)=O	156	Slightly soluble

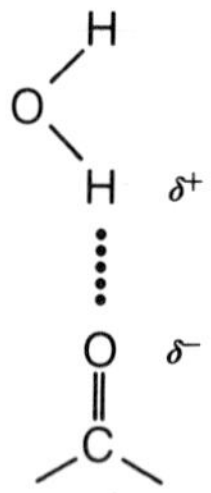

Hydrogen bond ($\cdots$) between a water molecule and a carbonyl group

The polarity of the carbonyl group affects boiling points and solubilities in water. The lack of the OH system, however, means that aldehydes and ketones cannot donate hydrogen bonds, only accept them. Thus, when comparing substances of nearly the same formula weights but from different families, as seen in Table 15.3, we find that aldehydes and ketones boil higher than alkanes, but lower than alcohols. As seen in the data of Tables 15.1 and 15.2, the low-formula-weight aldehydes and ketones are relatively soluble in water, but as the total carbon content increases, this solubility decreases.

15.2 NAMING ALDEHYDES AND KETONES

The IUPAC name ending for aldehydes is -al and for ketones is -one.

The Common Names of Simple Aldehydes Are Derived from Those of Carboxylic Acids   What is easy about the common names of aldehydes is that they all (well, nearly all) end in *-aldehyde.* The prefixes to this are the same as found in the common names of the

TABLE 15.3 Boiling Point versus Structure

Compound	Boiling Point (°C)
$CH_3CH_2CH_2CH_3$	0
$CH_3CH_2CH=O$	49
CH_3CCH_3 (C=O)	57
$CH_3CH_2CH_2OH$	98
$HOCH_2CH_2OH$	198

carboxylic acids to which the aldehydes are easily oxidized. We will, therefore, study the common names of these two families here in one place. (Common names are actually more often used than the IUPAC names.)

The common names of the simple carboxylic acids, known for centuries, are based on natural sources of the acids. Formic acid, for example, is present in the stinging fluid of ants, and the Latin root for ants is *formica*. So this one-carbon acid is called formic acid. The prefix in formic acid is *form-*, so the one-carbon aldehyde is called *formaldehyde*. Here are the four simplest carboxylic acids and their common names together with the structures and names of their corresponding aldehydes.

■ Formic acid also appears to have an aldehyde group, but it is classified as a carboxylic acid.

$$\underset{\text{Formic acid}}{\overset{\overset{\displaystyle O}{\|}}{HCOH}} \qquad \underset{\text{Formaldehyde}}{\overset{\overset{\displaystyle O}{\|}}{HCH}}$$

■ L. *acetum*, vinegar

$$\underset{\text{Acetic acid}}{\overset{\overset{\displaystyle O}{\|}}{CH_3COH}} \qquad \underset{\text{Acetaldehyde}}{\overset{\overset{\displaystyle O}{\|}}{CH_3CH}}$$

■ Gr. *proto*, first, and *pion*, fat

$$\underset{\text{Propionic acid}}{\overset{\overset{\displaystyle O}{\|}}{CH_3CH_2COH}} \qquad \underset{\text{Propionaldehyde}}{\overset{\overset{\displaystyle O}{\|}}{CH_3CH_2CH}}$$

■ L. *butyrum*, butter

$$\underset{\text{Butyric acid}}{\overset{\overset{\displaystyle O}{\|}}{CH_3CH_2CH_2COH}} \qquad \underset{\text{Butyraldehyde}}{\overset{\overset{\displaystyle O}{\|}}{CH_3CH_2CH_2CH}}$$

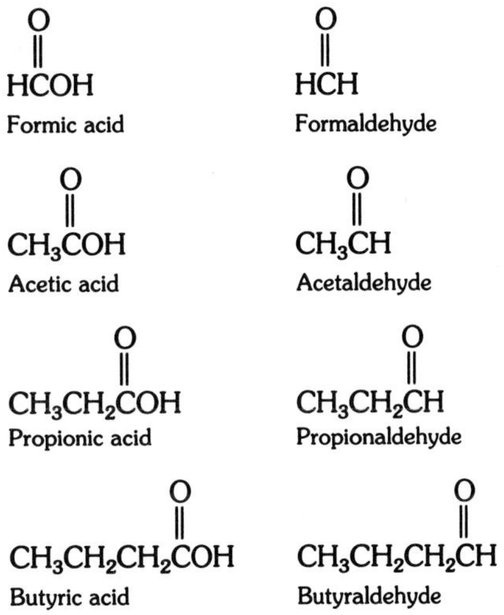

In the aromatic series we have the following examples.

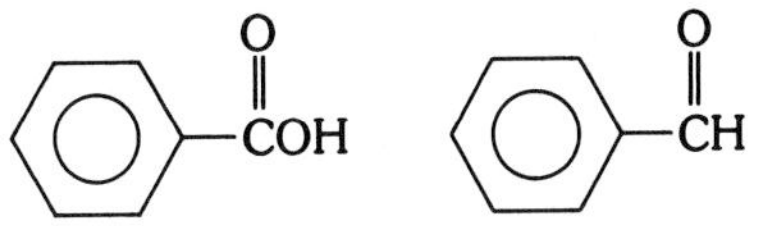

Benzoic acid   Benzaldehyde

The IUPAC Names of Aldehydes End in -*al*   As with the IUPAC names of alcohols, those of the aldehydes are based on the idea of a *parent aldehyde*. Here are the rules.

1.   Select as the parent aldehyde the longest chain *that includes the carbon atom of the aldehyde group.*

The parent aldehyde in the following structure is a five-carbon aldehyde.

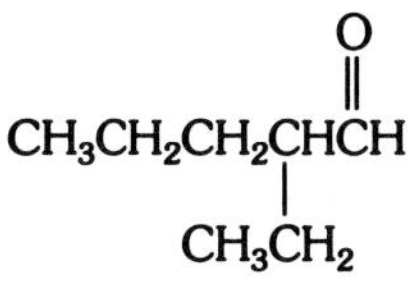

$$\underset{\underset{\displaystyle CH_3CH_2}{|}}{\overset{\overset{\displaystyle O}{\|}}{CH_3CH_2CH_2CHCH}}$$

There is a longer chain, one of six carbons, but it doesn't include the carbon of the aldehyde group, so this longer chain can't be used in the parent name.

2.   Name the parent by changing the *-e* ending of the corresponding alkane to *-al*.

In the example shown with rule 1, the alkane that corresponds to the correct chain is pentane, so the name of the parent aldehyde in this structure is pentanal.

3.   Number the chain to give the carbon atom of the carbonyl group number 1.

This is another instance of the precedence accorded the aldehyde group. Regardless of where other substituents on the parent chain occur, they have to take whatever numbers they receive following the assignment of 1 to the carbonyl carbon atom.

4. Assemble the rest of the name in the same way that was used in naming alcohols, except do not include "1" to specify the location of the aldehyde group.

The carbonyl carbon can't have any other number but 1, so we don't include this number. Thus, using the example begun under rule 1, we have

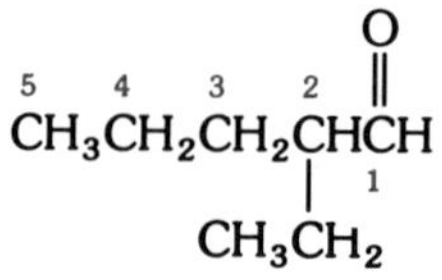

$$
\overset{5}{C}H_3\overset{4}{C}H_2\overset{3}{C}H_2\overset{2}{C}H\overset{1}{C}H\overset{\displaystyle O}{\parallel}
$$

$$
CH_3CH_2
$$

2-Ethylpentanal
not: 2-ethyl-1-pentanal

EXAMPLE 15.1   WRITING THE IUPAC NAME OF AN ALDEHYDE

Problem: What is the IUPAC name of the following compound?

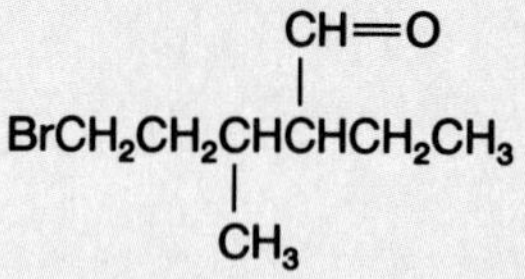

$$
\begin{array}{c}
CH{=}O \\
| \\
BrCH_2CH_2CHCHCH_2CH_3 \\
| \\
CH_3
\end{array}
$$

Solution: First, we identify the parent aldehyde. The longest chain that includes the carbon atom of the aldehyde group has five carbons, so the name of the parent aldehyde is *pentanal*. Next, we number the chain beginning with the carbon atom of the aldehyde group.

$$
\begin{array}{c}
\overset{1}{C}H{=}O \\
| \\
BrCH_2CH_2\overset{3}{C}H\overset{}{C}H\overset{}{C}H_2CH_3 \\
| \\
CH_3
\end{array}
$$

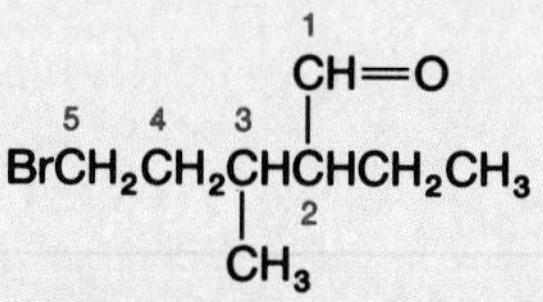

At position 2 there is an ethyl group; at 3, a methyl group; and at 5, a bromo group. Remember that we put the bromo group first in the name. We organize the names of the two alkyl groups in their alphabetical order. The name is

5-bromo-2-ethyl-3-methylpentanal

PRACTICE EXERCISE 1   Write the IUPAC names of the following aldehydes.

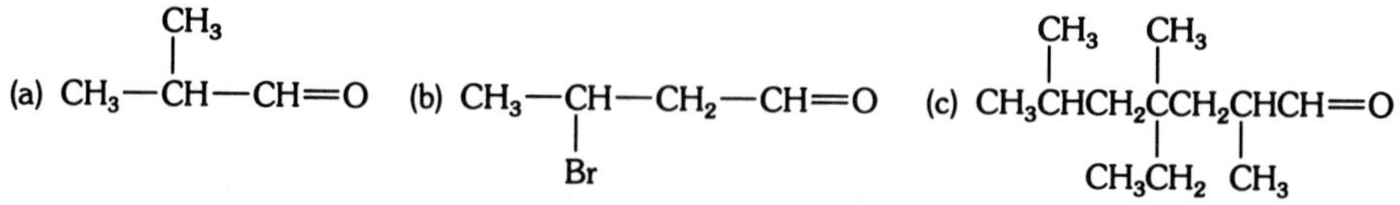

$$
\text{(a) } CH_3{-}\overset{\overset{\displaystyle CH_3}{|}}{C}H{-}CH{=}O
\qquad
\text{(b) } CH_3{-}\overset{\overset{\displaystyle }{|}}{C}H{-}CH_2{-}CH{=}O \atop \quad\quad\quad\quad Br
\qquad
\text{(c) } CH_3\overset{\overset{\displaystyle CH_3}{|}}{C}HCH_2\overset{\overset{\displaystyle CH_3}{|}}{C}CH_2\overset{}{C}HCH{=}O
$$

PRACTICE EXERICSE 2   What is wrong with the name 2-isopropylpropanal?

■ Pronouce *-one* as *own*.

IUPAC Names of Ketones End in *-one*   The IUPAC rules for naming ketones are identical to those for the aldehydes, except for one obvious change. The name of the parent ketone must end in *-one* (not *-al*). Otherwise, the location of the carbonyl group takes precedence in numbering the chain, as with aldehydes.

| EXAMPLE 15.2 | WRITING THE IUPAC NAME OF A KETONE |

Problem: What is the IUPAC name of the following ketone?

$$CH_3\!-\!\overset{\overset{\displaystyle CH_3}{|}}{CH}\!-\!\overset{\overset{\displaystyle CH_3}{|}}{\underset{\underset{\displaystyle CH_3\!-\!CH_2\!-\!CH_2}{|}}{C}}\!-\!\overset{\overset{\displaystyle O}{||}}{C}\!-\!CH_3$$

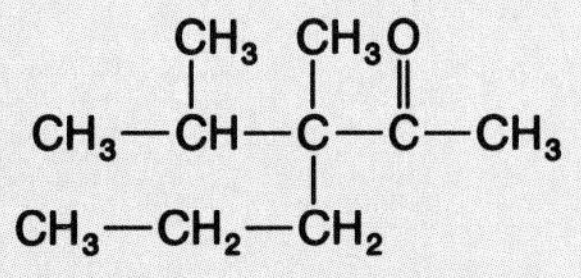

Solution: There are two chains that have six carbon atoms, but we have to use the one that has the carbon atom of the carbonyl group. We number this chain to give the location of the carbonyl group the lower number.

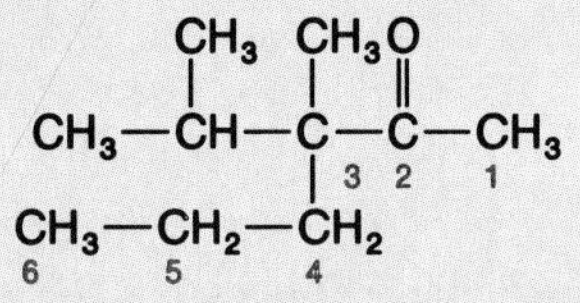

$$CH_3\!-\!\overset{\overset{\displaystyle CH_3}{|}}{CH}\!-\!\overset{\overset{\displaystyle CH_3}{|}}{\underset{\underset{\underset{\displaystyle 6\quad5\quad4}{\displaystyle CH_3\!-\!CH_2\!-\!CH_2}}{|}}{\underset{3\quad2}{C}}}\!-\!\overset{\overset{\displaystyle O}{||}}{\underset{1}{C}}\!-\!CH_3$$

The parent ketone is therefore 2-hexanone. At carbon 3 its chain has a methyl group plus an isopropyl group, so the full name of this compound is

3-isopropyl-3-methyl-2-hexanone

PRACTICE EXERCISE 3

Write the IUPAC names for the following ketones.

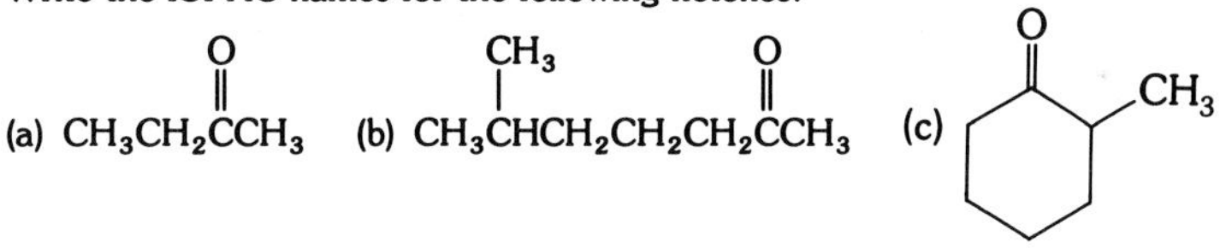

(a) $CH_3CH_2\overset{\overset{\displaystyle O}{||}}{C}CH_3$ (b) $CH_3\overset{\overset{\displaystyle CH_3}{|}}{C}HCH_2CH_2CH_2\overset{\overset{\displaystyle O}{||}}{C}CH_3$ (c)

The Simplest Ketone Is Usually Called Acetone, Not Propanone   Quite often the simpler ketones are given common names that are made by naming the two alkyl groups attached to the carbon atom of the carbonyl group and then following these names by the word *ketone*. For example,

■ The name *acetone* stems from the fact that this ket*one* can be made by heating the calcium salt of *acetic* acid.

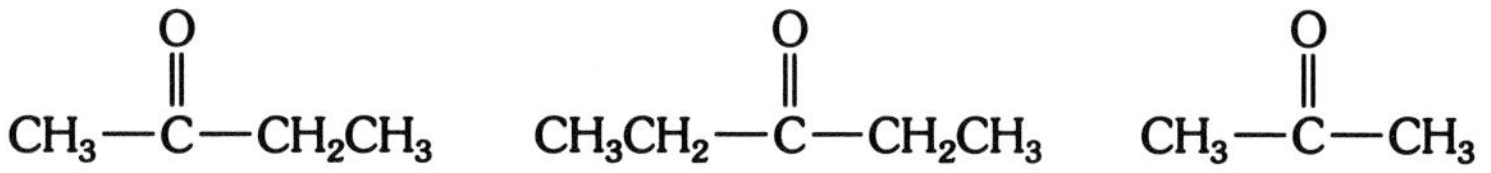

$$CH_3\!-\!\overset{\overset{\displaystyle O}{||}}{C}\!-\!CH_2CH_3 \qquad CH_3CH_2\!-\!\overset{\overset{\displaystyle O}{||}}{C}\!-\!CH_2CH_3 \qquad CH_3\!-\!\overset{\overset{\displaystyle O}{||}}{C}\!-\!CH_3$$

Methyl ethyl ketone   Diethyl ketone   (Dimethyl ketone)
                                                              Acetone

As we noted, the name *acetone* is almost always used for dimethyl ketone or propanone.

PRACTICE EXERCISE 4

Write the structures of the following ketones.

(a) ethyl isopropyl ketone   (b) methyl phenyl ketone
(c) dipropyl ketone   (d) di-*t*-butyl ketone

15.3 THE OXIDATION OF ALDEHYDES AND KETONES

The aldehyde group is easily oxidized to the carboxylic acid group, but the ketone system is difficult to oxidize.

We learned in the previous chapter that the oxidation of a 1° alcohol to an aldehyde requires care, because aldehydes are themselves easily oxidized. We also learned that much less care is needed to oxidize a 2° alcohol to a ketone, because ketones resist oxidation.

$$RCH_2OH + (O) \longrightarrow R-\overset{\overset{\displaystyle O}{\|}}{C}-H + H_2O$$

1° Alcohol   Oxidizing agent   Aldehyde

$$\overset{\overset{\displaystyle OH}{|}}{RCHR'} + (O) \longrightarrow R-\overset{\overset{\displaystyle O}{\|}}{C}-R' + H_2O$$

2° Alcohol   Ketone

The ease with which the aldehyde group is oxidized by even mild reactants has led to some simple test tube tests for aldehydes that we will study next. This study will also be our introduction to a kind of species new to our study and a kind of great importance at the molecular level of life, the complex ion.

Tollens' Test Produces a Silver Mirror   One very mild oxidizing agent consists of an alkaline solution of the diammonia complex of the silver ion, $[Ag(NH_3)_2]^+$, and this reagent is called **Tollens' reagent.** It oxidizes the aldehyde group to a carboxyl group (rather, to its anion form), as a reduction to metallic silver occurs. In general,

$$RCH{=}O + 2[Ag(NH_3)_2]^+ + 3OH^- \longrightarrow RCO_2^- + 2Ag + 2H_2O + 4NH_3$$

When this reaction occurs in a test tube thoroughly cleaned and made free of any greasy deposit, the silver plates out as a beautiful mirror. Its appearance is dramatic evidence that the reaction occurred, so the Tollens' reagent provides a simple test to tell whether an unknown compound is an aldehyde or a ketone. This is one technology used to make mirrors. The reagent has to be freshly made, because it deteriorates on standing.

The test is called **Tollens' test** (or, sometimes, the silver mirror test). A positive Tollens' test is the formation of metallic silver in any form, as a mirror in a clean test tube or as a grayish precipitate otherwise. Glucose, a carbohydrate that we will learn more about later, gives a positive Tollens' test.

Tollens' reagent is prepared by adding sodium hydroxide to dilute silver nitrate. This causes silver oxide, Ag_2O, to precipitate. Then dilute ammonia is added. Its molecules are able to pull silver ions out of the solid silver oxide by forming a soluble *complex ion,* the diammonia complex ion, $[Ag(NH_3)_2]^+$. Thus the silver oxide dissolves, and now the compound suspected of being an aldehyde or a ketone is added. The mixture is warmed in a hot-water bath for a few minutes. If the unknown is an aldehyde (and if the test tube was cleaned), the silver mirror slowly takes form. It's quite pretty to watch.

Metal Ions Form Many Complex Ions   As we indicated, the silver diammine ion, $[Ag(NH_3)_2]^+$, is an example of a **complex ion.** This is an ion consisting of a metal ion associated with one or more neutral but somewhat electron-rich molecules, like ammonia, or with negative ions.

Virtually all the trace metal ions required in nutrition have to exist as complex ions in cells and body fluids because these fluids are slightly alkaline. Uncomplexed transition metal ions are insoluble when the pH is greater than 7; they form their hydroxides or oxides and precipitate. (Ag^+, for example, precipitates as Ag_2O in base, which actually happens in the first step in the preparation of Tollens' reagent.) However, many electron-rich ions or molecules, like ammonia, are able to form water-soluble complex ions with metal ions and so allow them to be in solution even at pHs greater than 7. The $[Ag(NH_3)_2]^+$ ion illustrates how ammonia molecules can hold Ag^+ ions in solution in base.

The iron(II) ion is also insoluble in base, but in blood (pH 7.35) it occurs in a complex ion called *heme,* the red-colored species in hemoglobin. Inside cells, the phosphate ion level is sufficiently high to form insoluble phosphates with calcium ion, but this must be prevented for many reasons, not the least of which is that cells would mineralize and die. Cells avoid this by

■   Hemoglobin is the oxygen-carrier in blood

forming complex ions between Ca^{2+} and a variety of electron-rich molecular units on proteins. Complex ions thus have absolutely vital functions at the molecular level of life.

The Benedict's Test Produces a Brick-Red Precipitate **Benedict's reagent,** another mild oxidizing agent, consists of the copper(II) ion complexed with the citrate ion, the anion of citric acid. Provided the medium is slightly alkaline, this complex is able to oxidize the aldehyde group. The complex form of Cu^{2+} is therefore needed to keep it from precipitating in the alkaline solution as CuO.

$$HO—\overset{\displaystyle CH_2CO_2^-}{\underset{\displaystyle CH_2CO_2^-}{C}}—CO_2^-$$

Citrate ion

When an easily oxidized compound is added to a test tube that contains some Benedict's reagent, and the solution is warmed, Cu^{2+} ions are reduced to Cu^+ ions, and these cannot be protected from OH^- ions (or from water) by the citrate system. The newly formed Cu^+ ions are pulled out of the surrounding citrate ions, and are changed by the base into a precipitate of copper(I) oxide, Cu_2O.

Benedict's reagent has a brilliant blue color caused by the copper(II) complex, but Cu_2O has a brick-red color. Therefore the visible evidence of a positive **Benedict's test** is the disappearance of a blue color and the appearance of a reddish precipitate.

Simple aldehydes do not give the test as well as aldehydes with neighboring oxygens. Three systems, one not even an aldehyde, and all of which occur among various carbohydrates, give positive Benedict's tests:

■ A carbon atom immediately adjacent to a carbonyl group is often called an alpha (α) carbon:

$$-\overset{\displaystyle |}{\underset{\displaystyle |}{C}}-\overset{\displaystyle O}{\overset{\displaystyle \|}{C}}-$$

Alpha carbon

$$\overset{\displaystyle O}{\overset{\displaystyle \|}{R\underset{\displaystyle |}{\underset{\displaystyle OH}{C}}HCH}}$$
α-Hydroxy aldehyde

$$\overset{\displaystyle O \quad O}{\overset{\displaystyle \| \quad \|}{RC—CH}}$$
α-Keto aldehyde

$$\overset{\displaystyle O}{\overset{\displaystyle \|}{R\underset{\displaystyle |}{\underset{\displaystyle OH}{C}}HCR'}}$$
α-Hydroxy ketone

Glucose, for example, is an α-hydroxy aldehyde, and Benedict's test is a common method for detecting glucose in urine. In certain conditions, such as diabetes, the body cannot prevent some of the excess glucose in the blood from being present in the urine, so testing the urine for its glucose concentration has long been used in medical diagnosis.

Clinitest tablets, a convenient solid form of Benedict's reagent, contain all the needed reactants in their solid forms. To test for glucose, we mix a few drops of urine with a tablet. As the tablet dissolves, the heat needed for the test is generated. The color that develops is compared with a color code on a chart provided with the tablets. (Specialists in the control of diabetes prefer to monitor the carbohydrate status of a diabetic person by determining the glucose in the blood instead of in the urine. Not all patients, however, can or are willing to manage blood tests, particularly when they are needed frequently.) Other tests for glucose are based on enzyme-catalyzed reactions, and we will learn about them later.

15.4 THE REDUCTION OF ALDEHYDES AND KETONES

Aldehydes and ketones are reduced to alcohols when hydrogen adds to their carbonyl groups.

Aldehydes are reduced to 1° alcohols and ketones are reduced to 2° alcohols by a variety of conditions. We will study two methods, the direct addition of hydrogen and reduction by hydride ion transfer. Either method can be called the *hydrogenation* of an aldehyde or ketone.

Aldehyde and Keto Groups Add H_2 Catalytically Under heat and pressure and in the presence of a finely divided metal catalyst, the carbonyl groups of aldehydes and ketones add hydrogen. Although these *conditions* are impossible in living systems, of course, we study the reaction because the *effect* of the addition of hydrogen is routinely done in such systems.

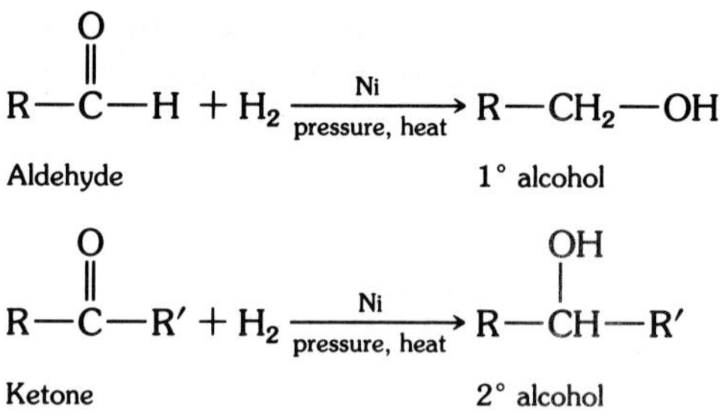

$$R-\overset{\overset{\textstyle O}{\|}}{C}-H + H_2 \xrightarrow[\text{pressure, heat}]{\text{Ni}} R-CH_2-OH$$

Aldehyde   1° alcohol

$$R-\overset{\overset{\textstyle O}{\|}}{C}-R' + H_2 \xrightarrow[\text{pressure, heat}]{\text{Ni}} R-\overset{\overset{\textstyle OH}{|}}{C}H-R'$$

Ketone   2° alcohol

Specfic examples include

$$CH_3CH_2CH_2CH{=}O + H_2 \xrightarrow[\text{pressure, heat}]{\text{Ni}} CH_3CH_2CH_2CH_2OH$$

Butanal   1-Butanol

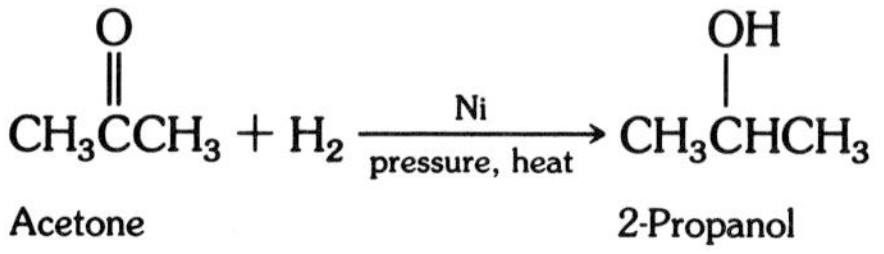

$$CH_3\overset{\overset{\textstyle O}{\|}}{C}CH_3 + H_2 \xrightarrow[\text{pressure, heat}]{\text{Ni}} CH_3\overset{\overset{\textstyle OH}{|}}{C}HCH_3$$

Acetone   2-Propanol

Hydride Ion Transfers to Aldehyde and Keto Groups   The hydride ion, $H{:}^-$, is a powerful reducing agent. It is also an extremely powerful base, so it cannot exist in the aqueous medium of cells. It reacts very vigorously with water to give hydrogen gas, leaving the *relatively* much weaker base, OH^-.

$$H{:}^- + H-OH \longrightarrow H-H + OH^-$$

If we added sodium hydride, NaH, to water, for example, the following reaction would occur and leave a caustic solution containing sodium hydroxide, lye.

$$NaH(s) + H_2O \longrightarrow H_2(g) + NaOH(aq)$$

The only way hydride ion could be supplied in living systems, therefore, would be by a donor that transfers it directly to the acceptor.

    The carbonyl group is an excellent acceptor of hydride ion. We'll represent an organic donor of hydride ion by the symbol $M{:}H$, where M refers to a *metabolite*, a chemical intermediate in metabolism. When an aldehyde or ketone group accepts a hydride ion, the following reaction occurs.

■ In the lab, $H{:}^-$ can be supplied by LiAlH$_4$ or NaBH$_4$ for these reductions.

■ $M{:}H$ in the body is often a B-vitamin unit in an enzyme.

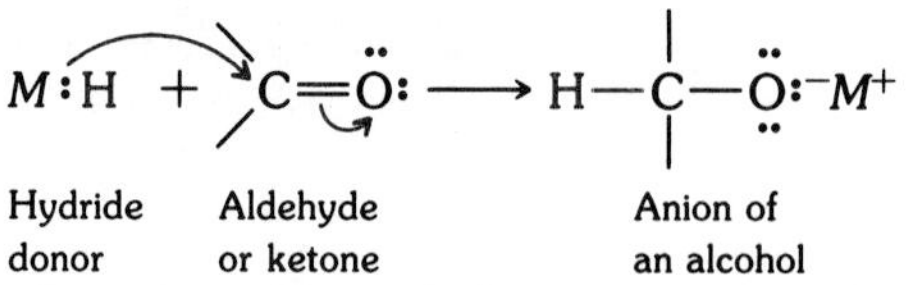

$$M{:}H \;+\; \overset{\diagup}{\underset{\diagup}{C}}{=}\overset{\cdot\cdot}{\underset{\cdot\cdot}{O}}{:} \longrightarrow H-\overset{|}{\underset{|}{C}}-\overset{\cdot\cdot}{\underset{\cdot\cdot}{O}}{:}^-M^+$$

Hydride   Aldehyde   Anion of
donor   or ketone   an alcohol

The anion of an alcohol is a stronger proton-acceptor than a hydroxide ion. So in the instant when the newly formed anion emerges, it takes a proton either from a water molecule or from some other proton-donor in the surrounding buffer system. Thus the final organic product is an alcohol.

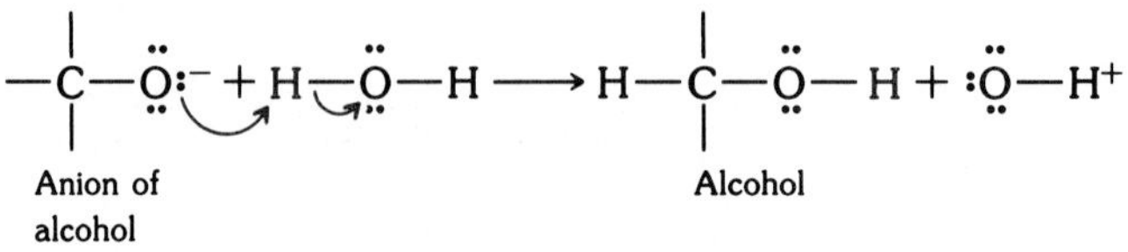

$$-\overset{|}{\underset{|}{C}}-\overset{\cdot\cdot}{\underset{\cdot\cdot}{O}}{:}^- + H-\overset{\cdot\cdot}{\underset{\cdot\cdot}{O}}-H \longrightarrow H-\overset{|}{\underset{|}{C}}-\overset{\cdot\cdot}{\underset{\cdot\cdot}{O}}-H + {:}\overset{\cdot\cdot}{\underset{\cdot\cdot}{O}}-H^+$$

Anion of   Alcohol
alcohol

    As we have already noted, another name for *hydrogenation* is *reduction,* and when a carbonyl carbon atom accepts the pair of electrons carried by the hydride ion, it *gains* this pair and so is reduced. (Remember, a gain of electrons is reduction because it makes oxidation numbers less positive.)

One of the many examples in cells of reduction by the donation of hydride ion is the reduction of the keto group in the pyruvate ion to form the lactate ion, a step in the metabolism of glucose.

■ NAD is a molecular unit present in several enzymes and made from a B vitamin.

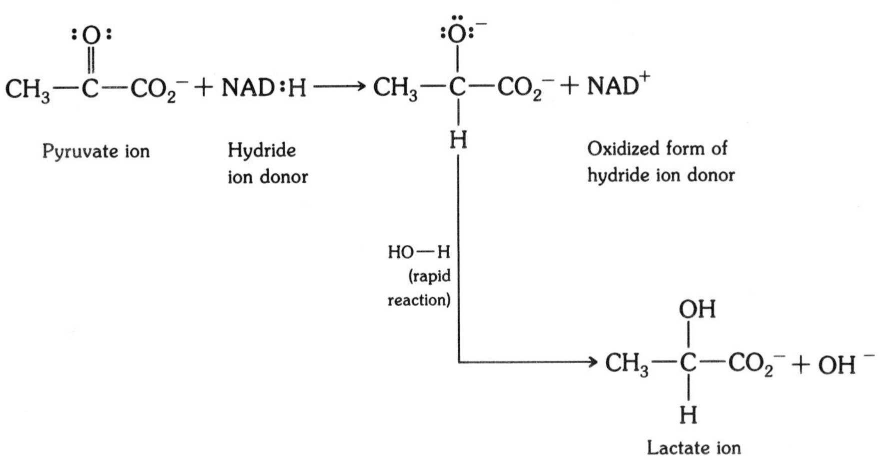

$$CH_3-\overset{\displaystyle :O:}{\overset{\|}{C}}-CO_2^- + NAD:H \longrightarrow CH_3-\overset{\displaystyle :\overset{..}{O}:^-}{\underset{\underset{H}{|}}{C}}-CO_2^- + NAD^+$$

Pyruvate ion   Hydride ion donor   Oxidized form of hydride ion donor

HO—H
(rapid reaction)

$$\longrightarrow CH_3-\overset{\displaystyle OH}{\underset{\underset{H}{|}}{C}}-CO_2^- + OH^-$$

Lactate ion

(In this sequence, NAD stands for *nicotinamide adenine dinucleotide,* a substance we will discuss further in a later chapter. Right now, all we need to know about NAD is that its reduced form, NAD:H, is a good donor of hydride ion).

EXAMPLE 15.3	**WRITING THE STRUCTURE OF THE PRODUCT OF THE REDUCTION OF AN ALDEHYDE OR KETONE**

Problem: What is the product of the reduction of propanal?

Solution: All the action is at the carbonyl group. It changes to an alcohol group. Therefore all we have to do is copy over the structure of the given compound, change the double bond to a single bond, and supply the two hydrogen atoms—one to the oxygen atom of the original carbonyl group and one to the carbon atom.

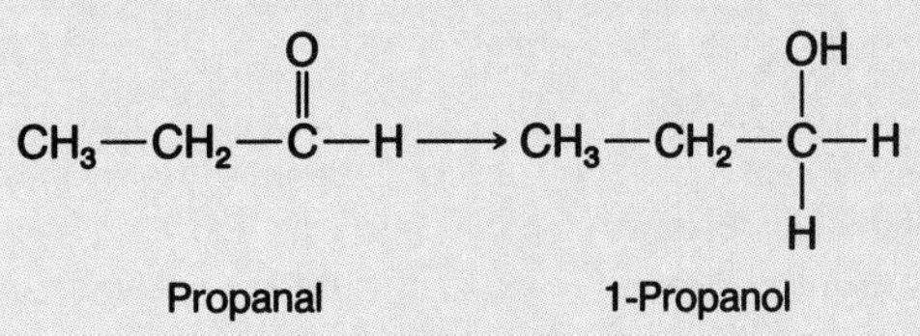

$$CH_3-CH_2-\overset{\displaystyle O}{\overset{\|}{C}}-H \longrightarrow CH_3-CH_2-\overset{\displaystyle OH}{\underset{\underset{H}{|}}{C}}-H \quad (or, CH_3CH_2CH_2OH)$$

Propanal   1-Propanol

PRACTICE EXERCISE 5   Write the structures of the products that form when the following aldehydes and ketones are reduced.

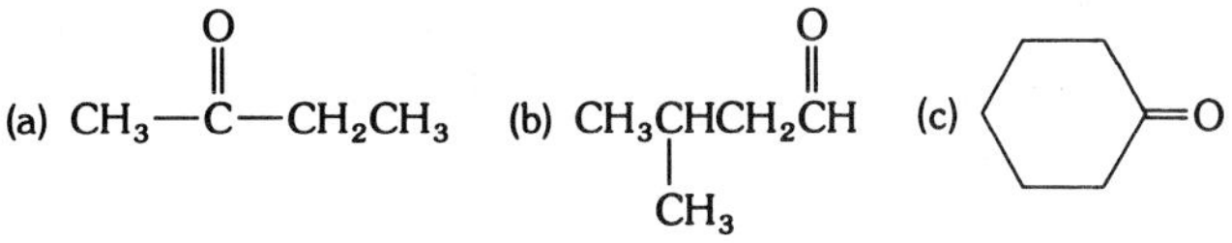

(a) $CH_3-\overset{\displaystyle O}{\overset{\|}{C}}-CH_2CH_3$ (b) $CH_3\underset{\underset{CH_3}{|}}{CH}CH_2\overset{\displaystyle O}{\overset{\|}{CH}}$ (c) ⬡=O

15.5 THE REACTIONS OF ALDEHYDES AND KETONES WITH ALCOHOLS

1,1-Diethers—acetals or ketals—form when aldehydes or ketones react with alcohols in the presence of an acid or enzyme catalyst.

This section is background to the study of carbohydrates whose molecules have the functional groups introduced here. We will study the simplest possible examples of these groups now so that carbohydrate structures will be easier to understand.

Hemiacetals Form When Alcohols Add to the Aldehyde Group When a solution of an aldehyde in an alcohol is prepared, molecules of the alcohol add to molecules of the aldehyde and the following equilibrium mixture forms.

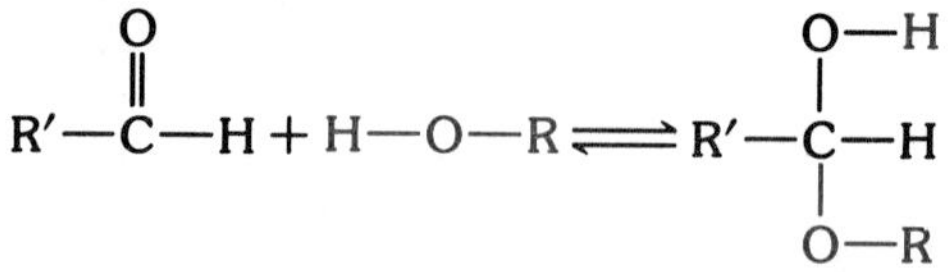

$$\underset{\text{Aldehyde}}{\overset{\overset{\displaystyle O}{\|}}{R'-C-H}} + \underset{\text{Alcohol}}{H-O-R} \rightleftharpoons \underset{\text{Hemiacetal}}{\overset{\displaystyle O-H}{\underset{\displaystyle O-R}{R'-C-H}}}$$

The product, the **hemiacetal,** has molecules that always have a carbon atom holding both an OH group and an OR group. When these two groups are this close to each other, they so modify each other's properties that it's useful to place the whole system into its own separate family.

In the formation of a hemiacetal, the O—R part of the alcohol molecule *always* ends up attached to the carbon atom of the original carbonyl group, and the H atom of the alcohol always goes to the carbonyl oxygen.

Except among carbohydrates, a hemiacetal system is too unstable to exist in a pure compound. If we try to isolate and purify an ordinary hemiacetal, it breaks back down, and only the original aldehyde and alcohol are obtained. Despite this, we're still interested in the hemiacetal system for two reasons. It is relatively stable among carbohydrates, and it is an intermediate in the formation of 1,1-diethers or acetals, which are stable enough to be isolated. The acetal system is also common among carbohydrates.

The relative ease with which hemiacetals break back down means that the hemiacetal system is a site of structural weakness, even among carbohydrates. For this reason, we have to learn how to recognize the system when it occurs in a structure.

■ The hemiacetal system:

$$\overset{\displaystyle O-H}{\underset{\displaystyle O-R}{C-C-H}}$$

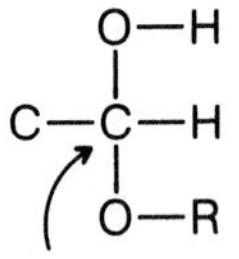

This originally was the carbon atom of an aldehyde group.

| **EXAMPLE 15.4** | **IDENTIFYING THE HEMIACETAL SYSTEM** |

Problem: Which of the following structures has the hemiacetal system? Draw an arrow pointing to any carbon atoms that were initially the carbon atoms of aldehyde groups.

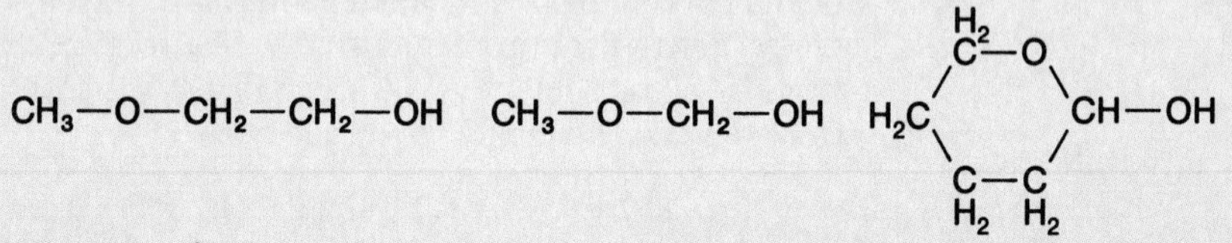

$$\underset{\textbf{1}}{CH_3-O-CH_2-CH_2-OH} \qquad \underset{\textbf{2}}{CH_3-O-CH_2-OH} \qquad \underset{\textbf{3}}{\overset{\displaystyle H_2C}{\underset{\displaystyle \underset{H_2\ H_2}{C-C}}{}}\overset{\overset{\displaystyle C-O}{H_2}}{}CH-OH}$$

Solution: To have the hemiacetal system, the molecule must have a carbon to which are attached one OH group, and one —O—C unit. Notice that in structure **1** there is an OH group and an —O—C unit, but they are not joined to the *same* carbon. Therefore **1** is not a hemiacetal. It just has an ordinary ether group and an alcohol group.

In structure **2** the OH and the —O—C are joined to the same carbon, so **2** is a hemiacetal. Similarly, in structure **3** the carbon on the far right corner of the ring holds both an OH group and a —O—C unit, and **3** is also a hemiacetal, a cyclic hemiacetal. Structure **3** shows the way in which the hemiacetal system occurs in many carbohydrates, as a cyclic hemiacetal.

■ The ring system of **3** also occurs in glucose.

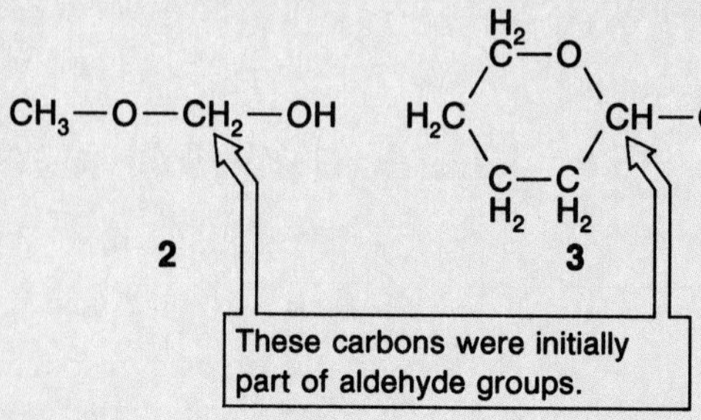

$$\underset{\textbf{2}}{CH_3-O-CH_2-OH} \qquad \underset{\textbf{3}}{\overset{\displaystyle H_2C}{\underset{\displaystyle \underset{H_2\ H_2}{C-C}}{}}\overset{\overset{\displaystyle C-O}{H_2}}{}CH-OH}$$

These carbons were initially part of aldehyde groups.

PRACTICE EXERCISE 6   Identify the hemiacetals among the following structures, and draw arrows that point to the carbon atoms that initially were part of the carbonyl groups of parent aldehydes.

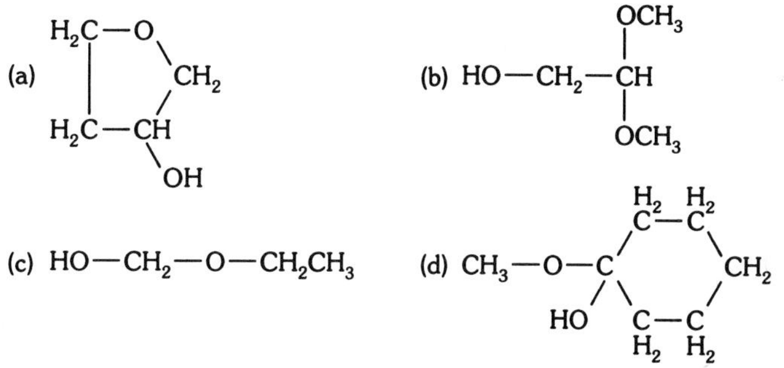

(a)
$$H_2C-O\diagdown \atop {| \qquad CH_2} \atop H_2C-CH \diagup \atop \diagdown OH$$

(b) $HO-CH_2-CH \begin{smallmatrix} OCH_3 \\ | \\ | \\ OCH_3 \end{smallmatrix}$

(c) $HO-CH_2-O-CH_2CH_3$

(d) $CH_3-O-C \diagdown {}^{H_2 \; H_2}_{C-C} \diagdown \atop {HO \diagup \diagdown \atop C-C \atop H_2 \; H_2} CH_2$

Another skill that will be useful in our study of carbohydrates is the ability to write the structure of a hemiacetal that could be made from a given aldehyde and alcohol.

WRITING THE STRUCTURE OF A HEMIACETAL GIVEN ITS PARENT ALDEHYDE AND ALCOHOL

EXAMPLE 15.5

Problem: Write the structure of the hemiacetal that is present at equilibrium in a solution of propanal in ethanol.

Solution: The best way to start is to rewrite the structure of the aldehyde, but show only one bond from carbon to oxygen:

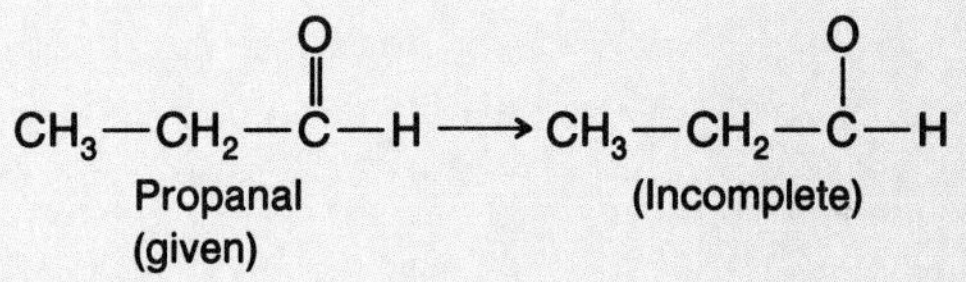

$$CH_3-CH_2-\overset{\overset{\displaystyle O}{\|}}{C}-H \longrightarrow CH_3-CH_2-\overset{\overset{\displaystyle O}{\|}}{C}-H$$
Propanal   (Incomplete)
(given)

Then look at the structure of the given alcohol, CH_3-CH_2-O-H. The H on its oxygen atom ends up on the oxygen atom of the developing structure:

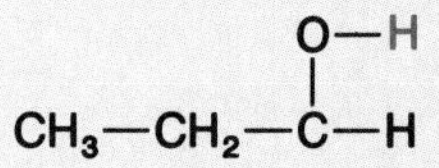

$$CH_3-CH_2-\overset{\overset{\displaystyle O-H}{|}}{C}-H \quad \text{(Incomplete)}$$

Finally the entire remainder of the alcohol molecule is attached by its oxygen atom to the carbon atom that presently has the O—H group in our developing structure:

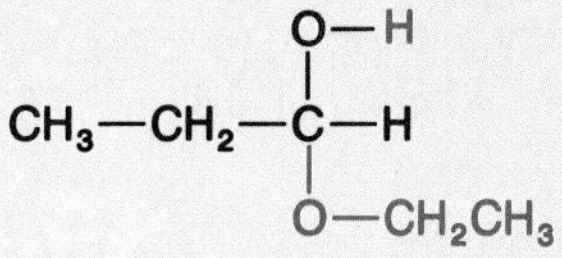

$$CH_3-CH_2-\underset{\underset{\displaystyle O-CH_2CH_3}{|}}{\overset{\overset{\displaystyle O-H}{|}}{C}}-H \qquad \text{(Final answer)}$$

We can leave the answer in this form, or we can rewrite it to condense it a little more:

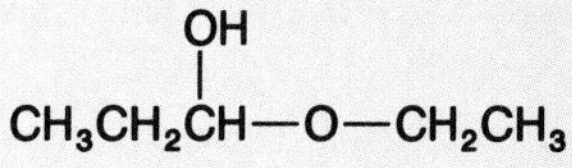

$$CH_3CH_2\overset{\overset{\displaystyle OH}{|}}{C}H-O-CH_2CH_3$$

PRACTICE EXERCISE 7   Write the structures of the hemiacetals that are present in the equilibria that involve the following pairs of compounds.

(a) ethanal and methanol   (b) butanal and ethanol
(c) benzaldehyde and 1-propanol   (d) methanal and methanol

Still another skill that will be useful in studying carbohydrates is the ability to write the structures of the aldehyde and alcohol that are liberated by the breakdown of a hemiacetal.

EXAMPLE 15.6   **WRITING THE BREAKDOWN PRODUCTS OF A HEMIACETAL**

Problem: What aldehyde and alcohol form when the following hemiacetal breaks down?

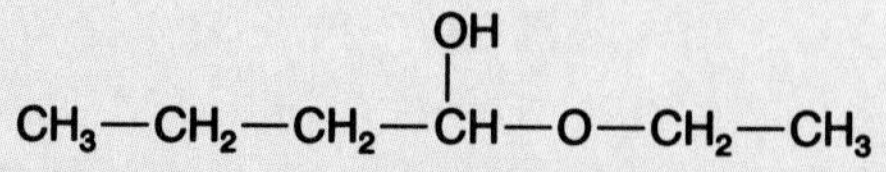

$$
\underset{\text{OH}}{\text{CH}_3-\text{CH}_2-\text{CH}_2-\overset{\mid}{\text{CH}}-\text{O}-\text{CH}_2-\text{CH}_3}
$$

Solution: This is the kind of problem for which the ability to pick out the carbon atom of the original carbonyl group is especially helpful. Remember that to find this carbon we look for one that holds both a OH group and a —O—R system. When we find this carbon, we break its bond to the —O—R unit and separate the pieces. (This bond was the bond that formed when the alcohol added to the aldehyde to form the hemiacetal system.) *Do not break any other bond in the given hemiacetal.*

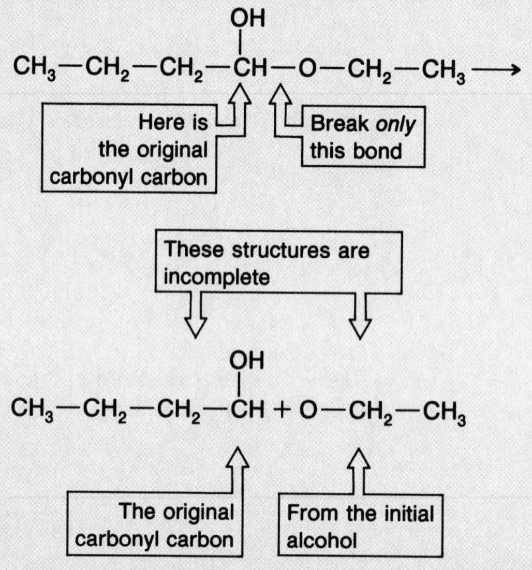

$$
\underset{\text{OH}}{\text{CH}_3-\text{CH}_2-\text{CH}_2-\overset{\mid}{\text{CH}}-\text{O}-\text{CH}_2-\text{CH}_3 \longrightarrow}
$$

Here is the original carbonyl carbon   Break *only* this bond

These structures are incomplete

$$
\underset{\text{OH}}{\text{CH}_3-\text{CH}_2-\text{CH}_2-\overset{\mid}{\text{CH}} + \text{O}-\text{CH}_2-\text{CH}_3}
$$

The original carbonyl carbon   From the initial alcohol

Now all we have to do is fix the structure of the fragment that has the original carbonyl carbon into a structure with an actual carbonyl group. We do this by moving the H atom on the oxygen over to the O atom of the other fragment. (This gives us the original alcohol molecule.) Then we write a carbon–oxygen double bond to make the carbonyl group, and we have the original aldehyde. The answer, then, is

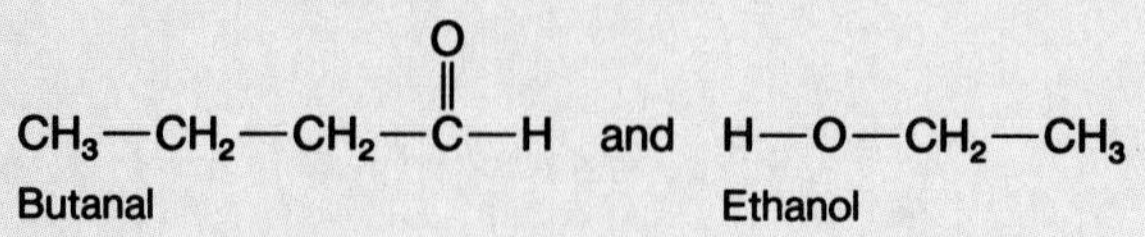

$$
\underset{\text{Butanal}}{\text{CH}_3-\text{CH}_2-\text{CH}_2-\overset{\overset{\textstyle O}{\|}}{\text{C}}-\text{H}} \quad \text{and} \quad \underset{\text{Ethanol}}{\text{H}-\text{O}-\text{CH}_2-\text{CH}_3}
$$

PRACTICE EXERICISE 8   Write the structures of the breakdown products of the following hemiacetals.

(a) 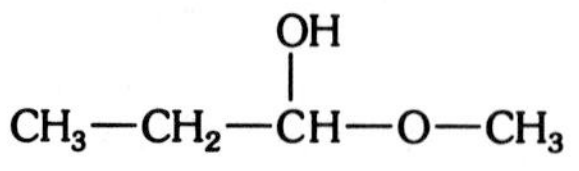 $\underset{\text{OH}}{\text{CH}_3-\text{CH}_2-\overset{\mid}{\text{CH}}-\text{O}-\text{CH}_3}$ (b) 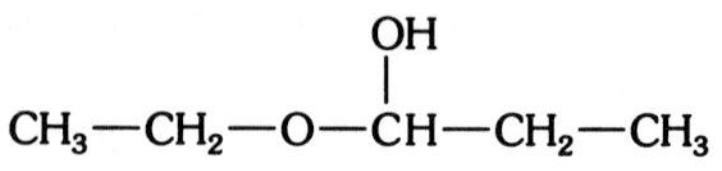 $\underset{\text{OH}}{\text{CH}_3-\text{CH}_2-\text{O}-\overset{\mid}{\text{CH}}-\text{CH}_2-\text{CH}_3}$

Hemiketals Form When Alcohols Add to Ketones   Toward alcohols ketones behave very much as aldehydes do. They add alcohols to form equilibria that contain a structure

■ The hemiketal system:

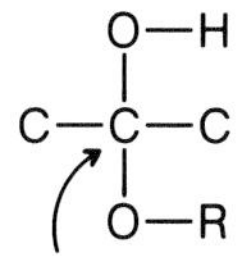

O—H
|
C—C—C
↗|
(O—R

This originally was
the carbon atom of
a keto group.

almost identical in type to that of a hemiacetal, only now it's called a **hemiketal.** Like the hemiacetal, the hemiketal has a carbon atom, originally the carbonyl carbon atom of the parent ketone, which holds both OH and O—R.

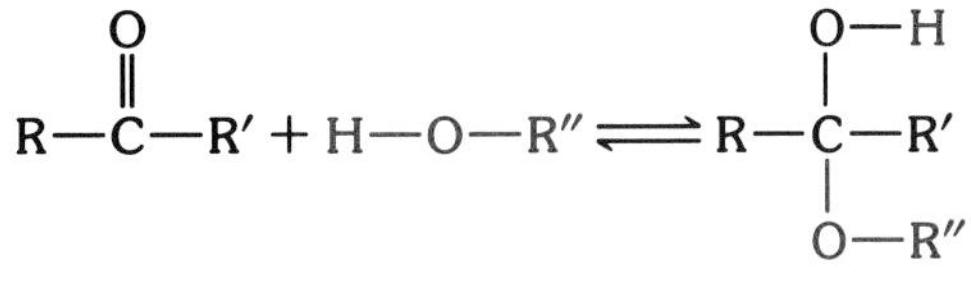

$$\underset{\text{Ketone}}{R-\overset{\overset{\displaystyle O}{\|}}{C}-R'} + \underset{\text{Alcohol}}{H-O-R''} \rightleftharpoons \underset{\text{Hemiketal}}{R-\overset{\overset{\displaystyle O-H}{|}}{\underset{\underset{\displaystyle O-R''}{|}}{C}}-R'}$$

Alcohols do not add as readily to ketones as they do to aldehydes, so the position of the equilibrium favors hemiketal formation less than corresponding equilibria favor hemiacetals. Among carbohydrates, however, fructose (levulose) has a relatively stable hemiketal system.

The kinds of problems that we studied under the hemiacetals are exactly analogous to those of the hemiketals. Try the following exercises to prove this.

PRACTICE EXERCISE 9

Examine the following structures and decide whether any represent hemiketals. Draw an arrow pointing to any carbon atoms that initially came from the carbonyl groups of ketones.

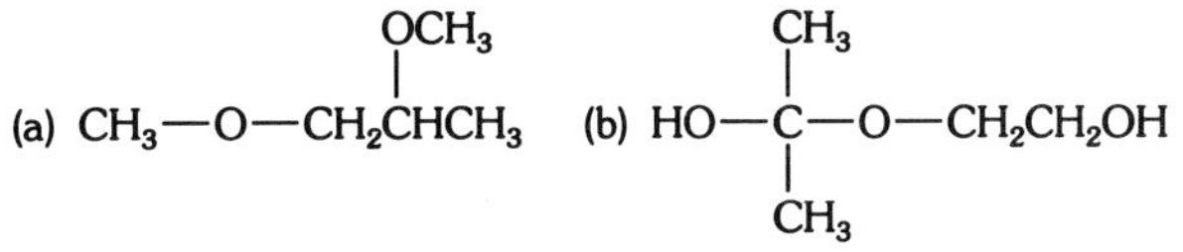

(a) $CH_3-O-CH_2\overset{\overset{\displaystyle OCH_3}{|}}{C}HCH_3$ (b) $HO-\overset{\overset{\displaystyle CH_3}{|}}{\underset{\underset{\displaystyle CH_3}{|}}{C}}-O-CH_2CH_2OH$

PRACTICE EXERCISE 10

Write the structure of the hemiketal that would be present at equilibrium in a solution of acetone in methanol.

PRACTICE EXERCISE 11

What ketone and alcohol would be needed to prepare (in an equilibrium) the following hemiketal?

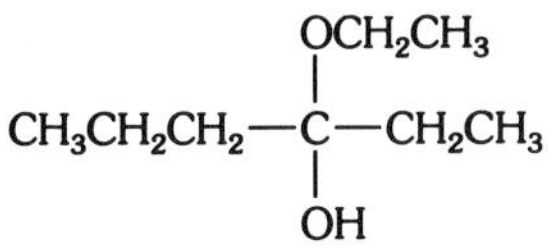

$$CH_3CH_2CH_2-\overset{\overset{\displaystyle OCH_2CH_3}{|}}{\underset{\underset{\displaystyle OH}{|}}{C}}-CH_2CH_3$$

Acetals and Ketals Form When Alcohols React Further with Hemiacetals and Hemiketals Hemiacetals and hemiketals are special kinds of alcohols, and they resemble alcohols in one important property. They can be converted into ethers, not ordinary ethers but special kinds of 1,1-diethers called **acetals** and **ketals.** The overall change that leads to an acetal is as follows.

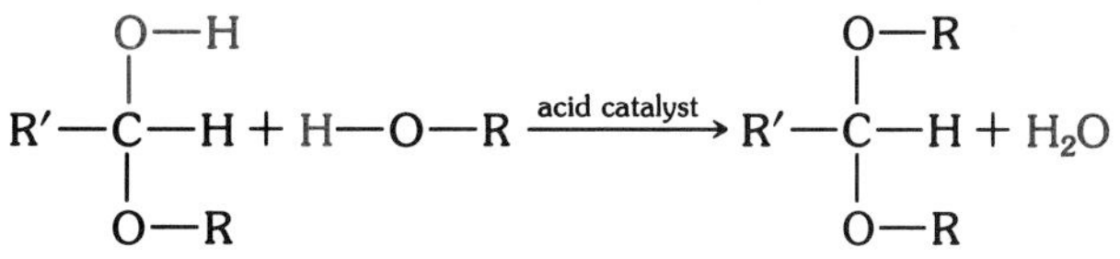

$$\underset{\text{Hemiacetal}}{R'-\overset{\overset{\displaystyle O-H}{|}}{\underset{\underset{\displaystyle O-R}{|}}{C}}-H} + H-O-R \xrightarrow{\text{acid catalyst}} \underset{\text{Acetal}}{R'-\overset{\overset{\displaystyle O-R}{|}}{\underset{\underset{\displaystyle O-R}{|}}{C}}-H} + H_2O$$

Hemiketals give the identical kind of reaction, but the products are called ketals. Unlike hemiacetals and hemiketals, both acetals and ketals are stable compounds that can be isolated and stored.

The difference between the formation of an acetal and an ordinary ether is that acetals form more readily. As a rule, when two functional groups are very close to each other in a molecule, each modifies the properties of the other in some way. Here, the O—R group makes the nearby OH group much more reactive toward forming an ether.

An acetal is a 1,1-diether. This doesn't mean that we have to number the chain this way. The 1,1 designation here means only that the two ether groups come to the same carbon. Ketals are also 1,1-diethers. Such common carbohydrates as sucrose (table sugar), lactose (milk sugar), and starch have the 1,1-diether system.

Acetals and ketals are stable, as we said, but only if they are kept out of contact with aqueous acids. In water, acids (or enzymes) catalyze the hydrolysis of these compounds. They break back down to give their parent alcohols and carbonyl compounds, aldehydes or ketones. The hydrolysis of acetals and ketals is the only one of their chemical reactions we need to study; it is the reaction by which carbohydrates are digested. Before we go into its chemistry, let's be sure we can recognize the acetal or ketal system when it occurs in a structure.

EXAMPLE 15.7

RECOGNIZING THE ACETAL OR KETAL SYSTEMS AND WHICH OF THEIR CARBON ATOMS CAME FROM PARENT CARBONYL CARBONS

Problem: Examine each structure to see whether it is an acetal or a ketal. If it is, identify the carbon atom that was the carbonyl carbon atom of the parent aldehyde or ketone.

$$CH_3-O-CH_2-O-CH_3 \qquad CH_3-O-\overset{\overset{\displaystyle O-CH_3}{|}}{C}H-CH_3$$

4   5   6

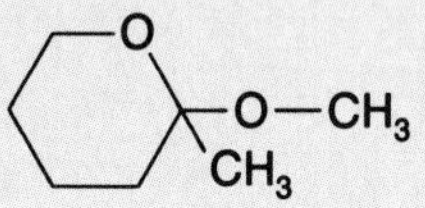

Solution: We have to find one carbon that holds two —O—R types of groups. Structure **4** has such a carbon in its central CH_2 unit. This carbon was initially the carbonyl carbon atom of an aldehyde (methanal), because it also holds at least one H atom. Structure **5** similarly has such a carbon, in the —CH— unit, and it also came from an aldehyde group (because it has at least one H atom). In structure **6**, we can also find a carbon that holds two —O—C networks. This carbon lacks an H-atom, however, so it must have come from the carbonyl group of a ketone system.

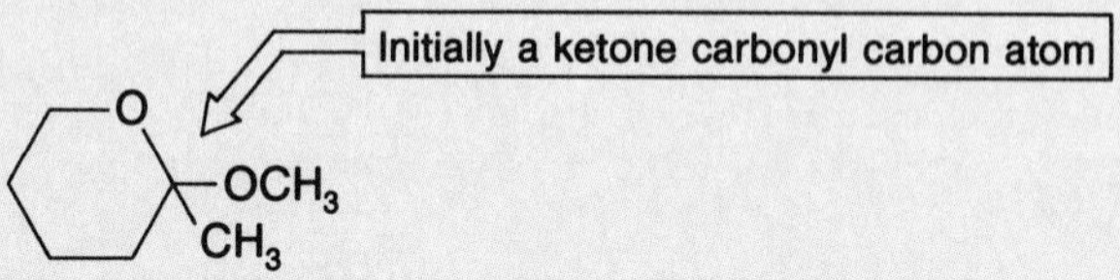

Initially a ketone carbonyl carbon atom

PRACTICE EXERCISE 12 Which of the following two compounds, if either, is an acetal or a ketal? If one is an acetal or a ketal, identify the carbon atom that came originally from the carbonyl group of a parent aldehyde or ketone.

(a) $CH_3-O-CH_2-CH_2-O-CH_3$ (b) $CH_3CH_2-O-\overset{\overset{\displaystyle CH_3}{|}}{\underset{\underset{\displaystyle CH_3}{|}}{C}}-O-CH_2CH_3$

Because acetals and ketals can be hydrolyzed, we have to be able to examine the structures of such compounds and write the structures of their parent alcohols and aldehydes (or ketones) — the hydrolysis products. A worked example shows how this can be done.

EXAMPLE 15.8

WRITING THE STRUCTURES OF THE PRODUCTS OF THE HYDROLYSIS OF ACETALS OR KETALS

Problem: What are the products of the following reaction?

$$CH_3-\overset{\overset{\displaystyle O-CH_3}{|}}{C}H-O-CH_3 + H_2O \xrightarrow{\text{acid catalyst}} ?$$

Solution: The best way to proceed is to find the carbon atom in the structure that holds *two* oxygen atoms. This carbon is the carbonyl carbon atom of the parent aldehyde (or ketone). Break both of its bonds to these oxygen atoms. *Do not break any other bonds.* Separate the fragments for further processing.

$$\begin{array}{c} \text{O}-\text{CH}_3 \\ | \\ \text{CH}_3-\text{CH}-\text{O}-\text{CH}_3 \end{array} \dashrightarrow \text{CH}_3-\text{CH} \qquad \begin{array}{c} -\text{O}-\text{CH}_3 \\ \\ -\text{O}-\text{CH}_3 \end{array} \qquad \text{(Incomplete)}$$

Initially, a carbonyl carbon

Next, we finish writing the carbonyl group where it belongs—at the identified carbon atom. Then we place H atoms on the oxygen atoms of the other fragments to finish writing the structures of the alcohol molecules that also form. The final products of the hydrolysis of the given acetal are

$$\begin{array}{c} \text{O} \\ \| \\ \text{CH}_3-\text{C}-\text{H} + 2\text{H}-\text{O}-\text{CH}_3 \end{array}$$

Notice that the oxygen atom for the new carbonyl group comes from the molecule of water that acted to hydrolyze the acetal. The two hydrogen atoms needed to complete the structures of the two alcohol molecules also come from the water molecule.

PRACTICE EXERCISE 13   Write the structures of the aldehydes (or ketones) and the alcohols that are obtained by hydrolyzing the following compounds. If they do not hydrolyze like acetals or ketals, write "no reaction."

(a) $\text{CH}_3-\text{O}-\text{CH}_2-\text{O}-\text{CH}_3$

(b) $\text{CH}_3-\text{O}-\text{CH}_2-\text{CH}_2-\text{O}-\text{CH}_2-\text{CH}_3$

(c) $\begin{array}{ccc} \text{CH}_3 & & \text{O}-\text{CH}_3 \\ | & & | \\ \text{CH}_3-\text{CH}- & -\text{C}-\text{O}-\text{CH}_3 \\ & & | \\ & & \text{CH}_3 \end{array}$

SUMMARY

Naming aldehydes and ketones   The IUPAC names of aldehydes and ketones are based on a parent compound, one with the longest chain that includes the carbonyl group. The names of aldehydes end in *-al* and of ketones in *-one,* and the chains are numbered to give the carbonyl carbons the lower of two possible numbers.

Physical properties of aldehydes and ketones   The carbonyl group confers moderate polarity, which gives aldehydes and ketones higher boiling points and solubilities in water than hydrocarbons but lower boiling points and solubilities in water than alcohols (that have comparable formula weights).

Chemical properties of aldehydes and ketones   Aldehydes are easily oxidized to carboxylic acids, but ketones resist oxidation. Aldehydes give a positive Tollens' test and ketones do not. α-Hydroxy aldehydes and ketones give Benedict's test. The test reagents involve two complex ions, the silver diammine complex in Tollens' reagent and the copper(II) citrate complex ion in the Benedict's test. Complex ions help to keep transition metal ions in solution, even in base.

When an aldehyde or a ketone is dissolved in an alcohol, some of the alcohol adds to the carbonyl group of the aldehyde or ketone. The equilibrium thus formed includes molecules of a hemiacetal (or hemiketal). The chart at the end of this summary outlines the chemical properties of the aldehydes and ketones we have studied.

Hemiacetals and hemiketals   Hemiacetals and hemiketals are usually unstable compounds that exist only in an equilibrium involving the parent carbonyl compound and the parent alcohol (which generally is the solvent). Hemiacetals and hemiketals readily break back down to their parent carbonyl compounds and alcohols. When an acid catalyst is added to the equilibrium, a hemiacetal or hemiketal reacts with more alcohol to form an acetal or ketal.

Acetals and ketals   Acetals and ketals are 1,1-diethers that are stable in aqueous base or in water, but not in aqueous acid. Acids catalyze the hydrolysis of acetals and ketals, and the final products are the parent aldehydes (or ketones) and alcohols.

Aldehydes

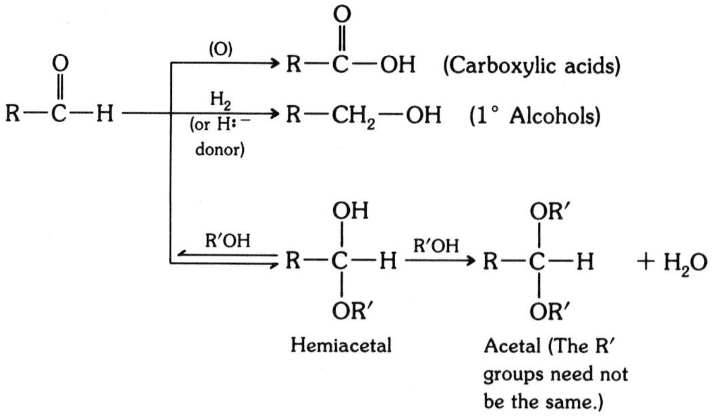

$$R-C(=O)-H \xrightarrow{(O)} R-C(=O)-OH \quad \text{(Carboxylic acids)}$$

$$\xrightarrow[\text{donor}]{\substack{H_2 \\ (\text{or } H:^-)}} R-CH_2-OH \quad (1° \text{ Alcohols})$$

$$\xrightleftharpoons{R'OH} R-\underset{OR'}{\overset{OH}{\underset{|}{\overset{|}{C}}}}-H \xrightarrow{R'OH} R-\underset{OR'}{\overset{OR'}{\underset{|}{\overset{|}{C}}}}-H \; + \; H_2O$$

Hemiacetal   Acetal (The R′ groups need not be the same.)

Ketones

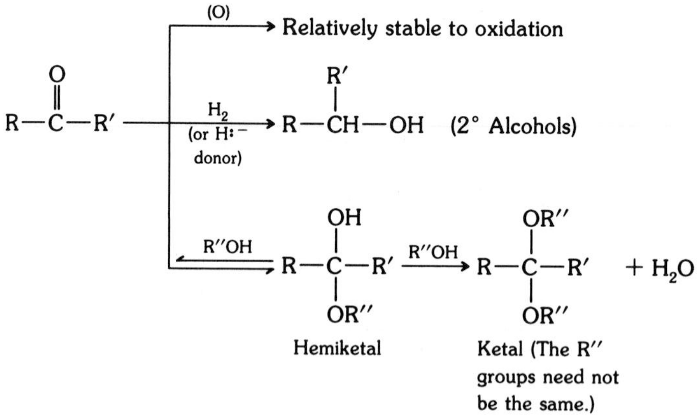

$$R-C(=O)-R' \xrightarrow{(O)} \text{Relatively stable to oxidation}$$

$$\xrightarrow[\text{donor}]{\substack{H_2 \\ (\text{or } H:^-)}} R-\underset{}{\overset{R'}{\underset{|}{CH}}}-OH \quad (2° \text{ Alcohols})$$

$$\xrightleftharpoons{R''OH} R-\underset{OR''}{\overset{OH}{\underset{|}{\overset{|}{C}}}}-R' \xrightarrow{R''OH} R-\underset{OR''}{\overset{OR''}{\underset{|}{\overset{|}{C}}}}-R' \; + \; H_2O$$

Hemiketal   Ketal (The R″ groups need not be the same.)

Acetals and Ketals

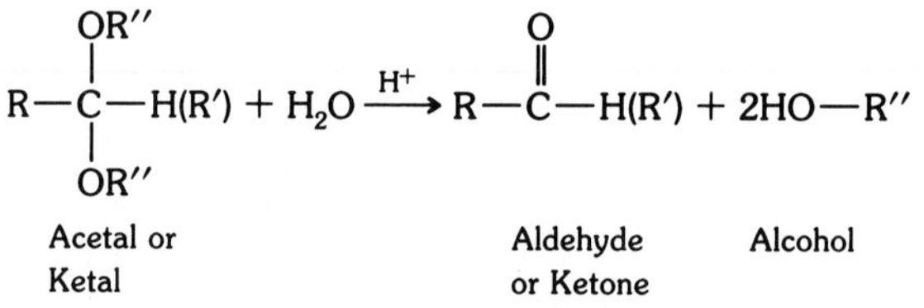

$$R-\underset{OR''}{\overset{OR''}{\underset{|}{\overset{|}{C}}}}-H(R') + H_2O \xrightarrow{H^+} R-C(=O)-H(R') + 2HO-R''$$

Acetal or   Aldehyde   Alcohol
Ketal   or Ketone

REVIEW EXERCISES

The answers to these Review Exercises are in the *Study Guide* that accompanies this book.

NAMES AND STRUCTURES

15.1 What is the *structural* difference between an aldehyde and a ketone?

15.2 Write the structure of each of the following compounds.
(a) 3-methylpentanal
(b) 2,3-dibromocyclopentanone
(c) 1-phenyl-1-butanone
(d) dibutyl ketone
(e) butane-2,3-dione

15.3 What are the structures of the following compounds?
(a) 2-cyclohexylcyclohexanone
(b) 2-ethylbutanal
(c) di-*sec*-butyl ketone
(d) 1,3-diphenyl-2-propanone
(e) 1,3,5-cyclohexanetrione

15.4 Although we can write structures that correspond to the following names, when we do, we find that the names aren't proper. How should these compounds be named in the IUPAC system?
(a) 6-methylcyclohexanone
(b) 1-hydroxy-1-propanone (Give common name.)

(c) 1-methylbutanal
(d) 2-methylethanal
(e) 2-propylpropanal

15.5 The following names can be used to write structures, but the names turn out to be improper. What should be their IUPAC names?
(a) 2-sec-butylbutanal
(b) 1-phenylethanal
(c) 4,5-dimethylcyclopentanone
(d) 1-hydroxyethanal (Give common name.)
(e) 1-butanone

15.6 If the IUPAC name of $CH_3-\overset{O}{\underset{\|}{C}}-CH_2-\overset{O}{\underset{\|}{C}}-H$ is 3-ketobutanal, what is the IUPAC name of the following compound?

$$H-\overset{O}{\underset{\|}{C}}-\overset{}{\underset{\underset{CH_3}{|}}{CH}}-\overset{\overset{CH_3}{|}}{CH}-\overset{O}{\underset{\|}{C}}-CH_3$$

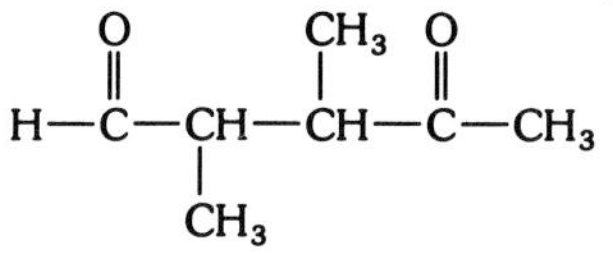

15.7 We can name compound **A** as 2-methylformylcyclohexane. Taking a clue from this, how might compound **B** be named?

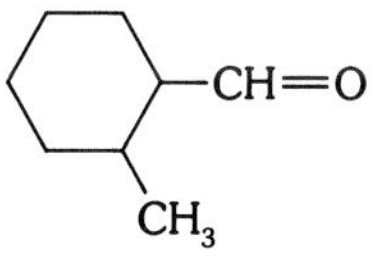

A 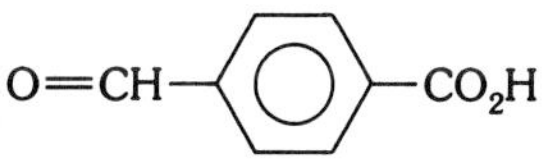   **B**

15.8 Write the IUPAC names of the following compounds.

(a) 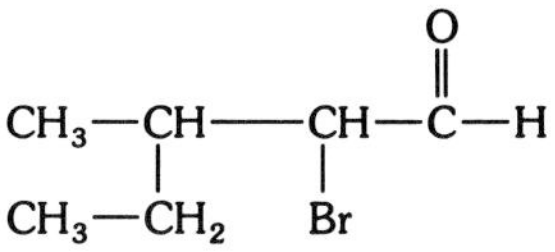 $CH_3-\overset{}{\underset{\underset{CH_3-CH_2}{|}}{CH}}-\overset{}{\underset{\underset{Br}{|}}{CH}}-\overset{O}{\underset{\|}{C}}-H$

(b) 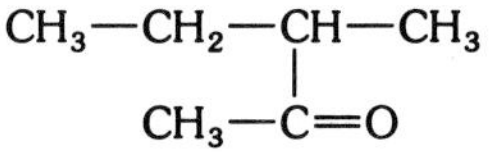 $CH_3-CH_2-\overset{}{\underset{\underset{CH_3-C=O}{|}}{CH}}-CH_3$

(c)

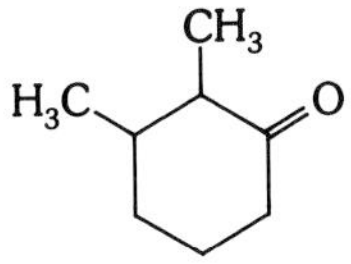

(d)

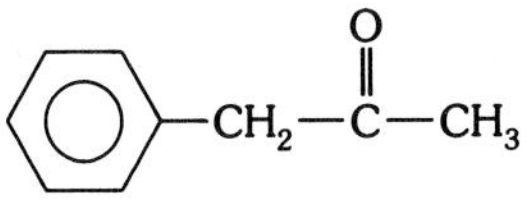

(e)

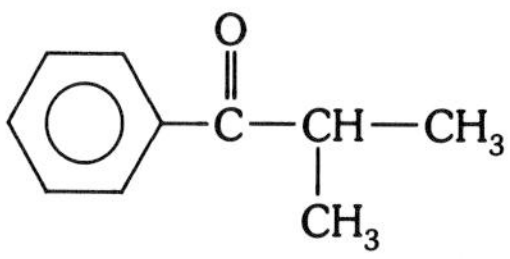

15.9 What are the IUPAC names of the following compounds?

(a) 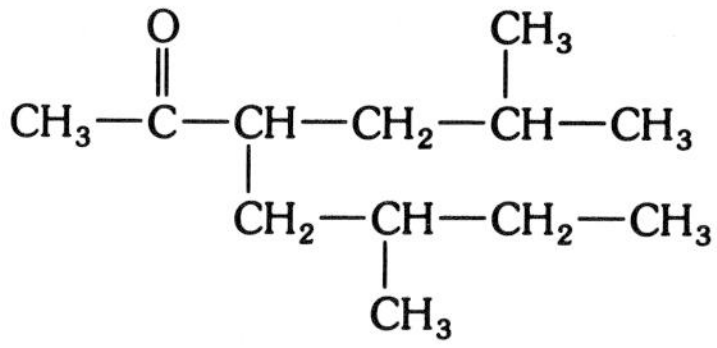 $CH_3-\overset{O}{\underset{\|}{C}}-CH-CH_2-\overset{\overset{CH_3}{|}}{CH}-CH_3$
    with $\underset{\underset{CH_3}{|}}{\underset{|}{CH_2-CH-CH_2-CH_3}}$

(b) $H-\overset{O}{\underset{\|}{C}}-CH_2-CH-C(CH_3)_3$
    with $\underset{\underset{CH_3}{|}}{\underset{|}{CH_2-CH-CH_3}}$

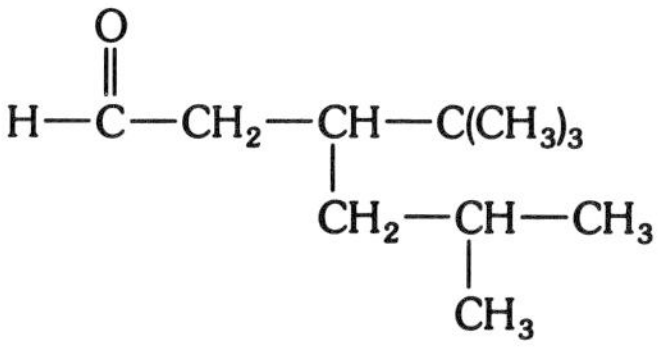

(c) $-CH_2-\overset{O}{\underset{\|}{C}}-H$

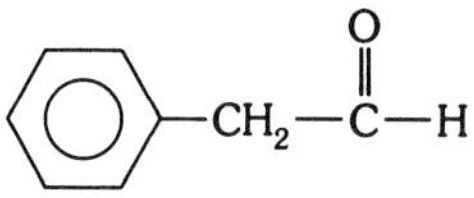

(d) 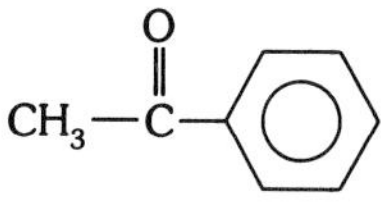 $CH_3-\overset{O}{\underset{\|}{C}}-$

(e) 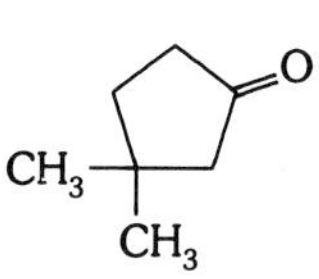 CH_3-

15.10 If the common name of $CH_3CH_2CH_2CH_2\overset{O}{\underset{\|}{C}}OH$ is valeric acid, what is the most likely common name of the following compound?

$$CH_3CH_2CH_2CH_2CH=O$$

15.11 If the common name of the following compound,

$$CH_3-O-\text{}-CH=O$$

is anisaldehyde, what is the most likely common name of

$$CH_3-O-\text{}-\overset{O}{\underset{\|}{C}}-OH?$$

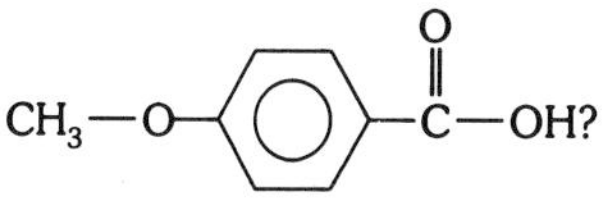

Physical Properties of Aldehydes and Ketones

15.12 Arrange the following compounds in their order of increasing boiling points. Do this by placing the letters that identify them in the correct order, starting with the lowest-boiling compound and moving in order to the highest-boiling compound.

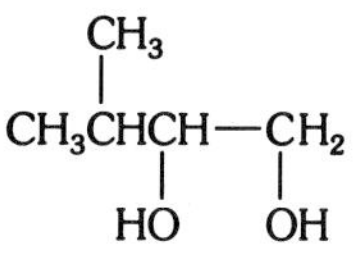

$$\underset{\underset{HO}{|}}{CH_3}\overset{}{CHCH}-\underset{\underset{OH}{|}}{CH_2} \qquad \overset{\overset{CH_3}{|}}{CH_3CHCH_2CH=O}$$
A 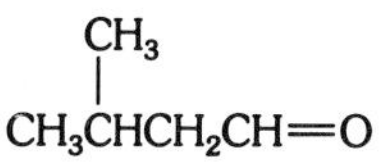   **B**

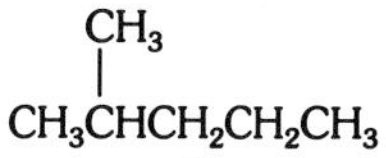

$$\overset{\overset{CH_3}{|}}{CH_3CHCH_2CH_2CH_3} \qquad \overset{\overset{CH_3}{|}}{CH_3CHCH_2CH_2OH}$$
C 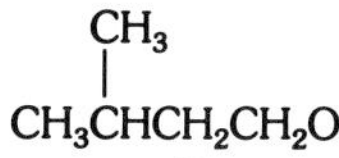   **D**

15.13 Arrange the following compounds in their order of increasing boiling points. Do this by placing the letters that identify them in the correct order, starting with the lowest-boiling compound on the left in the series and moving to the highest-boiling compound.

A   **B**   **C**   **D**

15.14 Reexamine the compounds of Review Exercise 15.12, and arrange them in their order of increasing solubility in water.

15.15 Arrange the compounds of Review Exercise 15.13 in their order of increasing solubility in water.

15.16 Draw the structure of a water molecule and an acetone molecule and align them on the page to show how the acetone molecule can accept a hydrogen bond from the water molecule. Use a dotted line to represent this hydrogen bond and place $\delta+$ and $\delta-$ symbols where they are appropriate.

15.17 Draw the structures of molecules of methanol and ethanal, and align them on the page to show how a hydrogen bond (which you are to indicate by a dotted line) can exist between the two. Place $\delta+$ and $\delta-$ symbols where they are appropriate.

Oxidation of Alcohols and Aldehydes

15.18 What are the structures and the IUPAC names of the aldehydes and ketones to which the following compounds can be oxidized?

(a) $HO-CHCH_2CH_3$ with CH_3 above   (b) $HO-$ cyclopentane

(c) phenyl$-CH_2OH$ (d) CH_3CCH_2OH with CH_3 above and CH_3 below

15.19 Examine each of the following compounds to see whether it can be oxidized to an aldehyde or to a ketone. If it can, write the structure and the IUPAC name of the aldehyde or ketone.

(a) CH_3CH_2OH (b) CH_3CH-OH with OH above

(c) cyclohexane with CH_3 and OH (d) CH_3CHCH_2COH with OH and O

15.20 An unknown compound, C_3H_6O, reacted with permanganate ion to give $C_3H_6O_2$, and the same unknown also gave a positive Tollens' test. Write the structures of C_3H_6O and $C_3H_6O_2$.

15.21 An unknown compound, $C_3H_6O_2$, could be oxidized easily by permanganate ion to $C_3H_4O_3$, and it gave a positive Benedict's test. Write structures for $C_3H_6O_2$ and $C_3H_4O_3$.

15.22 Which of the following compounds can be expected to give a positive Benedict's test? All are intermediates in metabolism.

(a) $HOCH_2CHCH$ with O and HO (b) $HOCH_2CCH_2OH$ with O

(c) CH_3CHCH_2COH with O and OH (d) CH_3CCH_2COH with O and O

15.23 Which of the following compounds give a positive Benedict's test? (Most are intermediates in metabolism.)

(a) $HOCH_2CH-CHCH$ with O, HO and OH (b) $HOCH_2CH_2CCH_3$ with O

(c) CH_3C-CH with O and O (d) $HOC-CCH_3$ with O and O

15.24 Concerning complex ions,
(a) The cations of what kinds of elements are usually involved?
(b) What kinds of particles become associated with these cations in a complex ion?

15.25 Concerning complex ions in test reagents,
(a) What is the formula of the complex ion in Tollens' reagent and why is it important that Ag^+ be so complexed?
(b) What is the function of the citrate ion in Benedict's reagent?

15.26 What is the formula of the precipitate that forms in a positive Benedict's test?

15.27 Clinitest tablets are used for what?

15.28 What is one practical commercial application of Tollens' test?

15.29 Neither the lactate ion nor the pyruvate ion gives a positive Tollens' test. When the body metabolizes the lactate ion, it oxidizes it to the pyruvate ion, $C_3H_3O_3^-$. Using these facts, write the structure of the lactate ion.

15.30 One of the steps in the metabolism of fats and oils in the diet is the oxidation of the following compound:

$$CH_3CHCH_2CO_2^- \text{ with } OH$$

Write the structure of the product of this oxidation.

Reduction of Aldehydes and Ketones

15.31 The hydride ion, as we learned, reacts as follows with water:

$$H:^- + H-OH \longrightarrow H_2 + OH^-$$

The hydride ion reacts in a similar way with $H-O-CH_3$. Write the net ionic equation for this reaction.

15.32 Based on our strategies for figuring out whether a particular negative ion is a strong Brønsted base, how can we tell whether CH_3-O^- is a strong or a weak Brønsted base?

15.33 Consider the reaction that occurs when a hydride ion transfers from its donor (which we can write as $M:H$) to ethanal. (We will see several examples of this kind of reaction in our later study of metabolism.)

(a) Write the structure of the organic anion that forms when the hydride ion is transferred to ethanal.

(b) What is the net ionic equation of the reaction of this anion with water?

(c) What is the IUPAC name of the organic product of this reaction with water?

15.34 If a donor of a hydride ion ($M:H$) transfers it to a molecule of acetone,

(a) What is the structure of the organic ion that forms?

(b) What happens to this anion in the presence of water? (Write a net ionic equation.)

(c) What is the IUPAC name of the organic product of this reaction with water?

15.35 The metabolism of aspartic acid, an amino acid, occurs by a succession of steps, one of which is indicated as follows.

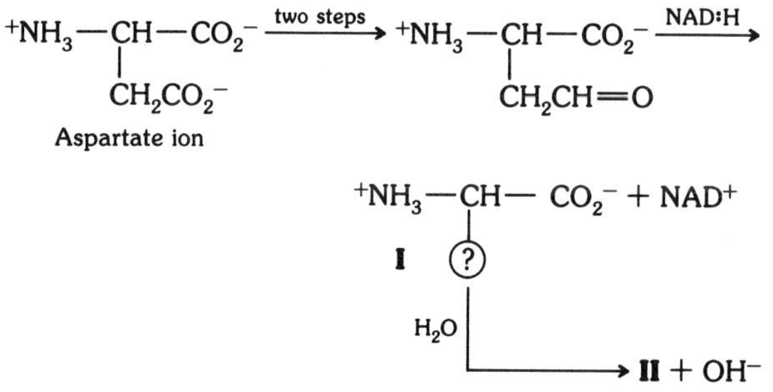

$$^+NH_3-CH-CO_2^- \xrightarrow{\text{two steps}} {}^+NH_3-CH-CO_2^- \xrightarrow{NAD:H}$$
$$\quad\quad | \quad\quad\quad\quad\quad\quad\quad\quad\quad\quad |$$
$$\quad\quad CH_2CO_2^- \quad\quad\quad\quad\quad\quad CH_2CH=O$$

Aspartate ion

$$^+NH_3-CH-CO_2^- + NAD^+$$
$$\mathbf{I} \quad \textcircled{?}$$
$$\quad\quad | \quad H_2O$$
$$\quad\quad \longrightarrow \mathbf{II} + OH^-$$

Complete the structure of **I**, and write the structure of **II**.

15.36 One of the steps the body uses to make long-chain carboxylic acids is a reaction similar to the following.

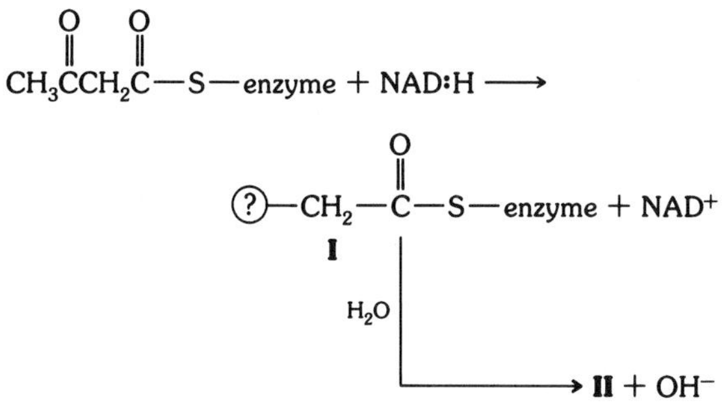

$$\overset{O}{\overset{||}{CH_3C}}CH_2\overset{O}{\overset{||}{C}}-S-\text{enzyme} + NAD:H \longrightarrow$$

$$\textcircled{?}-CH_2-\overset{O}{\overset{||}{C}}-S-\text{enzyme} + NAD^+$$
$$\mathbf{I}$$
$$\quad | \quad H_2O$$
$$\quad\quad \longrightarrow \mathbf{II} + OH^-$$

Complete the structure of **I** and write the structure of **II**.

15.37 Write the structures of the aldehydes or ketones that could be used to make the following compounds by reduction (hydrogenation).

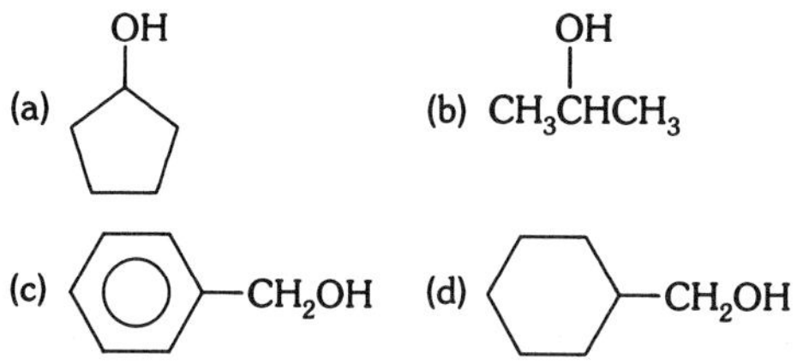

(a) [cyclopentanol structure with OH]

(b) $CH_3\overset{OH}{\overset{|}{CH}}CH_3$

(c) [benzene ring]—CH_2OH (d) [cyclohexane ring]—CH_2OH

Hemiacetals and Acetals. Hemiketals and Ketals

15.38 Examine each structure and decide whether it represents a hemiacetal, hemiketal, acetal, ketal, or something else.

(a) $CH_3-O-\overset{\overset{CH_3}{|}}{CH}-OH$

(b) $CH_3CH_2\overset{\overset{O-CH_3}{|}}{CH}-O-CH_3$

(c) $CH_3-O-\overset{\overset{CH_2-O-CH_3}{|}}{CH}-CH_3$

(d) $CH_3-O-\overset{\overset{O-CH_3}{|}}{C}(CH_3)_2$

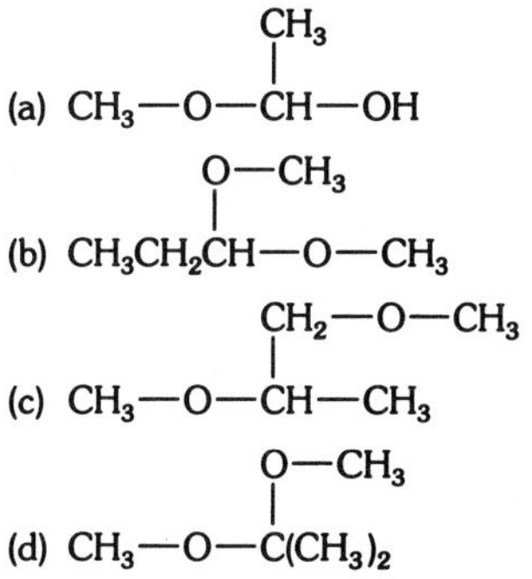

15.39 Examine each structure and decide whether it represents a hemiacetal, hemiketal, acetal, ketal, or something else.

(a) $CH_3-\overset{\overset{OH}{|}}{CH}CH_2-O-CH_3$

(b) $HOCH_2OCH_3$

(c) $HOCH_2\overset{\overset{OCH_3}{|}}{CH}OCH_3$

(d) [ring structure: H_2C-O, H_2C-CH_2, CH—O—CH$_3$]

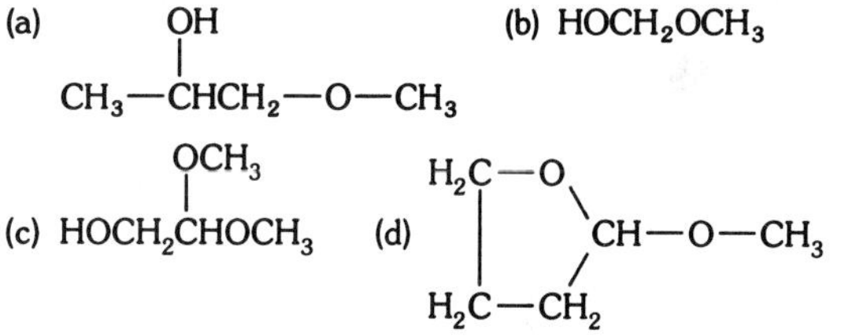

15.40 Either an aldehyde or a ketone could be used to make each of the following compounds by hydrogenation. Write the structure of the aldehyde or ketone suitable in each part.

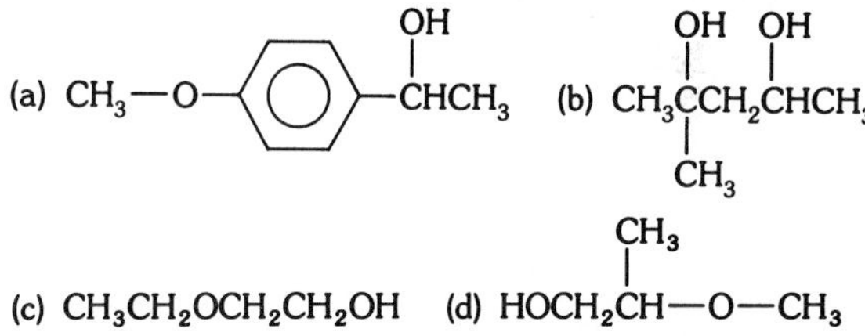

(a) CH_3-O-[benzene ring]$-\overset{\overset{OH}{|}}{CH}CH_3$

(b) $CH_3\overset{\overset{OH}{|}}{C}CH_2\overset{\overset{OH}{|}}{CH}CH_3$ with CH_3

(c) $CH_3CH_2OCH_2CH_2OH$

(d) $HOCH_2\overset{\overset{CH_3}{|}}{CH}-O-CH_3$

15.41 Write the structures of the hemiacetals and the acetals that can form between ethanal and these two alcohols.

(a) methanol   (b) ethanol

15.42 What are the structures of the hemiketals and the ketals that can form between acetone and these two alcohols?

(a) methanol   (b) ethanol

15.43 Write the structure of the hydroxyaldehyde (a compound having both the alcohol group and the aldehyde group in the same molecule) from which the following hemiacetal forms in a ring-closing reaction. (You may leave the chain of the open-chain compound somewhat coiled.)

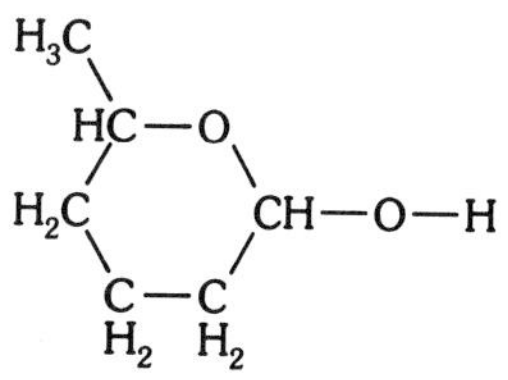

[ring structure: H$_3$C–HC–O, H$_2$C, H$_2$C–C–C–CH—O—H, C$_{H_2}$ C$_{H_2}$]

15.44 One form in which a glucose molecule exists is given by the following structure. (*Note:* The atoms and groups that are attached to the carbon atoms of the six-membered ring must be seen as projecting *above* or *below* the ring.)

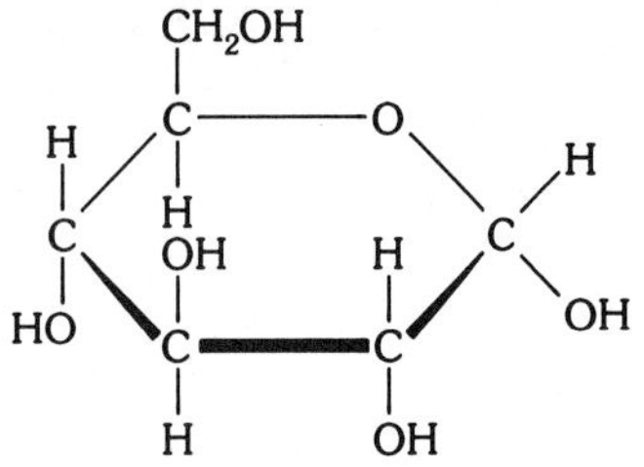

(a) Draw an arrow that points to the hemiacetal carbon.
(b) Write the structure of the open-chain form that has a free aldehyde group. (You may leave the chain coiled.)

15.45 Write the structure of a hydroxy ketone (a molecule that has both the —OH group and the keto group) from which the following hemiketal forms in a ring-closing reaction. (You may leave the chain of the open-chain compound somewhat coiled.)

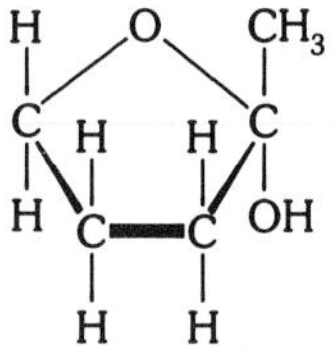

15.46 Fructose occurs together with glucose in honey, and it is sweeter to the taste than table sugar. One form in which a fructose molecule can exist is given by the following structure.

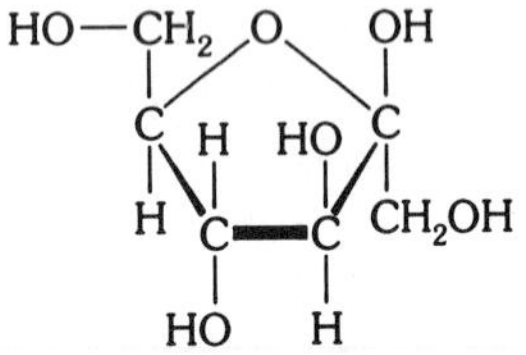

(a) Draw an arrow to the carbon of the hemiketal system that came initially from the carbon atom of a keto group.
(b) In water, fructose exists in an equilibrium with an open-chain form of the given structure. This form has a keto group in the same molecule as five OH groups. Draw the structure of this open-chain form (leaving the chain coiled somewhat as it was in the structure that was given).

15.47 The digestion of some carbohydrates is simply their hydrolysis catalyzed by enzymes. Acids catalyze the same kind of hydrolysis of acetals and ketals. Write the structures of the products, if any, that form by the action of water and an acid catalyst on the following compounds.

(a) CH_3—O—$\overset{\overset{\displaystyle CH_3}{|}}{CH}$—O—$CH_3$

(b) CH_3—O—$\overset{\overset{\displaystyle CH_3}{|}}{CH}$—$CH_2$—O—$CH_3$

(c) CH_3—O—$\overset{\overset{\displaystyle CH_3}{|}}{\underset{\underset{\displaystyle CH_3}{|}}{C}}$—O—$CH_3$

(d)

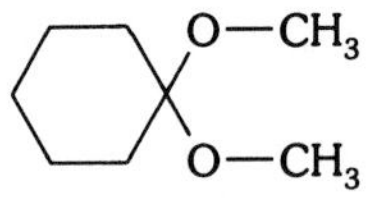

15.48 What are the structures of the products, if any, of the action of water that contains a trace of acid catalyst on the following compounds?

(a)

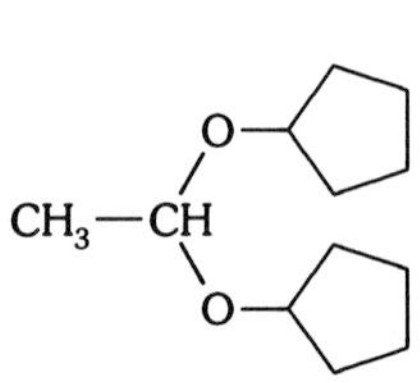

(b)

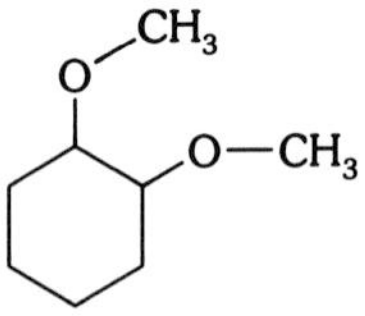

(c)

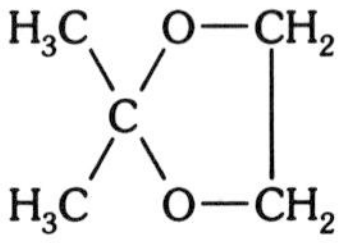

(d) $CH_3CH_2\overset{\overset{\displaystyle O-CH_3}{|}}{CH}$—O—$CH_2CH_3$

15.49 Complete the following reaction sequences by writing the structures of the organic products that form. If no reaction occurs, write "no reaction." (Reviewed here too are some reactions of earlier chapters.)

(a) $CH_3CH=CHCH_3 + H_2 \xrightarrow[\text{heat, pressure}]{\text{Ni}}$

(b) $CH_3\overset{\overset{\displaystyle OH}{|}}{CH}CH_3 + (O) \longrightarrow$

(c) CH_3—O—$\overset{\overset{\displaystyle OCH_3}{|}}{CH}CH_3 + H_2O \xrightarrow{H^+}$

(d) $CH_3\overset{\overset{\displaystyle O}{\|}}{CH} + H_2 \xrightarrow[\text{heat, pressure}]{\text{Ni}}$

(e) $CH_3CH_2\overset{\overset{\displaystyle O}{\|}}{CH} + (O) \longrightarrow$

(f) CH_3—$\overset{\overset{\displaystyle CH_3}{|}}{\underset{\underset{\displaystyle CH_3}{|}}{C}}$—OH + (O) $\longrightarrow$

(g) $CH_3OH + CH_3CH_2\overset{\overset{\displaystyle O}{\|}}{CH} \rightleftharpoons$

(h) CH_3CH_2—O—$CH_2CH_3 + (O) \longrightarrow$

(i) 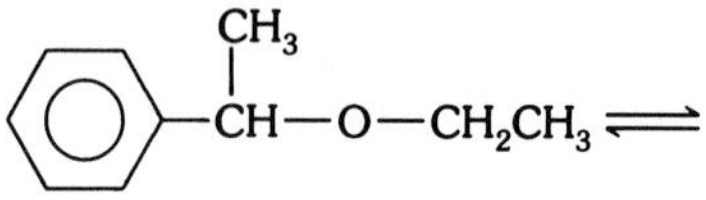 $\rightleftharpoons$

(j) $CH_3\overset{\overset{\displaystyle O}{\|}}{CH} + 2CH_3OH \xrightarrow{\text{acid catalyst}}$

15.50 Write the structures of the organic products that form in each of the following situations. If no reaction occurs, write "no reaction." (Some of the situations constitute a review of reactions in earlier chapters.)

(a)

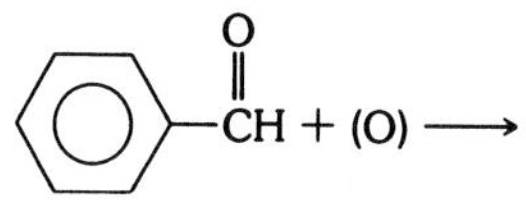

$$\text{(phenyl)}-\overset{\displaystyle O}{\overset{\|}{C}}H + (O) \longrightarrow$$

(b)

$$\text{(cyclopentane with OH)}-CH_3 + (O) \longrightarrow$$

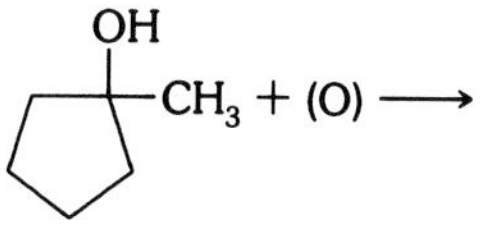

(c) $CH_3\overset{O}{\overset{\|}{C}}H + CH_3CH_2CH_2OH \rightleftharpoons$

(d) $CH_3-O-CH_2CH_2-O-CH_3 + H_2O \xrightarrow{H^+}$

(e) $CH_3CH_2-O-\overset{OH}{\underset{CH_3}{\overset{|}{\underset{|}{C}}}}-CH_3 \rightleftharpoons$

(f) $CH_3CH_2\overset{O}{\overset{\|}{C}}H + H_2 \xrightarrow[\text{heat, pressure}]{Ni}$

(g) $CH_3CH_2\overset{O-CH_2CH_3}{\underset{CH_3}{\overset{|}{\underset{|}{C}}}}-O-CH_2CH_3 + H_2O \xrightarrow{H^+}$

(h)

$$\text{(phenyl)}-\overset{OH}{\overset{|}{C}}HCH_3 + (O) \longrightarrow$$

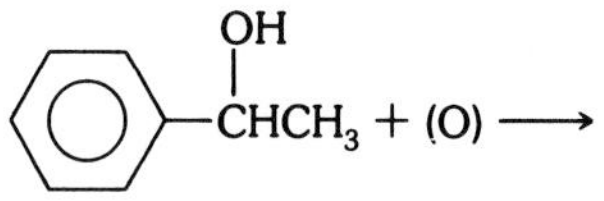

(i) $CH_3-O-CH_2CH{=}CH_2 + H_2 \xrightarrow[\text{heat, pressure}]{Ni}$

(j) $CH_3CH_2\overset{O}{\overset{\|}{C}}H + 2CH_3OH \xrightarrow{H^+}$

15.51 Catalytic hydrogenation of compound A (C_3H_6O) gave B (C_3H_8O). When B was heated strongly in the presence of sulfuric acid, it changed to compound C (C_3H_6). The acid-catalyzed addition of water to C gave compound D (C_3H_8O); and when D was oxidized, it changed to E (C_3H_6O). Compounds A and E are isomers, and compounds B and D are isomers. Write the structures of compounds A through E.

15.52 When compound F ($C_4H_{10}O$) was gently oxidized, it changed to compound G (C_4H_8O), but vigorous oxidation changed F (or G) to compound H ($C_4H_8O_2$). Action of hot sulfuric acid on F changed it to compound I (C_4H_8). The addition of water to I (in the presence of an acid catalyst) gave compound J ($C_4H_{10}O$), a compound that could not be oxidized. Compounds F and J are isomers. Write the structures of compounds F through J.

Important Aldehydes and Ketones (Special Topic 15.1)

15.53 Give the name of a specific aldehyde or ketone described in Special Topic 15.1 that is
(a) A female sex hormone
(b) A good nail polish remover
(c) A preservative
(d) A product of the digestion of starch

The Bonds in the Carbonyl Group (Special Topic 15.2)

15.54 What kinds of atomic orbitals (pure or hybridized) overlap to form the following bonds in formaldehyde?
(a) The C—H bonds
(b) The sigma bond in the carbonyl group
(c) The pi bond in the carbonyl group

15.55 What are the bond angles in formaldehyde? Do all its atoms lie in the same plane?

Carboxylic Acids and Esters

Above the morning fog near Half Dome mountain in Yosemite National Park, this pilot of a hang glider trusts his life to the strength and great resistance to tearing possessed by a polyester fabric, Dacron. Our study of simple esters in this chapter will help us understand polyesters better.

16.1 OCCURRENCE, NAMES, AND PHYSICAL PROPERTIES OF CARBOXYLIC ACIDS

The carboxylic acids are polar compounds whose molecules form strong hydrogen bonds to one another.

The two principal types of organic acids are the carboxylic acids and the sulfonic acids. Sulfonic acids are much less common than carboxylic acids, and we will not study them.

$$-\overset{\overset{\displaystyle O}{\|}}{C}-O-H \quad \text{or} \quad -CO_2H \quad \text{or} \quad -COOH \qquad -\overset{\overset{\displaystyle O}{\|}}{\underset{\underset{\displaystyle O}{|}}{S}}-O-H \quad \text{or} \quad -SO_3H$$

Carboxyl group   Sulfonic acid group

■ "Carboxyl" comes from *carb*onyl + hydr*oxyl*.

In **carboxylic acids,** the carbonyl carbon holds a hydroxyl group and either another carbon atom or a hydrogen atom. A number of specific examples are given in Table 16.1. The acids with straight, alkane-like chains are often called the **fatty acids,** because they are products of the digestion of fats (and oils) in the diet.

The simplest acid, the first one listed in Table 16.1, is formic acid. It has a sharp, irritating odor and is responsible for the sting of nettle plants and certain ants. The next acid, acetic acid, gives tartness to vinegar, where its concentration is 4% to 5%. Butyric acid causes the odor of rancid butter. Valeric acid gets its name from the Latin *valerum,* meaning "to be strong." What is strong about valeric acid is its odor. Other acids with vile odors are caproic, caprylic, and capric acids, which get their names from the Latin *caper,* meaning "goat", a reference to odor.

Some acids are dicarboxylic acids with two carboxyl groups. The simplest is oxalic acid, which gives the tart taste to rhubarb. The tartness of citrus fruits is caused by a tricarboxylic acid, citric acid. Lactic acid, which has both a carboxyl group and a 2° alcohol group, gives the tart taste to sour milk. These facts plus information in Table 16.1 on the origins of other acids show how widely carboxylic acids occur in nature.

$$\underset{\text{Oxalic acid}}{HO-\overset{\overset{\displaystyle O}{\|}}{C}-\overset{\overset{\displaystyle O}{\|}}{C}-OH} \qquad \underset{\text{Citric acid}}{HO-\overset{\overset{\displaystyle CH_2CO_2H}{|}}{\underset{\underset{\displaystyle CH_2CO_2H}{|}}{C}}-CO_2H} \qquad \underset{\text{Lactic acid}}{CH_3\overset{}{\underset{\underset{\displaystyle OH}{|}}{CH}}CO_2H}$$

All carboxylic acids are weak Brønsted acids, and they exist in the form of their anions both in basic solutions and in their salts. It is largely as their anions that they occur in living cells and body fluids.

■ The lactate ion is produced in muscles engaged in strenuous exercise.

$$\underset{\text{Symbols of anions of carboxylic acids}}{R-\overset{\overset{\displaystyle O}{\|}}{C}-O^- \quad \text{or} \quad RCO_2^- \quad \text{or} \quad RCOO^-}$$

IUPAC Names of Carboxylic Acids End in *-oic acid* The IUPAC rules for naming carboxylic acids are similar to those for the aldehydes, including the requirements that the parent acid have the longest chain that includes the carbonyl group and that the carbon atom of this group be given number 1. Once the parent acid is identified, change the ending of the name of the alkane that has the same number of carbons (the parent alkane) from *-e* to *-oic acid.* The names in parenthesis in Table 16.1 are IUPAC names.

■ Use the *name of the acid,* not the name of the alkane, to devise the name of the anion of the acid.

To name anions of carboxylic acids, the *carboxylate ions,* change the ending of the name of the parent *acid* from *-ic* to *-ate* (and omit the word *acid*). This rule applies both to the IUPAC names and to the common names. For example,

TABLE 16.1 Carboxylic Acids

n Structure	Name[a]	Origin of Name	M.Pt. (°C)	B.Pt. (°C)	Solubility (in g/100 g water at 20 °C)	K_a (25 °C)
Straight-chain saturated acids, $C_nH_{2n}O_2$						
1 HCO_2H	Formic acid (methanoic acid)	L. *formica*, ant	8	101	∞	1.8×10^{-4} (20°C)
2 CH_3CO_2H	Acetic acid (ethanoic acid)	L.*acetum*, vinegar	17	118	∞	1.8×10^{-5}
3 $CH_3CH_2CO_2H$	Propionic acid (propanoic acid)	L. *proto, pion*	−21	141	∞	1.3×10^{-5}
4 $CH_3(CH_2)_2CO_2H$	Butyric acid (butanoic acid)	L. *butyrum*, butter	−6	164	∞	1.5×10^{-5}
5 $CH_3(CH_2)_3CO_2H$	Valeric acid (pentanoic acid	L. *valere*, to be strong (valerian root)	−35	186	4.97	1.5×10^{-5}
6 $CH_3(CH_2)_4CO_2H$	Caproic acid (hexanoic acid)	L. *caper*, goat	−3	205	1.08	1.3×10^{-5}
7 $CH_3(CH_2)_5CO_2H$	Enanthic acid (heptanoic acid)	Gr. *oenanthe*, vine blossom	−9	223	0.26	1.3×10^{-5}
8 $CH_3(CH_2)_6CO_2H$	Caprylic acid (octanoic acid)	L. *caper*, goat	16	238	0.07	1.3×10^{-5}
9 $CH_3(CH_2)_7CO_2H$	Pelargonic acid (nonanoic acid)	Pelargonium, geranium	15	254	0.03	1.1×10^{-5}
10 $CH_3(CH_2)_8CO_2H$	Capric acid (decanoic acid)	L. *caper*, goat	32	270	0.015	1.4×10^{-5}
12 $CH_3(CH_2)_{10}CO_2H$	Lauric acid (dodecanoic acid)	Laurel	44	—	0.006	—
14 $CH_3(CH_2)_{12}CO_2H$	Myristic acid (tetradecanoic acid)	Myristica (nutmeg)	54	—	0.002	—
16 $CH_3(CH_2)_{14}CO_2H$	Palmitic acid (hexadecanoic acid)	Palm oil	63	—	0.0007	—
18 $CH_3(CH_2)_{16}CO_2H$	Stearic acid (octadecanoic acid)	Gr. *stear*, solid	70	—	0.0003	—
Miscellaneous carboxylic acids						
$C_6H_5CO_2H$	Benzoic acid	Gum benzoin	122	249	0.34 (25 °C)	6.5×10^{-5}
$C_6H_5CH{=}CHCO_2H$	Cinnamic acid (*trans* isomer)	Cinnamon	132	—	0.04	3.7×10^{-5}
$CH_2{=}CHCO_2H$	Acrylic acid	L. *acer*, sharp	13	141	soluble	5.6×10^{-5}
	Salicylic acid	L. *salix*, willow	159	211	0.22 (25 °C)	1.1×10^{-3} (19 °C)

[a] In parentheses below each common name is the IUPAC name.

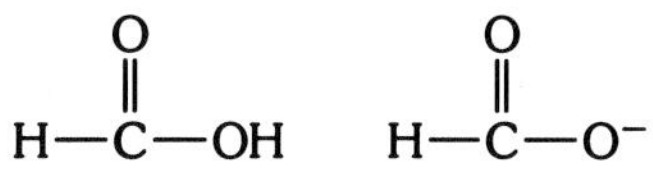

$$\underset{\substack{\text{Methanoic acid}\\\text{(formic acid)}}}{H-\overset{\overset{\displaystyle O}{\|}}{C}-OH} \qquad \underset{\substack{\text{Methanoate ion}\\\text{(formate ion)}}}{H-\overset{\overset{\displaystyle O}{\|}}{C}-O^-}$$

■ Pronounce "oate" as "oh-ate."

EXAMPLE 16.1   NAMING A CARBOXYLIC ACID AND ITS ANION

Problem: The following carboxylic acid has the common name of isovaleric acid. What is the IUPAC name of this acid and its sodium salt?

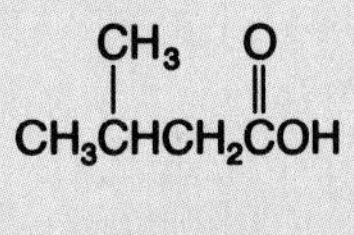

$$\underset{}{CH_3CHCH_2\overset{\overset{\displaystyle O}{\|}}{C}OH}$$
with CH_3 on the CH

Solution: The longest chain that includes the carboxyl group has four carbon atoms, so the parent acid is named by changing the name *butane*, the parent alkane, to *butanoic acid*. Then we have to number the chain, starting with the carboxyl group's carbon.

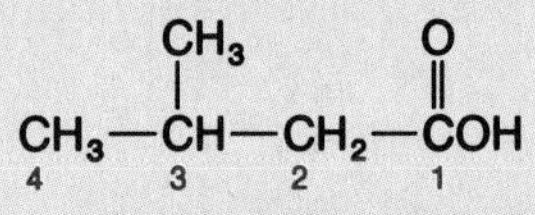

$$\underset{4}{CH_3}-\underset{3}{\underset{|}{\overset{\displaystyle CH_3}{CH}}}-\underset{2}{CH_2}-\underset{1}{\overset{\overset{\displaystyle O}{\|}}{C}OH}$$

The methyl group is at position 3, so the IUPAC name of this acid is 3-methylbutanoic acid.

To name its anion, we drop *-ic acid* from the name and add *-ate*. Therefore the name of the anion is 3-methylbutanoate, and the name of the sodium salt of this acid is sodium 3-methylbutanoate. (The common name is sodium isovalerate.)

PRACTICE EXERCISE 1   What are the IUPAC names of the following compounds?

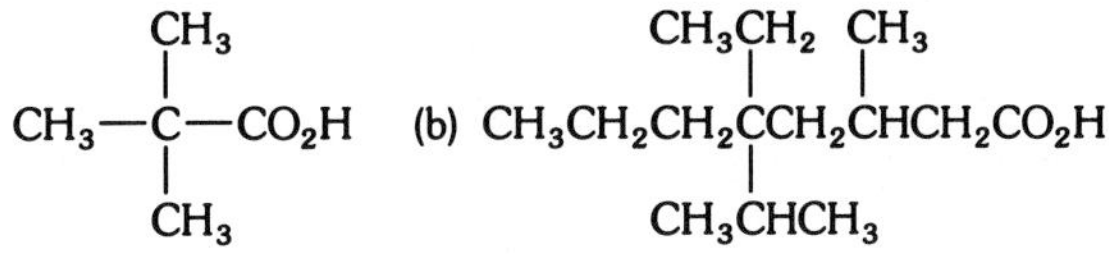

$$CH_3-\underset{\underset{\displaystyle CH_3}{|}}{\overset{\overset{\displaystyle CH_3}{|}}{C}}-CO_2H$$

(b) $CH_3CH_2CH_2\underset{\underset{\displaystyle CH_3CHCH_3}{|}}{\overset{\overset{\displaystyle CH_3CH_2}{|}}{C}}CH_2\overset{\overset{\displaystyle CH_3}{|}}{CH}CH_2CO_2H$

(c) CH_3CO_2Na

(d) $CH_3CH_2CHCH_2\overset{\overset{\displaystyle CH_3}{|}}{CH}CH_2CO_2Na$
with Cl below first CH

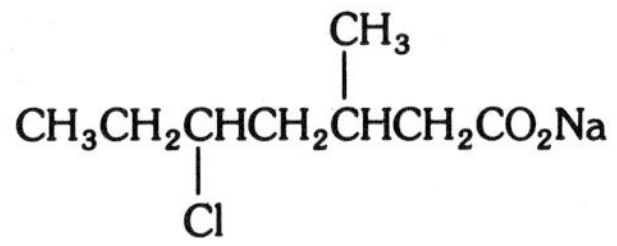

PRACTICE EXERCISE 2   If the IUPAC name of $HO\overset{\overset{\displaystyle O}{\|}}{C}CH_2\overset{\overset{\displaystyle O}{\|}}{C}OH$ is propanedioic acid (and not 1,3-propanedioic acid), what must be the IUPAC name for $HO\overset{\overset{\displaystyle O}{\|}}{C}CH_2CH_2CH_2\overset{\overset{\displaystyle O}{\|}}{C}OH$?

PRACTICE EXERCISE 3   If the IUPAC name of $CH_3CH{=}CHCH_2CH_2CO_2H$ is 4-hexenoic acid, what must be the IUPAC name of the following acid? Its common name is *oleic acid,* and it is one of the products of the digestion of almost any edible vegetable oil or animal fat. (The name of the straight-chain alkane with 18 carbon atoms is octadecane.)

■ Oleic acid is actually the *cis* isomer. The name of the *trans* isomer is elaidic acid.

$$CH_3CH_2CH_2CH_2CH_2CH_2CH_2CH_2CH{=}CHCH_2CH_2CH_2CH_2CH_2CH_2CH_2CO_2H$$
Oleic acid (common name)

Carboxylic Acid Molecules Hydrogen-Bond to Each Other   Carboxylic acids have higher boiling points than alcohols of comparable formula weights, because molecules of carboxylic acids form hydrogen-bonded pairs:

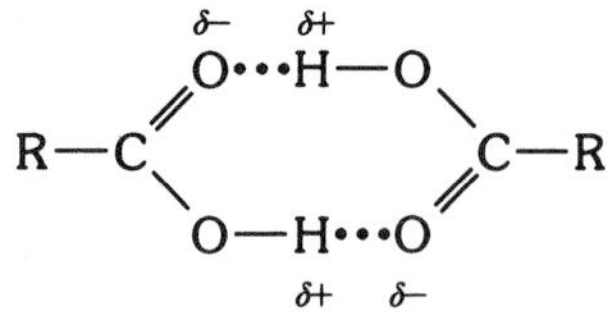

$$R-C \underset{\underset{\delta^+ \quad \delta^-}{\overset{O-H\cdots O}{\Big|}}}{\overset{\overset{\delta^- \quad \delta^+}{O\cdots H-O}}{\Big|}} C-R$$

■ Remember, we're interested in how structure affects solubility in water because water is the fluid medium in the body.

This makes the *effective* formula weight of a carboxylic acid much higher than its calculated formula weight, and therefore the boiling point is higher.

The lower-formula-weight carboxylic acids (C_1-C_4) are soluble in water largely because the carboxyl group has *two* oxygen atoms that can accept hydrogen bonds from water molecules. In addition, the carboxyl group has the OH group that can donate hydrogen bonds.

16.2 THE ACIDITY OF CARBOXYLIC ACIDS

The carboxylic acids are weak Brønsted acids toward water but strong Brønsted acids toward the hydroxide ion.

Aqueous solutions of carboxylic acids contain the following species in equilibrium:

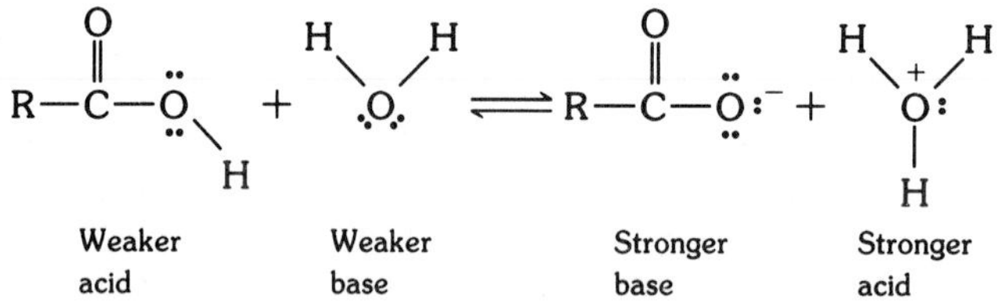

$$R-C\overset{O}{\underset{}{\parallel}}-\overset{..}{\underset{..}{O}}\diagdown_H \ + \ \overset{H}{\underset{}{\diagup}}\overset{..}{\underset{..}{O}}\overset{H}{\diagdown} \ \rightleftharpoons \ R-C\overset{O}{\underset{}{\parallel}}-\overset{..}{\underset{..}{O}}:^- \ + \ \overset{H}{\underset{H}{\diagup}}\overset{+}{\underset{|}{O}}:\overset{H}{\diagdown} \qquad K_a = \frac{[RCO_2^-][H^+]}{[RCO_2H]}$$

| Weaker acid | Weaker base | Stronger base | Stronger acid |

The K_a values of several carboxylic acids are given in Table 16.1, and you can see that most are on the order of 10^{-5}. Thus the carboxylic acids are weak acids toward water, and their percentage ionizations are low. For example, in a $1M$ solution at room temperature, acetic acid is ionized only to about 0.5%.

The Carboxylate Group, RCO_2^-, Is More Stable Than RO^- Carboxylic acids, although weak acids, are vastly stronger acids than alcohols, whose K_a values are on the order of 10^{-16}. This makes alcohols several billion times weaker acids than carboxylic acids. As we have said, alcohols are not proton-donors in water any more than water is.

This greater acidity of the carboxylic acids depends on the greater stability of carboxylate anions compared to that of the anions of alcohols, RO^-. As we indicated in our study of the (weak) acidity of phenols (Section 14.5), when a negative charge is adjacent to a pi-electron system, as it is in the carboxylate ion, the charge spreads out over it. Spreading a charge stabilizes the ion, and this helps to make the carboxylate ion more stable than the RO^- ion from an alcohol. This greater stability is part of the explanation for the greater acidity of carboxylic acids compared to alcohols.

Carboxylic Acids Are Neutralized by Strong Bases The hydroxide ion, the carbonate ion, and the bicarbonate ion are bases strong enough to neutralize carboxylic acids. This reaction is extremely important at the molecular level of life, because the carboxylic acids we normally produce by metabolism must be neutralized. Otherwise, the pH of body fluids, such as the blood, would fall too low (and we would die).

With hydroxide ion, the reaction is as follows.

$$RCO_2H + OH^- \longrightarrow RCO_2^- + H-OH$$

| Stronger acid | Stronger base | Weaker base | Weaker acid |

With bicarbonate ion, the chief base in the buffer systems of the blood, the following reaction occurs:

$$RCO_2H + HCO_3^- \longrightarrow RCO_2^- + H_2O + CO_2$$

Some specific examples are as follows:

$$CH_3CO_2H + OH^- \longrightarrow CH_3CO_2^- + H_2O$$

Acetic acid   Acetate ion

■ The stearate ion is one of several organic ions in soap.

$$CH_3(CH_2)_{16}CO_2H + OH^- \longrightarrow CH_3(CH_2)_{16}CO_2^- + H_2O$$

Stearic acid   Stearate ion
(insoluble in water)   (soluble in water)

$$C_6H_5CO_2H + HCO_3^- \longrightarrow C_6H_5CO_2^- + H_2O + CO_2$$

Benzoic acid   Benzoate ion
(insoluble   (soluble in
in water)   water)

PRACTICE EXERCISE 4   Write the structures of the carboxylate anions that form when the following carboxylic acids are neutralized.

(a) $CH_3CH_2CO_2H$ (b) 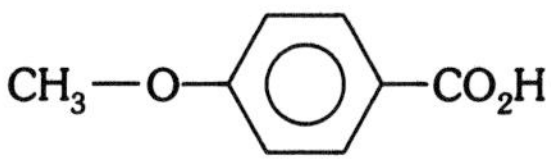 $CH_3—O—\langle\bigcirc\rangle—CO_2H$ (c) $CH_3CH{=}CHCO_2H$

Carboxylate Ions Are More Soluble in Water Than Their Parent Acids   The purified salts that combine carboxylate ions and metal ions are genuine salts, assemblies of oppositely charged ions, so all are solids at room temperature. Table 16.2 gives a few examples of the sodium salts. Like all sodium salts, they are soluble in water but completely insoluble in such nonpolar solvents as ether or gasoline. Several are used as decay inhibitors in foods, as described in Special Topic 16.1.

Carboxylate Ions Are Good Proton-Acceptors or Bases   Because carboxylate ions are the anions of *weak* acids, they themselves must be relatively good bases, especially toward a strong proton donor such as the hydronium ion. At room temperature, the following neutralization of a strong acid by a carboxylate ion occurs virtually instantaneously. It is the most important reaction of the carboxylate ion that we will study, because it makes the carboxylate ion group a neutralizer of excess acid at the molecular level of life.

TABLE 16.2   Some Sodium Salts of Carboxylic Acids

Common Name[a]	Structure	Melting Point (°C)	Solubility	
			Water	Ether
Sodium formate (sodium methanoate)	HCO_2Na	253	Soluble	Insoluble
Sodium acetate (sodium ethanoate)	CH_3CO_2Na	323	Soluble	Insoluble
Sodium propionate (sodium propanoate)	$CH_3CH_2CO_2Na$	—	Soluble	Insoluble
Sodium benzoate	$C_6H_5CO_2Na$	—	66 g/100 mL	Insoluble
Sodium salicylate	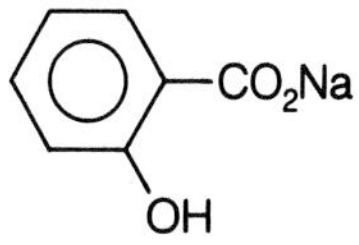 $\langle\bigcirc\rangle{-}CO_2Na$, OH	—	111 g/100 mL	Insoluble

[a] The IUPAC names are in parentheses.

SPECIAL TOPIC 16.1   **SOME IMPORTANT CARBOXYLIC ACIDS AND SALTS**

Acetic Acid   Most people experience acetic acid directly in the form of its dilute solution in water, which is called vinegar. Because blood is slightly alkaline, acetic acid circulates as the acetate ion, and we will meet this species many times when we study metabolic pathways. The acetate ion, in fact, is one of the major intermediates in the metabolism of carbohydrates, lipids, and proteins.

Acetic acid is also an important industrial chemical, and more than 3 billion pounds (23 billion moles) are manufactured each year in the United States. Acetate rayon is just one consumer product made using acetic acid.

Propanoic Acid and Its Salts   Propanoic acid occurs naturally in Swiss cheese, in a concentration that can be as high as 1%. Its sodium and calcium salts are food additives used in baked goods and processed cheese to retard the formation of molds or the growth of bacteria. (On ingredient labels, these salts are listed under their common names, sodium or calcium propionate.)

Sorbic Acid and the Sorbates   Sorbic acid, or 2,4-hexanedienoic acid, $CH_3CH=CHCH=CHCO_2H$, and its sodium or potassium salts are added in trace concentrations to a variety of foods to inhibit the growth of molds and yeasts. The sorbates often appear on ingredient lists for fruit juices, fresh fruits, wines, soft drinks, sauerkraut and other pickled products, and some meat and fish products. For food products that usually are wrapped, such as cheese and dried fruits, solutions of sorbate salts are sometimes sprayed onto the wrappers.

Sodium Benzoate   Traces of sodium benzoate inhibit molds and yeasts in products that normally have pH values below 4.5 or 4.0. (The sorbates work better at slightly higher pH values—up to 6.5.) You'll see sodium benzoate on ingredient lists for beverages, syrups, jams and jellies, pickles, salted margarine, fruit salads, and pie fillings. Its concentration is low—0.05% to 0.10%—and neither benzoic acid nor the benzoate ion accumulates in the body.

■ These rapid proton transfers don't require any heating, either.

$$R-CO_2^- + H-\overset{\overset{+}{H}}{\underset{H}{O}} \longrightarrow R-CO_2H + H-OH$$

Stronger base   Stronger acid   Weaker acid   Weaker base

For example,

$$C_6H_5CO_2^- + H_3O^+ \longrightarrow C_6H_5CO_2H + H_2O$$

Benzoate ion (soluble in water)   Benzoic acid (insoluble in water)

$$CH_3(CH_2)_{16}CO_2^- + H_3O^+ \longrightarrow CH_3(CH_2)_{16}CO_2H + H_2O$$

Stearate ion (soluble in water)   Stearic acid (insoluble in water)

The Carboxylic Acid Group Is a Solubility "Switch"   In these reactions, we have noted the solubilities in water of several species to draw attention to a very important property that the carboxylic acid group gives to a molecule. It can be used to switch on or off the solubility in water of any substance that contains this group. When we try to increase the pH of a solution—by adding a strong base—a water-insoluble carboxylic acid almost instantly dissolves, because it changes to its carboxylate ion. Similarly, when we try to decrease the pH of a solution—by adding a strong acid—a water-soluble carboxylate anion instantly changes to its much less soluble, free carboxylic acid form. In other words, by suitably adjusting the pH of an aqueous solution, we can make a substance with a carboxyl group more soluble or less soluble in water. The body often takes advantage of this kind of solubility "switch."

PRACTICE EXERCISE 5   Write the structures of the organic products of the reactions of the following compounds with dilute hydrochloric acid at room temperature.

(a) $CH_3-O-\langle\bigcirc\rangle-CO_2^-K^+$ (b) $CH_3CH_2CO_2^-Li^+$ (c) $(CH_3CH=CHCO_2^-)_2Ca^{2+}$

16.3 THE CONVERSION OF CARBOXYLIC ACIDS TO ESTERS

Carboxylic acids can be used directly or indirectly to make esters from alcohols.

■ We'll learn how to name esters soon, but we will not develop the rules for naming acid chlorides or acid anhydrides.

The carboxylic acids are the parent compounds for several families that collectively are called the **acid derivatives.** These include the **acid chlorides,** the **anhydrides** (both common and mixed anhydrides), the **esters,** and the **amides.** They are called acid *derivatives* because they can be made from the acids and they can be hydrolyzed back to the acids.

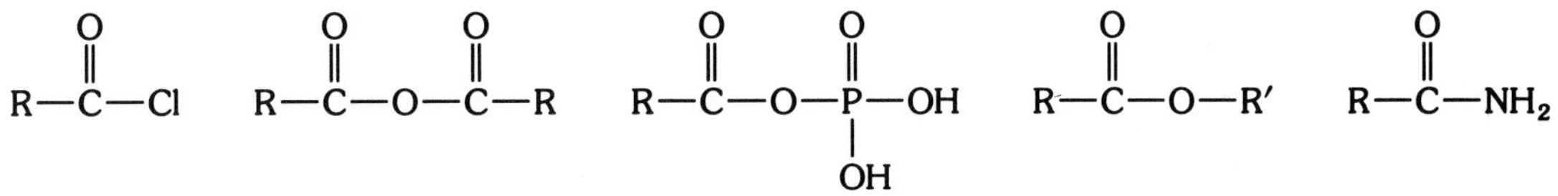

$$R-\overset{\overset{\displaystyle O}{\|}}{C}-Cl \qquad R-\overset{\overset{\displaystyle O}{\|}}{C}-O-\overset{\overset{\displaystyle O}{\|}}{C}-R \qquad R-\overset{\overset{\displaystyle O}{\|}}{C}-O-\underset{\underset{\displaystyle OH}{|}}{\overset{\overset{\displaystyle O}{\|}}{P}}-OH \qquad R-\overset{\overset{\displaystyle O}{\|}}{C}-O-R' \qquad R-\overset{\overset{\displaystyle O}{\|}}{C}-NH_2$$

| Acid chlorides | Acid anhydrides | Mixed anhydrides with phosphoric acid | Esters | Amides |

Neither the acid chlorides nor the simple acid anhydrides occur in the body, because these compounds react too readily with water and with alcohol groups. We include them in our study because they are often used in the lab to make esters (e.g., aspirin), and because their reactions leading to esters are simple examples of **acyl group transfer reactions.** An **acyl group** is a carboxylic acid minus its OH group.

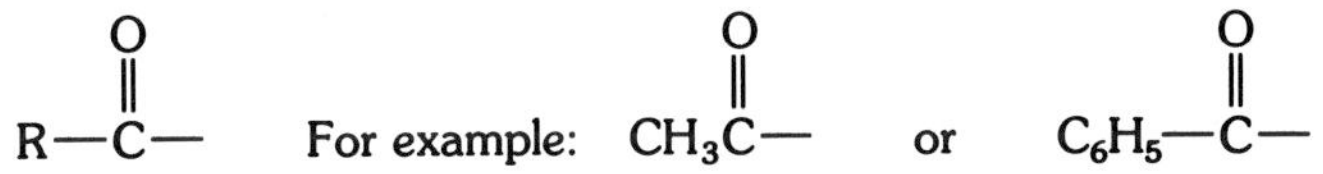

$$R-\overset{\overset{\displaystyle O}{\|}}{C}- \qquad \text{For example:} \quad CH_3\overset{\overset{\displaystyle O}{\|}}{C}- \quad \text{or} \quad C_6H_5-\overset{\overset{\displaystyle O}{\|}}{C}-$$

| Acyl group | Acetyl group | Benzoyl group |

Thus the acyl group is in the molecules of all carboxylic acids, esters, acid chlorides, anhydrides, and amides.

Acid Chlorides Are the Most Reactive of Acid Derivatives   Acid chlorides react readily and exothermically with water to give the parent acids and hydrogen chloride (which, because of the *excess water,* forms as hydrochloric acid). In this reaction an acyl group transfers from —Cl to OH. We call the chloride ion a *leaving group.*

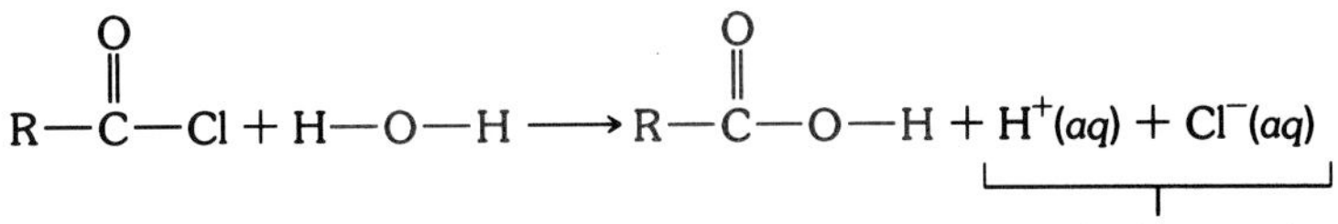

$$R-\overset{\overset{\displaystyle O}{\|}}{C}-Cl + H-O-H \longrightarrow R-\overset{\overset{\displaystyle O}{\|}}{C}-O-H + H^+(aq) + Cl^-(aq)$$

| Acid chloride | Carboxylic acid | Hydrochloric acid |

Acid chlorides also react vigorously with alcohols to give esters. In this reaction an acyl group transfers to an alcohol unit.

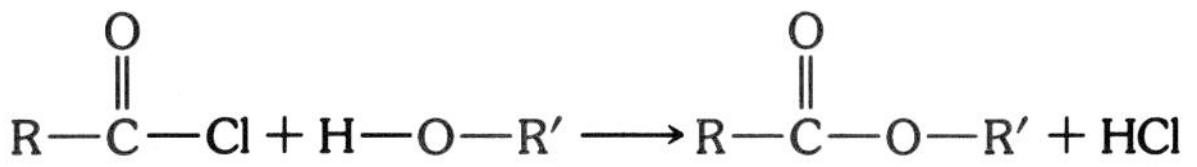

$$R-\overset{\overset{\displaystyle O}{\|}}{C}-Cl + H-O-R' \longrightarrow R-\overset{\overset{\displaystyle O}{\|}}{C}-O-R' + HCl$$

| Acid chloride | Alcohol | Ester |

For example,

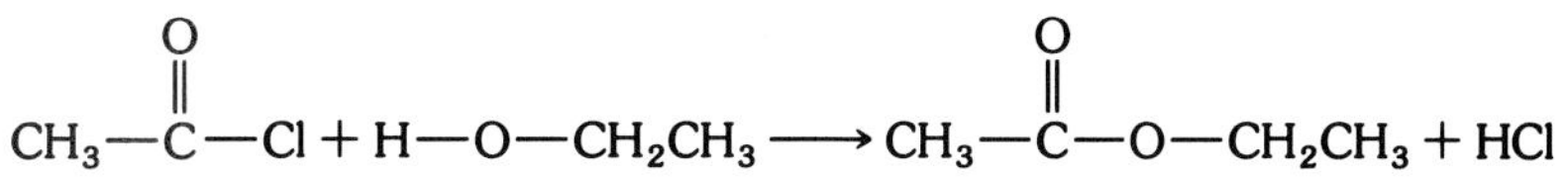

$$CH_3-\overset{\overset{\displaystyle O}{\|}}{C}-Cl + H-O-CH_2CH_3 \longrightarrow CH_3-\overset{\overset{\displaystyle O}{\|}}{C}-O-CH_2CH_3 + HCl$$

| Acetyl chloride | Ethyl alcohol | Ethyl acetate (ethyl ethanoate) |

This is an example of a reaction called an **esterification,** the synthesis of an ester. We say that the alcohol is *esterified*. We could also say that the acid has been esterified by this method.

Acid Anhydrides Are Good Acyl Transfer Reactants   When a carboxylic acid anhydride reacts with an alcohol, an acyl group transfers from a carboxylate group to OR. This reaction occurs with roughly the same ease as the reaction of an acid chloride with an alcohol. Acid anhydrides react with alcohols as follows:

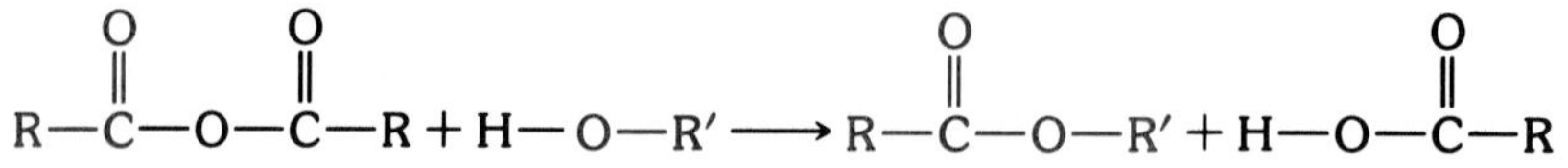

$$
\underset{\substack{\text{Acid}\\\text{anhydride}}}{R-\overset{\overset{\displaystyle O}{\|}}{C}-O-\overset{\overset{\displaystyle O}{\|}}{C}-R} + \underset{\text{Alcohol}}{H-O-R'} \longrightarrow \underset{\text{Ester}}{R-\overset{\overset{\displaystyle O}{\|}}{C}-O-R'} + \underset{\substack{\text{Carboxylic}\\\text{acid}}}{H-O-\overset{\overset{\displaystyle O}{\|}}{C}-R}
$$

Phenols, like alcohols, can be also esterifed by acid anhydrides. When the acid anhydride is acetic anhydride and the phenol group is in salicylic acid, one product is aspirin:

■ Both salicylic acid and acetic anhydride are common, readily available organic chemicals.

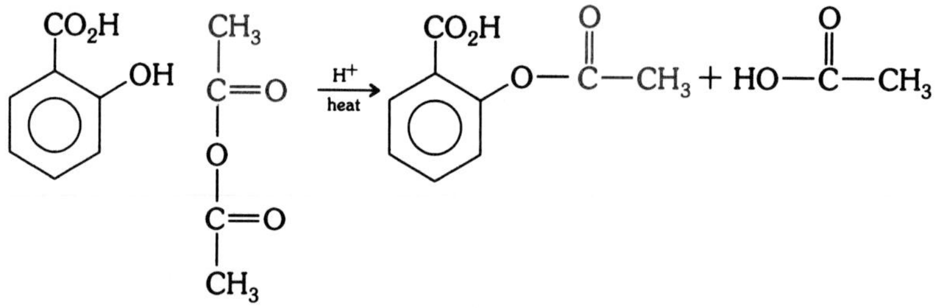

Salicylic acid   Acetic anhydride   Acetyl salicylic acid (aspirin)

Direct Esterification of Acids Is Another Synthesis of Esters   When a solution of a carboxylic acid in an alcohol is heated, and a strong acid catalyst is present, the following species become involved in an equilibrium.

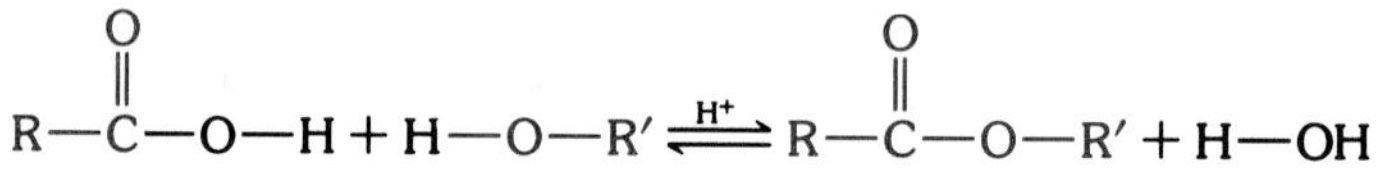

$$
\underset{\substack{\text{Carboxylic}\\\text{acid}}}{R-\overset{\overset{\displaystyle O}{\|}}{C}-O-H} + \underset{\text{Alcohol}}{H-O-R'} \underset{}{\overset{H^+}{\rightleftharpoons}} \underset{\text{Ester}}{R-\overset{\overset{\displaystyle O}{\|}}{C}-O-R'} + H-OH
$$

When the alcohol is in excess, Le Chatelier's principle operates and the equilibrium shifts so much to the right that this is a good method for making an ester. This synthesis of an ester is called *direct esterification*. Some specific examples are as follows.

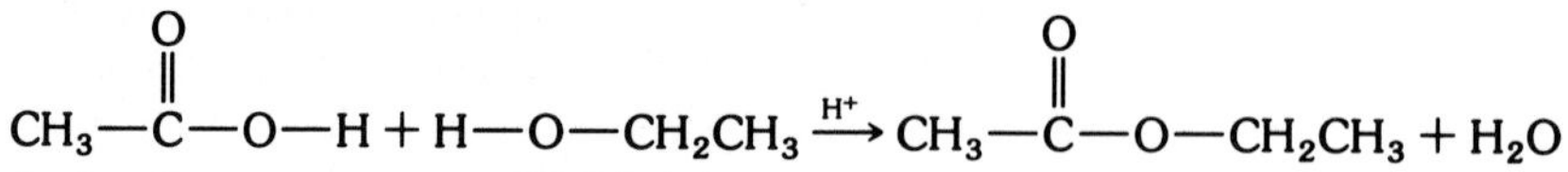

$$
\underset{\text{Acetic acid}}{CH_3-\overset{\overset{\displaystyle O}{\|}}{C}-O-H} + \underset{\substack{\text{Ethyl alcohol}\\\text{(large excess)}}}{H-O-CH_2CH_3} \overset{H^+}{\longrightarrow} \underset{\text{Ethyl acetate}}{CH_3-\overset{\overset{\displaystyle O}{\|}}{C}-O-CH_2CH_3} + H_2O
$$

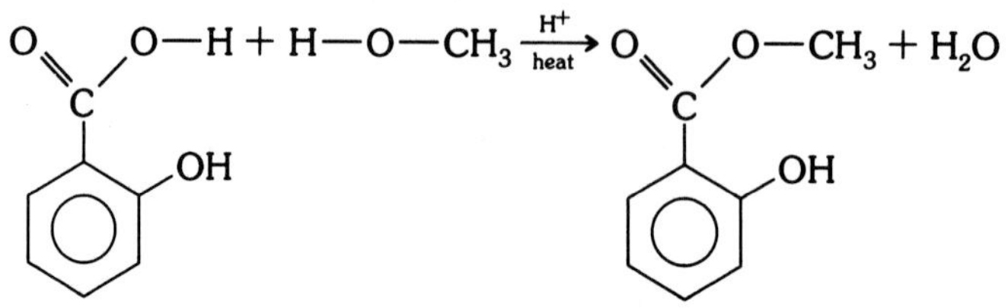

Salicylic acid   Methyl alcohol (large excess)   Methyl salicylate (oil of wintergreen)

EXAMPLE 16.2	WRITING THE STRUCTURE OF A PRODUCT OF DIRECT ESTERIFICATION

Problem: What is the ester that can be made from benzoic acid and methyl alcohol?

Solution: Write the structures of the two reactants. Sometimes it helps to let the OH groups "face" each other:

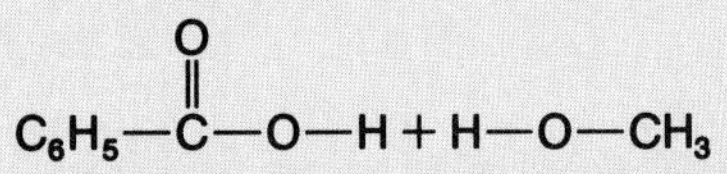

$$
\underset{\text{Benzoic acid}}{C_6H_5-\overset{\overset{\displaystyle O}{\|}}{C}-O-H} + \underset{\text{Methyl alcohol}}{H-O-CH_3}
$$

■ Although it is not important in predicting correct structures of products, always erase the OH group from the carboxylic acid, not the alcohol. This will make it easier to learn a reaction coming up in the next chapter.

To obtain the pieces of the water molecule, the other product of direct esterification, we have to remove the OH group from the acid and the proton on oxygen from the alcohol. This leaves us with the following fragments:

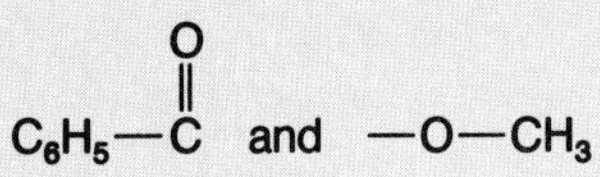

$$
C_6H_5-\overset{\overset{\displaystyle O}{\|}}{C} \quad \text{and} \quad -O-CH_3
$$

Now all that is left to do is join these fragments.

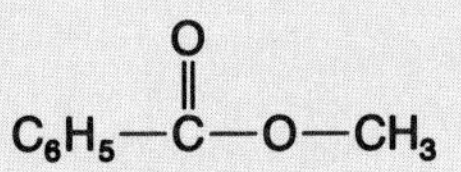

$$
\underset{\text{Methyl benzoate}}{C_6H_5-\overset{\overset{\displaystyle O}{\|}}{C}-O-CH_3} \quad \text{(The product of the esterification)}
$$

PRACTICE EXERCISE 6
Write the structures of the esters that form by the direct esterification of acetic acid by the following alcohols.

(a) methyl alcohol   (b) propyl alcohol   (c) isopropyl alcohol

PRACTICE EXERCISE 7
Write the structures of the esters that can be made by the direct esterification of ethyl alcohol by the following acids.

(a) formic acid   (b) propionic acid   (c) benzoic acid

The Acid Catalyst Helps the Transfer of the Acyl Group from the Acid to the Alcohol's Oxygen Atom Without the acid catalyst, direct esterification would proceed very slowly. The catalyst works by converting what is a very poor leaving group in the acid into one stable enough to be a good leaving group. (Somewhat arbitrarily, we designate the OH group as the leaving group and the acyl group as the transferring group.) If the acyl group had to transfer out of the carboxylic acid molecule, the OH group *as a hydroxide ion* would be the leaving group. This ion is a strong base and so is not a good leaving group. The acid catalyst, however, donates a proton to the OH group, and thus sets up the carboxylic acid molecule to drop off a stable water molecule as the acyl group transfers.

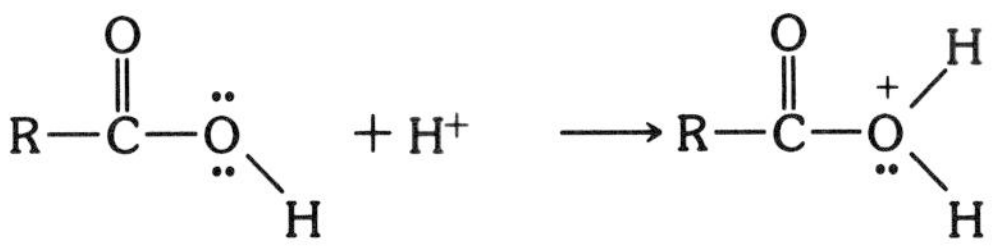

$$
R-\overset{\overset{\displaystyle O}{\|}}{C}-\overset{..}{\underset{..}{O}}\diagdown_{H} + H^+ \longrightarrow R-\overset{\overset{\displaystyle O}{\|}}{C}-\overset{+}{\underset{..}{O}}\diagdown^{H}_{H}
$$

Catalyst   Protonated form of the carboxylic acid

In its protonated form, as shown, the bond from the carbonyl carbon atom to the potential leaving group (water) is weak in comparison to this bond in the unprotonated form of the carboxylic acid. The extra positive charge in the protonated acid draws the electrons of this bond away from the carbonyl carbon. Moreover, this carbon now has a larger partial positive

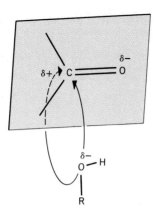

Figure 16.1
An alcohol molecule can attack a carbonyl carbon atom from either side of the planar carbonyl group. The other groups already attached to the carbonyl carbon atom interfere very little with this attack. Therefore when one of these other groups is a particularly stable leaving group, such as Cl or a carboxylate group, the carbonyl compound is especially reactive toward alcohols (and water, too).

charge, $\delta+$, so besides being wide open to attack (Figure 16.1), it attracts the alcohol molecule more strongly. For all these reasons, the alcohol more readily attacks the carboxylic acid when the strong acid catalyst is used. We can visualize the acyl group transfer as follows.

16.4 OCCURRENCE, NAMES, AND PHYSICAL PROPERTIES OF ESTERS

Esters are moderately polar compounds.

The functional group of an ester is the central structural feature of all the edible fats and oils as well as a number of constituents of body cells. Be sure you can recognize this group and pick out what we will call the *ester linkage*, the single bond between the carbonyl carbon atom and the oxygen atom that holds the ester's alkyl group. This linkage is where an ester breaks apart when it reacts with water.

Two general formulas for esters

Ester group (carbonyl-oxygen-carbon)

Table 16.3 lists several common esters.

One interesting feature about acids and their esters is that the low-formula-weight acids have vile odors, but their esters have some of the most pleasant fragrances in all of nature. (See Table 16.4.) Special Topic 16.2 describes some important esters in more detail.

The Acid Portions of Esters and Carboxylate Ions Have Identical Names Common and IUPAC names of esters are devised in the same way. For the moment, simply ignore the R′ group of an ester, the part supplied by the alcohol, and focus on the acid portion.

TABLE 16.3 Esters of Carboxylic Acids

Common Name[a]	Structure	Melting Point (°C)	Boiling Point (°C)	Solubility (in g/100 g water, 20 °C)
Ethyl esters of straight-chain carboxylic acids, $RCO_2C_2H_5$				
Ethyl formate (ethyl methanoate)	$HCO_2C_2H_5$	−79	54	Soluble
Ethyl acetate (ethyl ethanoate)	$CH_3CO_2C_2H_5$	−82	77	7.35 (25 °C)
Ethyl propionate (ethyl propanoate)	$CH_3CH_2CO_2C_2H_5$	−73	99	1.75
Ethyl butyrate (ethyl butanoate)	$CH_3(CH_2)_2CO_2C_2H_5$	−93	120	0.51
Ethyl valerate (ethyl pentanoate)	$CH_3(CH_2)_3CO_2C_2H_5$	−91	145	0.22
Ethyl caproate (ethyl hexanoate)	$CH_3(CH_2)_4CO_2C_2H_5$	−68	168	0.063
Ethyl enanthate (ethyl heptanoate)	$CH_3(CH_2)_5CO_2C_2H_5$	−66	189	0.030
Ethyl caprylate (ethyl octanoate)	$CH_3(CH_2)_6CO_2C_2H_5$	−43	208	0.007
Ethyl pelargonate (ethyl nonanoate)	$CH_3(CH_2)_7CO_2C_2H_5$	−45	222	0.003
Ethyl caproate (ethyl decanoate)	$CH_3(CH_2)_8CO_2C_2H_5$	−20	245	0.0015
Esters of acetic acid, CH_3CO_2R				
Methyl acetate	$CH_3CO_2CH_3$	−99	57	24.4
Ethyl acetate	$CH_3CO_2CH_2CH_3$	−82	77	7.39 (25 °C)
Propyl acetate	$CH_3CO_2CH_2CH_2CH_3$	−93	102	1.89
Butyl acetate	$CH_3CO_2CH_2CH_2CH_2CH_3$	−78	125	1.0 (22 °C)
Miscellaneous esters				
Methyl acrylate (methyl propenoate)	$CH_2{=}CHCO_2CH_3$		80	5.2
Methyl benzoate	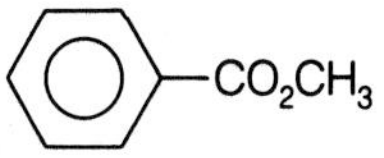 $C_6H_5{-}CO_2CH_3$	−12	199	Insoluble
Methyl salicylate	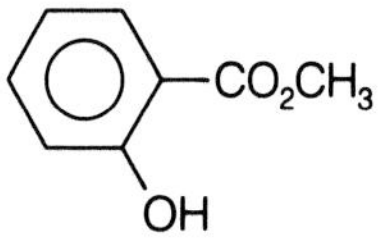 $C_6H_4(OH){-}CO_2CH_3$	−9	223	Insoluble
Acetylsalicylic acid	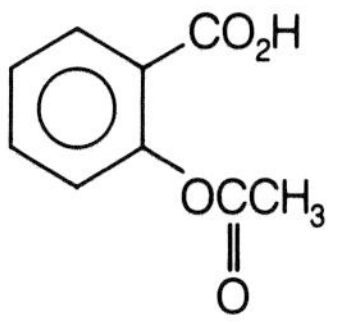 $C_6H_4(OCCH_3{=}O){-}CO_2H$	135		
Natural waxes	$CH_3(CH_2)_nCO_2(CH_2)_nCH_3$	$n = 23{-}33$: carnauba wax $= 25{-}27$: beeswax $= 14{-}15$: spermaceti		

[a] IUPAC names are in parentheses.

Esters of *p*-Hydroxybenzoic Acid — the Parabens Several alkyl esters of *p*-hydroxybenzoic acid — referred to as *parabens* on ingredient labels — are used to inhibit molds and yeasts in cosmetics, pharmaceuticals, and food.

Salicylates Certain esters and salts of salicylic acid are analgesics, the pain suppressants; and antipyretics; the fever reducers. The parent acid, salicylic acid, is itself too irritating to the stomach for these uses, but sodium salicylate and acetylsalicylic acid (aspirin) are commonly used. Methyl salicylate, a pleasant-smelling oil, is used in liniments, for it readily migrates through the skin.

Sodium salicylate

Acetyl salicylic acid (aspirin)

Methyl salicylate (oil of wintergreen)

Dacron Dacron, a polyester of exceptional strength, is widely used to make fabrics and film backing for recording tapes. (Actually, the name *Dacron* applies just to the fiber form of this polyester. When it is cast as a thin film, its name is *Mylar*.) Dacron fabrics have been used in surgery to repair or replace segments of blood vessels, as seen in Figure 16.2.

The formation of Dacron and many other polyfunctional polymers starts with two difunctional monomers, *aAa* and *bBb*. Their functional groups are able to react with each other to split out a small molecule, *ab*. The monomer fragments, *A* and *B*, join end to end to make a very long, polymer molecule. In principle, the polymerization can be represented as follows:

$$aAa + bBb + aAa + bBb + aAa + bBb + \ldots \text{ etc.} \longrightarrow$$
$$-A-B-A-B-A-B- \ldots \text{ etc.} + n(ab)$$

A copolymer

Because two monomers are used, the reaction is called *copolymerization.*

One monomer used to make Dacron, is ethylene gly-

Figure 16.2
The knitted tubing for this graft in an operative site is made of Dacron fibers.

col, which has two alcohol OH groups. The other monomer is dimethyl terephthalate, which has two methyl ester groups. The copolymerization of these two monomers depends on a reaction of esters with alcohols that we will not study in detail. It's a reaction, however, in which two alkyl groups switch places; the alcohol's alkyl group replaces the alkyl group on the ester molecule and a new ester and a new alcohol form. In the copolymerization of ethylene glycol and dimethyl terephthalate, the ester's two methyl groups end up in molecules of methyl alcohol. Thus the *ab* molecule that splits out is methyl alcohol, and the terephthalate unit has become an ester of ethylene glycol. The copolymerization proceeds as follows.

Ethylene glycol

Dimethyl terephthalate

(Repeating unit)
Dacron/Mylar

TABLE 16.4 Fragrances or Flavors of Some Esters

Name	Structure	Source of Flavor
Ethyl formate	$HCO_2CH_2CH_3$	Rum
Isobutyl formate	$HCO_2CH_2CH(CH_3)_2$	Raspberries
Pentyl acetate	$CH_3CO_2CH_2CH_2CH_2CH_2CH_3$	Bananas
Isopentyl acetate	$CH_3CO_2CH_2CH_2CH(CH_3)_2$	Pears
Octyl acetate	$CH_3CO_2(CH_2)_7CH_3$	Oranges
Ethyl butyrate	$CH_3CH_2CH_2CO_2CH_2CH_3$	Pineapples
Pentyl butyrate	$CH_3CH_2CH_2CO_2(CH_2)_4CH_3$	Apricots
Methyl salicylate	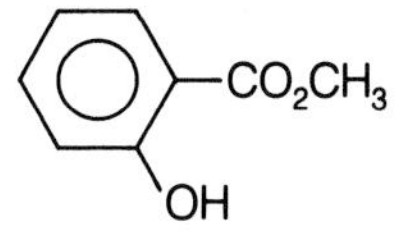 (benzene ring)—CO_2CH_3 with OH	Oil of wintergreen

Acid portion

$$R-\overset{\overset{\displaystyle O}{\|}}{C}-O-R'$$

Alcohol portion of ester

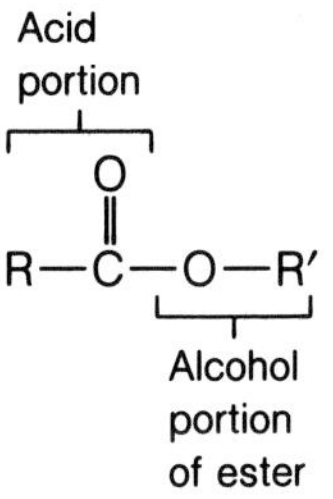

Pretend you are naming the *anion* of the acid. Remember that in both the common and the IUPAC names for this anion, the *-ic* ending of the name of the parent acid is changed to *-ate*. Thus salts of acetic acid (ethanoic acid) are called acetate salts (common name) or ethanoate salts (IUPAC). Similarly, esters of this acid are called acetate esters (common) or ethanoate esters (IUPAC).

Once you have the name of the acid portion of the ester, simply write the name of the alkyl group in the ester's alcohol portion in front of this name (as a separate word). Here are some examples that show the pattern. (The IUPAC names are in parentheses.)

Ester	Name of Parent Acid	Name of Acid Portion of Ester	Alkyl Group in Ester	Name of Ester
$CH_3-\overset{\overset{\displaystyle O}{\|}}{C}-O-CH_3$	Acetic acid (ethanoic acid)	Acetate (ethanoate)	Methyl	Methyl acetate (methyl ethanoate)
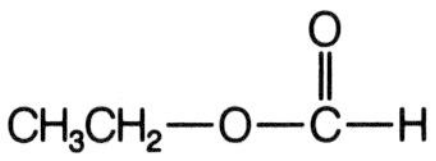 $CH_3CH_2-O-\overset{\overset{\displaystyle O}{\|}}{C}-H$	Formic acid (methanoic acid)	Formate (methanoate)	Ethyl	Ethyl formate (ethyl methanoate)

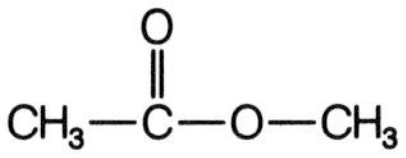

EXAMPLE 16.3   **WRITING IUPAC NAMES FOR ESTERS**

Problem: What is the IUPAC name for the following ester?

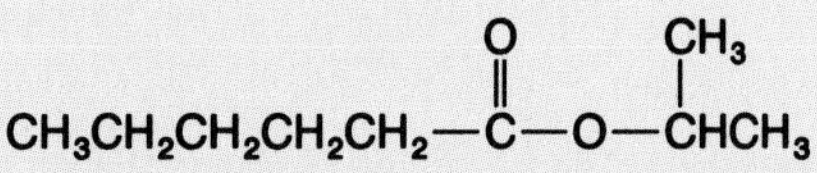

$$CH_3CH_2CH_2CH_2CH_2-\overset{\overset{\displaystyle O}{\|}}{C}-O-\overset{\overset{\displaystyle CH_3}{|}}{C}HCH_3$$

Solution: First, figure out what part of this structure came initially from a parent alcohol. This is the alkyl group, or the nonacyl group. In this ester, the alcohol part is the isopropyl group on the right in the structure. The parent acid of the ester, the part with the acyl group, has a chain six carbons long. Therefore the parent acid is hexanoic acid, so for the ester we change the *-ic acid* ending to *-ate* to give hexanoate. Finally, we have to add the name *isopropyl* (as a separate word). This ester is named

Isopropyl hexanoate   (The answer)

Write the IUPAC names of the following esters.

$$CH_3$$
$$|$$
(a) $CH_3CH_2CO_2CH_3$ (b) $CH_3CH_2CHCH_2CO_2CH_2CH_2CH_3$

Using the patterns developed, write the common names of the following esters.

$$CH_3$$
$$|$$
(a) $CH_3CO_2CCH_3$ (b) $CH_3CH_2CH_2CO_2CH_2CH_3$
$$|$$
$$CH_3$$

The Ester Group Is Polar But Cannot Donate Hydrogen Bonds   The inability of the ester group to donate hydrogen bonds affects boiling points. Esters of the lower-formula-weight alcohols, like methyl and ethyl alcohol, have lower boiling points than their parent acids. Even though methyl acetate, for example, has a higher formula weight than acetic acid, it boils at 57 °C, whereas acetic acid boils at 118 °C.

This ester group, because it has oxygen atoms, can *accept* hydrogen bonds, however. This allows the lower-formula-weight esters to be relatively soluble in water.

16.5   SOME REACTIONS OF ESTERS

Ester molecules are broken apart by water in the presence of either acids or bases.

The reaction of esters with water is very slow unless some catalyst or promoter is present. Strong acids as well as special enzymes are good catalysts, and strong bases promote the reaction while becoming neutralized. Ester hydrolysis, catalyzed by enzymes, is the chemistry of the digestion of fats and oils.

Esters Hydrolyze to Their Parent Acids and Alcohols   An ester reacts with water to give the carboxylic acid and the alcohol from which the ester could be made. This reaction is called the hydrolysis of an ester, and a strong acid catalyst is generally used. (In the body, an enzyme acts as the catalyst.) In general,

$$R-\overset{\overset{\displaystyle O}{\|}}{C}-O-R' + H-OH \xrightarrow[\text{heat}]{H^+} R-\overset{\overset{\displaystyle O}{\|}}{C}-O-H + H-O-R'$$

Specific examples are

$$CH_3-\overset{\overset{\displaystyle O}{\|}}{C}-O-CH_2CH_3 + H_2O \xrightarrow[\text{heat}]{H^+} CH_3-\overset{\overset{\displaystyle O}{\|}}{C}-OH + HO-CH_2CH_3$$ 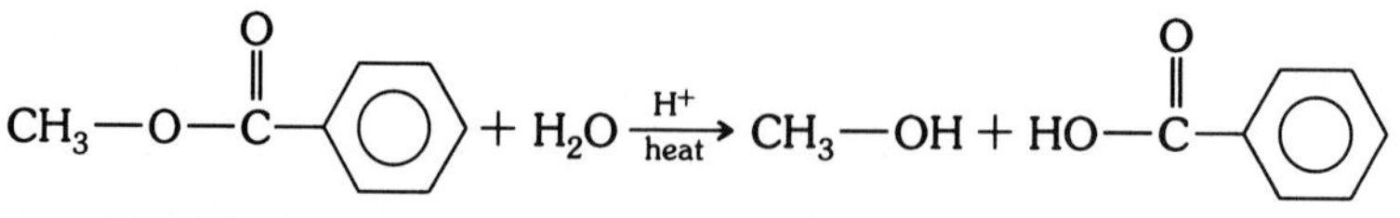
Ethyl acetate   Acetic acid   Ethyl alcohol

$$CH_3-O-\overset{\overset{\displaystyle O}{\|}}{C}-\bigcirc + H_2O \xrightarrow[\text{heat}]{H^+} CH_3-OH + HO-\overset{\overset{\displaystyle O}{\|}}{C}-\bigcirc$$
Methyl benzoate   Methyl   Benzoic acid
                          alcohol

To avoid a mistake that students often make, notice that the *only* bond to break in ester hydrolysis is the one that joins the carbonyl group to the oxygen atom, the "ester bond." Notice also that the products are always the "parents" of the ester and that the names of these parents are strongly implied in the name of the ester itself. Thus methyl benzoate hydrolyzes to *methyl* alcohol and *benz*oic acid. Now let's work an example.

| EXAMPLE 16.4 | PREDICTING THE PRODUCTS OF AN ESTER HYDROLYSIS |

Problem: What are the products of the hydrolysis of the following ester?

$$CH_3-\overset{\displaystyle O}{\overset{\displaystyle \|}{C}}-O-CH_2CH_2CH_3$$

Solution: The crucial step is to find the ester bond, the carbonyl-to-oxygen bond. It doesn't matter in which direction this bond happens to point on the page:

$$CH_3CH_2CH_2-O-\overset{\displaystyle O}{\overset{\displaystyle \|}{C}}-CH_3 \quad \text{or} \quad CH_3-\overset{\displaystyle O}{\overset{\displaystyle \|}{C}}-O-CH_2CH_2CH_3$$

Ester bond
(carbonyl-to-oxygen bond)

As we said, this bond is the only bond that breaks in ester hydrolysis, so break it. Erase it and separate the fragments. If the ester were written as follows:

$$CH_3CH_2CH_2-O-\overset{\displaystyle O}{\overset{\displaystyle \|}{C}}-CH_3 \dashrightarrow CH_3CH_2CH_2-O + \overset{\displaystyle O}{\overset{\displaystyle \|}{C}}-CH_3$$

On the other hand, if the ester's structure were written in the opposite direction:

$$CH_3-\overset{\displaystyle O}{\overset{\displaystyle \|}{C}}-O-CH_2CH_2CH_3 \dashrightarrow CH_3-\overset{\displaystyle O}{\overset{\displaystyle \|}{C}} + O-CH_2CH_2CH_3$$

Either way gives the same results. Next we attach the pieces of the water molecule to make the "parents" of the ester. We attach OH to the carbonyl carbon and we put H on the oxygen atom of the other fragment. The products therefore are the following, propyl alcohol and acetic acid.

■ Both the OH and the H are supplied by H—OH, the other reactant.

$$HOCH_2CH_2CH_3 + HO-\overset{\displaystyle O}{\overset{\displaystyle \|}{C}}-CH_3$$

PRACTICE EXERCISE 10   Write the structures of the products of the hydrolysis of the following esters.

(a) $CH_3-O-\overset{O}{\overset{\|}{C}}-CH_3$ (b) $CH_3CH_2-\overset{O}{\overset{\|}{C}}-O-\overset{CH_3}{\overset{|}{C}}HCH_3$ (c) $CH_3\overset{CH_3}{\overset{|}{C}}H-\overset{O}{\overset{\|}{C}}-O-CH_2CH_2CH_3$

Ester hydrolysis is a reverse of direct ester formation. Both involve the identical chemical equilibrium. So if we were to take an ester and water in a 1:1 mole ratio, not all the ester molecules would change into molecules of the parent acid and alcohol. Some of the ester molecules and some of the water molecules would still be unchanged. When we want to make sure that all the ester is hydrolyzed, we use a large excess of water. In accordance with Le Chatelier's principle, this excess of one reactant shifts the equilibrium in favor of making the products.

■ L. *sapo*, soap, and *onis*, to make. Ordinary soap is made by the saponification of the ester groups in fats and oils.

Esters Are Saponified By Strong Bases   If a strong base instead of a strong acid is used to promote the breakup of an ester, the products are the salt of the parent acid and the parent alcohol — a reaction called **saponification.** It requires a full mole (not just a catalytic trace) of base for each mole of ester bonds. The base *promotes* the reaction but, unlike a true catalyst, it is permanently changed (neutralized). No equilibrium forms, because one product, the *anion* of the parent acid, cannot be converted into an ester by a direct reaction with alcohols. In general,

$$
R—\overset{\overset{\displaystyle O}{\|}}{C}—O—R' \; + \; OH^- \xrightarrow{\text{heat}} R—\overset{\overset{\displaystyle O}{\|}}{C}—O^- \; + \; H—O—R'
$$

Specific examples are as follows. (Assume that OH^- comes from NaOH or KOH.)

$$
CH_3—\overset{\overset{\displaystyle O}{\|}}{C}—O—CH_2CH_3 \; + \; OH^- \underset{\text{heat}}{\rightleftharpoons} CH_3—\overset{\overset{\displaystyle O}{\|}}{C}—O^- \; + \; HO—CH_2CH_3
$$

Ethyl acetate · · · · · · Acetate ion · · · · Ethyl alcohol

$$
CH_3—O—\overset{\overset{\displaystyle O}{\|}}{C}—\text{(phenyl)} + OH^- \underset{\text{heat}}{\rightleftharpoons} CH_3—OH + {}^-O—\overset{\overset{\displaystyle O}{\|}}{C}—\text{(phenyl)}
$$

Methyl benzoate · · · · · · · Methyl · · · Benzoate ion
alcohol

WRITING THE STRUCTURES OF THE PRODUCTS OF SAPONIFICATION

Problem: What are the products of the saponification of the following ester?

$$
CH_3CH_2\overset{\overset{\displaystyle O}{\|}}{C}—O—CH_3
$$

Solution: Remember that saponification is very similar to ester hydrolysis. Therefore first break (erase) the ester bond—*break only this bond*—and separate the fragments:

$$
CH_3CH_2\overset{\overset{\displaystyle O}{\|}}{C}—O—CH_3 \dashrightarrow CH_3CH_2\overset{\overset{\displaystyle O}{\|}}{C} \; + \; O—CH_3 \quad \text{(Incomplete)}
$$

Now change the fragment that has the carbonyl group into the *anion* of a carboxylic acid. Do this by attaching —O^- to the carbonyl carbon atom. Then attach an H atom to the oxygen atom of the other fragment to make the alcohol molecule:

$$
CH_3CH_2\overset{\overset{\displaystyle O}{\|}}{C}—O^- \; + \; H—O—CH_3 \quad \text{(The products)}
$$

PRACTICE EXERCISE 11 Write the structures of the products of the saponification of the following esters.

(a) (phenyl)—O—$\overset{\overset{\displaystyle O}{\|}}{C}$—$CH_3$ (b) CH_3—O—$\overset{\overset{\displaystyle O}{\|}}{C}$—(phenyl)—O—$CH_3$

16.6 ORGANOPHOSPHATE ESTERS AND ANHYDRIDES

Some of the most widely distributed kinds of esters and anhydrides in living organisms are the anions of esters of phosphoric acid, diphosphoric acid, and triphosphoric acid.

Phosphoric acid appears in several forms and anions in the body, but the three fundamental parents of all these forms are phosphoric acid, diphosphoric acid, and triphosphoric acid.

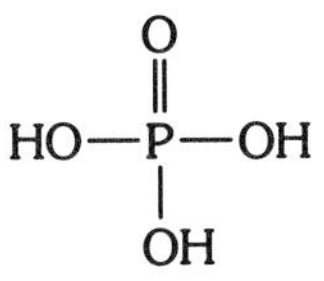

Phosphoric acid 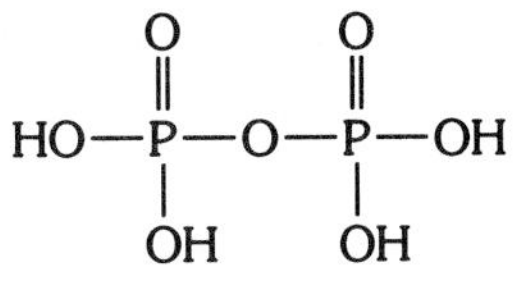   Diphosphoric acid 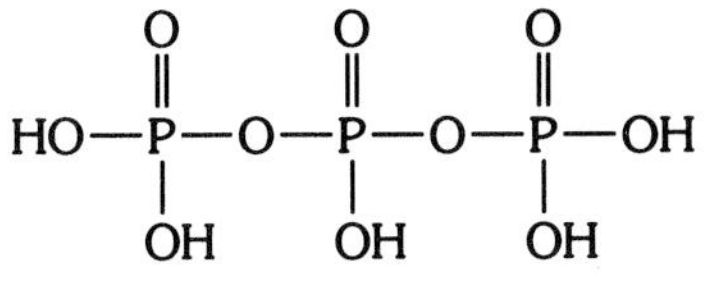   Triphosphoric acid

These are all polyprotic acids, but at the slightly alkaline pHs of body fluids, they cannot exist as free acids. They occur, instead, as a mixture of negative ions.

Esters of Alcohols and Phosphoric Acid Are Monophosphate Esters   If you look closely at the structure of phosphoric acid, you can see that part of it resembles a carboxyl group.

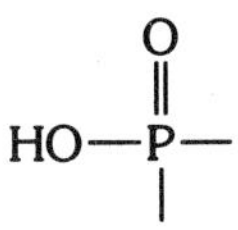

Part of a phosphoric acid molecule 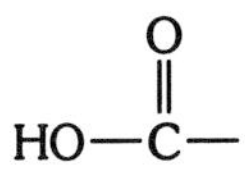   Part of a carboxylic acid molecule

It isn't surprising therefore that esters of phosphoric acid exist and that they are structurally similar to esters of carboxylic acids.

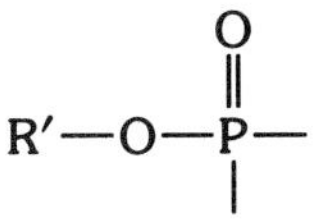

Part of a phosphate ester   compares to   Part of a carboxylate ester

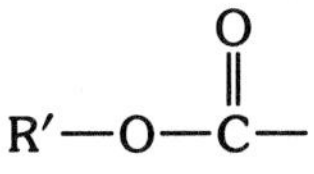

One large difference between a phosphate ester and a carboxylate ester is that a phosphate ester is still a diprotic acid. Its molecules still carry two proton-donating —O—H groups. Therefore, depending on the pH of the medium, a phosphate ester can exist in any one of three forms, and usually there is an equilibrium mixture of all three.

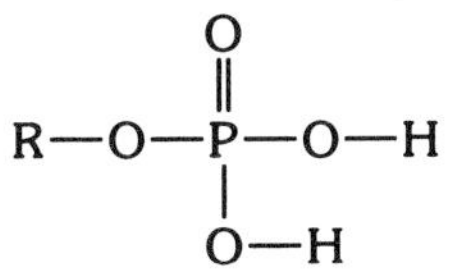

Phosphate ester (as a diprotic acid) —favored at low pH

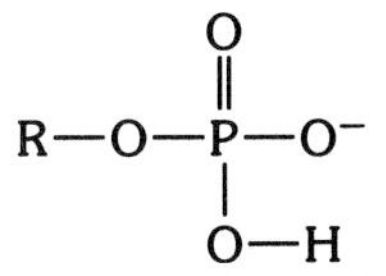

Phosphate ester (as a singly ionized species) —favored at pH values just below 7

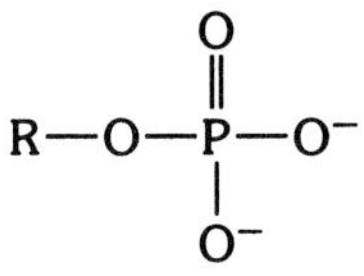

Phosphate ester (as a doubly ionized species) —favored at pH values above 7

At the pH of most body fluids (just slightly more than 7), phosphate esters exist mostly as the doubly ionized species—as the di-negative ion. All forms, however, are generally soluble in water, and one reason that the body converts so many substances into their phosphate esters may be to improve their solubilities in water.

Alcohols and Diphosphoric Acid Form Diphosphate Esters   A diphosphate ester actually has three functional groups: the phosphate ester group, the proton-donating OH group, and the phosphoric anhydride system.

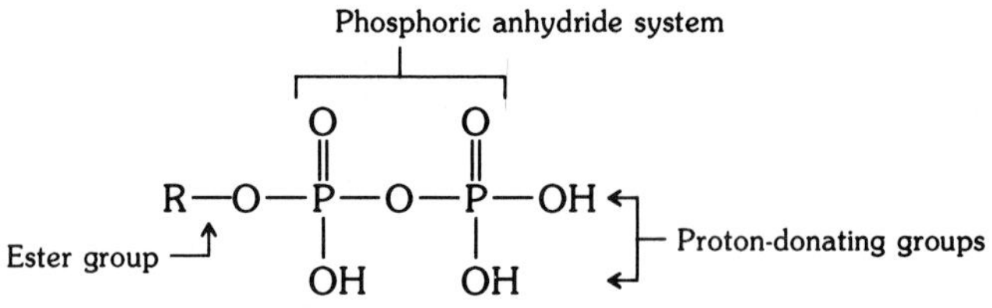

Phosphoric anhydride system

$$R-O-\overset{\overset{\displaystyle O}{\|}}{\underset{\underset{\displaystyle OH}{|}}{P}}-O-\overset{\overset{\displaystyle O}{\|}}{\underset{\underset{\displaystyle OH}{|}}{P}}-OH$$

Ester group ↑   Proton-donating groups

Diphosphate ester

Notice the similarity of part of the structure of a diphosphate ester to that of an anhydride of a carboxylic acid:

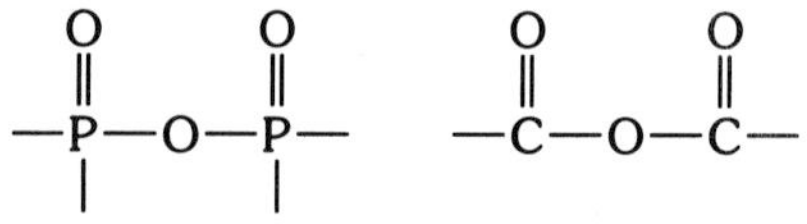

$$-\overset{\overset{\displaystyle O}{\|}}{\underset{\underset{\displaystyle |}{|}}{P}}-O-\overset{\overset{\displaystyle O}{\|}}{\underset{\underset{\displaystyle |}{|}}{P}}-$$

$$-\overset{\overset{\displaystyle O}{\|}}{C}-O-\overset{\overset{\displaystyle O}{\|}}{C}-$$

Part of the diphosphate system

The phosphoric anhydride group

Part of a carboxylic acid anhydride

The carboxylic anhydride group

One of the many diphosphate esters in the body is called adenosine diphosphate, or ADP. We will show its structure as its triply charged anion, because it exists largely in this fully ionized form at the pH of most body fluids.

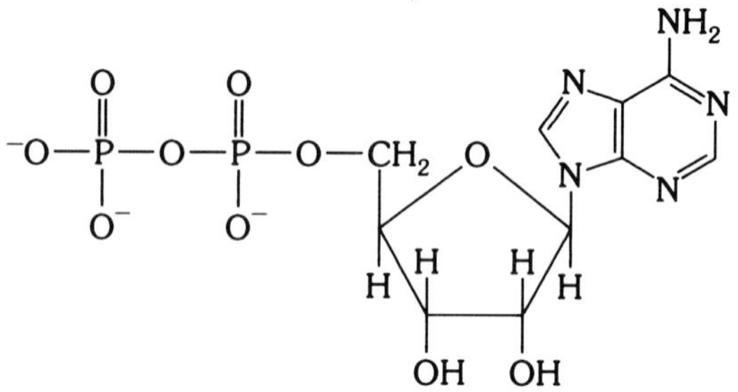

Adenosine diphosphate, ADP
(fully ionized form)

The Phosphoric Anhydride System Is a Major Storehouse of Chemical Energy in Living Systems

ADP can be hydrolyzed to adenosine and two phosphate ions, or to adenosine monophosphate and one phosphate ion. Although either hydrolysis is *very* slow in the absence of an enzyme, the breaking up of the phosphoric anhydride system generates considerable energy.

ADP can also react with alcohols. This reaction resembles hydrolysis because it breaks up the phosphoric anhydride system. This system in ADP and similar compounds (like ATP, below) turns out to be the chief means for storing chemical energy in cells. The phosphoric anhydride system is so important in this way that it is worthwhile to ask how it holds its chemical energy.

The source of the internal energy in the triply charged anion of ADP is the tension up and down the anhydride chain. This central chain bears oxygen atoms with full negative charges, and these charges repel each other. This internal repulsion primes the phosphoric anhydride system for breaking apart exothermically when it is attacked by a suitable reactant.

Molecules with alcohol groups are examples of such reactants in the body, but these reactions require enzymes for catalysis. Without a catalyst, the negatively charged ADP anion actually *repels* electron-rich species. Yet if an alcohol group is to attack the phosphoric anhydride system and break it apart, the oxygen atom of the alcohol group must be able to strike a phosphorus atom. We can visualize this attack as follows.

$$R-O-\overset{\overset{\displaystyle O}{\|}}{\underset{\underset{\displaystyle O^-}{|}}{P}}-O-\overset{\overset{\displaystyle O}{\|}}{\underset{\underset{\displaystyle O^-}{|}}{P}}-O^- \longrightarrow R-O-\overset{\overset{\displaystyle O}{\|}}{\underset{\underset{\displaystyle O^-}{|}}{P}}-O-\overset{\overset{\displaystyle O}{\|}}{\underset{\underset{\displaystyle O^-}{|}}{P}}-O^- \longrightarrow$$

$$\overset{\displaystyle \ddot{O}}{\underset{\displaystyle R' \qquad H}{}} \qquad\qquad \overset{\displaystyle \ddot{O}}{\underset{\displaystyle R' \qquad H \text{ --→} \ (\text{to be buffered})}{}}$$

$$R-O-\overset{\overset{\displaystyle O}{\|}}{\underset{\underset{\displaystyle O^-}{|}}{P}}-O^- + R'-O-\overset{\overset{\displaystyle O}{\|}}{\underset{\underset{\displaystyle O^-}{|}}{P}}-O^-$$

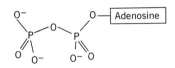

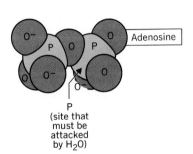

P
(site that
must be
attacked
by H_2O)

Figure 16.3
The oxygen atoms in the phosphoric anhydride system of ADP screen the phosphorus atoms. The negative charges on these oxygen atoms deflect incoming, electron-rich particles such as molecules of an alcohol or of water. Therefore this kind of anhydride system reacts very slowly with these reactants, unless a special catalyst such as an enzyme is also present.

As seen in Figure 16.3, however, the phosphorus atoms in the chain are buried within a clutch of negatively charged oxygen atoms that repel the alcohol molecule. Thus the internal tension cannot be relieved by this kind of reaction *unless an enzyme for the reaction is present.* You have probably already guessed that *the body exerts control over energy-releasing reactions of diphosphates by its control of the enzymes for these reactions.*

Water could make the same kind of exothermic attack on a diphosphate ester as an alcohol, but *the body has no enzymes inside cells that catalyze this reaction.* Hence, energy-rich diphosphates can exist in cells despite the abundance of water.

Alcohols and Triphosphoric Acid Form Triphosphate Esters   Adenosine triphosphate or ATP is the most common and widely-occurring member of a small family of energy-rich triphosphate esters. Because the triphosphates have two phosphoric anhydride systems in each molecule, on a mole-for-mole basis the triphosphates are among the most energy-rich substances in the body.

Adenosine triphosphate, ATP
(in its fully ionized form)

Triphosphates are much more widely used in cells as sources of energy than the diphosphates. The overall reaction for the contraction of a muscle, for example, can be written as follows. We now introduce the symbol P_i to stand for the set of inorganic phosphate ions, mostly $H_2PO_4^-$ and HPO_4^{2-}, produced in the breakup of ATP and present at equilibrium at body pH.

$$\text{Relaxed muscle} + \text{ATP} \xrightarrow{\text{enzyme}} \text{contracted muscle} + \text{ADP} + P_i$$

Muscular work requires ATP, and if the body's supply of ATP were used up *with no way to remake it,* we'd soon be helpless.

The resynthesis of ATP from ADP and P_i is one of the major uses of the chemical energy in the food we eat. What we have learned here is *how* these triphosphates and diphosphates can be energy-rich and, at the same time, not be destroyed by uncatalyzed reactions in the body. Later, we will study more details of how a cell makes and uses these phosphate systems.

SUMMARY

Acids and their salts The carboxyl group, CO_2H, is a polar group that confers moderate water solubility to a molecule without preventing its solubility in nonpolar solvents. This group is very resistant to oxidation and reduction. Carboxylic acids are strong proton-donors toward hydroxide ions, whereas alcohols are not. Toward water, carboxylic acids are weak acids. Therefore their conjugate bases, the carboxylate anions, are good proton-acceptors toward the hydronium ions of strong acids.

Salts of carboxylic acids are ionic compounds, and the potassium or sodium salts are very soluble in water. Hence, the carboxyl group is one of nature's important "solubility switches." An insoluble acid becomes soluble in base, but it is thrown out of solution again by the addition of acid.

The derivatives of acids—acid chlorides, anhydrides, and esters—can be made from the acids and are converted back to the acids by reacting with water. We can organize the reactions we have studied for the carboxylic acids as follows.

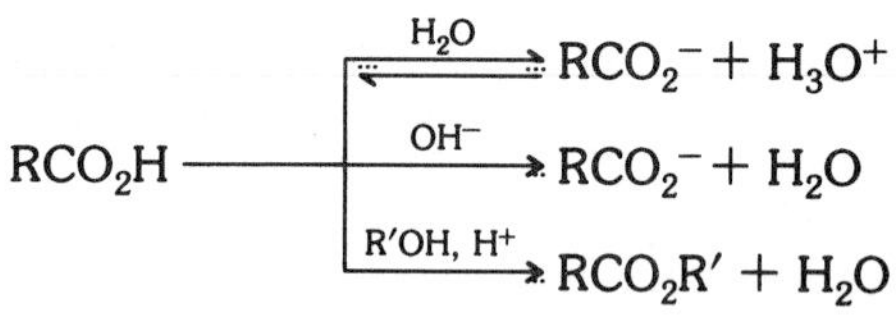

$$RCO_2H \begin{cases} \xrightarrow{H_2O} RCO_2^- + H_3O^+ \\ \xrightarrow{OH^-} RCO_2^- + H_2O \\ \xrightarrow{R'OH, H^+} RCO_2R' + H_2O \end{cases}$$

Esters We can organize the reactions used to make esters and the reactions of esters as follows.

Esterifications

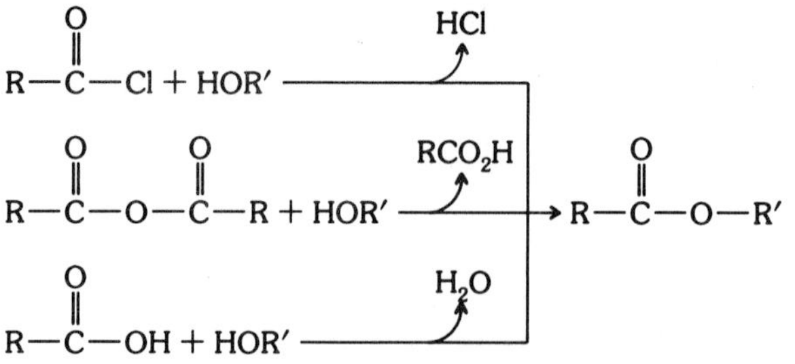

Reactions of esters:

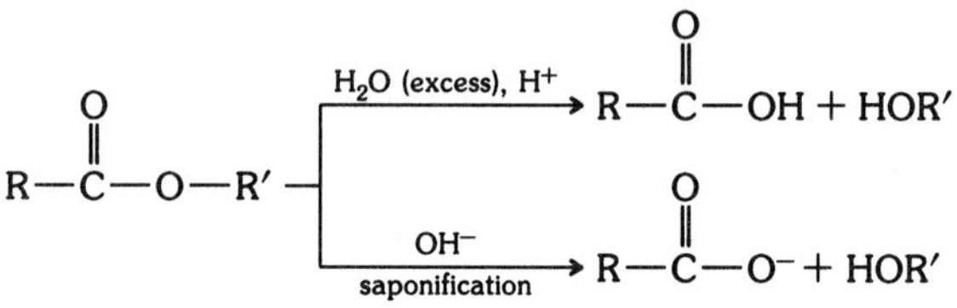

Esters and anhydrides of the phosphoric acid system Esters of phosphoric acid, diphosphoric acid, and triphosphoric acid occur in living systems largely as anions, because these esters are also polyprotic acids. In addition, those of diphosphoric and triphosphoric acid are phosphoric anhydrides. These anhydrides are energy-rich compounds. Their reactions with water or alcohols are very exothermic, but the reactions are also very slow unless a catalyst (an enzyme) is present.

REVIEW EXERCISES

The answers to these Review Exercises are in the *Study Guide* that accompanies this book.

Structures and Names of Carboxylic Acids and Their Salts

16.1 What is the structure of the carboxyl group, and in what way does it differ from the functional group in an alcohol? In a ketone?

16.2 Fatty acids are carboxylic acids obtained from what substances?

16.3 What is the common name of the acid in vinegar? In sour milk?

16.4 Write the structures of the following substances.
(a) butyric acid   (b) acetic acid
(c) formic acid   (d) benzoic acid

16.5 What are the structures of the following?
(a) 2,2-dimethylpropanoate ion
(b) 4-bromo-3-methylhexanoic acid
(c) pentanedioic acid
(d) 2-butenoate ion

16.6 Write the IUPAC names of the following compounds.

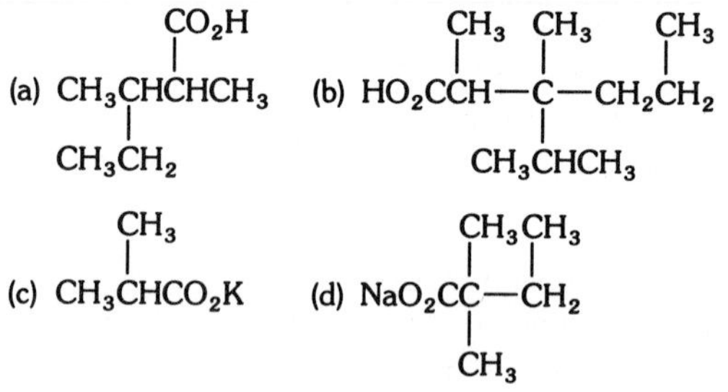

16.7 What are the IUPAC names of the following compounds?

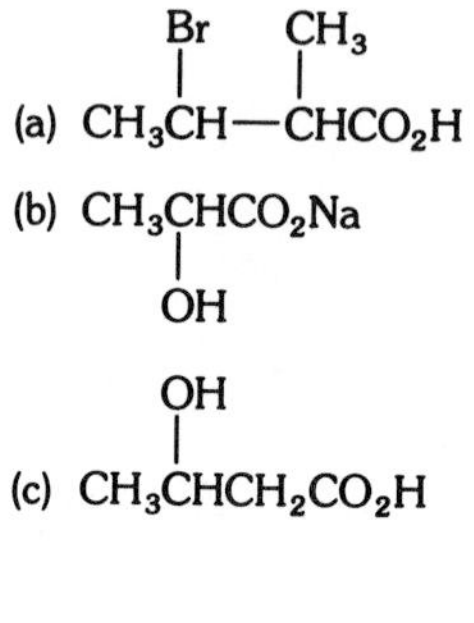

(d) 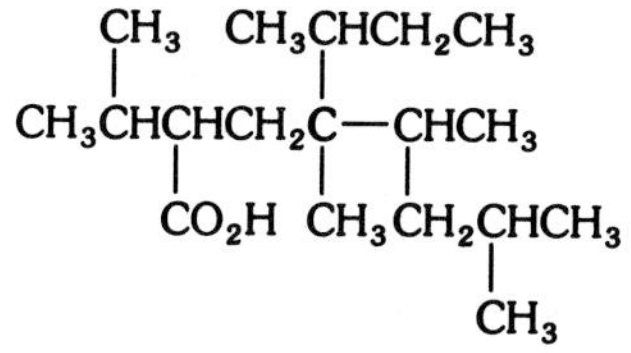
$$\underset{\underset{CO_2H}{|}}{CH_3CHCHCH_2} \overset{\overset{CH_3}{|}}{\underset{\underset{CH_3}{|}}{C}} \overset{\overset{CH_3CHCH_2CH_3}{|}}{\underset{\underset{CH_3}{|}}{CHCH_3}}$$

16.8 One of the *ketone bodies* whose concentration in blood rises in unchecked diabetes has the following structure.

$$CH_3\overset{\overset{O}{\|}}{C}CH_2CO_2H$$

If its IUPAC name is 3-ketobutanoic acid and its common name is acetoacetic acid, what are the IUPAC and common names for its sodium salt?

16.9 The tricarboxylic acid cycle is one of the major metabolic sequences of reactions in the body. One of the acids in this series of reactions is commonly called α-ketoglutaric acid, which has the following structure.

$$HO_2C\overset{\overset{O}{\|}}{C}CH_2CH_2CO_2H$$

What is the IUPAC name of this acid? (See Review Exercise 16.8.)

Physical Properties of Carboxylic Acids

16.10 Draw a figure that shows how two acetic acid molecules can pair in a hydrogen-bonded form.

16.11 The hydrogen bond system in formic acid includes an array of molecules, one after the other, each carbonyl oxygen of one molecule attracted to the HO group of the next molecule in line. Represent this linear array of hydrogen-bonded molecules of formic acid by a drawing.

16.12 Give the following compounds in their order of increasing solubility in water. Do this by arranging their identifying letters in a row in the correct order, placing the letter of the least soluble on the left.

$$\underset{\mathbf{A}}{CH_3CO_2H} \quad \underset{\mathbf{B}}{CH_3(CH_2)_5CO_2H} \quad \underset{\mathbf{C}}{CH_3(CH_2)_6CH_3}$$

16.13 Give the following compounds in their order of increasing boiling points by arranging their identifying letters in a row in the correct order. Place the letter of the lowest-boiling compound on the left.

$$\underset{\mathbf{A}}{HO_2CCO_2H} \quad \underset{\mathbf{B}}{CH_3CO_2H} \quad \underset{\mathbf{C}}{CH_3OH} \quad \underset{\mathbf{D}}{CH_3CH_2CH_3}$$

Carboxylic Acids as Weak Acids

16.14 Write the equation for the equilibrium that is present in an aqueous solution of acetic acid.

16.15 What is the equation for the equilibrium that is present in a solution of formic acid in water?

16.16 Give the following compounds in their order of increasing acidity by arranging their identifying letters in a row in the correct sequence. (Place the letter of the least acidic compound on the left.)

$$\underset{\mathbf{A}}{CH_3CO_2H} \quad \underset{\mathbf{B}}{HNO_3} \quad \underset{\mathbf{C}}{CH_3CH_2OH} \quad \underset{\mathbf{D}}{\text{⟨benzene ring⟩—OH}}$$

16.17 Give the order of increasing acidity of the following compounds. Arrange their identifying letters in the order that corresponds to their acidity, with the letter of the least acidic compound on the left.

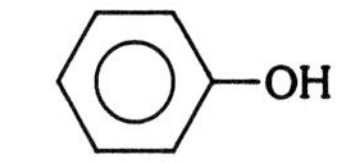

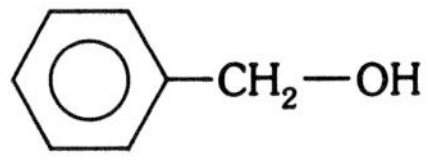

A ⟨benzene ring⟩—CH₂—OH   B CH₃—⟨benzene ring⟩—OH

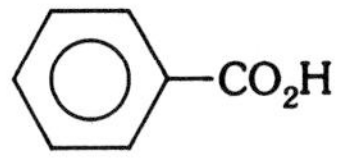

C ⟨benzene ring⟩—CO₂H   D H₂SO₄

16.18 Write the net ionic equation for the complete reaction, if any, of sodium hydroxide with the following compounds at room temperature.

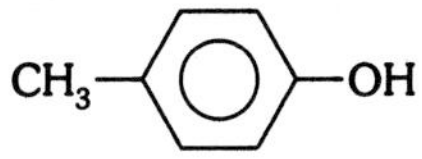

(a) $CH_3CH_2CO_2H$

(b)  HO_2C—⟨benzene ring⟩—CH_3

(c) CH_3CH_2OH

16.19 What are the net ionic equations for the reactions of the following compounds with aqueous potassium hydroxide at room temperature?

(a) 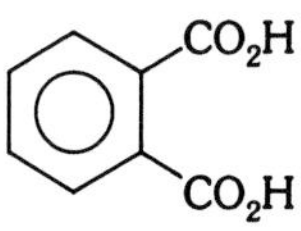 ⟨benzene ring with two CO₂H groups ortho⟩

(b) 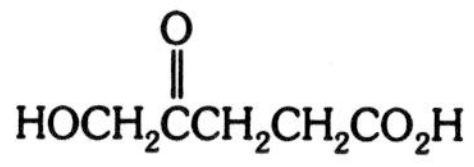 $HOCH_2\overset{\overset{O}{\|}}{C}CH_2CH_2CO_2H$

(c) ⟨benzene ring⟩—OH

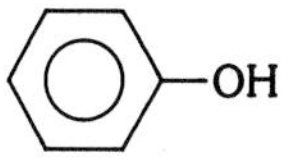

Salts of Carboxylic Acids

16.20 Which compound, **A** or **B**, is more soluble in water? Explain.

$$\underset{\mathbf{A}}{CH_3(CH_2)_8CO_2H} \quad \underset{\mathbf{B}}{CH_3(CH_2)_8CO_2Na}$$

16.21 Which compound, **A** or **B**, is more soluble in ether? Explain.

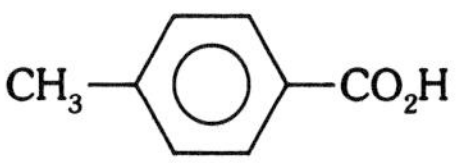

A CH₃—⟨benzene ring⟩—CO₂H   B CH₃—⟨benzene ring⟩—CO₂K

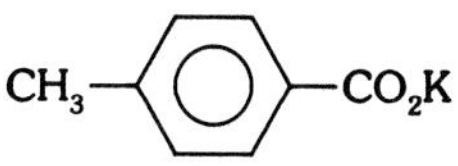

16.22 Suppose that you added 0.1 mol of hydrochloric acid to an aqueous solution that contains 0.1 mol of the compound given in each of the following parts. If any reaction occurs rapidly at room temperature, write its net ionic equation.

(a) CH_3—⟨○⟩—CO_2^- (b) CH_3CO_2H

(c) $^-O_2CCH_2CH_2CO_2^-$

16.23 Suppose that you have each of the following compounds in a solution in water. What reaction, if any, will occur rapidly at room temperature if an equimolar quantity of hydrochloric acid is added? Write net ionic equations.
(a) $CH_3CH_2CO_2H$
(b) $CH_3CH_2CH_2CO_2^-$
(c) $HOCH_2CH_2CH_2CO_2^-$

Esterification and Reactivity

16.24 What are the structures of the reactants that are needed to make methyl propanoate from methanol and each of the following kinds of starting materials?
(a) an acid chloride
(b) a carboxylic acid anhydride
(c) by direct esterification

16.25 In order to prepare ethyl benzoate, what are the structures of the reactants needed for each kind of approach?
(a) by direct esterification
(b) from an acid chloride
(c) from an acid anhydride

16.26 The reaction of methyl alcohol with acetyl chloride, $CH_3\overset{\overset{\text{O}}{\|}}{C}Cl$, is rapid.
(a) What is the structure of the organic product?
(b) How is the speed of this reaction explained?

16.27 Ethyl alcohol reacts rapidly with acetic anhydride, $CH_3\overset{\overset{\text{O}}{\|}}{C}-O-\overset{\overset{\text{O}}{\|}}{C}CH_3$, to give ethyl acetate and acetic acid. How can the very rapid rate of the reaction be explained?

16.28 What are the structures of the products of the esterification by methyl alcohol of each compound?
(a) formic acid
(b) 2-methylbutanoic acid
(c) *p*-chlorobenzoic acid
(d) Oxalic acid, $HO\overset{\overset{\text{O}}{\|}}{C}-\overset{\overset{\text{O}}{\|}}{C}OH$. (Show the esterification of both of the carboxyl groups.)

16.29 When propanoic acid is esterified by each of the following compounds, what are the structures of the esters that form?
(a) ethanol
(b) 2-methyl-1-propanol
(c) phenol
(d) $HOCH_2CH_2OH$ (1,2-ethanediol) (Show the esterification of both alcohol groups.)

16.30 Explain by means of equations how H^+ works as a catalyst in the direct esterification of acetic acid by ethyl alcohol.

16.31 The first of the following two reactions is very difficult to cause, but the second occurs fairly readily. What is a logical explanation for this difference?

(1) $H_2O + CH_3CH_2-\overset{\overset{\text{H}}{|}}{O^+}-CH_2CH_3 \longrightarrow$
$CH_3CH_2-\overset{\overset{+}{O}\diagdown H}{} + \overset{H}{\diagup}O-CH_2CH_3$

(2) $H_2O + CH_3\overset{\overset{\text{O}}{\|}}{C}-\overset{\overset{\text{H}}{|}}{O^+}-CH_2CH_3 \longrightarrow$
$CH_3\overset{\overset{\text{O}}{\|}}{C}-\overset{\overset{+}{O}\diagdown H}{} + \overset{H}{\diagup}O-CH_2CH_3$

16.32 Suppose that a way could be found to remove H_2O as rapidly as it is produced in direct esterification. What would this do to the equilibrium in this reaction, shift it to the right (favoring the ester) or to the left (favoring the carboxylic acid and the alcohol)? Explain.

16.33 How do we explain the fact that esters react much more slowly with water than acid chlorides do?

Structures and Physical Properties of Esters

16.34 Write the structures of the following compounds.
(a) methyl formate   (b) ethyl benzoate

16.35 What are the structures of the following compounds?
(a) isopropyl propanoate   (b) isobutyl 2-methylbutanoate

16.36 Arrange the following compounds in their order of increasing boiling points. Do this by placing their identifying letters in a row, starting with the lowest-boiling compound on the left.

$CH_3CH_2CH_2CH_2CO_2H$ $CH_3CH_2OCH_3$
A   **B**

$CH_3CH_2CO_2CH_3$ $CH_3CH_2CO_2CH_2CH_3$
C   **D**

16.37 Arrange the following compounds in their order of increasing solubilities in water by placing their identifying letters in the correct sequence, beginning with the least soluble on the left.

$CH_3(CH_2)_4CO_2Na$ $CH_3(CH_2)_2CO_2H$
A   **B**

$CH_3(CH_2)_4CO_2CH_3$ $CH_3(CH_2)_6OCH_3$
C   **D**

Reactions of Esters

16.38 Write the equation for the acid-catalyzed hydrolysis of each compound. If no reaction occurs, write "no reaction."

(a) $CH_3\overset{\overset{\text{CH}_3}{|}}{CH}-O-\overset{\overset{\text{O}}{\|}}{C}CH_3$ (b) $CH_3\overset{\overset{\text{O}}{\|}}{\underset{\underset{\text{CH}_3}{|}}{CHC}}-O-CH_3$

(c) $CH_3—O—CH_2CO_2H$ (d) $HOCH_2\overset{\displaystyle O}{\overset{\|}{C}}—O—CH_3$

16.39 What are the equations for the acid-catalyzed hydrolyses of the following compounds? If no reaction occurs, write "no reaction."

(a) 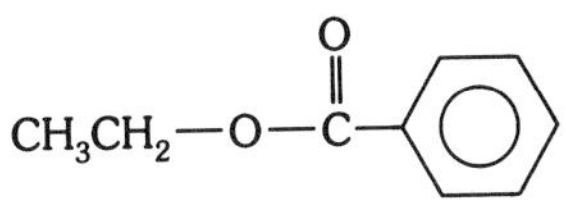 $CH_3CH_2—O—\overset{\displaystyle O}{\overset{\|}{C}}—$ [benzene ring]

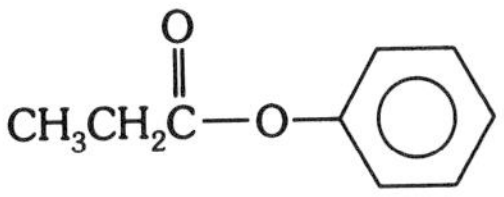

(b) $CH_3CH_2\overset{\displaystyle O}{\overset{\|}{C}}—O—$ [benzene ring]

(c) $CH_3CH_2—O—$ [benzene ring] $—\overset{\displaystyle O}{\overset{\|}{C}}CH_3$

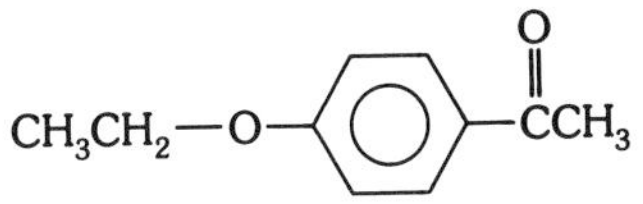

(d) $CH_3—O—\overset{\displaystyle O}{\overset{\|}{C}}CH_2CH_2\overset{\displaystyle O}{\overset{\|}{C}}—O—CH_3$

16.40 The digestion of fats and oils involves the complete hydrolysis of molecules such as the following. What are the structures of its hydrolysis products?

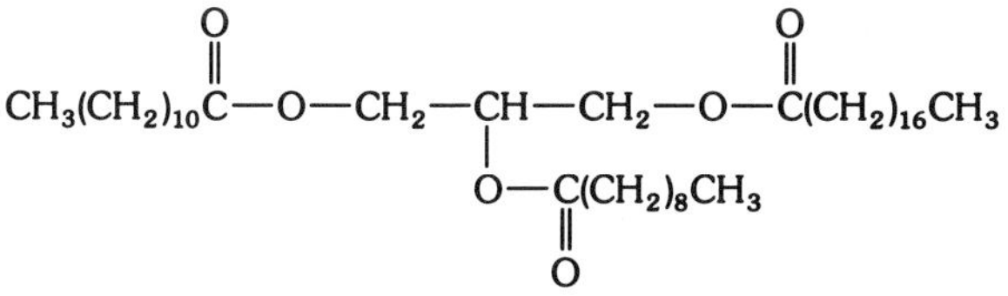

$CH_3(CH_2)_{10}\overset{\displaystyle O}{\overset{\|}{C}}—O—CH_2—CH—CH_2—O—\overset{\displaystyle O}{\overset{\|}{C}}(CH_2)_{16}CH_3$
$\qquad\qquad\qquad\qquad |$
$\qquad\qquad\qquad\quad O—\overset{}{C}(CH_2)_8CH_3$
$\qquad\qquad\qquad\qquad\quad \|$
$\qquad\qquad\qquad\qquad\quad O$

16.41 Cyclic esters are known compounds. What is the structure of the product when the following compound is hydrolyzed?

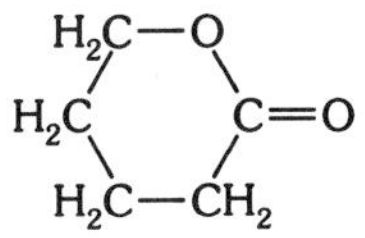

$H_2C—O$
$H_2C \qquad C=O$
$H_2C—CH_2$

16.42 What are the structures of the products of the saponification of the compounds in Review Exercise 16.38?

16.43 What forms, if anything, when the compounds of Review Exercise 16.39 are subjected to saponification by aqueous KOH? Write their structures.

16.44 What are the products of the saponification of the compound given in Review Exercise 16.40? (Assume that aqueous NaOH is used.)

16.45 Write the structure of the organic ion that forms when the compound of Review Exercise 16.41 is saponified.

16.46 A pharmaceutical chemist needed to prepare the ethyl ester of an extremely expensive and rare carboxylic acid in order to test this form of the drug for its side effects. Direct esterification had to be used. How could the conversion of the acid to its ethyl ester be maximized? Use RCO_2H as a symbol for the acid in any equations you write.

16.47 Write the steps in the mechanism of the acid-catalyzed hydrolysis of methyl acetate. (Remember, this is the exact re-

verse of the acid-catalyzed, direct esterification of acetic acid by methyl alcohol.)

Phosphate Esters and Anhydrides

16.48 Write the structures of the following compounds.
   (a) monoethyl phosphate
   (b) monomethyl diphosphate
   (c) monopropyl triphosphate

16.49 State one apparent advantage to the body of its converting many compounds into phosphate esters.

16.50 What part of the structure of ATP is particularly responsible for its being described as an *energy-rich* compound? Explain.

16.51 Why is ATP more difficult to hydrolyze than acetyl chloride?

Review of Organic Reactions

16.52 Complete the following reaction sequences by writing the structures of the organic products. If no reaction occurs, state so. (These constitute a review of this and earlier chapters on organic chemistry.)

(a) $CH_3\overset{\displaystyle O}{\overset{\|}{C}}H \xrightarrow{K_2Cr_2O_7}$

(b) $CH_3CH_2CH_3 + H_2SO_4 \longrightarrow$

(c) $CH_3OH + CH_3CO_2H \xrightarrow[heat]{H^+}$

(d) $CH_3CH_2\overset{\displaystyle OH}{\overset{|}{C}}HCH_3 \xrightarrow[heat]{KMnO_4}$

(e) $CH_3\overset{\displaystyle OH}{\overset{|}{C}}HCH_3 \xrightarrow[heat]{H_2SO_4}$

(f) $CH_3O\overset{\displaystyle O}{\overset{\|}{C}}\overset{}{C}HCH_3 + H_2O \xrightarrow{H^+}$
$\qquad\qquad |$
$\qquad\qquad CH_3$

(g) $CH_3CH_2CH=CH_2 + HCl(g) \longrightarrow$

(h) $CH_3\overset{\displaystyle O—CH_3}{\overset{|}{C}}H—O—CH_3 + H_2O \xrightarrow{H^+}$

(i) $CH_3\overset{}{C}H\overset{\displaystyle O}{\overset{\|}{C}}—O—CH_3 + NaOH(aq) \longrightarrow$
$\qquad |$
$\qquad CH_3$

(j) $CH_3—O—CH_2CH_2\overset{\displaystyle O}{\overset{\|}{C}}CH_3 + H_2O \longrightarrow$

(k) $CH_3CH_2\overset{\displaystyle O}{\overset{\|}{C}}—Cl + H_2O \longrightarrow$

(l) $CH_3CH_2CH_2CO_2H + NaOH \longrightarrow$

16.53 Write the structures of the organic products, if any, that form in the following situations. If no reaction occurs, state so.

(Some of these constitute a review of reactions from earlier chapters.)

(a) $CH_3CH_2CO_2^- + HCl(aq) \longrightarrow$

(b) 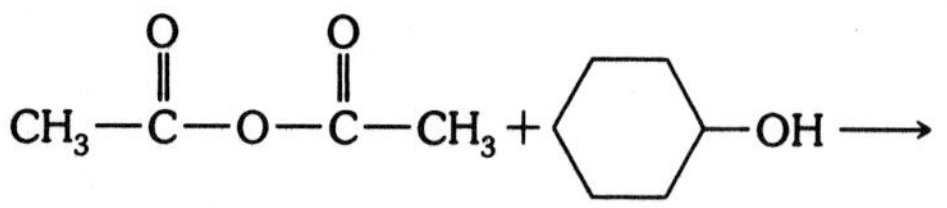

(c) $CH_3CH_2-O-CH_2CH_2\overset{O}{\overset{\|}{C}}CH_3 + NaOH \longrightarrow$

(d) $CH_3CH_2CH_2-O-\overset{O}{\overset{\|}{C}}-CH_2CH_2-O-\overset{O}{\overset{\|}{C}}-CH_3 + \underset{(excess)}{H_2O} \xrightarrow{H^+}$

(e) 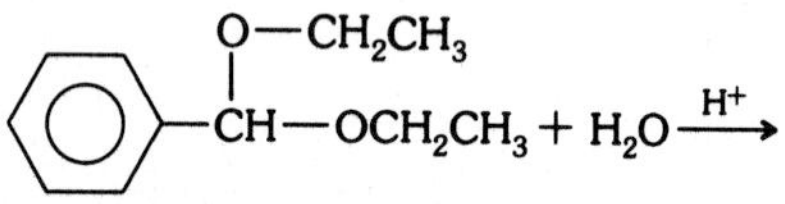

(f) $CH_3\underset{CH_3}{\underset{|}{\overset{OH}{\overset{|}{C}}}}CH_2CH_3 \xrightarrow{KMnO_4}$

(g) $CH_3CH_2CO_2H + CH_3\overset{CH_3}{\overset{|}{C}}HOH \xrightarrow[heat]{H^+}$

(h) $CH_3(CH_2)_9CH_3 + NaOH \longrightarrow$

(i) $CH_3-O-\overset{O}{\overset{\|}{C}}CH_2CH_2-O-\overset{O}{\overset{\|}{C}}CH_2CH_3 + \underset{(excess)}{NaOH(aq)} \longrightarrow$

(j) $CH_3(CH_2)_6CO_2H + NaOH(aq) \longrightarrow$

(k) $^-O_2CCH_2CH_2CH_2CO_2^- + \underset{(excess)}{HCl(aq)} \longrightarrow$

(l) $\underset{(excess)}{CH_3OH} + HO_2CCH_2CH_2CH_2CO_2H \xrightarrow[heat]{H^+}$

Common Acids and Salts (Special Topic 16.1)

16.54 Name a compound that is
- (a) Used to manufacture a kind of rayon
- (b) Present in vinegar
- (c) A food additive put into wrappers of cheese

Common Esters (Special Topic 16.2)

16.55 Esters of *p*-hydroxybenzoic acid are referred to by what common name? How are they used in commerce?

16.56 What is meant by a *copolymer?*

16.57 What copolymer has been used in surgical grafts?

16.58 Salicylates are described as *analgesics* and *antipyretics*. What do these terms mean?

16.59 Why is salicylic acid, the parent of the salicylates, structurally modified for medicinal uses?

16.60 Concerning salicylic acid,
- (a) What two functional groups does it have?
- (b) Which functional group is esterified in acetylsalicylic acid?
- (c) Which group is esterified in methyl salicylate?

CHAPTER SEVENTEEN

Amines and Amides

More strength per gram is present in nylon than in any other fabric, so parachutists have long used this polyamide. The amide function is essential to an understanding not just of nylon but also of all proteins.

17.1 OCCURRENCE, NAMES, AND PHYSICAL PROPERTIES OF AMINES

The amino group, NH_2, has some of the properties of ammonia, including the ability to be involved in hydrogen bonding.

Both the amino group and its protonated form occur in living things in molecules of proteins, enzymes, and genes. When a carbonyl group is attached to nitrogen, we have the amide system, and this also occurs widely in living things.

$$-NH_2 \qquad -NH_3^+ \qquad \overset{\displaystyle O}{\overset{\|}{-C}} -N-$$

Amino   Protonated   Amide
group   amino group   system

Amines Are Ammonia-like Compounds   The **amines** are organic relatives of ammonia in which one, two, or all three of the hydrogen atoms on an ammonia molecule have been replaced by a hydrocarbon group. Some examples are

■ These are the common names, not the IUPAC names.

$$CH_3NH_2 \qquad CH_3NHCH_3 \qquad \overset{\displaystyle CH_3}{\overset{\|}{CH_3NCH_3}} \qquad CH_3NHCH_2CH_3$$

Methylamine   Dimethylamine   Trimethylamine   Methylethylamine

Several amines are listed in Table 17.1. All these are classified as *amines,* and all are basic, like ammonia.

It's quite important to realize that for a compound to be an amine, not only must its molecules have a nitrogen with three bonds, but none of these bonds can be to a carbonyl group. If such a system is present — a carbonyl-nitrogen bond — the substance is an **amide.** Thus the structure given by **1** is an amide, not an amine. However, the structure given by **2** is not an amide, because there is no carbonyl–nitrogen bond. Instead, **2** has two functional groups — a keto group and an amino group. The chemical difference is that amines are basic and amides are not. Another difference is that the carbon–nitrogen bond in amines can't be broken by water, but the carbonyl–nitrogen bond in amides can.

$$\overset{\displaystyle O}{\overset{\|}{R-C}}-NH_2 \qquad\qquad \overset{\displaystyle O}{\overset{\|}{R-C}}-CH_2-NH_2$$

        1   **2**

TABLE 17.1 Amines

Common Name	Structure	Boiling Point (°C)	Solubility in Water	K_b (at 25 °C)
Methylamine	CH_3NH_2	−8	Very soluble	4.4×10^{-4}
Dimethylamine	CH_3NHCH_3	8	Very soluble	5.3×10^{-4}

Trimethylamine	CH_3NCH_3
	      $\|$
	     CH_3
		3	Very soluble	0.5×10^{-4}

Ethylamine	$CH_3CH_2NH_2$	17	Very soluble	5.6×10^{-4}
Diethylamine	$CH_3CH_2NHCH_2CH_3$	55	Very soluble	9.6×10^{-4}

Triethylamine	$CH_3CH_2NCH_2CH_3$
	        $\|$
	      CH_2CH_3
		89	14 g/dL	5.7×10^{-4}

Propylamine	$CH_3CH_2CH_2NH_2$	49	Very soluble	4.7×10^{-4}
Aniline	$C_6H_5NH_2$	184	4 g/dL	3.8×10^{-10}

If one or more of the groups attached directly to nitrogen in an amine is a benzene ring, then the amine is an *aromatic* amine. Otherwise, it is classified as an *aliphatic* amine. Thus benzylamine is an aliphatic amine and aniline, *N*-methylaniline, and *N,N*-dimethylaniline are all aromatic amines.

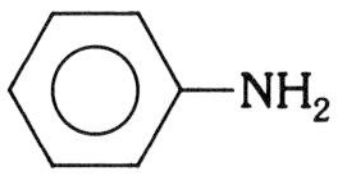

Aniline 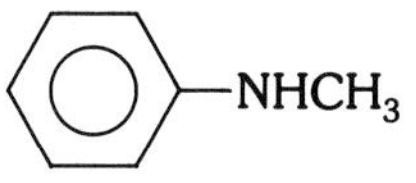   *N*-Methylaniline 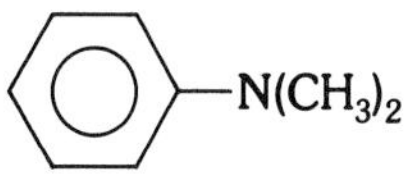   *N,N*-Dimethylaniline 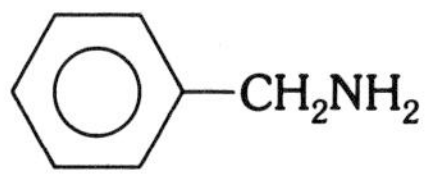   Benzylamine

The Common Names of Amines Usually End in *-amine* The common names of the simple, aliphatic amines are made by writing the names of the alkyl groups attached to nitrogen in front of the word *amine* (and leaving no space). We have already seen how this works. Here are three more examples.

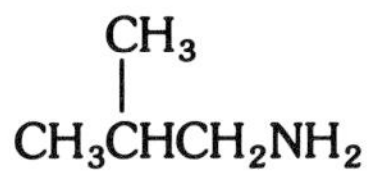

Isobutylamine 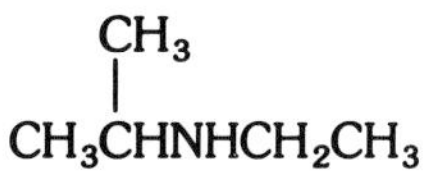   Ethylisopropylamine 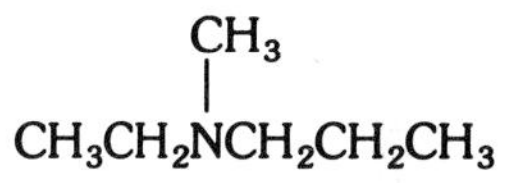   Methylethylpropylamine

In complex systems, the names of some amines use the name *amino* as a substituent name for the NH_2 group. Thus isobutylamine can be named 1-amino-2-methylpropane. We will not develop IUPAC names for amines.

PRACTICE EXERCISE 1

Give common names for the following compounds.

(a) $(CH_3)_2NCH(CH_3)_2$ (b) 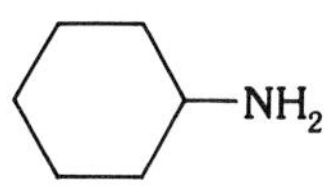 —NH_2 (c) $(CH_3)_2CHCH_2NHC(CH_3)_3$

PRACTICE EXERCISE 2

Write the structures of the following compounds.

(a) *t*-Butyl-*sec*-butylamine
(b) *p*-Nitroaniline
(c) *p*-Aminobenzoic acid (the PABA of sun-screening lotions)

Heterocyclic Amines Have N as a Ring Atom Both proteins and genes are rich in nitrogen-containing heterocyclic rings. For example, the amino acid proline has a saturated ring that includes a nitrogen atom. Unsaturated rings are present in other amino acids such as tryptophan.

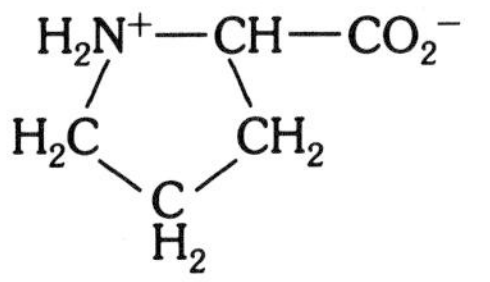

Proline

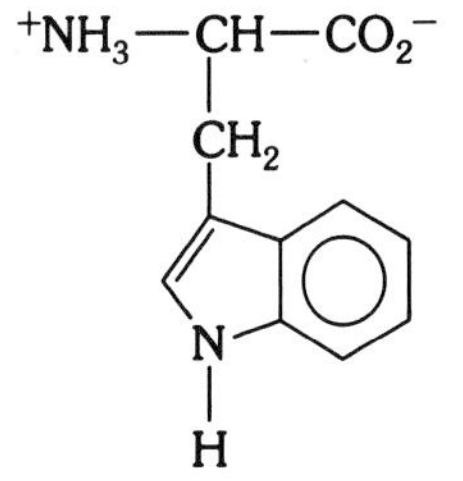

Tryptophan

In molecules of genes, heterocyclic amine systems generally involve either the pyrimidine ring or the purine ring system.

Figure 17.1
Hydrogen bonds (*a*) in amines and (*b*) in aqueous solutions of amines.

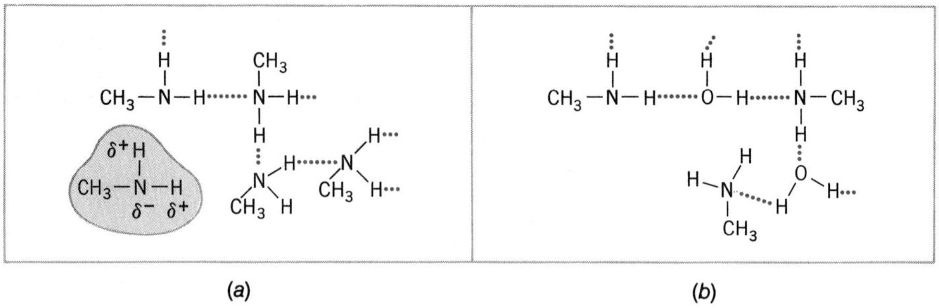

(a)   (b)

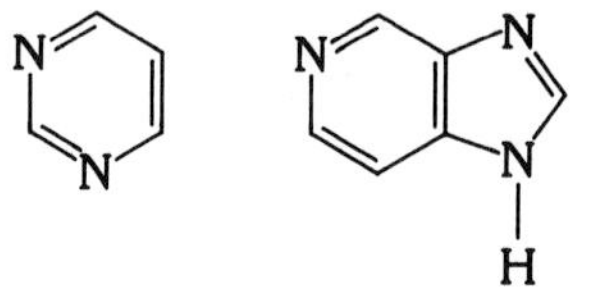

Pyrimidine   Purine

Compound	Boiling Point (°C)
CH_3CH_3	−89
CH_3NH_2	−6
CH_3OH	65

N—H Groups in Amines Are Involved in Hydrogen Bonding We have sometimes used boiling point data to tell us something about forces between molecules. The data in the margin tell us, for example, that when compounds of similar formula weights are compared, the boiling points of amines are higher than those of alkanes but lower than those of alcohols. This suggests that the forces of attraction between molecules are stronger in amines than in alkanes, but they are weaker in amines than in alcohols.

We can understand these trends in terms of hydrogen bonds. When a hydrogen atom is bound to oxygen or nitrogen but not to carbon, the system can donate and accept hydrogen bonds. Nitrogen, however, has a lower electronegativity than oxygen, so the polarity of the N—H bond in amines is weaker than the polarity of the O—H bond in alcohols. The N—H system, therefore, develops weaker hydrogen bonds than the O—H system. As a result, amine molecules can't attract each other as strongly as alcohol molecules, so amines boil lower than alcohols (of comparable formula weights). But amine molecules, nevertheless, do develop some hydrogen bonds (Figure 17.1), which alkane molecules cannot do, so amines boil higher than alkanes (of comparable formula weights).

Even though hydrogen bonding that involves amines is weaker than that which involves alcohols, it has a very important function at the molecular level of life among proteins and nucleic acids, where it stabilizes the special molecular shapes of these substances.

Hydrogen bonding also helps amines to be much more soluble in water than alkanes, as Figure 17.1 also depicts.

■ The processes in the body that lead to the sensations of odor or taste begin with *chemical* reactions.

Odor isn't actually a *physical* property, but we should note that the amines with lower formula weights smell very much like ammonia. The odors of amines become very "fishy" at slightly higher formula weights.

17.2 CHEMICAL PROPERTIES OF AMINES

The amino group is a proton acceptor, and the protonated amino group is a proton donor.

We will examine two chemical properties of amines that will be particularly important to our study of biochemicals: the basicity of amines, in this section, and their conversion to amides, in the next.

Aliphatic Amines Are About as Basic as Ammonia When either ammonia or any water-soluble amine is dissolved in water, the following equilibrium becomes established:

$$R-NH_2 + H_2O \rightleftharpoons R-NH_3^+ + OH^-$$

Amine (or
ammonia,
when R = H)

Protonated
amine (or
ammonium ion
when R = H)

How much the products are favored in this equilibrium is expressed by the **base ionization constant, K_b,**

■ Remember, the brackets [ ] denote the moles-per-liter concentration of the compound or ion that the brackets enclose.

$$K_b = \frac{[RNH_3^+][OH^-]}{[RNH_2]}$$

Table 17.1 gives the K_b values for several amines. The K_b of ammonia is 1.8×10^{-5}, so you can see that most amines have K_b values slightly larger than that of ammonia. Remember, the larger the K_b value, the *stronger* is the base, because a larger value means that the terms in the numerator, including [OH$^-$], have to be larger. Thus the aliphatic amines are generally slightly stronger bases than ammonia, and their aqueous solutions are basic solutions. Compounds with aliphatic amino groups, in other words, tend to raise the pH of an aqueous solution.

Compounds with amino groups can also neutralize hydronium ions. The following acid–base neutralization occurs rapidly and essentially completely at room temperature.

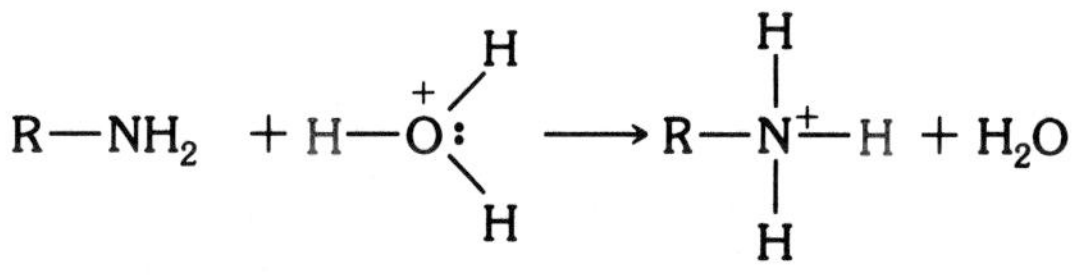

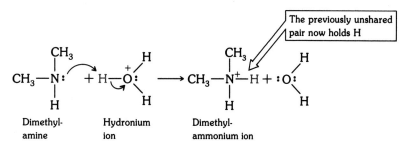

Amine (or
ammonia,
when R = H)

Hydronium
ion

Protonated
amine (or
ammonium ion
when R = H)

■ Tetraalkylammonium ions

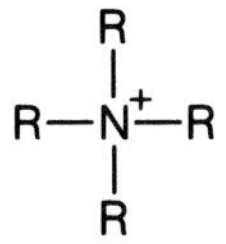

R—N⁺—R
with R above and R below

are also known species, but such cations can't be basic because they have no unshared pair of electrons on nitrogen.

For example,

$$CH_3NH_2 + HCl(aq) \longrightarrow CH_3NH_3^+Cl^- + H_2O$$

Methylamine   Hydrochloric
acid

Methylammonium
chloride

It doesn't matter if the nitrogen atom in an amine bears one, two, or three hydrocarbon groups. The amine can still neutralize strong acids, because the reaction involves just the unshared pair of electrons on the nitrogen, not any of the bonds to the other groups.

The previously unshared
pair now holds H

CH₃—N: + H—O: ⟶ CH₃—N⁺—H + :O:

Dimethyl-
amine

Hydronium
ion

Dimethyl-
ammonium ion

WRITING THE STRUCTURE OF THE PRODUCT WHEN AN AMINE IS NEUTRALIZED BY A STRONG ACID

EXAMPLE 17.1

Problem: What organic cation forms when hydrochloric acid (or any strong acid) neutralizes each of the following amines?

(a) $CH_3CH_2NH_2$ (b) $CH_3CH_2NCH_3$ (c) N—CH$_3$
                          |
                          CH$_3$

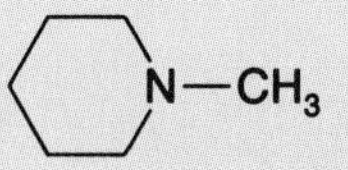

Solution: All that we have to do is increase the number of H atoms attached to the nitrogen atom by one, and then write a positive sign to show the charge. Thus the answers are

(a) $CH_3CH_2NH_3{}^+$ (b) $CH_3CH_2\overset{+}{N}HCH_3$ (c) $\overset{+}{N}H$—CH$_3$
                              |
                              CH$_3$

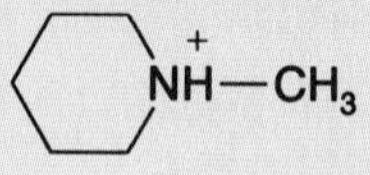

PRACTICE EXERCISE 3

What are the structures of the cations that form when the following amines react completely with hydrochloric acid?

(a) aniline   (b) trimethylamine   (c) $NH_2CH_2CH_2NH_2$

■ Some amine salts are internal salts, like all the amino acids, the building blocks of proteins.

$$^+NH_3—CH—CO_2{}^-$$
$$\underset{G}{|}$$

General formula of all amino acids.
G = an organic group

Protonated Amines Can Neutralize Strong Bases   A combination of a protonated amine and an anion make up an organic salt called an **amine salt.** Table 17.2 gives some examples and, like all salts, they are crystalline solids at room temperature. In addition, like the salts of the ammonium ion, nearly all amine salts of strong acids are soluble in water *even when the parent amine is not.* Amine salts are much more soluble in water than amines because the *full* charges carried by the ions of an amine salt can be much better hydrated by water molecules than the amine itself, where only the small, partial charges of polar bonds occur.

Protonated amine cations neutralize the hydroxide ion and revert to amines in the following manner (where we show only skeletal structures).

$$-\overset{|}{\underset{|}{N}}\overset{+}{—}H + OH^- \longrightarrow -\overset{|}{\underset{|}{N}}\!:\, + H—OH$$

Protonated amine   Amine

For example,

$$CH_3NH_3{}^+ + OH^- \longrightarrow CH_3NH_2 + H_2O$$
$$CH_3CH_2\overset{+}{N}H_2CH_3 + OH^- \longrightarrow CH_3CH_2NHCH_3 + H_2O$$

TABLE 17.2   Amine Salts

Name	Structure	Melting Point (°C)
Methylammonium chloride	$CH_3NH_3{}^+Cl^-$	232
Dimethylammonium chloride	$(CH_3)_2NH_2{}^+Cl^-$	171
Dimethylammonium bromide	$(CH_3)_2NH_2{}^+Br^-$	134
Dimethylammonium iodide	$(CH_3)_2NH_2{}^+I^-$	155
Tetramethylammonium hydroxide[a]	$(CH_3)_4N^+OH^-$	130–135 (decomposes)

[a] Because of its OH^- ion, which dissociates fully from the cation in water, this compound is as strong a base as NaOH.

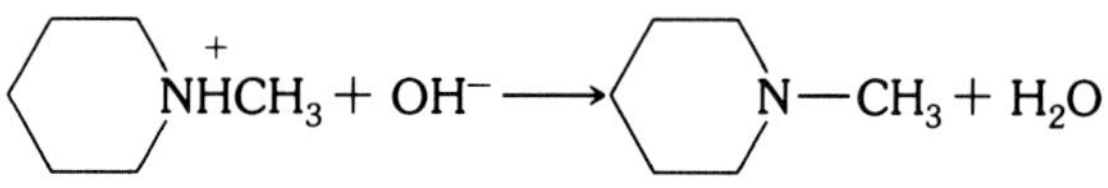

$$\text{(cyclohexyl)}\overset{+}{N}HCH_3 + OH^- \longrightarrow \text{(cyclohexyl)}N-CH_3 + H_2O$$

■ The other important solubility switch that we have studied involved the carboxylic acid group:

R—CO$_2$H
(Less soluble)

H$^+$ (⇵) OH$^-$

RCO$_2^-$
(More soluble)

The Amino Group Is a Solubility Switch   We have just learned that putting a proton on an amino group and taking it off are easily done at room temperature simply by adding an acid and then a base. We have also learned that the protonated amine is more soluble in water than the amine. This makes the amino group an excellent "solubility switch."

The solubility of an amine can be switched on simply by adding enough strong acid to protonate it. Triethylamine, for example, is insoluble in water, but we can switch on its solubility by adding a strong acid like hydrochloric acid. The amine dissolves as its protonated form is produced.

$$(CH_3CH_2)_3N\!:\ +\ HCl(aq) \longrightarrow (CH_3CH_2)_3\overset{+}{N}H\ Cl^-$$

Triethylamine   Triethylammonium chloride
(water-insoluble)   (water-soluble)

We can just as quickly and easily bring the amine back out of solution by adding a strong base, like the hydroxide ion. It takes the proton off the protonated amine and gives the less soluble form.

$$(CH_3CH_2)_3\overset{+}{N}H\ +\ OH^- \longrightarrow (CH_3CH_2)_3N\ +\ H_2O$$

Triethylammonium   Triethylamine
ion   (water-insoluble)
(water-soluble)

The significance of this "switching" relationship is that the solubilities of complex compounds that have the amine function can be changed almost instantly simply by adjusting the pH of the medium.

One application of this property involves medicinals. A number of amines obtained from the bark, roots, leaves, flowers, or fruit of various plants are useful drugs. These naturally occurring, acid-neutralizing, physiologically active amines are called **alkaloids,** and morphine, codeine, and quinine are just three examples.

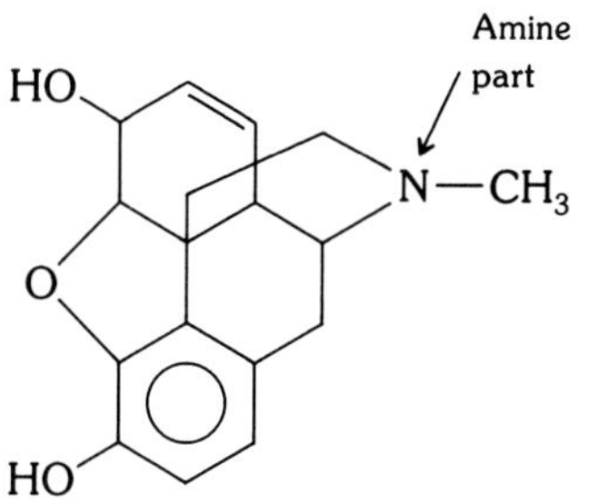

Morphine

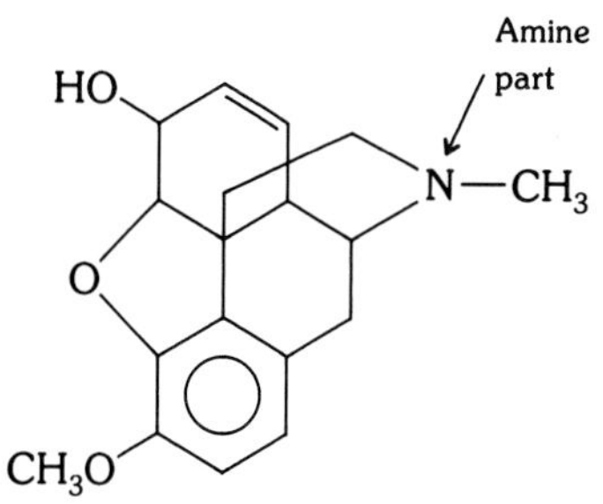

Codeine

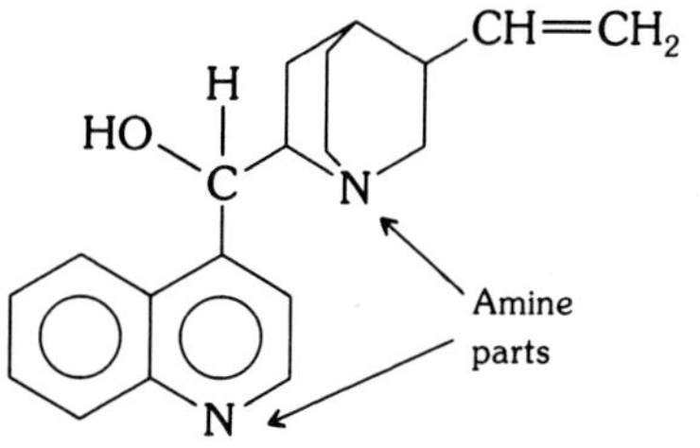

Quinine

To make it easier to administer alkaloidal drugs in the dissolved state, we often prepare them as their water-soluble amine salts. Morphine, for example, a potent sedative and painkiller, is often given as morphine sulfate, the salt of morphine and sulfuric acid. Quinine, an antimalarial drug, is available as quinine sulfate. Codeine, sometimes used in cough medicines, is often present as codeine phosphate. Special Topic 17.1 tells about a few other physiologically active amines, most of which are also prepared as their amine salts.

| EXAMPLE 17.2 | WRITING THE STRUCTURE OF THE PRODUCT OF DEPROTONATING THE CATION OF AN AMINE SALT |

■ Amphetamine sulfate (also known as benzedrine sulfate) is the form in which this drug is administered. It can be prescribed as an anorexigenic agent — one that reduces the appetite.

Problem: The protonated form of amphetamine is shown below. What is the structure of the product of its reaction with OH^-?

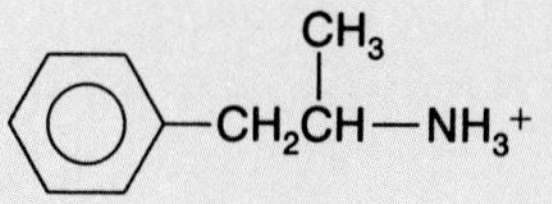

Solution: Because OH^- removes just one H^+ from the protonated amine's cation, all we have to do is reduce the number of H atoms on the nitrogen by one and cancel the positive charge. The answer, therefore is

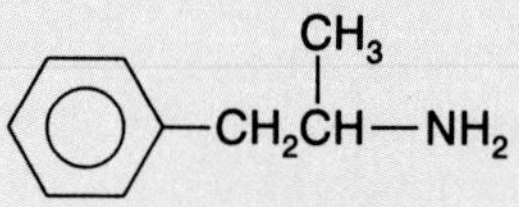

Amphetamine

(The structure of amphetamine, given here, appears to be identical with that of Dexedrine, shown in Special Topic 17.1. However, there is an important difference that we will explore in the next chapter.)

PRACTICE EXERCISE 4

■ *Hallucinogens* are drugs that cause illusions of time and place, make unreal experiences or things seem real, and distort the qualities of things.

Write the structures of the products after the following protonated amines have reacted with OH^- in a $1:1$ mole ratio.

(a)

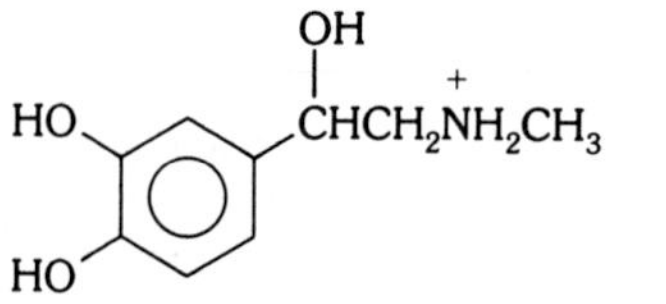

Epinephrine (adrenaline), a hormone given here in its protonated form. As the chloride salt in a 0.1% solution, it is injected in some cardiac failure emergencies. (See also Special Topic 17.1.)

(b)

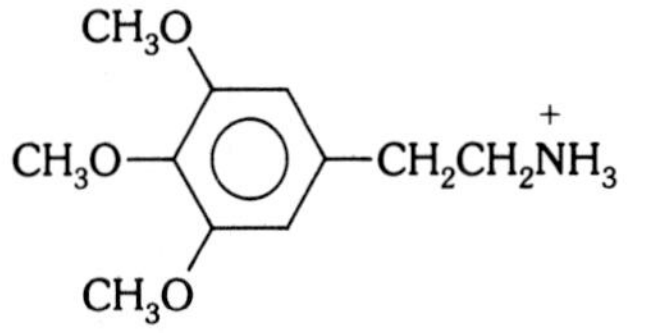

Mescaline, a mind-altering hallucinogen shown here in its protonated form. It is isolated from the mescal button, a growth on top of the peyote cactus. Indians in the southwestern United States have used it in religious ceremonies.

17.3   AMIDES OF CARBOXYLIC ACIDS

Amides are neutral nitrogen compounds that can be hydrolyzed to carboxylic acids and ammonia (or amines).

The carbonyl–nitrogen bond is sometimes called the **amide bond,** because it is the bond that forms when amides are made, and it is the bond that breaks when amides are hydrolyzed. As the following general structures show, an amide can be derived either from ammonia or from amines. Those derived from ammonia itself are often referred to as *simple* amides.

■ The amide bond is called the *peptide bond* in the chemistry of proteins.

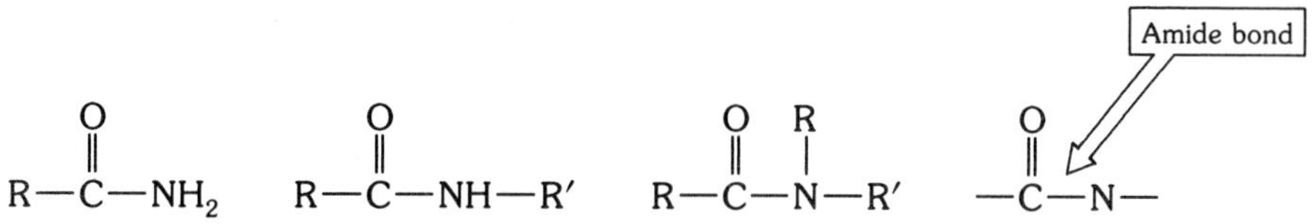

$$R-\overset{O}{\overset{\|}{C}}-NH_2 \qquad R-\overset{O}{\overset{\|}{C}}-NH-R' \qquad R-\overset{O}{\overset{\|}{C}}-\overset{R}{\overset{|}{N}}-R' \qquad -\overset{O}{\overset{\|}{C}}-N-$$

Amides of ammonia (simple amides) · Amides of amines · Amide group

We study the amide system because all proteins are essentially polyamides, polymers whose molecules have regularly spaced amide bonds. Nylon is a synthetic polymer with repeating amide groups. See Special Topic 17.2.

Table 17.3 lists several low-formula-weight amides. Their molecules are quite polar, and when they have an H atom bonded to N, they can both donate and accept hydrogen bonds. These forces add up so much in simple amides that all except methanamide are solids at room temperature. When we study proteins, we'll see how the hydrogen bond is involved in stabilizing the shapes of protein molecules, shapes that are as important to the functions of proteins as anything else about their structures.

The Names of Simple Amides End in -amide The common names of simple amides are made by replacing *-ic acid* by *-amide,* and their IUPAC names are devised by replacing *-oic acid* by *-amide.* In the following examples, notice how we can condense the structure of the amide group.

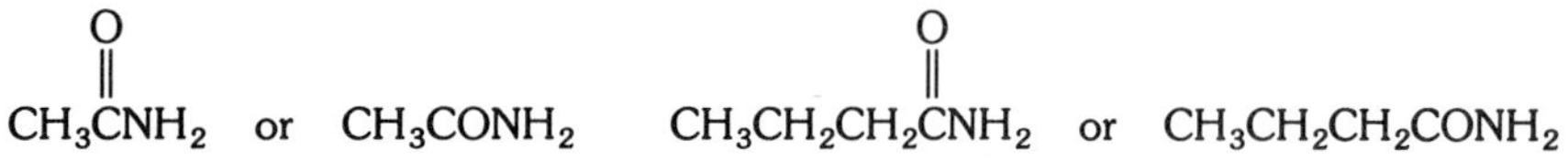

$$CH_3\overset{O}{\overset{\|}{C}}NH_2 \text{ or } CH_3CONH_2 \qquad\qquad CH_3CH_2CH_2\overset{O}{\overset{\|}{C}}NH_2 \text{ or } CH_3CH_2CH_2CONH_2$$

Acetamide (common name) · Butyramide (common name)
Ethanamide (IUPAC name) · Butanamide (IUPAC name)

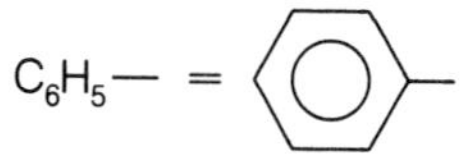

$C_6H_5- = $

The simplest aromatic amide is called benzamide, $C_6H_5CONH_2$, where C_6H_5 signifies the phenyl group. We'll not need to know the rules for naming other kinds of amides.

TABLE 17.3 Amides of Carboxylic Acids

IUPAC Name	Structure	Melting Point (°C)
Methanamide	$HCONH_2$	3
N-Methylmethanamide	$HCONHCH_3$	−5
N,N-Dimethylmethanamide	$HCON(CH_3)_2$	−61
Ethanamide	CH_3CONH_2	82
N-Methylethanamide	$CH_3CONHCH_3$	28
N,N-Dimethylethanamide	$CH_3CON(CH_3)_2$	−20
Propanamide	$CH_3CH_2CONH_2$	79
Butanamide	$CH_3CH_2CH_2CONH_2$	115
Pentanamide	$CH_3CH_2CH_2CH_2CONH_2$	106
Hexanamide	$CH_3CH_2CH_2CH_2CH_2CONH_2$	100
Benzamide	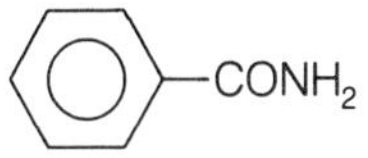 —$CONH_2$	133

SPECIAL TOPIC 17.1 SOME PHYSIOLOGICALLY ACTIVE AMINES

Epinephrine and norepinephrine are two of the many hormones in our bodies. We will study the nature of hormones in a later chapter, but we can use a definition here. **Hormones** are compounds the body makes in special glands to serve as chemical messengers. In response to a stimulus somewhat unique for each hormone, such as fright, food odor, sugar ingestion, and others, the gland secretes its hormone into circulation. The hormone then moves to some organ or tissue where it activates a particular metabolic series of reactions that constitute the biochemical response to the initial stimulus. Maybe you have heard the expression, "I need to get my adrenalin flowing." Adrenalin — or epinephrine, its technical name — is made by the adrenal gland. If you ever experience a sudden fright, a trace of epinephrine immediately flows and the results include a strengthened heartbeat, a rise in blood pressure, and a release of glucose into circulation from storage — all of which get the body ready to respond to the threat.

Norepinephrine has similar effects, and because these two hormones are secreted by the adrenal gland, they are called **adrenergic agents.**

Epinephrine

Norepinephrine

β-Phenylethanolamine

Several useful drugs mimic epinephrine and norepinephrine, and all are classified as *adrenergic drugs.* Most of them, like epinephrine and norepinephrine, are related structurally to β-phenylethanolamine (which is not a formal name, obviously). In nearly all their uses, these drugs are prepared as dilute solutions of their amine acid salts. Several of the β-phenylethanolamine drugs are even more structurally like epinephrine and norepinephrine, because they have the structural features of 1,2-dihydroxybenzene. This compound is commonly called *catechol,* so the catechol-like adrenergic drugs are called the **catecholamines.** Synthetic epinephrine (an agent in Primatene Mist), ethylnorepinephrine, and isoproterenol are examples.

Ethylnorepinephrine
(Used against asthma
in children)

Isoproterenol
(Used in treating emphysema
and asthma)

The β-phenylethylamines are another family of physiologically active amines. For example, dopamine (which is also a catecholamine) is the compound the body uses to make norepinephrine. Its synthetic form is used to treat shock associated with severe congestive heart failure.

The amphetamines are a family of β-phenylethylamines that include Dexedrine ("speed") and Methedrin ("crystal," "meth"). The amphetamines can be legally prescribed as stimulants and antidepressants, and sometimes they are prescribed for weight-control programs. However, millions of these "pep pills" or "uppers" are sold illegally, and this use of amphetamines constitutes a major drug abuse problem. The dangers of overuse include suicide, belligerence and hostility, paranoia, and hallucinations.

Dopamine

Dexedrine

Methedrine

In a later chapter we will discuss the mechanisms by which these drugs and the naturally occurring hormones work.

SPECIAL TOPIC 17.2   NYLON, A POLYAMIDE

The term *nylon* is a coined name that applies to any synthetic, long-chain, fiber-forming polymer with repeating amide linkages. One of the most common members of the nylon family, nylon-66, is made from 1,6-hexanediamine and hexanedioic acid.

$$NH_2CH_2CH_2CH_2CH_2CH_2CH_2NH_2$$

1,6-Hexanediamine
(hexamethylenediamine)

$$HOCCH_2CH_2CH_2CH_2COH$$
(with two C=O groups shown)

Hexanedioic acid
(adipic acid)

(The "66" means that each monomer has six carbon atoms.) To be useful as a fiber-forming polymer, each nylon-66 molecule should contain from 50 to 90 of each of the monomer units. Shorter molecules form weak fibers.

When molten nylon resin is being drawn into fibers, newly emerging strands are caught up on drums and stretched as they cool. Under this tension, the long polymer molecules within the fiber line up side by side, overlapping each other, to give a finished fiber of unusual strength and beauty. Part of nylon's strength comes from the innumerable hydrogen bonds that extend between the polymer molecules and that involve their many regularly spaced amide groups.

Nylon is more resistant to combustion than wool, rayon, cotton, or silk, and it is as immune to insect attack as Fiberglas. Molds and fungi do not attack nylon molecules. In medicine, nylon is used in specialized tubing, and as velour for blood contact surfaces. Nylon sutures were the first synthetic sutures and are still used.

$$\{CCH_2CH_2CH_2CH_2CNHCH_2CH_2CH_2CH_2CH_2NH\}_n C\text{—etc.}$$

Repeating unit in nylon-66

PRACTICE EXERCISE 5   Write the IUPAC names of the following amides.

(a) $CH_3CH_2CHCH_2CH_2CONH_2$
          |
         CH_3

(b) $CH_3CH_2CHCONH_2$
          |
        CH_3CH_2

Amides Are Not Proton-Acceptors, Like Amines   One reason for creating a separate family for the amides apart from the amines is that, unlike amines, amides are not bases. They're not proton-donors, either. Amides are neutral in an acid–base sense. The amide group, in other words, does not affect the pH of an aqueous system.

■ The oxygen atom of the carbonyl group is what makes the whole group electronegative.

The electronegative carbonyl group on the nitrogen atom causes the acid–base neutrality of amides. Both an amide and an amine have an unshared pair of electrons on nitrogen, but in the amide this pair is drawn back so tightly by the electron-withdrawing ability of the carbonyl group that the nitrogen atom cannot accept and hold a proton.

Amides Are Made from Amines by Acyl Group Transfer Reactions   Amides can be made from amines just as esters can be made from alcohols. Either acid chlorides or acid anhydrides react smoothly with ammonia or amines to give amides. (The amine, of course, must have at least one hydrogen atom on nitrogen, because one hydrogen has to be replaced as the amide forms.) We can illustrate these reactions using ammonia.

$$R\!-\!\overset{O}{\underset{\|}{C}}\!-\!Cl + 2NH_3 \longrightarrow R\!-\!\overset{O}{\underset{\|}{C}}\!-\!NH_2 + [NH_4^+ + Cl^-]$$

Acid chloride   Amide   Ammonium chloride

$$R\!-\!\overset{O}{\underset{\|}{C}}\!-\!O\!-\!\overset{O}{\underset{\|}{C}}\!-\!R + 2NH_3 \longrightarrow R\!-\!\overset{O}{\underset{\|}{C}}\!-\!NH_2 + [NH_4^+ + {}^-O\!-\!\overset{O}{\underset{\|}{C}}\!-\!R]$$

Acid anhydride   Ammonium salt of the
                                                                      carboxylic acid

These reactions are further examples of *acyl group transfer reactions*. The acyl group in the acid chloride, for example, transfers from the Cl atom to the N atom of the amine (or ammonia). An acyl group can transfer from an acid anhydride to N, also.

In the body, other kinds of acyl carrier molecules serve instead of ordinary acid chlorides and anhydrides as sources of the acyl group. When proteins are made from amino acids, for example, the acyl portions of amino acids — they are called *aminoacyl units* — are held by carrier molecules.

■ G is some organic group, but not necessarily an alkyl group. Hence, the symbol R is not used here.

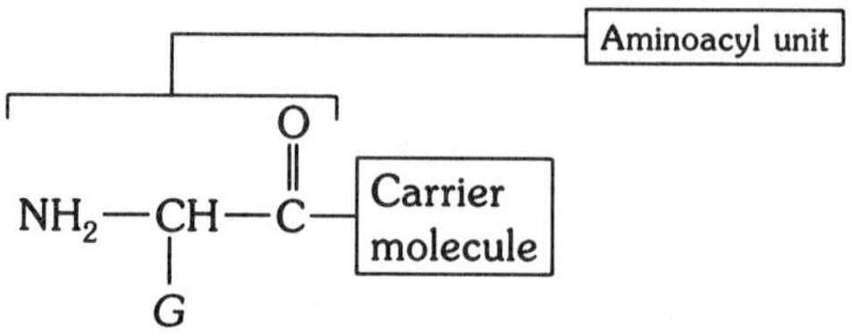

$$NH_2-\underset{\underset{G}{|}}{CH}-\overset{\overset{O}{||}}{C}-\boxed{\begin{array}{c}\text{Carrier}\\\text{molecule}\end{array}}\quad\boxed{\text{Aminoacyl unit}}$$

When a cell makes an amide bond, it transfers an aminoacyl group from its carrier molecule to the nitrogen atom of the amino group. The carrier molecule is released to be reused.

■ The molecule given here as NH_2-R can be another aminoacyl group that is bound to another carrier molecule.

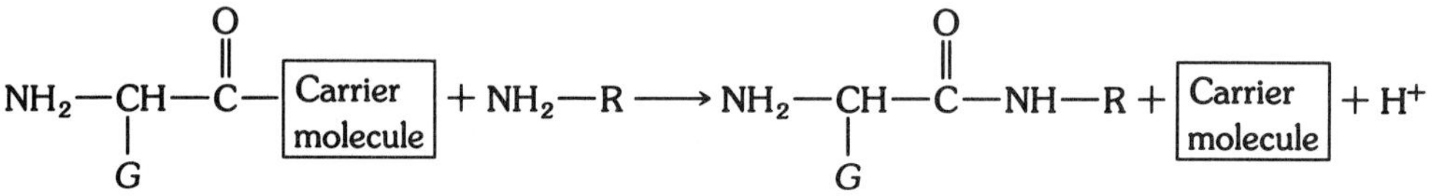

$$NH_2-\underset{\underset{G}{|}}{CH}-\overset{\overset{O}{||}}{C}-\boxed{\begin{array}{c}\text{Carrier}\\\text{molecule}\end{array}}+NH_2-R\longrightarrow NH_2-\underset{\underset{G}{|}}{CH}-\overset{\overset{O}{||}}{C}-NH-R+\boxed{\begin{array}{c}\text{Carrier}\\\text{molecule}\end{array}}+H^+$$

This is the aspect of making amides — aminoacyl transfers — that is of greatest interest as we prepare for our upcoming study of biochemistry. The skill we'll need is to figure out the structure of the amide that can be made from ammonia (or some amine) and a carboxylic acid regardless of the exact nature of the acyl transfer agent. We'll practice this in the next worked example.

| EXAMPLE 17.3 | WRITING THE STRUCTURE OF AN AMIDE THAT CAN BE MADE FROM THE ACYL GROUP OF AN ACID AND AN AMINE |

Problem: What amide can be made from the following two substances, assuming that a suitable acyl group transfer process is available?

$$\underset{}{CH_3CH_2\overset{\overset{O}{||}}{C}OH}\quad\text{and}\quad\underset{}{CH_3\overset{\overset{CH_3}{|}}{C}HNH_2}$$

Solution: The best way to proceed is to write the skeleton of the amide system and then build on it. It doesn't matter how we orient this skeleton, as we'll demonstrate.

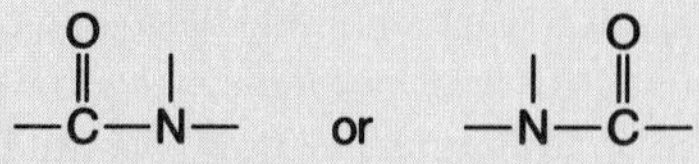

$$-\overset{\overset{O}{||}}{C}-\overset{\overset{|}{}}{N}-\quad\text{or}\quad-\overset{\overset{|}{}}{N}-\overset{\overset{O}{||}}{C}-\quad\text{(Incomplete)}$$

Then we look at the acid and see what else must be on the carbon atom of this skeleton. It's an ethyl group, so we write it in:

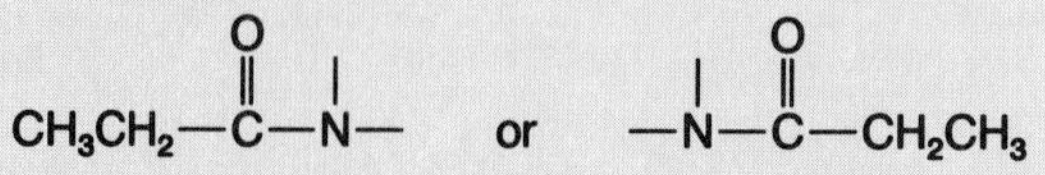

$$CH_3CH_2-\overset{\overset{O}{||}}{C}-\overset{\overset{|}{}}{N}-\quad\text{or}\quad-\overset{\overset{|}{}}{N}-\overset{\overset{O}{||}}{C}-CH_2CH_3\quad\text{(Incomplete)}$$

Then we look at the amine to see what group(s) it carries. It has an isopropyl group, so we attach it to the N atom. (If there *had been two* organic groups on N in the amine, we would attach both, of course.)

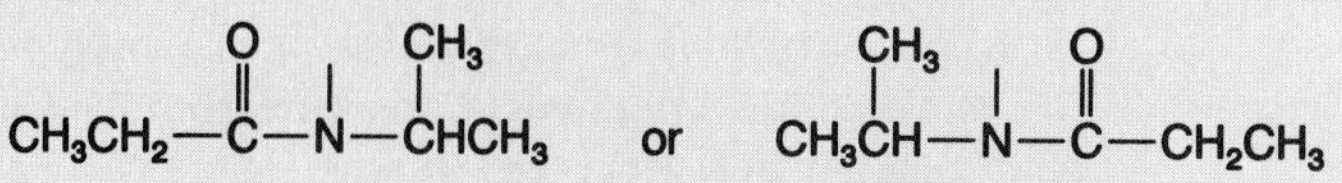

$$CH_3CH_2-\overset{\overset{O}{||}}{C}-\overset{\overset{|}{}}{N}-\overset{\overset{CH_3}{|}}{C}HCH_3\quad\text{or}\quad CH_3\overset{\overset{CH_3}{|}}{C}H-\overset{\overset{|}{}}{N}-\overset{\overset{O}{||}}{C}-CH_2CH_3\quad\text{(Incomplete)}$$

Finally, of the two H atoms on N in the amine, one survives, and our last step is to write it in. The final answer is

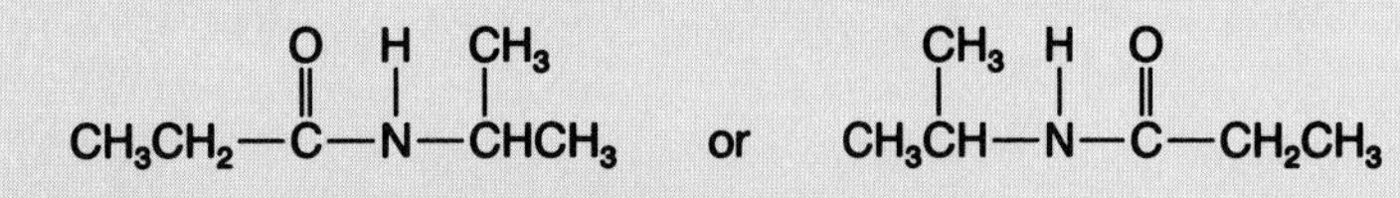

$$\underset{\substack{O\ \ \ \ H\ \ CH_3}}{CH_3CH_2-\overset{\displaystyle O}{\overset{\|}{C}}-\overset{\displaystyle H}{\overset{|}{N}}-\overset{\displaystyle CH_3}{\overset{|}{C}}HCH_3} \quad or \quad CH_3\overset{\displaystyle CH_3}{\overset{|}{C}}H-\overset{\displaystyle H}{\overset{|}{N}}-\overset{\displaystyle O}{\overset{\|}{C}}-CH_2CH_3$$

These structures, of course, are identical.

PRACTICE EXERCISE 6

What amides, if any, could be made by suitable acyl group transfer reactions from the following pairs of compounds?

(a) CH_3NH_2 and $CH_3\overset{\displaystyle CH_3}{\underset{|}{C}}HCO_2H$ (b) $NH_2C_6H_5$ and CH_3CO_2H

(c) $CH_3\overset{\displaystyle O}{\overset{\|}{C}}CH_2NH_2$ and CH_3NH_2 (d) CH_3CO_2H and $CH_3\overset{\displaystyle CH_3}{\underset{|}{N}}CH_3$

Amides Are Hydrolyzed to Their Parent Amines and Acids   The only reaction of amides we will study is their hydrolysis, a reaction in which the amide bond breaks and we obtain the amide's parent acid and amine (or ammonia). Either acids or bases promote this reaction, and enzymes catalyze it in the body. The hydrolysis of the amide bond is all that is involved in the overall chemistry of the digestion of proteins.

When an acid promotes the hydrolysis of an amide, one of the products, the amine, neutralizes the acid. (This is why we don't say that the acid *catalyzes* the hydrolysis. Catalysts, by definition, are reaction promotors that are not used up.) Thus instead of obtaining the amine itself, we get the salt of the amine. For example,

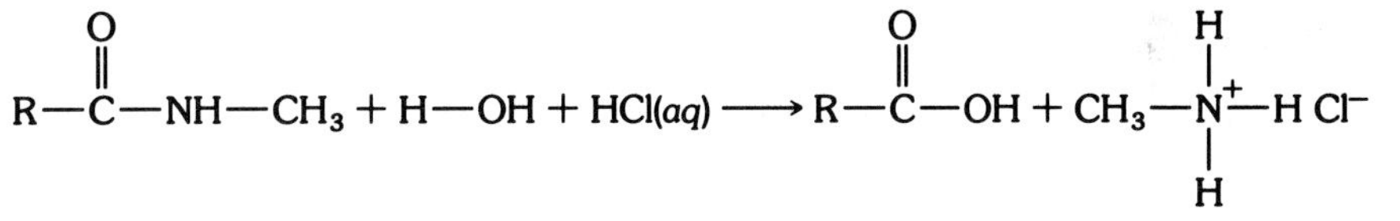

$$R-\overset{\displaystyle O}{\overset{\|}{C}}-NH-CH_3 + H-OH + HCl(aq) \longrightarrow R-\overset{\displaystyle O}{\overset{\|}{C}}-OH + CH_3-\overset{\displaystyle H}{\underset{\displaystyle H}{\overset{|}{\underset{|}{N^+}}}}-H\ Cl^-$$

On the other hand, if we use a base to promote this hydrolysis, then the carboxylic acid that forms neutralizes the base, and we get the salt of the carboxylic acid. For example,

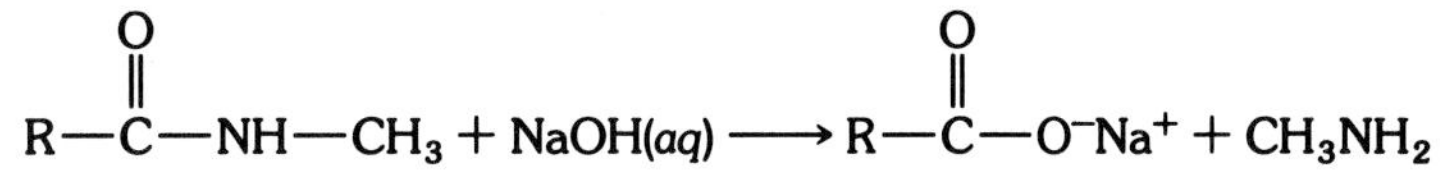

$$R-\overset{\displaystyle O}{\overset{\|}{C}}-NH-CH_3 + NaOH(aq) \longrightarrow R-\overset{\displaystyle O}{\overset{\|}{C}}-O^-Na^+ + CH_3NH_2$$

The hydrolysis of an amide can occur without any promoter; it is just much slower this way. Moreover, when enzymes catalyze this hydrolysis, they are not used up by the reaction. Therefore we'll write amide hydrolysis as a simple reaction with water to give the free carboxylic acid and the free amine. Here are some examples:

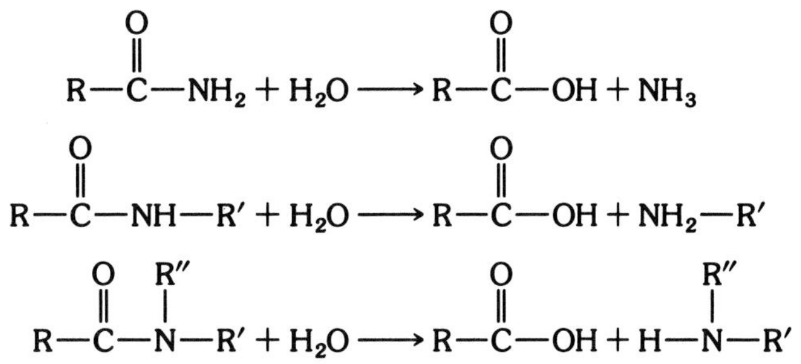

$$R-\overset{\displaystyle O}{\overset{\|}{C}}-NH_2 + H_2O \longrightarrow R-\overset{\displaystyle O}{\overset{\|}{C}}-OH + NH_3$$

$$R-\overset{\displaystyle O}{\overset{\|}{C}}-NH-R' + H_2O \longrightarrow R-\overset{\displaystyle O}{\overset{\|}{C}}-OH + NH_2-R'$$

$$R-\overset{\displaystyle O}{\overset{\|}{C}}-\overset{\displaystyle R''}{\overset{|}{N}}-R' + H_2O \longrightarrow R-\overset{\displaystyle O}{\overset{\|}{C}}-OH + H-\overset{\displaystyle R''}{\overset{|}{N}}-R'$$

| EXAMPLE 17.4 | WRITING THE PRODUCTS OF THE HYDROLYSIS OF AN AMIDE |

Problem: Acetophenetidin (phenacetin) has long been used in some brands of headache remedies. (APC tablets, for example, consist of aspirin, phenacetin, and caffeine.)

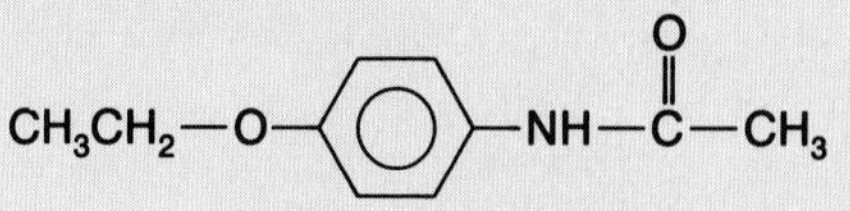

$$CH_3CH_2-O-\langle\bigcirc\rangle-NH-\overset{\overset{\textstyle O}{\|}}{C}-CH_3$$

Acetophenetidin

If this compound is an amide, what are the products of its hydrolysis?

Solution: Acetophenetidin does have the amide bond, so it can be hydrolyzed. (The functional group on the left side of this structure is an ether, and ethers do not react with water.)

Because the amide bond breaks when an amide is hydrolyzed, simply erase this bond from the structure and separate the parts. *Do not break any other bond.*

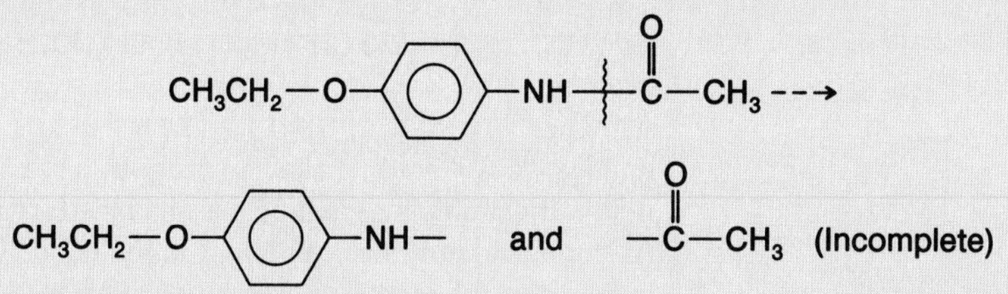

$$CH_3CH_2-O-\langle\bigcirc\rangle-NH-|-\overset{\overset{\textstyle O}{\|}}{C}-CH_3 \dashrightarrow$$

$$CH_3CH_2-O-\langle\bigcirc\rangle-NH- \quad \text{and} \quad -\overset{\overset{\textstyle O}{\|}}{C}-CH_3 \quad \text{(Incomplete)}$$

We know that the hydrolysis uses HO—H to give a carboxylic acid and an amine, so we put a HO— group on the carbonyl group we put H— on the nitrogen of the other fragment. The products, therefore, are

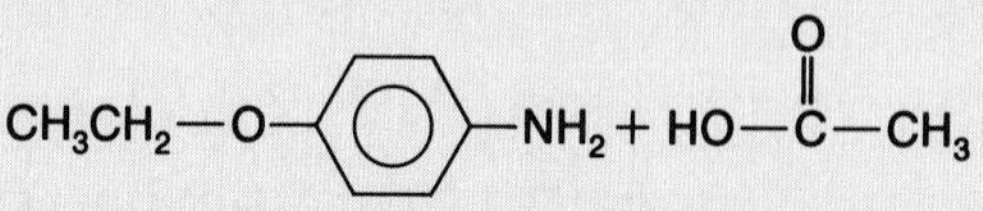

$$CH_3CH_2-O-\langle\bigcirc\rangle-NH_2 + HO-\overset{\overset{\textstyle O}{\|}}{C}-CH_3$$

PRACTICE EXERCISE 7   For any compounds in the following list that are amides, write the products of their hydrolysis.

(a) 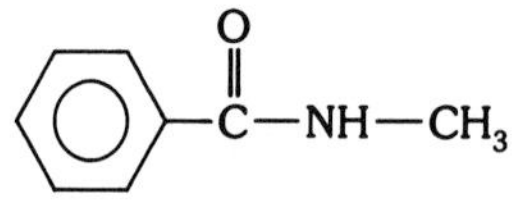 $\langle\bigcirc\rangle-\overset{\overset{\textstyle O}{\|}}{C}-NH-CH_3$ (b) $\langle\bigcirc\rangle-\overset{\overset{\textstyle O}{\|}}{C}-CH_2-NH_2$

(c) $\langle\bigcirc\rangle-NH-\overset{\overset{\textstyle O}{\|}}{C}-CH_3$ (d) 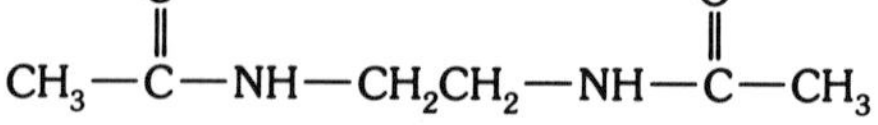 $CH_3-\overset{\overset{\textstyle O}{\|}}{C}-NH-CH_2CH_2-NH-\overset{\overset{\textstyle O}{\|}}{C}-CH_3$
(Use an excess of water)

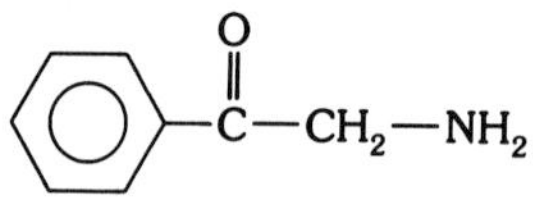

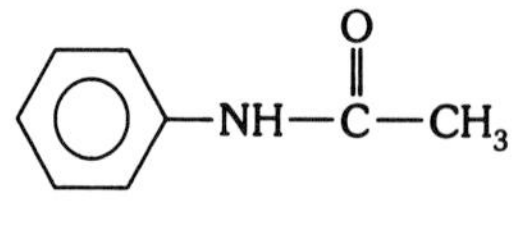

PRACTICE EXERCISE 8   The following structure illustrates some of the features of protein molecules. What are the products of the complete, enzyme-catalyzed hydrolysis (the digestion) of this substance? (A typical protein would hydrolyze to several hundred and, in some, several thousand of the kinds of molecules produced here.)

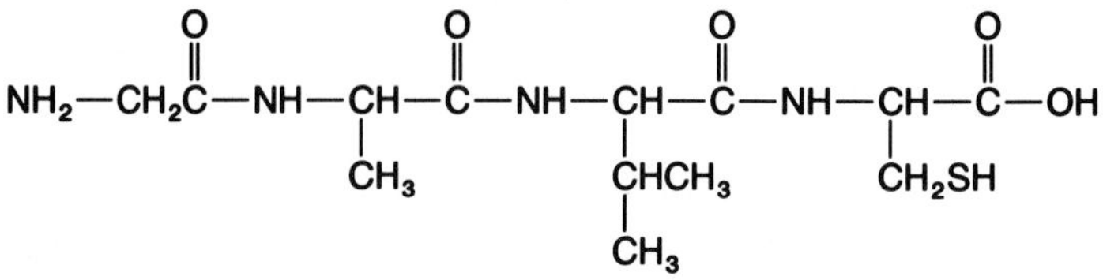

$$NH_2-CH_2\overset{\overset{\textstyle O}{\|}}{C}-NH-\underset{\underset{\textstyle CH_3}{|}}{CH}-\overset{\overset{\textstyle O}{\|}}{C}-NH-\underset{\underset{\textstyle \underset{\underset{\textstyle CH_3}{|}}{CHCH_3}}{|}}{CH}-\overset{\overset{\textstyle O}{\|}}{C}-NH-\underset{\underset{\textstyle CH_2SH}{|}}{CH}-\overset{\overset{\textstyle O}{\|}}{C}-OH$$

SUMMARY

Amines and protonated amines When one, two, or three of the hydrogen atoms in ammonia are replaced by an organic group (other than a carbonyl group), the result is an amine. The nitrogen atom can be part of a ring, as in heterocyclic amines. Like ammonia, the amines are weak bases, but all can form salts with strong acids. The cations in these salts are protonated amines.

Amine salts are far more soluble in water than their parent amines. Protonated amines are easily deprotonated by any strong base to give back the original, and usually far less soluble amine. Thus any compound with the amine function has a "solubility switch," because its solubility in an aqueous system can be turned on by adding acid (to form the amine salt) and turned off again by adding base (to recover the amine).

Amides The carbonyl–nitrogen bond, the amide bond, can be formed by letting an amine or ammonia react with anything that can transfer an acyl group (e.g., an acid chloride or an acid anhydride). Amides are neither basic nor acidic, but are neutral compounds. Amides can be made to react with water to give back their parent acids and amines. The accompanying chart summarizes the reactions studied in this chapter.

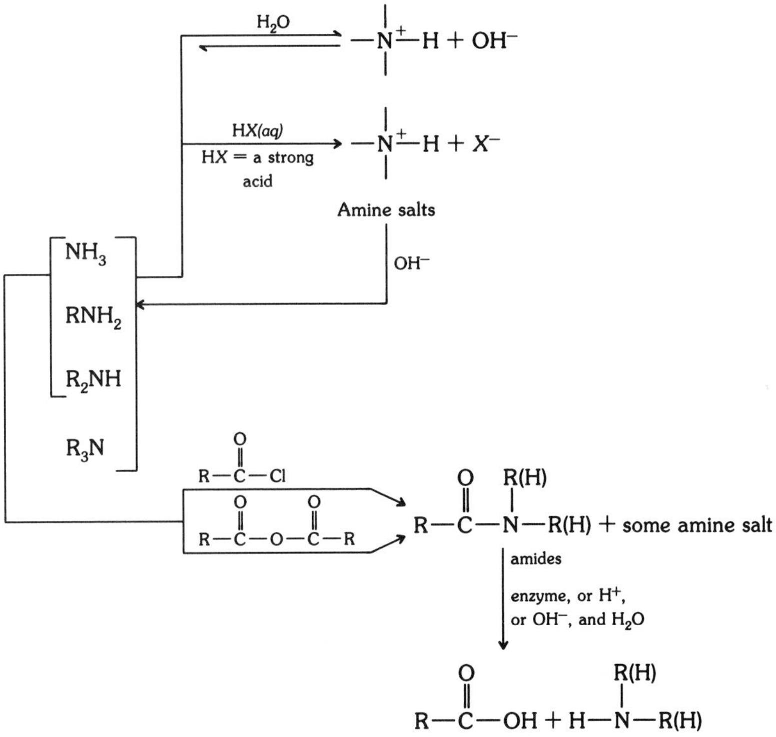

REVIEW EXERCISES

The answers to these Review Exercises are in the *Study Guide* that accompanies this book.

Structures of Amines and Amides — Review of Functional Groups

17.1 Classify the following as aliphatic, aromatic, or heterocyclic amines or amides, and name any other functional groups, too.

(a) $CH_3-O-CH_2-\overset{\overset{\displaystyle O}{\|}}{C}-NH_2$

(b) $CH_3-O-\overset{\overset{\displaystyle O}{\|}}{C}-CH_2-NH_2$

(c) 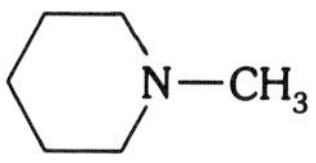 ⟨ring⟩$N-CH_3$

(d)  CH_3-⟨ring⟩$-NH_2$

17.2 Classify each of the following as aliphatic, aromatic, or heterocyclic amines or amides. Name any other functional groups that are present.

(a) 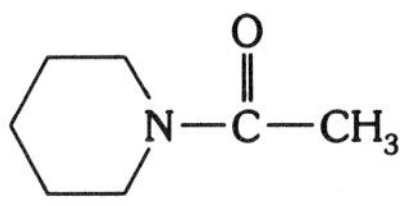 ⟨ring⟩$N-\overset{\overset{\displaystyle O}{\|}}{C}-CH_3$

(b) 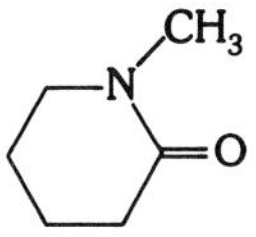 ⟨ring⟩ with $N-CH_3$ and $=O$

(c)

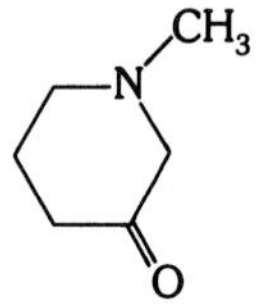

(d)

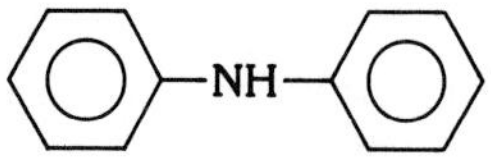

17.3 The following compounds are all very active physiological agents. Name the numbered functional groups that are present in each.

(a)

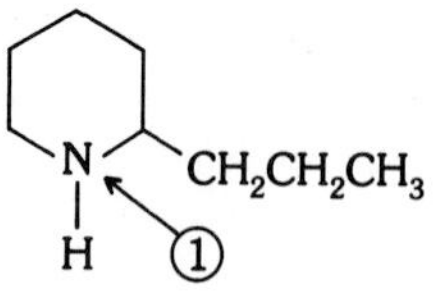

Coniine, the poison in the extract of hemlock that was used to execute the Greek philosopher Socrates.

(b)

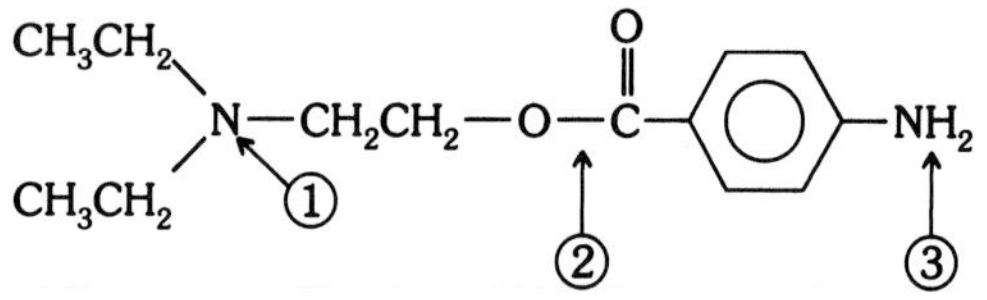

Novocaine, a local anesthetic

(c)

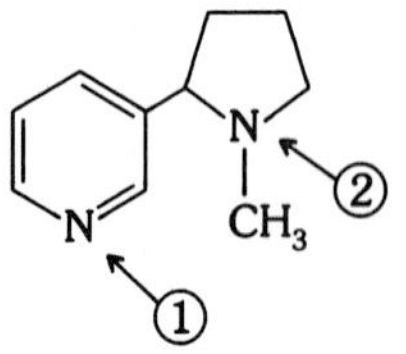

Nicotine, a poison in tobacco leaves

(d)

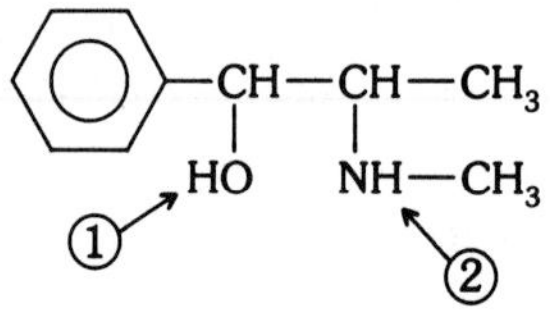

Ephedrine, a bronchodilator

17.4 Some extremely potent, physiologically active compounds are in the following list. Name the functional groups that they have.

(a)

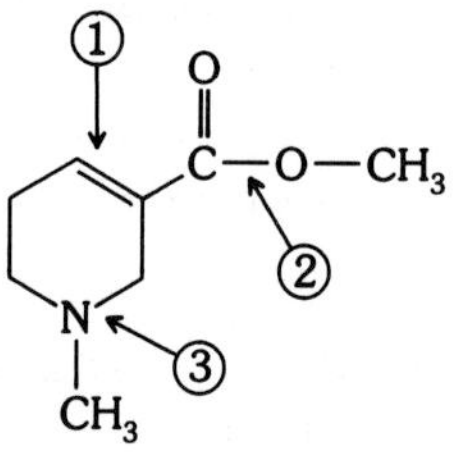

Arecoline, the most active component in the nut of the betel palm. This nut is chewed daily as a narcotic by millions of inhabitants of parts of Asia and the Pacific islands.

(b)

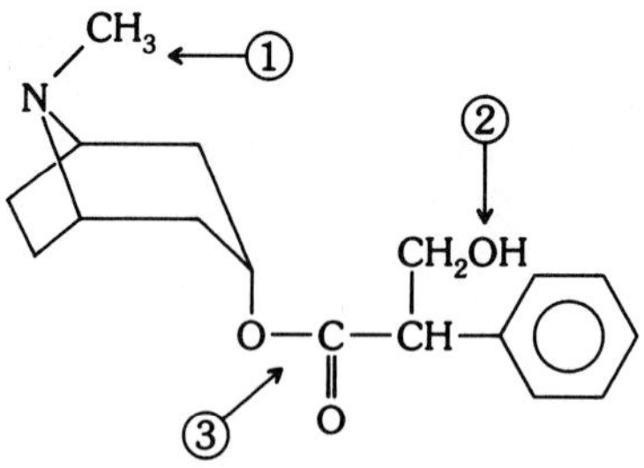

Hyoscyamine, a constituent of the seeds and leaves of henbane, and a smooth muscle relaxant. (A very similar form is called atropine, a drug used to counteract nerve poisons.)

(c)

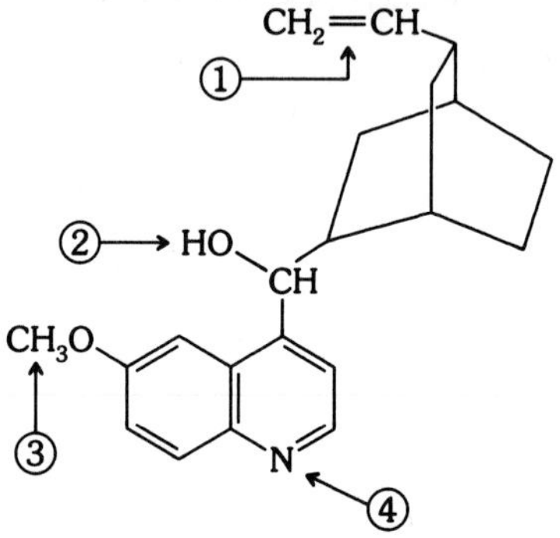

Quinine, a constituent of the bark of the chinchona tree in South America and used worldwide to treat malaria.

(d)

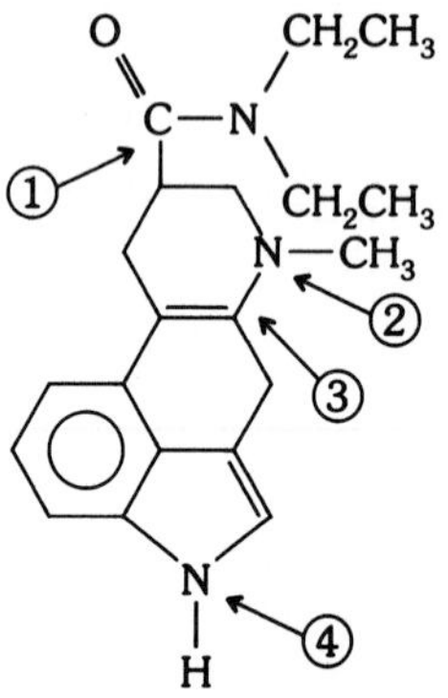

LSD (lysergic acid diethylamide), a constituent of diseased rye and a notorious hallucinogen.

Nomenclature of Amines and Amine Salts

17.5 Give the common names of the following compounds or ions.

(a)

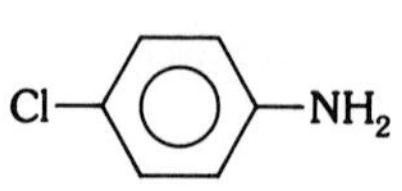

(b)

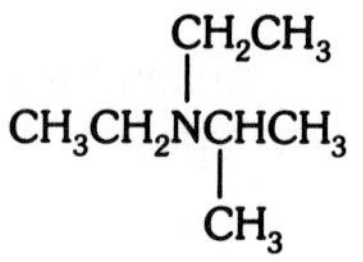

(c)

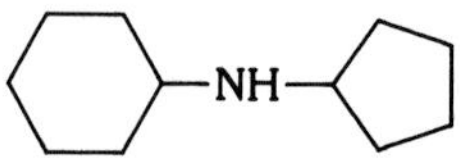

(d)

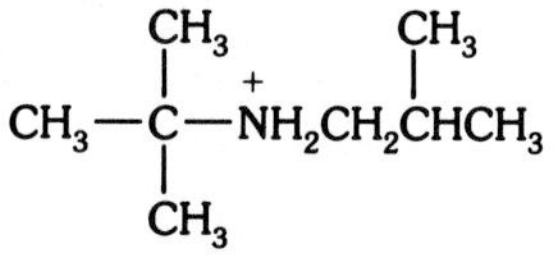

17.6 What are the common names of the following compounds?

(a) $[(CH_3)_3C]_3N$

(b) 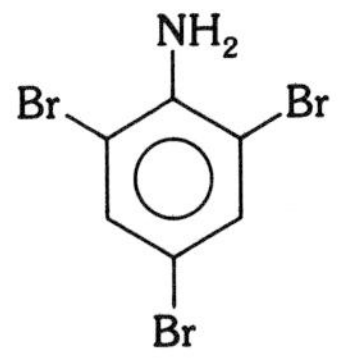

(c) $(CH_3)_2CHNHCH_2CH_2CH_2CH_3$

(d) $(CH_3CH_2)_3\overset{+}{N}H\ Cl^-$

Chemical Properties of Amines and Amine Salts

17.7 Complete the following reaction sequences by writing the structures of the organic products. If no reaction occurs, write "no reaction."

(a) $CH_3NH_2 + NaOH(aq) \rightarrow$

(b) 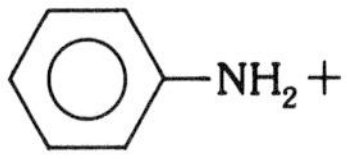 $+ HBr(aq) \longrightarrow$

(c) $NH_4Cl(aq) + NaOH(aq) \rightarrow$

(d) 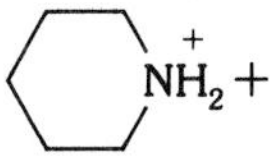 $+ OH^- \longrightarrow$

(e) $^+NH_3CH_3 + OH^- \rightarrow$

(f) $^+NH_3-CH_2-\overset{O}{\overset{\|}{C}}-O^- + OH^- \rightarrow$

17.8 Write the structures of the organic products that form in each situation. Assume that all reactions occur at room temperature. (Some of the named compounds are described in Review Exercises 17.3 and 17.4.) If no reaction occurs, write "no reaction."

(a) 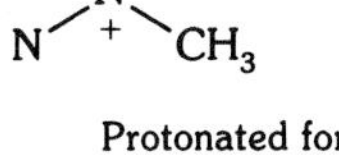 $+ HCl(aq) \longrightarrow$

(b) 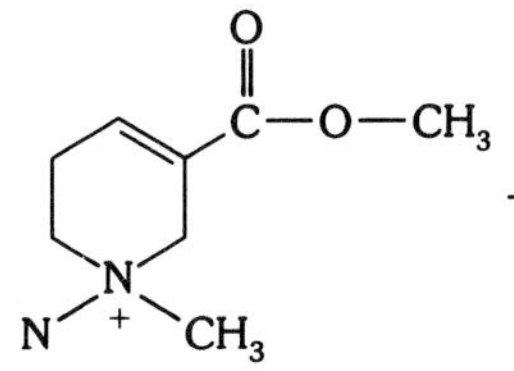 $+ OH^- \longrightarrow$

Protonated form of arecoline

(c) 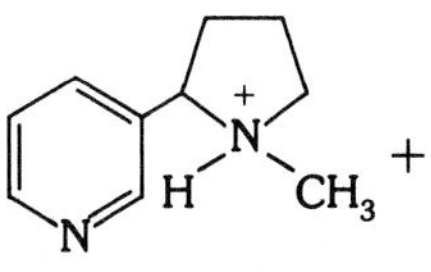 $+ OH^- \longrightarrow$

Protonated form of nicotine

(d) 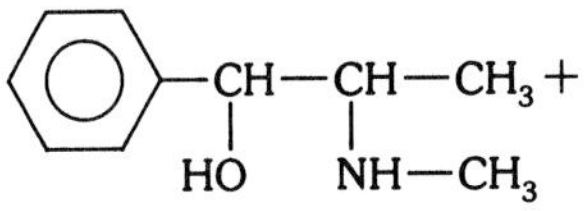 $+ HCl(aq) \longrightarrow$

Ephedrine

(e) 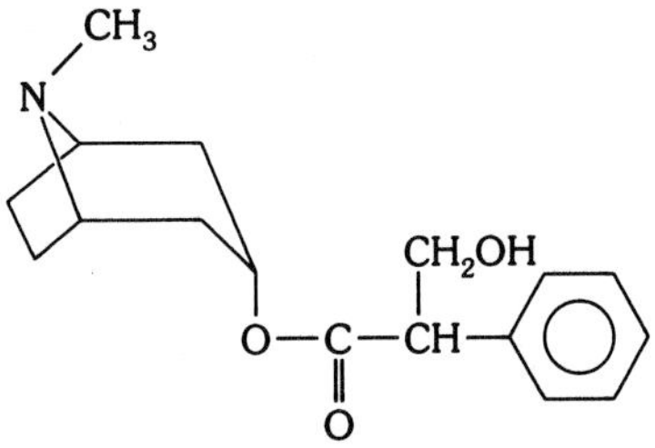 $+ HCl(aq) \longrightarrow$

Hyoscamine

17.9 Which is the stronger base, **A** or **B**? Explain.

$CH_3CH_2\overset{O}{\overset{\|}{C}}NHCH_3$	$CH_3\underset{NH_2}{\underset{\|}{C}H}\overset{O}{\overset{\|}{C}}CH_3$
A	**B**

17.10 Which is the stronger proton-acceptor, **A** or **B**? Explain.

$CH_3-\overset{CH_3}{\overset{\|}{N}}-CH_3$	$CH_3-\underset{CH_3}{\underset{\|}{\overset{CH_3}{\overset{\|}{N^+}}}}-CH_3$
A	**B**

Names and Structures of Amides

17.11 What are the IUPAC names of the following compounds?

(a) $CH_3-\underset{CH_3}{\underset{\|}{\overset{CH_3}{\overset{\|}{C}}}}-\overset{O}{\overset{\|}{C}}-NH_2$

(b) $CH_3\underset{Br}{\underset{\|}{C}H}\overset{CH_3}{\overset{\|}{C}H}-\overset{O}{\overset{\|}{C}}-NH_2$

17.12 If the common name of hexanoic acid is caproic acid, what is the common name of its simple amide?

17.13 If $C_6H_5CONHCH_3$ is the structure of *N*-methylbenzamide, what is the structure of *N,N*-dimethylbenzamide?

17.14 If $NH_2-\overset{O}{\overset{\|}{C}}-\overset{O}{\overset{\|}{C}}-NH_2$ is the structure of ethanediamide, what is the structure of butanediamide?

17.15 What is the structure of lysergic acid? The structure of its *N,N*-diethylamide was given in Review Exercise 17.4, part (d).

17.16 What is the structure of the amide between ephedrine, given in part (d) of Review Exercise 17.3, and acetic acid?

Synthesis of Amides

17.17 Write the equations for two ways to make acetamide using ammonia as one reactant.

17.18 What are two different ways to make N-methylacetamide if methylamine is one reactant? Write the equations.

17.19 Examine the following acyl group transfer reaction.

$$
\underset{\text{NH}_2\text{CH}_2\text{CNHCHC}}{\overset{O\quad O}{\|\quad\|}}\underset{\text{CH}_3}{}\boxed{\begin{array}{c}\text{Carrier}\\\text{molecule}\end{array}}_{1}
$$

$$
+ \ \underset{\text{NH}_2\text{CHC}}{\overset{O}{\|}}\boxed{\begin{array}{c}\text{Carrier}\\\text{molecule}\end{array}}_{2} \longrightarrow
$$

$$
\underset{\text{CHCH}_3}{\underset{\text{CH}_3}{}}
$$

$$
\underset{\text{NH}_2\text{CH}_2\text{CNHCHCNHCHC}}{\overset{O\quad O\quad O}{\|\quad\|\quad\|}} \boxed{\begin{array}{c}\text{Carrier}\\\text{molecule}\end{array}}_{2} + \boxed{\begin{array}{c}\text{Carrier}\\\text{molecule}\end{array}}_{1}
$$

$$
\underset{\text{CH}_3\quad\text{CHCH}_3}{}
$$

$$
\underset{\text{CH}_3}{}
$$

(a) Which specific acyl group transferred? (Write its structure.)

(b) How many amide bonds are in the product?

17.20 If the following anhydride is mixed with ammonia, what organic products that are not salts can form? Write their structures.

$$
\text{CH}_3\overset{O}{\overset{\|}{-}}\text{C}-\text{O}-\overset{O}{\overset{\|}{\text{C}}}-\text{CH}_2\text{CH}_3
$$

Reactions of Amides

17.21 What are the products of the hydrolysis of the following compounds? (If no hydrolysis occurs, state so.)

(a) $\text{CH}_3\text{NHCCH}_2\text{CH}_3$ (with $\overset{O}{\|}$)

(b) $\text{CH}_3\text{NHCH}_2\text{CCH}_3$ (with $\overset{O}{\|}$)

(c) CH_3CNCH_3 (with $\overset{O}{\|}$ and CH_3 below)

(d) $\text{CH}_3\text{CHCNHCH}_3$ (with $\overset{O}{\|}$ and CH_3 below)

17.22 Write the structures of the products of the hydrolysis of the following compounds. If no reaction occurs, state so. If more than one bond is subject to hydrolysis, be sure to hydrolyze all of them.

(a) $\text{NH}_2\text{CH}_2\overset{O}{\overset{\|}{\text{C}}}\text{NHCH}_2\overset{O}{\overset{\|}{\text{C}}}\text{OH}$

(b) $\text{CH}_3\text{N}\underset{\text{CH}_3}{}\text{CH}_2\overset{O}{\overset{\|}{\text{C}}}\text{NHCH}_2\text{CH}_2\overset{O}{\overset{\|}{\text{C}}}\text{NHCH}_3$

(c) $\begin{array}{c}\text{H}_2\text{C}-\text{NH}\\\text{H}_2\text{C}\text{C}=\text{O}\\\text{H}_2\text{C}-\text{CH}_2\end{array}$

(d) $\text{CH}_3\text{N}\underset{\text{CH}_3}{}\text{CH}_2\text{CH}_2\text{NHCCH}_2\text{CH}_2\text{CNHCH}_3$ (with two $\overset{O}{\|}$)

Review of Organic Reactions

17.23 Which of all the functional groups that we have studied can be changed by each of the following reactants? Write the equations for the reactions, using general symbols such as ROH or RCO_2H and so forth to illustrate these reactions, and name the organic families to which the reactants and products belong.

(a) Water, with either an acid or an enzyme catalyst.

(b) Hydrogen (or a hydride ion-donor) and any needed catalysts and special conditions.

(c) An oxidizing agent represented by (O), such as $Cr_2O_7^{2-}$ or MnO_4^-, but not ozone or oxygen used in combustion.

17.24 We have described three functional groups that typify those involved in the chemistry of the digestion of carbohydrates, fats and oils, and proteins. What are the names of these groups and to which type of food does each belong?

17.25 Write the structures of the organic products that would form in the following situations. If no reaction occurs, state so. These constitute a review of nearly all the organic reactions we have studied, beginning with Chapter 12.

(a) $\text{CH}_3\text{CH}_2\text{CO}_2\text{H} + \text{NaOH}(aq) \rightarrow$

(b) $\text{CH}_3-\hexagon + \text{MnO}_4^-(aq) \longrightarrow$

(c) $\text{CH}_3\overset{O}{\overset{\|}{\text{C}}}\text{CH}_3 + \text{H}_2 \xrightarrow[\text{heat, pressure}]{\text{Ni}}$

(d) $\text{CH}_3\text{O}\overset{O}{\overset{\|}{\text{C}}}\text{CH}_3 + \text{H}_2\text{O} \xrightarrow[\text{heat}]{\text{H}^+}$

(e) $\text{CH}_3-\overset{O}{\overset{\|}{\text{C}}}-\text{Cl} + 2\text{CH}_3\text{CHCH}_3 \rightarrow$ (with NH_2 below)

(f) $\text{CH}_3(\text{CH}_2)_8\text{CH}_3 + \text{NaOH}(aq) \rightarrow$

(g) $CH_3CH_2CHOCH_3 + H_2O \xrightarrow[heat]{H^+}$ (with OCH_3 above the CH)

(h) (benzene ring)$-\overset{\overset{\displaystyle O}{\|}}{C}-H + (O) \longrightarrow$

(i) $CH_3CH_2\overset{\overset{\displaystyle O}{\|}}{C}-O-CH_2CH_3 + NaOH(aq) \xrightarrow[heat]{}$

(j) $CH_3-\overset{\overset{\displaystyle O}{\|}}{C}-H + 2CH_3OH \xrightarrow[heat]{H^+}$

(k) $CH_3\overset{\overset{\displaystyle O}{\|}}{C}CH_3 + (O) \longrightarrow$

(l) $CH_3-O-CHCH_2CH_2CH_3 + NaOH(aq) \longrightarrow$ (with OCH_3 above the CH)

(m) $CH_3CH_2CO_2H + CH_3OH \xrightarrow[heat]{H^+}$

(n) $CH_3CH_2CH_2NH_2 + HCl(aq) \xrightarrow[25\,°C]{}$

(o) $H\overset{\overset{\displaystyle O}{\|}}{C}NH_2 + H_2O \xrightarrow[heat]{}$

(p) $CH_3SH + (O) \longrightarrow$

17.26 What are the structures of the organic products that form in the following situations? (If there is no reaction, state so.) These reactions review most of the chemical properties of functional groups we have studied, beginning with Chapter 12.

(a) (benzene ring)$-\overset{\overset{\displaystyle O}{\|}}{C}-O-CH_2CH_3 + NaOH(aq) \xrightarrow[heat]{}$

(b) (benzene ring)$-\overset{\overset{\displaystyle O}{\|}}{C}-H + 2CH_3OH \xrightarrow[heat]{H^+}$

(c) $CH_3(CH_2)_3CH_3 + Cr_2O_7^{2-} \longrightarrow$

(d) $CH_3\overset{\overset{\displaystyle O}{\|}}{C}CH_2CH_3 + (O) \longrightarrow$

(e) $HO\overset{\overset{\displaystyle O}{\|}}{C}CH_2CH_2CH_3 + NaOH(aq) \xrightarrow[25\,°C]{}$

(f) $CH_3-\overset{\overset{\displaystyle OCH_2CH_3}{|}}{\underset{\underset{\displaystyle CH_3}{|}}{C}}-O-CH_2CH_3 + H_2O \xrightarrow{H^+}$

(g) (cyclopentane ring)$ + NaOH(aq) \longrightarrow$

(h) $CH_3-O-\overset{\overset{\displaystyle O}{\|}}{C}CH_2CH_2\overset{\overset{\displaystyle O}{\|}}{C}-O-CH_3 + H_2O \xrightarrow{enzyme}$ (excess)

(i) $NH_2CH_2CH_2CH_2NH_2 + HCl(aq) \xrightarrow[25\,°C]{}$ (excess)

(j) $CH_3-O-CH_2CH_2\overset{\overset{\displaystyle O}{\|}}{C}-H + (O) \longrightarrow$

(k) $CH_3CH_2OH + CH_3(CH_2)_4CO_2H \xrightarrow[heat]{H^+}$

(l) $CH_3CH_2-O-\overset{\overset{\displaystyle CH_3}{|}}{CH}-O-CH_2CH_3 + H_2O \xrightarrow[heat]{H^+}$

(m) $CH_3CH_2\overset{\overset{\displaystyle O}{\|}}{C}CH_2CH_3 + H_2 \xrightarrow[heat, pressure]{Ni}$

(n) $2CH_3NH_2 + CH_3\overset{\overset{\displaystyle O}{\|}}{C}-O-\overset{\overset{\displaystyle O}{\|}}{C}CH_3 \longrightarrow$

(o) $CH_3NH\overset{\overset{\displaystyle O}{\|}}{C}CH_2CH_2\overset{\overset{\displaystyle O}{\|}}{C}NHCH_3 + H_2O \xrightarrow{enzyme}$ (excess)

(p) $CH_3S-SCH_3 + 2(H) \longrightarrow$

Physiologically Active Amines (Special Topic 17.1)

17.27 What are hormones and, in very broad terms, what is their function?

17.28 Hormones secreted by the adrenal gland are called what kinds of agents?

17.29 Name two hormones secreted by the adrenal gland.

17.30 Drugs that tend to mimic the two hormones secreted by the adrenal gland are called what kinds of drugs?

17.31 To be a *catecholamine* as well as a *β*-phenylethanol amine, a compound must have what structural features?

17.32 Is dopamine, a *β*-phenylethylamine, also a catecholamine?

17.33 In what general family of the physiologically active amines are the amphetamines found?

17.34 What is the chemical name of each?
(a) "Speed"   (b) "Uppers"

Nylon (Special Topic 17.2)

17.35 What functional group is present in nylon-66?

17.36 The strength of a nylon fiber is attributed in part to what relative weak bond?

Optical Isomerism

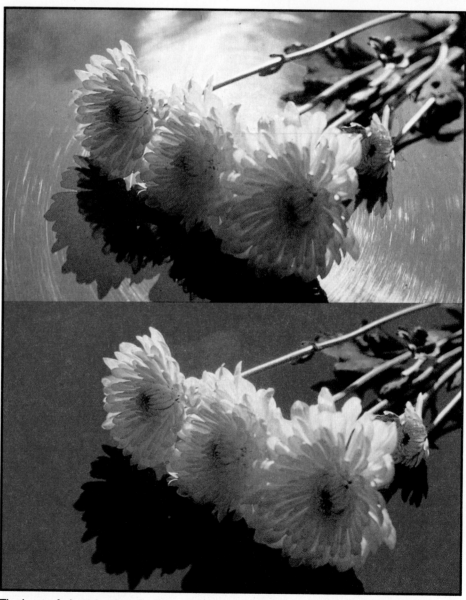

The bane of photographers is glare, and most of the glare is polarized light (top). A polarizing filter takes out such glare and makes possible a much better picture (bottom). In this chapter we study a helpful use of polarized light.

Structural isomers and stereoisomers are the two broad classes of isomers.

Compounds that have identical molecular formulas can be different in two general ways, as structural isomers or as stereoisomers.

Structural Isomers Differ in Molecular Frameworks Butane and isobutane, both C_4H_{10}, have different chains. Ethanol and dimethyl ether, both C_2H_6O, have different functional groups. Each pair illustrates **structural isomerism** because their members differ in their skeletons.

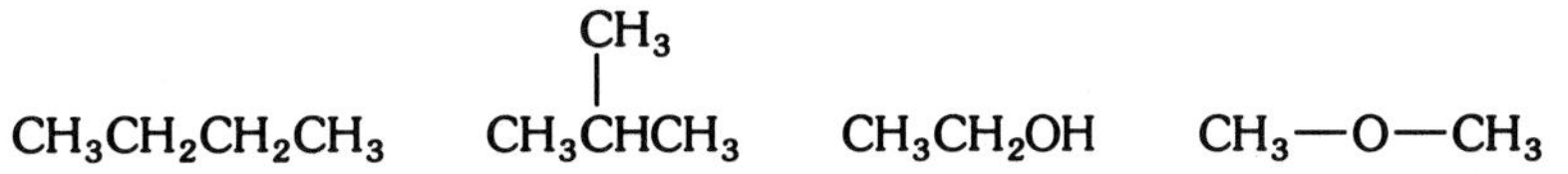

$$CH_3CH_2CH_2CH_3 \qquad CH_3\overset{\overset{\displaystyle CH_3}{|}}{C}HCH_3 \qquad CH_3CH_2OH \qquad CH_3{-}O{-}CH_3$$

Butane   Isobutane   Ethanol   Dimethyl ether

Stereoisomers Differ Only in Geometry *cis*-2-Butene and *trans*-2-butene illustrate **stereoisomerism** because they have identical molecular formulas, functional groups, and heavy-atom skeletons but display different geometries.

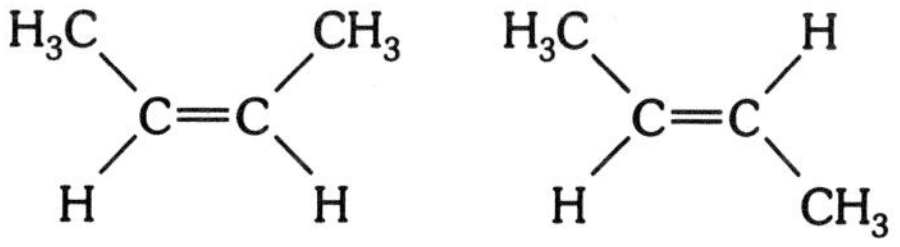

cis-2-Butene   trans-2-Butene

There is one more kind of stereoisomerism, **optical isomerism,** which we will study in this chapter. Although optical isomers come as close to being identical as your left and right hands, they display some very dramatic differences in chemistry at the molecular level of life. One such difference is illustrated by the bittersweet story of asparagine.

■ Asparagine is a building block for making proteins in the body.

Asparagine is a white solid that was first isolated in 1806 from the juice of asparagus. When from this source, asparagine has a bitter taste. Its molecular formula is $C_4H_8N_2O_3$, and its structure is given by structure **1.**

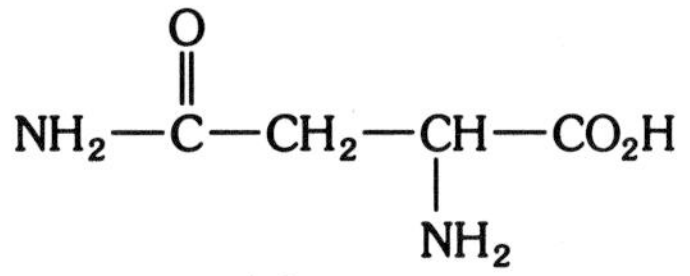

$$NH_2{-}\overset{\overset{\displaystyle O}{\|}}{C}{-}CH_2{-}\underset{\underset{\displaystyle NH_2}{|}}{C}H{-}CO_2H$$

1 Asparagine

■ Vetch is a member of a genus of herbs, some of which are useful as fodder for cattle.

In 1886, a chemist isolated from sprouting vetch a white substance with the same molecular formula *and structure,* but it had a sweet taste. To have names for these, the one isolated from asparagus we now call L-asparagine, and the one from vetch sprouts D-asparagine.

■ The letters D and L will acquire more specific meaning in the next chapter. Consider them to be only labels now.

Here were two substances seemingly answering to the same structure despite what is almost a dogma in chemistry, the principle of *one substance–one structure.* If two samples of matter have identical physical and chemical properties, then they have to be identical at the level of their individual formula units. If two samples differ in even one way in their fundamental properties, then there has to be at least one difference in the way that their molecules are put together.

Taste is a chemical sense, so the two samples of asparagine do have one difference in chemical property. Under the one-substance–one-structure law, the molecules of D- and L-asparagine must be structurally different in at least one way. This difference arises from a peculiar lack of symmetry in their molecules that makes possible two different relative configurations of their molecular parts.

18.2 MOLECULAR CHIRALITY

The molecules of many substances have a handedness like that of the left and the right hands.

Two partial ball-and-stick molecular models of asparagine are shown in part *(a)* of Figure 18.1. Examine each to make sure that it faithfully represents asparagine, structure **1.** To make the study of these models easier, we have simplified them as shown in part *(b)* of Figure 18.1. Notice again how alike the two molecular structures are. Notice particularly that the same four groups are attached to a central carbon atom, and that there is no cis – trans kind of difference between them. Yet the fact remains that one represents a bitter-tasting compound, and the other is of a sweet-tasting compound. In some way these two similiar structures have to be different, and the difference isn't something that can be removed by rotating groups around single bonds.

Two Materials Whose Molecules Can Be Superimposed Are Samples of the Same Compound   To understand how the two asparagine structures are different, we first have to learn the ultimate test for deciding whether two structures are the same. For two structures to be identical, it must be possible to superimpose them. This is a manipulation you

Figure 18.1

The two stereoisomers of asparagine.
(a) Two ways of joining the four groups to the carbon marked by the asterisk.
(b) Simplified representations of the models in part *a*. (c) What is in front of the mirror is identical with the model on the left in part *b*. What is seen in the mirror as the image is identical with the model on the right in part *b*. You'll mentally have to spin the mirror image 120° counterclockwise about the bond from C to g to see that they are the same. The object and its mirror image do not superimpose, so they can't be identical. Instead, they are enantiomers.

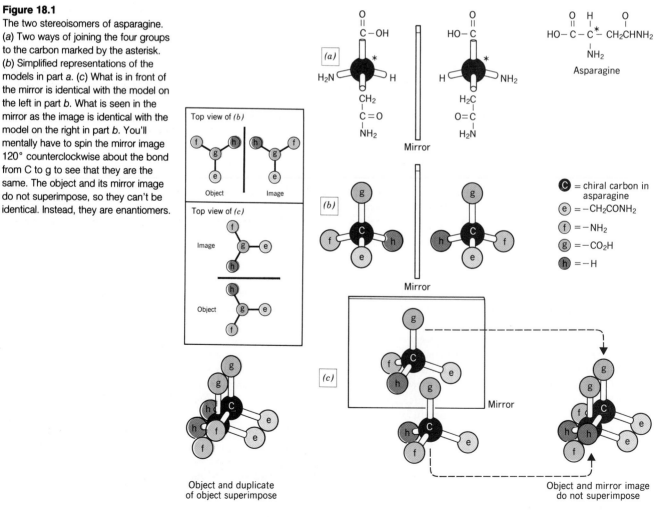

In some references you'll see the word *superposition* used for *superimposition*.

can carry to completion only in your mind, but molecular models are a great help. **Superimposition** is the mental blending of one molecular model with another so that the two would coincide in every atom and bond simultaneously if the operation could actually be completed. (When working with molecular models, it's fair to twist parts about single bonds to find conformations that can be superimposed, but it's not legal to break any bonds.) Superimposition is illustrated in the left-hand side of part *(c)* of Figure 18.1 where two identical models of one of the asparagines is used.

As we said, the fundamental criterion of identity of two structures is that they pass the test of superimposition, a test that we will see is failed by the two *different* asparagines, part *(b)* of Figure 18.1. In part *(c)*, the model on the left in part *(b)* has been turned counterclockwise by 120° around the vertical bond from C to group g and then placed as the object in front of the mirror. Now look at its reflection in the mirror. If you made an exact model of this reflection, it would be identical to that of the other asparagine. This is how nearly identical the two asparagines are. In the lower right of part *(c),* you can see that these two models, the one in front of the mirror and the model of its reflection, do not superimpose.

The Molecules of Enantiomers Are Related as Object to Mirror Image But Cannot Be Superimposed

As we said, the two different asparagines are so alike that the molecules of one are the mirror images of the molecules of other. Yet the model and its mirror image do not superimpose. Isomers whose molecules are related as object to mirror image but cannot be superimposed are called **enantiomers** of each other.

Always remember two general facts about isomers of any kind. They are truly *different substances,* different compounds, but they share the same molecular formula while differing in the arrangements of their parts. Enantiomers are just special kinds of isomers, but unlike structural isomers they also have identical atom-to-atom sequences. The fundamental difference between two enantiomers lies only in their configurations, so they fall into the general family of stereoisomers. To distinguish them from geometric (cis–trans) isomers, which are also stereoisomers, remember that the existence of two geometric isomers depends on a lock against free rotation, either a double bond or a ring.

Stereoisomers that are not geometric isomers are called **optical isomers.** Thus the two main families of stereoisomers are geometric isomers and optical isomers. See also Figure 18.2. Enantiomers constitute one way in which optical isomers can occur, the only way that we'll study apart from a Special Topic later in the chapter.

Molecules of Two Enantiomers Have Opposite Configurations

Lack of free rotation is not the cause of the asparagine enantiomers. Their molecules, instead, are described as having *opposite configurations.* To show what this means, we have repositioned their abbre-

Figure 18.2
The relationships of various kinds of isomers.

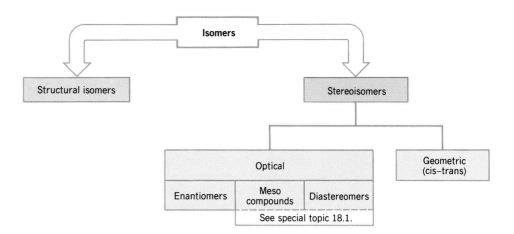

Figure 18.3
When the two stereoisomers of asparagine are viewed down the same axis, the C—H bond axis, the remaining three groups at the central carbon atom have opposite configurations.

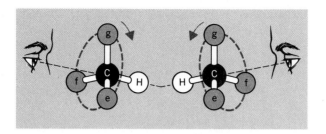

viated molecular models in Figure 18.3. (Imagine a mirror standing between the two and perpendicular to the page to see that they are related as object to mirror image.)

You're now going to let your eyes make a special scanning trip around each molecule. Imaging that the bond from C to H in each model is the steering column of the steering wheel of a car. Then imagine that the remaining three groups — **e, f,** and **g** — are distributed around the steering wheel itself. Now move your eyes from **g** to **e** and then to **f.** When you do this with the asparagine model on the left in Figure 18.3, your eyes move clockwise. But to make the identical trip — **g** to **e** to **f** — in the model on the right, your eyes move counterclockwise. These clockwise versus counterclockwise arrangements of identical parts around the same central axis are what having opposite configuration means. The four groups on the central carbon in one asparagine are the same four groups as in the other, but they are configured oppositely in space.

Molecules of Two Enantiomers Have Opposite Chirality   We have to remind ourselves here that any object has a mirror image. Spheres, cubes, broom handles, water glasses, and whatever can all be reflected in a mirror. It's only when the model of the object and the model of the mirror image can't be superimposed that we call the two enantiomers.

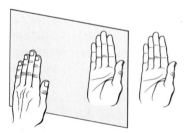

The image of the left hand is just like the right hand in the relative orientations of the fingers, thumb, and palm.

Your two hands are like a pair of enantiomers, if you disregard small differences such as wrinkles, scars, rings, and fingerprints. Now place your left hand in front of a mirror near its edge. Place your other hand just off the edge of the mirror and notice that the reflection of your left hand in the mirror is the same as your right hand (disregarding, as we said, the small differences). Your right hand is the mirror image reflection of your left hand.

Next, try to superimpose the two hands. Because the mirror image of your left hand is your real right hand, use your two hands to see whether they superimpose. If you put them palm to palm it seems as though all the fingers do superimpose. But remember, you have to carry this blending through to completion (in your mind), and when you do, the palm of one hand comes out on the back side of the other. The palms won't superimpose when the fingers seem to. And if you try to get the palms to come out right, then the fingers come out all wrong. Left and right hands, although related as object to mirror image, don't superimpose. They are related as enantiomers.

Notice, now, how the two hands have opposite configurations. Look at them down the same axis, as we did with the asparagine models in Figure 18.3, say, down the axis from palm to backside. This means that both palms will face you. To make the trip from thumb to little finger, touching every other finger on the way, you have to scan in one direction for one hand and in exactly the opposite direction for the other. Thus the two hands have opposite configurations.

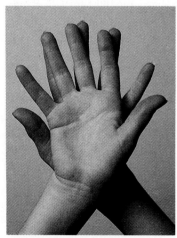

The two hands are related as an object to its mirror image, but they can't be superimposed.

The little experiment with the hands has been used for decades to teach about configurational differences of enantiomers, and this is why we say that molecules of different enantiomers have different *handedness*. The technical term for this configurational property is **chirality** (from the Greek word for hand, which is *cheir*). We say that the molecules of enantiomers have opposite chirality, meaning opposite handedness. We also say that the molecules of any given enantiomer are **chiral** — they possess handedness or chirality.

The opposite of chiral is **achiral.** An achiral molecule is one that is symmetrical enough so that its model and the model of its mirror image do superimpose. The methane molecule is

A left-hand glove does not fit the right hand.

achiral, for example. Some examples of larger achiral objects include a cube, a sphere, a broom handle, and a water glass.

Chirality Can Make Enormous Differences at the Molecular Level of Life
One asparagine enantiomer tastes sweet and the other tastes bitter—a large (although a somewhat trivial) difference that chirality can make. The details are not fully known, but the taste mechanism probably begins with a chemical reaction that is catalyzed by an enzyme. The enzymes involved, *like all enzymes,* themselves consist of very large, chiral molecules with molecular surfaces that are different for each enzyme.

The substance whose reaction an enzyme catalyzes is called the **substrate** for that enzyme. An enzyme works by letting a molecule of the substrate come and temporarily fit into the contours on the enzyme's surface. This idea of fitting can be illustrated by a return to our hands, only now we'll add gloves. Gloves, like hands, are chiral, and a glove fits well only to its matching hand. The left hand fits well into the left glove, not the right glove. Now suppose that an enzyme responsible ultimately for the sensation of a sweet taste is like a glove for the right hand. This means that only the substrate molecules that have the matching handedness can interact with this enzyme. Substrate molecules of the opposite handedness can't fit to this enzyme.

We can now shift back from this analogy of hands and gloves to chiral molecules with the aid of Figure 18.4. To make it easier, we have used simple geometric forms to create two enantiomers, and indentations that match these forms are part of the enzyme surface. One enantiomer can fit to the enzyme surface, but no matter how you turn the model of the other enantiomer you can't get it to fit to the same enzyme surface.

There is, evidently, a different enzyme whose surface chirality matches the other asparagine enantiomer that lets us know that this other enantiomer has a different taste. The phenomenon of chirality is absolutely central to this difference. And the different chemical properties that relate to the taste of asparagine are illustrated in countless ways at the molecular level of life. We'll see time after time that differences in geometry and configuration are as important as functional groups to the chemical reactions of life.

Chirality Does Not Affect Reactions with Achiral Compounds
If the enzyme molecule weren't chiral, it couldn't discriminate between enantiomers. In fact, *enantiomers have identical chemical properties toward all reactants whose molecules are achiral*—reactants such as H_2O, NaOH, HCl, Cl_2, NH_3, and H_2. A broom handle, which isn't chiral, is an analogy. It fits just as easily to the left hand as to the right. It can't discriminate between the hands. In like manner, the molecules of an achiral reactant can't tell the difference between molecules of enantiomers. To summarize, enantiomers react differently toward reactants whose molecules are chiral but identically toward achiral reactants.

Figure 18.4
Since an enzyme is chiral, it can accept substrate molecules of only one of a pair of enantiomers. To illustrate this difference, we have used simple geometric forms. On the left, the enzyme can accept as a substrate the molecule of one enantiomer. On the right, the same enzyme can't accept a molecule of the other enantiomer, because the shapes don't match.

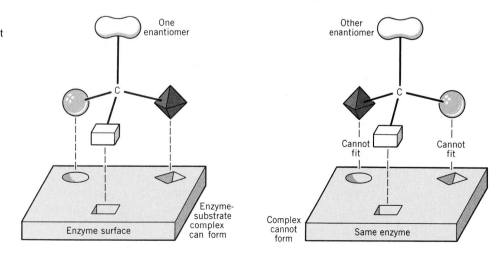

Two Enantiomers Have Identical Physical Properties, with One Exception   Two enantiomers have identical melting points, boiling points, densities, and solubilities in common (i.e., achiral) solvents like water, ether, gasoline, or ethanol. This *must* be so, because the molecules of two enantiomers *must* have identical molecular polarities. They have, after all, identical intranuclear distances and bond angles.

Returning once again to our analogy with the hands, you can see that the distance, say, from the tip of the thumb to the tip of the little finger is the same in both hands. You can pick any other such intrahand distance that you please, and it is the same in both hands. Similarly, the angle between any two fingers is the same in both hands. In like manner, if we pick any distance between atoms or any bond angle in one asparagine enantiomer, we will find it to be the same in the other. When all these distances and angles are identical in the two enantiomers, their molecules as a whole must have identical polarities. This is responsible for the identical physical properties that we mentioned. There is one difference in physical property, which we will study in Section 18.3.

Molecules with One Carbon Holding Four Different Groups Are Chiral   It is important that we be able to recognize when a potential substrate is chiral, because molecules of opposite chirality have such different chemical properties at the molecular level of life. How, then, can we look at a structure and tell whether its molecules are chiral without making molecular models of both object and mirror image?

■ There are some substances — both organic and inorganic — whose molecules have no chiral carbon atoms and yet are chiral molecules, but we won't encounter any of these in our study.

In all the examples of chiral molecules that we'll encounter, there is always at least one carbon to which *four different groups* are attached. A carbon that holds four different atoms or groups is called a **chiral carbon,** because its presence usually (although not always) guarantees that a molecule with such a carbon is itself chiral.

The asparagine molecule has one (and just one) chiral carbon, and when a molecule has only one chiral carbon, we can be absolutely certain that the molecule is itself chiral. Here, then, is one way to predict whether a substance consists of chiral molecules; we look for a chiral carbon. If we find one, we can be certain that the molecules are chiral. If we find more than one, we have to be careful, but this brings us to a complication that we'll use Special Topic 18.1 to examine. Probably 99.99% of all examples of substances that have two or more chiral carbons also have chiral molecules, but a few exceptions do exist where the molecule is achiral despite having chiral carbon atoms. (These are the *meso compounds* discussed in Special Topic 18.1.)

| **EXAMPLE 18.1** | **IDENTIFYING CHIRAL CARBONS** |

Problem: Amphetamine, which we introduced in Example 17.2, exists as a pair of enantiomers. One of them has its own name — Dexedrine. Find the chiral carbon in amphetamine, and list the four groups attached to it.

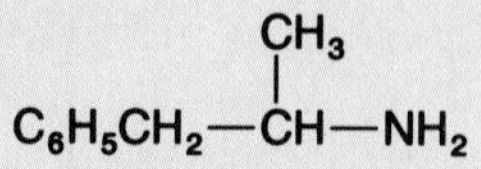

$$
\begin{array}{c}
CH_3 \\
| \\
C_6H_5CH_2\!-\!CH\!-\!NH_2
\end{array}
$$
Amphetamine

Solution: There is one chiral carbon in amphetamine, the one labeled with the asterisk:

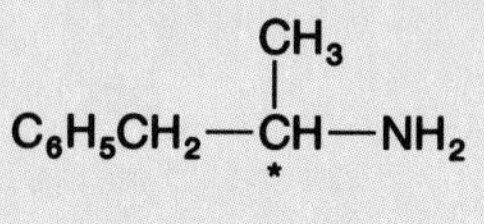

$$
\begin{array}{c}
CH_3 \\
| \\
C_6H_5CH_2\!-\!CH\!-\!NH_2 \\
{}^{*}
\end{array}
$$

The four groups are:

$$C_6H_5CH_2,\ H,\ CH_3,\ \text{and}\ NH_2$$

PRACTICE EXERCISE 1   Place an asterisk next to each chiral carbon in the following structures.

(a) 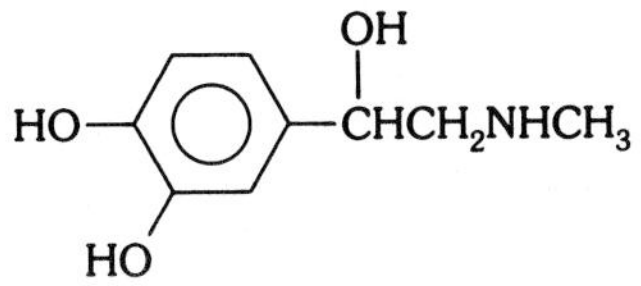 HO—⬡—$\overset{\overset{\displaystyle OH}{|}}{C}HCH_2NHCH_3$ Epinephrine, a hormone (See Special Topic 17.1.)

HO

(b) 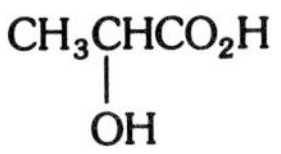 $CH_3\overset{}{C}HCO_2H$ Lactic acid, the sour constituent in sour milk
     $\overset{|}{OH}$

(c) 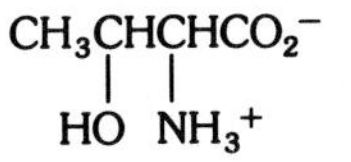 $CH_3CHCHCO_2^-$ Threonine, one of the amino acid building blocks of pro-
     $\overset{|}{HO}\ \overset{|}{NH_3{}^+}$ teins

(d) 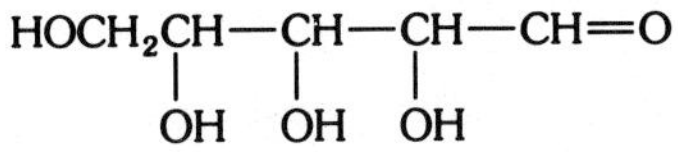 $HOCH_2CH—CH—CH—CH{=}O$ Ribose, a sugar unit at the molecular level of heredity
     $\quad\quad\overset{|}{OH}\ \ \overset{|}{OH}\ \ \overset{|}{OH}$

A Molecule with *n* Different Chiral Carbons Has 2^n Optical Isomers   When a molecule has two or more chiral carbons, as in parts (c) and (d) of Practice Exercise 1, it becomes useful to judge whether the chiral carbons are *different*. When used in this context, *different* means that the sets of four atoms or groups at the various chiral carbons have at least one difference. Two chiral carbons are said to be *different* if the set of four groups at one is not duplicated by the set at the other. Whenever the chiral carbons in a molecule are different in this sense — as they were in parts (c) and (d) of Practice Exercise 1 — the substance can exist in the forms of 2^n optical isomers, where *n* is the number of different chiral carbons. These 2^n optical isomers occur as half as many *pairs* of enantiomers. We'll see this illustrated in the next worked example.

EXAMPLE 18.2

JUDGING WHETHER CHIRAL CARBONS ARE DIFFERENT AND CALCULATING THE NUMBER OF OPTICAL ISOMERS

Problem: The threonine molecule, part (c) of Practice Exercise 1, has two chiral carbons, labeled here by asterisks.

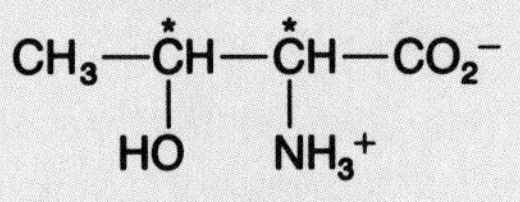

$$CH_3—\overset{*}{C}H—\overset{*}{C}H—CO_2^-$$
$$\quad\ \ \overset{|}{HO}\quad\ \ \overset{|}{NH_3{}^+}$$
$$Threonine$$

Are these chiral carbons different? If so, how many optical isomers of threonine are there?

Solution: Make a list of the sets of four different groups at each chiral carbon and compare the sets. If they're not identical in every respect, then the two chiral carbons are different.

At one chiral carbon: At the other chiral carbon:
CH_3, H, OH, —$\overset{}{C}H—CO_2^-$ $CH_3—\overset{}{C}H—$, H, CO_2^-, $NH_3{}^+$
$\quad\quad\quad\quad\quad\overset{|}{NH_3{}^+}$ $\quad\ \overset{|}{HO}$

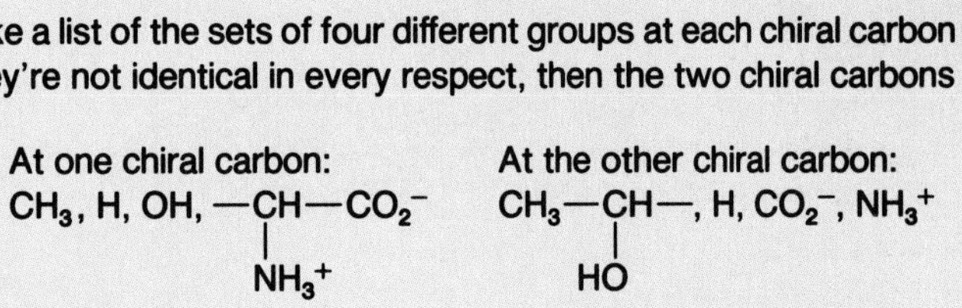

■   Only L-threonine works as a building block for making proteins in the body. There is no enzyme that can accept any of the other optical isomers as substrates.

The sets are obviously different, so $n = 2$ is the number of different chiral carbons in a threonine molecule. Therefore $2^n = 2^2 = 4$, the number of optical isomers of threonine. These occur as half of 4 or 2 pairs of enantiomers. The complete set has the following structures. One pair of enantiomers is on the left. Just imagine that the mirror is between them and is perpendicular to the page. The other pair of enantiomers is on the right.

■ The labels D and L will be explained in the next chapter. The meaning of the experimental values given for the symbol $[\alpha]_D^{26}$ is explained in the next section.

D-Threonine
$[\alpha]_D^{26}$ +28.3°

L-Threonine
$[\alpha]_D^{26}$ −28.3°

D-Allothreonine
$[\alpha]_D^{26}$ −9.6°

L-Allothreonine
$[\alpha]_D^{26}$ +9.6°

PRACTICE EXERCISE 2   Examine the structure of ribose that was given in part (d) of Practice Exercise 1. (a) How many different chiral carbons does it have? (b) How many optical isomers are there of this structure? (Only one is actually the ribose that can be used by the body.) (c) How many pairs of enantiomers correspond to this structure?

PRACTICE EXERCISE 3   Write the structure of 2,3-butanediol and place an asterisk by each carbon that is chiral. Are they *different* chiral carbons?

18.3   OPTICAL ACTIVITY

Enantiomers affect polarized light in equal and opposite ways when they are compared under identical conditions.

We mentioned earlier that there is one physical property in which enantiomers differ, and to describe it we first have to learn something about polarized light.

The Electromagnetic Oscillations of Polarized Light Are in the Same Plane

Light is electromagnetic radiation in which the intensities of the electric and magnetic fields set up by the light source oscillate in a regular way. In ordinary light, these oscillations occur equally in all directions about the line that defines the path of the light ray.

Certain materials, such as the polarizing film in the lenses of Polaroid sunglasses, affect ordinary light in a special way. Polarizing film interacts with the oscillating electrical field of any light passing through it to make this field oscillate in just one plane. The light that emerges is now **plane-polarized light.** See Figures 18.5 and Figure 18.6a.

Figure 18.5
When light passes through polarizing film, it becomes polarized light.

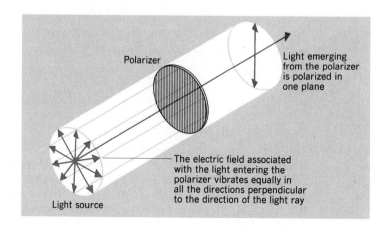

Polarizer

Light emerging from the polarizer is polarized in one plane

The electric field associated with the light entering the polarizer vibrates equally in all the directions perpendicular to the direction of the light ray

Light source

SPECIAL TOPIC 18.1

OTHER KINDS OF OPTICAL ISOMERS: DIASTEREOMERS AND MESO COMPOUNDS

In Example 18.2, the structures of the four optical isomers of threonine were given. There were four of them, and they occurred as two pairs of enantiomers. D-Threonine is the enantiomer of L-threonine, and D-allothreonine is the enantiomer of L-allothreonine. Thus all four belong to the same set of stereoisomers. The members of such a set that are *not* related as enantiomers are called **diastereomers.** Thus either D- or L-threonine is a diastereomer of either D- or L-allothreonine.

Unlike enantiomers, diastereomers do have many differences in physical properties. The set of intramolecular distances and bond angles in one diastereomer isn't exactly duplicated in any other diastereomer. Hence, molecules of one diastereomer should be expected to have at least slightly different polarities than those of any other diastereomer. You can see an illustration of one such difference in physical property in the values of the specific rotation of the diastereomers of the threonine–allothreonine system.

Another kind of optical isomer, the *meso compound,* occurs among the stereoisomers of tartaric acid. Tartaric acid is 2,3-dihydroxybutanedioic acid, and it has two chiral carbons. However, these two chiral carbons are identical.

You can see that two are related as enantiomers, because their models are related as an object to its mirror image and they can't be superimposed. There is no enantiomer for the third stereoisomer, the one labeled *meso*-tartaric acid. The model of its mirror image is shown, but if you rotated it 180° about the correct axis (can you find it?), the model and its mirror image would superimpose. So here is an example of a compound with chiral carbons that is optically inactive. Each has the same set of attached atoms or groups as the other: CO_2H, H, HO, and $HOCHCO_2H$. There is no simple equation for calculating how many optical isomers exist of a compound that has two or more identical chiral carbons. Tartaric acid happens to have three optical isomers.

Remember that the molecule as a *whole* has to be chiral for the compound to be able to affect plane-polarized light. We still call *meso*-tartaric acid an optical isomer even though it is itself optically inactive, because it belongs to a set of stereoisomers that does include optically active forms. Optical isomers that are achiral are classified as **meso compounds,** and this is why the achiral form of tartaric acid is called *meso*-tartaric acid.

Tartaric acid

D-Tartaric acid
$[\alpha]_D^{20} -11.98°$
m.p. 170°C

L-Tartaric acid
$[\alpha]_D^{20} +11.98°$
m.p. 170°C

meso-Tartaric acid
$[\alpha]_D^{20}$ 0°
m.p. 140°C

■ You can try this out using two Polaroid sunglass lenses. The lenses of these glasses reduce glare by cutting out the plane-polarized light produced when sunlight reflects from a plane surface such as a road, a snowfield, or a lake.

If we look at some object through polarizing film and then place a second film in front of the first, we can rotate one film until the object no longer can be seen, as shown in Figure 18.6b and Figure 18.7. If we now rotate one film by 90°, we'll see the object at maximum brightness again. The first film seems to act as a lattice fence, forcing any light that goes through it to vibrate only in the direction allowed by the long spaces between the slats. This light then moves on to the molecular slats of the second film. If its slats are perpendicular to those of the first, the light has no freedom to oscillate, and it cannot get through. At intermediate angles, fractional amounts of light can go through the second polarizing film. Only when the slats of

Figure 18.6

The principal working parts of a polarimeter and how optical rotation is measured.

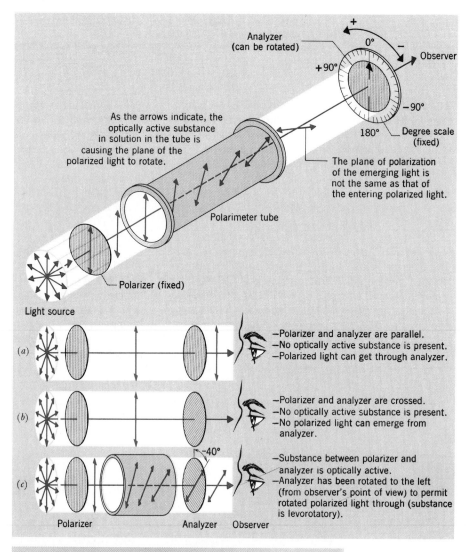

As the arrows indicate, the optically active substance in solution in the tube is causing the plane of the polarized light to rotate.

Analyzer (can be rotated)

Observer

Degree scale (fixed)

The plane of polarization of the emerging light is not the same as that of the entering polarized light.

Polarimeter tube

Polarizer (fixed)

Light source

(a)
—Polarizer and analyzer are parallel.
—No optically active substance is present.
—Polarized light can get through analyzer.

(b)
—Polarizer and analyzer are crossed.
—No optically active substance is present.
—No polarized light can emerge from analyzer.

(c)
—Substance between polarizer and analyzer is optically active.
—Analyzer has been rotated to the left (from observer's point of view) to permit rotated polarized light through (substance is levorotatory).

Polarizer   Analyzer   Observer

Figure 18.7

When two polarizing films are "crossed," no light can get through to the observer.

the two films are *parallel* to each other can the light leaving the first film slip easily through the second.

An Enantiomer Can Rotate the Plane of Plane-Polarized Light

When a solution of D-asparagine in water is placed in the path of plane-polarized light, the plane of polarization of the light is rotated. Any substance that can rotate the plane of plane-polarized light is said to be **optically active.** We have not actually explained how this phenomenon happens — we are unable to do so. We have only reported that it does happen. It's because of this physical property that the term *optical isomerism* was first applied to compounds that were found to be optically active.

The Polarimeter Measures the Degree of Optical Activity

The instrument used to detect and measure optical activity is called a **polarimeter.** See the top part of Figure 18.6. Its principal working parts consist of a polarizer for the light, a tube for holding solutions in the path of the polarized light, an analyzer (actually, just another polarizing device), and a circular scale for measuring the number of degrees of rotation. When the "slats" of the polarizer and the analyzer are parallel and the tube contains no optically active material, the polarized light emerges from the solution with maximum intensity. Let's assume that we start with this parallel orientation of analyzer and polarizer.

When a solution of one pure enantiomer is placed in the light path, the plane-polarized light encounters molecules of just one chirality. They cause the plane of oscillation of the polarized light to be rotated. The plane of oscillation of the polarized light that leaves the solution is now no longer parallel with the analyzer, as shown in Figure 18.6c. Consequently, not as much light gets through the solution, so now the intensity of the observed light is less than the original maximum. To restore the original maximum intensity, the operator must rotate the analyzer to the right or to the left a definite number of degrees until the analyzer is parallel with the light *that emerges from the tube.*

■ Latin, *dextro,* right, and *levo,* left.

The operator, looking *toward* the light source, might find that rotating the analyzer to the right restores the light intensity with fewer degrees of rotation than rotating the analyzer to the left. When such a rightward rotation works, the degrees are recorded as positive, and the optically active substance is said to be **dextrorotatory.** If the fewer degrees of rotation are found by a leftward or counterclockwise rotation, then the degrees are recorded as negative. In this case, the substance is said to be **levorotatory.** In Figure 18.6c the reading is $\alpha = -40°$, where α stands for the **optical rotation,** the *observed* number of degrees of rotation for the solution.

The observed number of degrees of rotation varies both with the temperature and the frequency of the light used. There is no simple, direct relationship, however, so both of these data simply have to be recorded. For example, $\alpha_D^{20} = -40°$ means that the solution had a temperature of 20 °C and that the so-called D light of a sodium vapor lamp was the light source. (This is the intense yellow light given by a sodium vapor lamp such as used in some streetlights.)

The Specific Rotation of an Optically Active Compound Is One of Its Physical Constants

The observed rotation of a compound is not just a function of temperature or of the light frequency but also of the population of its molecules interacting with the light. This population can be changed by changing the solution's concentration or by using tubes of different length. Thus

$$\alpha \propto \text{concentration}$$
$$\alpha \propto \text{path length}$$

Since α is *directly* proportional to both concentration and path length, it is also proportional to the products of these two:

$$\alpha \propto (\text{concentration})(\text{path length}) \tag{18.1}$$

We can convert this to an equation by inserting a constant of proportionality. Before we do this, we have to define the units of concentration and path length. Traditionally, the unit used for length is the decimeter, the only time that this unit of length appears routinely in chemistry (1 dm = 10 cm), and the symbol used here is ℓ. The unit used for concentration is g/100 mL and the symbol for this is c, but to bring what we will finally calculate into an easy range, the concentration in g/100 mL is divided by 100. With these changes the relationship of Equation 18.1 becomes

$$\alpha \propto \frac{c}{100} \times \ell \tag{18.2}$$

Now we can introduce the constant of proportionality, which is given the symbol $[\alpha]$ and has the name of **specific rotation:**

$$\alpha = [\alpha] \times \frac{c \times \ell}{100}$$

By rearranging terms, we define specific rotation by the following equation, in which symbols for temperature and wavelength are associated with $[\alpha]$ to remind us that these are variables and that a given value of $[\alpha]$ is good only for definite values of them. We have

$$[\alpha]_\lambda^t = \frac{100\alpha}{c\ell} \tag{18.3}$$

where c = concentration in grams per 100 mL of solution
ℓ = length of the light path in the solution in decimeters (1 dm = 10 cm)
α = observed rotation in degrees (plus or minus)
λ = wavelength of light
t = temperature of the solution in degrees Celsius

■ L-Asparagine is the more common form.

The value of $[\alpha]_D^{20}$ for D-asparagine is $+5.42°$; for L-asparagine, $[\alpha]_D^{20} = -5.42°$. Here, then, is an illustration of the only physical difference between a pair of enantiomers. All their physical properties are identical, including the number of *degrees* of specific rotation, but not the *direction* of rotation. One enantiomer is always dextrorotatory and the other is always levorotatory by the same number of degrees.

A 50:50 Mixture of Enantiomers Is Optically Inactive It is important to realize that optical activity and optical isomerism are not the same. *Optical activity* refers to a phenomenon we can observe with the right kind of instrument. We can see the number of degrees of rotation. *Optical isomerism* is a factor in our explanation of optical activity. We *infer* optical isomerism (and other things) from the observation of optical activity.

It's possible to have a sample of a substance that consists entirely of chiral molecules but that still is optically inactive. All we have to do is mix two enantiomers in an equimolar ratio. The activity of the molecules of one enantiomer to rotate the plane of polarized light, say, clockwise, is canceled by the activity of the molecules of the other enantiomer. Such 50:50 mixtures of enantiomers, called **racemic mixtures,** are common.

It's both interesting and significant that if a racemic mixture of the asparagine enantiomers is given in the diet, the body will use one and excrete the other entirely unused. Naturally occurring glucose is dextrorotatory, and it's often named (+)-glucose to distinguish it from its synthetic enantiomer (−)-glucose, which the body can't use. Naturally occurring fructose, another sugar, is levorotatory and is often named (−)-fructose. The body can use (−)-fructose, but it would be unable to metabolize (+)-fructose, its synthetic enantiomer.

■ This is why glucose is often called *dextrose* and fructose is sometimes called *levulose.*

The specific rotation of an optically active compound is an important physical constant, comparable to its melting point or its boiling point. If we want to know the concentration of, say, (+)-glucose in water, all we have to do is measure the observed rotation in a tube of known path length. Then we can calculate the concentration of the solution by Equation 18.3, because we know $[\alpha]$, α, and ℓ.

SUMMARY

Optical activity Optical activity is a natural phenomenon detected by means of a polarimeter if polarized light that passes through a substance or its solution undergoes a rotation in its plane of polarization. Substances that do this are called optically active.

Optical isomerism At the molecular level, optically active compounds consist of chiral molecules. Models of such molecules and models of their mirror images do not superimpose. Substances whose molecules are related as object to mirror image that do not superimpose are enantiomers. Almost always, an enantiomer molecule has a chiral carbon, one that holds four different atoms or groups. If a molecule has n different chiral carbons, then the number of optical isomers is 2^n, and these occur as half as many pairs of enantiomers. Each enantiomer is an example of one kind of optical isomer, which places it in the broad family of stereoisomers. A 50:50 mixture of enantiomers, a racemic mixture, is optically inactive.

Properties of enantiomers Enantiomers are identical in every physical property except the sign of their specific rotation. They are also identical in every chemical respect provided that the molecules or ions of the reactant are achiral. When the reactant particles are chiral, then one enantiomer reacts differently with it than the other enantiomer, a phenomenon always observed when an enzyme is involved.

Specific rotation The specific rotation of an optically active substance is its observed rotation at one unit of concentration (1 g/100 mL) in one unit of path length (1 dm). It varies, but not in a simple way, with the temperature and the wavelength of the light used. Values of specific rotation can be used to determine concentrations of optically active substances.

REVIEW EXERCISES

The answers to the Review Exercises marked with an asterisk are in Appendix D. The answers to the other Review Exercises are in the *Study Guide* that accompanies this book.

Structural Isomers and Stereoisomers

18.1 What are the structures of the simplest chloroalkanes that can exhibit structural isomerism?

18.2 Draw the structures of the simplest chloroalkenes that can exist as a set of stereoisomers. (Be sure to draw these carefully to show the geometric relationships.)

18.3 Classify the following pairs of structures as structural isomers or as stereoisomers.

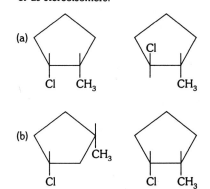

18.4 What is the "one-substance–one-structure" principle?

Optical Isomers

18.5 The general structure of several optical isomers that include glucose is that of 2,3,4,5,6-pentahydroxyhexanal:

$$HO-CH_2-CH-CH-CH-CH-CH=O$$
$$\qquad\ \ \ |\quad\ \ |\quad\ \ |\quad\ \ |$$
$$\qquad\ \ OH\ \ OH\ \ OH\ \ OH$$

(a) Place an asterisk by each chiral carbon.
(b) How many of these chiral carbons qualify as *different* chiral carbons?
(c) How many optical isomers of this compound are possible?
(d) These optical isomers occur as how many *pairs* of enantiomers?

18.6 One of the building blocks of nucleic acids used in transmitting genetic information from a cell nucleus to the place in a cell where enzymes are made is adenosine monophosphate, AMP.

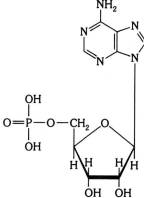

Adenosine monophosphate, AMP

(a) Place an asterisk by each chiral carbon in AMP.
(b) How many optical isomers can be calculated for AMP? (Only one is usable by the cell.)

18.7 One of the approximately 20 building blocks of protein molecules is glycine: $^{+}NH_3-CH_2-CO_2^-$. Does glycine have optical isomers? How can you tell?

18.8 One of the very important intermediate substances in the body's energy-producing metabolism is an anion of citric acid.

$$CH_2CO_2H$$
$$HO-C-CO_2H$$
$$CH_2CO_2H$$

Does citric acid have optical isomers? How can you tell?

18.9 Cholesterol is involved in a beneficial way in making some of the sex hormones and in a harmful way by plugging small capillaries.

Cholesterol

(a) Place an asterisk by each carbon in the cholesterol molecule that is chiral.
(b) How many optical isomers can be calculated for cholesterol? (Cholesterol is just one of these.)

18.10 Vitamin D_2 is one of a few members of the vitamin D family of substances.

Vitamin D_2

(a) Put an asterisk by each of the chiral carbons in the structure of vitamin D_2.
(b) How many optical isomers are there of this compound?

Properties of Enantiomers

18.11 The melting point of (−)-cholesterol is 148.5 °C. What is the melting point of (+)-cholesterol? How can we know this without actually making the measurement?

18.12 Explain why enantiomers should have identical physical properties (except for the sign of specific rotation).

18.13 Explain why enantiomers cannot have different chemical properties toward reactants whose molecules or ions are achiral. (Use an analogy if you wish.)

18.14 Explain why enantiomers have different chemical properties toward reactants whose molecules or ions are chiral. (Use an analogy if you wish.)

Specific Rotation

18.15 Pantothenic acid was once called vitamin B_3.

Pantothenic acid

Only its dextrorotatory form can be used by the body, and its specific rotation is $[\alpha]_D^{25} = +37.5°$. In a tube 1.00 dm long and at a concentration of 1.00 g/dL, what is the *observed* optical rotation of the levorotatory enantiomer of (+)-pantothenic acid?

18.16 Ascorbic acid is also known as vitamin C. Only its dextrorotatory enantiomer can be used by the body.

Ascorbic acid

Its specific rotation is $[\alpha]_D^{25} = +21°$. What is the specific rotation of (−)-ascorbic acid?

18.17 Explain why the observed rotation is proportional to the concentration of the optically active compound and to the length of the tube through which the polarized light travels.

18.18 What becomes of the optical activity of a substance if it consists of a mixture of equal numbers of moles of its two enantiomers? Explain.

•18.19 A solution of sucrose (table sugar) in water at 25 °C in a tube that is 10.0 cm long gives an observed rotation of +2.00°. The specific rotation of sucrose in water at this temperature and the same wavelength of light is +66.4°. What is the concentration of the sucrose solution in g/dL?

18.20 Quinine sulfate, an antimalarial drug, has a specific rotation in water at 17 °C of −214°. If a solution of quinine sulfate in this solvent in a 1.00-dm tube and under the same conditions of temperature and wavelength has an observed rotation of −10.4°, what is its concentration in g/dL?

•18.21 Strychnine and brucine are structurally similar compounds that have extremely bitter tastes, and both are very poisonous. The specific rotation in chloroform at 20 °C of brucine is −127° and that of strychnine under identical conditions is −139°. If a solution of one of these in chloroform at a concentration of 1.68 g/dL in a tube 1.00 dm long gave an observed rotation of −2.34°, which of the two compounds was it? Do the calculation needed for the answer.

18.22 Corticosterone and cortisone are two substances used to treat arthritis. Under identical conditions of solvent and temperature, the specific rotation of corticosterone is +223°

and that of cortisone is $+209°$. If a solution of one of these at a concentration of 1.48 g/dL and in a tube 1 dm long has an observed rotation of $+3.10$, which compound was in the solution? Do the calculation.

Other Optical Isomers (Special Topic 18.1)

18.23 Examine the structures of D-threonine and D-allothreonine as given in Example 8.2.

(a) Why don't these qualify as enantiomers?

(b) Why are they described as being members of the *same set* of optical isomers?

(c) Why aren't they called geometric isomers?

(d) What kind of stereoisomers are they?

18.24 Two models of methane, related as object to mirror image, superimpose. Why isn't methane called a meso compound?

18.25 Despite the fact that *meso*-tartaric acid is optically inactive, it is described as an *optical isomer* of D- or L-tartaric acid. Why?

Carbohydrates

A wheat harvest gathers both materials and chemical energy for living. The energy, which comes originally from the sun, is trapped in plants by chlorophyll, a green pigment. With this energy plus small molecules and ions in soil, plants carry out photosynthesis to make complex compounds, like the carbohydrates studied in this chapter.

19.1 BIOCHEMISTRY: AN OVERVIEW

Building materials, energy, and information are basic essentials for life.

Biochemistry is the systematic study of the chemicals of living systems, their organization, and the principles of their participation in the processes of life.

The Cell Is the Smallest Unit That Lives The molecules of living systems are lifeless, yet life has a molecular basis. Whether studied in cells or when isolated from them, the chemicals at the foundation of life obey all the known laws of chemistry and physics. Yet, in isolation, not one compound of a cell has life. The intricate organization of compounds in a cell is as important to life as the chemicals themselves. Thus the cell is the smallest unit of matter that lives and that can make a new cell like itself.

The Life of a Cell Requires Materials, Energy, and Information Our purpose in the remainder of this book is to study the molecular basis of meeting the three basic needs of a living system: its needs for materials, energy, and information. Without the daily satisfaction of these, life at any of the many loftier levels — creativity, relationships, and love — would be severely constrained. Most of our focus will be on the molecular basis of life in the human body.

We will begin in the next three chapters to study the organic materials of life, starting with the three great classes of foodstuffs: carbohydrates, lipids, and proteins. We use their molecules to build and run ourselves and to try to stay in some state of repair. Proteins are particularly important in both the structures and functions of cells, whether of plants or of animals. Plants rely heavily on carbohydrates for cell walls, and animals obtain considerable energy from carbohydrates made by plants. Lipids (fats and oils) serve many purposes and are rich in energy.

■ Cornstarch, potato starch, table sugar, and cotton are all carbohydrates.

■ Meat is rich in protein.

■ Butter, lard, margarine, and corn oil are all lipids.

What Controls Enzymes Controls Life Because of their central catalytic role in regulating chemical events in cells, we will study a special family of proteins, the enzymes. Enzymes are components of the intricate information system in an organism. Without information — plans or blueprints — materials and energy could combine to produce only rubble and rubbish. Monkeys swinging hammers would only reduce a stack of lumber to splinters. Carpenters, using the same materials and expending no more raw energy, can build a building, because they possess information in the form of plans and experience.

Enzymes, however, do not originate the plans of a living system. They only help to carry them out. The blueprint for any one member of a species is encoded in the molecular structures of nucleic acids. These compounds are able to direct the synthesis of a cell's enzymes, and each individual has a unique set. Before we study how enzymes work, therefore, we will study enzyme-makers and see how different species can take essentially the same raw materials and energy and make unique enzymes.

■ Individual genes are sections of molecules of a polymer called DNA, which is one kind of nucleic acid.

Materials and Energy in the Diet Are First Processed by Digestion To supply materials for any use — parts, energy, or information — each organism has basic nutritional needs. These include not just organic materials, but also minerals, water, and oxygen. We'll survey these aspects of the biochemistry of life, too.

All the materials taken in the diet have to be processed by the digestive system and distributed by the bloodstream. We must, therefore, study some of the chemical aspects of how this work is done. One of the special emphases, already begun in our study, is the molecular basis of using oxygen and releasing carbon dioxide.

Some Materials Are Used Mainly for Their Chemical Energy The molecular basis of energy for life forms the final broad topic of our study, the last four chapters. One of the kinds of questions that we will address is "How can one get the energy for running, skipping, and laughing out of a peanut butter sandwich?" As we study biochemical energetics and its enzymes and metabolic pathways, we'll have numerous occasions to peer deeply into the molecular basis of some disorders and diseases.

We Launch a New Beginning with the Study of Carbohydrates We have an exciting trip ahead. In the preceding chapters we have slowly and carefully built a solid foundation of chemical principles. It's been like a mountain-climbing trip where the route for a large part of the trek is through country with few grand vistas, and yet with a beauty of its own. Now we're moving to elevations where the vistas begin to open. It's like a new beginning, and we start it with a study of the first of the three chief classes of food materials, the carbohydrates.

19.2 MONOSACCHARIDES

The structure of glucose is the key to the structures of most carbohydrates.

■ The oxidized and reduced forms of polyhydroxy aldehydes and ketones as well as certain amino derivatives are also in the family of carbohydrates.

Carbohydrates are aldehydes and ketones with many OH groups, or substances that form these by hydrolysis. They include the simple sugars, like glucose, as well as sugar, starch, and cellulose. Carbohydrates are the primary products of **photosynthesis,** the complex series of reactions in plants that are powered by solar energy as it is absorbed by the green pigment chlorophyll. By the process CO_2, H_2O, and minerals are converted to plant chemicals and oxygen. Special Topic 19.1 discusses this further.

The Simple Sugars Do Not React with Water The carbohydrates that cannot be hydrolyzed are called the **monosaccharides** or **simple sugars.** Their empirical formula is $(CH_2O)_n$. Those with aldehyde groups are called **aldoses** and those with keto groups are **ketoses.** Like these terms, virtually all the names of carbohydrates end in *-ose.*

Whether they are aldoses or ketoses, monosaccharides with three carbons are trioses, those with four are tetroses, and this pattern continues with pentoses, hexoses, and higher sugars as well. Two trioses, glyceraldehyde and dihydroxyacetone, occur in metabolism, and two pentoses, ribose and 2-deoxyribose, are essential to the nucleic acids, the chemicals of heredity.

| Glyceraldehyde | Dihydroxyacetone | Ribose | 2-Deoxyribose |

■ *Deoxy* means lacking an oxygen where one normally is.

Glucose is a hexose, $(CH_2O)_6$ or $C_6H_{12}O_6$, with an aldehyde group, so it is also called an **aldohexose.** Galactose is also an aldohexoses, an optical isomer of glucose. Fructose, also $(CH_2O)_6$ or $C_6H_{12}O_6$, has a keto group, so it's a **ketohexose.** You can see how parts of words can be combined into one very descriptive term. Glucose, galactose, and fructose are the nutritionally important monosaccharides.

■ *Oligosaccharide* molecules yield three to ten monosaccharide molecules when they are hydrolyzed.

Disaccharides and Polysaccharides Make Up the Other Families of Carbohydrates Carbohydrates that can be hydrolyzed to two monosaccharides are called **disaccharides.** Sucrose, maltose, and lactose are common examples. Starch and cellulose are called **polysaccharides,** because when one of their molecules reacts with water, it gives hundreds of monosaccharide molecules.

All Monosaccharides Are Reducing Carbohydrates Carbohydrates are sometimes described by their abilities to react with Tollens' and Benedict's reagents. Something is reduced in these tests (e.g., Ag^+ or Cu^{2+}), so carbohydrates that give these tests are called **reducing carbohydrates.** All monosaccharides and nearly all disaccharides are reducing carbohydrates. Sucrose (table sugar) is not, and neither are the polysaccharides.

The energy released when a piece of wood burns came originally from the sun. The wood, of course, isn't just bottled sunlight. It's a complex, highly organized mixture of compounds, mostly organic. The solar energy needed to make these compounds is temporarily stored in wood in the form of distinctive arrangements of electrons and nuclei that characterize energy-rich molecules.

They are made from very simple, energy-poor substances such as carbon dioxide, water, and soil minerals. In the living world only plants have the ability to use solar energy to convert energy-poor substances into complex, energy-rich, organic compounds. The overall process by which plants do this is called **photosynthesis.**

The simplest statement of photosynthesis in equation form is

$$CO_2 + H_2O + \text{solar energy} \xrightarrow[\text{plant enzymes}]{\text{chlorophyll}} (CH_2O) + O_2$$

Fundamental
unit in all
carbohydrates

The symbol (CH_2O) stands for a molecular unit in carbohydrates, but plants can use the energy of carbohydrates (which came from the sun) to make other substances as well—proteins, lipids, and many others. In the final analysis, the synthesis of all the materials in our bodies consumed solar energy, and all our activities that use energy ultimately depend on a steady flow of solar energy through plants to the plant materials we eat. The meat and dairy products in our diets also depend on the consumption of plants by animals.

Chlorophyll is the green pigment in the solar-absorbing systems of plants, usually their leaves. Chlorophyll molecules absorb solar energy, and in their energized states trigger the subsequent reactions leading to carbohydrates. A large number of steps and several enzymes are involved.

The other product of photosynthesis is oxygen, so this process continuously regenerates the world's oxygen supply. Roughly 400 billion tons of oxygen are set free by photosynthesis each year, and about 200 billion tons of carbon (as CO_2) is converted into compounds in plants. Of all this activity, only about 10% to 20% occurs in land plants. The rest is done by phytoplankton and algae in the earth's oceans. In principle it would be possible to dump so much poison into the oceans that the cycle of photosynthesis would be gravely affected. It is quite clear that the nations of the world must see that this does not happen.

When plants die and decay, their carbon atoms end up eventually in carbon dioxide again, and the reactions of decay consume oxygen. The combustion of fuels such as petroleum, coal, and wood also uses oxygen. And animals consume oxygen during respiration. Thus there exists a grand cycle in nature in which atoms of carbon, hydrogen, and oxygen move from CO_2 and H_2O into complex forms plus molecular O_2. The latter then interact in various ways to regenerate CO_2 and H_2O.

Someone has estimated that all the oxygen in our earth's atmosphere is renewed by this cycle once in about 20 centuries, and that all the CO_2 in the atmosphere and the earth's waters goes through this cycle every three centuries.

A reference: G. M. Woodwell, "The Energy Cycle of the Biosphere," *Scientific American*, September 1970, page 64.

■ Glucose is also called corn sugar, because it can be made by the hydrolysis of cornstarch.

■ Fructose has a much sweeter taste than glucose or sucrose.

■ Human blood has 100 mg glucose per 100 mL.

■ A 1,1-diol consists of the following system:

$$\begin{array}{c} | \\ -C-OH \\ | \\ OH \end{array}$$

Glucose Is Nature's Most Widely Used Organic Monomer   If we count all its combined forms, (+)-glucose is perhaps the most abundant organic species on earth. It's the building block for molecules of cellulose, a polysaccharide that makes up about 10% of all the tree leaves of the world (on a dry weight basis), about 50% of the woody parts of plants, and nearly 100% of cotton. Glucose is also the monomer for starch, another polysaccharide, which is in many of our foods, particularly grains and tubers. Glucose and fructose are the major components of honey. Glucose is also commonly found in plant juices. Because it is by far the most common carbohydrate in blood, glucose is often called **blood sugar,** although this term strictly applies to the mixture of all of the carbohydrates in blood.

One Form of Glucose Is a Pentahydroxy Aldehyde   Simple alcohols, ROH, can form acetate esters, CH_3CO_2R. Glucose forms a pentaacetate, so five of the six oxygens in $C_6H_{12}O_6$ are in alcohol groups. The sixth oxygen is in an aldehyde group because glucose is easily oxidized to a C_6 monocarboxylic acid by reagents, like Tollens' reagent, that do not oxidize alcohol groups

Under strong, forcing conditions, glucose can be reduced to a straight-chain derivative of hexane, so the six carbons in glucose must be in a straight chain. The five —OH groups must be strung out, one on each of five carbons, because 1,1-diols are not stable. These data support the conclusion that glucose is 2,3,4,5,6-pentahydroxyhexanal. In fact, all aldohexoses are optical isomers of each other and so all have the same basic skeleton:

$$
\overset{6}{C}H_2 - \overset{5}{C}H - \overset{4}{C}H - \overset{3}{C}H - \overset{2}{C}H - \overset{1}{\overset{\overset{\displaystyle O}{\|}}{C}} - H
$$
$$
\underset{OH}{|} \quad \underset{OH}{|} \quad \underset{OH}{|} \quad \underset{OH}{|} \quad \underset{OH}{|}
$$

Basic structure of all
aldohexoses, including glucose

Carbons 2, 3, 4, and 5 in the glucose chain are all chiral and all different. We learned in the previous chapter that the number of optical isomers of a compound whose molecules have n different chiral carbons is 2^n. 2,3,4,5,6-Pentahydroxyhexanal, therefore, must have $2^4 = 16$ optical isomers, or eight pairs of enantiomers. (+)-Glucose is one of these 16; galactose is another.

Fresh Glucose Solutions Gradually Change in Optical Rotation Although glucose is optically active, when we try to measure its optical activity, it behaves in a very strange way. A *freshly prepared* solution of (+)-glucose has a specific rotation of $[\alpha]_D^{20} = +113°$. As this solution ages, however, its specific rotation changes until it stabilizes at a value of $+52°$. We'll call a glucose solution with this specific rotation an "aged glucose solution."

By a special method of recovery (which we'll not discuss), we can recover crystalline (+)-glucose from the aged solution, the same glucose in every respect as before. A freshly prepared solution of this recovered glucose again shows a specific rotation of $+113°$. This new solution ages in the identical way until its specific rotation stabilizes at $+52°$. This cycle can be repeated as often as we please.

It is possible by another method of recovering glucose from an aged solution to obtain a slightly different crystalline compound. Its freshly prepared solution has a specific rotation of $+19°$, but it also changes with time to $+52°$, the same value that was observed for the other aged solution. Using this second method to recover glucose, we can repeat this cycle as often as we please, too.

To summarize, from the original aged solution we can use one method to recover the solute and get back glucose with a specific rotation of $+113°$. With the second recovery technique, we get a glucose with a specific rotation of $+19°$. We can interconvert these forms through the aged solution as often as we please. This change over time of the optical rotation of an optically active substance, one that can be recovered from an aged solution without any other apparent change, is called **mutarotation.** All the hexoses and most of the disaccharides mutarotate. Let us now see what is behind it.

Glucose Molecules Exist Mostly in Cyclic Forms Built into the *same* molecule of 2,3,4,5,6-pentahydroxyhexanal are the two functional groups needed to make a hemiacetal, the OH group and the CH=O group. Recall that hemiacetal formation is represented as follows:

$$
\overset{\overset{\displaystyle O}{\|}}{R - C - H} + H - O - R' \rightleftharpoons R - \overset{\overset{\displaystyle O - H}{|}}{\underset{\underset{\displaystyle H}{|}}{C}} - O - R'
$$

Aldehyde   Alcohol   Hemiacetal

Suppose now that the OH group is on the *same chain* as the CH=O group. We would have something like

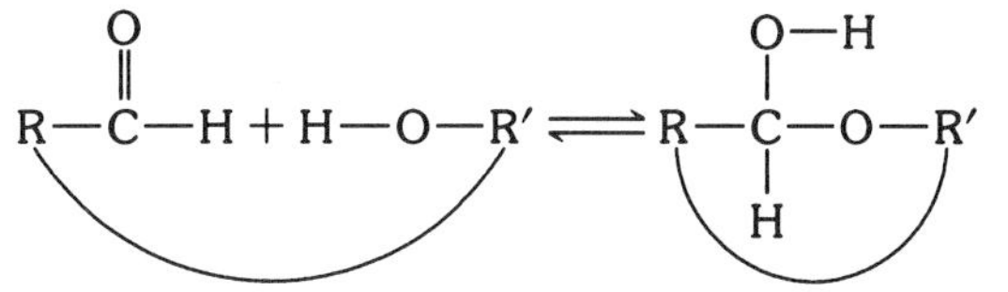

A cyclic
hemiacetal

This is what happens to the open form of glucose. The C-5 OH group adds to the aldehyde group. The open structure has to coil for this to happen, as shown in structure **2**, below. It undergoes ring closure, and a new OH group, the hemiacetal OH, appears at C-1. This C-1 OH, however, can emerge on one side of the ring or the other. It depends on the way the O atom of the C=O group points just before ring closure.

If, at the moment of ring closure, the C-1 OH comes out on the side of the ring opposite to the CH_2OH unit (involving C-6), one cyclic form of glucose emerges. It is the alpha form, **1**, called α-glucose. If the new C-1 OH group comes out on the same side of the ring as the CH_2OH unit, the beta form of glucose, **3**, called β-glucose, forms.

■ The H at C-2 and C-5 and the OH at C-3 do not stick *inside* the ring. They stick *above or below the plane* of the ring.

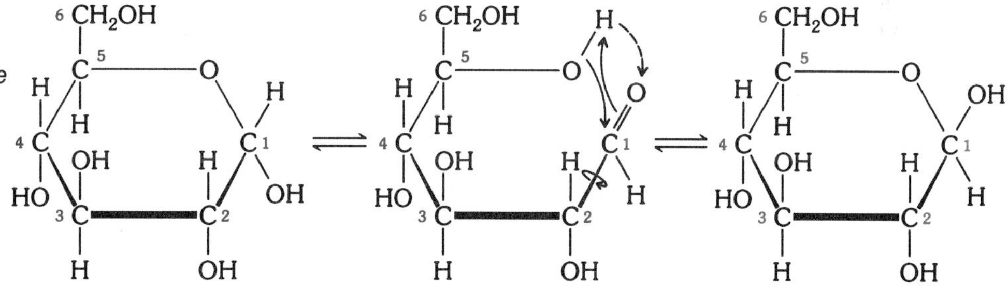

1
α-Glucose

2
Open form of glucose

3
β-Glucose

The Six-Membered Rings of Glucose Are Actually Not Flat The carbon atoms in glucose are all tetrahedral, so the bonds from them normally are at angles of 109.5°. The two bonds from the O atom in the ring are also close to this. A *flat* hexagon ring, however, would have internal angles of 120°. A *saturated* six-membered ring, therefore, cannot be flat as indicated by structures **1** or **3**. Instead, such rings are nonplanar so that normal bond angles are possible. We show next the three forms of glucose as they are known to exist in nonplanar conformations called *chair forms*.

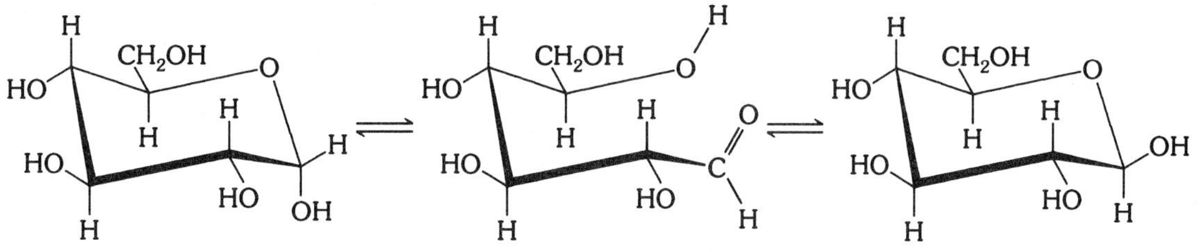

4 (= 1)
α-Glucose

5 (= 2)
Open form of glucose

6 (= 3)
β-Glucose

Special Topic 19.2 discusses these conformations in more detail and indicates why they are preferred. Having called this to your attention, we will continue to use the planar designations, because major references in biochemistry do so. When occasions arise in which the fact of nonplanarity is critical, we will use the nonplanar forms.

In Aged Glucose Solutions, All Three Forms of Glucose Exist in Equilibrium α-Glucose is the form of the glucose molecules when a freshly prepared aqueous solution has a

SPECIAL TOPIC 19.2   **THE BOAT AND CHAIR FORMS OF SATURATED, SIX-MEMBERED RINGS**

The inside angle of a regular hexagon is 120°, so the six atoms of a saturated six-membered ring cannot lie in the same plane and also have the tetrahedral bond angles of 109.5°. The cyclohexane ring resolves this by twisting into a nonplanar shape called the **chair form.**

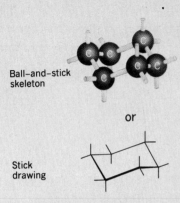

Ball–and–stick skeleton

or

Stick drawing

A chair form of cyclohexane

Even when one CH_2 unit of this ring is replaced by an oxygen atom, as in the rings of the glucose forms, the same kind of chair conformation predominates.

A chair form of the glucose ring

or

A chair form of the glucose ring

The **boat form** is another conformation of the ring that permits normal bond angles, and the ring has enough flexibility to be able to twist from the chair to the boat form. As the drawings show, if you twist one end of the chair form upward, you get the boat, and if you twist the opposite end downward, you get an alternative chair form. Thus there are *two* chair forms and one boat. All three have normal bond angles.

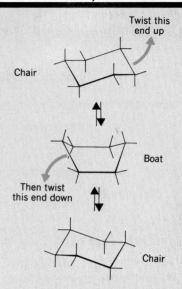

Twist this end up

Chair

Boat

Then twist this end down

Chair

The two chair forms of cyclohexane are equally stable, but the boat form is less stable than a chair. In the boat form, as you can see in the scale model, the electron clouds by the hydrogen atoms are closer to one another, particularly the two hydrogens at opposite ends, marked *a*, one at the "prow" and one at the "stern." They nudge each other in the boat form, but are as far from each other as possible in the chair form.

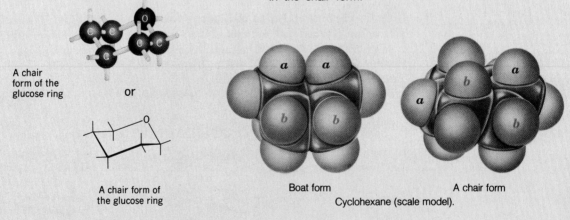

Boat form   A chair form

Cyclohexane (scale model).

Similarly, the electron clouds marked *b* are closer to each other in the boat than in the chair form. Electron clouds repel each other, so the boat form is less stable than the chair form.

When the six-membered ring holds substituents, as it does among the carbohydrates, the alternative chair forms are no longer equivalent. We must, therefore, have labels to distinguish the two ways that bonds and substituents can be oriented. Positions around the perimeter are called *equatorial positions* because they are located roughly on the ring's equator. They are indicated by the black bonds and Hs in structure **A**. The positions that project above or below the average plane alongside the axis through this plane are called *axial substituents,* indicated in color in **A**.

A

B

When chair form **A** twists into its alternative chair form, **B**, every equatorial position changes to axial and every axial to equatorial.

In an actual sample of cyclohexane, the two chair forms exist in equilibrium, and they constantly flip-flop back and forth. In a sense, the flat hexagonal structure that we usually draw for the ring of cyclohexane is an average of these two forms, and in most situations we can ignore the true bond angles of the six-membered ring.

The equivalency of the two chair forms vanishes, as we said, when the ring bears substituents. The electron clouds of axial substituents nudge one another more than do those of equatorial substituents. Thus equatorial orientations are more stable. As a rule, therefore, saturated six-membered rings take up whichever chair form puts the maximum number of bulky substituents in equatorial positions. This important fact dominates the conformations of the ring forms of the aldohexoses. The beta form of glucose, for example, is able to have every ring substituent oriented equatorially, the only aldohexose in which this is possible. In its alternative chair form, however, all substituents would be oriented axially, and this form does not occur.

β-Glucose
(more stable;
all substituents
are equatorial)

β-Glucose
(less stable;
all substituents
are axial)

Since most people find it easier to draw flat rings for the aldohexoses, and most references in biochemistry use them widely, we will generally use them also. They correctly show *relative* projections of groups on a ring—the up or down orientations—but their bond angles are not correct.

---

specific rotation of +113°. Hemiacetals are unstable, however, and glucose in its cyclic forms is a hemiacetal. First one molecule of **1** and then another opens up to give form **2**. As soon as molecules of **2** appear, they can and do reclose. Figure 19.1 shows how free rotation about the C-1 to C-2 bond can reposition the aldehyde group, so that either one side or the other side of the carbonyl system faces the C-5 OH group at the moment of ring closure.

To keep the two glucose forms straight, use the CH₂OH group and the ring O atom as points of reference. Notice that in both of the cyclic forms of glucose the CH₂OH unit sticks upward from the plane *when the ring is drawn with its oxygen in the upper right-hand corner.* Now notice that the OH group at C-1 projects upward in *β*-glucose and downward in *α*-glucose. (The projections of all the other OH groups are the same in the two forms. If we changed any of them, we would have something that isn't any form of glucose, but one of its optical isomers instead.)

Thus the two cyclic forms of glucose differ only in the orientation of the OH group at C-1. With this in mind, let's review what happens during mutarotation.

As we said, when *α*-glucose is freshly dissolved in water, it has a specific rotation of +113°. But its molecules open and close, because the hemiacetal system easily breaks apart and reforms. Some of the newly formed open-chain molecules reclose as *α*-glucose, and some as *β*-glucose. These events take place during mutarotation, whether we start with *α*- or *β*-glucose, until one grand, dynamic equilibrium involving all three forms of glucose is established. The identical equilibrium develops from either cyclic form of glucose, because we

■ This arrangement of CH₂OH relative to the ring O atom also ensures that the optical configurations at all chiral carbons of natural glucose are correctly displayed in our structures.

Figure 19.1
The α- and β-forms of glucose arise from the same intermediate, the open-chain form. Depending on how the aldehyde group, CH=O, is pointing when the ring closes, one ring form or the other results.

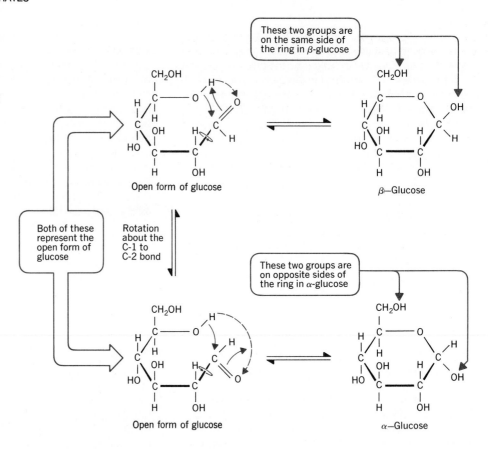

obtain an aged solution that has the identical specific rotation, +52°. We can express the equilibrium in words as follows:

$$\alpha\text{-Glucose} \rightleftharpoons \text{open-chain form of glucose} \rightleftharpoons \beta\text{-glucose}$$

At equilibrium, the solute molecules are 36% α-glucose, 64% β-glucose and scarcely a trace (<0.05%) of the open-chain form.

The method of recovering solid glucose from an aged solution determines the form of glucose in the crystals. One recovery method succeeds in getting just α-glucose molecules to start the formation of crystals. The molecules of β-glucose can't fit to this crystal and help it grow, so they remain in solution. But the loss of molecules of α-glucose from the equilibrium puts a stress on it, and the equilibrium shifts (in accordance with Le Chatelier's principle) to replace the lost molecules. In this way, all the β-glucose molecules eventually get changed to α-glucose molecules and nestle into the growing crystals.

The other method of crystallization succeeds in getting crystals started from just the β-glucose molecules, so eventually all the α-glucose molecules get switched over to the β-form and join the growing crystals.

■ This is another example of Le Chatelier's principle in action.

Molecules of the open-chain form never crystallize. They occur only in the solution. Of course, they are the ones attacked by Tollens' or Benedict's reagents, and as they are removed they are replaced by a steady shifting of the equilibrium from closed forms to the open form. This is why glucose, despite the fact that in the solid state it is in either one cyclic form or the other, gives the chemical properties of a pentahydroxy aldehyde. This is also why it is still acceptable to define a monosaccharide as an aldehyde (or ketone) with multiple OH groups rather than as a cyclic hemiacetal.

Before continuing, you should now pause to learn how to write the cyclic forms of glucose (using flat rings). Figure 19.2 outlines the steps in mastering this that have worked well for many students. Although six-membered rings are not *flat*, as we said, the projections of the

Figure 19.2
How to draw the cyclic forms of
glucose in a highly condensed way.

1. First write a six-membered ring with an oxygen in the upper right-hand corner.

2. Next "anchor" the CH₂OH on the carbon the left of the oxygen. (Let all the Hs attached to ring carbons be "understood.")

3. Continue in a *counterclockwise* way around the ring, placing the OHs first down, then up, then down.

4. Finally, at the last site on the trip, how the last OH is positioned depends on whether the alpha or the beta form is to be written. The alpha is "down," the beta "up."

If this detail is immaterial, or if the equilibrium mixture is intended, the structure may be written as

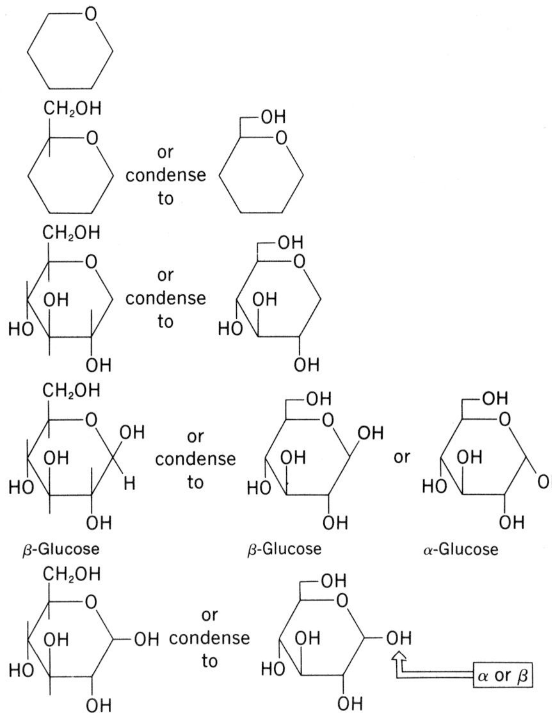

groups on the ring, relative to the CH₂OH unit, are faithfully shown by these kinds of drawings.

Galactose Is an Optical Isomer of Glucose   Galactose is an aldohexose that occurs in nature mostly as a structural unit in larger molecules such as the disaccharide lactose. Galactose differs from glucose only in the orientation of the C-4 OH group. Like glucose, it is a reducing sugar, it mutarotates, and it exists in solution in three forms, alpha, beta, and open.

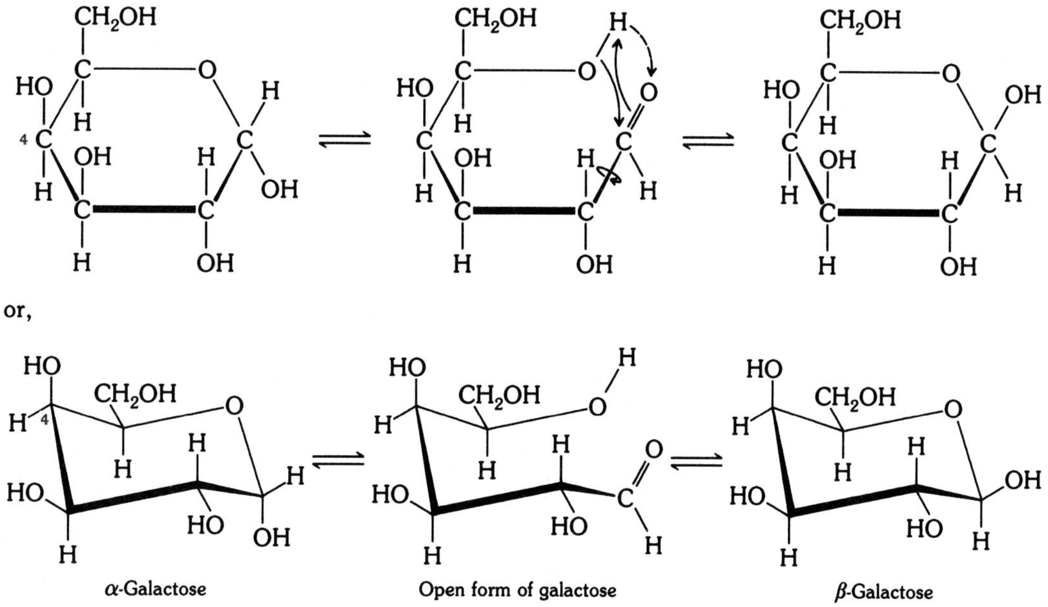

■ Lactose is milk sugar.

or,

α-Galactose   Open form of galactose   β-Galactose

Fructose Occurs in a Five-Membered, Cyclic Hemiketal Form Fructose, the most important ketohexose, is found together with glucose and sucrose in honey and in fruit juices. It, too, can exist in more than one form, including cyclic hemiketals. The hemiketal carbon is C-2.

■ The internal angle of a pentagon (108°) is very close to the tetrahedral angle, so the five-membered ring is nearly flat.

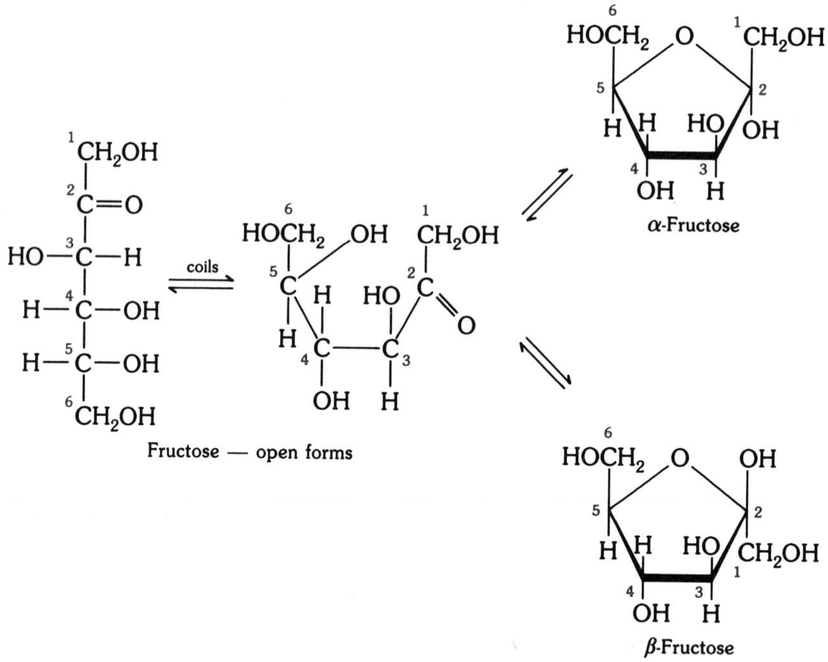

Fructose — open forms

α-Fructose

β-Fructose

■ An old name for fructose is *levulose*, after its strong levorotatory power.

Fructose is strongly levorotatory, with a specific rotation of $[\alpha]_D^{20} = -92.4°$. Because its molecules have the α-hydroxyketone system, fructose is a reducing sugar. Monophosphoric and diphosphoric acid esters of fructose are important compounds in the metabolism of carbohydrates.

Deoxycarbohydrates Have Fewer OH Groups A deoxycarbohydrate is one with a molecule that lacks an OH group where normally such a group is expected. Thus 2-deoxyribose is the same as ribose except that there is no OH group at C-2, just two Hs instead. Both ribose and 2-deoxyribose, as we noted earlier, are building blocks of nucleic acids, and each of these aldopentoses can exist in three forms, two cyclic hemiacetals and an open form. We show just one form of each.

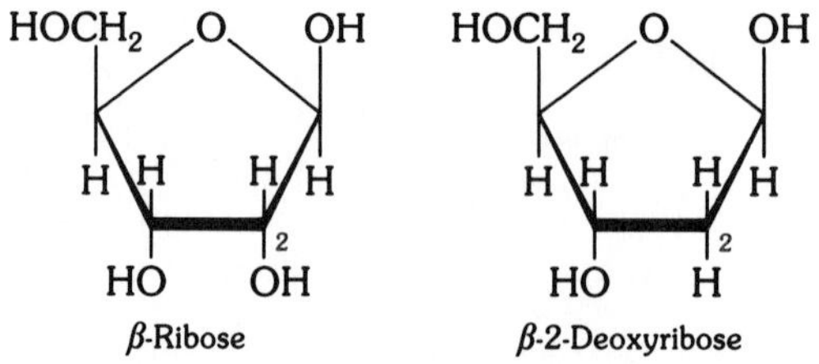

β-Ribose   β-2-Deoxyribose

19.3 D- AND L-FAMILIES OF CARBOHYDRATES

When the chiral carbon farthest from the carbonyl group of a monosaccharide has the same configuration as (+)-glyceraldehyde, the monosaccharide is in the D-family.

In this section we will study the question of the actual orientations or configurations of the chiral carbons in the monosaccharides.

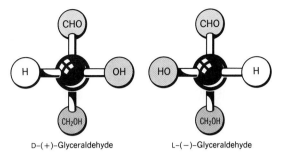

D-(+)-Glyceraldehyde   L-(−)-Glyceraldehyde

Figure 19.3
The absolute configurations of the enantiomers of glyceraldehyde.

All Naturally Occurring Monosaccharides Belong to the Same Optical Family

To simplify this study, we'll retreat from the complexities of (+)-glucose and go back to the simplest aldose, glyceraldehyde. The structures of the two enantiomers of glyceraldehyde are shown in Figure 19.3. Both are known, and the enantiomer labeled D-(+)-glyceraldehyde actually has the absolute configuration shown. **Absolute configuration** refers to the actual arrangement in space about each chiral center in a molecule. When we know the absolute configuration of (+)-glyceraldehyde, we also know that of (−)-glyceraldehyde, because it has to be the mirror image of (+)-glyceraldehyde. (See also Figure 19.3.)

Chemists have used the absolute configurations of the enantiomers of glyceraldehyde to devise configurational or optical families for the rest of the carbohydrates. Any compound that has a configuration like that of (+)-glyceraldehyde and can be related to it by known reactions is said to be in the **D-family.** For example, (−)-glyceric acid is in the D-family because it can be made from D-(+)-glyceraldehyde by an oxidation that doesn't disturb any of the four bonds to the chiral carbon, as the following equation shows.

D-(+)-Glyceraldehyde   D-(−)-Glyceric acid

When the molecules of a compound are the mirror images of an enantiomer in the D-family, the compound is in the **L-family.**

The letters D and L are only family names. They have nothing to do with actual signs of rotation. There exists, in fact, no way to tell from the sign of rotation whether a compound is in the D- or L-family. These letters signify something about absolute configurations only.

■ Emil Fischer (1852–1919) won the second Nobel prize in chemistry in 1902.

Fischer Projection Formulas Simplify Absolute Configurations
When a molecule has several chiral centers, it becomes quite difficult for most people to make a perspective, three-dimensional drawing of an absolute configuration. Emil Fischer, a chemist who unraveled most of the carbohydrate structures, devised a way around this, and his structural representations are called *Fischer projection formulas*. To make them, we follow a set of rules that let us project onto a plane surface the three-dimensional configuration of each chiral carbon in a molecule.

Rules for Writing Fischer Projection Formulas

1. Visualize the molecule with its main carbon chain vertical and with the bonds that hold the chain together projecting to the rear at each chiral carbon. Carbon-1 is at the top.

2. Mentally flatten the structure, chiral carbon by chiral carbon, onto a plane surface. (See Figures 19.4 and 19.5.)

3. In the projected structure, represent each chiral carbon either as the intersection of two lines or conventionally as C.

4. The horizontal lines at a chiral center actually represent bonds that project *forward,* out of the plane of the paper.

5. The vertical lines at a chiral center actually represent bonds that project rearward, behind the plane.

A Fischer projection formula can have more than one intersection of lines, each representing a chiral carbon, as seen in Figure 19.5. Always remember that at each chiral carbon, a horizontal line is a bond coming toward you and a vertical line is a bond going away from you.

Once we have one plane projection structure, it's easy to draw the mirror image, as we see in Figures 19.4 and 19.5. We can easily test for superimposition, too, provided we strictly heed one important additional rule. We may never (mentally) lift a Fischer projection formula out of the plane of the paper. We may only slide it and rotate it within the plane. This rule is necessary because if we turn a Fischer projection formula out of the plane and over, we actually make groups that project in one direction project oppositely, but the operation will not show this reversal.

| EXAMPLE 19.1 | WRITING FISCHER PROJECTION FORMULAS |

Problem: Write the Fischer projection formulas for the optical isomers of glyceric acid.

$$HOCH_2CHCO_2H$$
$$|$$
$$OH$$

Glyceric acid

Solution: There are three carbons in the chain, but only the center carbon is chiral. Therefore glyceric acid has two optical isomers, two enantiomers. We represent its chiral carbon by the intersection of two perpendicular lines, and we make two of these, one for each enantiomer:

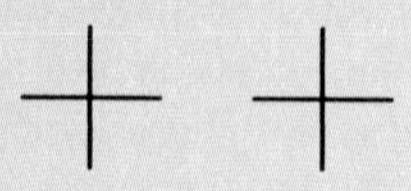

$$+ \qquad + \qquad \text{(Incomplete)}$$

Then we attach the other two, nonchiral carbons. According to the rules, we have to put C-1, the carbon with the carbonyl group in CO_2H, at the top:

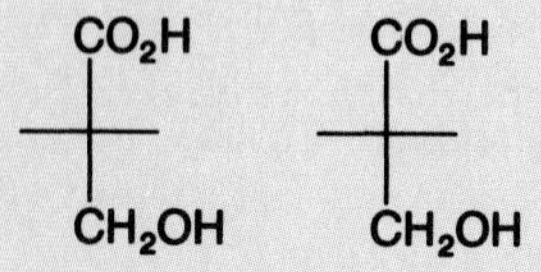

$$
\begin{array}{cc}
CO_2H & CO_2H \\
+ & + \\
CH_2OH & CH_2OH
\end{array}
\qquad \text{(Incomplete)}
$$

We know that the OH group at C-2 can be either on the right or the left, so we finish the Fischer projection formulas:

$$
\begin{array}{cc}
\text{CO}_2\text{H} & \text{CO}_2\text{H} \\
\text{H}-\!\!\!-\text{OH} & \text{HO}-\!\!\!-\text{H} \qquad \text{(Complete)} \\
\text{CH}_2\text{OH} & \text{CH}_2\text{OH}
\end{array}
$$

These are the two enantiomers of glyceric acid. The one on the left is D-glyceric acid, and the other is L-glyceric acid.

Figure 19.4
The relationships of the perspective (three-dimensional) drawings of D-(+)-glyceraldehyde and L-(−)-glyceraldehyde to their corresponding Fischer projection formulas.

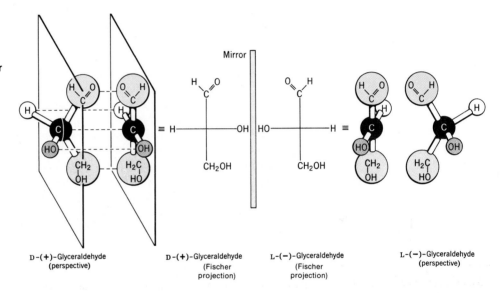

D-(+)-Glyceraldehyde (perspective)   D-(+)-Glyceraldehyde (Fischer projection)   L-(−)-Glyceraldehyde (Fischer projection)   L-(−)-Glyceraldehyde (perspective)

Figure 19.5
The four aldotetroses in their perspective and Fischer projection formulas. There are two different chiral carbons, so there are $2^2 = 4$ optical isomers that occur as two pairs of enantiomers, those of erythrose and those of threose.

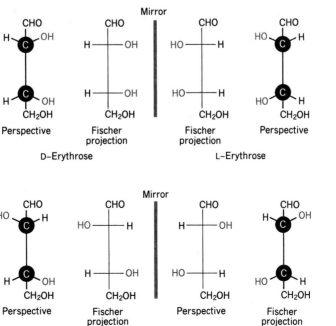

Fischer projection formulas that correspond to the various optical isomers of tartaric acid are given below. (a) Which are identical? (b) Which are related as enantiomers? (c) One is a *meso*-compound (Special Topic 18.1). Which is it?

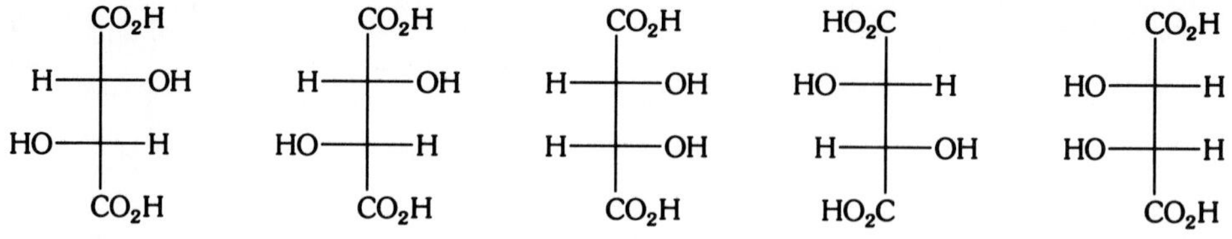

(a)   (b)   (c)   (d)   (e)

Write Fischer projection formulas for the optical isomers of the following compound:

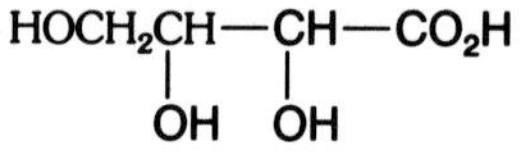

$$HOCH_2CH—CH—CO_2H$$
$$\quad\quad\quad | \quad\quad |$$
$$\quad\quad\quad OH \quad OH$$

All Naturally Occurring Carbohydrates Are in the D-Family

Monosaccharides are assigned to the D-family or the L-family according to the projection of the OH group at the chiral carbon farthest from the carbonyl group. The compound is in the D-family when this OH group projects to the right *in a Fischer projection formula* oriented so that the carbonyl group is at or near the top. When this OH group projects to the left, the substance is in the L-family. We have already illustrated these rules by D- and L-glyceraldehyde (Figure 19.4), and by the enantiomers of threose and erythrose in Figure 19.5. It doesn't matter how the other OH groups at the other chiral carbons project. Membership in the D- or L-family is determined solely by the projection of the OH on the chiral carbon farthest from the carbonyl carbon.

The nutritionally important carbohydrates are all in the D-family. Therefore throughout the rest of this book, if the family membership of a carbohydrate isn't given, assume that the D-family is meant.

Figure 19.6 gives the Fischer projection formulas of all the aldoses in the D-family from the aldotriose through the aldohexoses. There are eight D-aldohexoses. The enantiomers of these constitute eight L-aldohexoses (not shown). In all, therefore, there are 16 optical isomers of the aldohexoses, as we calculated earlier.

19.4 DISACCHARIDES

The disaccharides are glycosides that can be hydrolyzed to monosaccharides.

The aldoses, as we have just seen, are hemiacetals. Like all hemiacetals, they react with alcohols in the presence of a catalyst to give acetals and water.

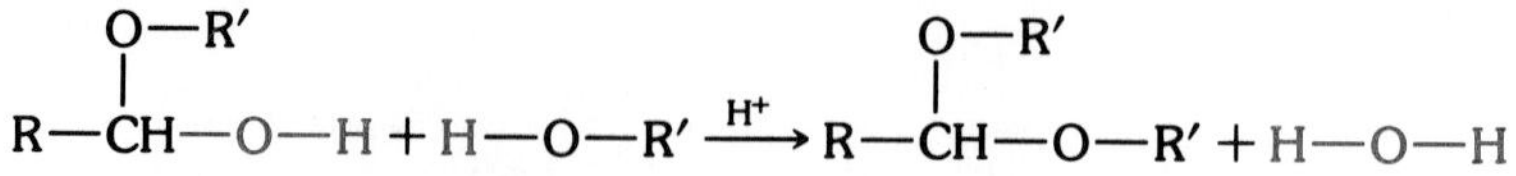

The Sugar Acetals Are Called Glycosides

Like all hemiacetals, those of the cyclic forms of the monosaccharides can also form acetals. Methanol, for example, can be made to react with the cyclic hemiacetal system in glucose to give either an α- or a β-acetal, depending on how the new O—CH₃ group becomes oriented at the ring. If it's on the same side of the ring as our reference CH₂OH group, then we have the β-form. If it is on the opposite side, then we have the α-form.

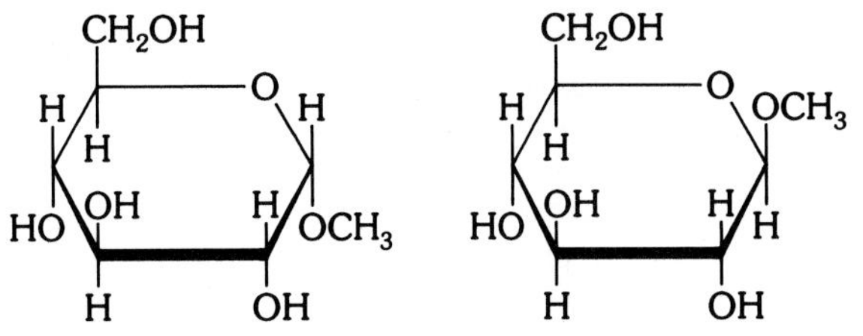

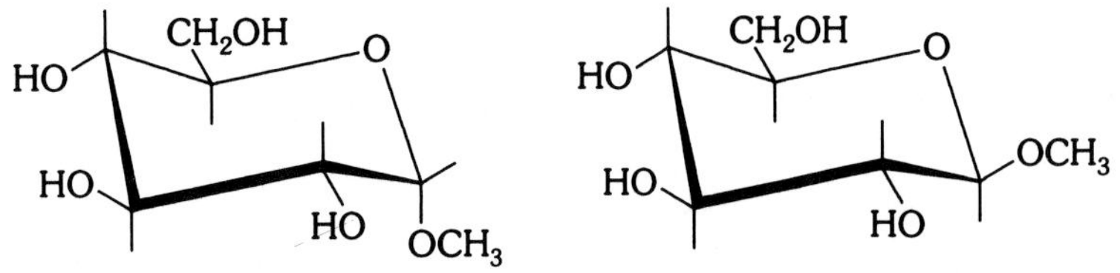

Methyl α-D-glucoside
$[\alpha]_D^{25} = +158°$

Methyl β-D-glucoside
$[\alpha]_D^{25} = -33°$

■ There are also galactosides, fructosides, and so forth.

All sugar acetals have the general name of **glycosides.** To name the glycoside of a specific sugar, we replace the *-ose* in the sugar's name by *-oside,* as in *glucoside.*

The sugar acetals made from simple alcohols are stable enough to isolate, but they readily react with water when an acid catalyst (or the appropriate enzyme) is present. They do not mutarotate and do not give positive Benedict's tests because their rings cannot open to expose an aldehyde group.

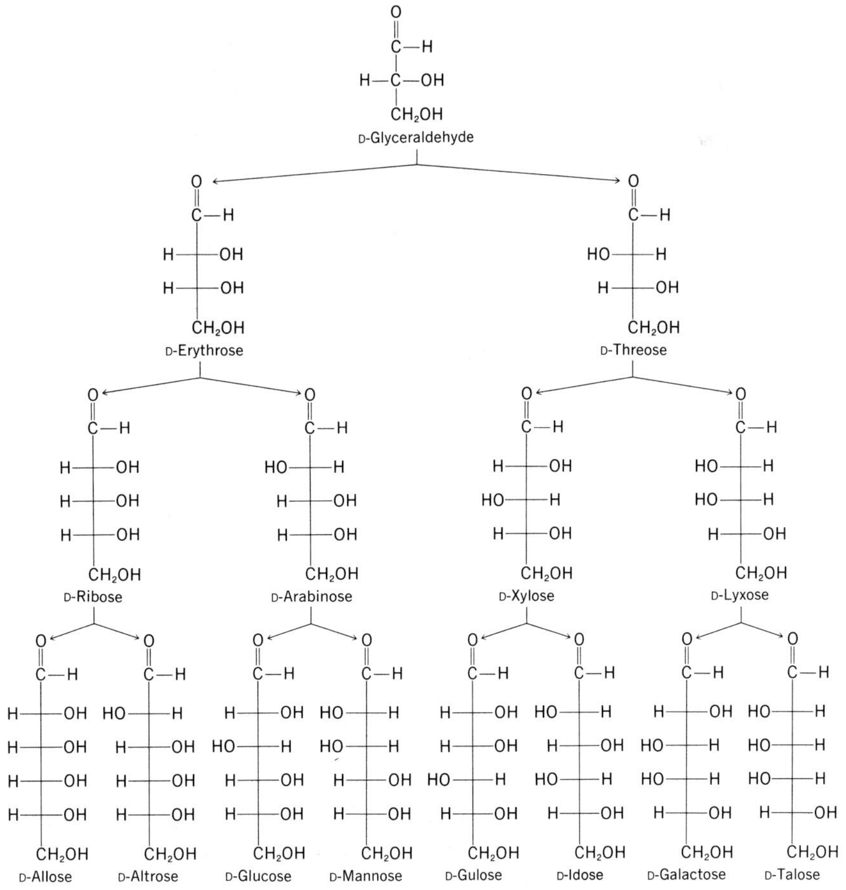

Figure 19.6
The D-family of aldoses through the aldohexoses. Notice that in all of them, the OH group on the chiral center that is farthest from the carbonyl group projects to the right. Each pair of arrows points to a pair of aldoses whose configurations are identical except at C-2.

The Disaccharides Are Glycosides That Use a Second Sugar as the Alcohol All the disaccharides are glycosides made from the cyclic hemiacetal unit of one sugar and one of the alcohol groups of another. An acetal oxygen "bridge" thus links two monosaccharide units in disaccharides. This acetal unit, like all acetals, reacts readily with water in the presence of an acid or enzyme catalyst, and this hydrolysis frees the original monosaccharide molecules.

The three nutritionally important disaccharides are maltose, lactose, and sucrose. All are in the D-family. We'll first show their relationships to monosaccharides by word equations, and then we'll look more closely, but briefly, at their structures.

■ You can see why glucose is of such central interest to carbohydrate chemists.

$$\text{Maltose} + \text{H}_2\text{O} \longrightarrow \text{glucose} + \text{glucose}$$
$$\text{Lactose} + \text{H}_2\text{O} \longrightarrow \text{glucose} + \text{galactose}$$
$$\text{Sucrose} + \text{H}_2\text{O} \longrightarrow \text{glucose} + \text{fructose}$$

■ If the OH group at C-1 on the far-right glucose unit projected downward instead of upward, the structure would be that of α-D-maltose.

Maltose Is Made from Two Glucose Units Maltose or malt sugar does not occur widely as such in nature, although it is present in germinating grain. It occurs in corn syrup, which is made from cornstarch, and it forms from the partial hydrolysis of starch. As the first equation indicated, maltose is made from two glucose units. They are joined by an acetal oxygen bridge that in carbohydrate chemistry is called a **glycosidic link.**

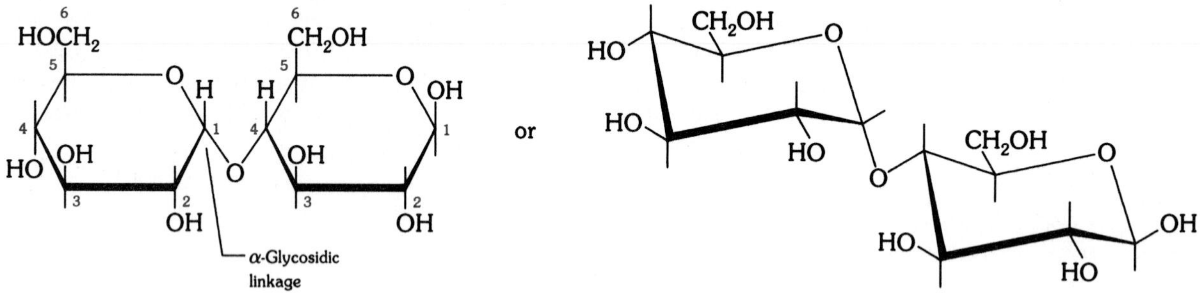

β-Maltose

In maltose, the oxygen of the glycosidic link joins the C-1 position of the glucose unit that served as the hemiacetal partner, the unit on the left, to the C-4 of the glucose unit that was the alcohol partner, on the right in the structure. Such a glycosidic link is designated as (1 → 4).

The bond to the bridging oxygen from C-1 (on the left) points in the *alpha* direction, so the glycosidic link is more fully described as α(1 → 4). Had this link pointed in the beta direction, it would have been described as β(1 → 4). But then the disaccharide would not have been maltose but a different disaccharide, cellobiose.

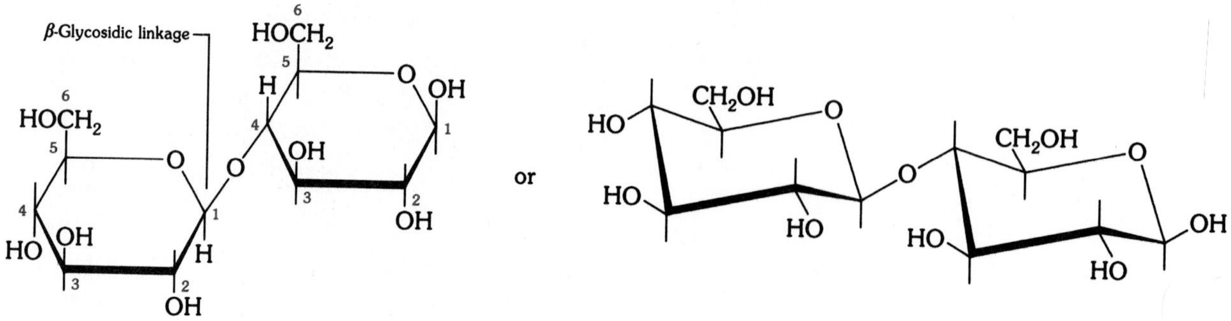

β-Cellobiose

The purely geometric difference between α(1 → 4) and β(1 → 4) that marks the difference between maltose and cellobiose may seem to be a trifle, but the difference to us is that we can digest maltose but not cellobiose. Just this difference in *geometry* bars humans from an enormous potential food source, for nature could supply much of it from the polysaccharide cellulose. We have an enzyme, maltase, that catalyzes the digestion (the hydrolysis) of maltose. We have no enzyme for cellobiose (or, for that matter, cellulose), although some organisms do.

Maltose Retains a Hemiacetal Unit, So It Is a Reducing Sugar and Mutarotates The glucose unit on the 4-side of a (1 → 4) glycosidic link in maltose still has a hemiacetal group. This part of maltose, therefore, can open and close, so maltose can exist in three forms, α-, β-, and the open form. Maltose therefore mutarotates and is a reducing sugar. The ring-opening action occurs only at the hemiacetal part, not at the oxygen bridge.

Lactose Links Galactose by a β(1 → 4) Bridge to Glucose Lactose or milk sugar occurs in the milk of mammals — 4% to 6% in cow's milk and 5% to 8% in human milk. It is also a by-product in the manufacture of cheese.

Lactose is a galactoside. From C-1 of its galactose unit there is a β(1 → 4) glycosidic link to C-4 of a glucose unit. The glucose unit therefore still has a free hemiacetal system, so lactose mutarotates and is a reducing sugar.

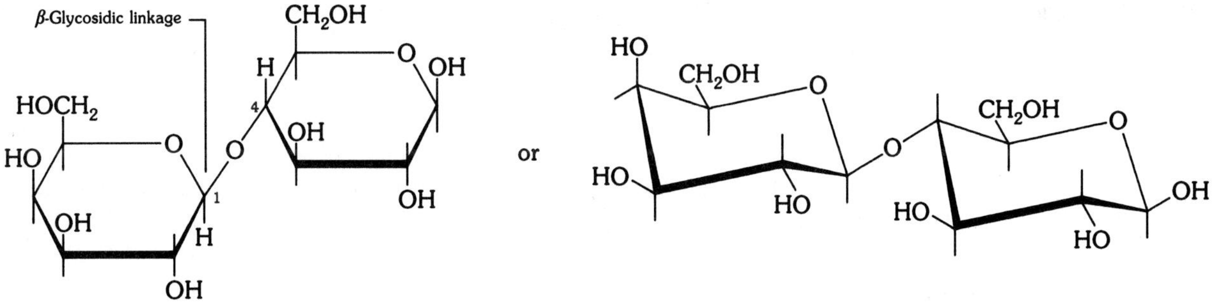

β-Lactose

Sucrose Links a Glucose Unit to a Fructose Unit Sucrose, our familiar table sugar, is obtained from sugarcane or from sugar beets. Its structure links a glucose to a fructose unit by an oxygen bridge in such a way that *no hemiacetal or hemiketal group remains*. Neither ring in sucrose, therefore, can open and close spontaneously in water. Hence, sucrose neither mutarotates nor gives positive tests with Tollens' or Benedict's reagents. It's our only common nonreducing disaccharide.

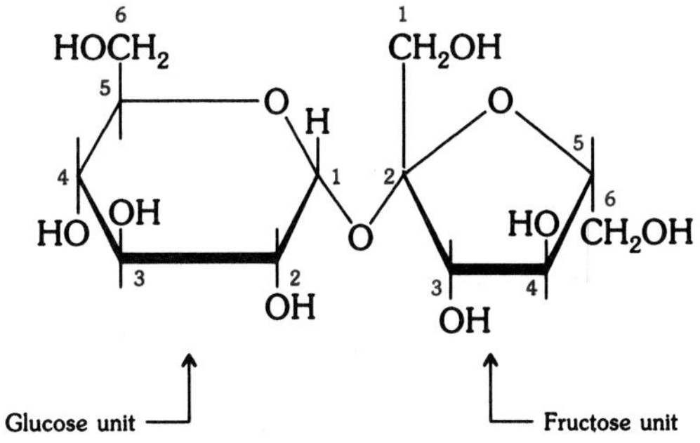

■ Beet sugar and cane sugar are identical compounds, sucrose.

Sucrose

The 50 : 50 mixture of glucose and fructose that forms when sucrose is hydrolyzed is called *invert sugar*, and it makes up the bulk of the carbohydrate in honey. (The sign of specific rotation inverts from + to − when sucrose, $[\alpha]_D^{20} + 66.5°$, changes to invert sugar, $[\alpha]_D^{20} - 19.9°$ and this inversion of the sign is the origin of the term *invert* sugar.)

19.5 POLYSACCHARIDES

Starch, glycogen, and cellulose are all polyglucosides.

In this section we will study the structures and some of the properties of three polymers of glucose: starch, glycogen, and cellulose.

Plants Store the Chemical Energy of Glucose in Starch Molecules When glucose is made by photosynthesis, solar energy becomes stored as chemical energy, which the plants can use for chemical work. Free glucose, however, is very soluble in water, so a plant would also have to retain considerable moisture to hold glucose in solution. This problem is avoided by the conversion of glucose to its much less soluble polymer, starch. It is particularly abundant in plant seeds and tubers, where its energy is used for sprouting and growth. Animals that have plants in their diets also take advantage of the chemical energy in starch.

Starch is a mixture of two kinds of polymers of α-glucose, amylose and amylopectin. In amylose, the glucose units are joined by a linear succession of $\alpha(1 \rightarrow 4)$ glycosidic links, as seen in Figure 19.7. The lengths of the amylose "chains" vary within the same sample, but over 1000 glucose units occur per amylose molecule. Formula weights ranging from 150,000 to 600,000 have been measured. The long amylose molecules coil into spiral-like helices, which tuck a significant fraction of the OH groups inside and away from contact with water. Thus amylose is only slightly soluble in water.

Amylopectin molecules have both $\alpha(1 \rightarrow 4)$ and $\alpha(1 \rightarrow 6)$ glycosidic links, as seen in Figure 19.8. The $\alpha(1 \rightarrow 6)$ bridges link the C-1 ends of linear amylose-type units to C-6 positions of glucose units in other long amylose chains, as seen in Figure 19.7. There are hundreds of such links per molecule, so amylopectin is heavily branched, and the branches prevent any coiling of the polymer. This leaves many more OH groups exposed to water than in amylose, so amylopectin tends to be somewhat more soluble in water than is amylose. However, neither dissolves well. The "solution" is actually a colloidal dispersion, because it gives the Tyndall effect.

Natural starches are about 10% to 20% amylose and 80% to 90% amylopectin. Neither is a reducing carbohydrate and neither gives a positive Tollens' or Benedict's test. One unique test that starch does give is called the **iodine test,** and it can detect extremely minute traces of starch.[1] When a drop of iodine reagent is added to starch, an intensely purple color develops as the iodine molecules become trapped within the vast network of starch molecules. In a starch sample undergoing hydrolysis, this network gradually breaks up so the system slowly loses its ability to give the iodine test.

The glycosidic links in starch are easily hydrolyzed in the presence of acids or the appropriate enzyme, which humans have. Thus the complete digestion of starch gives us only glucose. The partial hydrolysis of starch produces smaller polymer molecules that make up a substance known as *dextrin,* which has been used to manufacture mucilage and paste.

■ So-called *soluble* starch is partially hydrolyzed starch, and its smaller molecules more easily dissolve in water.

[1] The starch–iodine reagent is made by dissolving iodine, I_2, in aqueous sodium iodide, NaI. Iodine by itself is very insoluble in water, but iodine molecules combine with iodide ions to form the triiodide ion, I_3^-. Molecular iodine is readily available from this ion if some reactant is able to react with it.

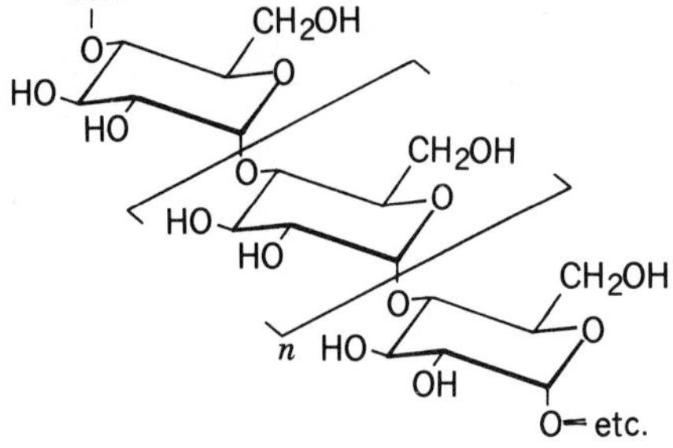

Figure 19.7
Amylose — partial structure.

$n > 1000$

Figure 19.8
Amylopectin—partial structure.

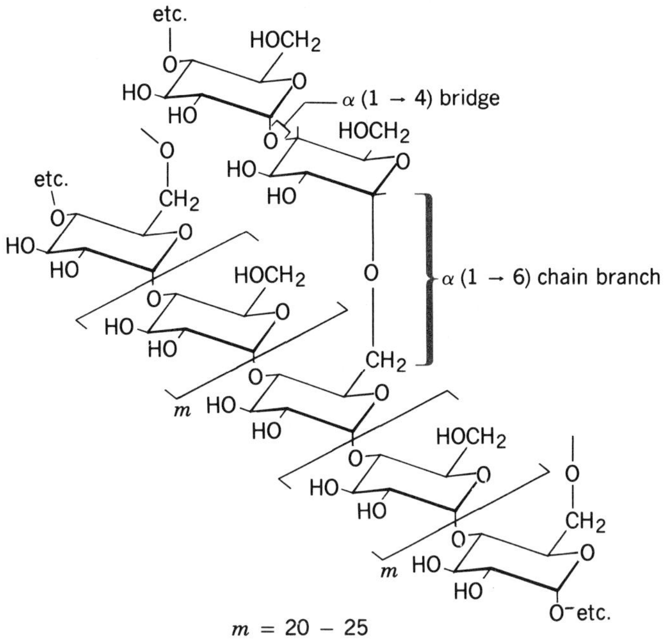

$m = 20 - 25$

We and many animals use plant starch for food. Digestion hydrolyzes starch, and what glucose our bodies cannot use right away is changed into an amylopectin-like polymer called glycogen. In this form, we can store the chemical energy of glucose units. Normally we don't excrete any excess glucose. If we eat enough to replenish glycogen reserves in various tissues, any additional glucose is converted to fat (to the satisfaction of a huge weight-watcher industry).

■ Glycogen is sometimes called animal starch.

Glycogen Is the Storage Form of Glucose in Animals Glycogen molecules are essentially like those of amylopectin, perhaps even more branched. The formula weights of various samples of glycogen have been reported in the range of 300,000 to 100,000,000, which correspond roughly to the range of 1700 to 600,000 glucose units per molecule. We store glucose as glycogen principally in the liver and in muscle tissue.

Cellulose Is a Polymer of β-Glucose Much of the glucose a plant makes by photosynthesis goes to make cellulose and other substances that it needs to build its cell walls and its rigid fibers. Cellulose, unlike starch or glycogen, has a geometry that allows its molecules to line up side by side, overlapping each other, and twist into fibers.

■ Cellobiose is to cellulose what maltose is to starch.

The huge geometric difference that allows cellulose to form fibers but not amylose is the orientation of the oxygen bridge. Cellulose is a polymer of the beta form of glucose. All the oxygen bridges are $\beta(1 \rightarrow 4)$. See Figure 19.9. Cellulose molecules, moreover, have no branches, like the $\alpha(1 \rightarrow 6)$ branches in amylopectin. All the substituents in the rings in cellulose project in the most stable directions (the equatorial directions as discussed in Special Topic 19.2). The cellulose molecule is thus quite ribbon-like, so it's easy for neighboring molecules to nestle to each other where hydrogen bonds between molecules stabilize the

Figure 19.9
Cellulose—partial structure. In cotton, this polymer of β-D-glucose has from 2000 to 26,000 glucose units, depending on the variety. The strength of a cotton fiber comes in part from the thousands of hydrogen bonds that can exist between parallel and overlapping cellulose molecules.

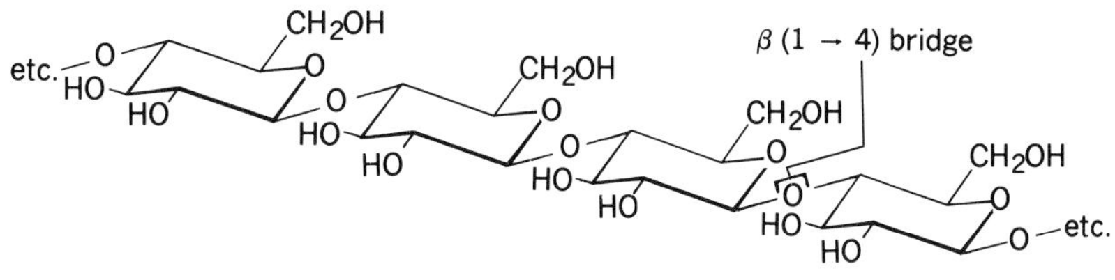

■ If you spill *concentrated* acid on your clothes or skin, deluge the area with water immediately.

aggregations. With twistings of these collections, cellulose fibers of considerable strength are possible.

As we have noted, humans have no enzyme that can catalyze the hydrolysis of a beta-glycosidic link, so none of the huge supply of cellulose in the world, or the cellobiose that could be made from it, is nutritionally useful to us. Many bacteria have this enzyme, however, and some strains dwell in the stomachs of cattle and other animals. Bacterial action converts cellulose in hay and other animal feed into molecules that the larger animals can then use.

The oxygen bridges in the cellulose of cotton fabrics, being acetal systems, are hydrolyzed when a trace of acid catalyst is present. Perhaps you discovered this the morning after you spilled some acid on your jeans in lab. (If you know that you have spilled a small amount of dilute acid on jeans, put a small spatulaful of sodium bicarbonate or sodium carbonate on a towel, make a paste, and daub the spot with it. A towel moistened with dilute ammonia also works, but watch out for the ammonia odor. You might be able to save the fabric if you act quickly.)

SUMMARY

Carbohydrates Carbohydrates are aldehydes or ketones with multiple OH groups or are glycosides of these. Those that can't be hydrolyzed are the monosaccharides, which in pure forms exist as cyclic hemiacetals or cyclic hemiketals that can mutarotate and that are reducing sugars.

Monosaccharides The three nutritionally important monosaccharides are glucose, galactose, and fructose—all in the D-family. Glucose is the chief carbohydrate in blood. Galactose, which differs from glucose only in the orientation of the OH at C-4, is obtained (together with glucose) from the hydrolysis of lactose. Fructose, a reducing ketohexose, differs from glucose only in the location of the carbonyl group. It's at C-2 in fructose and at C-1 in glucose.

Disaccharides The disaccharides are glycosides whose molecules break up into two monosaccharide molecules when they react with water. Maltose is made of two glucose units joined by an $\alpha(1 \rightarrow 4)$ glycosidic link. In a molecule of lactose (milk sugar)—a galactoside—a galactose unit joins a glucose unit by a $\beta(1 \rightarrow 4)$ oxygen bridge. In sucrose (cane or beet sugar), there is an oxygen bridge from C-1 of a glucose unit to C-2 of a fructose unit. Both maltose and lactose retain hemiacetal systems, so both mutarotate and are reducing sugars. They also exist in α- and β-forms. Sucrose is a nonreducing disaccharide. The digestion of these disaccharides is by the following reactions:

$$\text{Maltose} + H_2O \longrightarrow \text{glucose} + \text{glucose}$$
$$\text{Lactose} + H_2O \longrightarrow \text{glucose} + \text{galactose}$$
$$\text{Sucrose} + H_2O \longrightarrow \text{glucose} + \text{fructose}$$

Polysaccharides Three important polysaccharides of glucose are starch (a plant product), glycogen (an animal product), and cellulose (a plant fiber). In molecules of each, $(1 \rightarrow 4)$ glycosidic links occur. They're alpha bridges in starch and glycogen and beta bridges in cellulose. In the molecules of the amylopectin portion of starch as well as in glycogen, numerous $\alpha(1 \rightarrow 6)$ bridges also occur. No polysaccharide gives a positive test with Tollens' or Benedict's reagents. Starch gives the iodine test. As starch is hydrolyzed, its molecules successively break down to dextrins, maltose, and finally, glucose. Humans have enzymes that catalyze the hydrolysis of $\alpha(1 \rightarrow 4)$ glycosidic links, but not the $\beta(1 \rightarrow 4)$ glycosidic links of cellulose.

Absolute configuration Fischer projection structures of open-chain forms are made according to a set of rules. The carbon chain is positioned vertically with any carbonyl group as close to the top as possible. At each chiral carbon, this chain projects rearward. Any groups on bonds that appear horizontal project forward. If the OH group of a carbohydrate that is farthest from the carbonyl group projects to the right in a Fischer projection structure, the carbohydrate is in the D-family. If this OH group projects to the left, the substance is in the L-family.

REVIEW EXERCISES

Except where noted, flat hexagon structures can be used for cyclic six-membered rings.

The answers to these Review Exercises are in the *Study Guide* that accompanies this book.

Biochemistry

19.1 Substances in the diet must provide raw materials for what three essentials for life?

19.2 What are the three broad classes of foods?

19.3 What two kinds of compounds are most involved in the molecular basis of information? Which one carries the genetic "blueprints"?

19.4 What is as important to the life of a cell as the chemicals that make it up and that it receives?

Carbohydrate Terminology

19.5 Examine the following structures and identify by letter(s) which structure(s) fit(s) each of the labels. If a particular label is not illustrated by any structure, state so.

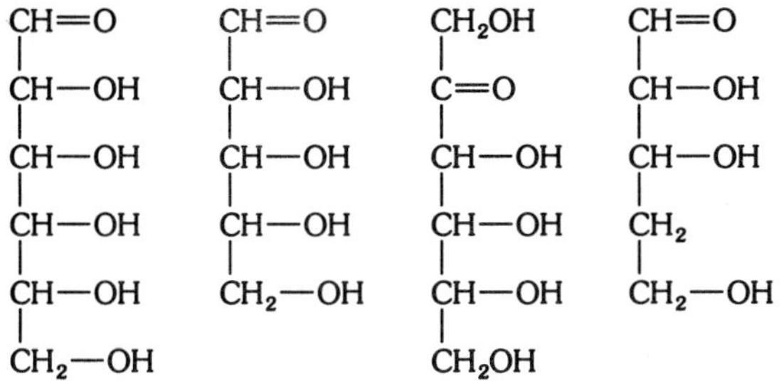

    A   **B**   **C**   **D**

(a) ketose(s)   (b) deoxy sugar(s)
(c) aldohexose(s)   (d) aldopentose(s)

19.6 Write the structure (open-chain form) that illustrates
(a) any aldopentose
(b) any ketotetrose

19.7 What is the structure and the common name of the simplest aldose?

19.8 What is the structure and the common name of the simplest ketose?

19.9 A sample of 0.0001 mol of a carbohydrate reacted with water in the presence of a catalyst, and 1 mol of glucose was produced. Classify this carbohydrate as a mono-, di-, or polysaccharide.

19.10 An unknown carbohydrate failed to give a positive Benedict's test. Classify it as a reducing or a nonreducing carbohydrate.

Monosaccharides

19.11 What is the name of the most abundant carbohydrate (a) in blood and (b) in corn syrup?

19.12 What is the name of the ketose present in honey?

19.13 Write the structure (open-chain form) of any carbohydrate that has all of the following properties. It forms a tetraacetate ester. It is oxidized without loss of carbon or hydrogen by Tollens' reagent to give a carboxylic acid. It can be reduced by a series of steps to pentane.

19.14 An unknown carbohydrate could be reduced by a series of steps to butane. It gave a positive Benedict's test, and its molecules had just one chiral carbon. What is a structure consistent with these facts?

19.15 What is the structure of the open form of the following cyclic hemiacetal? (Write the open form with its chain coiled in the same way it is coiled in the closed form.)

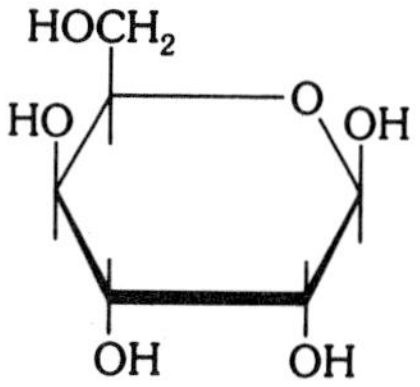

19.16 Examine the following structure. If you judge that it is either a cyclic hemiketal or a cyclic hemiacetal, write the structure of the open-chain form (coiled in like manner as the chain of the ring).

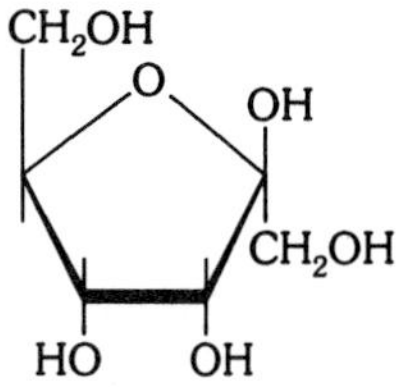

19.17 Mannose mutarotates like glucose. Mannose is identical with glucose except that in the cyclic structures the OH at C-2 in mannose projects on the same side of the ring as the CH_2OH group. Write the structures of the three forms of mannose that are in equilibrium after mutarotation gives a steady value of specific rotation. Identify which corresponds to α-mannose and which to β-mannose.

19.18 Allose is identical with glucose except that in its cyclic forms the OH group at C-3 projects on the opposite side of the ring from the CH_2OH group. Allose mutarotates like glucose. Write the structures of the three forms of allose that are in equilibrium after mutarotation gives a final value of specific rotation. Which structures are α-allose and β-allose?

19.19 If less than 0.05% of all galactose molecules are in their open-chain form at equilibrium in water, how can galactose give a strong, positive Tollens' test, a test good for the aldehyde group?

19.20 At equilibrium, after mutarotation, a glucose solution consists of 36% α-glucose and 64% β-glucose (and just a trace of the open form). Suppose that in some enzyme-catalyzed process the beta form is removed from this equilibrium. What becomes of the other forms of glucose?

19.21 Study the cyclic form of fructose on page 496 again. If its designation as β-fructose signifies a particular relationship between the CH_2OH group at C-5 and the OH group at C-2, what must be the cyclic form of fructose in sucrose?

19.22 Is the following structure that of α-fructose, β-fructose, or something else? Explain.

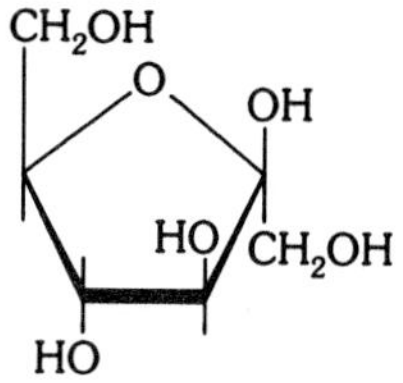

19.23 Write the cyclic structure of α-3-deoxyribose and draw an arrow that points to its hemiacetal carbon.

19.24 Could 4-deoxyribose exist as a cyclic hemiacetal with a five-membered ring (one of whose atoms is O)? Explain.

Absolute Configurations

19.25 Write the Fischer projection formula of L-glucose. (Refer to Figure 19.6.)

19.26 What is the Fischer projection formula of D-2-deoxyribose? (Refer to Figure 19.6.)

19.27 Suppose that the aldehyde group of D-glyceraldehyde is oxidized to a carboxylic acid group, and that this is then converted to a methyl ester under conditions that do not touch any of the four bonds to C-2. What is the Fischer projection formula of this methyl ester? To what family, D or L, does it belong? Explain.

19.28 Sorbose has the structure given below. It is made by the fermentation of sorbitol, and hundreds of tons of sorbose are used each year to make vitamin C. In what configurational family, D or L, is sorbose?

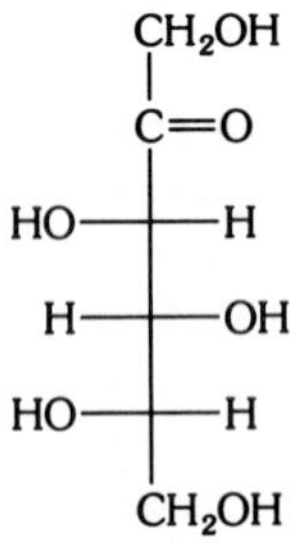

19.29 Sorbitol, $C_6H_{14}O_6$, is found in the juices of many fruits and berries (e.g., pears, apples, cherries, and plums). It can be made by the addition of hydrogen to D-glucose:

$$C_6H_{12}O_6 + H_2 \xrightarrow[\text{heat, pressure}]{\text{Ni}} C_6H_{14}O_6$$

D-Glucose D-Sorbitol

Write the Fischer projection formula of D-sorbitol.

19.30 The magnesium salt of D-gluconic acid (Glucomag) is used as an antispasmodic and to treat dysmenorrhea. D-Gluconic acid forms by the mild oxidation of D-glucose:

$$C_6H_{12}O_6 + (O) \longrightarrow C_6H_{12}O_7$$

D-Glucose D-Gluconic acid

What is the Fischer projection formula of D-gluconic acid?

Glycosides

19.31 Using cyclic structures, write the structures of ethyl α-glucoside and ethyl β-glucoside. Are these two enantiomers or are they some other kind of stereoisomers?

19.32 What are the structures of methyl α-galactoside and methyl β-galactoside? Could these be described as cis-trans isomers? Explain.

Disaccharides

19.33 What are the names of the three nutritionally important disaccharides?

19.34 What is invert sugar?

19.35 Why isn't sucrose a reducing sugar?

19.36 Examine the following structure and answer the questions about it.

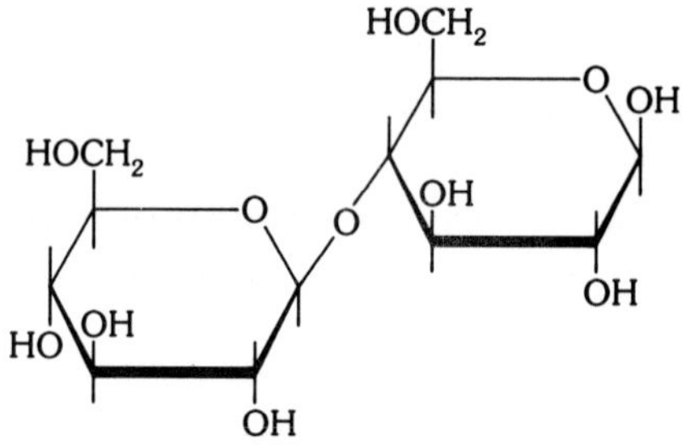

(a) Does it have a hemiacetal system? Where? (Draw an arrow to it or circle it.)

(b) Does it have an acetal system? Where? (Circle it.)

(c) Does this substance give a positive Benedict's test? Explain.

(d) In what specific structural way does it differ from maltose?

(e) Write the cyclic structures and names of the products of the acid-catalyzed hydrolysis of this compound. (This compound, incidentally, is cellobiose.)

19.37 Trehalose is a disaccharide found in young mushrooms and yeast, and it is the chief carbohydrate in the hemolymph of certain insects. On the basis of its structural features, answer the following questions.

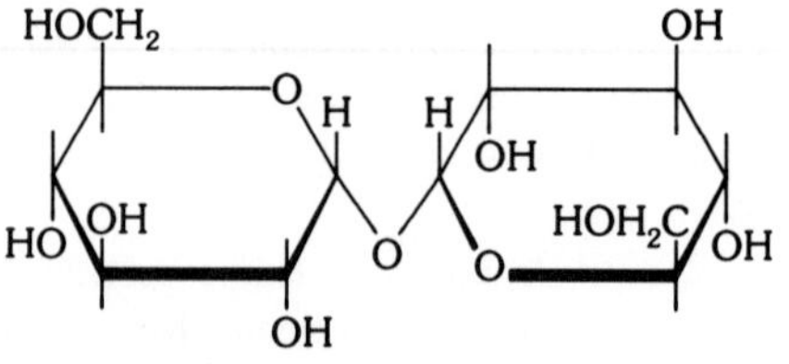

(a) Is trehalose a reducing sugar? Explain.

(b) Can trehalose mutarotate? Explain.

(c) Identify, by name only, the products of the hydrolysis of trehalose.

19.38 Maltose has a hemiacetal system. Write the structure of maltose in which this group has changed to the open form.

19.39 When lactose undergoes mutarotation, one of its rings opens up. Write this open form of lactose.

Polysaccharides

19.40 Name the polysaccharides that give only D-glucose when they are completely hydrolyzed.

19.41 What is the main structural difference between amylose and cellulose?

19.42 How are amylose and amylopectin alike structurally?

19.43 How are amylose and amylopectin different structurally?

19.44 Why can't humans digest cellulose?

19.45 What is the iodine test? Describe the reagent and state what it is used to test for and what is seen in a positive test.

19.46 How do amylopectin and glycogen compare structurally?

19.47 How does the body use glycogen?

Photosyntheses (Special Topic 19.1)

19.48 The energy available in glucose originated in the sun. Explain in general terms how this happened.

19.49 Write the simple, overall equation for photosynthesis.

19.50 What is the name and color of the energy-absorbing pigment in plants?

19.51 In what general region of the planet earth is most of the photosynthesis carried out? By what organisms?

19.52 Describe in general terms the oxygen cycle of our planet including the function of photosynthesis in it.

Boat and Chair Forms of Saturated Six-Membered Rings (Special Topic 19.2)

Start by simply tracing the structures; then practice drawing the skeletons of the two chair forms of six-membered rings.

19.53 Why are chair forms of saturated, six-membered rings more stable than boat forms?

19.54 Why are equatorial positions more stable than axial?

19.55 Draw the structures of the following.
(a) A chair form of cyclohexane. Label the bonds that can hold substituents as being axial (a) or equatorial (e).
(b) The least stable structure of *trans*-1,2-dimethylcyclohexane.
(c) The most stable structure of *trans*-1,2-dimethylcyclohexane.
(d) The most stable form of D-glucose.
(e) The most stable form of D-allose. (*Hint:* Refer to the Fischer projection structure of D-allose in Figure 19.6 and note where it is the same as the Fischer projection structure of D-glucose and where it differs.)

CHAPTER TWENTY

Lipids

- WHAT LIPIDS ARE
- CHEMICAL PROPERTIES OF TRIACYLGLYCEROLS
- PHOSPHOLIPIDS
- STEROIDS
- CELL MEMBRANES

In pioneer days, before people obtained paraffin from petroleum, candles were made from natural waxes, like beeswax. Waxes are esters whose molecules are mostly hydrocarbon-like. We study waxes and other natural esters of the lipid family in this chapter.

20.1 WHAT LIPIDS ARE

The edible fats and oils consist of hydrocarbon-like molecules that are esters of long-chain fatty acids and glycerol.

When undecomposed plant or animal material is crushed and ground with a nonpolar solvent such as ether, whatever dissolves is classified as a **lipid.** This operation catches a large variety of relatively nonpolar substances, and all are lipids. Thus this broad family is defined not by structure but by the technique used to isolate its members, solvent extraction. Among the many substances that won't dissolve in nonpolar solvents are carbohydrates, proteins, other very polar organic substances, inorganic salts, and water.

◼ Extraction means to shake or stir a mixture with a solvent that dissolves just part of the mixture.

Lipids Are Broadly Subdivided According to the Presence of Saponifiable Groups One of the major classes of lipids—the **saponifiable lipids,** consists of compounds with one or more groups that can be hydrolyzed or saponified. In nearly all examples, these are ester groups. A number of families are in this class, including the waxes, the neutral fats, the phospholipids, and the glycolipids. The **nonsaponifiable lipids** lack groups that can be hydrolyzed or saponified. These include cholesterol and many sex hormones. The chart in Figure 20.1 outlines the many kinds of lipids.

◼ Butterfat and salad oils are neutral fats.
◼ Cholesterol and several sex hormones are steroids.

Figure 20.1
Lipid families.

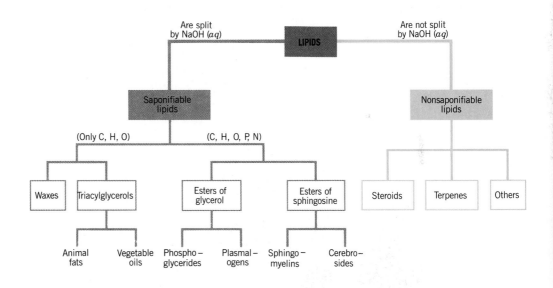

Plant Waxes Are Simple Esters with Long Hydrocarbon Chains The waxes, the simplest of the saponifiable lipids, occur as protective coatings on fruit and leaves as well as on fur, feathers, and skin. Nearly all **waxes** are esters of long-chain monohydric alcohols and long-chain monocarboxylic acids in both of which there is an even number of carbons. As many as 26 to 34 carbon atoms can be incorporated in *each* of the alcohol and the acid units, which makes the waxes almost totally hydrocarbon-like.

◼ An acyl group has the general structure:

$$R-\overset{\displaystyle O}{\overset{\displaystyle \|}{C}}-$$

■ Lanolin is used to make cosmetic skin lotions.

Any particular wax, like beeswax, consists of a mixture of similar compounds that share the kind of structure shown above. In molecules of lanolin (wool fat), however, the alcohol portion is contributed by steroid alcohols, which have large ring systems (to be studied in Section 20.4). Waxes exist in sebum, a secretion of human skin that helps to keep the skin supple.

PRACTICE EXERCISE 1 One particular ester in beeswax can be hydrolyzed to give a straight-chain primary alcohol with 26 carbons and a straight-chain carboxylic acid with 28 carbons. Write the structure of this ester.

■ In the older literature, the triacylglycerols are called the **triglycerides.**

The Triacylglycerols Are Triesters of Glycerol The molecules of the most abundant lipids are the **triacylglycerols,** which are esters of glycerol and long-chain monocarboxylic acids, the **fatty acids.** Unlike more complex lipids, triacylglycerol molecules have no ionic sites, so sometimes they are called the *neutral fats*. Their general structure is

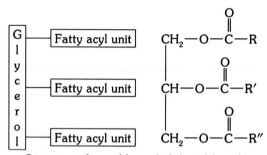

Components of neutral fats and oils (triacylglycerols)

The triacylglycerols include lard (hog fat), tallow (beef fat), butterfat — all animal fats — as well as such plant oils as olive oil, cottonseed oil, corn oil, peanut oil, soybean oil, coconut oil, and linseed oil.

The three acyl units in a typical triacylglycerol molecule are from three different fatty acids. Fats and oils are thus mixtures of different molecules that share common structural features. Although we can't write, for example, the structure of cottonseed oil, we can describe a typical molecule, like that of structure **1.**

■ Notice that the middle carbon of the glycerol unit in **1** is a chiral carbon.

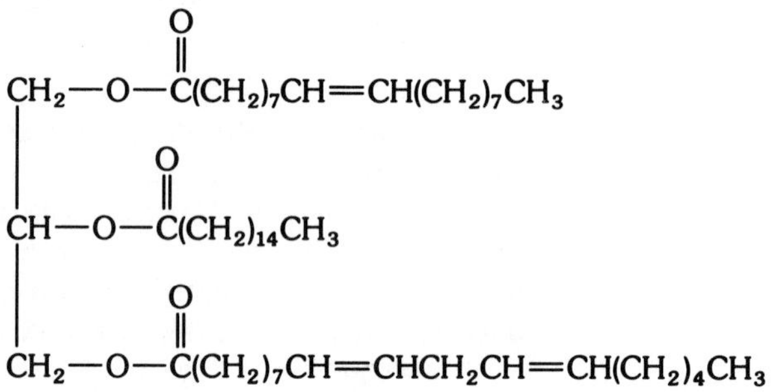

$$CH_2-O-\overset{\overset{\displaystyle O}{\|}}{C}(CH_2)_7CH=CH(CH_2)_7CH_3$$

$$CH-O-\overset{\overset{\displaystyle O}{\|}}{C}(CH_2)_{14}CH_3$$

$$CH_2-O-\overset{\overset{\displaystyle O}{\|}}{C}(CH_2)_7CH=CHCH_2CH=CH(CH_2)_4CH_3$$

1

In a particular fat or oil, certain fatty acids predominate, others either are absent or are present in trace amounts, and virtually all the molecules are triacylglycerols. Data on the fatty acid compositions of several fats and oils are listed in Table 20.1.

TABLE 20.1   Fatty Acids Obtained from Neutral Fats and Oils

Type	Fat or Oil	Average Composition of Fatty Acids (%)					
		Myristic Acid	Palmitic Acid	Stearic Acid	Oleic Acid	Linoleic Acid	Others
Animal	Butter	8–15	25–29	9–12	18–33	2–4	a
Fats	Lard	1–2	25–30	12–18	48–60	6–12	b
	Beef tallow	2–5	24–34	15–30	35–45	1–3	b
Vegetable	Olive	0–1	5–15	1–4	67–84	8–12	
Oils	Peanut	—	7–12	2–6	30–60	20–38	
	Corn	1–2	7–11	3–4	25–35	50–60	
	Cottonseed	1–2	18–25	1–2	17–38	45–55	
	Soybean	1–2	6–10	2–4	20–30	50–58	c
	Linseed	—	4–7	2–4	14–30	14–25	d
Marine	Whale	5–10	10–20	2–5	33–40	—	e
Oils	Fish	6–8	10–25	1–3	—	—	e

[a] Also, 3–4% butyric acid, 1–2% caprylic acid, 2–3% capric acid, 2–5% lauric acid.

[b] Also, linolenic acid, 1%.

[c] Also, linolenic acid, 5–10%.

[d] Also, linolenic acid, 45–60%.

[e] Large percentages of other highly unsaturated fatty acids.

The Fatty Acids Are Mostly Long-Chain, Unbranched Monocarboxylic Acids   The fatty acids obtained from the lipids of most plants and animals share the following features.

1.   They are usually monocarboxylic acids, RCO_2H.

2.   The R group is usually an unbranched chain.

3.   The number of carbon atoms is almost always even.

4.   The R group can be saturated, or it can have one or more double bonds, which are cis. CH_2 units occur between double bonds

The most abundant saturated fatty acids are palmitic acid, $CH_3(CH_2)_{14}CO_2H$, and stearic acid, $CH_3(CH_2)_{16}CO_2H$, which have 16 and 18 carbons, respectively. Refer back to Table 16.1 for the other saturated fatty acids used to make triacylglycerols. They are the acids below acetic acid with even number of carbons, like butanoic, hexanoic, octanoic, and decanoic acids. Their acyl units, however, are present in only relatively small amounts in triacylglycerols.

The unsaturated fatty acids most commonly obtained from triacylglycerols are listed in Table 20.2 and include oleic, linoleic, and linolenic acids, all with 18-carbon skeletons. Oleic acid is the most abundant and most widely distributed fatty acid in nature. The double bonds in the unsaturated fatty acids of Table 20.2 are cis.

The vegetable oils rely more on the unsaturated fatty acids, like oleic and linoleic acid, for acyl groups than the animal fats, so they have more double bonds per molecule. See Table 20.1. The vegetable oils are therefore described as *polyunsaturated*. The saturated fatty acyl units of palmitic and stearic acids are far more common in animal fats.

The presence of cis alkene groups, which give kinks to the side chains, affects the melting points of the fatty acids, as you can see in Table 20.2. As more alkene groups are added, the melting points decrease because the structural kinks at double bonds inhibit the kind of close

TABLE 20.2 Common Unsaturated Fatty Acids

Name	Number of Double Bonds	Total Number of Carbons	Structure	Melting Point (°C)
Palmitoleic acid	1	16	$CH_3(CH_2)_5CH{=}CH(CH_2)_7CO_2H$	32
Oleic acid	1	18	$CH_3(CH_2)_7CH{=}CH(CH_2)_7CO_2H$	4
Linoleic acid	2	18	$CH_3(CH_2)_4CH{=}CHCH_2CH{=}CH(CH_2)_7CO_2H$	−5
Linolenic acid	3	18	$CH_3CH_2CH{=}CHCH_2CH{=}CHCH_2CH{=}CH(CH_2)_7CO_2H$	−11
Arachidonic acid	4	20	$CH_3(CH_2)_4CH{=}CHCH_2CH{=}CHCH_2CH{=}CHCH_2CH{=}CH(CH_2)_3CO_2H$	−50

packing in crystals required for stronger, higher-melting systems. This is why the animal fats, with fewer alkene groups, are likely to be solids at room temperature and the vegetable oils are liquids.

PRACTICE EXERCISE 2

Omega (ω) designation

CH_3 ω
|
CH_2 ω-2
|
CH ω-3
‖
CH
|
(remainder of fatty acid)

To visualize how a cis double bond introduces a kink into a molecule, write the structure of oleic acid in a way that correctly shows the cis geometry of the alkene group. (Without the double bond, as in stearic acid, the entire sidechain can stretch out into a perfect zigzag conformation, which makes it easy for two sidechains to nestle very close to each other.)

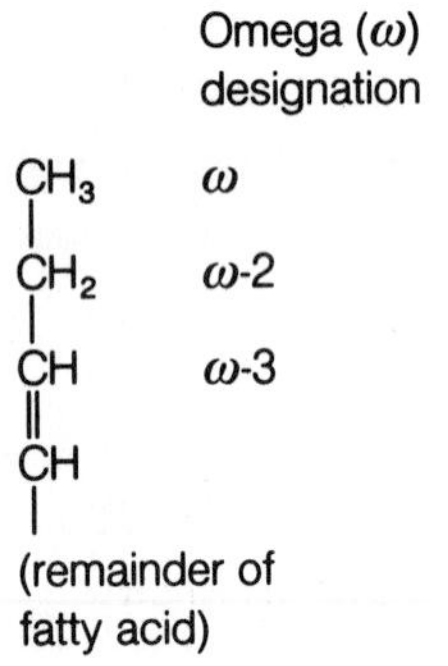

The properties of the fatty acids are those to be expected of compounds with carboxyl groups, double bonds (where present), and long hydrocarbon chains. Thus they are insoluble in water and soluble in nonpolar solvents. They are neutralized by bases and form salts. They can be esterified. Those that have alkene groups react with bromine and they take up hydrogen in the presence of a catalyst.

The *prostaglandins* are an unusual family of fatty acids with 20 carbons, five-membered rings, and a wide variety of effects in the body. See Special Topic 20.1.

In the late 1980s, one small group of fatty acids, the omega-3 fatty acids, were discussed in scientific debates about the value of fish or marine oils in the diet. Special Topic 20.2 describes them further.

20.2 CHEMICAL PROPERTIES OF TRIACYLGLYCEROLS

Triacylglycerols can be hydrolyzed (digested), saponified, and hydrogenated.

■ This hydrolysis of triacylglycerols is what happens when we digest fats and oils.

During Digestion, Triacylglycerols Are Hydrolyzed Enzymes in the digestive tracts of humans and animals catalyze the hydrolysis of the ester links in triacylglycerols. In general,

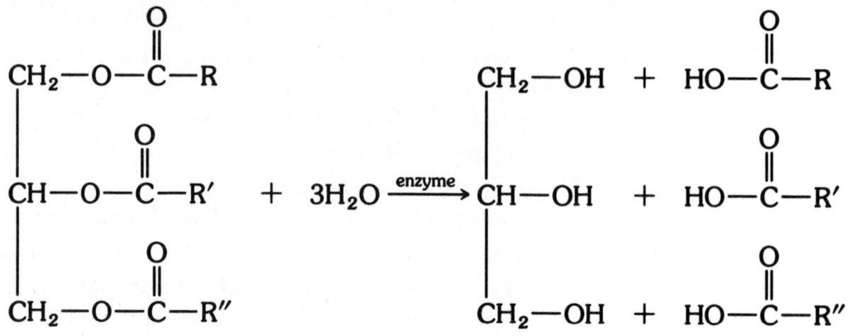

Triacylglycerol   Glycerol   Fatty acids

A specific example is

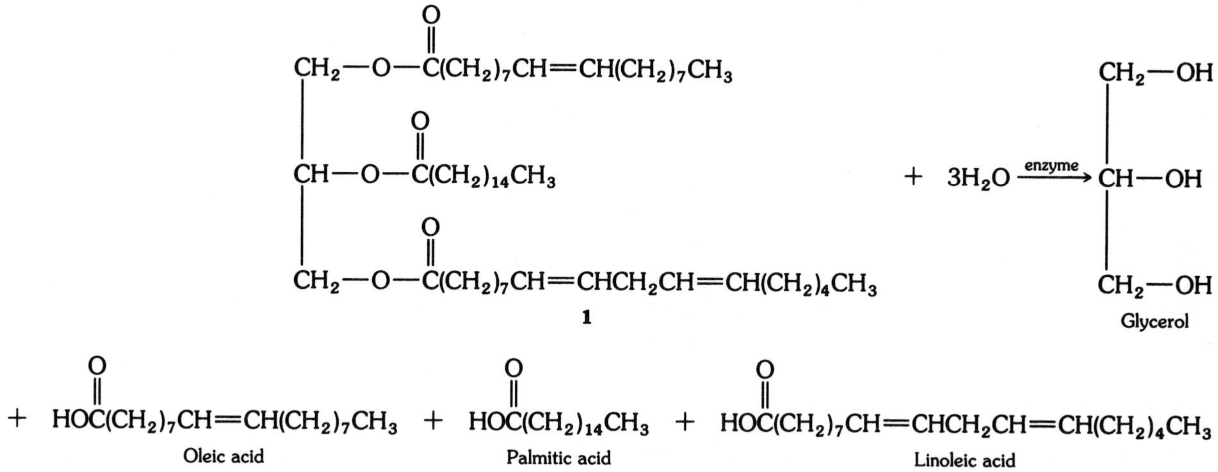

$$CH_2-O-\overset{\overset{O}{\|}}{C}(CH_2)_7CH=CH(CH_2)_7CH_3$$

$$CH-O-\overset{\overset{O}{\|}}{C}(CH_2)_{14}CH_3 \qquad + \quad 3H_2O \xrightarrow{enzyme}$$

$$CH_2-O-\overset{\overset{O}{\|}}{C}(CH_2)_7CH=CHCH_2CH=CH(CH_2)_4CH_3$$

1

$$CH_2-OH$$
$$CH-OH$$
$$CH_2-OH$$
Glycerol

$$+ \quad HO\overset{\overset{O}{\|}}{C}(CH_2)_7CH=CH(CH_2)_7CH_3 \quad + \quad HO\overset{\overset{O}{\|}}{C}(CH_2)_{14}CH_3 \quad + \quad HO\overset{\overset{O}{\|}}{C}(CH_2)_7CH=CHCH_2CH=CH(CH_2)_4CH_3$$

Oleic acid · · · Palmitic acid · · · Linoleic acid

Soaps Are Made by the Saponification of Triacylglycerols The saponification of the ester links in triacylglycerols by the action of a strong base (e.g., NaOH or KOH) gives glycerol and a mixture of the salts of fatty acids. These salts are soaps, and how they exert their detergent action is described in Special Topic 20.3. In general,

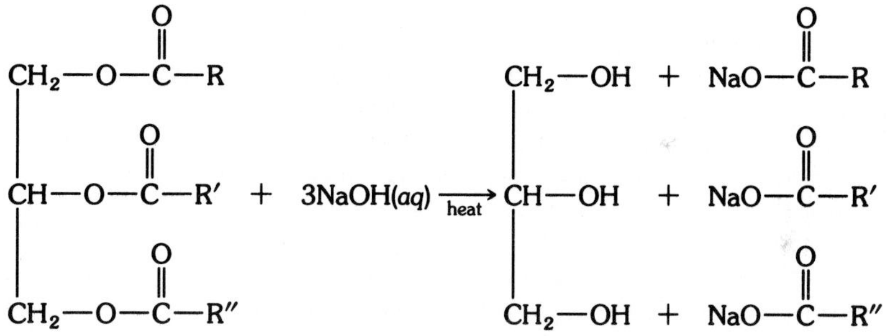

$$CH_2-O-\overset{\overset{O}{\|}}{C}-R$$
$$CH-O-\overset{\overset{O}{\|}}{C}-R' \quad + \quad 3NaOH(aq) \xrightarrow{heat}$$
$$CH_2-O-\overset{\overset{O}{\|}}{C}-R''$$

$$CH_2-OH \quad + \quad NaO-\overset{\overset{O}{\|}}{C}-R$$
$$CH-OH \quad + \quad NaO-\overset{\overset{O}{\|}}{C}-R'$$
$$CH_2-OH \quad + \quad NaO-\overset{\overset{O}{\|}}{C}-R''$$
Glycerol · · · Mixture of salts

PRACTICE EXERCISE 3 Write a balanced equation for the saponification of **1** with sodium hydroxide.

■ Hydrogenated vegetable oils are chemically identical to animal fats.

Hydrogenation of Vegetable Oils Gives Solid Shortenings When hydrogen is made to add to some of the double bonds in vegetable oils, the oils become like animal fats, both physically and structurally. One very practical consequence is that they change from being liquids to solids at room temperature. Many people prefer solid, lard-like shortening for cooking, instead of liquid oils. Therefore the manufacturers of such products as Crisco and Spry use inexpensive, readily available vegetable oils, like corn oil and cottonseed oil, and catalytically add hydrogen to some (not all) of the alkene groups in their molecules. Unlike natural lard, these vegetable shortenings have no cholesterol.

PRACTICE EXERCISE 4 Write the balanced equation for the complete hydrogenation of the alkene links in structure **1**.

The chief lipid material in margarine is produced from vegetable oils in the same way. The hydrogenation is done with special care so that the final product can melt on the tongue, a property that makes butterfat so pleasant. (If all the alkene groups in a vegetable oil were hydrogenated, instead of just some of them, the product would be just like beef or mutton fat, relatively hard materials that would not melt on the tongue.)

The popular brands of peanut butter whose peanut oils do not separate are made by the partial hydrogenation of the oil in real peanut butter. The lipid present becomes a solid at room temperature (and therefore it can't separate).

SPECIAL TOPIC 20.1 | THE PROSTAGLANDINS

The prostaglandins were discovered in the mid-1930s by a Swedish scientist, Ulf von Euler (Nobel prize, 1970), but they didn't arouse much interest in medical circles until the late 1960s, largely through the work of Sune Bergstrom. It became apparent that these compounds, which occur widely in the body, affect a large number of processes. Their general name comes from an organ, the prostate gland, from which they were first obtained. About 20 are known, and they occur in four major subclasses designated as PGA, PGB, PGE, and PGF. (A subscript is generally placed after the third letter to designate the number of alkene double bonds that occur outside of the five-membered ring.) The structures of some typical examples are shown here.

Prostaglandins are made from C-20 fatty acids such as arachidonic acid. By coiling a molecule of this acid, as shown, you can see how its structure needs only a ring closure (suggested by the dashed arrow) and three more oxygen atoms to become PGF$_2$. The oxygen atoms are all provided by molecular oxygen itself.

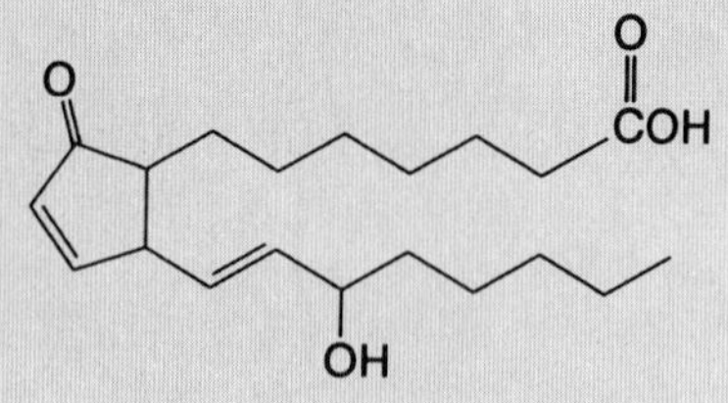

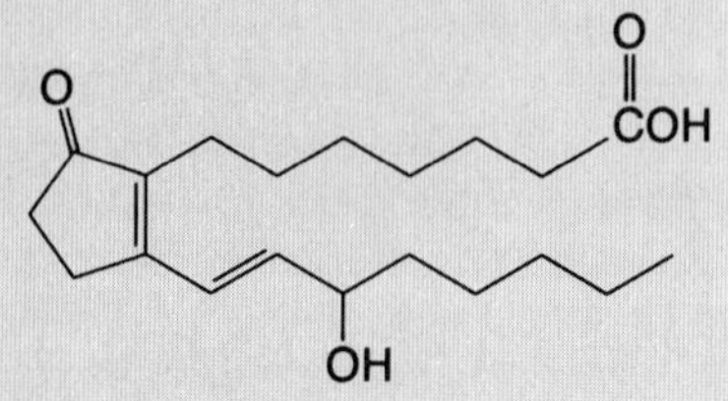

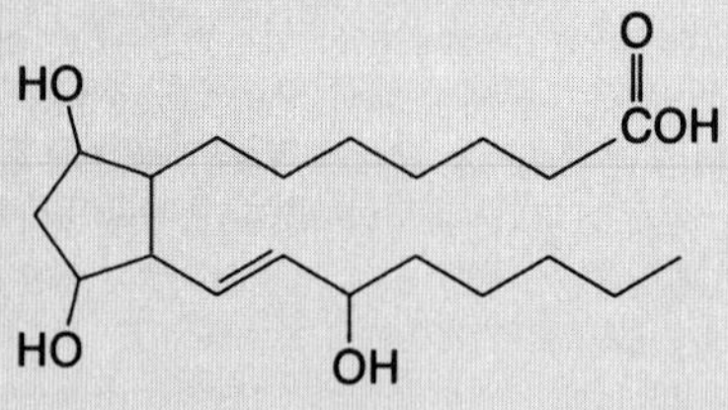

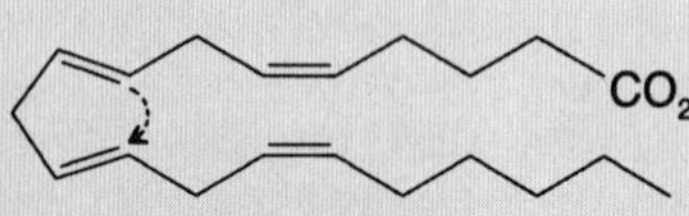

Prostaglandins as Chemical Messengers The prostaglandins are like hormones in many ways, except that they do not act globally, that is, over the entire body. They do their work within the cells where they are made or in nearby cells, so they are sometimes called *local hormones*. This is perhaps why the prostaglandins have such varied functions: they occur and express their roles in such varied tissues. They work together with hormones to modify the chemical messages that hormones bring to cells. In some cells, the prostaglandins inhibit enzymes and in others they activate them. In some organs, the prostaglandins help to regulate the flow of blood within them. In others, they affect the transmission of nerve impulses.

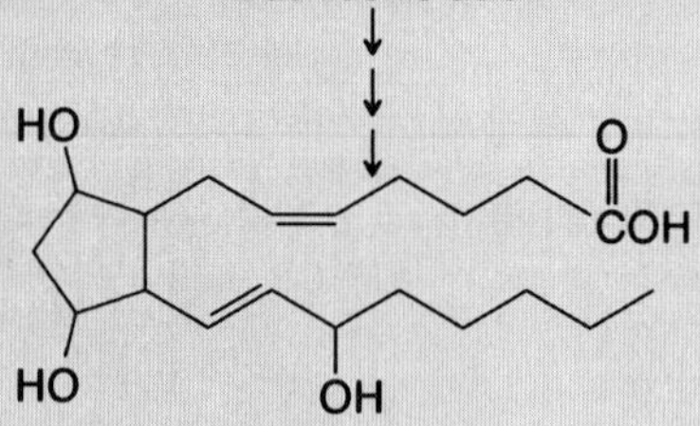

Some prostaglandins enhance inflammation in a tissue, and it is interesting that aspirin, an inflammation reducer, does exactly the opposite. This effect is caused by aspirin's ability to inhibit the work of an enzyme needed in the synthesis of prostaglandins.

Prostaglandins as Pharmaceuticals In experiments that use prostaglandins as pharmaceuticals, they have been found to have an astonishing variety of effects. One prostaglandin induces labor at the end of a pregnancy. Another stops the flow of gastric juice while the body heals an ulcer. Other possible uses are to treat high blood pressure, rheumatoid arthritis, asthma, nasal congestion, and certain viral diseases.

20.3 PHOSPHOLIPIDS

Phospholipid molecules have very polar or ionic sites in addition to long hydrocarbon chains.

Phospholipids are esters either of glycerol or of sphingosine which is a long-chain, dihydric amino alcohol with one double bond.

Omega-3 refers to the location of a double bond third in from the far end of a long-chain fatty acid, particularly those with 18, 20, and 22 carbons. Just as ω is the last letter in the Greek alphabet, so the ω position in a fatty acid is the one farthest from the carboxyl group. Arachidonic acid (Table 20.2) is an omega-6 C-20 fatty acid because it has a double bond at the sixth carbon from the omega end. Linolenic acid (Table 20.2) is an omega-3 fatty acid. Two other omega-3 acids are considered by some to be important in metabolism:

$$CH_3CH_2CH=CH(CH_2CH=CH)_4CH_2CH_2CH_2CO_2H$$
ω-3-eicosapentaenoic acid

$$CH_3CH_2CH=CH(CH_2CH=CH)_5CH_2CH_2CO_2H$$
ω-3-docosahexaenoic acid

The basis of the interest in these is that Eskimos have low incidences of heart disease despite relatively high cholesterol levels in their diets (from fish oils and fish liver). Some scientists believe that the high level of the omega-3 fatty acids in marine oils provides protection against disease.

Soap Water is a very poor cleansing agent because it can't penetrate greasy substances, the "glues" that bind soil to skin and fabrics. When just a little soap is present, however, water cleans very well, especially warm water. Soap is a simple chemical, a mixture of the sodium or potassium salts of the long-chain fatty acids obtained by the saponification of fats or oils.

Detergents Soap is just one kind of detergent. All detergents are surface-active agents that lower the surface tension of water. All consist of ions or molecules that have long hydrocarbon portions plus ionic or very polar sections at one end. The accompanying structures illustrate these features and show the varieties of detergents that are available.

Although soap is manufactured, it is not called a synthetic detergent. This term is limited to detergents that are not soap, that is, not the salts of naturally-occurring fatty acids obtained by the saponification of lipids. Most synthetic detergents are salts of sulfonic acids, but others have different kinds of ionic or polar sites. The great advantage of synthetic detergents is that they work in hard water and are not precipitated by the hardness ions—Mg^{2+}, Ca^{2+}, and the two ions of iron. The anions of the fatty acids present in soap form messy precipitates with these ions. The anions of synthetic detergents do not have this property.

The accompanying figure shows how detergents work. In part *a* we see the hydrocarbon tails of the detergent work their way into the hydrocarbon environment of the grease layer. ("Like dissolves like" Is the principle at work here.) The ionic heads stay in the water phase, and the grease layer becomes pincushioned with electrically charged sites. In part *b* we see the grease layer breaking up, aided with some agitation or scrubbing. Part *c* shows a magnified view of grease globules studded with ionic groups; being like-charged, these globules repel one another. They also tend to dissolve in water, so they are ready to be washed down the drain.

$$CH_3(CH_2)_{14}CO_2^-Na^+$$
Soap—an anionic detergent

$$CH_3(CH_2)_{13}OSO_3^-Na^+$$
A sodium alkyl sulfate—an anionic detergent

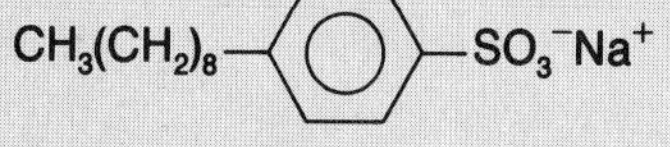

$$CH_3(CH_2)_8-\!\!\bigcirc\!\!-SO_3^-Na^+$$
A sodium alkylbenzenesulfonate—an anionic detergent

$$CH_3(CH_2)_{11}\overset{+}{N}(CH_3)_3Cl^-$$
A trimethylalkylammonium ion—a cationic detergent

$$CH_3(CH_2)_8(OCH_2CH_2O)_nH$$
A nonionic detergent

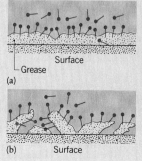

(a) Surface / Grease

(b) Surface

(c) Surface

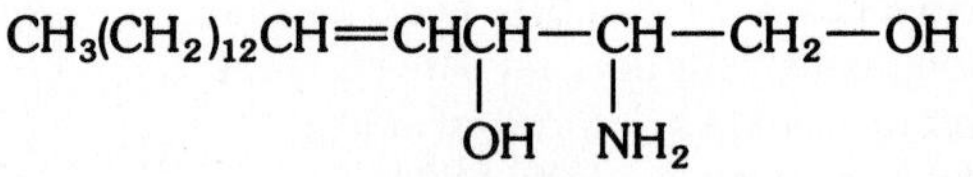

$$CH_3(CH_2)_{12}CH=CHCH-CH-CH_2-OH$$
$$\underset{OH}{|} \quad \underset{NH_2}{|}$$

Sphingosine

The phospholipids all have very polar but small molecular parts that are extremely important in the formation of cell membranes. We will survey their structures largely to demonstrate how they are both polar and hydrocarbon-like.

Phosphoglycerides Have Phosphate Units Plus Two Acyl Units   Molecules of **phosphoglycerides** have two ester bonds from glycerol to fatty acids plus one ester bond to phosphoric acid. The phosphoric acid unit, in turn, is joined by a phosphate ester link to a small alcohol molecule. Without this link, the compound is called phosphatidic acid.

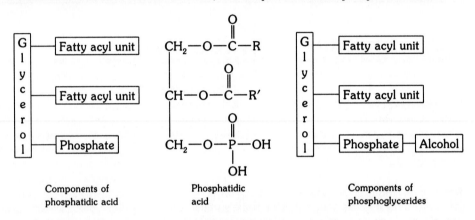

Components of   Phosphatidic   Components of
phosphatidic acid   acid   phosphoglycerides

The three principal phosphoglycerides are esters between phosphatidic acid and either choline, ethanolamine, or serine, forming, respectively, phosphatidylcholine (lecithin), **2**, phosphatidylethanolamine (cephalin), **3**, and phosphatidylserine, **4**.

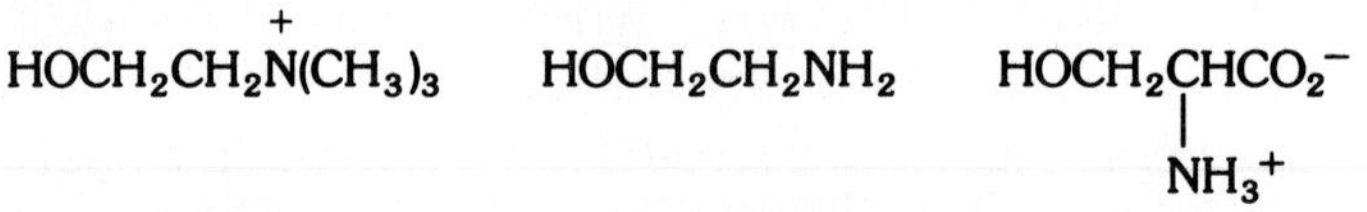

■ *Lecithin* is from the Greek *lekitos,* egg yolk—a rich source of this phospholipid.

$$\overset{+}{HOCH_2CH_2N(CH_3)_3} \qquad HOCH_2CH_2NH_2 \qquad HOCH_2\underset{\underset{NH_3^+}{|}}{C}HCO_2^-$$

Choline   Ethanolamine   Serine
(a cation)   (an amino acid)

■ *Cephalin* is from the Greek *kephale,* head. Cephalin is found in brain tissue.

As the structures of **2, 3,** and **4** show, one part of each phosphoglyceride molecule is very polar because it carries full electrical charges. The remainder is nonpolar and hydrocarbon-like.

$$CH_2-O-\overset{O}{\overset{||}{C}}-R$$
$$CH-O-\overset{O}{\overset{||}{C}}-R'$$
$$CH_2-O-\overset{O}{\overset{||}{P}}-OCH_2CH_2\overset{+}{N}(CH_3)_3$$
$$\underset{O^-}{|}$$

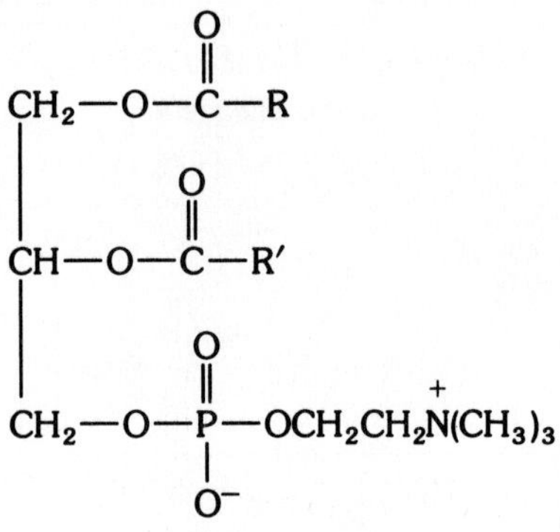

2
Phosphatidylcholine
(lecithin)

$$CH_2-O-\overset{O}{\overset{||}{C}}-R$$
$$CH-O-\overset{O}{\overset{||}{C}}-R'$$
$$CH_2-O-\overset{O}{\overset{||}{P}}-OCH_2CH_2NH_3^+$$
$$\underset{O^-}{|}$$

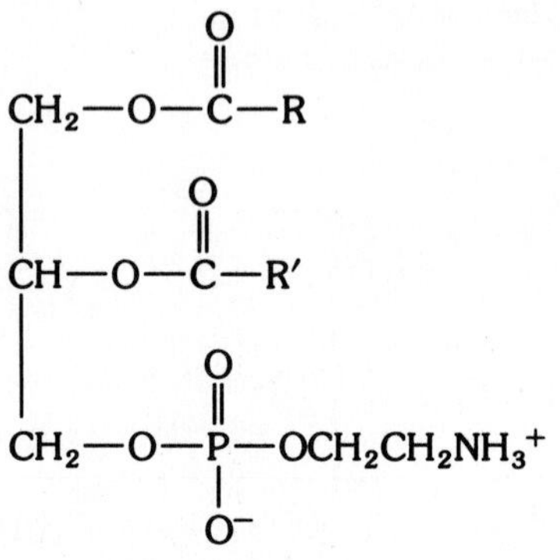

3
Phosphatidylethanolamine
(cephalin)

$$CH_2-O-\overset{O}{\overset{||}{C}}-R$$
$$CH-O-\overset{O}{\overset{||}{C}}-R'$$
$$CH_2-O-\overset{O}{\overset{||}{P}}-OCH_2CHCO_2^-$$
$$\underset{O^-}{|} \qquad \underset{NH_3^+}{|}$$

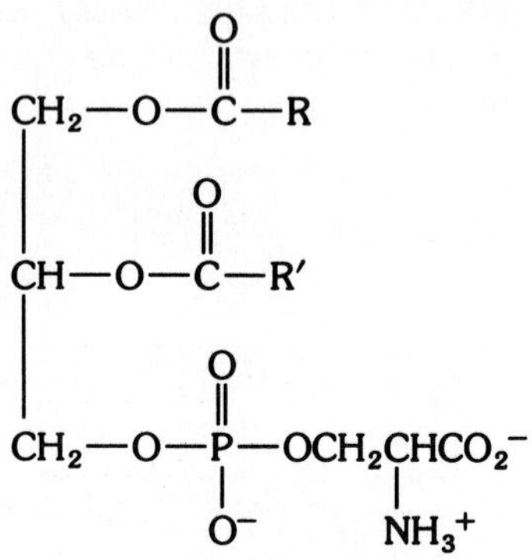

4
Phosphatidylserine

When pure, lecithin is a clear, waxy solid that is very hygroscopic. In air, it is quickly attacked by oxygen, which makes it turn brown in a few minutes. Lecithin is a powerful emulsifying agent for triacylglycerols, and this is why egg yolks, which contain it, are used to make the emulsions found in mayonnaise, ice cream, custards, and cake dough.

The Plasmalogens Have Both Ether and Ester Groups   The **plasmalogens** make up another family of glycerol-based phospholipids, and they occur widely in the membranes of nerve cells and muscle cells. They differ from the other phosphoglycerides by the presence of an unsaturated ether group instead of an acyl group at one end of the glycerol unit.

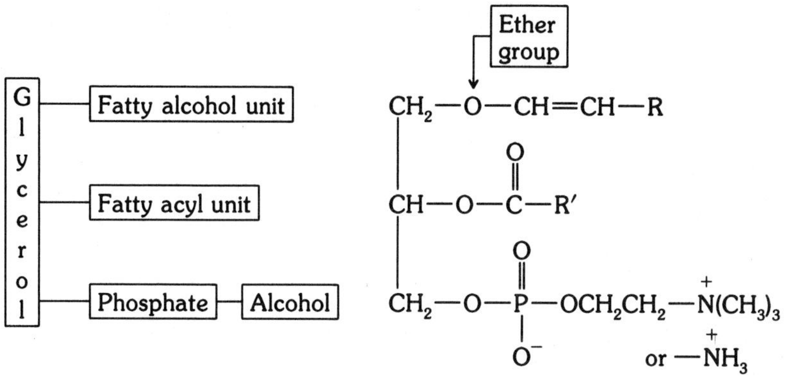

Components of plasmalogens   Plasmalogens

The Sphingolipids Are Based on Sphingosine, Not Glycerol   The two types of sphingosine-based lipids or **sphingolipids** are the sphingomyelins and the cerebrosides, and they are also important constituents of cell membranes. The sphingomyelins are phosphate diesters of sphingosine. Their acyl units occur as acylamido parts, and they come from unusual fatty acids that are not found in neutral fats.

The cerebrosides are not actually phospholipids. Instead they are **glycolipids,** lipids with a sugar (i.e., glycose) unit and not a phosphate ester system. The sugar unit, with its many OH groups, provides a strongly polar site, and it is usually a D-galactose, or a D-glucose unit, or an amino derivative of these.

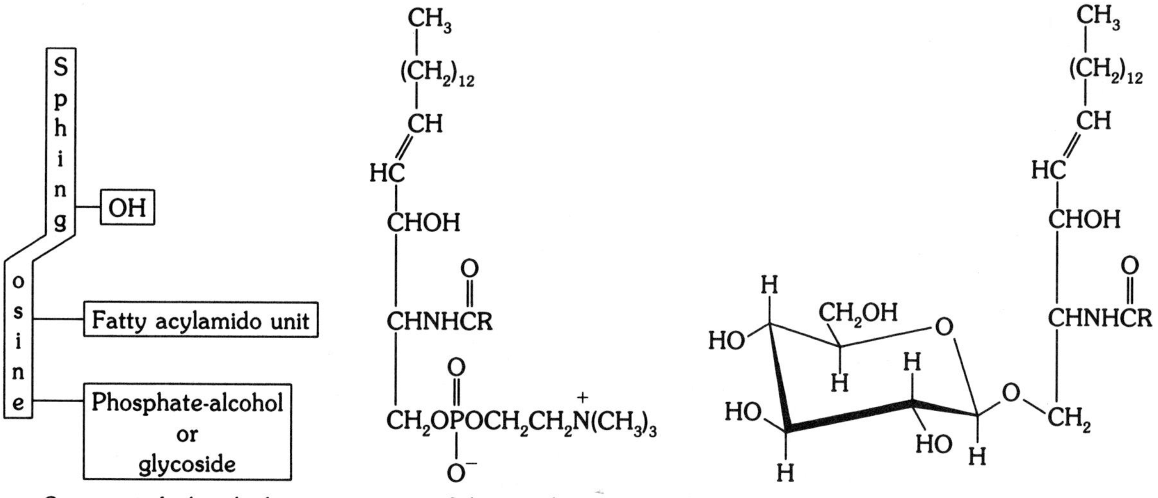

Component of sphingolipids   Sphingomyelins   Cerebrosides

20.4 STEROIDS

Cholesterol and other steroids are nonsaponifiable lipids.

Steroids are high-formula-weight aliphatic compounds whose molecules include the characteristic four-ring feature called the steroid nucleus. It consists of three six-membered rings and one five-membered ring, as seen in structure **5**. Several steroids are very active, physiologically.

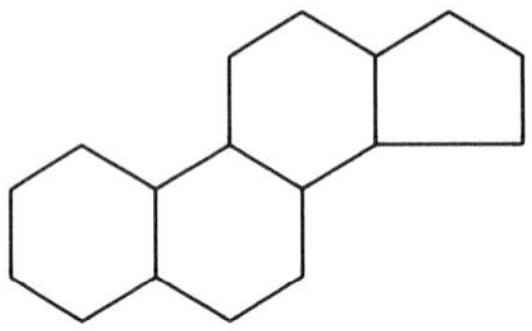

Steroid nucleus
5

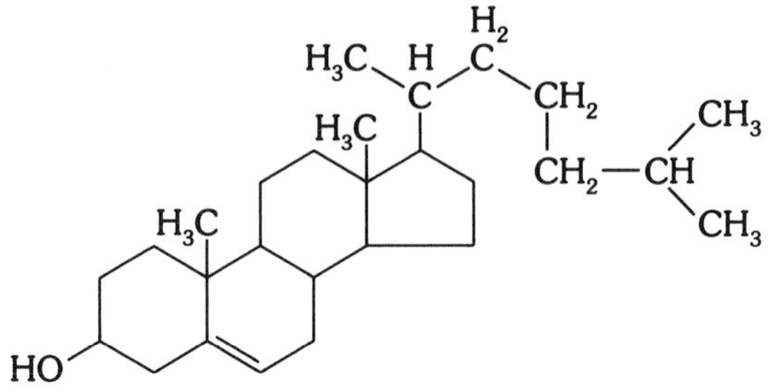

Cholesterol
(Greek: *chole*, bile; *stereos*, solid; -ol, alcohol)

Table 20.3 lists several steroids and their functions, and you can see the large range of properties they have in the body.

■ Steroid alcohols are called *sterols*.

Cholesterol Molecules Are Built into Cell Membranes   Cholesterol is an unsaturated steroid alcohol that makes up a significant part of the membranes of cells and is the chief constituent in gallstones. It's the body's raw material for making the bile salts and the steroid hormones, including the sex hormones listed in Table 20.3.

Cholesterol enters the body via the diet, but about 800 mg per day is normally synthesized in the liver from acetate units. The relationship between cholesterol and the risk of heart disease will be discussed when we study the metabolism of lipids. We need to know more about proteins, genes, and enzymes before we can discuss this relationship.

20.5 CELL MEMBRANES

Cell membranes consist of a lipid bilayer that includes molecules of proteins and cholesterol.

Cell membranes are made of both lipids and proteins. The principal lipids are the phospholipids, the glycolipids, and cholesterol. Some proteins provide closable molecular channels through which ions and molecules pass across the membrane. Other proteins act as "pumps" to move solutes across a cell membrane.

■ *Hydrophilic* — from the Greek *hydor*, water, and *philos*, loving. *Hydrophobic* — from the Greek *phobikos*, hating.

Both Hydrophilic and Hydrophobic Groups Are Necessary for Cell Membranes   The molecules in cell membranes have parts that are either very polar or fully ionic and others that are nonpolar. The polar or ionic sites are called **hydrophilic groups,** because they are able to attract water molecules. They become positioned in membranes where they can be in contact with the water in body fluids. In the phospholipids these hydrophilic groups are the phosphate diester units, which have ionic sites. In a glycolipid the sugar unit with its many OH groups is the hydrophilic group.

The nonpolar, hydrocarbon sections of membrane lipids are called **hydrophobic groups** because they are water-avoiding. They become positioned in the membrane away from water as much as possible. Substances like the phospholipids or glycolipids, with both hydrophilic and hydrophobic groups, are called **amphipathic compounds.**

Figure 20.2
Cell membrane.

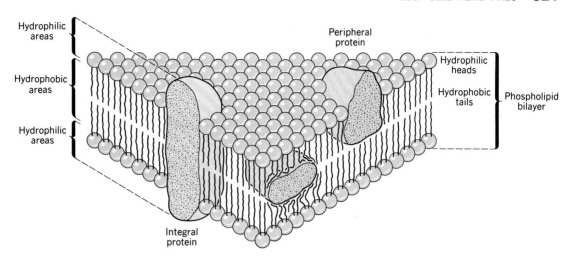

In The Lipid Bilayer of Cell Membranes, Hydrophobic Groups Intermingle Between the Membrane Surfaces, Peripheral protein, Hydrophilic areas, Hydrophobic areas, Hydrophilic areas, Hydrophilic heads, Hydrophobic tails, Phospholipid bilayer, Integral protein

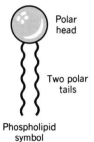

Polar head

Two polar tails

Phospholipid symbol

In The Lipid Bilayer of Cell Membranes, Hydrophobic Groups Intermingle Between the Membrane Surfaces

When phospholipids or glycolipids are mixed with water, their molecules spontaneously form a **lipid bilayer,** a sheet-like array that consists of two layers of lipid molecules aligned side by side, as illustrated in Figure 20.2. The hydrophobic "tails" of the lipid molecules intermingle in the center of the bilayer away from water molecules. In a sense, these "tails" dissolve in each other, following the "like-dissolves-like" rule. The hydrophilic "heads" stick out into the aqueous phase in contact with water. These water-avoiding and water-attracting properties, not covalent bonds, are the major "forces," that stabilize the membrane.

Cholesterol Stabilizes Membranes

Molecules of cholesterol and cholesterol esters, also found in cell membranes, are somewhat long and flat. In the lipid bilayer they occur with their long axes lined up side by side with the hydrocarbon chains of the other lipids. In contrast to these chains, the cholesterol units are more rigid, so they keep the membrane from being too fluid-like.

The Lipid Bilayer Is Self-Sealing

If a pin is stuck through a cell membrane and then pulled out, the lipid layer will close back spontaneously. This flexibility is allowed because, as we said, no covalent bonds hold neighboring lipid molecules to each other. Only the net forces of attraction that we imply when we use the terms *hydrophobic* and *hydrophilic* are at work. Yet the bilayer is strong enough to hold a cell together, and it is flexible enough to let things in and out. Water molecules move back and forth freely, but other molecules and ions vastly less so. Their migrations depend on the protein components of the membrane.

Membrane Proteins Help To Maintain Concentration Gradients

If the cell membrane were an ordinary dialyzing membrane, any kind of small molecule or ion could move freely back and forth. The health of cells, however, demands that only some things be let in and that others be let out. This means that between one side and the other of the membrane there have to be many concentration gradients. A **gradient** is the existence of an unevenness in the value of some physical property throughout a system. A concentration gradient exists in a solution, for example, when one region of the solution has a higher concentration of solute than another.

As the data in the table in the margin show, both sodium ions and potassium ions have quite different concentrations in the fluids on the inside of a cell as compared to the fluids on the outside. Thus between the inside and the outside of a cell there is a considerable concentration gradient for both of these ions. *This gradient must be maintained at all costs* against nature's spontaneous tendency to remove concentration gradients.

Ion	Concentration mmol/L	
	Plasma	Cells
Na^+	135–145	10
K^+	3.5–5.0	125

TABLE 20.3 Important Steroids

Vitamin D₃ Precursor

Irradiation of this derivative of cholesterol by ultraviolet light opens one of the rings to produce vitamin D₃. Meat products are sources of this compound.

Vitamin D₃ is an antirachitic factor. Its absence leads to rickets, an infant and childhood disease in which there is faulty deposition of calcium phosphate and poor bone growth.

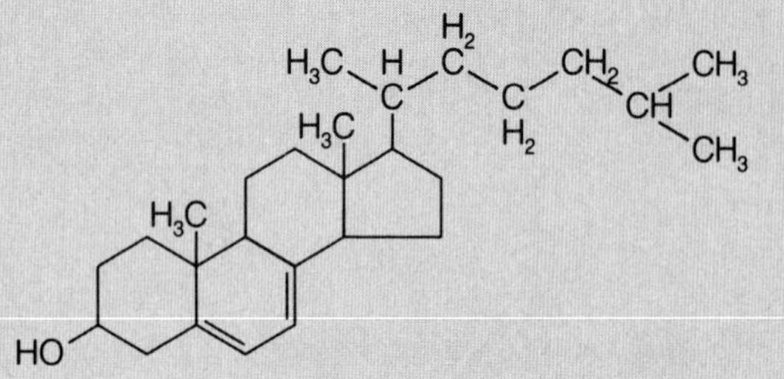

7-Dehydrocholesterol

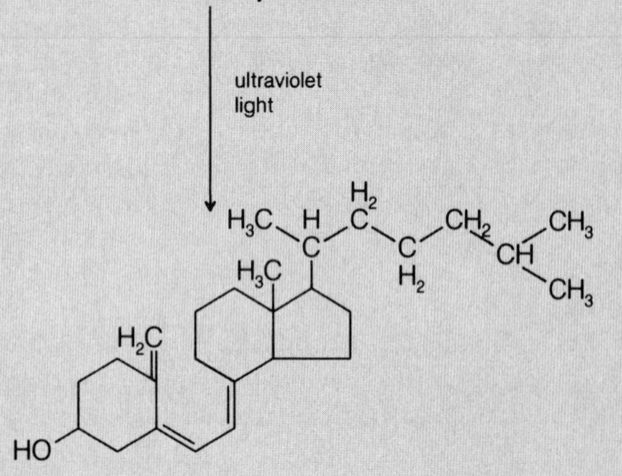

ultraviolet light

Vitamin D₃

Bile Acid

Cholic acid is found in bile in the form of its sodium salt. This and closely related salts are the bile salts; they are powerful surface active agents that aid in the digestion of lipids and in the absorption of vitamins A, D, E, and K from the intestinal tract.

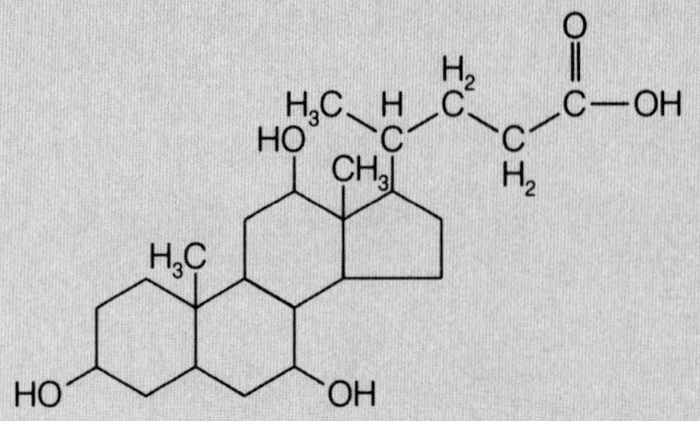

Cholic acid

Adrenocortical Hormone

Cortisol is one of the 28 hormones secreted by the cortex of the adrenal gland. Cortisone, very similar to cortisol, is another such hormone. When cortisone is used to treat arthritis, the body changes much of it to cortisol by reducing a keto group to the 2° alcohol group that you see in the structure of cortisol.

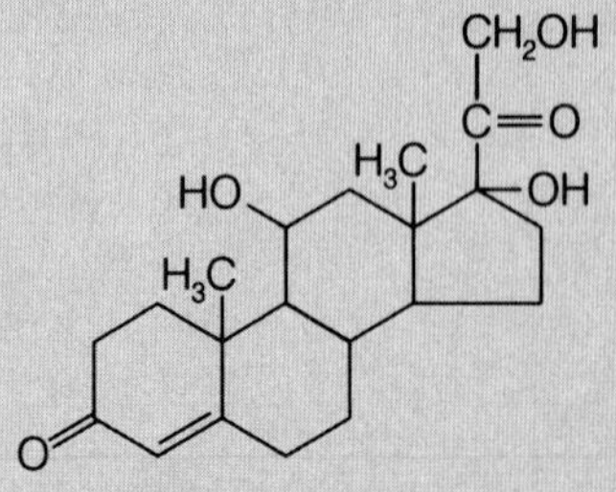

Cortisol

Cardiac Aglycone

Digitoxigenin is found in many poisonous plants, notably digitalis, as a complex glycoside. In small doses it stimulates the vagus mechanism and increases heart tone. In larger doses it acts as a potent poison.

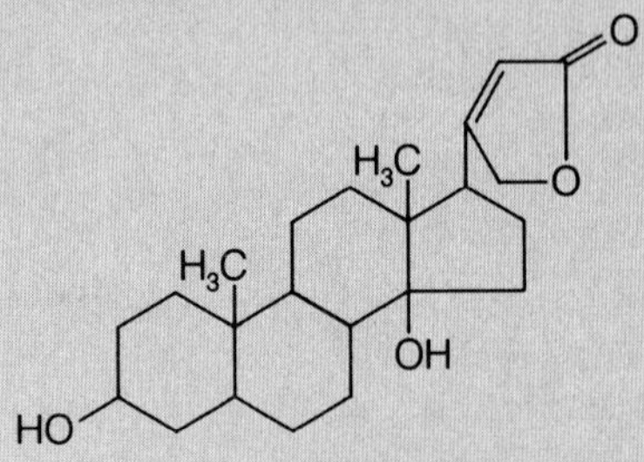

Digitoxigenin

TABLE 20.3 *(Continued)*

Sex Hormones

Estradiol is a human estrogenic hormone.

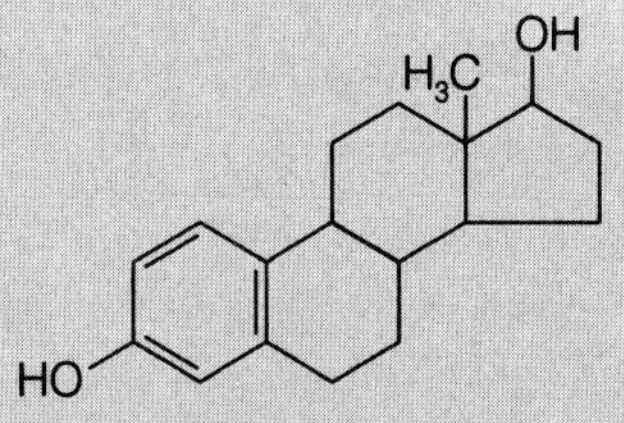

Estradiol

Progesterone, a human pregnancy hormone, is secreted by the corpus luteum.

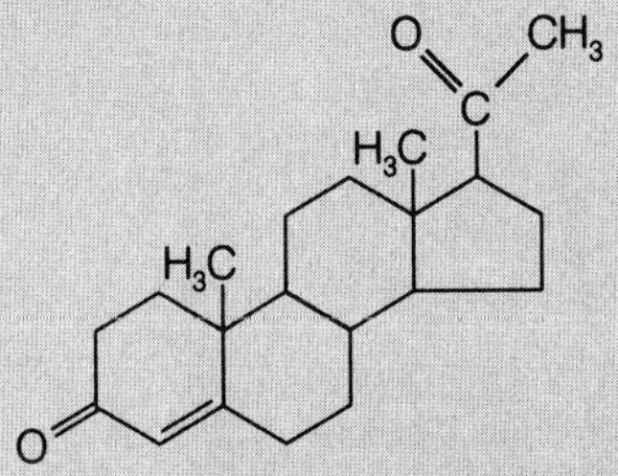

Progesterone

Testosterone, a male sex hormone, regulates the development of reproductive organs and secondary sex characteristics.

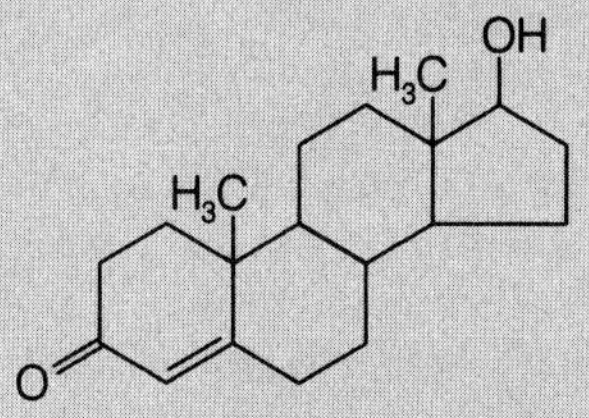

Testosterone

Androsterone is another male sex hormone.

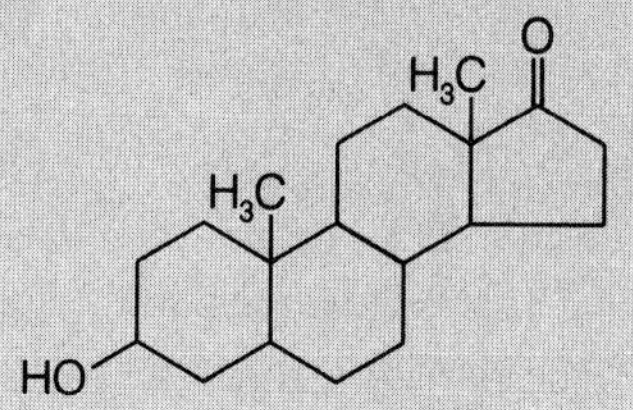

Androsterone

Synthetic Hormones in Fertility Control

Most oral contraceptive pills contain one or two synthetic, hormone-like compounds. (Synthetics must be used because the real hormones are broken down in the body.)

Synthetic estrogens

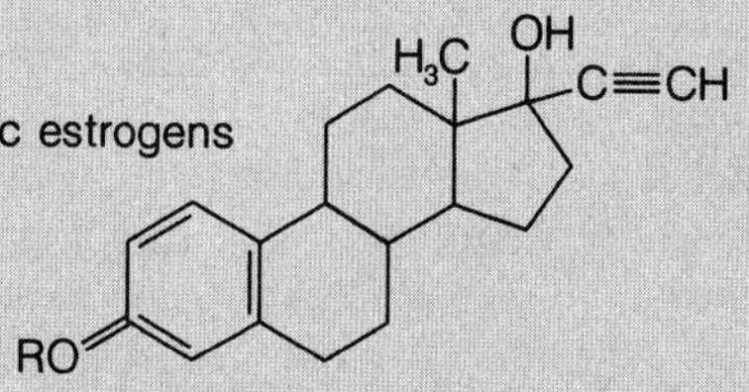

If R = H, ethynylestradiol
R = CH$_3$, mestranol

Synthetic progestins

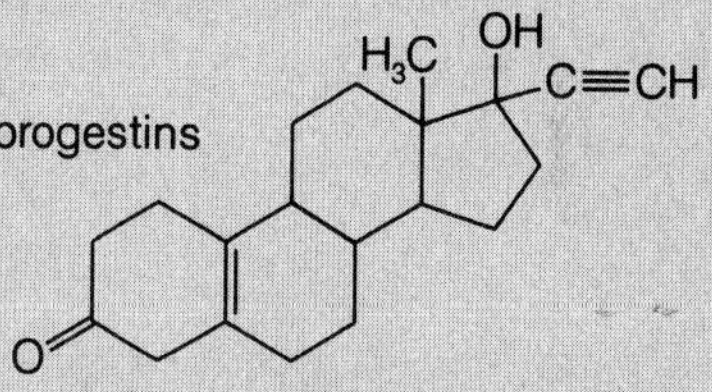

Norethynodrel

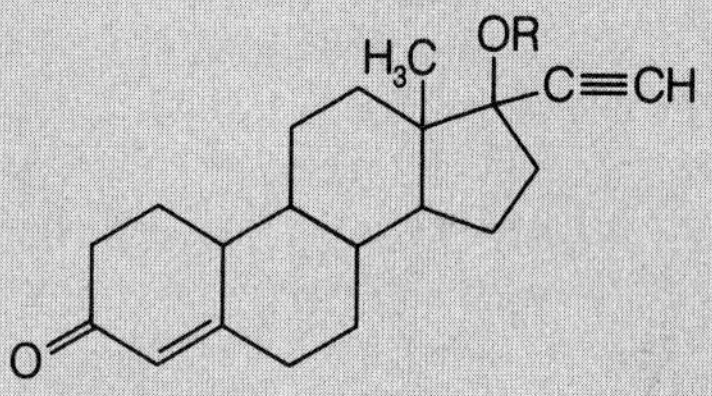

If R = H, norethindrone

$$R = \overset{\displaystyle O}{\overset{\|}{C}}—CH_3, \text{ norethindrone acetate}$$

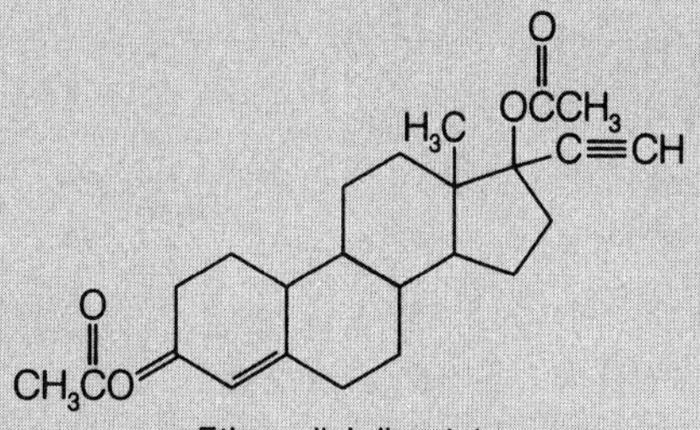

Ethynodiol diacetate

The most widely used pills have a combination of an estrogen (20 to 100 μg if mestranol, and 20 to 50 μg if ethinyl estradiol) plus a progestin (0.35 to 2.5 mg depending on the compound).

Here is where some of the proteins in cell membranes carry out a vital function. One kind of membrane protein can move sodium ions against their gradient. When too many sodium ions leak to the inside of a cell, they are "pumped" back out by a special molecular machinery called the sodium – potassium pump. The same pump can move potassium ions back inside a cell. This movement of any solute against its concentration gradient is an example of **active transport,** and other reactions in cells supply the chemical energy that lets it work.

■ Neurotransmitters are organic molecules that help carry nerve signals from the end of one nerve cell to the beginning of the next.

Some Proteins in Cell Membranes Are Receptors for Hormones and Neurotransmitters   A **receptor molecule** is one whose unique shape enables it to fit only to the molecule of a compound that it is supposed to receive, its substrate. It is thus able to "recognize" the molecules of just one compound from among the hundreds whose molecules bump against it. This is roughly how specific hormones are able to find only the cells that use them and bypass all others. The hormone molecule stops only where it is able to fit to a receptor. This mechanism also helps neurotransmitter molecules to act quickly in moving from one nerve cell to the next across the very narrow gap between them. Once a receptor molecule in a cell membrane accepts its unique substrate, further biochemical changes occur. An enzyme or a gene in the cell might be activated, for example.

SUMMARY

Lipids   Lipids are ether-extractable substances in animals and plants, and they include saponifiable esters and nonsaponifiable compounds. The esters are generally of glycerol or sphingosine with their acyl portions contributed by long-chain carboxylic acids (fatty acids). Because molecules of all lipids are mostly hydrocarbon-like, lipids are soluble in nonpolar solvents but not in water. The fatty acids obtained from lipids by hydrolysis generally have long chains of even numbers of carbons, seldom are branched, and often have one or more alkene groups. The alkene groups are generally cis.

Molecules of the waxy coatings on leaves and fruit, or in beeswax or sebum, are simple esters between long-chain monohydric alcohols and fatty acids.

Triacylglycerols   Molecules of neutral fats, those without electrically charged sites or sites that are similarly polar, are esters of glycerol and a variety of fatty acids, both saturated and unsaturated. Vegetable oils have more double bonds per molecule than animal fats. The triacylglycerols can be hydrogenated, hydrolyzed (digested), and saponified.

Phosphoglycerides   Molecules of the phosphoglycerides are esters both of glycerol and of phosphoric acid. A second ester bond from the phosphate unit goes to a small alcohol molecule that can also have a positively charged group. Thus this part of a phosphoglyceride is strongly hydrophilic.

Sphingomyelins   Sphingomyelins are esters of sphingosine, a dihydric amino alcohol. They also have a strongly hydrophilic phosphate system.

Glycolipids   Also sphingosine-based, the glycolipids use a monosaccharide instead of the phosphate-to-small-alcohol unit to provide the hydrophilic section. Otherwise, they resemble the sphingomyelins.

Steroids   Steroids are nonsaponifiable lipids with the steroid nucleus of four fused rings (three being C-6 rings and one a C-5 ring). Several steroids are sex hormones, and oral fertility-control drugs mimic their structure and functions. Cholesterol, the raw material used by the body to make other steroids, is also manufactured by the body.

Membranes   A double layer of phospholipids or glycolipids plus cholesterol and proteins make up the lipid bilayer part of a cell membrane. The hydrophobic tails of these amphipathic lipids intermingle within the bilayer, away from the aqueous phase. The hydrophilic heads are in contact with the aqueous medium.

The proteins on or in the bilayer serve as conduits and receptors or are parts of pumps, such as the sodium – potassium pump, that work to maintain important concentration gradients; or the proteins act as channels for small ions or molecules.

REVIEW PROBLEMS

The answers to these Review Problems are in the *Study Guide* that accompanies this book.

Lipids in General

20.1   Crude oil is soluble in ether, yet it isn't classified as a lipid. Explain.

20.2   Cholesterol has no ester group, yet we classify it as a lipid. Why?

20.3   Ethyl acetate has an ester group, but it isn't classified as a lipid. Explain.

20.4   What are the criteria for deciding whether a substance is a lipid?

Waxes

20.5 One component of beeswax has the formula $C_{34}H_{68}O_2$. When it is hydrolyzed, it gives $C_{16}H_{32}O_2$ and $C_{18}H_{38}O$. Write the most likely structure of this compound.

20.6 When all the waxes from the leaves of a certain shrub are separated, one has the formula of $C_{60}H_{120}O_2$. Its structure is **A, B,** or **C.** Which is it most likely to be? Explain why the others can be ruled out.

$$CH_3(CH_2)_{56}CO_2CH_2CH_3 \qquad CH_3(CH_2)_{29}CO_2(CH_2)_{28}CH_3$$
$$\textbf{A} \qquad\qquad\qquad \textbf{B}$$

$$CH_3(CH_2)_{28}CO_2(CH_2)_{29}CH_3$$
$$\textbf{C}$$

Fatty Acids

20.7 What are the structures and the names of the two most abundant saturated fatty acids?

20.8 Write the structures and names of the unsaturated fatty acids that have 18 carbons each and that have no more than three double bonds. Show the correct geometry at each double bond.

20.9 Write the equations for the reactions of palmitic acid with (a) $NaOH(aq)$ and (b) CH_3OH (when heated in the presence of an acid catalyst).

20.10 What are the equations for the reactions of oleic acid with (a) Br_2, (b) $KOH(aq)$, (c) H_2 (in the presence of a catalyst and under pressure), and (d) CH_3CH_2OH (heated in the presence of an acid catalyst)?

20.11 Which of the following acids, **A** or **B,** is more likely to be obtained by the hydrolysis of a lipid? Explain.

$$\overset{\displaystyle CH_3}{\underset{\displaystyle |}{}}$$
$$CH_3CH(CH_2)_{11}CO_2H \qquad CH_3(CH_2)_{12}CO_2H$$
$$\textbf{A} \qquad\qquad\qquad \textbf{B}$$

20.12 Without writing structures, state what kinds of chemicals the prostaglandins are.

Triacylglycerols

20.13 Write the structure of a triacylglycerol that involves linolenic acid, oleic acid, and myristic acid, besides glycerol.

20.14 What is the structure of a triacylglycerol made from glycerol, stearic acid, oleic acid, and palmitic acid?

20.15 Write the structures of all the products that would form from the complete digestion of the following lipid.

$$
\begin{array}{l}
CH_2-O-\overset{\displaystyle O}{\overset{\displaystyle \|}{C}}(CH_2)_7CH{=}CH(CH_2)_7CH_3 \\[4pt]
| \\[2pt]
\overset{\displaystyle O}{} \\[-4pt]
CH-O-\overset{\displaystyle \|}{C}(CH_2)_{12}CH_3 \\[4pt]
| \\[2pt]
\overset{\displaystyle O}{} \\[-4pt]
CH_2-O-\overset{\displaystyle \|}{C}(CH_2)_7CH{=}CH(CH_2)_7CH_3
\end{array}
$$

20.16 Write the structures of the products that are produced by the saponification of the triacylglycerol whose structure was given in Review Exercise 20.15.

20.17 The hydrolysis of a lipid produced glycerol, lauric acid, linoleic acid, and oleic acid in equimolar amounts. Write a structure that is consistent with these results. Is there more than one structure that can be written? Explain.

20.18 The hydrolysis of 1 mol of a lipid gave 1 mol each of glycerol and oleic acid and 2 mol of lauric acid. This lipid was optically active. Write its structure. Is more than one structure possible? Explain.

20.19 What is the structural difference between the triacylglycerols of the animal fats and the vegetable oils?

20.20 Products such as corn oil are advertised as being "polyunsaturated." What does this mean in terms of the structures of the molecules that are present? And corn oil is "more polyunsaturated" than what?

20.21 What chemical reaction is used in the manufacture of oleomargarine?

20.22 Lard and butter are chemically almost the same substances, so what is it about butter that makes it so much more desirable a spread for bread than, say, lard or tallow?

Phospholipids

20.23 What are the names of the two chief kinds of phospholipids?

20.24 In structural terms, how do the phosphoglycerides and plasmalogens differ?

20.25 How are the sphingomyelins and cerebrosides different structurally?

20.26 What structural unit provides the most polar group in a molecule of a glycolipid? (Name it.)

20.27 Phospholipids are not classified as neutral fats. Explain.

20.28 Phospholipids are particularly common in what part of a cell?

20.29 What are the names of the two types of sphingosine-based lipids?

20.30 Are the sugar units that are incorporated into the cerebrosides bound by glycosidic links or by ordinary ether links? How can one tell? Which kind of link is more easily hydrolyzed (assuming an acid catalyst)?

20.31 The complete hydrolysis of 1 mol of a phospholipid gave 1 mol each of the following compounds: glycerol, linolenic acid, oleic acid, phosphoric acid, and the cation, $HOCH_2CH_2\overset{+}{N}(CH_3)_3$.
(a) Write a structure of this phospholipid that is consistent with the information given.
(b) Is the substance a phosphoglyceride or a sphingolipid? Explain.
(c) Are its molecules chiral or not? How can you tell?
(d) Is it an example of a lecithin or a cephalin? Explain.

20.32 When 1 mol of a certain phospholipid was hydrolyzed, there was obtained 1 mol each of lauric acid, oleic acid, phosphoric acid, glycerol, and $HOCH_2CH_2NH_2$.

(a) What is a possible structure for this phospholipid?

(b) Is it a sphingolipid or a phosphoglyceride? Explain.

(c) Can its molecules exist as enantiomers or not? Explain.

(d) Is it a cephalin or a lecithin? Explain.

Steroids

20.33 What is the name of the steroid that occurs as a detergent in our bodies?

20.34 What is the name of a vitamin that is made in our bodies from a dietary steroid by the action of sunlight on the skin?

20.35 Give the names of three steroidal sex hormones.

20.36 What is the name of a steroid that is part of the cell membranes in many tissues?

Cell Membranes

20.37 Describe in your own words what is meant by the *lipid bilayer* structure of cell membranes.

20.38 How do the hydrophobic parts of phospholipid molecules avoid water in a lipid bilayer?

20.39 Besides lipids, what kinds of substances are present in a cell membrane?

20.40 What kinds of forces are at work in holding a cell membrane together?

20.41 Immediately after you add a teaspoon of sugar to a hot cup of coffee, can a concentration gradient for sugar be present? Explain what this is. What happens to it, given enough time, even without stirring the mixture? What causes this change to occur? What are the chances of the original gradient ever restoring itself spontaneously?

20.42 Which has the higher level of sodium ion, plasma or cell fluid?

20.43 Does cell fluid or plasma have the higher concentration of potassium ion?

20.44 In which fluid, plasma or cell fluid, would the level of sodium ion increase if the sodium ion gradient could not be maintained?

20.45 What is meant by *active transport* in a cell membrane?

20.46 What does the sodium–potassium pump in a cell membrane do?

20.47 Name the functions that the proteins of a cell membrane can serve.

The Prostaglandins (Special Topic 20.1)

20.48 Name the fatty acid that is used to make the prostaglandins.

20.49 What effect is aspirin believed to have on prostaglandins, and how is this related to aspirin's medicinal value?

The Omega-3 Fatty Acids and Heart Disease (Special Topic 20.2)

20.50 What is it about the structure of linolenic acid that lets us call it an omega-3 acid?

20.51 What source of the omega-3 acids is relatively rich in the C-20 and C-22 acids?

20.52 Why have the omega-3 acids aroused the interests of people in nutrition and in medicine?

Detergent Action (Special Topic 20.3)

20.53 Which is the more general term, soap or detergent? Explain.

20.54 What kind of chemical is soap?

20.55 For household laundry work, which product is generally preferred, a synthetic detergent or soap? Why?

20.56 Why are soap and sodium alkyl sulfates called *anionic* detergents?

20.57 Explain in your own words how a detergent can loosen oils and greases from fabrics.

Proteins

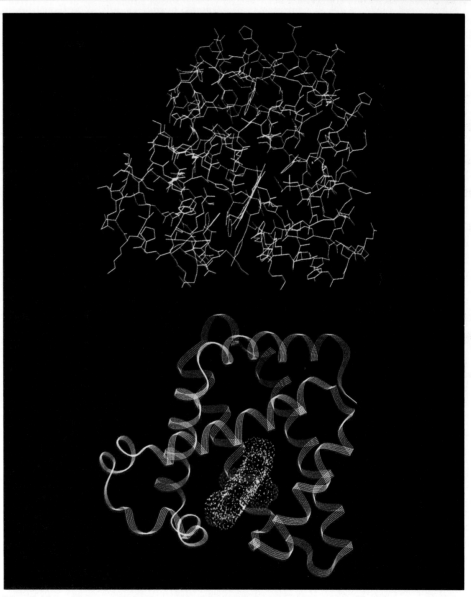

Myoglobin, a heme-containing protein that stores oxygen in muscles. *Top:* A conventional model showing all side chains. The heme unit appears edge on. *Bottom:* A ribbon model emphasizing the coiling of the polypetide backbone and showing the heme unit by a dotted area.

21.1 AMINO ACIDS. THE BUILDING BLOCKS OF PROTEINS

Living things select from among the molecules of about 20 α-amino acids to make the polypeptides in proteins.

Proteins, found in all cells and in virtually all parts of cells, constitute about half of the body's dry weight. They give strength and elasticity to skin. As muscles and tendons, they function as the cables that enable us to move the levers of our bones. They reinforce our teeth and bones much as thick steel rods reinforce concrete. The molecules of antibodies, of hemoglobin, and of the various kinds of albumins in our blood serve as protectors and as the long-distance haulers of substances, such as oxygen or lipids, that otherwise do not dissolve well in blood. Other proteins form parts of the communications network of our nervous system. Some proteins are enzymes, hormones, and gene regulators that direct and control all forms of repair, construction, and energy conversion in the body. No other class of compounds is involved in such a variety of functions, all essential to life. They deserve the name *protein*, taken from the Greek *proteios*, "of the first rank."

Polypeptides Are Made from α-Amino Acids The dominant structural units of **proteins** are high-formula-weight polymers called **polypeptides.** Metal ions and small organic molecules or ions are often present as well. The relationship of these parts to whole proteins is shown in Figure 21.1. Many proteins, however, are made entirely of polypeptides.

The monomer units for polypeptides are **α-amino acids,** which have the general structure given by **1,** and about 20 are used, most being used several times in the same polypeptide. Hundreds of **amino acid residues,** often called **amino acyl groups,** each derived from one or another of the various α-amino acids, are joined together in a single polypeptide molecule, but before we can study how polypeptides are put together we must learn more about amino acids.

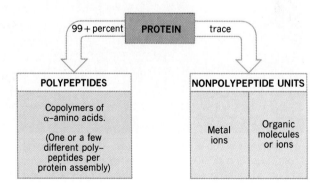

■ Hereafter, when we say "amino acid," we'll mean α-amino acid.

α-Amino acids
(general formula)

Amino acid residue
(an amino acyl group)

1

The same set of 20 amino acids, Table 21.1, is used by all species of plants and animals. In rare instances, a few others are present in certain polypeptides, and some of the 20 in Table 21.1 occur in slightly modified forms.

Figure 21.1
Components of proteins. Some proteins consist exclusively of polypeptide molecules, but most also have nonpolypeptide units such as small organic molecules or metal ions, or both.

TABLE 21.1 Amino Acids: $^+NH_3{-}CH{-}CO_2^-$ with G side chain

Type	Side Chain, G	Name	Symbol	pI
Side chain is nonpolar	$-H$	Glycine	Gly	5.97
	$-CH_3$	Alanine	Ala	6.00
	$-CH(CH_3)_2$	Valine	Val	5.96
	$-CH_2CH(CH_3)_2$	Leucine	Leu	5.98
	$-CHCH_2CH_3$ ($\mid$ CH_3)	Isoleucine	Ile	6.02
	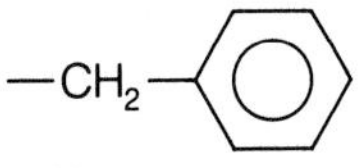 $-CH_2-C_6H_5$	Phenylalanine	Phe	5.48
	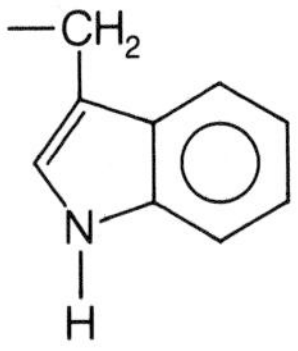 $-CH_2$–(indole)	Tryptophan	Trp	5.89
	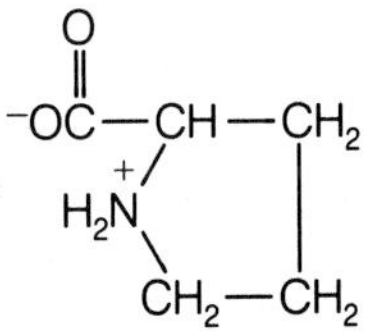 (complete structure, proline ring)	Proline	Pro	6.30
Side chain has a hydroxyl group	$-CH_2OH$	Serine	Ser	5.68
	$-CHOH$ ($\mid$ CH_3)	Threonine	Thr	5.64
	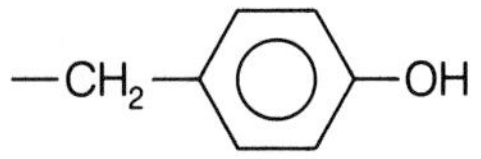 $-CH_2-C_6H_4-OH$	Tyrosine	Tyr	5.66
Side chain has a carboxyl group (or an amide)	$-CH_2CO_2H$	Aspartic acid	Asp	2.77
	$-CH_2CH_2CO_2H$	Glutamic acid	Glu	3.22
	$-CH_2CONH_2$	Asparagine	Asn	5.41
	$-CH_2CH_2CONH_2$	Glutamine	Gln	5.65
Side chain has a basic amino group	$-CH_2CH_2CH_2CH_2NH_2$	Lysine	Lys	9.74
	$-CH_2CH_2CH_2NH-C(=NH)-NH_2$	Arginine	Arg	10.76
	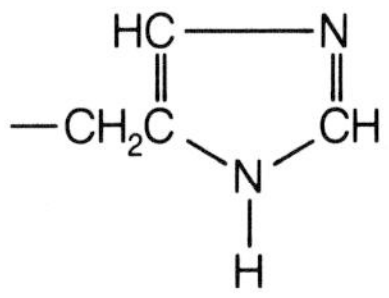 $-CH_2$–(imidazole)	Histidine	His	7.59
Side chain contains sulfur	$-CH_2SH$	Cysteine	Cys	5.07
	$-CH_2CH_2SCH_3$	Methionine	Met	5.74

The α-Amino Acids Are Based on a Dipolar Form of α-Amino Acetic Acid But Have Different Side Chains at the α-Position

As you can see in Table 21.1, the amino acids differ in the groups, **G**, called **side chains**, located at the α-position in **1**.

In the solid state, amino acids exist entirely in the form shown by **1**, which is called a **dipolar ion**. It is a neutral particle but has a positive and a negative charge on different sites. (We can call them molecules because they are electrically neutral.) Because they are exceedingly polar, amino acids, like salts, have melting points that are considerably higher than those of most molecular compounds, and they are insoluble in nonpolar solvents, but soluble in water.

Structure **1** is actually an internally neutralized molecule. We can imagine that it started out with a regular amino group, NH_2, and an ordinary carboxyl group, CO_2H. But then the amino group, a proton-acceptor, took a proton from the carboxyl group, a proton-donor, to give **1**. Of course, **1**, has its own (weaker) proton-donating group, NH_3^+, and its own (also weaker) proton-accepting group, CO_2^-, so these dipolar ions can neutralize acids or bases of sufficient strength, such as H_3O^+ and OH^-. (In fact, amino acids can serve as buffers.)

For most amino acids to exist as dipolar ions, **1**, in water, the pH has to be about 6 to 7. If we make the pH much lower (more acidic) or much higher (more basic), the form of the amino acid changes. If we add enough strong acid like HCl(*aq*), for example, to a solution of an amino acid at a pH initially about 6 to 7, and lower the pH to about 1, the CO_2^- groups take on protons. They change to structure **2**. Now they are cations that can migrate to a cathode.

■ These shifts of H+ ions are illustrations of Le Chatelier's principle at work.

$$^+NH_3 - CH - CO_2^-$$
$$|$$
$$G$$
1

$$^+NH_3 - CH - CO_2H \qquad\qquad NH_2 - CH - CO_2^-$$
$$| \qquad\qquad\qquad\qquad\qquad\qquad |$$
$$G \qquad\qquad\qquad\qquad\qquad\qquad G$$
2 $\qquad\qquad\qquad\qquad\qquad\qquad$ **3**

If we add enough strong base to raise the pH to about 11, then most of the amino acid molecules transfer protons from their NH_3^+ groups to OH^- ions, and change to structure **3**. This is an anion, so it can migrate to an anode.

A pH Exists for Each Amino Acid, Its Isoelectric Point, at Which No Net Migration in an Electric Field Occurs

In an aqueous solution of an amino acid, a dynamic equilibrium exists between **1**, **2**, and **3**. If now a current is passed between electrodes dipping into such a solution, cations of form **2** migrate to the cathode. Anions of form **3** migrate to the anode. Neutral molecules, **1**, migrate nowhere. A molecule with equal numbers of positive and negative charges, like **1**, is said to be an **isoelectric molecule,** and it won't migrate in an electric field.

Because the equilibrium is *dynamic*, a migrating cation could flip a proton to some acceptor, thereby become **1** and isoelectric (neutral) and stop dead. In another instant, it could shed another proton, become **3**, and so turn around and head for the anode. Similarly, an anion on its way to the anode might pick up a proton, become neutral, and also stop dead. Then it might take another proton, become **2**, and turn itself around. In the meantime, an isoelectric molecule, **1**, might either donate or accept a proton, become electrically charged, and start its own migration. (It rather reminds one of amusement park bumper cars that move in every direction.) The question is, what overall net migration occurs and how is this net effect influenced by the pH of the solution?

Although much coming and going occurs in an amino acid solution, the net molar concentrations of the species stay the same at equilibrium. If either **2** or **3** is in any molar excess, because of the pH, then some *net* migration will occur toward one electrode or the other. If the net molar concentration of **2,** for example, is greater than that of **3,** some statistical net movement to the cathode will occur.

Remember, however, that these equilibria can be shifted by adding acid or base. By carefully adjusting the pH, in fact, we can so finely tune the concentrations at equilibrium that no net migration occurs. At the right pH, the rates of proton exchange are such that each unit that is not **1** spends an equal amount of time as **2** and as **3.** (And the concentrations of **2** and **3** are very low.) In this way any net migration toward one electrode is blocked.

The pH at which no net migration of an amino acid can occur in an electric field is called the **isoelectric point** of the amino acid, and its symbol is **pI.** Table 21.1 includes a column of the pI values. Now let's see what this has to do with proteins.

Proteins, Like Amino Acids, Have Isoelectric Points   As we will soon see, all proteins have NH_3^+ or CO_2^- groups or can acquire them by a change in pH. Whole protein molecules, therefore, can also be isoelectric at the right pH. Each protein thus has its own isoelectric point. But now think of what can happen if the pH is changed. The entire electrical condition of a huge protein molecule can be made either cationic or anionic almost instantly, at room temperature, by adding strong acid or base — by changing the pH of the medium.

Such changes in the electrical charge of a protein have serious consequences at the molecular level of life. Being electrically charged can dramatically affect chemical reactions, for example, or greatly alter protein solubility. If proteins are to serve their biological purposes, some must not be allowed to go into solution and others must not be permitted to precipitate. We'll return to this concept in this and later chapters, but the discussion focuses our attention again on how important it is that an organism control the pH values of its fluids.

We will next survey the types of side chains in amino acids and how they affect the properties of polypeptides and proteins. These properties include how a polypeptide molecule will spontaneously fold and twist into its distinctive and absolutely vital final shape. You should memorize the structures of a minimum of five amino acids that illustrate the types we are about to study: glycine, alanine, cysteine, lysine, and glutamic acid are suggested. How to use Table 21.1 to write their structures is described in the following worked example.

EXAMPLE 21.1   **WRITING THE STRUCTURE OF AN AMINO ACID**

Problem: What is the structure of cysteine?

Solution: Doing this kind of problem depends on two things—on remembering what is common to all amino acids:

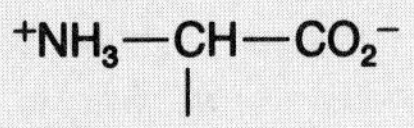

$$^+NH_3-\underset{|}{CH}-CO_2^-$$

and then either looking up or remembering the side chain for the particular amino acid. For cysteine, this is CH_2SH, so simply attach this group to the α-carbon. Cysteine is

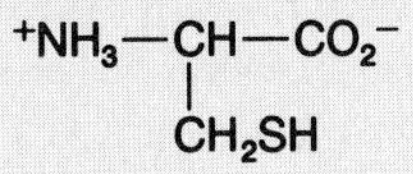

$$^+NH_3-\underset{\underset{CH_2SH}{|}}{CH}-CO_2^-$$

The memorization of amino acid structures involves learning the structures of the side chains and fixing them in the mind to the name of the amino acid.

PRACTICE EXERCISE 1 Write the structures of the dipolar ionic forms of glycine, alanine, lysine, and glutamic acid.

Several Amino Acids Have Hydrophobic Side Chains The first amino acids in Table 21.1, including alanine, have essentially nonpolar, hydrophobic side chains. When a long polypeptide molecule folds into its distinctive shape, these hydrophobic groups tend to be folded next to each other rather than next to highly polar groups or to water molecules in the solution.

Some Amino Acids Have Hydrophilic OH Groups on Their Side Chains The second set of amino acids in Table 21.1 consists of those whose side chains carry alcohol or phenol OH groups, which are polar and hydrophilic. They can donate and accept hydrogen bonds. As a long polypeptide chain folds into its final shape, these side chains tend to stick out into the surrounding aqueous phase to which they are attracted.

Two Amino Acids Have Carboxyl Groups on Their Side Chains The side chains of aspartic and glutamic acid carry proton-donating CO_2H groups. Because body fluids are generally slightly basic, the protons available from them have been neutralized, so these groups actually occur mostly as CO_2^- groups. The solution has to be made quite acidic to prevent this. This forces protons back onto the side-chain CO_2^- groups, and this is why the pI values of aspartic and glutamic acid are low.

Aspartic acid and glutamic acid often occur as asparagine and glutamine in which their side-chain CO_2H groups have become amide groups, $CONH_2$, instead. These are also polar, hydrophilic groups, but they are not electrically charged. They are neither proton-donors nor proton-acceptors, so the pI values of asparagine and glutamine are higher than those of aspartic or glutamic acids.

PRACTICE EXERCISE 2 Write the structure of aspartic acid (in the manner of **1**) with the side-chain carboxyl (a) in its carboxylate form, and (b) in its amide form.

Lysine, Arginine, and Histidine Have Basic Groups on Their Side Chains The extra NH_2 group on lysine makes its side chain basic and hydrophilic. A solution of lysine has to be made basic to prevent this group from existing in its protonated form, NH_3^+. This is why the pI value of lysine, 9.47, is relatively high. Arginine and histidine have similarly basic side chains.

PRACTICE EXERCISE 3 Write the structure of arginine in the manner of **1**, but with its side-chain amino group in its protonated form. (Put the extra proton on the $=NH$ unit, not the $-NH_2$ unit of the side chain.)

PRACTICE EXERCISE 4 Classify the side chain of the following amino acid as hydrophilic or hydrophobic. Does this side chain have an acidic, basic, or neutral group?

$$\begin{array}{l} ^{+}NH_3\underset{|}{C}HCO_2^- \\ \quad\quad\; CH_2CH_2CONH_2 \end{array}$$

Cysteine and Methionine Have Sulfur-Containing Side Chains The side chain in cysteine has an SH group. As we studied in Section 14.4, molecules with this group are easily oxidized to disulfide systems, and disulfides are easily reduced to SH groups:

$$2RSH \underset{(H)}{\overset{(O)}{\rightleftharpoons}} R{-}S{-}S{-}R + H_2O$$

Cysteine and its oxidized form, cystine, are interconvertible by oxidation and reduction, a property of far-reaching importance in some proteins.

$$\text{}^-OCCHCH_2\text{---S---H} \quad \xrightarrow[\text{oxidation}]{\text{(O)}} \quad \text{}^-OCCHCH_2\text{---S}$$

reduction
2(H)

Cysteine

Cystine

■ The three-letter symbol for cystine is

Cys
|
Cys

■ The mirror-image molecules of the L-amino acids are the D-amino acids, which can be synthesized in the laboratory.

The **disulfide link** contributed by cystine is especially prevalent in the proteins that have a protective function, such as those in hair, fingernails, and the shells of certain crustaceans.

The Alpha Position in All Amino Acids Except Glycine Is Chiral   All the amino acids except glycine are optically active and can exist as enantiomers. For each possible pair of enantiomers, however, nature supplies just one of the two (with a few rare exceptions). All the naturally occurring amino acids, moreover, belong to the same optical family, the L-family. What this means is illustrated in Figure 21.2. It also means that all the proteins in our bodies, including all enzymes, are made from L-amino acids and are all chiral.

21.2 PRIMARY STRUCTURES OF PROTEINS

The backbones of all polypeptides of all plants and animals have a repeating series of N—C—C(═O) units.

Protein structures are more complicated by far than those of carbohydrates or lipids, and every aspect of their structures is vital at the molecular level of life. We'll begin, therefore, with a broad overlook at the levels of protein structure.

Protein Structure Involves Four Features   There are four levels of complexity in the structures of most proteins. Disarray at any level almost always renders the protein biologically useless. The first and most fundamental level, the **primary structure** of a protein, concerns only the sequence of amino acyl units joined by carbonyl-to-nitrogen covalent bonds called *peptide bonds,* in the polypeptide(s) of the protein.

The next level, the **secondary structure,** also concerns just individual polypeptides. It entails noncovalent forces, particularly the hydrogen bond, and it consists of the particular way in which a long polypeptide strand has coiled or in which strands have intertwined or lined up side to side.

The **tertiary structure** of a polypeptide concerns the further bending, kinking, or twisting of secondary structures. If you've ever played with a coiled door spring, you know that the coil (secondary structure) can be bent and twisted (tertiary structure). Noncovalent forces, generally hydrogen bonds, stabilize these shapes.

Finally, we deal with the intact protein. Its **quaternary structure** is the way in which individual polypeptides (each with all previous levels of structure), and any other molecules or ions, come together in one grand whole.

In this section, we'll study the primary structural features of polypeptides, whose central feature is the peptide bond.

The Peptide Bond Joins Amino Acyl Units Together in a Polypeptide   The **peptide bond** is the chief covalent bond that forms when amino acids are put together in a cell to make a polypeptide. It's nothing more than an amide system, carbonyl to nitrogen. To

Figure 21.2
The two possible enantiomers of α-amino acids whose molecules have just one chiral center. The absolute configuration on the right, which is in the L-family, represents virtually all the naturally occurring α-amino acids.

■ Simple amides are

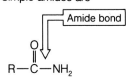

illustrate it and to show how polypeptides acquire their primary structure, we will begin by simply putting just two amino acids together.

Suppose that glycine acts at its carboxyl end and alanine acts as its amino end such that, by a series of steps (not given in detail but indicated by a dashed arrow, ------>), a molecule of water splits out and a carbonyl-to-nitrogen bond is created.

How a cell causes a peptide bond to form is a major topic under the chemistry of heredity.

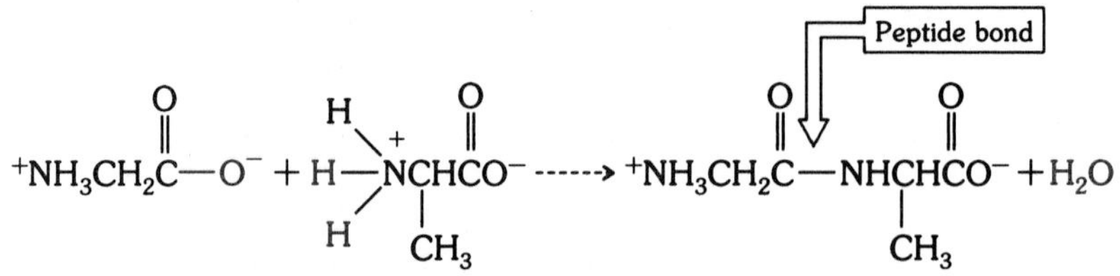

$$\overset{O}{\overset{\|}{^+NH_3CH_2C}}-O^- + H-\overset{H}{\overset{+}{\underset{H}{N}}}\overset{O}{\overset{\|}{C}}HCO^- \cdots\rightarrow \overset{O}{\overset{\|}{^+NH_3CH_2C}}-NH\overset{O}{\overset{\|}{C}}HCO^- + H_2O$$

Peptide bond

Glycine, Gly   Alanine, Ala   A dipeptide, Gly·Ala

4

Of course, there is no reason why we could not picture the roles reversed so that alanine acts at its carboxyl end and glycine at its amino end. This results in a different dipeptide (but an isomer of the first).

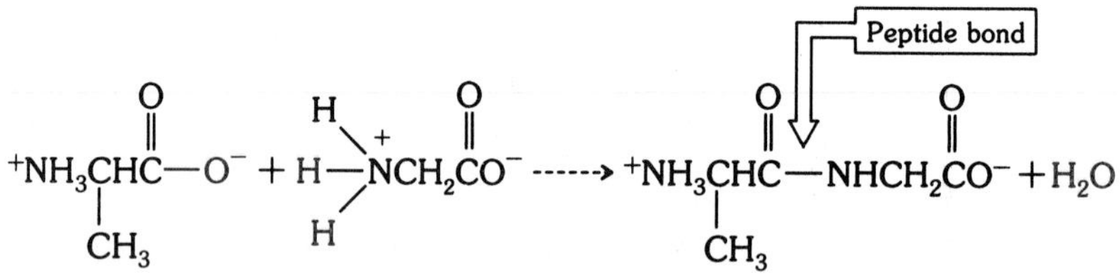

$$\overset{O}{\overset{\|}{^+NH_3CHC}}-O^- + H-\overset{H}{\overset{+}{\underset{H}{N}}}CH_2\overset{O}{\overset{\|}{C}}O^- \cdots\rightarrow \overset{O}{\overset{\|}{^+NH_3CHC}}-NHCH_2\overset{O}{\overset{\|}{C}}O^- + H_2O$$

Peptide bond

Alanine, Ala   Glycine, Gly   Another dipeptide, Ala·Gly

5

The product of the union of any two amino acyl units by a peptide bond is called a **dipeptide,** and all dipeptides have the following features:

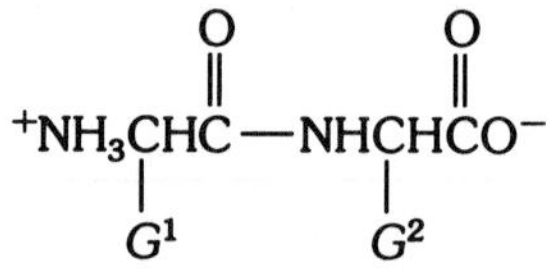

$$\overset{O}{\overset{\|}{^+NH_3CHC}}-\overset{O}{\overset{\|}{NHCHCO^-}}$$
$$\underset{G^1}{\quad}\qquad\underset{G^2}{\quad}$$

Dipeptide

Structures **4** and **5** differ only in the sequence in which the side chains, H and CH_3, occur on α-carbons. This is fundamentally how polypeptides also differ, in their sequences of side chains.

EXAMPLE 21.2   **WRITING THE STRUCTURE OF A DIPEPTIDE**

Problem: What are the two possible dipeptides that can be put together from alanine and cysteine?

Solution: Both must have the same backbone, so we write two of these first (and we follow the convention that such backbones are always written in the N to C—left to right—direction):

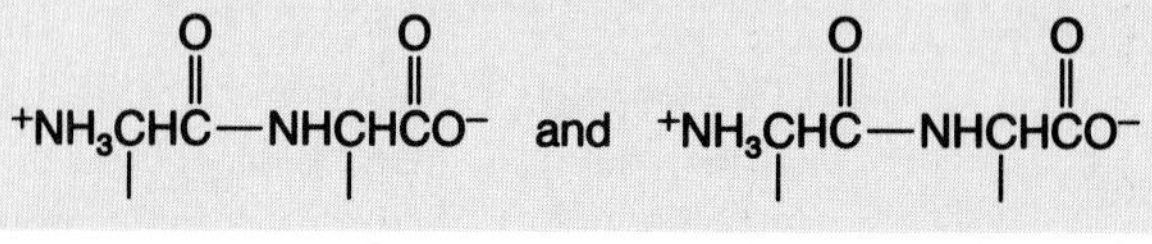

$$\overset{O}{\overset{\|}{^+NH_3CHC}}-\overset{O}{\overset{\|}{NHCHCO^-}} \quad \text{and} \quad \overset{O}{\overset{\|}{^+NH_3CHC}}-\overset{O}{\overset{\|}{NHCHCO^-}}$$

Then, either from memory or by the use of Table 21.1, we recall the two side chains, CH_3 for alanine and CH_2SH for cysteine. We simply attach these in their two possible orders to make the finished structures:

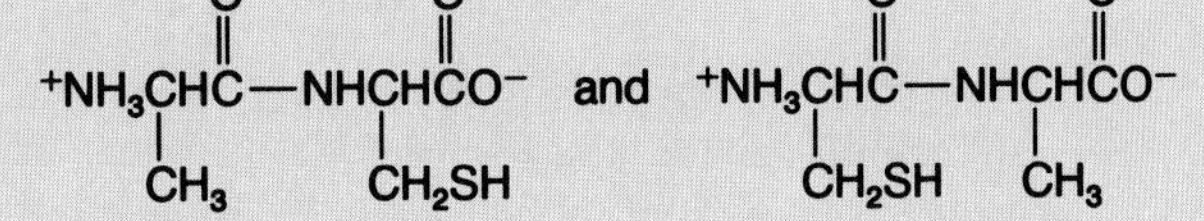

$$^+NH_3CHC-NHCHCO^- \quad \text{and} \quad ^+NH_3CHC-NHCHCO^- \qquad \text{(The answers)}$$

with side chains CH_3, CH_2SH on the first and CH_2SH, CH_3 on the second.

It would be worthwhile at this time simply to memorize the easy repeating sequence in a dipeptide, because it carries forward to higher peptides:

nitrogen – carbon – carbonyl – nitrogen – carbon – carbonyl

PRACTICE EXERCISE 5 Write the structures of the two dipeptides that can be made from alanine and glutamic acid.

Three-Letter Symbols for Amino Acyl Units Simplify the Writing of Polypeptide Structures Each amino acid has been assigned a three-letter symbol, given in Table 21.1. To use them in writing a polypeptide structure, we have to follow certain rules. The convention is that a series of three-letter symbols, each separated by a raised dot, represents a polypeptide structure, provided that the first symbol (reading left to right) is the free amino end, $^+NH_3$, and the last symbol has the free carboxylate end, CO_2^-. The structure of the dipeptide **4**, for example, can be rewritten as Gly · Ala, and its isomer **5** as Ala · Gly. In both, the backbones are identical.

Dipeptides still have $^+NH_3$ and CO_2^- groups, so a third amino acid can react at either end. In general,

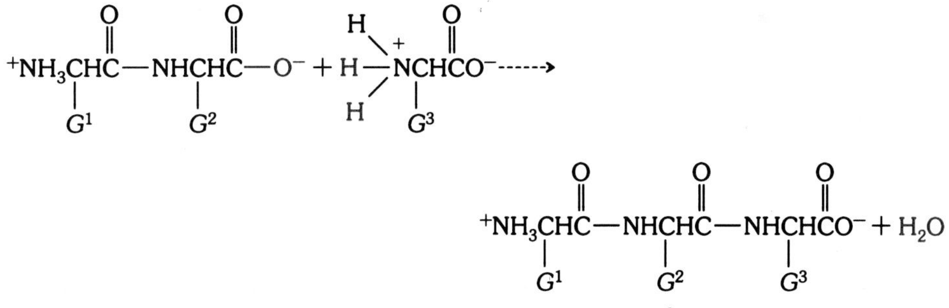

$$^+NH_3CHC-NHCHC-O^- + H-NCHCO^- \cdots\rightarrow$$

with side chains G^1, G^2 and G^3

$$^+NH_3CHC-NHCHC-NHCHCO^- + H_2O$$

with side chains G^1, G^2, G^3

6
A tripeptide

A specific example is:

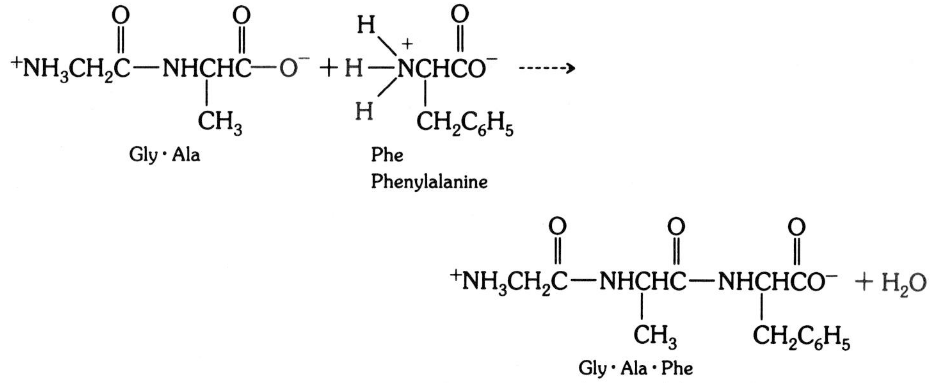

$$^+NH_3CH_2C-NHCHC-O^- + H-NCHCO^- \cdots\rightarrow$$

with side chains CH_3 and $CH_2C_6H_5$

Gly · Ala   Phe
Phenylalanine

$$^+NH_3CH_2C-NHCHC-NHCHCO^- + H_2O$$

with side chains CH_3 and $CH_2C_6H_5$

Gly · Ala · Phe
(a tripeptide)

This tripeptide, Gly·Ala·Phe, is only one of six possible tripeptides that involve these three different amino acids. The set of all possible sequences for a tripeptide made from glycine, alanine, and phenylalanine is as follows:

Gly·Ala·Phe Ala·Gly·Phe Phe·Gly·Ala

Gly·Phe·Ala Ala·Phe·Gly Phe·Ala·Gly

Each of these tripeptides still has groups at each end, $^+NH_3$ and CO_2^-, that can interact with still another amino acid to make a tetrapeptide. And this product would still have the end groups from which the chain could be extended still further. You can see how a repetition of this many hundreds of times can produce a long polymer, a polypeptide.

The Sequence of Side Chains on the Repeating N—C—C(=O) Backbone Is the Primary Structure of All Polypeptides All polypeptides have the following skeleton in common. They differ in length (*n*) and in the kinds and sequences of side chains.

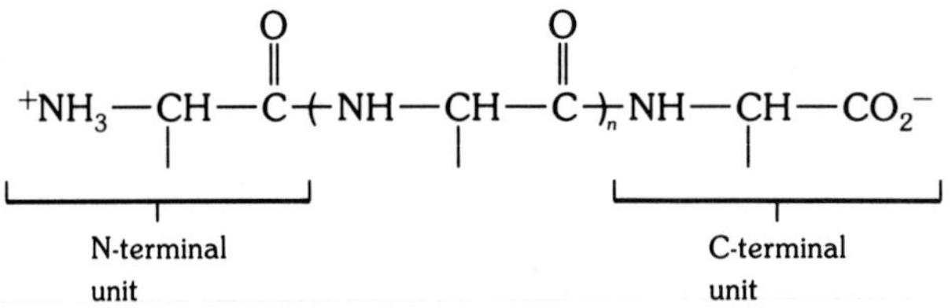

$$^+NH_3—CH—C(=O)[NH—CH—C(=O)]_n NH—CH—CO_2^-$$ (*n* can be several thousand)

N-terminal unit   C-terminal unit

(Notice, for later reference, the designations N-terminal unit and C-terminal unit for the residues with the free α-NH_3^+ and the free α-CO_2^- groups, respectively.) The peptide bond, as we said, is the chief covalent bond that holds amino acyl units together in polypeptides. The disulfide bond is the only other covalent bond at the primary level that affects the amino acyl units.

As the number of amino acyl residues increases, some used several times, the number of possible polypeptides rises rapidly. For example, if 20 different amino acids are incorporated, each used only once, there are 2.4×10^{18} possible isomeric polypeptides! (And a polypeptide with only 20 amino acid residues in its molecule is a very small polypeptide.)

Disulfide Bonds Can Give Loops in Polypeptides or Join Two Strands Together If the SH group on the side chain of cysteine appears on two neighboring polypeptide molecules, then mild oxidation is all it takes to link the two molecules by a disulfide bond, as shown in Figure 21.3. This cross-linking can also occur between parts of the same polypeptide molecule, in which case a closed loop results.

Some polypeptides feature both kinds of S—S cross-linking, and one example is the hormone insulin (Figure 21.4), which is considered to be a relatively simple polypeptide. You can find three disulfide bonds, one that creates a loop, and two that hold the two insulin subunits together.

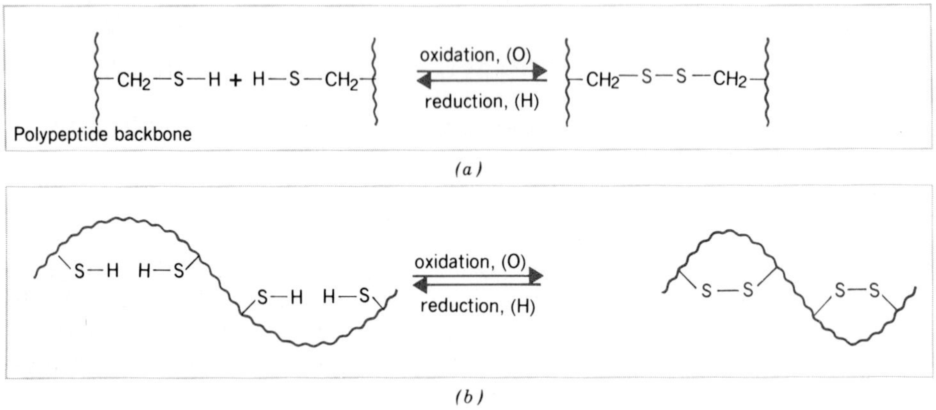

Figure 21.3
The disulfide link in polypeptides. (*a*) Two neighboring strands are joined. (*b*) Loops can form within the same strand.

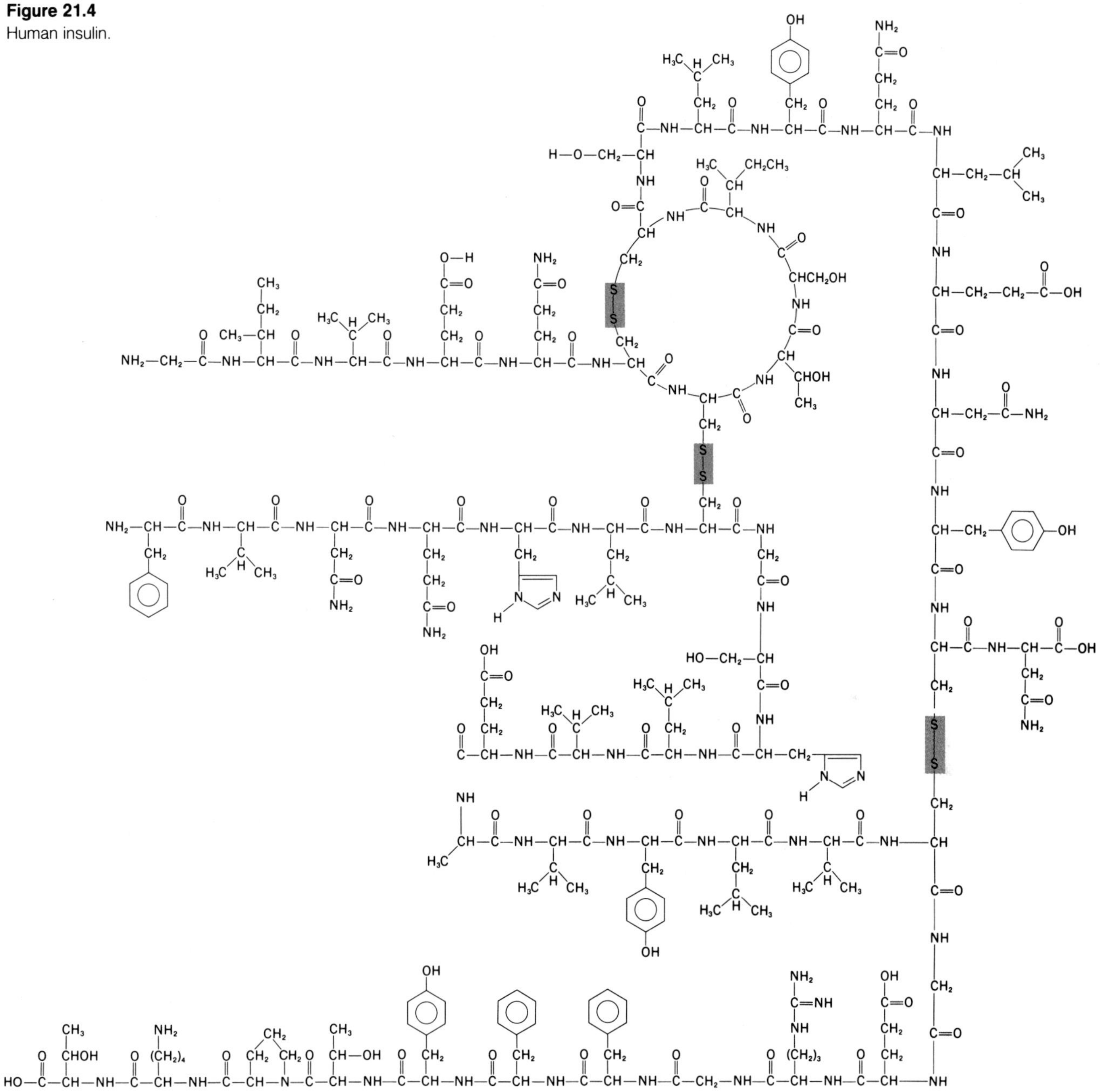

Figure 21.4
Human insulin.

21.3 SECONDARY STRUCTURES OF PROTEINS

The α-helix, the β-pleated sheet, and the triple helix are three kinds of secondary protein structures.

Once a cell puts together a polypeptide, noncovalent forces of attraction between parts of the molecule make the molecule twist into a particular shape. The hydrogen bond is the chief noncovalent force, and we'll see in this section how it can stabilize shapes of polypeptides. Bear in mind that the proteins can become biologically useless if any aspect of their shapes is altered.

Figure 21.5
The α-helix. (a) The polypeptide backbone atoms on a helical thread. (b) The H atoms and the side-chain groups, G, on the alpha carbons. (c) Expanded view down the long axis of an α-helix showing how the side chains project to the outside. (Adapted by permission from L. Stryer, *Biochemistry*, 3rd ed., W. H. Freeman and Company, New York, 1988, page 26.)

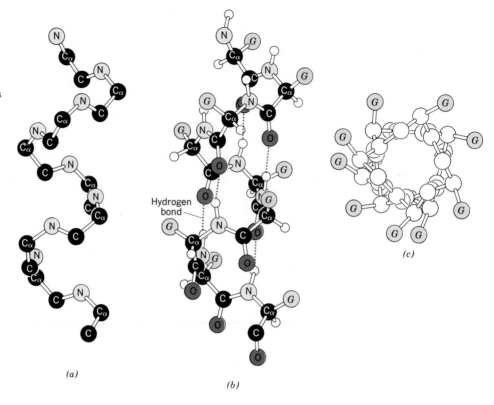

Hydrogen bond

(a)

(b)

(c)

■ Linus Pauling won the 1954 Nobel prize in chemistry for this work.

—N—H•••O=C

Hydrogen bond

■ The designation α was picked only because this secondary structure was the first to be identified.

The α-Helix Is a Major Secondary Structure of Polypeptides   The α-helix is a coiled configuration of a polypeptide strand. See Figure 21.5. Linus Pauling and R. B. Corey discovered it from a study of X-ray data. In the **α-helix,** the polypeptide backbone coils as a right-handed screw with all its side chains sticking to the outside.

Hydrogen Bonds Stabilize α-Helices   Hydrogen bonds extend from the oxygen atoms of carbonyl groups to hydrogen atoms of NH groups farther along the backbone. Individually, a single hydrogen bond is a weak force of attraction, but when there are hundreds of them up and down a coiled polypeptide, they add up much as the individual "forces" that hold a zipper strongly shut. Generally, only segments of polypeptides, not entire lengths, are in an α-helix configuration.

The β-Pleated Sheet Is a Side-by-Side Array of Polypeptide Molecules   Pauling and Corey also discovered that molecules in some proteins line up side by side, to form a sheet-like array that is somewhat pleated. See Figure 21.6. This is another kind of secondary structure in which hydrogen bonds hold things together. The pleated sheet is the dominant feature in fibroin, the protein in silk. In other proteins these sheets seldom contribute much to the overall structure.

The Polypeptides in Collagen Are in a Triple Helix   The third important secondary structure is found in a small family of proteins called the collagens. These are the proteins that give strength to bone, teeth, cartilage, tendons, and skin.

The polypeptide units in collagen are called tropocollagen, and each tropocollagen molecule consists of three polypeptide chains. Each chain has about 1000 amino acid residues, which are twisted together to form a **triple helix.**

Some of the amino acyl units are hydroxylated derivatives of lysine and proline made with the help of vitamin C *after* the initial polypeptide is made. Thus vitamin C is essential to

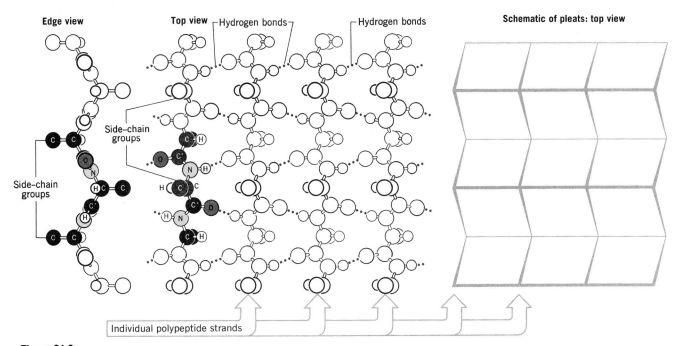

Figure 21.6
The β-pleated sheet.

■ A collagen fibril only 1 mm in diameter can hold a mass as large as 10 kg (22 lb).

the formation of strong bones. In some of the types of collagen, sugar molecules are incorporated as glycosides of side-chain OH groups.

The individual strands in tropocollagen helices are in a very open helix that is not stabilized by hydrogen bonds. These open helices, however, wrap around each other into a right-handed helical cable within which hydrogen bonds are at work. In addition, some disulfide cross-links are present.

A microfiber or *fibril* of collagen forms when individual tropocollagen cables overlap lengthwise, as seen in Figure 21.7. The mineral deposits in bones and teeth become tied into the protein at the gaps between the heads of tropocollagen molecules and the tails of others.

21.4 TERTIARY AND QUATERNARY STRUCTURES OF PROTEINS

Tertiary structures are the results of folding, bending, and twisting of secondary structures.

Once primary and secondary structures are in place, the final shaping of a protein occurs. All these activities happen spontaneously in cells, sometimes in a matter of seconds after the polypeptide molecule has been made and sometimes it takes several minutes. The "rules" followed by the polypeptide to give these shapes are still not known with any confidence. It's one of the remaining frontiers of protein research.

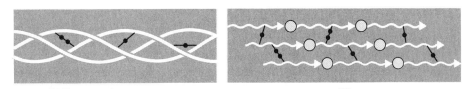

Figure 21.7   *(a)*   *(b)*
Collagen. (*a*) The tropocollagen cable is made of three polypeptide molecules, each in an α-helix (not pictured), wrapped together. (*b*) Individual tropocollagen cables, shown here by wavy lines, line up side by side with overlapping to give collagen fibrils. The circles represent gaps into which minerals can deposit in bones and teeth. The colored lines with solid color dots represent cross-links.

Figure 21.8
Myoglobin. The tube-like forms outline the segments that are in an α-helix. The flat, red structure is the heme unit. The black dots identify α-carbons. The side-chain groups at FG2, H16, H24, CD2, and CD3 are hydrophilic and are somewhat exposed to the aqueous medium. Hydrophobic groups that are somewhat tucked inside are at A7, A8, A9, A11, and A12, to note a few. (Reproduced by permission from R. E. Dickerson, ''X-Ray Analysis of Proteins,'' in H. Neurath (ed), *The Proteins,* Academic Press, New York; copyright 1964, all rights reserved.)

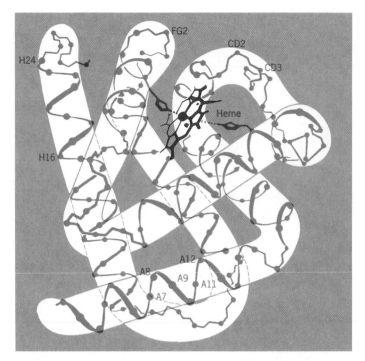

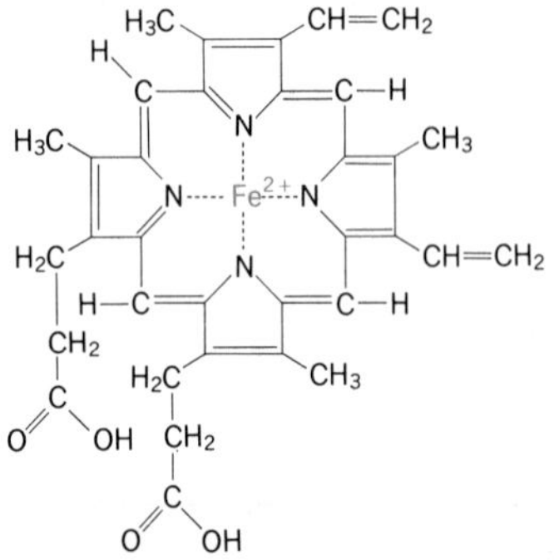

Figure 21.9
The heme molecule with its Fe^{2+} ion.

■ ''Prosthetic'' is from the Greek *prosthesis,* an addition.

Those who manufacture proteins by genetic engineering, which we'll describe in a later chapter, have sometimes been surprised and disappointed that their products have been biologically useless lumps of unshaped molecules. Even though the correct primary structure was manufactured, the exact conditions in the solution needed for the higher levels to appear spontaneously could not be duplicated.

Tertiary Protein Structure Involves the Folding and Kinking of Secondary Structure When α-helices take shape, their side chains tend to project outward where, in an aqueous medium, they would be in contact with water molecules. Even in water-soluble proteins, however, as many as 40% of the side chains are hydrophobic. Because such groups can't break up the hydrogen-bonding networks among the water molecules, the entire α-helix undergoes further twisting and folding until the hydrophobic groups are, as much as possible, tucked to the inside, away from the water, and the hydrophilic groups stay exposed to the water. Thus the final shape of the polypeptide, its **tertiary structure,** emerges in response to simple molecular forces set up by the water-avoiding and the water-attracting properties of the side chains.

The tertiary structure of myoglobin, the oxygen-holding protein in muscle tissue, is given in Figure 21.8. It consists of just one polypeptide plus a nonprotein, heme (Figure 21.9). About 75% of the myoglobin molecule is in an α-helix that is further folded as the figure shows. Virtually all its hydrophobic groups are folded inside and its hydrophilic groups are on the outside.

Polypeptides Incorporate Any Prosthetic Groups into Their Tertiary Structures A nonprotein, organic compound that associates with a polypeptide, like heme in myoglobin, is called a **prosthetic group.** It is often the focus of the protein's biological purpose. Heme, for example, is the actual oxygen-holder in myoglobin. It serves the same function in **hemoglobin,** the oxygen-carrier in blood.

Ionic Bonds Also Stabilize Tertiary Structures Another force that can stabilize a tertiary structure is the attraction between a full positive and a full negative charge, each occurring on a particular side chain. At the pH of body fluids, the side chains of both aspartic

Figure 21.10
The salt bridge. This attraction between full and unlike charges can (a) hold one polypeptide to another or (b) stabilize a loop or coil within the same molecule.

acid and glutamic acid carry CO_2^- groups. The side chains of lysine and arginine carry NH_3^+ groups. These oppositely charged groups naturally attract each other, like the attraction of oppositely charged ions in an ionic crystal. The attraction is called a **salt bridge.** See Figure 21.10.

When Polypeptides Group Together, the Quaternary Structures of Some Proteins Take Final Form   Proteins, like myoglobin, have finished shapes at the tertiary level. They are made up of single polypeptide molecules, sometimes with prosthetic groups.

Many proteins, however, are aggregations of two or more polypeptides, and these aggregations constitute **quaternary structures.** One molecule of the enzyme phosphorylase, for example, consists of two tightly aggregated molecules of the same polypeptide. If the two become separated, the enzyme can no longer function. Individual molecules of polypeptides that make up an intact protein molecule are called the protein's *subunits*.

Hemoglobin has four subunits, two of one kind (designated α-subunits) and two of another (called the β-subunits). Each of the four subunits carries a heme molecule. See Figure 21.11. Salt bridges and hydrogen bonds hold the subunits together. These forces do not work unless each subunit has the appropriate primary, secondary, and tertiary structural features. If even one amino acid residue is wrong, the results can be very serious, as in the example of sickle-cell anemia, described in Special Topic 21.1.

Figure 21.11
Hemoglobin. Four polypeptide chains, each with one heme molecule represented here by the colored, flat plates that contain spheres (Fe^{2+} ions), are nestled together. (From R. E. Dickerson and I. Geis, *The Structure and Action of Proteins,* W. A. Benjamin, Menlo Park, Calif., copyright 1969. All rights reserved. Used by permission.)

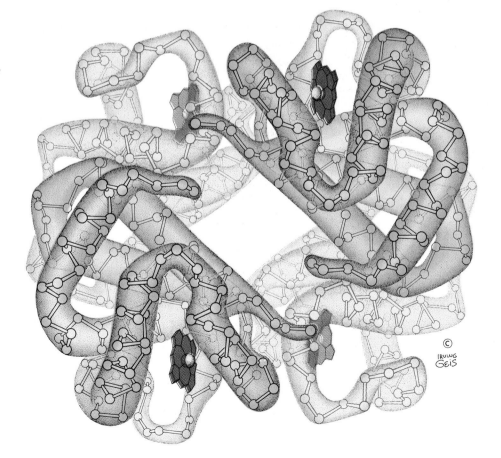

SICKLE-CELL ANEMIA AND ALTERED HEMOGLOBIN

The decisive importance of the primary structure to all other structural features of a polypeptide or its associated protein is illustrated by the grim story of sickle-cell anemia. This inherited disease is widespread among those whose roots are in central and western Africa.

In its mild form, where only one parent carries the genetic trait, the symptoms of sickle-cell anemia are seldom noticed except when the environment has a low partial pressure of oxygen, as at high altitudes. In the severe form, when both parents carry the trait, the infant usually dies by the age of 2 unless treatment is begun early. The problem is an impairment in blood circulation traceable to the altered shape of hemoglobin in sickle-cell anemia, particularly after the hemoglobin has delivered oxygen and is on its way back to the heart and lungs for more.

The fault at the molecular level lies in a β-subunit of hemoglobin. One of the amino acid residues should be glutamic acid but is valine, instead. Thus instead of a side-chain CO_2^- group, which is electrically charged and hydrophilic, there is an isopropyl side chain, which is neutral and hydrophobic. Normal hemoglobin, symbolized as HHb, and sickle-cell hemoglobin, HbS, therefore have different patterns of electrical charges. Both have about the same solubility in well-oxygenated blood, but HbS without its oxygen load tends to precipitate inside red cells. This distorts the cells into a telltale sickle shape. The distorted cells are harder to pump, and they sometimes clump together and plug capillaries. Sometimes they split open. Any of these events places a greater strain on the heart. The error in one side chain seems miniscule, but it is far from small in human terms.

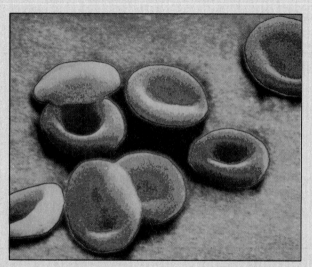

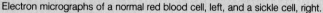
Electron micrographs of a normal red blood cell, left, and a sickle cell, right.

21.5   COMMON PROPERTIES OF PROTEINS

Even small changes in the pH of a solution can affect a protein's solubility and its physiological properties.

Although proteins come in many diverse biological types, they generally have similar chemical properties because they have similar functional groups.

Protein Digestion Is Hydrolysis   The digestion of a protein is nothing more than the hydrolysis of its peptide bonds (amide linkages), as illustrated in Figure 21.12. The end product is a mixture of amino acids. Since all animals use the same amino acids to make proteins, and since they can obtain the same set from plants (or each other!), a rather remarkable kinship exists throughout the living kingdom at its molecular level.

Protein Denaturation Is the Loss of Protein Shape   It isn't necessary to hydrolyze peptide bonds to denature a protein, that is, to destroy its ability to perform its biological

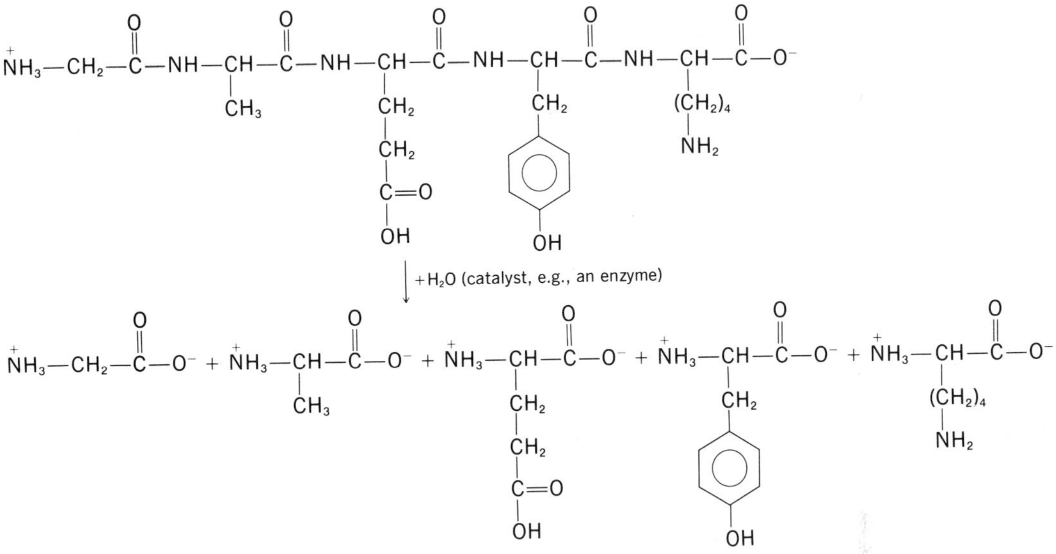

Glycine Alanine Glutamic acid Tyrosine Lysine

Figure 21.12
The digestion of a polypeptide, illustrated here by the hydrolysis of a pentapeptide. Only the peptide bonds (in color) break.

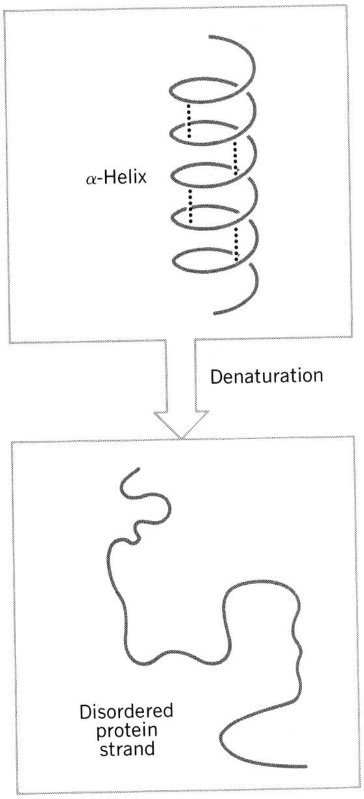

Figure 21.13
A protein is denatured when it loses secondary, tertiary, or quaternary structure.

function. All that has to happen is some disruption of secondary or higher structural features. **Denaturation** is the disorganization of the overall molecular shape of a protein. It can occur as an unfolding or uncoiling of helices, or as the separation of subunits. See Figure 21.13.

Usually, denaturation is accompanied by a major loss in solubility. When egg white is whipped or is heated, for example, as when you cook an egg, the albumin molecules unfold and become entangled among themselves. The system no longer blends with water—it's insoluble—and it no longer allows light to pass through.

Table 21.2 has a list of several reagents or physical forces that cause denaturation, together with explanations of how they work. How effective a given denaturating agent is depends on the kind of protein. The proteins of hair and skin and of fur or feathers quite strongly resist denaturation because they are rich in disulfide links.

Protein Solubility Depends Greatly on pH Because some side chains as well as the end groups of polypeptides bear electrical charges, the entire molecule bears a net charge. Because these groups are either proton-donors or proton-acceptors, the net charge is easily changed by changing the pH. CO_2^- groups, for example, become electrically neutral CO_2H groups when they pick up protons as a strong acid is added.

Suppose that the net charge on a polypeptide is 1−, and that one extra CO_2^- is responsible for it. When acid is added, we might imagine the following change, where the elongated shape is the polypeptide system.

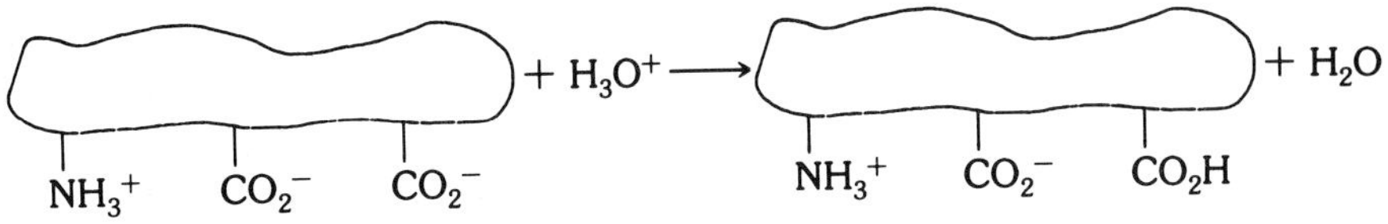

Now the polypeptide is isoelectric and neutral. On the other hand, a polypeptide might have a net charge of 1+, caused by an excess of one NH_3^+ group. The addition of OH^- can cause the following change, which makes the polypeptide isoelectric and neutral.

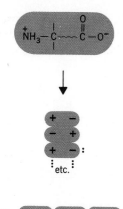

Figure 21.14
Several isoelectric protein molecules (top) can aggregate into very large clusters that no longer dissolve in water.

TABLE 21.2 **Denaturing Agents for Proteins**

Denaturing Agent	How the Agent May Operate
Heat	Disrupts hydrogen bonds by making molecules vibrate too violently. Produces coagulation, as in the frying of an egg.
Microwave radiation	Causes violent vibrations of molecules that disrupt hydrogen bonds.
Ultraviolet radiation	Probably operates much like the action of heat (e.g., sunburning)
Violent whipping or shaking	Causes molecules in globular shapes to extend to longer lengths and then entangle (e.g., beating egg white into meringue).
Detergents	Probably affect hydrogen bonds and salt bridges.
Organic solvents (e.g., ethanol, 2-propanol, acetone)	May interfere with hydrogen bonds because these solvents can also form hydrogen bonds. Quickly denature proteins in bacteria, killing them (e.g., the disinfectant action of 70% ethanol).
Strong acids and bases	Disrupt hydrogen bonds and salt bridges. Prolonged action leads to actual hydrolysis of peptide bonds.
Salts of heavy metals (e.g., salts of Hg^{2+}, Ag^+, Pb^{2+})	Cations combine with SH groups and form precipitates. (These salts are all poisons.)
Solutions of urea	Disrupt hydrogen bonds. (Urea, being amide-like, can form hydrogen bonds of its own.)

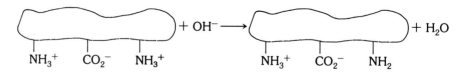

Like each amino acid, each protein has a characteristic pH, its isoelectric point, at which its net charge is zero and at which it cannot migrate in an electric field. One major significance is that polypeptide molecules that are neutral can aggregate and clump together to become particles of enormous size, which simply drop entirely out of solution. See Figure 21.14. A protein is least soluble in water when the pH equals the protein's isoelectric point. Therefore, whenever a protein must be in solution to work, as is true for many enzymes, the pH of the medium must be kept away from the protein's isoelectric point. Buffers in body fluids have the task of ensuring this.

An example of the effect of pH on solubility is given by casein, milk protein, whose pI value is 4.7. As milk turns sour, its pH drops from its normal value of 6.3 to 6.6 down to 4.7, and more and more casein molecules become isoelectric, clump together, and separate as curds. As long as the pH of milk is something *other than* the pI for casein, the protein remains colloidally dispersed.

21.6 CLASSES OF PROTEINS

Three criteria for classifying proteins are their solubility in aqueous systems, their compositions, and their biological functions.

We began this chapter with hints about the wide diversities of the kinds and uses of proteins. Now that we know about their structures, we can better understand how so many types of proteins with so many functions are possible. The following three major classifications of proteins and their several examples give substance to the chapter's introduction.

Proteins Can Be Classified According to Solubility   When proteins are classified according to their solubilities, two major families are the **fibrous proteins** and the **globular proteins.** The fibrous proteins are insoluble in water, and they including the following special types.

■ When meat is cooked, some of its collagen changes to gelatin, which makes the meat easier to digest.

■ Elastin is not changed to gelatin by hot water.

1. **Collagens.** In bone, teeth, tendons, skin, and soft connective tissue. When such tissue is boiled with water, the portion of its collagen that dissolves is called gelatin.

2. **Elastins.** In many places where collagen is found, but particularly in ligaments, the walls of blood vessels, and the necks of grazing animals. Elastin is rich in hydrophobic side chains. Cross-links between elastin strands are important to its recovery after stretching.

3. **Keratins.** In hair, wool, animal hooves, nails, and porcupine quills. The keratins are rich in disulfide links.

4. **Myosins.** The proteins in contractile muscle.

5. **Fibrin.** The protein of a blood clot. During clotting, it forms from its precursor, fibrinogen, by an exceedingly complex series of reactions.

Globular proteins, which are soluble in water or in water that contains certain salts, include the following.

1. **Albumins.** In egg white and in blood. In the blood the albumins serve many functions. Some are buffers. Some carry water-insoluble molecules of lipids or fatty acids. Some carry metal ions that could not be dissolved in water that is even slightly alkaline, such as Cu^{2+} ions.

2. **Globulins.** Including the gamma globulins that are part of the body's defense mechanism against diseases. The globulins need the presence of dissolved salts to be soluble in water.

Proteins Can Be Classified According to Composition   The nature of the prosthetic group in these proteins provides another way of classifying proteins.

1. Glycoproteins. Proteins with sugar units. Gamma globulin is an example.

2. Hemoproteins. Proteins with heme units such as hemoglobin, myoglobin, and certain cytochromes (enzymes that help cells use oxygen).

3. Lipoproteins. Proteins that carry lipid molecules, including cholesterol.

4. Metalloproteins. Proteins that incorporate a metal ion, such as many enzymes do.

5. Nucleoproteins. Proteins bound to nucleic acids, such as ribosomes and some viruses.

6. Phosphoproteins. Proteins with a phosphate ester to a side chain OH group, such as in serine. Milk casein is an example.

Proteins Can Be Classified According to Biological Function   Perhaps no other system more clearly dramatizes the importance of proteins than classifying them by their biological function.

1. Enzymes. The body catalysts.

2. Contractile muscle. With stationary filaments, myosin, and moving filaments, actin.

3. Hormones. Such as growth hormone, insulin, and others.

4. Neurotransmitters. Such as the enkephalins and endorphins.

5. Storage proteins. Those that store nutrients the organism will need such as seed proteins in grains, casein in milk, ovalbumin in egg white, and ferritin, the iron-storing protein in human spleen.

6. Transport proteins. Those that carry things from one place to another. Hemoglobin and the serum albumins are examples already mentioned. Ceruloplasmin is a copper-carrying protein.

7. Structural proteins. Proteins that hold a body structure together, such as collagen, elastin, keratin, and proteins in cell membranes.

8. Protective proteins. Those that help the body to defend itself. Examples are the antibodies and fibrinogen.

9. Toxins. Poisonous proteins. Examples are snake venom, diphtheria toxin, and clostridium botulinus toxin (a toxic substance that causes some types of food poisoning).

SUMMARY

Amino acids About 20 α-amino acids supply the amino acid residues that make up a polypeptide. All but one (glycine) are optically active and in the L-family. In the solid state or in water at a pH of roughly 6 to 7, most amino acids exist as dipolar ions. Their isoelectric points, the pH values of solutions in which they are isoelectric, are in this pH range of 6 to 7. Those with CO_2H groups on side chains have lower pI values. Those with basic side chains have higher pI values. Several amino acids have hydrophobic side chains, but the side chains in others are strongly hydrophilic. The SH group of cysteine opens the possibility of disulfide cross-links between polypeptide units.

Polypeptides Amino acid residues are held together by peptide (amide) bonds, so the repeating unit in polypeptides is —NH—CH—CO—. Each amino acyl unit has its own side chain. This repeating system with a unique sequence of side chains constitutes the primary structure of a polypeptide.

Once this is fashioned, the polypeptide coils and folds into higher features — secondary and tertiary — that are stabilized largely by hydrogen bonds and the water-avoiding or water-attracting properties of the side chains. The most prominent secondary structures are the α-helix, the β-pleated sheet, and the collagen triple helix.

Proteins Many proteins consist just of one kind of polypeptide. Many others have nonprotein, organic groups — prosthetic groups — or metal ions. And still other proteins — those with quaternary structure — involve two or more polypeptides whose molecules aggregate in definite ways, stabilized sometimes by salt bridges. Thus the terms *protein* and *polypeptide* are not synonyms, although for some specific proteins they turn out to be.

Because of their higher levels of structure, proteins can be denatured by agents that do nothing to peptide bonds. The acidic and basic side chains of polypeptides affect protein solubility, and when a protein is in a medium whose pH equals the protein's isoelectric point, the substance is least soluble. The amide bonds (peptide bonds) of proteins are hydrolyzed during digestion.

REVIEW EXERCISES

The answers to the following Review Exercises are in the *Study Guide* that accompanies this book.

Amino Acids

21.1 What structure will nearly all the molecules of glycine have at a pH of about 1?

21.2 In what structure will most of the molecules of alanine be at a pH of about 12?

21.3 Pure alanine does not melt, but at 290 °C it begins to char. However, the ethyl ester of alanine, which has a free NH_2 group, has a low melting point, 87 °C. Write the structure of this ethyl ester, and explain this large difference in melting point.

21.4 The ethyl ester of alanine (Review Exercise 21.3) is a much stronger base — more like ammonia — than alanine. Explain this.

21.5 Which of the following amino acids has the more hydrophilic side chain? Explain.

A : $^+NH_3CHCO_2^-$, CH, H_3C, CH_3

B : $^+NH_3CHCO_2^-$, $CH_2CH_2CH_2NHCNH_2$ (NH)

21.6 Which of the following amino acids has the more hydrophobic side chain? Explain.

A : $^+NH_3CHCO_2^-$, CH_2, (benzene ring)

B : $^+NH_3CHCO_2^-$, CH_2, (benzene ring), OH

21.7 One of the possible forms for lysine is

$$^+NH_3CHCO_2H$$
$$CH_2CH_2CH_2CH_2NH_3{}^+$$

(a) Is lysine most likely to be in this form at pH 1 or at pH 11? Explain.

(b) Would lysine in this form migrate to the anode, to the cathode, or not migrate at all in an electric field?

21.8 Aspartic acid can exist in the following form.

$$NH_2CHCO_2{}^-$$
$$CH_2CO_2{}^-$$

(a) Would this form predominate at a pH of 2 or a pH of 10? Explain.

(b) To which electrode, the anode or the cathode — or to neither — would aspartic acid in this form migrate in an electric field?

21.9 Complete the following Fischer projection formula to show correctly the absolute configuration of L-serine.

$$CO_2{}^-$$
$$+$$
$$CH_2OH$$

21.10 The molecules of all but one of the amino acids have at least one chiral carbon. Two of the amino acids have molecules with two chiral carbons. Write the structures and names of these two, and place asterisks by their chiral carbons.

Polypeptides

21.11 Write the conventional, condensed structure of the dipeptides that can be made from lysine and glycine.

21.12 What are the condensed structures of the dipeptides that can be made from cysteine and glutamic acid? (Do not use the three-letter symbols.)

21.13 Using three-letter symbols, write the structures of all of the tripeptides that can be made from lysine, glutamic acid, and alanine.

21.14 Write the structures in three-letter symbols of all of the tripeptides that can be made from cysteine, glycine, and alanine.

21.15 What is the conventional structure of Val · Ile · Phe?

21.16 The artificial sweetener in aspartame (the chief ingredient in NutraSweet) is the methyl ester of Asp · Phe. When the peptide bond in aspartame is hydrolyzed (and only this bond), one of the products cannot exist as an anion in water, even when the pH is 12. Write a conventional, condensed structure for aspartame.

21.17 Write the conventional structure for Ala · Val · Phe · Gly · Leu.

21.18 Write the conventional structure for
Asp · Thr · Lys · Glu · Tyr.

21.19 Compare the side chains in the pentapeptide of Review Exercise 21.17 (call it A) with those in

Lys · Glu · Asp · Thr · Ser   (which we can call B)

(a) Which of the two, A or B, is the more hydrocarbon-like?
(b) Which is probably more soluble in water? Explain.

21.20 Compare the side chains in the pentapeptide of Review Exercise 21.18, which we'll label C, with those in Phe · Leu · Gly · Ala · Val, which we can label D. Which of the two would tend to be less soluble in water? Explain.

21.21 If the tripeptide Gly · Cys · Ala were subjected to mild oxidizing conditions, what would form? Write the structure of the product using three-letter symbols.

21.22 Write the structure(s) of the product(s) of the mild reduction of the following polypeptide:

$$^+NH_3CH_2\overset{\displaystyle O}{\overset{\|}{C}}NHCH\overset{\displaystyle O}{\overset{\|}{C}}NHCHCO_2{}^-$$
$$CH_2 \quad CH_3$$
$$S$$
$$S$$
$$CH_2$$
$$^+NH_3CH_2\overset{\displaystyle O}{\overset{\|}{C}}NHCH\text{———}\overset{\displaystyle O}{\overset{\|}{C}}NHCHCO_2{}^-$$
$$CH_3$$

Higher Levels of Protein Structure

21.23 What kind of force makes it possible for a polypeptide to be stabilized in the shape of an α-helix?

21.24 The side-by-side alignment of polypeptides in a β-pleated sheet is maintained through the agency of what kind of force?

21.25 Give a brief description of the way in which polypeptide strands are organized in collagen.

21.26 What function does vitamin C perform in the formation of strong bones?

21.27 What factors affect the bending and folding of α-helices in the presence of an aqueous medium? Are enzymes required?

21.28 What is meant by a salt bridge? Draw structures to illustrate your answer.

21.29 In what way does hemoglobin represent a protein with quaternary structure (in general terms only)?

21.30 How do myoglobin and hemoglobin compare (in general terms only)?
(a) Structurally — at the quaternary level.
(b) Where they are found in the body?
(c) In terms of their prosthetic group(s).
(d) In terms of their functions in the body.

Properties of Proteins

21.31 What products form when the following polypeptide is completely digested?

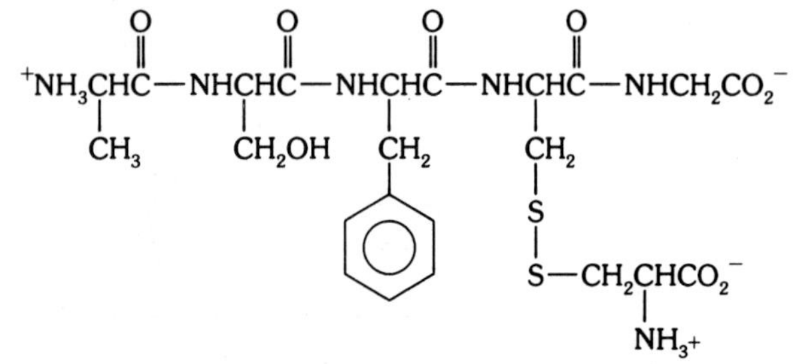

$$^+NH_3CHC\!-\!NHCHC\!-\!NHCHC\!-\!NHCHC\!-\!NHCH_2CO_2^-$$

with side chains:
CH_3, CH_2OH, CH_2–(phenyl), CH_2–S–S–$CH_2CHCO_2^-$ (NH_3^+)

21.32 The *partial* digestion of a polypeptide gave several products that were not amino acids. Some were dipeptides, for example. Which of the following compounds are possible products, and which could not possibly have formed? Explain.

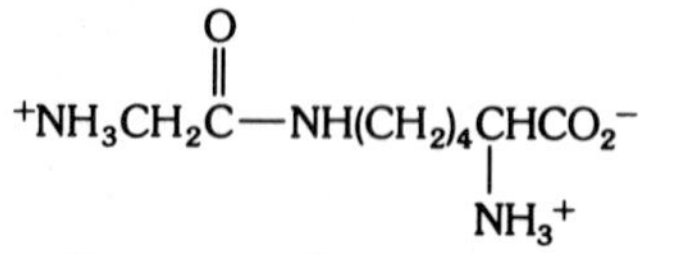

(a) $^+NH_3CHCO_2^-$
CH_2
S
S
CH_2
$^+NH_3CHCO_2^-$

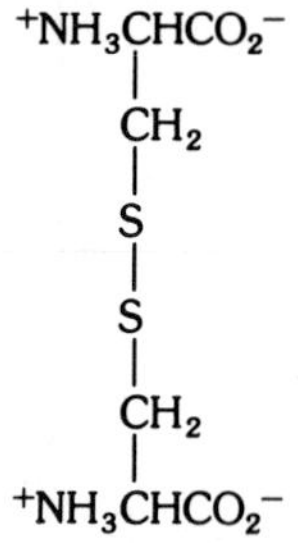

(b) $^+NH_3CH_2\overset{O}{\overset{\|}{C}}\!-\!NH(CH_2)_4CHCO_2^-$ (NH_3^+)

(c) $^-O\overset{O}{\overset{\|}{C}}CH_2NH\!-\!\overset{O}{\overset{\|}{C}}CH_2NH_3^+$

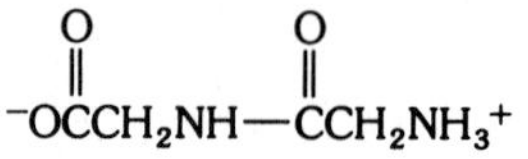

(d) $^+NH_3(CH_2)_4\overset{O}{\overset{\|}{CHC}}\!-\!NHCH_2CO_2^-$ (NH_3^+)

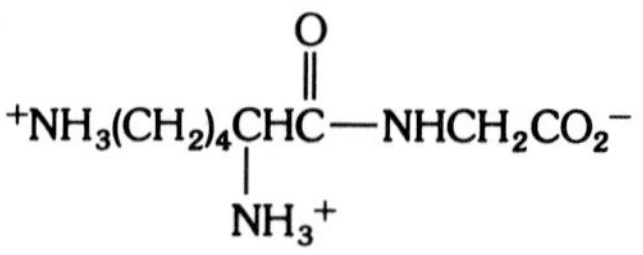

21.33 Explain why a protein is least soluble in an aqueous medium that has a pH equal to the protein's pI value.

21.34 What is the difference between the digestion and the denaturation of a protein?

Types of Proteins

21.35 What experimental criterion distinguishes between fibrous and globular proteins?

21.36 What is the relationship between collagen and gelatin?

21.37 How are collagen and elastin alike? How are they different?

21.38 What experimental criterion distinguishes between the albumins and the globulins?

21.39 What is fibrin and how is it related to fibrinogen?

21.40 What general name can be given to a protein that carries a lipid molecule?

Sickle-Cell Anemia (Special Topic 21.1)

21.41 What is the primary *structural* fault in the hemoglobin of sickle-cell anemia?

21.42 What happens in blood cells in sickle-cell anemia that causes their shapes to become distorted?

21.43 What problems are caused by the distorted shapes of the red cells?

CHAPTER TWENTY-TWO

Nucleic Acids

Have you ever wondered why camels have camel babies and not flamingo babies, for example? There is a chemical basis to this particularity, which we study in this chapter.

22.1 HEREDITY AND THE CELL

The chemicals associated with living things are organized in structural units called cells.

We have learned that nearly every reaction in a living organism requires its special catalyst, and that these catalysts are proteins called enzymes. The set of enzymes in one organism is not exactly the same as in another, although many enzymes in different species are quite similar. A major chemical requirement of reproduction is that each organism transmits to its offspring the capacity to possess the set of enzymes that are unique to the organism.

Nucleic Acids Carry Instructions for Making Enzymes In reproduction, an organism does not duplicate the enzymes themselves and then pass them on directly to its offspring. Instead, it sends on the *instructions* for making its unique enzymes from amino acids. It does this by duplicating the compounds of a different family, the nucleic acids. These then direct the synthesis of enzymes (and all other proteins) in the offspring. Our purpose in this chapter is to study how nucleic acids carry genetic instructions and act on them, but we have to learn something about the biological context first.

Every Cell Carries Nucleic Acids The cell is the smallest unit of an organism that has life and can duplicate itself in the organism. Cells of different systems vary widely in shape and size, but they generally have similar subunits. Figure 22.1 outlines the major features of animal and plant cells. The remainder of our discussion will concern the cells of higher animals, but plant cells work similarly.

In animal cells, the cell boundary is the cell membrane, which we studied in Section 20.5. Everything enclosed by it is called *protoplasm,* which contains several discrete particles or cellular bodies. Prominent among them are the **mitochondria,** which make adenosine triphosphate (ATP) for the cell's needs for chemical energy.

■ The English scientist Robert Hooke was the first to use the word *cell* when, in 1665, he described the hollow compartments he saw with the aid of a microscope in thin slices of cork.

■ German biologists M. J. Schleiden and T. Schwann in 1839 proposed a formal theory of the cell as an organism and of plants and animals as composed of these organisms.

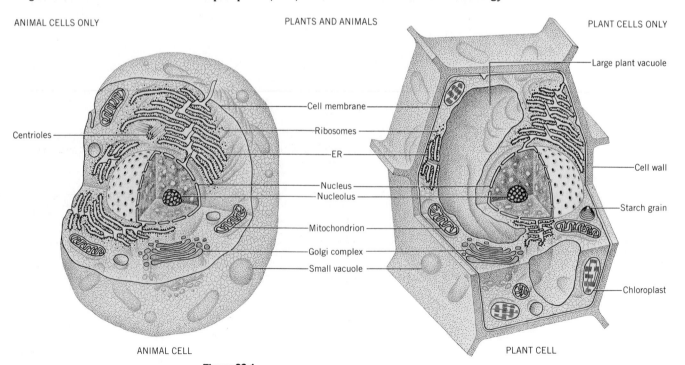

ANIMAL CELLS ONLY   PLANTS AND ANIMALS   PLANT CELLS ONLY

Centrioles

Cell membrane
Ribosomes
ER
Nucleus
Nucleolus
Mitochondrion
Golgi complex
Small vacuole

Large plant vacuole
Cell wall
Starch grain
Chloroplast

ANIMAL CELL   PLANT CELL

Figure 22.1
Models of generalized animal and plant cells. Although cells differ greatly from tissue to tissue, most have the features shown here. (From G. C. Stephens and B. B. North, *Biology, A Contemporary Perspective,* John Wiley & Sons, New York, 1974. Used by permission.)

The part of the cell outside of its nucleus is called the *cytoplasm*. It holds **ribosomes,** example, which consist mostly of nucleic acids and polypeptides and have an essentı. function in the synthesis of polypeptides, including those of enzymes. Polypeptide synthesis, however, is under the primary control of nucleic acids inside the cell's nucleus. Nucleic acids thus occur in both the cytoplasm and nucleus.

Genes Are the Fundamental Units of Heredity   The nucleus has its own membrane, and inside is a web-like network of protein. The nucleus also contains twisted and intertwined filaments of nucleoprotein called *chromatin*. Chromatin is like a strand of pearls, each pearl made of proteins called *histones* around which are tightly coiled one of the kinds of nucleic acid called DNA for short. DNA also links the "pearls." We'll study the structure of DNA in the next section, but DNA molecules have sections that constitute individual **genes,** the fundamental units of heredity. A single gene, for example, is responsible for a single enzyme, so unique genes translate into unique enzymes. A major goal of this chapter is to learn how the chemical structure of a gene enables it to do this.

■ Each "pearl" is called a *nucleosome.*

■ Every human cell has about 100,000 genes.

Prior to Cell Division, Genes Replicate   When cell division begins, the chromatin strands thicken and become rod-like bodies that accept staining agents and so can be seen under a microscope. These discrete bodies are called **chromosomes.** The thickening of chromatin into chromosomes is caused by the synthesis of new DNA and histones. The new chromosomes, including their DNA, are exact copies of the old, if all goes well as it does to a remarkable extent. This reproductive duplication of DNA is called **replication,** so by the replication of DNA, the genetic message of the first cell is passed to each of the two new cells.

When two germ cells, a sperm and an ovum, unite at conception to form the single cell from which the entire organism will grow, DNA from both germ cells combine. Genetic characteristics of both parents thus are passed on to the offspring. Every cell made from the first cell has the entire set of genes, but obviously most genes in the older organism are turned off most of the time. Genes that are behind the formation of fingernails, for example, must not operate in heart muscle cells! Another goal of our study is to learn how (some) genes might be regulated.

22.2   THE STRUCTURE OF NUCLEIC ACIDS

Genetic information is carried by the side chains of a twisted, double-stranded polymer called the DNA double helix.

The nucleic acids that store and direct the transmission of genetic information are polymers nicknamed DNA and RNA. **DNA** is **deoxyribonucleic acid,** and **RNA** is **ribonucleic acid.** The monomer molecules for the nucleic acids are called **nucleotides.**

Nucleotides Are Monophosphate Esters of Pentoses to Which Heterocyclic Bases Are Joined   Unlike the monomers of proteins, the nucleotides can be further hydrolyzed. As outlined in Figure 22.2, the hydrolysis of a representative mixture of nucleotides produces three kinds of products: inorganic phosphate, a pentose sugar, and a group of heterocyclic amines called the **bases,** which have single-letter symbols:

Bases from DNA		Bases from RNA	
Adenine	A	Adenine	A
Thymine	T	Uracil	U
Guanine	G	Guanine	G
Cytosine	C	Cytosine	C

Three bases are thus common to both DNA and RNA, and one base is different. The sugar unit is also different. It is a pentose in both, but the hydrolysis of RNA gives ribose — hence the R in RNA — and that of DNA gives deoxyribose — which lends the D to DNA.

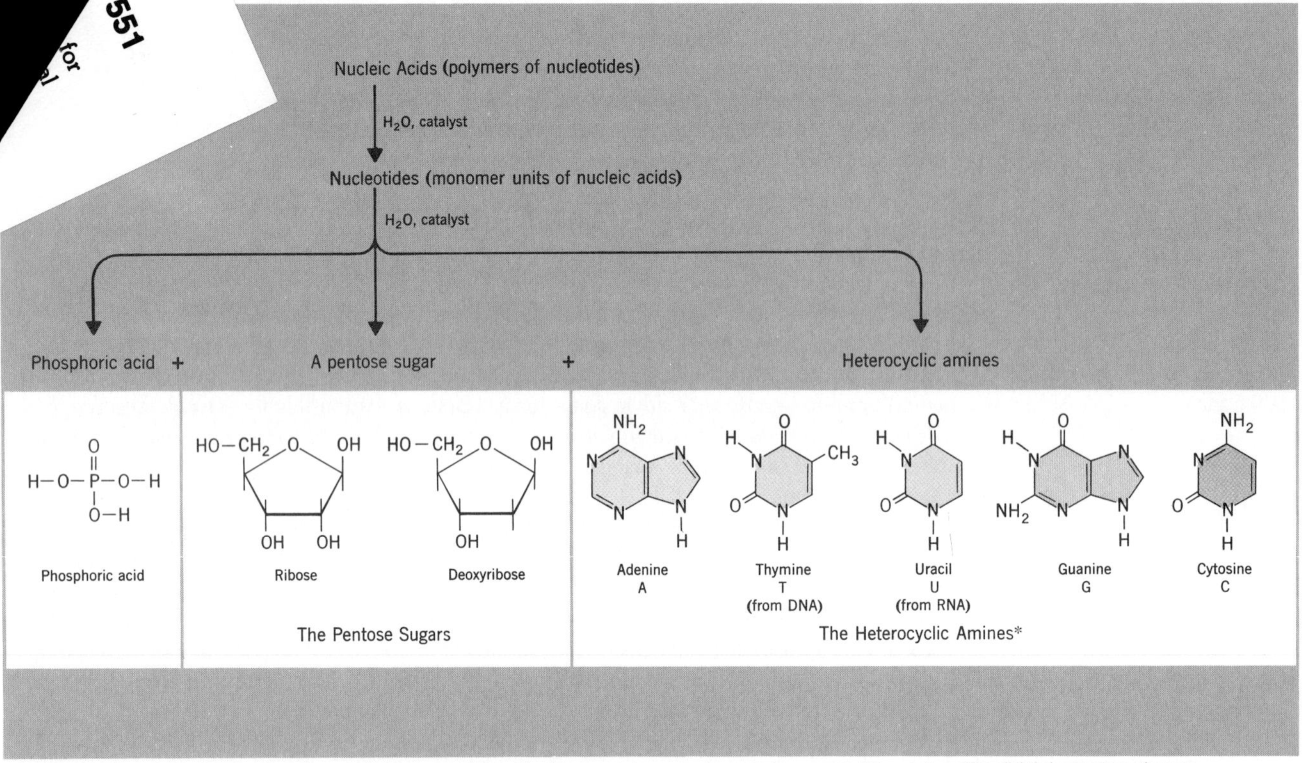

Nucleic Acids (polymers of nucleotides)

H_2O, catalyst

Nucleotides (monomer units of nucleic acids)

H_2O, catalyst

Phosphoric acid +   A pentose sugar   +   Heterocyclic amines

Phosphoric acid

Ribose   Deoxyribose

The Pentose Sugars

Adenine
A

Thymine
T
(from DNA)

Uracil
U
(from RNA)

Guanine
G

Cytosine
C

The Heterocyclic Amines*

These are the five principal heterocyclic amines obtainable from nucleic acids. Others, not shown, are known to be present. Although they differ slightly in structure, they are informationally equivalent to one or another of the five shown here.

Figure 22.2
The hydrolysis products of nucleic acids.

■ Ring carbon number 1 is the carbon of the aldehyde group when the pentose ring is open.

The structure of a typical nucleotide of RNA, adenosine monophosphate (AMP), is given in Figure 22.3. (The nucleotides of DNA are very similar.) The base, adenine (A), fits to the hemiacetal carbon (C-1) of the pentose, and the C-5 OH group of the pentose has been changed into an ester of phosphoric acid. All nucleotides are monophosphate esters like this. In making its nucleotides, the cell splits out two molecules of water as indicated in Figure 22.3 (but by *several* steps that we won't discuss).

When the OH at C-2 is replaced by H, and the pentose is deoxyribose, the resulting nucleotide is one for DNA. The pattern for all nucleotides, therefore, is as follows.

$$\text{HO---phosphate---pentose---OH}$$
$$\overset{\displaystyle\text{base}}{\underset{\displaystyle|}{}}$$

The Bases Project from the Backbones of Nucleic Acids Figure 22.4 shows the general scheme of how the nucleotides are linked in nucleic acids. Many steps and many

Figure 22.3
A typical nucleotide, AMP, and the smaller units from which it is assembled.

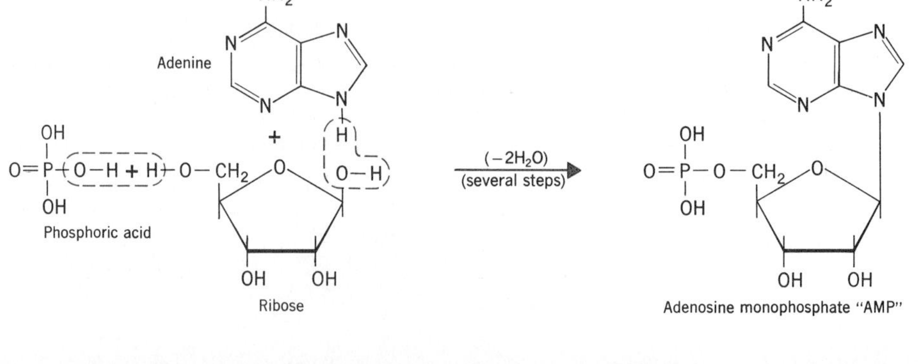

Adenine

Phosphoric acid

Ribose

$(-2H_2O)$
(several steps)

Adenosine monophosphate "AMP"

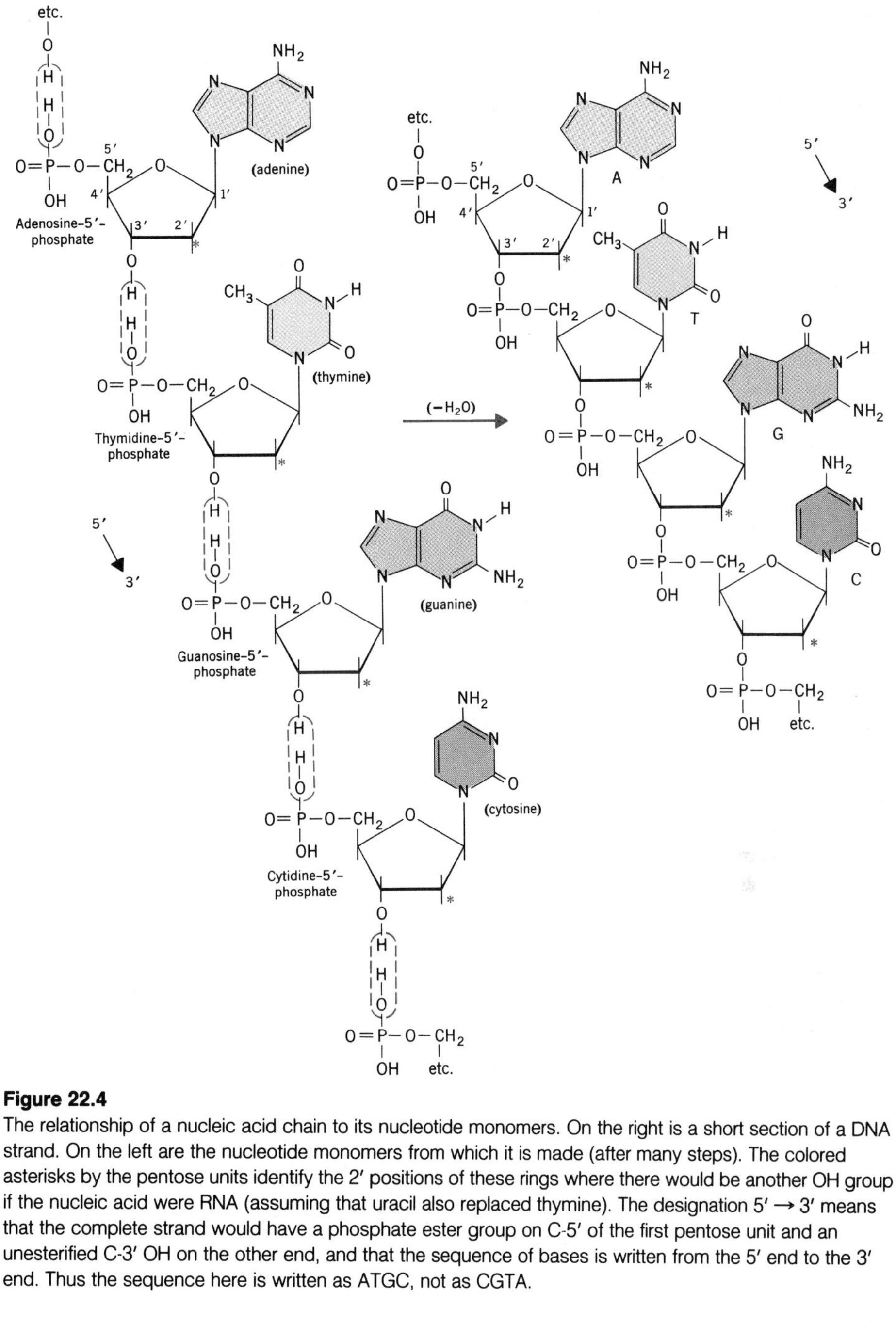

Figure 22.4
The relationship of a nucleic acid chain to its nucleotide monomers. On the right is a short section of a DNA strand. On the left are the nucleotide monomers from which it is made (after many steps). The colored asterisks by the pentose units identify the 2′ positions of these rings where there would be another OH group if the nucleic acid were RNA (assuming that uracil also replaced thymine). The designation 5′ → 3′ means that the complete strand would have a phosphate ester group on C-5′ of the first pentose unit and an unesterified C-3′ OH on the other end, and that the sequence of bases is written from the 5′ end to the 3′ end. Thus the sequence here is written as ATGC, not as CGTA.

■ Some 20 enzymes are required, the chief being DNA polymerase, discovered in 1958 by Arthur Kornberg (Nobel prize, 1959), and his co-workers.

enzymes are required but, in the overall result, water splits out between an OH group of the phosphate unit of one nucleotide and the C-3 OH of the pentose of the next. The result is a phosphodiester system. When this is repeated thousands of times, a nucleic acid is the product.

The pattern for the backbone of a nucleic acid is thus alternating phosphate and pentose units, and projecting from each pentose is one of the bases. The backbone holds the system together, and the bases — their selection and sequence — carry the genetic information. *The distinctiveness of any one nucleic acid is in the sequence of bases and the length of the backbone.*

Figure 22.5
Condensed structures of nucleic acids. Shown here is a representation of the same short segment of DNA that was given in Figure 22.4. The same representations could be used for RNA if U replaced T, and if the pentose units were understood to be ribose instead of deoxyribose.

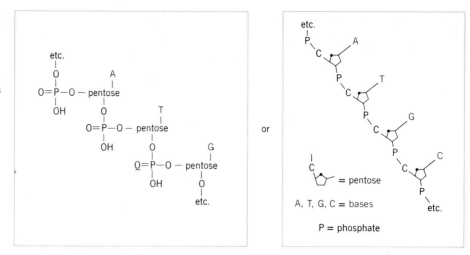

Simpler representations for nucleic acids will help our study, and Figure 22.5 shows how a nucleic acid structure can be condensed without loss of information.

Pairs of Bases Are Attracted to Each Other by Hydrogen Bonds The side-chain bases have functional groups so arranged geometrically that they can fit to each other in pairs by means of hydrogen bonds, as seen in Figure 22.6. This phenomenon is called **base pairing.** The locations and geometries of the functional groups of the bases permit only certain base pairs to exist. In DNA, G and C always form a pair, and A and T form another pair. In RNA, G and C always pair, and U and T always pair. Neither G nor C ever pairs with A, T, or U.

DNA Occurs as Two Paired Strands Twisted into a Double Helix In 1953, Francis Crick of England and James Watson of the United States proposed a structure for DNA, the **DNA double helix,** that made possible an understanding of how heredity works at the molecular level. Using X-ray data obtained by Rosalind Franklin, they deduced that two complementary DNA molecules occur side by side to form a double strand that then twists into a right hand helix.

The idea of complementary strands is a key feature of the double helix. Two irregular objects are *complementary* when one fits to the other, as your right hand would fit to its impression in clay. In DNA chemistry, *strand complementarity* also refers to a kind of fitting, to the pairing of bases *between* the strands. The idea was suggested by two significant 1 : 1 mole ratios discovered earlier by Erwin Chargaff. He had found that A and T are always present in DNA *in all species studied* in this ratio, and that G and C occur in a 1 : 1 mole ratio, also. As we have seen, A pairs to T and G pairs to C, so each pair *must* be in a 1 : 1 ratio. Crick and Watson

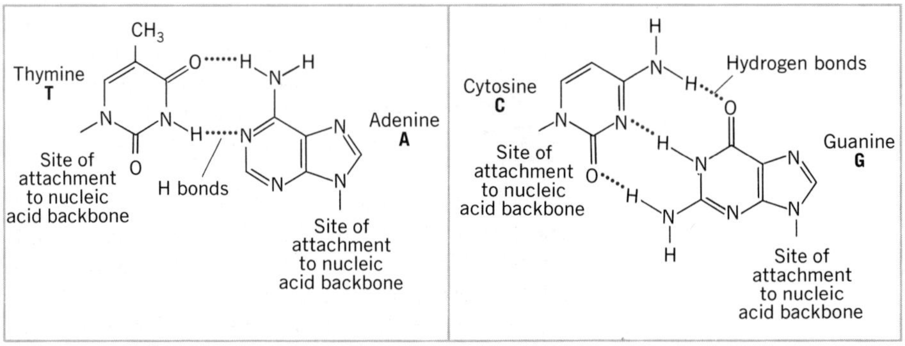

■ Crick and Watson shared the 1962 Nobel prize in medicine and physiology with Maurice Wilkins.

■ The ratios of A to T or of C to G *within the same DNA strand* varies within a species as well as between species.

Figure 22.6
Hydrogen bonding between base pairs. (*a*) Thymine (T) and adenine (A) form one base pair between which are two hydrogen bonds. (*b*) Cytosine (C) and guanine (G) form another base pair between which are three hydrogen bonds. Adenine can also base-pair to uracil (U).

Figure 22.7
A model of a short section of a DNA double helix. The two main backbones, made up of repeating phosphate–sugar units, are in blue. The bases of one side chain are in red and those of the opposite chain are in yellow.

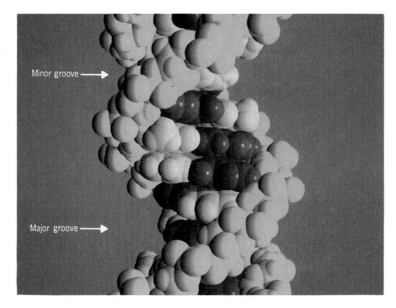

made sense of the simple $1:1$ ratios by proposing that A pairs to T *between the two strands*, and that G pairs to C also *between the strands*.

Whenever adenine (A) is one strand, then thymine (T) is opposite it on the other strand. And whenever guanine (G) projects from one strand, then cytosine (C) is opposite it on the other strand. The hydrogen bonds between A and T and between G and C hold the strands together.

A molecular model of the DNA double helix discovered by Crick and Watson is shown in Figure 22.7. The system resembles a spiral staircase in which the steps, which are perpendicular to the long axis of the spiral, consist of the base pairs. Hydrogen bonds between the pairs are centered around the long axis. The double helix (Figure 22.7) has two grooves, one major and one minor. These are binding sites for molecules of proteins that are involved in several gene functions, including gene repression and gene activation. The grooves are also sites for the initial molecular interactions of certain drugs, antibiotics, carcinogens (cancer-causing agents), and poisons.

Figure 22.8 is a schematic representation of the double helix that points out an additional feature. The two DNA strands run in opposite directions, indicated in this figure by the $5' \rightarrow 3'$ specifications by the pentose units. (By convention, primed numbers, like $5'$, are for ring positions of the pentose ring when the pentose is part of a nucleotide. Ring atoms in the bases, when needed, have unprimed numbers.)

Figures 22.7 and 22.8 show only short segments of DNA double helices. They do not show that these helices are further twisted and coiled into superhelices. This looping and coiling is necessary if the cell's DNA is to fit into its nucleus. A typical human cell nucleus, for example, is only about 10^{-7} m across, but if all its DNA double helices were stretched out, they would measure a little over 1 m, end to end.

The double helix discovered by Crick and Watson, now called DNA-B, has turned out to be one of a few forms of DNA. They differ in the ways in which the double helix is twisted and folded. Our study, however, does not require that we study these variations.

■ There are 3 to 5 billion base pairs in one nucleus of a human cell.

In DNA Replication, the Bases on Each Strand Guide the Formation of New Complementary Strands
When DNA replicates, the cell makes an exact complementary strand for each of the two original strands, so two identical double helices are made. The built-in guarantee that each new strand will be the complement of one of the old is the requirement that A pairs to T and C to G. A very general picture showing how this works is

Figure 22.8
A schematic representation of the DNA double helix. The two spiraling strands are held side by side by the hydrogen bonds (the rows of colored dots) between base pairs on opposite strands. (See the legend to Figure 22.4 for the meaning of the $5' \rightarrow 3'$ designations.)

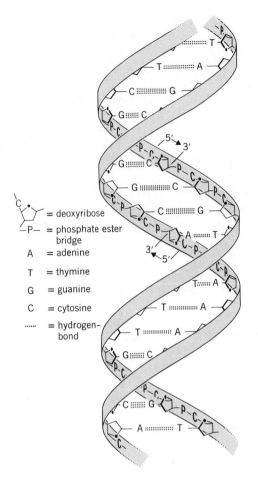

= deoxyribose
—P— = phosphate ester bridge
A = adenine
T = thymine
G = guanine
C = cytosine
······ = hydrogen-bond

given in Figure 22.9. Realize that this figure explains only one of the many aspects of replication, how base pairing ensures two new complementary strands. Some of the details of how replication occurs without everything becoming hopelessly tangled in the nucleus are understood, but we leave them to more advanced references.

In Higher Organisms, Sections of DNA Molecules Called Exons Collectively Carry the Message of One Gene   A gene was once thought to be one *continuous* segment of a DNA molecule, but since 1977 it has been known that virtually all single genes are divided or split. This means that a gene is made up of *sections,* called **exons,** of a DNA chain. Interrupting the exons and separating them are other, usually longer sections of the DNA molecule called **introns.** The gene for the β-subunit of human hemoglobin, for example, consists of 990 bases, but two intron units, 120 and 550 bases long, interrupt the gene, as illustrated in Figure 22.10. Some introns are as short as 65 bases in length and others are as long as 100,000 bases.

■ *Exon* refers to the part that is expressed and *intron* to the segments that *int*errupt the exons.

A single gene can have as many as 50 introns, but not all DNA molecules in higher organisms have them. A few genes exist with completely continuous sequences of bases. Just what purposes are served by the introns is currently under considerable speculation.

We'll see later in this chapter how the exons of one gene manage to get the gene's message together. For the present, we can consider that a gene is a particular section of a DNA strand minus all the introns in this section. A gene, in other words, is a specific series of bases strung in a definite sequence along a DNA backbone. In human beings, a single gene has between 900 and 3000 bases, and something like 100,000 genes are required to account for all our proteins.

■ There are no introns in human genes that code for histones or for α-interferon.

Figure 22.9
The accuracy of the replication of DNA is related to the exclusive pairing of A with T and G with C. The two new strands at the bottom are replicas of the original parent strand at the top.

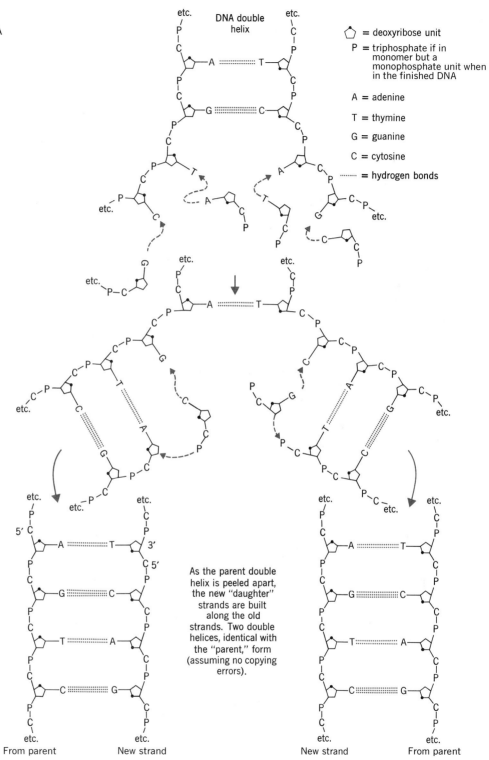

As the parent double helix is peeled apart, the new "daughter" strands are built along the old strands. Two double helices, identical with the "parent," form (assuming no copying errors).

Figure 22.10
The gene for the β-subunit of hemoglobin is a split gene with two long intron sections.

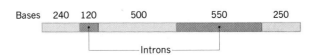

SPECIAL TOPIC 22.1   GENETIC FINGERPRINTING AND CRIME PROSECUTION

In the entire set of human genes, the human *genome,* there are many regions consisting of nucleotide sequences repeated in tandem. These regions, called *minisatellites,* all have a common core sequence, but the *number* of repeated sequences in the minisatellites varies from individual to individual. These variations, which can be measured, are so considerable between individuals, that they are the basis of a major new technique in crime prosecution.

Suppose, for example, a sample of semen can be obtained from the sperm left by a rapist. The sample is first hydrolyzed with the use of a specific enzyme, called a *restriction enzyme,* which is able to cut a DNA strand only at specific sites and releases the core segments. The fragments can then be separated and made to bind (by base pairing) to short, radioactively labeled, specially made DNA that has been designed to be able to bind to core segments. Now the fragments can be detected by the way in which the atomic radiations affect X-ray film. A series of 30 to 40 dark bands appears, roughly analogous to the bar codes on groceries that are used for pricing at checkout counters. Each

individual has a unique genetic "bar code." Since every cell in the body has the entire genome, a single cut hair of a rape suspect can provide enough material to measure the person's genetic "bar code" and compare it to that obtained from the semen sample. The accompanying figure shows how one suspect was trapped.

When the two "bar codes" match, the jury has evidence as powerful as fingerprints for a conviction. If "bar codes" do not match, the district attorney looks for another suspect. This kind of evidence is thus as powerful an ally of the innocent as it is an enemy of the guilty. If a crime site specimen is old or has been subjected to harsh environmental conditions and has deteriorated, it will give either a true test or none at all. It does not give a false test that will lead to the conviction of an innocent person. (Thus far several states have permitted genetic fingerprinting in court cases, but defense attorneys will eventually appeal convictions to the Supreme Court for a final test of the admissibility of such evidence.)

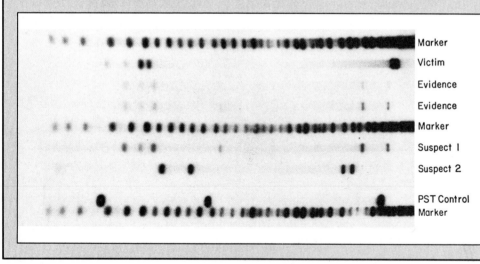

Marker	
Victim	
Evidence	
Evidence	
Marker	
Suspect 1	
Suspect 2	
PST Control Marker	

DNA fingerprinting. The banding pattern of the DNA of suspect 1 matches that of the evidence. Neither the rape victim's DNA nor that of suspect 2 does.

Gene Sequencing Has Been Automated   Chemists have developed automatic gene sequencing instruments that determine the sequences of bases in individual genes. The genes of one human being have to be very similar, of course, to those of another for the two to be members of the same species. However, every individual human being who has ever lived or ever will live, except for identical twins, has genes unique in some ways. This uniqueness of individuals is so analogous to the uniqueness of fingerprints that crime laboratories now use genetic "fingerprinting" as evidence in criminal trial. Special Topic 22.1 describes the technique.

22.3   RIBONUCLEIC ACIDS

The triplets of bases of the genetic code correlate with individual amino acids.

The general scheme that relates DNA to polypeptides is illustrated in Figure 22.11. We'll refer to it often, but first we need to learn more about RNA and its various types, particularly the four that participate in expressing genes in higher organisms.

Figure 22.11

The relationships of nuclear DNA to the various RNAs and to the synthesis of polypeptides.

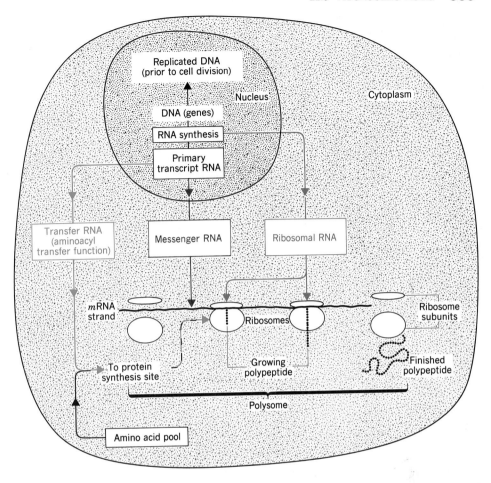

Ribosomal RNA (*r*RNA) Is the Most Abundant RNA

We have already mentioned the small particles in the cytoplasm, called ribosomes (Figure 22.1). Each forms from two subunits, as shown in Figure 22.11, which come together to form a complex with messenger RNA, another type that we'll study soon.

■ Over 50 kinds of polypeptides exist in one ribosome.

Ribosomes contain proteins and a ribonucleic acid called **ribosomal RNA,** abbreviated **rRNA.** Except in a few viruses, *r*RNA is single-stranded, but its molecules often have hairpin loops in which base pairing occurs.

The precise purpose of *r*RNA has yet to be worked out, but ribosomes are the sites of polypeptide synthesis. Their *r*RNA does not itself direct this work. Messenger RNA does this, and it's made from the second kind of RNA of our study.

Primary Transcript RNA (*pt*RNA) Is Complementary to DNA — Exons and Introns

■ *pt*RNA was initially called *heterogeneous nuclear RNA, hn*RNA.

■ At the 3′ end of *pt*RNA molecules there is a long poly-A tail (about 200 adenosine units long), and at the other end there is a nucleotide triphosphate "cap."

When a cell uses a gene to direct the synthesis of a polypeptide, its first step is to use the single DNA strand bearing the polypeptide's gene to guide the assemblage of a complementary molecule of RNA, called **primary transcript RNA,** abbreviated **ptRNA.** Figure 22.12 shows how this takes place. Uracil is now used instead of thymine, so when a DNA strand has an adenine side chain, then uracil not thymine takes the position opposite it on the complementary RNA.

The next general step in gene-directed polypeptide synthesis is the processing of *pt*RNA to form still another kind of RNA, messenger RNA.

Each Messenger RNA (*m*RNA) Is Complementary to One Gene

Molecules of *pt*RNA have large sections complementary to the introns of the DNA, and these sections must be deleted. Special enzymes catalyze reactions that snip these pieces out of *pt*RNA and splice

Figure 22.12
DNA-directed synthesis of *pt*-RNA in the nucleus of a cell in a higher organism. The shaded oval on the left represents a complex of enzymes that catalyze this step. (Notice that the direction of the *pt*RNA strand is opposite to that of the DNA strand.)

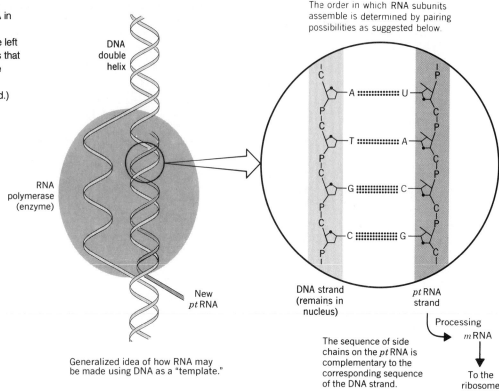

The order in which RNA subunits assemble is determined by pairing possibilities as suggested below.

DNA double helix

RNA polymerase (enzyme)

New *pt* RNA

Generalized idea of how RNA may be made using DNA as a "template."

DNA strand (remains in nucleus)

pt RNA strand

The sequence of side chains on the *pt* RNA is complementary to the corresponding sequence of the DNA strand.

Processing

m RNA

To the ribosome

■ A small family of nuclear ribonucleoproteins, *sn*RNPs (or "snurps"), helps this resplicing process.

■ F. Jacob and J. Monod (Nobel prizes, 1965) conceived the idea that a messenger RNA must exist.

■ *m*RNA is rapidly degraded in the cell, so fresh supplies must be made as needed.

together just the units corresponding to the exons of the divided gene. See Figure 22.13. The result is a much shorter RNA molecule called **messenger RNA,** or *m***RNA.**

In *m*RNA we have a sequence of bases complementary just to the gene's exons, so this *m*RNA now carries the unsplit genetic message. We have now moved the genetic message from a split gene on DNA to a molecule of *m*RNA, and the name for this overall process is **transcription.**

Triplets of Bases on *m*RNA Are Genetic Codons   Each group of three adjacent bases on a molecule of *m*RNA constitutes a unit of genetic information called a **codon** (taken from the word *code*). Thus it is a sequence of *codons* on the *m*RNA backbone more than a sequence of individual bases that now carries the genetic message. (We'll explain shortly why *three* bases per codon are necessary.)

Once they are made, the *m*RNAs move from the nucleus to the cytoplasm where they attach ribosomes. Many ribosomes can be strung like beads along one *m*RNA chain, and such a collection is called a *polysome* (short for *polyribosome*).

Ribosomes are traveling packages of enzymes intimately associated with *r*RNA. Each ribosome moves along its *m*RNA chain while the codons on the *m*RNA guide the synthesis of a polypeptide. To complete this system, we need a way to bring individual amino acids to the polysome's polypeptide assembly sites. For this, the cell uses still another type of RNA.

Transfer RNA (*t*RNA) Molecules Can Recognize Both Codons and Amino Acids   The substances that carry aminoacyl units to *m*RNA *in the right order for a particular polypeptide* are a collection of similar compounds called **transfer RNA** or *t***RNA.** Their molecules are small, each typically having only 75 nucleotides. As seen in Figure 22.14, they are single-stranded but with hairpin loops.

We're now dealing with the molecular basis of *information,* so we can use language analogies. On a human level, we use language to convey information, and language involves

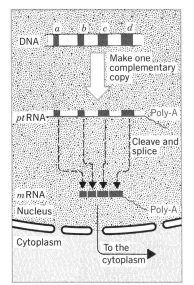

Figure 22.13
The RNA made directly at a DNA strand is ptRNA. Only the segments made at sites *a*, *b*, *c*, and *d*—the exons—are needed to carry the genetic message to the cytoplasm. The ptRNA is processed, therefore, and its segments that matched the introns of the gene are snipped out. Then the segments that matched the exons are rejoined to make the *m*RNA strand.

words built from a common alphabet. We are aware that many languages exist among human societies and that the world knows several alphabets. To communicate between languages, we have to translate. The same need for translation occurs at the level of genes and polypeptides. *t*RNA is the master translator in cells.

*t*RNA is able to work with two "languages," the genetic and the polypeptide. The genetic language is expressed in an alphabet of four letters, the four bases, A, T(or U), G, and C. The polypeptide language has an alphabet of 20 letters, the side chains on the 20 amino acids. To translate from a 4-letter language to a 20-letter language requires that the 4 genetic letters be used in groups of a minimum of 3 letters. Then there will be enough combinations of letters for the larger alphabet of the amino acids. Then there can be at least one genetic "word", built of 3 letters, for each of the 20 amino acids. This is exactly how *t*RNA is structured for its work with the genetic language. It is able to connect the three-letter codon "words" aligned along an *m*RNA backbone to a matching alignment of side chains of individual amino acids in a polypeptide being made.

One part of a *t*RNA molecule can recognize a codon because it carries a triplet of bases complementary to the codon. This triplet on *t*RNA is called an **anticodon.** Each of the 20 unique *t*RNAs, one for each of the 20 amino acids, carries a particular anticodon. In the *t*RNA molecule in Figure 22.14, the triplet CUU is its anticodon.

Another part of a *t*RNA molecule, an OH group at an end ribose unit, can attach a particular aminoacyl unit (by an ester bond). We can use the symbol *t*RNA–aa for this new compound, where we use "aa" for the aminoacyl group. Twenty such *t*RNA–aa molecules, one for each amino acid exist, but the anticodon on each is unique. A given *t*RNA–aa molecule, therefore, can be brought into alignment only with one codon of *m*RNA at a polysome.

To be able to work with the polypeptide language, each *t*RNA is somehow able to recognize the amino acid that "belongs" to it. Exactly how it can do this is the subject of intense research by several teams. It's a major frontier in nucleic acid studies. All we can do is accept the obvious fact that *t*RNAs can do this.

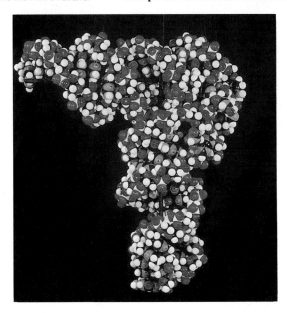

(a)

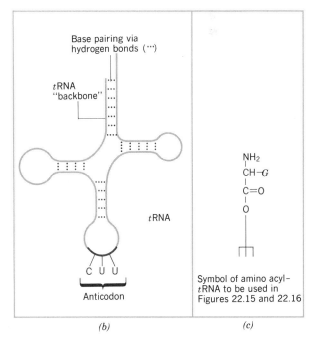

(b)

(c)

Figure 22.14
Transfer RNA (*t*RNA). (*a*) The *t*RNA for phenylalanine. Its anticodon occurs at the tip of the base, and the place where the phenylalanyl residue can be attached is at the upper left point. (*b*) This is a highly schematic representation of the model to highlight the occurrence of double-stranded regions. (*c*) The symbol of the aminoacyl–*t*RNA unit that will be used in succeeding figures.

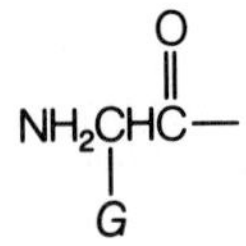

$$\underset{\underset{G}{|}}{NH_2CHC-} \overset{\overset{O}{||}}{}$$

An aminoacyl unit

As each *t*RNA−aa molecule comes to *m*RNA, its aminoacyl unit is transferred to a growing polypeptide chain. You can see that a unique series of codons *can allow the polypeptide chain to grow only with an equally unique sequence of amino acid residues.* The pairing of the triplets of bases between the codons and anticodons can permit only one sequence.

The Genetic Code Is the Correlation Between Codons and Amino Acids   Table 22.1 displays the known assignments of codons to amino acids, the **genetic code.** Most amino acids are associated with more than one codon, which apparently minimizes the harmful effects of genetic mutations. (These, in molecular terms, are small changes in the structures of genes.) Phenylalanine, for example, is coded either by UUU or by UUC. Alanine is coded by any one of the four triplets: GCU, GCC, GCA, or GCG. Only two amino acids go with single codons, tryptophan (Trp) and methionine (Met).

■ UUU and UUC are called *synonyms* for Phe.

The Genetic Code Is Almost Universal for All Plants and Animals   A few single-celled species have been found with codon assignments not given in Table 22.1. Moreover, some of the genes in human mitochondria, which we pointed out in Figure 22.1, have unique codons. Apart from these exceptions, the genetic code of Table 22.1 is shared from the lowest to the highest forms of life in both the plant and animal kingdoms. Once again we see a remarkable kinship with nature.

■ DNA also occurs in mitochondria, and there are some variations in the code for this DNA.

mRNA Codons Also Relate to DNA Triplets   It's important to remember that a codon cannot appear on a strand of *m*RNA unless a complementary triplet of bases was on an exon unit of the original DNA strand. For example, there could not be the UUC codon on *m*RNA unless the DNA strand had the triplet AAG, because G pairs with C and A of DNA pairs with U of *m*RNA.

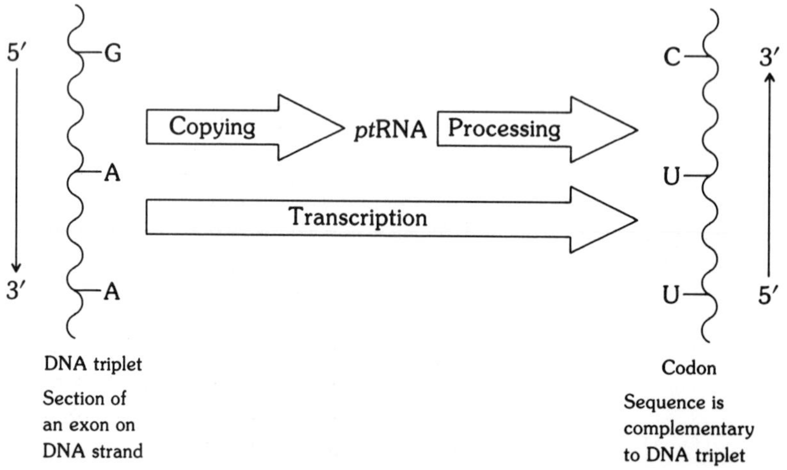

DNA triplet

Section of
an exon on
DNA strand

Codon

Sequence is
complementary
to DNA triplet

The Direction in Which a Codon Triplet is Expressed Has Structural Meaning   As shown here, a DNA strand and the RNA strand made directly from it run in opposite directions. To avoid confusion in writing codons on a horizontal line, scientists use the following conventions. The 5′ end of a codon is written on the left end of the three-letter symbol, and the direction, left to right, is 5′ to 3′. (See also Figure 22.5.) This is why the codon given above is written as UUC, not as CUU. Opposite this codon is the triplet GAA on the DNA strand, which is also written from the 5′ to 3′ end. To give another example, the complement to the *m*RNA codon, AAG, is the DNA triplet, CTT.

PRACTICE EXERCISE 1

Using Table 22.1, what amino acids are specified by each of the following codons on an *m*RNA molecule?

(a) CCU   (b) AGA   (c) GAA   (d) AAG

TABLE 22.1 Codon Assignments

First	Second				Third
	U	C	A	G	
U	Phenylalanine	Serine	Tyrosine	Cysteine	U
	Phenylalanine	Serine	Tyrosine	Cysteine	C
	Leucine	Serine	CT[a]	CT	A
	Leucine	Serine	CT	Tryptophan	G
C	Leucine	Proline	Histidine	Arginine	U
	Leucine	Proline	Histidine	Arginine	C
	Leucine	Proline	Glutamine	Arginine	A
	Leucine	Proline	Glutamine	Arginine	G
A	Isoleucine	Threonine	Asparagine	Serine	U
	Isoleucine	Threonine	Asparagine	Serine	C
	Isoleucine	Threonine	Lysine	Arginine	A
	Methionine[b]	Threonine	Lysine	Arginine	G
G	Valine	Alanine	Aspartic acid	Glycine	U
	Valine	Alanine	Aspartic acid	Glycine	C
	Valine	Alanine	Glutamic acid	Glycine	A
	Valine	Alanine	Glutamic acid	Glycine	G

[a] The codon CT is a signal codon for chain-termination.

[b] The codon for methionine, AUG, serves also as the codon form N-formylmethionine, the chain-initiating unit in polypeptide synthesis in bacteria and mitochondria.

PRACTICE EXERCISE 2

What amino acids are specified by the following base triads on DNA?

(a) GGA   (b) TCA   (c) TTC   (d) GAT

22.4 *m*RNA-DIRECTED POLYPEPTIDE SYNTHESIS

tRNA molecules carry aminoacyl groups, one by one, to an mRNA strand at a ribosome.

In the previous section we saw how a particular genetic message can be transcribed from the exons of a split gene to a series of codons on *m*RNA. In this section we will learn in broad terms how the next general step is accomplished, called **translation.** This step is the *m*RNA-directed assemblage of a polypeptide.

Genetic *Translation* Follows Transcription We will now use the fork-like symbol in part *c* of Figure 22.14 for *t*RNA–aa. The three tines of the fork stand for the anticodon triplet. We will assume that all the needed *t*RNA–aa combinations have been assembled and are waiting like so many spare parts to be used at the polypeptide assembly line.

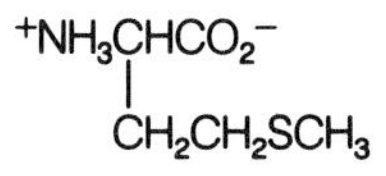

A polypeptide is started with an N-terminal methionine residue. After the polypeptide has been made, it is left in place only if methionine is supposed to be the N-terminal unit. Otherwise, methionine will be removed, and the second aminoacyl group will be the N-terminal unit.

The principal steps in genetic translation are the following.

1. **Formation of the elongation complex.** As shown in Figure 22.15, the elongation complex is made of several pieces: two subunits of the ribosome, the first aminoacyl–*t*RNA unit (which is Met–*t*RNA₁), and the *m*RNA molecule, beginning at its first

$^+NH_3CHCO_2^-$
|
$CH_2CH_2SCH_3$
Methionine, Met

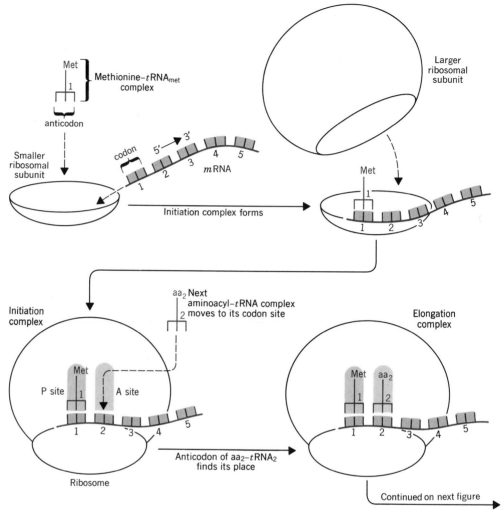

Figure 22.15
Formation of the elongation complex at the beginning of the synthesis of a polypeptide.

■ The "P" in P site refers to the peptidyl transfer site. The A site is the aminoacyl binding site.

codon end. The Met–$tRNA_1$ comes to rest with its anticodon matched to the first codon and with the bulk of its system in contact with a portion of the ribosome's surface called the P site. This is a site where there are enzymes that can catalyze the transfer of a growing polypeptide chain to a newly arrived aminoacyl unit.

Now the second $tRNA$ unit, $tRNA_2$, which holds the second aminoacyl group, aa_2, has to find the $mRNA$ codon that matches its own anticodon, and it does this at another site on the ribosome called the A site.

We now have two aminoacyl units, Met and aa_2, aligned side by side, one over the P site and the second over the A site, held in place with the aid of the hydrogen bonds of the matched codon–anticodon pairs. The work of completing the elongation complex is now complete, and actual chain lengthening can start.

2. **Elongation of the polypeptide chain.** There is now a series of repeating steps, illustrated in Figure 22.16. The methionine residue moves from its $tRNA$ to the newly arrived, second aminoacyl unit. This makes the first peptide bond, and it takes place by acyl transfer, much as we discussed when we studied the synthesis of amides in an earlier chapter.

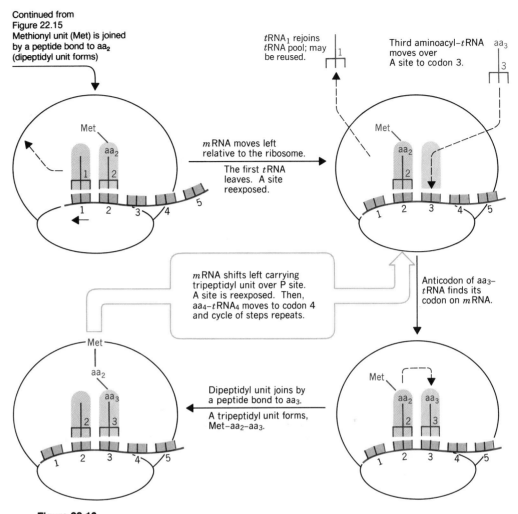

Figure 22.16
The elongation steps in the synthesis of a polypeptide. The dipeptidyl unit, Met–aa$_2$, formed by the process of Figure 22.15, now has a third amino acid residue, aa$_3$, added to it.

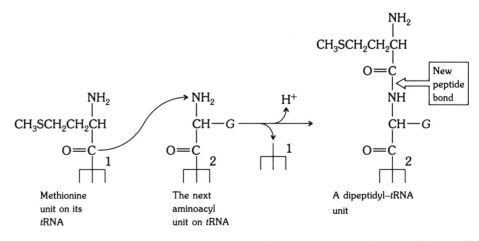

■ This kind of translocation of the growing polypeptide to the next amino acid is what is blocked by the toxin of the diphtheria bacillus.

The *m*RNA unit now shifts one codon over — leftward as we have drawn it. (It's actually a relative motion of the *m*RNA and the ribosome.) This movement positions what is now a *di*peptidyl–*t*RNA unit over the P site. Now the third aminoacyl–*t*RNA finds its anticodon-to-codon matching at the third codon of the *mRNA* strand, and it's over the recently vacated A site.

Elongation now occurs; the dipeptide unit transfers to the amino group of the third amino acid. Another peptide bond forms. And a tripeptidyl system has been made.

The cycle of steps can now occur again, starting with a movement of the *mRNA* chain relative to the ribosome that shifts this tripeptidyl – *tRNA* and positions it over the P site. The fourth amino acid residue is carried to the *mRNA*; the tripeptidyl unit transfers to it to make a tetrapeptidyl unit, and so forth. This cycle of steps continues until a special chain-terminating codon is reached.

3.   **Termination of polypeptide synthesis.** Once a ribosome has moved down to one of the chain-terminating codons of the *mRNA* strand (UAA, UAG, or UGA), the polypeptide synthesis is complete, and the polypeptide is released. The ribosome can be reused, and the polypeptide spontaneously acquires its higher levels of structure.

A *Repressor* Can Keep a Gene Switched Off Until an *Inducer* Acts   As we have said, every cell in the body carries the entire set of genes. In any given tissue, therefore, most must be permanently switched off. It wouldn't do, for example, for a cell to be making a protein-digesting enzyme that would then catalyze the destruction of its own proteins.

Because so many steps occur between the divided gene and the finished polypeptide, there are a large number of points at which the cell can control the overall process. We briefly discuss only one way this is done, and we have to rely heavily on Figure 22.17. It comes from discoveries involving a bacterium called *Escherichia coli,* or *E. coli,* a one-celled organism found in our intestinal tracts.

E. coli are able to obtain all the carbon atoms they need from the metabolism of lactose, milk sugar. They must first hydrolyze this disaccharide to galactose and glucose, and the enzyme β-galactosidase is essential for this reaction. The enzyme, of course, is not needed until lactose is available, so the gene for the enzyme is switched off until lactose molecules arrive. We'll leave some details to more advanced treatments. Our aim is only to illustrate in broad outline one of the most important kinds of activities at the molecular level of life, the control of gene expression. What we describe here is an **inducible gene,** and just one strategy for the control of genes.

The DNA segment responsible for the structure of β-galactosidase is in a region of the DNA strand called the *structural gene.* See Figure 22.17. Next to it, on the same DNA strand, is a segment of DNA to which a **repressor** molecule can bind. Because this DNA unit is part of the switch for the operation of the structural gene, it is named the *operator site.* Immediately next to it, down the same DNA chain, is a small segment called the *promoter site.* It holds in readiness the enzyme, DNA polymerase, needed to transcribe the structural gene. But this enzyme cannot work until the operator site is switched on. The structural gene plus the repressor and operator sites, taken together, make up a unit called the *lac operon.*

The repressor is a polypeptide made at the direction of its own gene, a *regulator gene,* located just above the promoter site in Figure 22.17. When repressor molecules are present, they bind to the DNA of the operator site. *This binding of the repressor is what prevents gene transcription and translation.*

Now suppose that some molecules of lactose appear. The enzyme made with the aid of the structural gene is now needed. The first of the lactose molecules to arrive are altered slightly (by steps we will not discuss) into **inducer** molecules. These have shapes that enable them to fit in some way to the repressor molecule at the operator site. As they attach to the repressor, the shape of the repressor becomes changed so that it no longer can stick to the operator gene, *and it drops off.* DNA polymerase is now released to work with the structural gene to help to make the *mRNA* needed for the manufacture of β-galactosidase.

The overall process we have described is called **enzyme induction,** and β-galactosidase is one of many *inducible enzymes.* Don't let the beauty of it be smothered by the details. If no substrate (lactose in this example) is in the cell, an enzyme isn't needed, and the genetic machinery for making it stays switched off. Only when the enzyme is needed, signaled by the arrival of its substrate, is it manufactured. Many human enzymes no doubt work in the same

■ Polypeptide synthesis can occur at several ribosomes moving along the *mRNA* strand at the same time.

■ In mammals, it takes only about one second to move each amino acid residue into place in a growing polypeptide.

Figure 22.17
Repression and induction of the enzyme *β*-galactosidase in *E. coli*. The inducer is lactose whose hydrolysis requires this enzyme. The first lactose molecules to arrive bind to and remove the repressor from the operator gene. Now the structural gene is free to direct the synthesis of *m*RNA coded to make the enzyme. The repressor is made at the direction of another gene (top), the regulator gene.

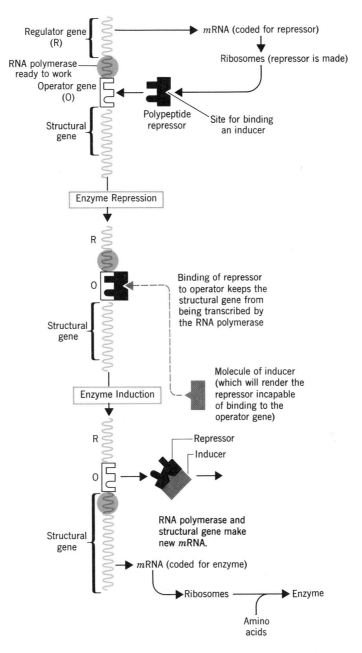

way. Without thousands of events at the molecular level of life happening *automatically,* that is, without human thought, we couldn't imagine minds free enough for any higher thoughts.

Many Antibiotics Kill Bacteria by Interfering with Genetic Translation or Transmission Bacteria, like us, have to manufacture polypeptides to stay alive and multiply. Inhibiting the synthesis of bacterial polypeptides at any one of several steps in the overall process will kill the bacteria. Streptomycin, for example, inhibits the initiation of polypeptide synthesis. Chloramphenicol inhibits the ability to transfer newly arrived aminoacyl units to the elongating strand. The tetracyclines inhibit the binding of *t*RNA – aa units when they arrive at the ribosome. Actinomycin binds tightly to DNA. Erythromycin, puromycin, and cycloheximide interfere with elongation.

■ These inhibiting activities render the *enzymes* for the various steps inactive.

A family of new antibiotics, the quinolones (e.g., ciprofloxacin and norfloxacin) inhibit a bacterial enzyme called gyrase needed to get newly made bacterial DNA into a properly coiled form. (We have the same kind of enzyme, but it is different enough in structure so the quinolones do not affect it.) The quinolones have been found effective with staph and strep infections and with Legionnaire's disease.

X Rays and Atomic Radiations Can Damage Genes   Atomic radiations, particularly X rays and gamma rays, go right through soft tissue where they create unstable ions and radicals (particles with unpaired electrons). New covalent bonds might form. Even side-chain bases might be annealed together. If such events were to happen to DNA molecules, the polypeptide eventually made at their direction might be faulty. And the DNA made by replication might be seriously altered. If the initial damage to the DNA is severe enough, replication won't be possible and the cell involved is reproductively dead. This, in fact, is the *intent* when massive radiation doses are used in cancer therapy—to kill cancer cells.

Chemicals that are used in cancer therapy often mimic radiations by interfering with the genetic apparatus of cancer cells. Such chemicals are called **radiomimetic substances.**

22.5   VIRUSES

Viruses take over the genetic machinery of host cells to make more viruses.

They are at the borderline of living systems and are generally regarded only as unique packages of dead chemicals, except when they get inside their host cells. They then seem to be living things, because they reproduce. They are a family of materials called **viruses.**

■ Viruses are intracellular parasites.

Viruses Consist of Nucleic Acids and Proteins   Viruses are agents of infection made of nucleic acid molecules surrounded by overcoats of protein molecules. Unlike a cell, a virus has either RNA or DNA, but not both. Viruses must use host cells to reproduce because they can neither synthesize polypeptides nor generate their own energy for metabolism. The simplest virus has only four genes and the most complex has about 250.

The protein overcoat of some viruses includes an enzyme that catalyzes the breakdown of the cell membrane of the host cell. When such a virus particle sticks to the surface of a host cell, its overcoat catalyzes the opening of a hole into the cell. Then the viral nucleic acid squirts into the cell, or the whole virus might move in. Each virus that works this way evidently has its own unique membrane-dissolving enzyme, so any one virus can affect only those cells in the host whose own membranes are susceptible to this enzyme. At least, this theory helps us understand how viruses are so unusually selective. A virus that attacks, for example, the nerve cells in the spinal cord has no effect on heart muscle cells. A large number of viruses exist that do not affect any kind of human cell. Many viruses attack only plants.

■ A complete virus particle *outside* its host cell is called a *virion.*

Once a virus gets inside its host cell, one of two possible fates awaits it. It may become turned off and change into a *silent gene;* or it may take over the genetic machinery of the cell and reproduce so much of itself that it bursts the host cell walls. The new virus particles that spill out then infect neighboring host cells, and in this way the infection spreads. A virus that has become a silent gene might later be activated. Some cancer-causing agents, including ultraviolet light, are believed to initiate cancer by this mechanism.

Most viruses are RNA-based, not DNA-based, so the manufacture of more of their RNA must somehow be managed without the direction of DNA.

RNA-Based Viruses Either Carry or Make Enzymes for Synthesizing More RNA   RNA-based viruses have to solve a major problem if they are to infect a host cell. These cells normally (in health) have no enzyme that can direct the synthesis of a copy of an RNA molecule *from the instructions of another RNA.* In healthy host cells, copies of RNA molecules are made by the direction of DNA, not RNA, like the synthesis of *pt*RNA directed by DNA.

Two basic solutions to this problem occur involving two different enzymes. One is called *RNA replicase,* and it can catalyze the manufacture of RNA *from the directions encoded on*

Figure 22.18
Overall strategies used by RNA viruses to make their messenger RNA.

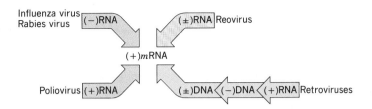

RNA. Some viruses carry this enzyme. Others are able to use the host cell's chemicals to direct its synthesis. Either way, once RNA replicase is inside the host cell, it handles the manufacture of the *m*RNA needed to make more viral RNA, and new virus particles can form.

The second solution occurs with viruses whose RNA directs the synthesis of a DNA polymerase that then directs the synthesis of more RNA. This polymerase is called *reverse transcriptase.*

Four Basic Strategies Are Used by RNA-Based Viruses To Make More RNA

Figure 22.18 outlines the strategies used by four kinds of RNA-based viruses to manufacture more of their own RNA. The (+) and (−) signs denote single-stranded RNA molecules of opposite complementarity. A (±) sign denotes a double-stranded nucleic acid. By convention, the messenger RNA that the virus must make is designated (+)*m*RNA. Refer to this figure as we briefly discuss four kinds of RNA viruses.

The poliovirus contains a single-stranded RNA molecule. Inside its host cell, it functions as a messenger RNA at the host's ribosomes for the synthesis of both overcoat proteins and molecules of RNA replicase. This enzyme then synthesizes (−)RNA molecules which, in turn, direct the synthesis of the (+)*m*RNA that now takes over the host cell's genetic machinery.

The rabies virus has (−)RNA molecules, but they are not messengers in their host cells. This virus carries its own RNA replicase into the host cells, where it directs the synthesis of (+)RNA. This is then used to make the new (−)RNA molecules required for additional virus particles.

The influenza virus also has (−)RNA, each molecule bearing 10 genes. During infection, segments of the RNA exist that can become reassorted as intact, new (−)RNA forms. In this way the influenza virus is able to change into new strains that make the job of immunizing large populations against influenza for long periods particularly difficult.

The reovirus of Figure 22.18 is present in the intestinal and respiratory tracts of mammals without causing disease. Its RNA is double-stranded RNA, or (±)RNA, and it carries its own RNA polymerase. It can use this on both (+) and (−) strands to make more viral (±)RNA.

The retroviruses (Figure 22.18) form a family of viruses with (+)RNA that cannot make more RNA without first making double-stranded DNA. To do this, retroviruses carry an unusual enzyme, *reverse transcriptase,* which can use RNA information to make DNA. This is unusual because it's normally the other way around; DNA information is used to make RNA. But in retroviruses, the flow of information goes in the reverse direction, hence the name, *reverse* transcriptase. (Hence also the *retro,* suggesting reversal or retrograde, in the name retrovirus.) Reverse transcriptase uses retroviral (+)RNA to direct the formation of (−)DNA, which directs the formation of (±)DNA. This then directs the synthesis of the (+)*m*RNA needed to make more retrovirus particles.

Cancer-Causing Viruses Transform Normal Genes in Host Cells   The retroviruses
include the only known cancer-causing RNA viruses, technically termed the *oncogenic RNA viruses.* (Several DNA-based viruses also cause cancer.) They transform host cells so that they grow chaotically and continuously. They do this by changing normal genes in the host cell to *oncogenes,* genes that henceforth are able to continue the cancerous growth.

The Host Cell of the AIDS Virus Is Part of the Human Immune System   The
acquired immunodeficiency syndrome, AIDS, is also caused by a retrovirus, the human

■ In the 1919 worldwide influenza epidemic, 20 million people died.

■ *Reo* in reovirus is from **r**espiratory, **e**nteric **o**rphan — a virus in search of a disease.

■ *Oncogenic* means cancer-inducing.

INTERFERON

The term *interferon* refers to a family of similar polypeptides that are chiefly characterized by an ability to inhibit viruses. There are at least three types in humans, designated as α-, β-, and γ-interferon. The interferons are glycoproteins that have about 150 amino acid residues per molecule.

Viruses are potent stimuli for the induction of interferon synthesis in humans. When an invading virus particle first encounters a white blood cell, particularly the type made in lymph tissue, the mechanism in the cell for making the *m*RNA coded for interferon is switched on. In a short time, the cell is manufacturing and releasing interferon, which then acts as a signal to other cells to make interferon, too. The interferon activates the circulating cells, called killer cells, that attack and destroy virus particles. In this way, interferon works to inhibit a viral infection.

The discovery of interferon in 1957 came about when two scientists, Alick Isaacs and Jean Lindenmann, wondered why victims of one viral disease never seemed to come down with a second viral disease at the same time. It seemed to them that something in the first viral attack triggered a mechanism that provided protection against an attack by a different virus. The search for this "something" led to interferon.

In the earliest clinical trials, interferon provided relief and sometimes a cure to a few patients who had rapidly acting cancer, such as osteogenic sarcoma (bone cancer), multiple myeloma, melanoma (a form of skin cancer), breast cancer, and some forms of leukemia and lymphoma. However, it takes nearly 25,000 pints of blood to make 100 mg of interferon, at a cost of a few billion dollars, so large-scale clinical tests really depend on interferon made by recombinant DNA technology.

The initial excitement that interferon would be the cure-all, free of side effects, for any kind of viral disease or any kind of cancer has faded. Yet tests with experimental animals continue to be promising, and several medical groups and biotechnology companies are continuing their testing efforts. In 1986 the U.S. Food and Drug Administration approved the first interferon for use against one specific cancer, hairy cell leukemia. In the same year α-interferon was shown to be effective in ordinary family settings to prevent those common colds caused by rhinovirus infections. (Early fall colds are often such infections.) In 1988 an immune system primer (prednisone, a steroid) followed by α-interferon caused the disappearance of the hepatitis B virus in half the patients tested who had chronic cases of this condition. (This virus in its acute stage can cause cirrhosis of the liver and liver cancer. Worldwide, an estimated 200 million people carry the virus.)

In 1988, the U.S. Food and Drug Administration approved the use of α-interferon for the treatment of genital warts. In a clinical trial, it eliminated these warts in over 40% of the patients, and in another 24% the warts were reduced in size. About 8 million Americans suffer from this sexually transmitted virus, which has been linked to cervical cancer. Other treatments were usually ineffective. Pregnant women were advised against this treatment because it could induce abortions.

immunodeficiency virus or HIV. One reason why this virus is so dangerous is that its host cell, the T4 lymphocyte, is a vital part of the human immune system. By destroying T4 lymphocytes, HIV exposes the body to other infectious diseases, like pneumonia, or to certain rare types of cancer.

Some Viral Infections Produce Interferons, Which Fight Further Infection One of the many features of the body's defense against some viral infections is a small family of polypeptides called the interferons. Currently, intensive research is in progress to make individual interferons and to test them in the treatment of viral diseases and cancer. Special Topic 22.2 discusses the interferons further. Supplies of interferons are now available by genetic engineering, which we will study next.

22.6 RECOMBINANT DNA TECHNOLOGY AND GENETIC ENGINEERING

Single-celled organisms can be made to manufacture the proteins of higher organisms.

Human insulin, human growth hormone, and human interferons are now being manufactured by a technology that involves the production of *recombinant DNA*. With the aid of Figure 22.19, we'll learn how this technology works. It represents one of the important advances in scientific technology of this century. It has permitted the *cloning,* the synthesis of identical

Figure 22.19
Recombinant DNA is made by inserting a DNA strand, coded for some protein not made by the bacteria, into the circular DNA of the bacterial plasmid.

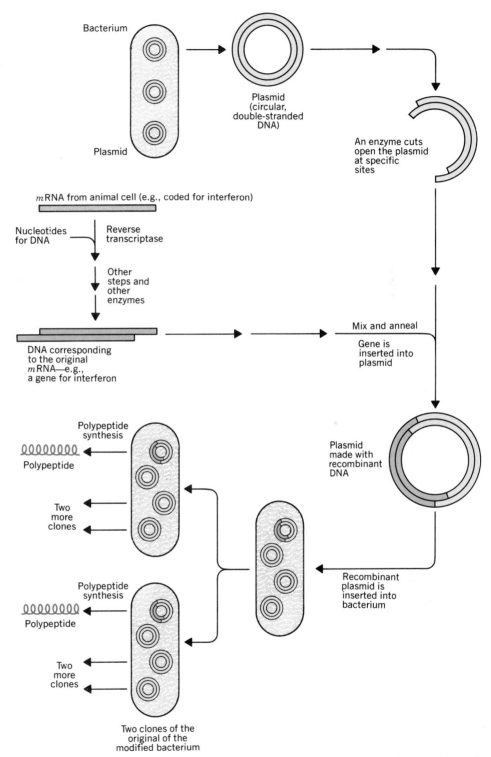

Bacterium

Plasmid

Plasmid
(circular,
double-stranded
DNA)

An enzyme cuts
open the plasmid
at specific
sites

*m*RNA from animal cell (e.g., coded for interferon)

Nucleotides
for DNA

Reverse
transcriptase

Other
steps and
other
enzymes

DNA corresponding
to the original
*m*RNA—e.g.,
a gene for interferon

Mix and anneal

Gene is
inserted into
plasmid

Plasmid
made with
recombinant
DNA

Recombinant
plasmid is
inserted into
bacterium

Polypeptide
synthesis

Polypeptide

Two
more
clones

Polypeptide
synthesis

Polypeptide

Two
more
clones

Two clones of the
original of the
modified bacterium

■ The term *cloning* is used for the operation that places new genetic material into a cell where it becomes a part of the cell's gene pool. The new cells that follow this operation are called *clones*.

copies, of a number of genes. The use of recombinant DNA to make genes and the products of such genes is called **genetic engineering.**

Genes Alien to Bacteria Can Be Inserted into Bacterial Plasmids   Bacteria make polypeptides using the same genetic code as humans. There are some differences in the machinery, however. An *E. coli* bacterium, for example, has DNA not only in its single

■ The isolation and purification of the many enzymes involved in the reactions of nucleic acids have been major accomplishments in molecular biology.

chromosome but also in large, circular, supercoiled DNA molecules called **plasmids.** Each plasmid carries just a few genes, but several copies of a plasmid can exist in one bacterial cell. Each plasmid can replicate independently of the chromosome.

The plasmids of *E. coli* can be removed and given new DNA material, such as a new gene, with base triplets for directing the synthesis of a particular polypeptide. It can be a gene completely alien to the bacteria, like the subunits of human insulin, or human growth hormone, or a human interferon. The DNA of the plasmids is snipped open by special enzymes called *restriction enzymes* absorbed from the surrounding medium. This medium can also contain naked DNA molecules, such as those of the gene to be cloned. Then, with the aid of a DNA-knitting enzyme called DNA *ligase,* the new DNA combines with the open ends of the plasmid. This recloses the plasmid loops. The DNA of these altered plasmids is called **recombinant DNA.** The altered plasmids are then allowed to be reabsorbed by bacterial cells.

The remarkable feature of bacteria with recombinant DNA is that when they multiply, the plasmids in the offspring also have this new DNA. When these multiply, still more altered plasmids are made.

Between their cell divisions, the bacteria manufacture the proteins for which they are genetically programmed, including the proteins specified by the recombinant DNA. In this way bacteria can be tricked into making the *human* proteins we have mentioned. The technology isn't limited to bacteria; yeast cells work, too.

People who rely on the insulin of animals, like cows, pigs, or sheep, sometimes experience allergic responses. They are also vulnerable to the availability of the pancreases of these animals, because they used to be the only sources of insulin. The ability to make *human* insulin, therefore, has been a welcome development for diabetics..

If an interferon should prove effective in treating various types of viruses, hepatitis, and possibly even certain kinds of cancer, the ability to make this unusually rare and costly substance in large quantities at low cost by recombinant DNA technology will truly be a major technological advance. In fact, just the clinical tests alone would be too costly without the availability of manufactured interferon.

Recombinant DNA technology has interacted with archeology in an interesting way. In the early 1980s scientists were able to remove segments of DNA molecules from an Egyptian mummy and from an extinct horse-like animal (a quagga) and reproduce these segments using bacteria. No segment was long enough to include a complete gene, but the technique no doubt will be developed as another tool for the study of evolutionary history.

Recombinant DNA Can Be Inserted into Cells of Higher Organisms Sometimes a desired polypeptide has to be "groomed" by a cell *after* it has been made by genetic translation before it will function. It might have to be attached to a carbohydrate molecule, for example. Bacteria lack the enzymes for such grooming work, so cells of higher organisms are used. When these cells are large enough, the new DNA can be inserted directly into them using glass pipets of extremely small diameters (0.1 μm). Although only a small fraction of such inserted DNA becomes taken up into the cells chromosomes, it can be enough when amplified by successive cell divisions.

Since viruses are able to get inside cells, some have been used to carry new DNA along. Retroviruses can be customized for this purpose, for example.

Genetic Engineering Offers Major Advances in Medicine One of the hopes of genetic engineering research is to have ways to correct genetic faults. As we will study in the next section, a number of undesirable conditions are caused by flawed or absent genes. Dwarfism, for example, is caused by a lack of growth hormone, a relatively small polypeptide. In experiments with mice, genetic engineering has successfully introduced growth hormone into mice, with dramatic effects on the mouse size.

In another medical application of genetic engineering, the smallpox vaccine is being remodeled to provide altered forms that might give immunity to many other diseases, ranging from malaria to influenza.

■ This hormone, called the atrial natriuretic factor (ANF), was discovered in the mid-1980s, but had been long-suspected.

A polypeptide hormone made by the heart, which reduces blood pressure, can be manufactured by genetic engineering and used by victims of high blood pressure. A clot-dissolving enzyme called tissue plasminogen activator or tPA has been genetically engineered for use in reducing the damage to heart tissue following a sudden heart attack.

The alteration of a sticky protein that mussels use to cling to underwater surfaces is being studied to find an adhesive that can be used after surgery.

The list of potential applications of genetic engineering to health problems grows yearly. It seems likely that kidney dialysis patients will need fewer blood transfusions if a blood-cell-producing substance, erythropoietin, can be made by this technology. Hemophiliacs who lack a blood-clotting factor may have it available. The synthesis of a number of drugs by genetic engineering is being studied, some that might be used against cancer.

Agriculture Is Affected by Genetic Engineering   In agriculture, genetic engineering is being tried for developing pest-resistant strains of plants, even plants that manufacture their own fertilizer. Gene manipulations have developed cows that yield much larger quantities of milk. Pigs with leaner meat have been produced. The list of similar applications is certain to grow.

The list of problems for society will also grow. In an age of large milk surpluses, some ask, who needs cows that can make more? What of the dairy farmers with huge investments already? These and questions like them are serious enough that if you follow newspapers and news magazines, you no doubt will read of the debates. There has never been a technology yet that had no associated problems. The extent to which these problems are accepted depends on human values expressed through laws and the acceptance of laws.

22.7   HEREDITARY DISEASES

About 2500 diseases in human beings are caused directly or indirectly by flawed genes.

A Defective Gene Can Make a Defective Enzyme   The victims of cystic fibrosis overproduce a thick mucus in the lungs and the digestive system, which clogs them and which often leads to death in children. About one person in 20 carries the defective gene associated with this disease, and it hits about one in every 1000 newborns. The defective gene directs the synthesis of an abnormal enzyme involved in biological oxidations, an enzyme that leads to excessive oxygen consumption and the overproduction of mucous.

Sickle-cell anemia is another disease caused by a defective gene. It was described in Special Topic 21.1.

Albinism, the absence of pigments in the skin and the irises of the eyes, is caused by a defect in a gene that directs the synthesis of an enzyme that is needed to make these pigments. The pigments absorb the ultraviolet rays in sunlight, radiation that can induce cancer, so victims of albinism are more susceptible to skin cancer.

Phenylketonuria, or PKU disease, is a brain-damaging genetic disease in which abnormally high levels of the phenylketoacid called phenylpyruvic acid occur in the blood. This condition causes permanent brain damage in the newborn. Because of a defective gene, an enzyme needed to handle phenylalanine is not made, and this amino acid is increasingly converted to phenylpyruvic acid.

$$C_6H_5CH_2\overset{\overset{\displaystyle O}{\displaystyle \|}}{C}CO_2H \qquad\qquad C_6H_5CH_2\underset{\underset{\displaystyle NH_3^+}{\displaystyle |}}{C}HCO_2^-$$

Phenylpyruvic acid   Phenylalanine

PKU can be detected by a simple blood test within four or five days after birth. If the infant's diet is kept very low in phenylalanine, it can survive the critical danger period and experience no brain damage. The infant's diet should include no aspartame, a low-calorie sweetener (contained in NutraSweet), because it is hydrolyzed by the digestive processes to give phenylalanine.

$$^+NH_3CHC-NHCHCOCH_3 + 2H_2O \longrightarrow {}^+NH_3CHCO_2^- + {}^+NH_3CHCO_2^- + CH_3OH$$

Aspartame   Aspartic acid Phenylalanine Methanol

■ There is enough phenylalanine in just one slice of bread to be potentially dangerous to a PKU infant.

■ If successfully launched (and it's a scientific project as massive as almost any underwritten by the U.S. government), the *Whole Human Genome Sequencing Project* will determine the base sequences in every human gene. The information would be useful in planning gene therapy.

Maintaining a low phenylalanine diet, of course, is not the easiest and best solution, so genetic engineers are working to correct the fundamental gene defect.

The techniques of genetic engineering have also been used to locate the chromosomes that hold the defective genes for a number of neurologic disorders, like several varieties of dystrophy, familial Alzheimer's disease, manic-depressive illness, and Huntington's chorea. Once the chromosome is known, the gene can be found and its defect analyzed. The hope is that gene therapy will someday be able to correct these disorders.

The possible fruits of the research outlined are in most cases many years down the road, maybe not even in your lifetime for most of them. But the indications to date are that the research is warranted. Such success stories that may develop will make front-page news, and because of your background in the chemical basis of heredity, you will be better able to follow it.

SUMMARY

Hereditary information The genetic apparatus of a cell is mostly in its nucleus and consists of chromatin, a complex of DNA and proteins. Strands of DNA, a polymer, carry segments that are individual genes. Chromatin replicates prior to cell division, and the duplicates segregate as the cell divides. Each new cell thereby inherits exact copies of the chromatin of the parent cell. If copying errors are made, the daughter cells (if they form at all) are mutants. They may be reproductively dead—incapable of themselves dividing—or they may transmit the mutant character to succeeding cells. The expression of this might be as a cancer, a tumor, or a birth defect. Atomic radiations, particularly X rays and gamma rays, are potent mutagens, but many chemicals, those that are radiomimetic, mimic these rays.

DNA Complete hydrolysis of DNA gives phosphoric acid, deoxyribose, and a set of four heterocyclic amines, the bases adenine (A), thymine (T), guanine (G), and cytosine (C). The molecular backbone of the DNA polymer is a series of deoxyribose units joined by phosphodiester groups. Attached to each deoxyribose is one of the four bases. The order in which triplets of bases occur is the cell's way of storing genetic information.

In higher organisms, a gene consists of successive groups of triplets, the exons, separated by introns. Thus the gene is a split system, not a continuous series of nucleotide units. DNA strands exist in cell nuclei as double helices, and the helices are held near each other by hydrogen bonds that extend from bases on one strand to bases on the other. The base A always pairs with the base T and C

always pairs with G. Using this structure and the faithfulness of base pairing, Crick and Watson explained the accuracy of replication. After replication, each new double helix has one of the parent DNA strands and one new, complementary strand.

RNA RNA is similar to DNA except that in RNA ribose replaces deoxyribose and uracil (U) replaces thymine (T). Four main types of RNA are involved in polypeptide synthesis. One is *r*RNA, which is in ribosomes. A ribosome contains both *r*RNA and proteins that have enzyme activity needed during polypeptide synthesis.

*m*RNA is the carrier of the genetic message from the nucleus to the site where a polypeptide is assembled. *m*RNA results from a chemical processing of the longer RNA strand, *pt*RNA, which is made directly under the supervision of DNA.

*t*RNA molecules are the smallest RNAs, and their function is to convey aminoacyl units to the polypeptide assembly site. They recognize where they are to go by base pairing between an anticodon on *t*RNA and its complementary codon on *m*RNA. Both codon and anticodon consist of a triplet of bases.

Polypeptide synthesis Genetic information is first transcribed when DNA directs the synthesis of *m*RNA. Each base triplet on the exons of DNA specifies a codon on *m*RNA. The *m*RNA moves to the cytoplasm to form an elongation complex with subunits of a ribosome and the first and second *t*RNA–aa unit to become part of the developing polypeptide.

The ribosome then rolls down the *mRNA* as *tRNA*−aa units come to the *mRNA* codons during the moment when the latter are aligned over the proper enzyme site of a ribosome. Elongation of the polypeptide then proceeds to the end of the *mRNA* strand or to a chain-terminating codon. After chain termination, the polypeptide strand leaves, and it may be further modified to give it its final N-terminal amino acid residue.

The whole operation can be controlled by a feedback mechanism in which an inducer molecule removes a repressor of the gene, thus letting the gene work.

Several antibiotics inhibit bacterial polypeptide synthesis, which causes the bacteria to die.

Viruses Viruses are packages of DNA or RNA encapsulated by protein. Once they get inside their host cell, virus particles take over the cell's genetic machinery, make enough new virus particles to burst the cell, and then repeat this in neighboring cells. Some viruses are implicated in human cancer. Some viruses make new RNA under the direction of existing RNA, using RNA replicase. Others, the retroviruses, use RNA to make DNA, and this then directs the synthesis of new RNA.

Recombinant DNA Recombinant DNA is DNA made from bacterial plasmids and DNA obtained from another source and encoded to direct the synthesis of some desired polypeptide. The altered plasmids are reintroduced into the bacteria, where they become machinery for synthesizing this polypeptide (e.g., human insulin, or growth hormone, or interferon). Yeast cells can be used instead of bacteria for this technology.

Cells of higher organisms are also used as places for inserting new DNA. In this kind of genetic engineering, microsyringes or tailored viruses have been used to insert the DNA. Many applications in medicine and agriculture exist.

Gene therapy Hereditary diseases stem from defects in DNA molecules that either prevent the synthesis of necessary enzymes or make the enzymes in forms that won't work. The identification of which chromosomes bear the defective genes has enabled the analyses of the genes themselves. In gene therapy, it is hoped that healthy genes can be substituted for those that are defective.

REVIEW EXERCISES

The answers to these Review Exercises are in the *Study Guide* that accompanies this book.

The Cell

22.1 What is protoplasm?

22.2 What are the mitochondria, and what do they do?

22.3 The cytoplasm makes up what part of a cell?

22.4 Chromatin is made up of what kinds of substances?

22.5 What is the name of the chemical that makes up genes?

22.6 What is the relationship between a chromosome and chromatin?

22.7 The duplication of a gene occurs in what part of the cell?

Structural Features of Nucleic Acids

22.8 What is the general name for the chemicals that are most intimately involved in the storage and the transmission of genetic information?

22.9 The monomer units for the nucleic acids have what *general* name?

22.10 What are the names of the two sugars produced by the complete hydrolysis of all the nucleic acids in a cell?

22.11 What are the names and symbols of the four bases that are liberated by the complete hydrolysis of (a) DNA and (b) RNA?

22.12 How are all DNA molecules structurally alike?

22.13 How do different DNAs differ structurally?

22.14 How are all RNA molecules structurally alike?

22.15 What are the principal structural differences between DNA and RNA?

22.16 When DNA is hydrolyzed, the ratios of A to T and of G to C are each very close to 1 : 1, *regardless of the species investigated*. Explain.

22.17 What is the principal noncovalent force in a DNA double helix?

22.18 What does base pairing mean, in general terms?

22.19 If the AGTCGGA sequence appeared on a DNA strand, what would be the sequence on the DNA strand opposite it in a double helix?

22.20 What does replication (of DNA) mean, in general terms?

22.21 The accuracy of replication is assured by the operation of what factors?

22.22 What is the relationship between a single molecule of single-stranded DNA and a single gene?

22.23 Suppose that a certain DNA strand has the following groups of nucleotides, where each lowercase letter represents a group several side chains long.

$$a \quad b \quad c\ d\ e\ f\ g$$

Which sections are likelier to be the introns? Why?

22.24 In general terms only, what particular contribution does a gene make to the structure of a polypeptide?

Ribonucleic Acids

22.25 What is the general composition of a ribosome, and what function does this particle have?

22.26 What is *pt*RNA, and what role does it have?

22.27 What is a codon, and what kind of nucleic acid is a continuous, uninterrupted series of codons?

22.28 Suppose that sections *x*, *y*, and *z* of the following hypothetical DNA strand are the exons of one gene:

3′   5′

AAA	GAA TAT CTC	AGG	GGT	TGT CTA
x		*y*		*z*

What is the structure of each of the following substances made under its direction?
(a) The *pt*RNA
(b) The *m*RNA

22.29 What is an anticodon, and on what kind of RNA is it found?

22.30 Which triplet, ATA or CGC, cannot be a codon? Explain.

22.31 Which amino acids are specified by the following codons?
(a) UUU   (b) UCC   (c) ACA   (d) GAU

22.32 What are the anticodons for the codons of Review Exercise 22.31?

Polypeptide Synthesis

22.33 What is meant by *translation,* as used in this chapter? And what is meant by *transcription?*

22.34 To make the pentapeptide, Met·Ala·Try·Ser·Tyr,
(a) What do the sequences of bases on the *m*RNA strand have to be?
(b) What is the anticodon on the first *t*RNA to move into place?

22.35 In general terms, what is a repressor, and what does it do?

22.36 What does an inducer do (in general terms)?

22.37 How do some of the antibiotics work at the molecular level?

22.38 The genetic code is the key to translating between what two "languages"?

22.39 What is meant by the statement that the genetic code is universal? And is the code strictly universal?

22.40 In general terms, how do X rays cause cancer?

22.41 How do X rays and gamma rays work in cancer therapy?

22.42 What is a radiomimetic substance?

Viruses

22.43 What is a virus made of?

22.44 How do at least some viruses get into their host cells?

22.45 What do viruses do, chemically, in host cells (in general terms)?

22.46 Viruses that can make RNA from RNA have to have or have to make what enzyme?

22.47 What enzymes must viruses have (or make) that manufacture DNA from RNA?

22.48 What does the prefix *retro* signify in retrovirus?

22.49 What is the full name of the HIV system?

22.50 What is the host cell of HIV and how does this fact make AIDS so dangerous?

Recombinant DNA

22.51 What is a plasmid, and what is it made of?

22.52 Recombinant DNA is made from the DNA of two different kinds of sources. What are they?

22.53 Recombinant DNA technology is carried out to accomplish the synthesis of what kind of substance (in general terms)?

22.54 What does genetic engineering refer to?

Hereditary Diseases

22.55 At the molecular level of life, what kind of defect is the fundamental cause of a hereditary disease?

22.56 What is the molecular defect in PKU, and how does it cause the problems of the victims? How is it treated?

22.57 What does *gene therapy* refer to?

Genetic DNA Fingerprinting (Special Topic 22.1)

22.58 What fact about cells makes it possible to use them from any part of the body of a suspect for genetic fingerprinting in a rape case for which a semen sample has been obtained?

22.59 A restriction enzyme separates DNA molecules into pieces given what general name? How are they used to give the genetic "bar code"?

Interferon (Special Topic 22.2)

22.60 What kinds of compounds are the interferons and what are they able to do that protects us from disease?

22.61 What kinds of infectious agents stimulate the production of interferons?

22.62 How are interferons made for clinical trials?

22.63 α-Interferon has been approved in the United States for use against what specific kind of cancer?

CHAPTER TWENTY-THREE

- **GENERAL NUTRITIONAL REQUIREMENTS**
- **PROTEIN REQUIREMENTS**
- **VITAMINS**
- **MINERALS AND TRACE ELEMENTS IN NUTRITION**

Nutrition

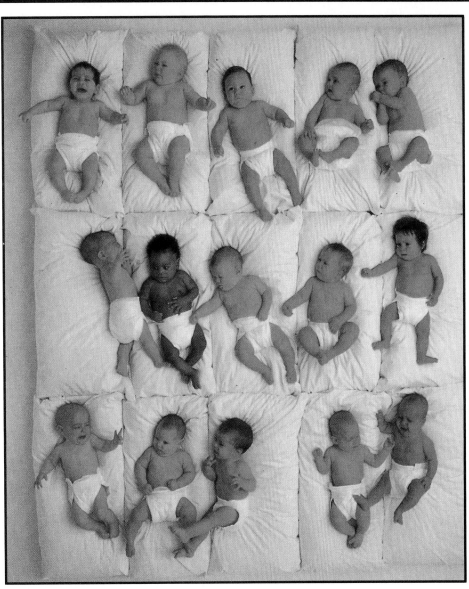

They obviously have had a great start in life. From here on nurture and nutrition will make the difference between wellness and sickliness. This chapter explains how vital amino acids and vitamins are.

23.1 GENERAL NUTRITIONAL REQUIREMENTS

The intent of the recommended dietary allowances (RDAs) is to help meal planners provide for the nutritional needs of practically all healthy people.

■ Two of the great scientific triumphs of the nineteenth century were the germ theory of disease and the birth of the science of nutrition.

Nutrition can be defined in both technical and personal terms. Technically, nutrition is a field of science that investigates the identities, the quantities, and the sources of substances, called *nutrients,* that are needed for health.

In personal terms, we speak of our own nutrition, the sum of the foods taken in the proper proportions at the best moments as we try to maintain a state of well-being and avoid diet-related diseases and infirmities.

The science of **dietetics** is the application of the findings of the science of nutrition to feeding individual human beings, whether they are ill or well.

This chapter is mostly about some of the major findings of the science of nutrition, a field so huge and complex that we can do little more than introduce some of its most important features and terms.

Nutrients Are Chemicals Required by Healthy Metabolism, and Foods Are Substances That Supply Them   When James Lind discovered in 1852 that oranges, lemons, and limes could cure scurvy, and K. Takadi in the 1880s found that a proper diet could cure beriberi, the science of nutrition was on its way. Good personal nutrition prevents a number of specific diseases and it cures several. It provides the correct nutrients for whatever happens to be the metabolic or health status of the body.

■ When the British navy required its sailors to eat limes regularly to combat scurvy, the sailors came to be called "limeys."

TABLE 23.1   Recommended Daily Dietary Allowances[a] of the Food and Nutrition Board, National Academy of Sciences National Research Council, Revised 1980

Persons	Age (years)	Weight (kg)	Weight (lb)	Height (cm)	Height (in.)	Protein (g)	Fat-Soluble Vitamins A (μg)[b]	D (μg)[c]	E (mg)[d]
Infants	0.0–0.5	6	13	60	24	kg $\times$ 2.2	420	10	3
	0.5–1.0	9	20	71	28	kg $\times$ 2.0	400	10	4
Children	1–3	13	29	90	34	23	400	10	5
	4–6	20	44	112	44	30	500	10	6
	7–10	28	62	132	54	36	700	10	7
Males	11–14	45	99	157	63	45	1000	10	8
	15–18	66	145	176	69	56	1000	10	10
	19–22	70	154	177	69	56	1000	7.5	10
	23–50	70	154	178	69	56	1000	5	10
	51+	70	154	178	69	56	1000	5	10
Females	11–14	46	101	157	62	46	800	10	8
	15–18	55	120	163	65	46	800	10	8
	19–22	55	120	163	65	44	800	7.5	8
	23–50	55	120	163	65	46	800	5	8
	51+	55	120	163	65	44	800	5	8
Pregnant						+30	+200	+5	+2
Lactating						+20	+400	+5	+3

[a] The allowances are intended to provide for individual variations among most normal persons as they live in the United States under usual environmental stresses. Diets should be based on a variety of common foods in order to provide other nutrients for which human requirements have been less well defined.

[b] Retinol equivalents. 1 retinol equivalent = 1 μg retinol or 6 μg β-carotene.

[c] As cholecalciferol. 10 μg cholecalciferol = 400 IU of vitamin D.

[d] α-Tocopherol equivalents. 1 mg d-α-tocopherol = 1 α-tocopherol equivalent.

The **nutrients** are any chemical substances that take part in any nourishing, health-supporting or health-promoting metabolic activity. Carbohydrates, lipids, proteins, vitamins, minerals, and trace elements are nutrients. Oxygen and water are usually not called nutrients, although they formally qualify under the definition. (We'll be saying more about these two later, anyway.) Materials that supply one or more nutrients are called **foods.**

The Recommended Dietary Allowances Describe What Nutrients Are Adequate for Healthy People   For several decades, the Food and Nutrition Board of the National Research Council of the National Academy of Sciences has published what are known as the **recommended dietary allowances,** or the **RDAs.** In the judgment of this Board, these allowances are the intake levels of essential nutrients that are "adequate to meet the known nutritional needs of practically all healthy persons." The values of the RDAs, as revised in 1980, are given in Table 23.1.

A number of points and qualifications about the RDAs must be emphasized.

1.   *The RDAs are not the same as the U.S. Recommended Daily Allowances (USRDA).*

The USRDAs are set by the U.S. Food and Drug Administration, based on the RDAs, as standards for nutritional information on food labels.

2.   *The RDAs are not the same as the Minimum Daily Requirements (the MDRs) for any one individual.*

The MDRs are just that, minimums. They are set very close to the levels at which actual signs of deficiencies occur. The RDAs are two to six times the MDRs. Just as individuals differ

TABLE 23.1   *(continued)*

Water-Soluble Vitamins							Minerals					
Ascorbic Acid (mg)	Folacin (µg)	Niacin (mg)	Ribo-flavin (mg)	Thiamine (mg)	Vitamin B_6 (mg)	Vitamin B_{12} (µg)	Calcium (mg)	Phos-phorus (mg)	Iodine (µg)	Iron (mg)	Mag-nesium (mg)	Zinc (mg)
35	30	6	0.4	0.3	0.3	0.5*g*	360	240	40	10	50	3
35	45	8	0.6	0.5	0.6	1.5	540	360	50	15	70	5
45	100	9	0.8	0.7	0.9	2.0	800	800	70	15	150	10
45	200	11	1.0	0.9	1.3	2.5	800	800	90	10	200	10
45	300	16	1.4	1.2	1.6	3.0	800	800	120	10	250	10
50	400	18	1.6	1.4	1.8	3.0	1200	1200	150	18	350	15
60	400	18	1.7	1.4	2.0	3.0	1200	1200	150	18	400	15
60	400	19	1.7	1.5	2.2	3.0	800	800	150	10	350	15
60	400	18	1.6	1.4	2.2	3.0	800	800	150	10	350	15
60	400	16	1.5	1.2	2.2	3.0	800	800	150	10	350	15
60	400	15	1.3	1.1	1.8	3.0	1200	1200	150	18	300	15
60	400	14	1.3	1.1	2.0	3.0	1200	1200	150	18	300	15
60	400	14	1.3	1.1	2.0	3.0	800	800	150	18	300	15
60	400	13	1.2	1.0	2.0	3.0	800	800	150	18	300	15
60	400	13	1.2	1.0	2.0	3.0	800	800	150	10	300	15
+20	+400	+2	+0.3	+0.4	+0.6	+1.0	+400	+400	+25	*h*	+150	+5
+40	+100	+5	+0.5	+0.5	+0.5	+1.0	+400	+400	+50	*h*	+150	+10

e The folacin allowances refer to dietary sources as determined by *Lactobacillus casei* assay under standard conditions for the assay.

f Niacin equivalents. 1 niacin equivalent (NE) = 1 mg of niacin or 60 mg of dietary tryptophan tocopherols.

g This is based on the average concentration of vitamin B_{12} in human milk.

h This increased requirement cannot be met by ordinary American diets, nor do many women have enough iron in existing stores. Therefore the use of supplemental iron is recommended.

greatly in height, weight, and appearance, they also differ greatly in specific biochemical needs. Therefore an effort has been made to set the RDAs far enough above average requirements so that "practically all healthy people" will thrive. Most will receive more than they need; a few will not receive enough.

One of the controversies over the RDAs concerns the validity of the statistical research and analysis by which "average requirements" were determined. Moreover, some nutritionists insist that among healthy people the range of daily need for a particular nutrient can vary far more widely than the Food and Nutrition Board has determined.

3. *The RDAs do not define therapeutic nutritional needs.*

 It's the job of hospital dieticians to devise the large variety of diets needed by the patient population.

People with chronic diseases such as prolonged infections or metabolic disorders; people who take certain medications on a continuing basis; and prematurely born infants all require special diets.

The RDAs do cover people according to age, sex, and size, and they indicate special needs for pregnant and lactating women, but they do not include any other special needs. Therapeutic needs for water and salt rise during strenuous physical activity and prolonged exposure to high temperatures.

In some areas of the United States and in many other parts of the world, intestinal parasites are common. These organisms rob the affected people of some of their food intake each day, and these people also need special diets.

4. *The RDAs can (and ought to) be provided in the diet from a number of combinations and patterns of food.*

No single food contains all nutrients. People take dangerous risks with their health when they go on fad diets limited to one particular food, like brown rice, gelatin, yogurt, or liquid protein. The ancient wisdom of a varied diet that includes meat, fruit, vegetables, grains, nuts, pulses (e.g., beans), and dairy products may seem to be supported solely by cultural and aesthetic factors. A varied diet, however, also assures us of getting any trace and needed nutrients that might not yet have been discovered.

■ Except for water, the nutrients in Table 23.2 are arranged in their order of requirements expressed in *moles.*

Table 23.2 is a compilation of the nutrients that are known to be required by every adult, according to American scientists and those with the United Nations. Some of the listed nutrients are not included in official U.S. tabulations either because they are so common that a deficiency is almost impossible or because it hasn't been possible to determine the minimum requirements.

Table 23.2 includes several elements such as iron and zinc. These are known as *trace elements,* and we'll return to them in Section 23.4.

Adults Have a Water Budget of 2.5 to 3 L per Day   Our water intake comes from the fluids we drink, the water in the foods we eat, and the water made by the oxidations of nutrients in cells. Most comes in response to the thirst mechanism.

Water leaves the body via the urine, the feces, exhaled air, and perspiration. Figure 23.1 gives the relative quantities by each route for adults and infants.

Figure 23.1
Water intake and outgo by the principal routes (excluding sensible perspiration —sweating). The dashed lines at "M" are the minimal volumes of urine at the maximal concentrations of solutes. "Ox" refers to water formed by the oxidation of foods. (*Source: Recommended Dietary Allowances,* 9th ed., National Academy of Sciences, Washington, D.C., 1980.

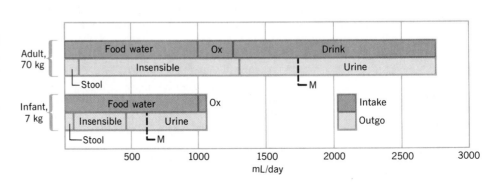

■ No amount of physical training or willpower can condition anyone to go without water.

Not shown in Figure 23.1 is the water that can be lost by sensible perspiration (sweat). An activity in the hot sun of an arid desert can cause the loss of as much as 10 L of water per day along with body salts. If these losses aren't made up at a reasonable rate, the results can be heat exhaustion, heat stroke, heat cramps, and even death.

Energy Needs Determine Oxygen Requirements Our daily oxygen needs are given in Table 23.2, because they indirectly tell us how much chemical energy we have to import each day to maintain metabolism under various activities. Our energy needs vary, of course, with the kinds of activities we have, and Table 23.3 shows the ranges, from the relative inactivity of sleep to heavy work.

At rest, the largest user of oxygen in the body is the brain. Its mass is only about 2% of the body mass, but it consumes 20% of the oxygen used by the resting body. Much of the energy used in the brain goes to keep up concentration gradients of ions across the membranes of the billions of brain cells.

■ High-protein diets, if eaten for an extended period, can make the kidneys overwork and become damaged.

Fad Diets Meant To Control Energy Intake Can Cause Grave Harm The energy obtained from food should not come exclusively either from carbohydrates alone or from fats alone. If you went on a zero-carbohydrate diet, your body would make glucose to meet its needs. (The brain derives nearly all its energy from the breakdown of glucose.) If the body has to make glucose over a long period of time, say weeks, a slow buildup of toxic wastes would cause harm. On the other hand, if you were to go on a zero-fat diet, then some fatty acids that are essential to the body would be unavailable, and your system would not absorb the fat-soluble vitamins very well. A daily diet that includes at least 15 to 25 g of food fat (the equivalent of two to four pats of margarine or butter) and 50 to 100 g of digestible carbohydrate prevents these problems.

Two Fatty Acids Must Be in the Diet Linoleic and arachidonic acid (Table 20.2) are called the **essential fatty acids,** and they are needed for the health and growth of infants. If they are not in the diet, the victims experience skin problems and problems in the transportation of lipids in the bloodstream.

Linoleic acid apparently is also essential to adults, but its widespread presence in all edible vegetable oils makes it virtually impossible for an adult not to obtain enough. Linoleic acid in adults can be used to make what arachidonic acid is needed. However, arachidonic acid is present in trace amounts in animal fats. This acid is used to make the prostaglandins that were described in Special Topic 20.1, page 516.

23.2 PROTEIN REQUIREMENTS

A protein's biological value is determined largely by its digestibility and its ability to supply the essential amino acids.

■ This is only about 2 ounces per day.

The total protein requirement (Table 23.2) is 56 g/day for adult men and 46 g/day for adult women. Small as these numbers are, they are still more than the bare minimum. Their intent is to allow about 30% extra to cover a wide range of variations in the protein needs of individuals. Moreover, they assume that we digest and absorb into the bloodstream only 75% of the protein in the diet. (These allowances are considered too narrow by some nutritionists.)

Essential Amino Acids
_____

Isoleucine
Leucine
Lysine
Methionine
Phenylalanine
Threonine
Tryptophan
Valine
_____
Histidine is believed to be essential to infants.

Our Protein Requirement Actually Means a Requirement for Essential Amino Acids Proteins supply α-amino acids, and these are what protein requirements are all about. We need daily intakes in particular of a small number of specific amino acids whose presence in the diet is so critical that they are called the **essential amino acids.**

Of the 20 amino acids used to make proteins, adults can synthesize 12 from parts and pieces of other molecules, including other amino acids. This leaves eight essential amino acids, those that the body cannot synthesize, at least not at rates rapid enough to make much difference. They are listed in Table 23.2 as well as in the margin.

TABLE 23.2 Adult Human Nutritional Requirements

Nutrient	Mass		Moles	
	Man[a]	Woman[b]	Man[a]	Woman[b]
Oxygen	800 g	593 g	25.0	18.5
	560 L[c]	414 L[c]		
As air, 21% oxygen	2930 L[d]	2173 L[d]		
Water[e]	2800 g	2000 g	155	111
Energy	2700 kcal	2000 kcal		
If all from glucose	675 g	500 g	3.75	2.78
If all from fat	300 g	222 g	0.338	0.25
Protein	56 g	46 g	0.47[f]	0.38[f]
Essential amino acids				
Tryptophan	0.5 g		0.0025	
Phenylalanine	2.2 g		0.0133	
Lysine	1.6 g		0.0110	
Threonine	1.0 g		0.0085	
Methionine[h]	2.2 g		0.0150	
Leucine	2.2 g		0.0168	
Isoleucine	1.4 g		0.0106	
Valine	1.6 g		0.0137	
Sodium chloride[j]	3.0 g		0.051	
Potassium	1.0 g		0.026	
Phosphorus	0.8 g		0.026	
Calcium	0.8 g		0.020	
Magnesium	0.35 g		0.015	
Essential fatty acids[j]	3.0 g		0.010	
Iron[k]	0.018 g		3.2×10^{-4}	
Vitamin C	0.045 g		2.5×10^{-4}	
Zinc	0.015 g		2.2×10^{-4}	
Niacin	0.018 g		1.5×10^{-4}	
Fluorine	0.002 g		1.0×10^{-4}	
Vitamin E[l]	0.015 g		3.5×10^{-5}	
Copper	0.0015 g		2.4×10^{-5}	
Pantothenic acid[m]	0.005 g		2.3×10^{-5}	
Manganese[m]	0.001 g		1.8×10^{-5}	
Vitamin K[l]	0.005 g		1.1×10^{-5}	
Vitamin B_6	0.002 g		1.0×10^{-5}	
Vitamin A[l]	0.0015 g		5.2×10^{-6}	
Riboflavin	0.0016 g		4.2×10^{-6}	
Thiamin	0.0014 g		4.2×10^{-6}	
Iodine	0.00012 g		9.4×10^{-7}	
Folic acid	0.0004 g		9.0×10^{-7}	
Biotin[m]	0.00015 g		6.0×10^{-7}	
Vitamin D[n]	0.00001 g		2.6×10^{-8}	
Chromium	0.000001 g		2.0×10^{-8}	

TABLE 23.2 *(continued)*

Nutrient	Mass		Moles	
	Man[a]	Woman[b]	Man[a]	Woman[b]
Vitamin B_{12}	0.0000005 g		3.7×10^{-9}	
Cobalt	0.00000002 g		3.7×10^{-9}	
Molybdenum[o]				
Vanadium[o]				
Selenium[o]				
Tin[o]				

Source of data: F. E. Deatherage, *Food for Life,* Plenum Publishing Corporation, New York, 1975. Used by permission.

[a] Man: Weight, 70 kg (154 lb). Height, 175 cm (5 ft 8 in.). Age, 22 to 50 years.

[b] Woman: Weight, 58 kg (128 lb). Height, 163 cm (5 ft 5 in.). Age, 22 to 50 years.

[c] At 0 °C and 760 mm Hg pressure.

[d] At 20 °C and 740 mm Hg — room conditions.

[e] Includes water consumed directly and as a component in food plus the water made by the oxidation of nutrients.

[f] Average formula weight of amino acids is 120.

[g] 0.22 g if tyrosine is available.

[h] 0.35 g if cystine is available.

[i] 2 to 3 g is minimum, but the salt requirement as well as the water requirement may increase in warm climates and during heavy work.

[j] As linoleic, linolenic, and/or arachidonic acid.

[k] Recommended for menstruating women; for men about 0.01 g is recommended.

[l] A number of closely related chemical compounds may serve this vitamin function. 1 IU (International Unit) of A = 0.3 μg of retinol or 0.6 μg of β-carotene. 1 IU of E = 1.0 mg of DL-α-tocopherol acetate or 0.81 mg D-α-tocopherol.

[m] Although definitely required, the amount of this nutrient's daily requirement has not been established. Sufficient amounts are in many foods.

[n] Vitamin D may not be required by the adult but is required by growing children; it is made from normal skin constituents by ultraviolet light or it may be fed in the diet. 1 IU of D = 0.025 μg of D_3, activated 7-dehydrocholesterol.

[o] It is known that this trace element is an integral part of vital enzyme systems, but the daily requirement has not been established. Sufficient amounts are in many foods.

TABLE 23.3 Daily Energy Expenditures of Adult Men and Women in Light Occupations

Activity Category	Time (hr)	Man (70 kg)		Woman (58 kg)	
		Rate		Rate	
		kcal/min	Total (kcal)	kcal/min	Total (kcal)
Sleeping, reclining	8	1.0–1.2	540	0.9–1.1	440
Very light[a]	12	up to 2.5	1300	up to 2.0	900
Light[b]	3	2.5–4.9	600	2.0–3.9	450
Moderate[c]	1	5.0–7.4	300	4.0–5.9	240
Heavy[d]	0	7.5–12.0	___	6.0–10.0	___
Total	24		2740		2030

Source: J. V. G. A. Durin and R. Passmore, 1967. In *Recommended Dietary Allowances,* 9th ed., National Academy of Sciences, Washington, D.C., 1980.

[a] Seated and standing activities, driving cars and trucks, secretarial work, laboratory work, sewing, ironing, playing musical instruments.

[b] Walking (on the level, 2.5 to 3 mph), tailoring and pressing, carpentry, electrical trades, restaurant work, washing clothes, light recreation such as golf, table tennis, volleyball, sailing.

[c] Walking at 3.5 to 4 mph, garden work, scrubbing floors, shopping with heavy load, moderate sports such as skiing, tennis, dancing, bicycling.

[d] Uphill walking with a load, pick-and-shovel work, lumbering, heavy sports such as swimming, climbing, football, or basketball.

Our total daily needs for the essential amino acids add up only to about 13 g, less than half an ounce. When a cell is actually making a protein, however, all the amino acids needed for it must be available *at the same time,* even if only a trace of any one is required. The absence of lysine, for example, when a protein that includes it has to be made, would prevent the synthesis of the protein altogether.

The Availability of Amino Acids Varies with the Digestibility of the Dietary Protein Not all proteins are easily and completely digested. The variations are expressed by a **coefficient of digestibility,** defined by Equation 23.1.

$$\text{Coefficient of digestibility} = \frac{(\text{N in food eaten}) - (\text{N in feces})}{(\text{N in food eaten})} \tag{23.1}$$

The difference of terms in the numerator:

$$(\text{N in food eaten}) - (\text{N in feces})$$

is the nitrogen that is actually absorbed by the bloodstream.

Animal proteins have higher coefficients of digestibility than those of plants or fruits. For the average animal protein this coefficient is 0.97, which means 97% digestible. The coefficients for the proteins in fruits and fruit juices average about 0.85; for whole wheat flour 0.79; and for whole rye flour 0.67. Milling improves the digestibility coefficients, raising them to 0.83 for all-purpose bread flour and 0.89 for cake flour.

Milling does the same to rice. The digestibility coefficient for brown rice is 0.75 but 0.84 for polished white rice. Milling, unfortunately, also reduces the quantities of vitamins, minerals, and fiber in the grain product. But these are usually put back, as in enriched flours, for example.

The average digestibility coefficient of the proteins in legumes and nuts is 0.78, and in vegetables the range is 0.65 to 0.74.

Proteins Low in Essential Amino Acids Have Low Biological Value The digestibility of a protein is just one factor in the quality of a protein source. If a protein is lacking or low in one or more of the essential amino acids, it is a low-quality protein.

When the body gets amino acids from a low-quality protein, it simply will not be able to use the amino acids efficiently *to make protein.* When a low-quality protein diet fails to supply one essential amino acid, like lysine, the body still gets a load of other amino acids it can't use to make lysine-containing proteins. There is no way to store these excess amino acids until lysine arrives, and they cannot be excreted as amino acids. To get rid of them, the body has to break them down so their nitrogen can be excreted as urea. This leaves other compounds.

The remaining, nitrogen-free products can be used by the body for energy, as we'll study later. But if the body isn't demanding this energy by its level of activity, then it converts these breakdown products into fat. You can get fat on a high-protein, low-activity diet, and you strain your kidneys besides.

Urea

One Measure of Protein Quality Is Called the Protein's Biological Value Measured when the body operates under the stress of receiving not quite enough protein overall, the percent of the nitrogen retained out of the total nitrogen eaten is called the **biological value** of the protein. It is a measure of the efficiency with which the body uses the nitrogen *of the actually absorbed amino acids* furnished by the protein.

The largest single factor in a protein's biological value is its amino acid composition. What most limits biological value is the extent to which the protein supplies the essential amino acids in sufficient quantities for human use. Human milk protein is the best of all proteins in terms of digestibility and biological value. Whole-egg protein is very close, and it is often taken as the reference for experimental work.

When the diet is well balanced in absorbable amino acids, the amount of nitrogen ingested equals the amount excreted. This condition is called **nitrogen balance.** Most 70-kg

TABLE 23.4 Comparisons of Food Proteins with Human Milk Protein

Food	Limiting Amino Acid	Food's Protein Equivalent to 35 g Human Milk Protein (g)	Digestibility Coefficient of Food's Protein	Amount of Food's Protein[a] (g)	Percentage of Protein in the Food	Amount of Food Needed[b]	Kilocalories of Food Received
Wheat	Lysine	80.6	79.0	102	13.3%	767 g (1.7 lb)	2560
Corn	Tryptophan and lysine	72.4	60.0	120	7.8%	1540 g (3.4 lb)	5660
Rice	Lysine	51.7	75.0	68.9	7.5%	919 g (2.0 lb)	3310
Beans	Valine	50.5	78.0	64.8	24.0%	270 g (0.59 lb)	913
Soybeans	Methionine and cysteine	43.8	78.0	56.2	34.0%	165 g (0.36 lb)	665
Potatoes	Leucine	71.6	74.0	96.7	2.1%	4600 g (10.1 lb)	3500
Cassava	Methionine and cysteine	82.4	60.0	137	1.1%	12,500 g (27.5 lb)	16,400
Eggs	Leucine	36.6	97.0	37.8	12.8%	295 g (0.65 lb)	477
Meat	Tryptophan	43.1	97.0	44.4	21.5%	206 g (0.45 lb)	295
Cow's milk	Methionine and cysteine	43.8	97.0	45.2	3.2%	1410 g (3.1 lb)	903

Source: Data from F. E. Deatherage, *Food for Life,* Plenum Press, New York, 1975. Used by permission.

[a] The grams of protein that have to be obtained from each food source for the protein to be nutritionally equivalent (with respect to essential amino acids) to 35 g of human milk protein, allowing for the poorer digestibility of that food's protein (i.e., its digestibility coefficient).

[b] The grams of each food that are equivalent in nutritional value (with respect to essential amino acids) to 35 g human milk protein, allowing for the digestibility coefficient and the percent protein in the food.

■ Infants and schoolchildren must have a positive nitrogen balance, meaning that they must ingest more nitrogen than they excrete, in order to grow.

men could be in nitrogen balance by ingesting 35 g/day of the proteins in human milk. This value is used as a reference standard in rating other proteins.

The Essential Amino Acids Most Poorly Supplied Put an Upper Limit on a Protein's Biological Value Table 23.4 summarizes some information about most of the proteins, named in the first column, that are prominent in various diets of the world's peoples. We now study what the data in the other columns mean.

Column 2 The essential amino acid that is most poorly supplied by a given protein is called its **limiting amino acid.** These are named in this column of Table 23.4.

Column 3 This column gives the number of grams of each food that a 70-kg man would have to digest *and absorb* per day to get the same amount of its limiting amino acid that is available from 35 g of human milk protein. Such an intake, of course, would also supply all the other needed but nonlimiting amino acids. For example, 80.6 g of wheat protein — not wheat, but wheat protein — would have to be digested and absorbed to obtain the lysine in 35 g of human milk protein. But this figure, 80.6 g, assumes 100% digestion, so we have to adjust for a lower percentage digestion.

Column 4 This column gives the digestibility coefficients of all the proteins listed. Wheat protein has a digestibility coefficient of 0.790 so, by a factor of 100/79.0, we need more wheat protein than 80.6 g in order to get the necessary lysine.

Column 5 Here is the result of multiplying 80.6 by (100/79.0). We need 102 g of wheat protein to get the necessary limiting amino acid, lysine. But remember, we're talking about wheat *protein,* not actual wheat, so we move on to the next column.

Column 6 Wheat, on the average, is only 13.3% protein, so we have to multiply our 102 g of wheat protein by the factor 100/13.3. The grim result, 767 g, is in the next column.

Column 7 A 70-kg man would have to eat 767 g (1.69 lb) of wheat if his daily needs for all amino acids are to be met by wheat alone. But all this wheat also has calories. The implication of a daily diet of 767 g of wheat is in the last column.

Column 8 Anyone eating 767 g of wheat also gets 2560 kcal of food energy. This is nearly as much total energy per day as a 70-kg man should have, so the amount isn't prohibitive, but can you imagine a diet this boring? Just imagine the man's problems if he had to get all his amino acids from potatoes, 10.1 lb/day, or cassava, 27.5 lb/day!

The data in Table 23.4 are of tremendous importance to those concerned about supplying both the protein and total calorie needs of the world's burgeoning population. Neither children nor adults can eat enough corn, rice, potatoes, or cassava per day to meet both their protein and energy needs.

Proteins That Provide a Balanced Supply of Essential Amino Acids Are Called Adequate Proteins

Proteins of eggs and meat, as you can see in Table 23.4, are particularly good. They are said to be **adequate proteins,** because they include all the essential amino acids in suitable proportions to make it possible to satisfy amino acid and total nitrogen needs without excess intake of calories.

Soybeans are the best of the nonanimal sources of proteins. Cassava, a root, is an especially inadequate protein, and corn (or maize) is also poor. Unhappily, huge numbers of the world's peoples, especially those in Africa, Central and South America, India, and the countries of the Middle and Far East, rely heavily on these two foods. Although they adequately provide energy needs, not enough of them can be eaten per day to give the essential amino acids, so there are widespread dietary deficiency diseases in these regions.

Variety in the Diet Offers Many Nutritional Advantages

The data in Table 23.4 also provide scientific support for the long-standing practices in all major cultures of including a wide variety of foods in the daily diet. Meat and eggs can ensure adequate protein while they leave room for an attractive variety that is important to good eating habits. Milk, soybeans, and other beans also leave room for variety.

With Planning and Good Timing, Vegetarians Obtain All Essential Amino Acids

When both rice (low in lysine) and beans (low in valine) are included in equal proportions, about 43 g of a rice–bean combination is equal in protein value to 35 g of human milk protein. Less of this combined diet is needed than rice alone or beans alone, which means that room is left for other foods that our taste buds crave.

The rice and beans should, of course, be eaten fairly closely together to ensure that all essential amino acids are simultaneously available during protein synthesis. Eating just the rice early in the morning and the beans in the evening works against efficient protein synthesis. All of us, including vegetarians, must also include adequate amounts of another family of substances the body cannot make, the vitamins.

23.3 VITAMINS

The vitamins essential to health must be in the diet because the body cannot make them.

■ Vitamin = "vital amine," from an early belief that vitamins might all be amines.

The term **vitamin** applies to any compound or a closely related group of compounds satisfying the following criteria:

1. It is organic rather than inorganic or an element.

2. It cannot be synthesized at all (or at least in sufficient amounts) by the body and it must be in the diet.

3. Its absence causes a specific **vitamin deficiency disease.**

4. Its presence is essential to normal growth and health.

5. It is present in foods in *small* concentrations, and it is not a carbohydrate, a saponifiable lipid, an amino acid, or a protein.

Sometimes Any Member of a Set of Compounds Prevents a Vitamin-Deficiency Disease The members of a set of related compounds that prevent a specific vitamin-deficiency disease are called *vitamers*. The body can convert any one of them into the active forms needed. Our needs for vitamin A, for example, are satisfied by several structurally related compounds, including a family of plant pigments called the carotenoids.

Some Individuals Require Greater Daily Vitamin Intakes Because of Genetic Defects In addition to vitamin deficiency diseases, there are at least 25 disorders classified as *vitamin-responsive inborn errors of metabolism*. These are caused by genetic faults that can be partly and sometimes entirely overcome by the daily ingestion of 10 to 1000 times as much of a particular vitamin as normally should be present in the diet.

Genetic faults can compromise the body's use of a vitamin at several places along the vitamin's metabolic path. There might be impaired absorption of the vitamin, or impaired transport in the blood. Many vitamins are needed to provide a prosthetic group for an enzyme, so the genetic error could be a defect in building the vitamin molecule into the enzyme.

Vitamins Are Classified as Fat-Soluble or Water-Soluble As we should now expect, fat-soluble vitamins are largely hydrocarbon-like, and water-soluble vitamins are polar or ionic.

As a group, the fat-soluble vitamins pose dangers when taken in excess. We all have at least some fatty tissue, and "like dissolves like." So when we ingest surpluses of the fat-soluble vitamins, fatty tissue absorbs some of the excess. Such accumulations can be dangerous, as we will see. Dietary surpluses of water-soluble vitamins leave the body in the urine.

In this section we study what the vitamins are, their related deficiency diseases, and their sources. In the next chapter, we will see how the body uses them at the molecular level.

The Fat-Soluble Vitamins Are A, D, E, and K The fat-soluble vitamins occur in the fat fractions of living systems. Table 23.2 gives their requirements for adults. Because molecules of these vitamins have alkene double bonds or phenol rings, oxidizing agents readily attack them. These vitamins are destroyed, therefore, by prolonged exposures to air or to organic peroxides found in fats and oils becoming rancid.

Vitamin A activity is given by several vitamers. In the body the active forms — retinol, retinal, and retinoic acid — all have five alkene groups. β-carotene is a source for all three because the liver has enzymes that can cleave its molecules to give the retinol skeleton. This is why β-carotene, the yellow pigment in many plants and available in liver and egg yolk, is an important source of vitamin A activity. It is an example of a *provitamin*, a compound that the body can change into an active vitamin.

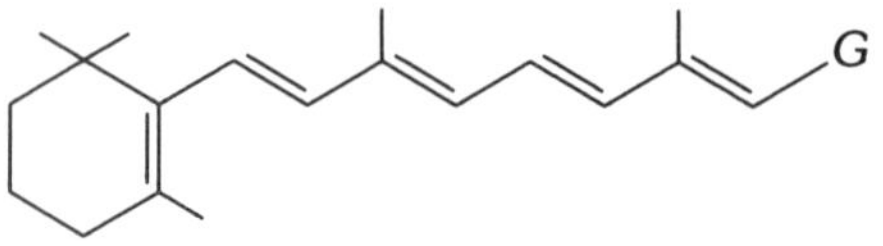

Retinol, $G = CH_2OH$
Retinal, $G = CH{=}O$
Retinoic acid, $G = CO_2H$

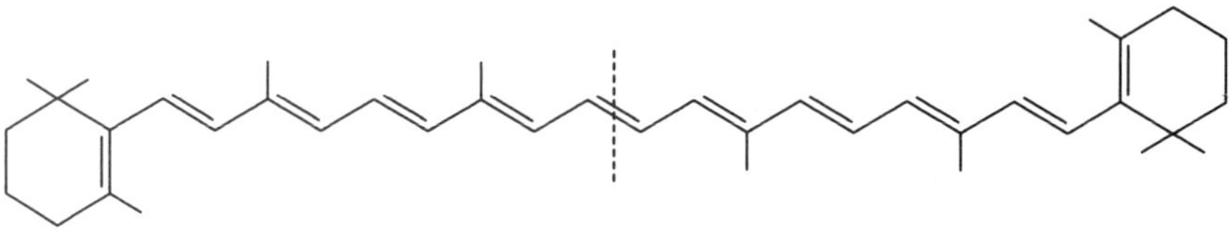

*β-*Carotene

The deficiency disease for vitamin A is nyctalopia, or night blindness — impaired vision in dim light. We also need vitamin A for healthy mucous membranes.

Several studies have shown that a high intake of β-carotene in a diet rich in vegetables and fruit is associated with a reduced risk of cancer of the epithelial cells in several locations. (Epithelial cell cancers, like colon cancer and lung cancer, account for over 90% of cancer deaths in the United States.) The ease of oxidation of the multiply unsaturated skeleton of β-carotene might account for this. Two kinds of oxidizing agents, excited (activated) oxygen and free radicals, have been implicated in the onset of cancer, and β-carotene might serve to trap and destroy them.

Excess doses of vitamin A must not be taken because it is toxic to adults. The livers of polar bears and seals are particularly rich in vitamin A, and Eskimos are careful about eating these otherwise desirable foods. Siberian huskies also have very high levels of vitamin A in their livers, and early explorers, when driven to eating their sled dogs to survive, risked serious harm and death by eating too much husky liver. In early 1913 the Antarctic explorer X. Mertz almost certainly died in just this way, and his companion, Douglas Mawson, barely survived.

Some and maybe all forms of vitamin A, when taken in excess, are also known to be teratogenic (they cause birth defects), so vitamin supplements with extra vitamin A should not be taken by pregnant women.

Vitamin D also exists in a number of forms. Cholecalciferol (D_3) and ergocalciferol (D_2) are two that occur naturally.

■ Epithelial cells make up the tissue that lines tubes and cavities.

■ Those suffering from excess vitamin A recover quite quickly when they stop taking vitamin A.

■ Notice the alkene groups, which are easily oxidized and so can trap undesirable oxidizing agents, like peroxides.

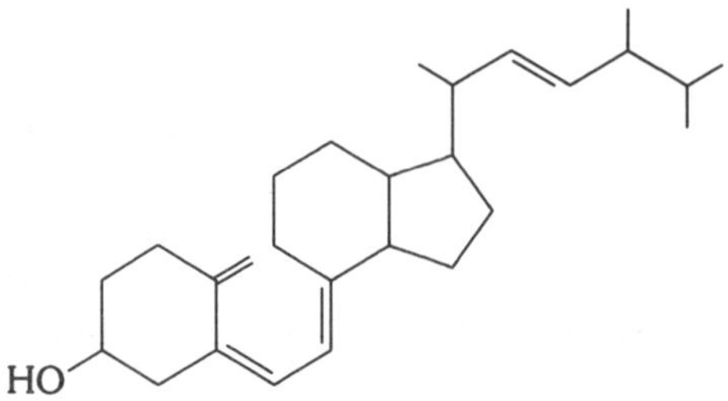

HO

Ergocalciferol (D_2)

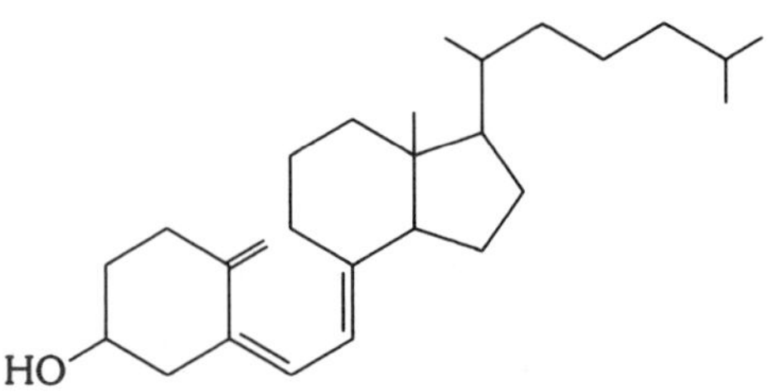

HO

Cholecalciferol (D_3)

These two are equally useful in humans, and either can be changed in the body to the slightly oxidized forms that the body uses as hormones to stimulate the absorption and uses of calcium ions and phosphate ions. Vitamin D is especially important during the years of early growth when bones and teeth, which need calcium and phosphate ions, are developing. Lack of vitamin D causes the deficiency disease known as rickets, a bone disorder.

Eggs, butter, liver, fatty fish, and fish oils such as cod-liver oil are good natural sources of vitamin D precursors. The most common source today is vitamin-D-fortified milk. We are able to make some vitamin D ourselves from certain steroids that we can manufacture, provided we get enough direct sunlight on the skin. Energy absorbed from sunlight converts these steroids to the vitamin. Youngsters who worked from dawn to dusk in dingy factories or mines during the early years of the industrial revolution were particularly prone to rickets, simply because they saw little if any sun.

No advantage is gained by taking large doses of vitamin D, and in sufficient excess it is dangerous. Excesses promote a rise in the calcium ion level of the blood, and this damages the kidneys and causes soft tissue to calcify and harden.

Vitamin E needs are satisfied by any member of the tocopherol family. The most active member is α-tocopherol.

■ Poor management of Ca^{2+} metabolism contributes to a disfiguring bone condition of old age called osteoporosis.

■ The benzene ring with the phenolic OH is easily oxidized, which makes the tocopherols effective in trapping unwanted oxidizing agents.

α-Tocopherol

Vitamin E detoxifies organic peroxides, those with structures such as $R\!-\!O\!-\!O\!-\!H$. These can form when oxygen attacks CH_2 groups that are adjacent to alkene double bonds, as in the many $-CH_2\!-\!CH\!=\!CH-$ units in molecules of the unsaturated fatty acids. Because the acyl units of these acids are present in the phospholipids of which cell membranes are made, vitamin E is needed to protect all membranes.

In the absence of vitamin E, the activities of certain enzymes are reduced, and red blood cells hemolyze more readily. Anemia and edema are reported in infants whose feeding formulas are low in vitamin E. According to some studies, a lack of vitamin E can contribute to an increased susceptibility to sudden heart attacks, especially in males under stress.

Vitamin E occurs so widely in vegetable oils that it is almost impossible not to obtain enough of it. It is generally considered to be relatively nontoxic to humans, but because it's a fat-soluble vitamin, it can accumulate in fatty tissue. Caution must be used in taking it as a supplement, but intakes in the range of 200 to 600 mg/day appear to be acceptable in humans.

Vitamin K is the antihemorrhagic vitamin. It is present in green, leafy vegetables, and deficiencies are rare. It works as a cofactor in the blood-clotting mechanism. Sometimes women about to give birth and later their newborn infants are given vitamin K to provide an extra measure of protection against possible hemorrhaging.

■ Much of the vitamin K that we need is made for us by our own intestinal bacteria.

The Water-Soluble Vitamins Are Vitamin C, Choline, Thiamin, Riboflavin, Nicotinamide, Folacin, Vitamin B₆, Vitamin B₁₂, Pantothenic Acid, and Biotin

These are the water-soluble vitamins recognized by the Food and Nutrition Board. It is widely believed that they are among the safest substances known, but this generalization is much too broad, as we will see.

Vitamin C, or ascorbic acid, prevents scurvy, a sometimes fatal disease in which collagen is not well made. Whether it prevents other diseases is the subject of enormous controversy, speculation, and research. It is an antioxidant, much as is vitamin E. A variety of

■ Collagen is the protein in bone that holds the minerals together, much as steel rods work in reinforced concrete.

studies have found that vitamin C is involved in the metabolism of amino acids, in the synthesis of some adrenal hormones, and in the healing of wounds. There are probably millions of people who believe that vitamin C in sufficient dosages — up to several grams per day — acts to prevent or to reduce the severity of the common cold. The vitamin appears to be nontoxic at these high levels.

Vitamin C is present in citrus fruits, potatoes, leafy vegetables, and tomatoes. It is destroyed by extended cooking, heating over steam tables, or prolonged exposure to air or to ions of iron or copper. Even when vitamin C is kept in a refrigerator in well-capped bottles, it slowly deteriorates.

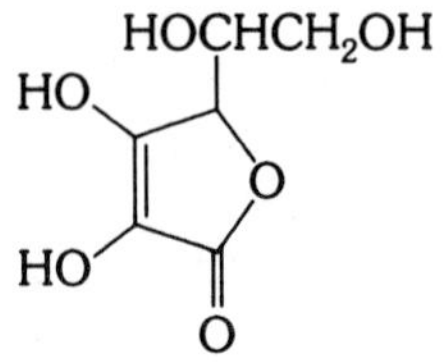

Vitamin C (ascorbic acid)

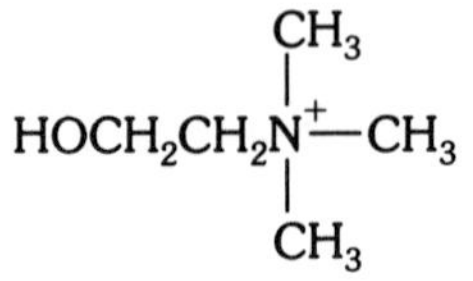

Choline

■ Acetylcholine is one of several neurotransmitters.

Choline is needed to make complex lipids, as we discussed in Section 20.3. Acetylcholine, which is made from choline, is one of several substances that carry nerve signals from one nerve cell to another. The body can make choline, but the Food and Nutrition Board calls it a vitamin because there are ten species of higher animals that have dietary requirements for it. We make it too slowly to meet all our daily needs, so having it in the diet provides protection. It occurs widely in meats, egg yolk, cereals, and legumes. No choline deficiency disease has been demonstrated in humans, but in animals the lack of dietary choline leads to fatty livers and to hemorrhagic kidney disease.

■ In rice, most of the thiamine is in the husk, which is lost when raw rice is milled.

Thiamine is needed for the breakdown of carbohydrates. Its deficiency disease is beriberi, a disorder of the nervous system. Good sources are lean meats, legumes, and whole (or enriched) grains. It is stable when dry but destroyed by alkaline conditions or prolonged cooking. Thiamine is not stored, and excesses are excreted in the urine. One's daily thiamine requirement is proportional to the number of calories that are represented by the diet. The Food and Nutrition Board recommends 0.5 mg/1000 kcal for children and adults.

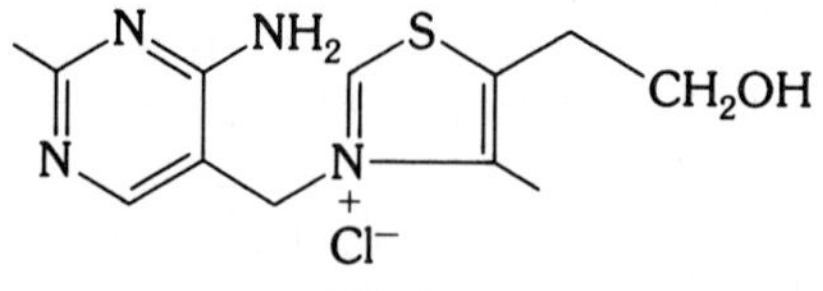

Thiamine

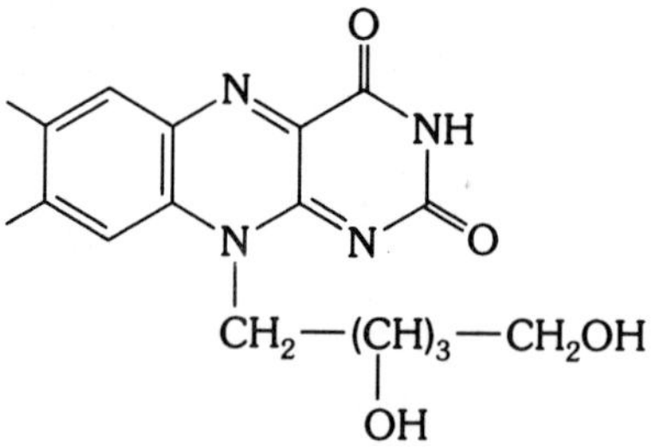

Riboflavin

Riboflavin is required by a number of oxidative processes in metabolism. Deficiencies lead to the inflammation and breakdown of tissue around the mouth and nose as well as the tongue, a scaliness of the skin, and burning, itching eyes. Wound healing is impaired. The best source is milk, but certain meats (e.g., liver, kidney, and heart) also supply it. Cereals are poor sources unless they have been enriched. Little if any riboflavin is stored, and excesses in the diet are excreted. Alkaline substances, prolonged cooking, and irradiation by light destroy this vitamin.

■ Severe niacin deficiency can cause delerium and dementia.

Niacin, meaning both nicotinic acid and nicotinamide, is essential for nearly all biological oxidations. It's needed by every cell of the body every day. Its deficiency disease is pellagra, a deterioration of the nervous system and the skin. Pellagra is particularly a problem where corn (or maize) is the major item of the diet. Corn (maize) is low in niacin and the essential amino acid tryptophan, from which we are able to make some of our own niacin. Where the diet is low in tryptophan, niacin must be provided in other foods, such as enriched grains. Prolonged cooking destroys niacin.

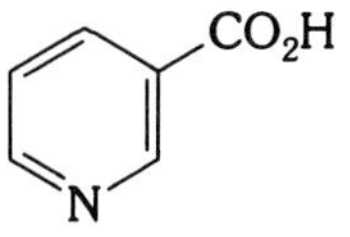

■ We can make about 1 mg of niacin for every 60 mg of dietary tryptophan — nearly all we need.

Nicotinic acid (niacin) 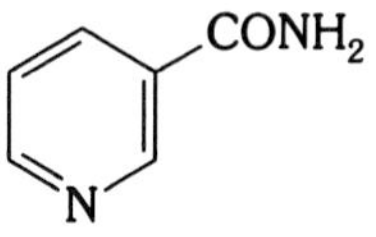 Nicotinamide (niacinamide)

■ Chronic alcoholism causes folacin deficiency.

Folacin is the name used by the Food and Nutrition Board for folic acid and related compounds. Its deficiency disease is megaloblastic anemia. Several drugs, including alcohol, promote folic acid deficiency. It is needed for the synthesis of nucleic acids and heme. Good sources are fresh, leafy green vegetables, asparagus, liver, and kidney. Folacin is relatively unstable to heat, air, and ultraviolet light, and its activity is often lost in both cooking and food storage.

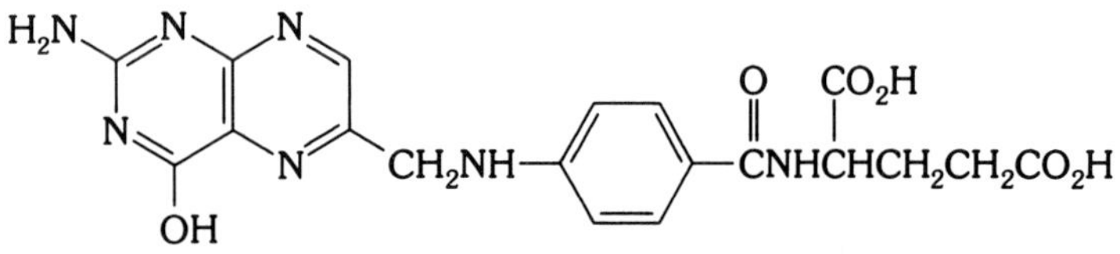

Folic acid

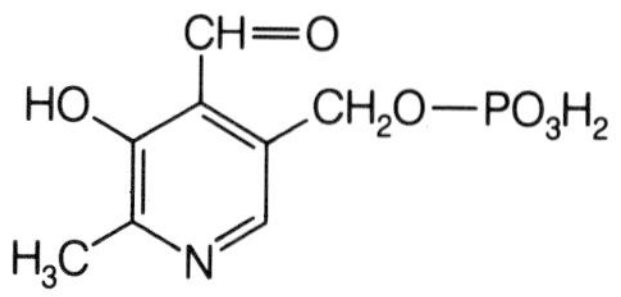

Vitamin B₆ activity is supplied by pyridoxine, pyridoxal, or pyridoxamine. All can be changed in the body to the active form, pyridoxal phosphate. The activities of at least 60 enzymes involved in the metabolism of various amino acids depend on pyridoxal phosphate. One deficiency disease is hypochromic microcytic anemia, and disturbances in the central nervous system also occur. The vitamin is present in meat, wheat, yeast, and corn. It is relatively stable to heat, light, and alkali.

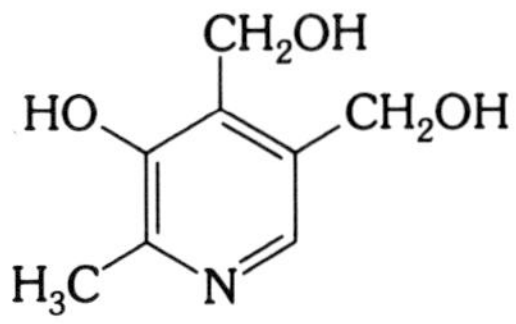

Pyridoxal phosphate

Pyridoxine 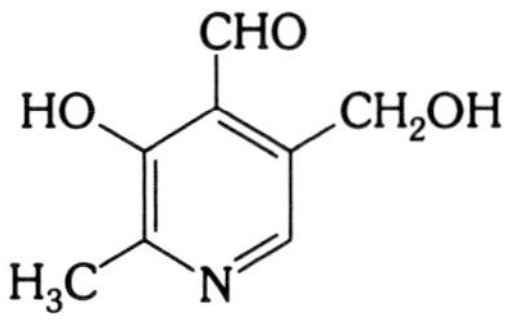 Pyridoxal 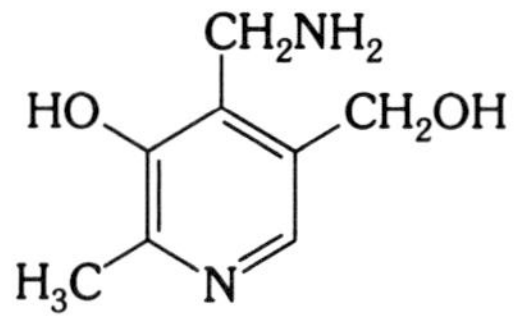 Pyridoxamine

Pyridoxine is widely used as a component of body-building diets and in the treatment of premenstrual syndrome. Massive doses ("megavitamin doses") at levels of 500 mg/day and higher, however, can severely disable parts of the nervous system and should be avoided. Pyridoxine is clearly not "among the safest substances known."

Vitamin B₁₂, or cobalamin, is a specific controlling factor for pernicious anemia. This deficiency disease, however, is very rare, because it is very difficult to design a diet that lacks this vitamin. Animal products such as liver, kidney, and lean meats as well as milk products and eggs are good sources — and virtually the only sources. Thus most people who develop B₁₂ deficiency are true vegetarians (or are infants born of true vegetarian mothers). Any symptoms of B_{12} deficiency have a slow onset because the body stores the vitamin fairly well and because such minute traces are needed.

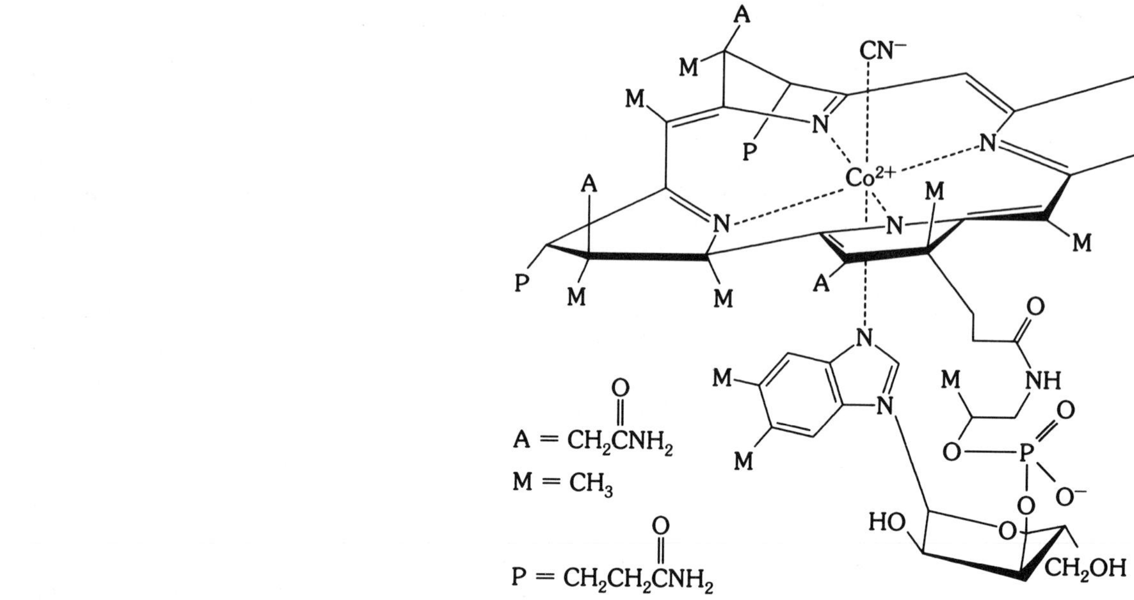

$A = CH_2\overset{\displaystyle O}{\overset{\|}{C}}NH_2$

$M = CH_3$

$P = CH_2CH_2\overset{\displaystyle O}{\overset{\|}{C}}NH_2$

Cyanocobalamin

Pantothenic acid is used to make a coenzyme, coenzyme A (symbol: CoASH), which the body needs to metabolize fatty acids. Signs of a deficiency disease for this vitamin have not been observed clinically in humans, but the deliberate administration of compounds that work to lower the availability of pantothenic acid in the body causes symptoms of cellular damage in vital organs. This vitamin is supplied by many foods, and especially by liver, kidney, egg yolk, and skim milk.

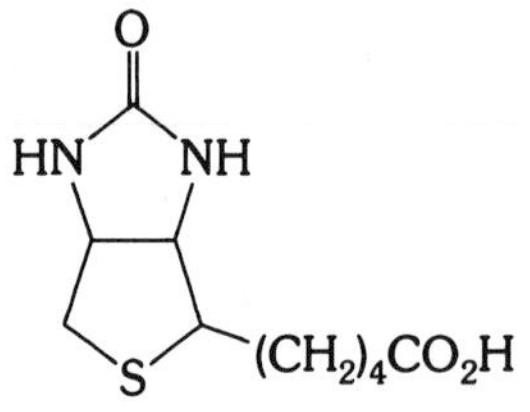

Biotin

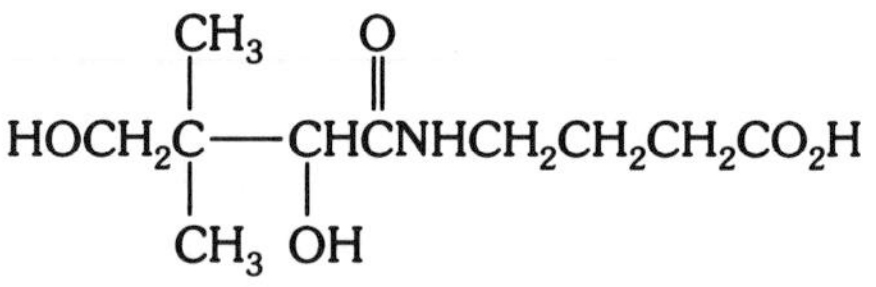

$HOCH_2\overset{\displaystyle CH_3}{\underset{\displaystyle CH_3}{C}}-\overset{\displaystyle }{\underset{\displaystyle OH}{CH}}\overset{\displaystyle O}{\overset{\|}{C}}NHCH_2CH_2CH_2CO_2H$

Pantothenic acid

Biotin is required for all pathways in which carbon dioxide is temporarily used as a reactant, as in the synthesis of fatty acids that we'll study in Chapter 28. Signs of biotin deficiency are difficult to find, but when such a deficiency is deliberately induced, the person experiences nausea, pallor, dermatitis, anorexia, and depression. When biotin is given again, the symptoms disappear. Our own intestinal microorganisms probably make biotin for us. Egg yolks, liver, tomatoes, and yeast are good sources.

23.4 MINERALS AND TRACE ELEMENTS IN NUTRITION

Many metal ions are necessary for the activities of enzymes.

Most of the minerals and trace elements needed in the diet are metal ions, but some anions are also required. The distinction between a *mineral* and a *trace element* is a matter of quantity.

Minerals Are Needed at Levels of 100 mg/day or More   The dietary **minerals** are calcium (Ca^{2+}), phosphorus (phosphate ion, P_i), magnesium (Mg^{2+}), sodium (Na^+), potassium (K^+), and chlorine (Cl^-). These are the chief electrolytes in the body. The uses of these minerals will be described elsewhere, principally in Chapter 25.

Trace Elements Are Needed at Levels of 20 mg/day or Less   The Food and Nutrition Board recognizes 17 **trace elements,** all of which have been found to have various biological functions in animals, and which therefore are quite likely used in the human body. Ten of them are *known* to be needed by humans: fluorine (as F^-) and iodine (as I^-), and the ions of chromium, manganese, iron, cobalt, copper, zinc, selenium, and molybdenum. All are toxic in excessive amounts. They occur widely in food and drink, but some are removed by food refining and processing.

   Fluorine (as fluoride ion) is essential to the growth and development of sound teeth, and the Food and Nutrition Board recommends that public water supplies be fluoridated at a level of about 1 ppm wherever natural fluoride levels are too low. Both the medical and dental associations in the United States strongly support this. Those in some other countries do not, France, West Germany, Denmark, for example. A controversy over the appropriateness of fluoridating drinking water supplies has gone on for nearly half a century.

   Iodine (as iodide ion) is essential in the synthesis of certain hormones made by the thyroid gland. Diets deficient in iodide ion cause an enlargement of the thyroid gland known as a goiter. It takes only about 1 μg (1×10^{-6} g) of I^- per kilogram of body weight each day to prevent a goiter.

   Seafood is an excellent source of iodide ion, but iodized salt with 75 to 80 μg of iodide ion equivalent per gram of salt is the surest way to obtain the iodine that is needed. Before the days of iodized salt, goiters were quite common, especially in regions where little if any fish or other seafood was in the diet.

   Chromium (Cr^{3+}) is required for the work of insulin and normal glucose metabolism. Chromium that occurs naturally in foods is absorbed significantly more easily than chromium given as the simple salts added to vitamin–mineral supplements. Most animal proteins and whole grains supply this trace element. The daily intake should be 0.05 to 0.2 mg.

   Manganese (Mn^{2+}) is required for normal nerve function, for the development of sound bones, and for reproduction. It is essential to the activities of certain enzymes in the metabolism of carbohydrates. Nuts, whole grains, fruits, and vegetables supply this element, but a recommended daily allowance has yet to be set by the Food and Nutrition Board. Some nutritionists recommend a daily intake of 2.5 to 5.0 mg/day.

   Iron (Fe^{2+}) is needed in heme and several enzymes. The intestines regulate how much dietary iron is absorbed, so a proper level of iron in circulation is maintained in this way. A high serum iron level apparently renders an individual more susceptible to infections. Pregnant women must have larger than usual amounts of iron to keep pace with the needs of fetal blood.

   Cobalt (Co^{2+}) is part of the vitamin B_{12} molecule (cyanocobalamin, page 592). Apparently there is no other use for it in humans. But without it there can be anemia and growth retardation.

   Copper (Cu^{2+}) occurs in a number of proteins and enzymes. If deficient in copper, the individual synthesizes lower-strength collagen and elastin and will tend to suffer anemia, skeletal defects, and degeneration of the myelin sheaths of nerve cells. Ruptures and aneurysms of the aorta become more likely. The structure of hair is affected, and reproduction tends to fail.

   Fortunately, copper occurs widely in foods, particularly in nuts, raisins, liver, kidney, certain shellfish, and legumes. An intake of just 2 mg/day assures a copper balance for nearly all people. Unfortunately, however, the copper contents of the foods in a typical American diet have declined over the last four decades. Some scientists believe that the increase in the incidence of heart disease in the United States during this period has been caused partly by diets low in copper. In one study that involved women, the lower the copper level in the blood, the higher were their blood cholesterol levels. (We'll discuss cholesterol and heart disease in Chapter 28.)

■ 1 ppm $F^- = 1$ mg/L

■ High-fiber diets can work against the absorption of some of the trace elements.

Zinc (Zn^{2+}) is required for the activities of several enzymes. Without sufficient zinc in the diet, an individual will experience loss of appetite and poor wound healing. Insufficient zinc in an infant's diet, which is a chronic problem in the Middle East, causes dwarfism and poor development of the gonads. If too much zinc is in the diet, and too little copper is present, the extra zinc acts to inhibit the absorption of copper. The ratio of zinc to copper probably doesn't matter as long as sufficient copper is available. When enough zinc is present, it acts to inhibit the absorption of a rather toxic pollutant, cadmium (as Cd^{2+}), which is just below zinc in the periodic table.

Selenium is known to be essential in many animals, including humans. How much we need is not known, but probably we need 0.05 to 0.2 mg/day. *Too much is very toxic.*

A strong statistical correlation exists between high levels of selenium in livestock crops and low incidences of human deaths by heart disease. In the United States, those who live where selenium levels are high — the Great Plains between the Mississippi River and the eastern Rocky Mountains — have one-third the chance of dying from heart attack and strokes as those who live where levels are very low — the northeastern quarter of the United States, Florida, and the Pacific Northwest. Rats, lambs, and piglets on selenium-poor diets develop damage to heart tissue and abnormal electrocardiograms.

Selenium reduces the occurrence of certain cancers in animals, and it may possibly provide a similar benefit in humans, but at excessive levels it causes cancer in experimental animals.

Molybdenum is in an enzyme required for the metabolism of nucleic acids as well as in some enzymes that catalyze oxidations. Deficiencies in humans are unknown, meaning that almost any reasonable diet furnishes enough.

Nickel, silicon, tin, and vanadium are possibly trace elements for humans, because deficiency diseases for these elements have been induced in experimental animals.

SUMMARY

Nutrition Good nutrition entails the ingestion of all the substances needed for health — water, oxygen, food energy, essential amino acids and fatty acids, vitamins, minerals, and trace elements. Foods that best supply various nutrients have been identified. The Food and Nutrition Board of the National Academy of Sciences regularly publishes *recommended daily allowances* that are intended to be amounts that will meet the nutritional needs of practically all healthy people. Some people need more, most need less. But neither more nor less of anything is necessarily better. The RDAs should be obtained by a varied diet because it promotes good eating habits and because such a diet might supply a nutrient no one yet knows is essential.

Water needs The thirst mechanism leads to our chief source of water. Our principal routes of exporting water are the urine, perspiration (both sensible and insensible), and exhaled air. When excessive water is lost during vigorous exercise, the body also loses electrolytes.

Energy Both carbohydrates and lipids should be in the diet as sources of energy. Without carbohydrates for several days, certain poisons build up in the blood as the body works to make glucose internally from amino acids. A zero-lipid diet means zero ingestion of essential fatty acids. Our oxygen requirements adjust to the caloric demands of our activities.

Protein in the diet What we need most from proteins are certain essential amino acids, and we need some extra nitrogen if we have to make the nonessential amino acids. When a diet excretes as much nitrogen as it takes in, the individual is in nitrogen balance. The most superior, balanced proteins — those that are highly digestible and that supply the essential amino acids in the right proportions — are proteins associated with animals such as the proteins in milk and whole eggs. (Human milk protein is the standard of excellence, and whole-egg protein is very close to it.)

The most important factor in the biological value of a protein is its limiting amino acid — the essential amino acid that it supplies in the lowest quantity. Another factor is the digestibility of the protein. For several reasons — poor source of an essential amino acid, low digestibility coefficients, low concentration of the protein — several foods cannot be used as exclusive or even major components of a healthy diet. Foods that have inadequate proteins include corn (maize), rice, potatoes, cassava, and manioc.

Vitamins Organic compounds, called vitamins, or sets of closely related compounds that satisfy the same need, must be in the diet in at least trace amounts or an individual will suffer from a vitamin deficiency disease. Vitamins can't be made by the body. (Essential amino acids and essential fatty acids are generally not classified as vitamins, nor are carbohydrates, proteins, or triacylglycerols and other saponifiable lipids.) Excessive amounts of the fat-soluble vitamins (A, D, E, and K) — especially A and D — must be avoided. These vitamins accumulate in fatty tissue, and in excess they can cause serious trouble. Any excesses of the water-soluble vitamins are eliminated.

Minerals and trace elements The minerals are inorganic cations and anions that are needed in the diet in amounts in excess of 100 mg/day. The trace elements are needed at levels of 20 mg/day or less. The whole-body quantities of the minerals are large relative to the trace elements. (More about minerals is given in later chapters.)

The trace elements that are metal ions are essential to several enzyme systems. Two anions are trace elements, F^- and I^-. Fluoride ion is needed to make strong teeth, and iodide ion is needed to make thyroid hormones and to prevent goiter.

REVIEW EXERCISES

The answers to these Review Exercises are in the *Study Guide* that accompanies this book.

Nutrition

23.1 What does the science of nutrition study?

23.2 What is meant by the term *nutrient?*

23.3 What is the relationship of nutrients to foods?

23.4 What is the relationship of the science of dietetics to nutrition?

23.5 Why are the recommended dietary allowances higher than minimum daily requirements?

23.6 What are seven situations that require special therapeutic diets?

23.7 Why should our diets be drawn from a variety of foods?

23.8 What is potentially dangerous about the following diets?
(a) A carbohydrate-free diet
(b) A lipid-free diet

Protein and Amino Acid Requirements

23.9 Because the full complement of 20 amino acids is required to make all the body's proteins, why are fewer than half of this number considered essential amino acids?

23.10 If we are able to make all the nonessential amino acids, why should our daily protein intake include more than what is represented solely by the essential amino acids?

23.11 What does the body do with the amino acids that it absorbs from the bloodstream but doesn't use?

23.12 What is the equation that defines the coefficient of digestibility of a protein? What does the numerator in this equation stand for?

23.13 Which kind of protein is generally more fully digested by the body, the protein from an animal or a plant source?

23.14 What can be done to whole grains to improve the digestibility of their proteins? What also happens in this process that reduces the food value of the grains?

23.15 What is the most important factor in determining the biological value of a given protein?

23.16 Which specific protein has the highest coefficient of digestibility and the highest biological value for humans? Which protein comes so close to this on both counts that it is possible to use it as a substitute for research purposes?

23.17 What is meant by the *limiting* amino acid of a protein?

23.18 Why does the protein in corn have a lower biological value than the protein in whole eggs?

23.19 In one variety of hybrid corn, the limiting amino acids are lysine and tryptophan. It takes 75 g of this corn to provide the protein equivalent to 35 g of human milk protein. The coefficient of digestibility of the protein in this corn is 0.59.
(a) In order to match the nutritional value of human milk protein, how many grams of the protein in this corn must be ingested?
(b) To get this much protein from this variety of corn, how many grams of the corn must be eaten? The corn is only 7.6% protein.
(c) How many kilocalories are also consumed with the quantity of corn calculated in part (b) if the corn has 360 kcal/100 g?
(d) Could a child eat enough corn per day to satisfy all its protein needs and still have room for any other food?

23.20 The limiting amino acid in peanuts is lysine, and 62 g of protein obtained from peanuts is equivalent to 35 g of human milk protein. The coefficient of digestibility of peanut protein is 0.78. In order to match human milk protein in nutritional value,
(a) How many grams of peanut protein must be eaten?
(b) How many grams of peanuts must be eaten if peanuts are 26.2% protein?
(c) How many kilocalories are also ingested with this many grams of peanuts if peanuts have 282 kcal/100 g?
(d) Could a child eat enough peanuts per day to satisfy its protein needs and still have room for other foods?

Vitamins

23.21 Make a table that lists each vitamin, at least one good source of each, and a serious consequence of a deficiency of each. (Use just the information available in this book.) Set up the table with the following column heads.

Vitamin	Source(s)	Problem(s) If Deficient

23.22 Why aren't the essential amino acids listed as vitamins?

23.23 On a strict vegetarian diet — no meat, eggs, and dairy products of any sort — which one vitamin is the most difficult to obtain?

23.24 Why should strict vegetarians use two or more different sources of proteins?

23.25 Which are the fat-soluble vitamins?

23.26 Which vitamin is activated when the skin is exposed to sunlight?

23.27 Which vitamin acts as a hormone in its active forms?

23.28 Which vitamin has been shown to be teratogenic when used in excess?

23.29 The yellow-orange pigment in carrots, carotene, can serve as a source of the activity of which vitamin?

23.30 The vitamin needed to participate in the blood-clotting mechanism is which one?

23.31 The Food and Nutrition Board of the National Academy of Sciences recognizes which substances as the water-soluble vitamins?

23.32 Scurvy is prevented by which vitamin?

23.33 Name two vitamins that tend to be destroyed by prolonged cooking.

23.34 Which vitamin prevents beriberi?

23.35 When corn (maize) is the chief food in the diet, which vitamin is likely to be in short supply because a raw material for making it is in short supply?

Minerals and Trace Elements

23.36 What criterion makes the distinction between *minerals* and *trace elements?*

23.37 Name and give the chemical forms of the six minerals.

23.38 Make a table of the ten trace elements and at least one particular function of each.

23.39 What can be the body's response to an iodine-deficient diet?

CHAPTER TWENTY-FOUR

Enzymes, Hormones, and Neurotransmitters

What an outpouring of adrenaline must occur in a race, not just in the running but also in the exaltation of winning. Adrenaline, more properly called epinephrine, is one of the hormones that helps the body mobilize glucose for energy.

24.1   ENABLES

24.1   ENZYMES

The catalytic abilities of enzymes often depend on cofactors that are made from B vitamins.

Virtually all enzymes are proteins. A few have been discovered that are made of RNA, but they are rare exceptions. In this chapter we will study only enzymes that are proteins.

■ All enzyme molecules and most substrate molecules are chiral: they have handedness.

Enzymes Are Very Specific in the Substrates They Accept   Enzyme specificity is one property that a theory of enzyme action has to explain. Few enzymes are so specific, however, that they catalyze just one particular reaction of one particular compound. Most enzymes possess *relative specificity*. Enzymes that catalyze the hydrolysis of esters, for example, usually handle a variety of esters, not just one. They do not work as well if at all, however, for the hydrolysis of any other kind of functional group.

Enzymes that work with the hydrolysis of biopolymers, like starch, polypeptides, and nucleic acids, frequently are specific about the points on the biopolymer they attack. Some digestive enzymes catalyzing the hydrolysis of peptide bonds specialize, for example, in bonds adjacent to particular aminoacyl side chains. Their work splits long polypeptides into shorter molecules. Another digestive enzyme then goes to work exclusively on the C-terminal aminoacyl units of these shorter chains, and still another enzyme works on the N-terminal units.

Enzymes Display Remarkable Rate Enhancements   Enzymes, like all catalysts, affect the *rates* of reactions by providing a reaction pathway with a lower energy of activation than the uncatalyzed reaction can take. Even small reductions of energy barriers can cause spectacular increases in rates. The enzyme carbonic anhydrase (CA) is an example. It catalyzes the interconversion of bicarbonate ion and protons with carbon dioxide and water:

$$CO_2 + H_2O \xrightleftharpoons[\text{carbonic anhydrase}]{} HCO_3^- + H^+$$

■ The equilibrium *must* shift to the right to make H_2CO_3 when the supply of CO_2 is high — a consequence of Le Chatelier's principle.

In actively metabolizing cells, where the supply of CO_2 is relatively high, this equilibrium shifts to the right, and each molecule of carbonic anhydrase aids in the conversion of 600,000 molecules of CO_2 *each second!* This is the fastest known rate for any enzyme-catalyzed reaction, and it is ten million times faster than the uncatalyzed reaction. In blood that circulates into the lungs, where exhaling keeps the supply of CO_2 low, this equilibrium must shift to the left, and the same enzyme participates in this change.

Enzymes Get Equilibria Established Extremely Rapidly   In a chemical equilibrium, like that involving carbonic anhydrase, it is important to remind ourselves that the catalyst speeds up *equilibration*. It accelerates *both* the forward and the reverse reactions. Whether the equilibrium shifts to the right or to the left doesn't depend on the catalyst at all. It depends strictly on the inherent equilibrium constants; on the relative concentrations of reactants and products; on whether other reactions feed substances into the equilibrium or continuously remove them; and on the temperature. All the catalyst does is to make whatever shift is mandated by these conditions occur very rapidly.

Most Enzymes Consist of Polypeptides Plus Cofactors   The molecules of most enzymes include a nonpolypeptide component called a **cofactor.** The polypeptide is called the **apoenzyme,** but without the cofactor there is no enzymic activity.

The cofactor of some enzymes is simply a metal ion. Zn^{2+} is the metal ion in carbonic anhydrase. Fe^{2+} occurs in a family of enzymes, the cytochromes, involved in biological oxidations. Most of the trace metal ions of nutrition are enzyme cofactors.

In other enzymes the cofactor is an organic molecule or ion, called a **coenzyme.** Some enzymes have both a coenzyme and a metal ion cofactor.

■ Thiamine is vitamin B$_1$.

B Vitamins Are Used To Make Coenzymes   Thiamine diphosphate, a coenzyme with structure **1,** is a diphosphate ester of thiamine, a B vitamin.

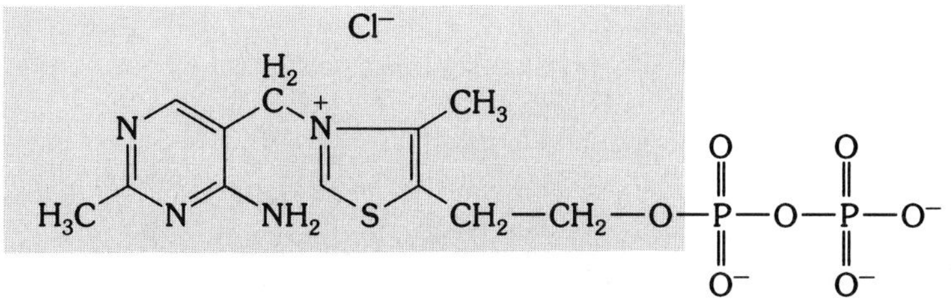

1
Thiamine diphosphate

When pure, this coenzyme is a triprotic acid, but at the pH of body fluids it is ionized as shown.

■ *Dinucleotide* means that two nucleotides are joined together.

Nicotinamide, another B vitamin, is part of the structure of nicotinamide adenine dinucleotide, **2a,** another important coenzyme. Mercifully, its long name is usually shortened to NAD$^+$ (or, sometimes, just NAD). Notice that the bottom half of the NAD$^+$ molecule is from adenosine monophosphate, AMP. Its upper half is almost like this except that a molecule of nicotinamide has replaced adenine.

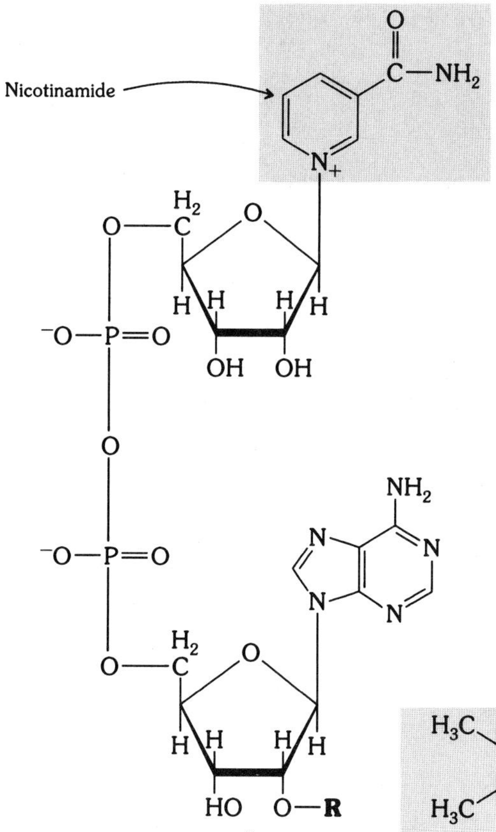

2
a NAD$^+$ **R** = H
b NADP$^+$ **R** = OPO$_3{}^{2-}$

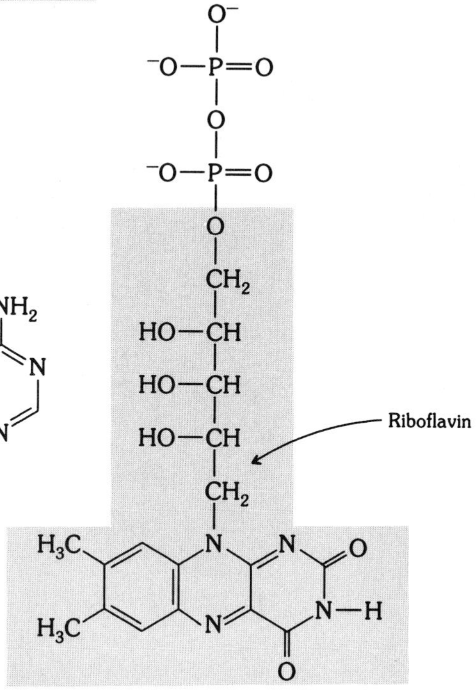

3
FMN

■ The P in NADP$^+$ refers to the extra phosphate ester unit.

Nicotinamide occurs in yet another important coenzyme, nicotinamide adenine dinucleotide phosphate, **2b,** a phosphate ester of NAD$^+$. Its name is usually shortened to NADP$^+$ (or,

---

SPECIAL TOPIC 24.1   **HOW NAD⁺ AND FAD (OR FMN) PARTICIPATE IN ELECTRON TRANSFER**

In the nicotinamide unit of both NAD^+ and $NADP^+$ there is a positive charge on the nitrogen atom, an atom that is also part of an aromatic ring. Despite how rich this ring is in electrons, the positive charge on N makes it an electron acceptor. Without the charge, the ring would otherwise be very similar to the ring in benzene, and it would strongly resist any reaction that disrupted its closed-circuit electron system. The positive charge on N, however, places the ring of the nicotinamide unit on an energy teeter-totter which, the cell can tip either way without too much energy cost.

As seen in the following equations, when the donor of an electron pair, such as an oxidizable alcohol, arrives at the enzyme, the donor can transfer the electron pair (as $H{:}^-$) to the ring. Even though the ring will temporarily lose its aromatic character, the positive charge of the ring nitrogen atom encourages this transfer of negative charge. In the next step of this metabolic pathway, the pair of electrons, still as $H{:}^-$, transfers to a riboflavin unit, also shown in the equations below. As this occurs, the ring of the nicotinamide unit recovers its stable, benzene-like nature.

Eventually, the pair of electrons winds up on an oxygen atom when, in the last step of this long metabolic pathway, oxygen that has been supplied by the air we breathe is reduced to water. We'll return to these steps in Chapter 26.

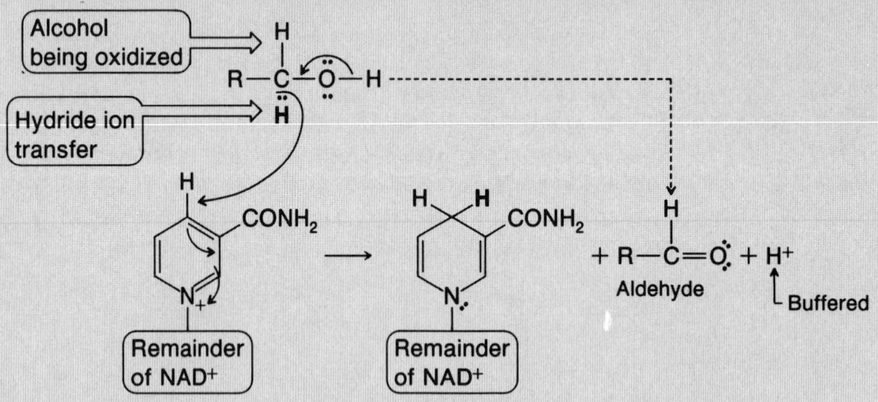

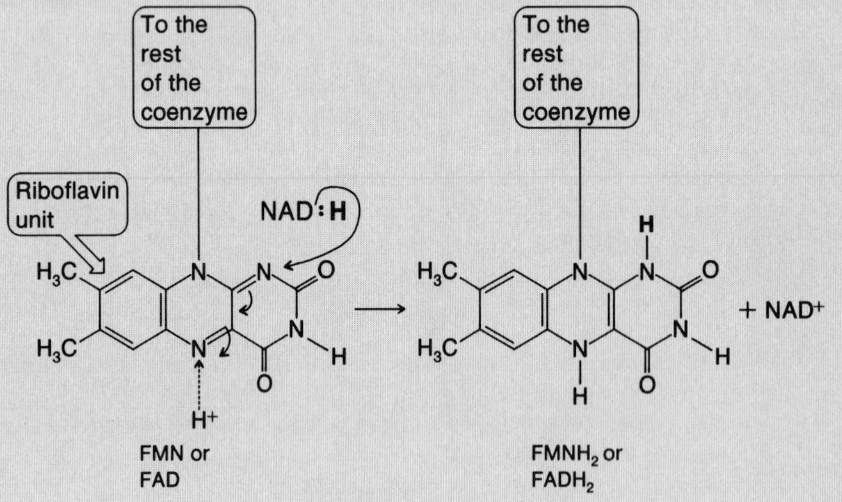

---

sometimes, just NADP). Both NAD^+ and $NADP^+$ are coenzymes in major biological oxidation–reduction reactions.

Quite often equations that involve enzymes with recognized coenzymes are written with the symbol of the coenzyme as a reactant or as a product. NAD^+, for example, is the cofactor for the enzyme that catalyzes the body's oxidation of ethyl alcohol to acetaldehyde. It serves, in fact, as the actual acceptor of the hydride ion, $H{:}^-$, given up by ethyl alcohol. The details are reserved to Special Topic 24.1, but the overall equation is written simply as follows.

$$CH_3CH_2OH + NAD^+ \longrightarrow CH_3CH{=}O + NAD{:}H + H^+$$

Ethyl alcohol   Ethanal   Reduced form of NAD^+ Hydrogen ion (buffered)

When the symbol of a coenzyme is used in an equation, remember that it stands for the entire enzyme that bears the coenzyme. In this reaction the NAD^+ unit in the enzyme accepts $H{:}^-$ from the alcohol, and we can write this part of the reaction by the following equation:

$$NAD^+ + H{:}^- \longrightarrow NAD{:}H$$

By accepting the *pair of electrons* in $H{:}^-$, NAD^+ is reduced, and $NAD{:}H$ (usually written as NADH) is called the *reduced form* of NAD^+. $NADP^+$ can also accept hydride ion, and its reduced form is written as NADPH.

We learned earlier that we may not call something a catalyst unless it undergoes no *permanent* change, but the foregoing examples seem to contradict this. In the body, however, a reaction that alters an enzyme is followed at once by one that regenerates the enzyme. The NADH produced by the oxidation of ethyl alcohol, for example, is recovered in the next step. The next enzyme, FAD (for flavin adenine dinucleotide), **3**, employs still another B vitamin, riboflavin. FAD accepts $H{:}^-$ from $NAD{:}H$, changes to $FADH_2$ (the second H is H^+ from the buffer), and restores NAD^+. This is also shown in Special Topic 24.1, but the overall reaction is

■ Riboflavin is vitamin B_2.

$$NADH + FAD + H^+ \longrightarrow NAD^+ + FADH_2$$

The FAD-containing enzyme is, of course, now in its reduced form, $FADH_2$. $FADH_2$ passes on its load of hydrogen and electrons in yet another step and so is reoxidized and restored to FAD. The steps continue, but we'll stop here. The main points are that B vitamins are key parts of coenzymes, and that the catalytic activities of the associated enzymes involve the molecules of these vitamins directly.

Flavin mononucleotide or FMN is a near relative of FAD that contains riboflavin. Its reduced form is $FMNH_2$, and it is also involved in biological oxidations.

Enzymes Are Named after Their Substrates or Reaction Types   Nearly all enzymes have names that end in *-ase*. The prefix is either from the name of the substrate or from the kind of reaction. For example, an **esterase** aids the hydrolysis of esters. A **lipase** works on the hydrolysis of lipids. A **peptidase** catalyzes the hydrolysis of peptide bonds. Similarly, an **oxidase** is an enzyme that catalyzes an oxidation, and a **reductase** handles a reduction. An **oxidoreductase** handles a redox equilibrium. A **transferase** catalyzes the transfer of a group from one molecule to another, and a **kinase** is a special transferase that handles phosphate groups.

■ Whenever we see *-ase* as a suffix in the name of any substance or type of reaction, the word is the name of an enzyme.

These names are chemically informative, but not all enzyme names are. The peptidases *trypsin* and *pepsin*, for example, have old names that tell us nothing. To ensure clear, informative names of enzymes, an International Enzyme Commission has developed a system of classifying and naming enzymes. The names of the principal reactants, separated by a colon, are written first and then the name of the kind of reaction is written as a prefix to *-ase*. For example, in moving from left to right in the following equilibrium, an amino group transfers from the glutamate ion to the pyruvate ion:

■ This reaction, incidentally, is an example of how the body can make an amino acid — here, alanine — from other substances.

$$^-O_2CCH_2CH_2CHCO_2^- + CH_3\overset{\overset{\displaystyle O}{\|}}{C}CO_2^- \rightleftharpoons {}^-O_2CCH_2CH_2\overset{\overset{\displaystyle O}{\|}}{C}CO_2^- + CH_3CHCO_2^-$$

$$\underset{NH_3^+}{\big|} \qquad\qquad\qquad\qquad\qquad\qquad\qquad\qquad\qquad\qquad \underset{NH_3^+}{\big|}$$

Glutamate ion   Pyruvate ion α-Ketoglutarate ion   Alanine

The systematic name for the enzyme is *glutamate : pyruvate aminotransferase.* In all but formal publications, such a cumbersome (but unambiguous) name is seldom used. This enzyme, for example, is most often referred to simply as GPT.

Enzymes Often Occur as a Family of Similar Compounds Called Isoenzymes with Identical Functions

Identical reactions are often catalyzed by enzymes with identical cofactors but slightly different apoenzymes. These variations are called **isoenzymes** or **isozymes.**

Creatine kinase or CK, for example, consists of two polypeptide chains M (for skeletal muscle) and B (for brain). It occurs as three isoenzymes. All catalyze the transfer of a phosphate group in the following equilibrium:

■ When supplies of ATP are low and those of ADP are therefore high, the *reverse* of this equilibrium becomes a major path for making more ATP in muscle cells.

■ ATP is adenosine triphosphate, which we described together with ADP in Section 16.6.

$$\underset{\text{Creatine}}{\overset{\overset{\displaystyle NH_2^+}{\|}}{NH_2CNCH_2CO_2^-} \overset{|}{\underset{CH_3}{}}} + ATP \underset{\substack{\text{creatine}\\\text{kinase}}}{\rightleftharpoons} \underset{\text{Creatine phosphate}}{\overset{\overset{\displaystyle O NH_2^+}{\| \|}}{^-OPONHCNCH_2CO_2^-}} \overset{|}{\underset{O^- CH_3}{}} + ADP$$

One CK isoenzyme, called CK(MM), has two M units and occurs in skeletal muscle. Another, CK(BB), has two B units and occurs in brain tissue. The third, CK(MB), has one M and one B polypeptide, and it is present almost exclusively in heart muscle, where it accounts for 15% to 20% of the total CK activity. The rest is contributed by CK(MM).

We have given this much detail about creatine kinase because this and similar enzymes have an extraordinarily important function in clinical analysis and diagnosis, as we'll see later in the chapter.

24.2 THE ENZYME–SUBSTRATE COMPLEX

The flexibility of an enzyme and its aminoacyl side chains allow only the enzyme's substrate to fit to it and to become activated for a reaction.

When an enzyme catalyzes a reaction of a substrate, molecules of each must momentarily fit to each other. This temporary combination is called an **enzyme–substrate complex.** It is part of a series of chemical equilibria that carry the substrate through a number of changes until the products of the overall reaction form.

$$\underset{\text{Enzyme}}{E} + \underset{\text{Substrate}}{S} \rightleftharpoons \underset{\substack{\text{Enzyme–}\\\text{substrate}\\\text{complex}}}{E-S} \rightleftharpoons \underset{\substack{\text{Substrate–}\\\text{activated}\\E-S \text{ complex}}}{E-S^*} \rightleftharpoons \underset{\substack{\text{Enzyme–}\\\text{product}\\\text{complex}}}{E-P} \rightleftharpoons \underset{\substack{\text{Enzyme}\\\text{(recovered)}}}{E} + \underset{\text{Product}}{P}$$

■ Hormone uptake by just specific cells also depends on a lock- and-key recognition.

The first equilibrium is the binding of the enzyme to the substrate and is like the fitting of a key (the substrate molecule) to a tumbler lock (the enzyme). This theory is thus often called the **lock-and-key theory** of enzyme action. See Figure 24.1.

For the key to fit, however, the tumblers in the lock must adapt to the key. An enzyme molecule has similar flexibility. According to the **induced-fit theory,** as the substrate molecule nestles onto the enzyme molecule, the molecular groups of the substrate induce the enzyme into an even better fit. See Figure 24.2. Thus an enzyme–substrate complex, $E-S$, forms. This initial fitting largely explains why enzymes are so *specific* in the types of reactions that they catalyze.

The polypeptide in the enzyme has aminoacyl side chains (or groups of them), called **binding sites.** They have shapes and electrical charges that help to bind the substrate to the enzyme. Other groups on the enzyme, called **catalytic sites,** handle the actual catalytic work

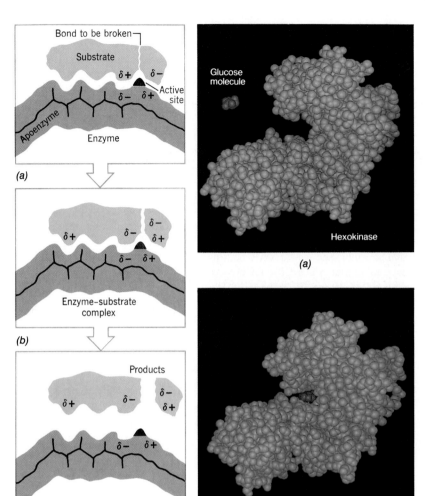

(a)

(b)

(c)

Figure 24.1
The lock-and-key model for enzyme action. (a) The enzyme and its substrate fit together to form an enzyme–substrate complex. (b) A reaction, such as the breaking of a chemical bond, occurs. (c) The product molecules separate from the enzyme.

(a)

(b)

Figure 24.2
Induced-fit theory. (a) A molecule of an enzyme, hexokinase, has a gap into which a molecule of its substrate, glucose, can fit. (b) The entry of the glucose molecule induces a change in the shape of the enzyme molecule, which now surrounds the substrate entirely.

in the complex. As stated in Section 24.1, catalytic sites are often supplied by molecules of coenzymes, and these must be bound to the apoenzyme to become integral parts of whole enzyme. See Figure 24.3.

The Activation of the Substrate Changes It into Its Transition State The fit achieved by the enzyme and the substrate molecules in the $E-S$ complex is not perfect. But the intermolecular forces that caused the complex to begin to form in the first place now continue to work. These forces distort and stretch chemical bonds in the substrate to improve the fit. The result of such changes is the conversion of the initial enzyme–substrate complex, $E-S$, into a substrate-activated complex, $E-S^*$.

The fit is now as good as it can be, and the substrate molecule has reached a unique condition of both shape and internal energy, called its *transition state*. The perfecting of the enzyme–substrate fit as the transition state forms, replacing the initial, somewhat imperfect fitting of enzyme to substrate, largely accounts for the high catalytic power of an enzyme.

The conversion of the substrate into the product now proceeds, as in Figure 24.1b. We can easily imagine that a molecule of the product has a different distribution of electrical charges and even a different shape than that of the reactant. See Figure 24.1c. The enzyme–

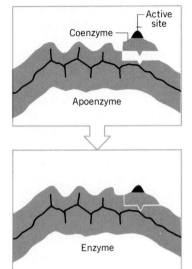

Figure 24.3
A coenzyme, which contributes the active site, joins to an apoenzyme in the formation of many kinds of complete enzymes.

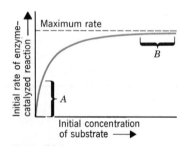

Figure 24.4
Initial rates of an enzyme-catalyzed reaction plotted versus the initial concentrations of substrates when the concentration of the enzyme is fixed in each experiment. The sections labeled A and B are discussed in the text.

product complex, $E - P$, therefore cannot hold together. The product molecule P slips off and the enzyme is ready to receive another substrate molecule.

At High Substrate Concentrations, an Enzyme's Rate Enhancement Levels Off One significant aspect of many enzyme-catalyzed reactions is that they display abnormal changes in rates as substrate concentrations are increased. To see this, we first must learn what is considered normal.

We know that reaction rates are sensitive to the concentrations of reactants. In many reactions between two species, if you double the initial concentration of one species, holding the other's constant, the rate doubles. Many enzyme-catalyzed reactions are like this if we treat their enzymes as actual (although temporary) reactants. At some fixed initial enzyme concentration, doubling the concentration of the substrate doubles the reaction rate. What is significant about enzyme-catalyzed reactions is that this cannot be indefinitely extended to higher and higher initial substrate concentrations. Eventually, at some higher initial substrate concentration, no further rate acceleration occurs. The rate levels off.

This is normal behavior, and we can see what this means with the aid of Figure 24.4, a plot of initial rates versus initial values of [S]. Imagine a series of experiments in all of which the molar concentration of the enzyme, [E], is the same. We will vary only the initial concentration of the substrate, [S], from experiment to experiment. As we said, in most ordinary reactions, the initial rate would double each time we doubled the initial concentration of one reactant.

In our series of experiments, we do observe something like this, but only in trials that have *low* initial values of [S], as in part A of the plot in Figure 24.4. In this part, a small increase in [S] does cause a proportionate increase in initial rate. The curve rises steadily.

In succeeding experiments, however, at higher and higher initial values of [S], the initial rates respond less and less until, in part B of the plot, the initial rates are constant *regardless of the value of* [S]. The reason is that we now have enough substrate molecules to saturate all the active sites of all the enzyme molecules. Any additional substrate molecules have to wait their turns, so to speak.

Now let's see what we meant by an abnormal response of rate to substrate concentration and what it signifies.

Some Enzymes Display an Initial Resistance to the Formation of an Enzyme–Substrate Complex One of the very significant features of several enzymes is that the initial sharp rise of the curve in Figure 24.4 does not occur when [S] is low. It's as though the enzyme is inactive at low substrate concentrations. For these enzymes the plots of initial values of [S] versus initial rates look more like the curve in Figure 24.5. The plot has a lazy "ess" shape, so it's called a *sigmoid plot* (after *sigma*, Greek for S). The rate increases very slowly, then takes off in a normal response of rate to concentration, and finally levels off in the usual way.

Sigmoid plots of rates versus substrate concentration are found among enzymes that remain inactive until a sufficient concentration of substrate forces them into active forms. What the curve suggests is something about enzyme activation, as we'll learn in the next section, as well as in our study of the behavior of hemoglobin in the next chapter.

24.3 THE REGULATION OF ENZYMES

Enzymes are switched on and off by initiators, effectors, inhibitors, genes, poisons, hormones, and neurotransmitters.

A cell cannot be allowed to do everything at once. Some of its possible reactions have to be shut down while others occur. One way to keep a reaction switched off is to prevent its enzyme from forming, as we learned when we studied how genes can be controlled. Another but harmful way is to deny the cell the amino acids, vitamins, and minerals that it needs to

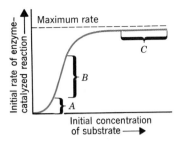

Figure 24.5
Initial rates of enzyme-catalyzed reactions plotted versus initial values of substrate concentrations, at fixed enzyme concentration, when an allosteric effect is observed. Sections labeled *A* and *B* of the curve — a sigmoid curve — are discussed in the text.

■ *Allo-*, other; *-steric,* space — the other space or the other site.

make enzymes. Hormones and neurotransmitters are natural regulators of enzymes, and we'll learn about them in the next section. In this section we study several other means to control enzymes.

The Catalytic Sites in Some Enzymes Are Given Active Shapes by Reactions at Other Sites Enzymes with sigmoid rate curves (Figure 24.5) have two or more catalytic sites that normally are inactive, even in the presence of some substrate. They are activated by the substrate, but only when its initial concentration has risen enough. Such enzymes generally have two or more polypeptide units, each with a catalytic site, and these units interact.

Let's suppose, for simplicity, that our enzyme is made of just two polypeptide chains. It has two catalytic sites, one on each polypeptide. We'll represent each site by a geometric shape, as shown in Figure 24.6. We have to suppose that the shape of each site is not quite complementary to the substrate, that the substrate must itself induce the correct fit, because the enzyme's response is sluggish at low substrate concentration. We're in region *A* of the sigmoid rate curve (Figure 24.5), the region of the slower than normal rate.

When a substrate molecule, however, does induce a fit to one catalytic site, it simultaneously causes a conformational change at the second site. This allows the same enzyme molecule to accept a second substrate molecule much more easily than the first. Now the enzyme is being used at maximum efficiency, and the rate takes off.

This phenomenon in which one active site is activated by an event that occurs elsewhere on the enzyme is called **allosteric activation.** The enzyme's subunits cooperate with each other to cause full activation. But this doesn't happen unless the level of substrate concentration has climbed high enough to start the process. The activity of an enzyme is thus regulated by how much its services are needed.

In the next chapter, we'll see how a similar allosteric effect is caused by oxygen when it interacts with hemoglobin, which is not an enzyme, and how this enables hemoglobin to operate at 100% efficiency, or very nearly so.

Allosteric Activation Can Be Caused by Effectors Instead of Substrates The catalytic sites of some enzymes are activated by substances called **effectors** that are not substrates. When their molecules bind allosterically to the enzyme, that is, at a location distinct from the catalytic site, they force a configurational change that activates the enzyme. See Figure 24.6*b*, where circles represent the effector molecules. The effector might, for example, be a molecule whose own metabolism *needs the products* made by the enzyme it activates.

Figure 24.6
Allosteric activations. (*a*) Allosteric activation by substrate. (*b*) Allosteric activation by effector.

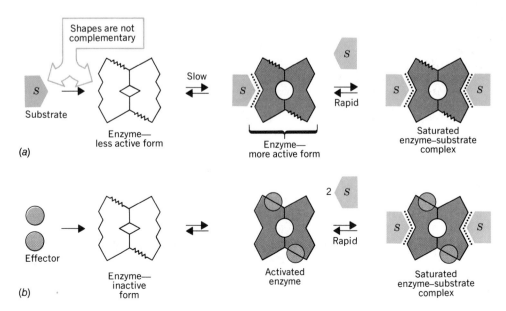

Figure 24.7
Conversion of a zymogen (proenzyme) into its active enzyme. The active site of the enzyme lies hidden in the zymogen. This site is exposed by cleaving a bond to split off a fragment (the idea illustrated here) or by opening the polypeptide up.

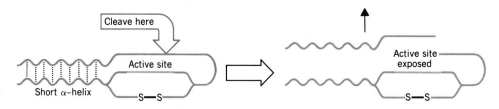

Nerve Signals Can Indirectly Tell an Effector To Work

Two of the very important effectors are *calmodulin,* a protein found in most cells, and *troponin,* present in muscle cells. Neither works as an effector, however, until it has itself been activated. Its activator is calcium ion, and cells control their calcium ion levels by active transport mechanisms mediated by nerve signals.

■ The cytosol is the *solution* in the cytoplasm and does not include the organelles in the cytoplasm.

Normally, the level of calcium ion free in solution in the cytosol is only about 10^{-7} mol/L. It must be kept extremely low, because the cytosol contains phosphate ion, which forms an insoluble salt with Ca^{2+}. The level of this ion just outside the cell is about 10^{-3}, very considerably higher. Despite the concentration gradient, which nature would normally erase by diffusion, the calcium ions stay outside until something changes the cell's permeability to them. Nerve signals do this.

The overall sequence is roughly as follows. A nerve signal opens channels in the cell membrane for Ca^{2+} ions and they enter the cell, where they bind to calmodulin or troponin. The effector is thus activated and it then activates an enzyme to cause some chemical work or, in muscles, to cause muscle contraction. When the signal is over, the channels close, and Ca^{2+} ions are pumped back out through other portals. The effector is thus inactivated. This mechanism thus connects nerve signals to specific chemical activities in cells.

Some Enzymes Are Activated by the Removal of a Polypeptide Unit

Several digestive enzymes are first made in inactive forms called **zymogens** or **proenzymes.** Their polypeptide strands have several more amino acid residues than the enzyme, and these extra units cover over the active site. Then, when the active enzyme is needed, a complex process is launched that clips off the extra units and, by exposing the active site, activates the enzyme. See Figure 24.7.

One of the functions of enteropeptidase, a compound released in the upper intestine when food moves in from the stomach, is to convert the zymogen, trypsinogen, into the enzyme, trypsin, which helps to digest proteins. Trypsin is activated by the deletion of a small polypeptide unit in trypsinogen. When no food is present, there is no need for trypsin, but when food enters, enteropeptidase comes in as well, and then trypsin is activated.

We'll look at plasminogen, one of the important zymogens in blood plasma, in the next section. Its activation to plasmin, a proteolytic blood-clot-dissolving enzyme, resembles the activation of trypsin, except that a peptide bond breaks in a disulfide loop. The plasminogen molecule thus does not split into two pieces but opens up into one with the flexibility it apparently needs to get the side chains of the active site exposed.

Phosphorylation Activates Some Enzymes

■ Kinases are the enzymes for this phosphorylation, and they must themselves be activated (usually by Ca^{2+}) only when needed.

The enzyme that catalyzes the hydrolysis of glucose units from glycogen—glycogen phosphorylase—is made in an inactive state. When a serine side chain, which is CH_2OH, is changed to a phosphate ester, $CH_2OPO_3^{2-}$ the enzyme is activated.

Inhibitors Can Keep Enzymes Switched Off Until They Are Needed

Some substance, called **inhibitors,** bind reversibly to the enzyme and prevent it from working. In **allosteric inhibition,** molecules of the inhibitor bind to the enzyme somewhere other than the active site. This affects the shape of the active site or a binding site, and the enzyme–substrate complex cannot form. See Figure 24.8a. Then if some reaction occurs to the inhibitor so that it no longer sticks to the enzyme, the catalyst is released.

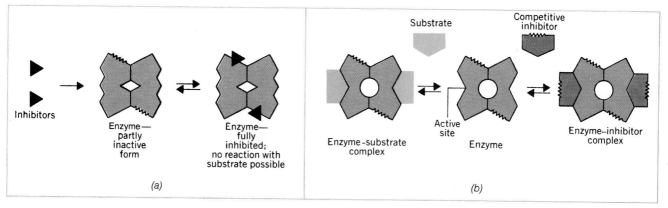

Figure 24.8
Enzyme inhibition. (a) Allosteric inhibition. (b) Competitive inhibition.

In **competitive inhibition,** the inhibitor is a nonsubstrate whose molecules have shapes similar enough to those of the true substrate that they compete with it for the active site. When the inhibitor molecules lock to the enzyme's active sites, but do not undergo a reaction and leave, then the enzyme has become useless to the true substrate. See Figure 24.8b.

When the competitive inhibitor is the *product* of the reaction or a product later in a series, we have **feedback inhibition.** As the level of such a product increases, its molecules 'feed back' with increasing success as inhibitors to an enzyme that helped to make them. The amino acid isoleucine, for example, is a feedback inhibitor. It is made from another amino acid, threonine, by a series of steps, each with its own enzyme. As more and more isoleucine is made, its molecules more and more inhibit the enzyme involved with threonine in the first step, E_1, of the series:

$$
\begin{array}{ccc}
\overset{+}{NH_3}CHCO_2^- & \xrightarrow{E_1}\xrightarrow{E_2}\xrightarrow{E_3}\xrightarrow{E_4}\xrightarrow{E_5} & \overset{+}{NH_3}CHCO_2^- \\
| & & | \\
CHOH & \text{Inhibition of } E_1 & CHCH_3 \\
| & \text{by molecules} & | \\
CH_3 & \text{of isoleucine} & CH_2CH_3 \\
\text{Threonine} & \text{Feedback inhibition} & \text{Isoleucine}
\end{array}
$$

The beautiful feature of feedback inhibition is that the system for making a product shuts down automatically when enough is made. Then, as the cell consumes this product, it eventually uses even product molecules that have been serving as inhibitors. The result is that when the product concentration has dropped very low, the enzyme needed to make more is released from its bondage.

Feedback inhibition is very common in nature. It helps to maintain a condition of **homeostasis** in which disturbances to systems by stimuli are minimized, because the stimulus is able to start a series of events that restore the system to the original state. Body temperature is an example of a condition maintained by homeostatic mechanisms. The body does this so well that even small changes in temperature tell us that something is wrong.

A familiar homeostatic mechanism in a home is the work of a furnace controlled by a thermostat. When the room becomes hot enough (the desired "product"), the thermostat trips and the furnace shuts off. In time, the temperature drops, the thermostat trips back, and the furnace restarts.

A competitive inhibitor doesn't have to be a product of the enzyme's own work. It can be something else the cell makes, or it could be a medication. What its molecules must do is resemble those of the normal substrate enough to bind to the active site of the enzyme.

■ An antimetabolite is called an *antibiotic* when it is the product of the growth of a fungus or a natural strain of bacteria.

Inhibition by Antibiotics   A broad family of compounds called **antimetabolites** includes some made by bacteria and fungi and called **antibiotics.** They are substances that inhibit or prevent the normal metabolism of a disease-causing bacterial system. Some antibiotics work by inhibiting an enzyme that the bacterium needs for its own growth. Both the sulfa drugs and penicillin work in this way.

Poisons Often Cause Irreversible Enzyme Inhibition   The most dangerous **poisons** are effective even at very low concentrations because they are powerful inhibitors of enzymes. The cyanide ion, for example, forms a strong complex with one of the metal ion cofactors in an enzyme needed for our use of oxygen.

Enzymes that have SH groups are denatured and deactivated by such heavy metal ions as Hg^{2+}, Pb^{2+}, Cu^{2+}, and Ag^+, all poisons.

Nerve gases and their weaker cousins, the organophosphate insecticides, inactivate enzymes of the nervous system.

24.4   ENZYMES IN MEDICINE

The specificity of the enzyme for its substrate and the slight differences in properties of isoenzymes provide several unusually sensitive methods of medical diagnosis.

Enzymes that normally work only inside cells are not found in the blood, except at extremely low concentrations. When cells are diseased or injured, however, their enzymes spill into the bloodstream. Much can be learned about the disease or injury by detecting such enzymes and measuring their levels.

Enzyme Assays of Blood Use Substrates as Chemical "Tweezers"   Despite the enormous complexity of blood and the very low levels of enzymes in it, enzyme assays are relatively easy to carry out. The substrate for the enzyme is used to find its own enzyme, and the specificity of the enzyme–substrate system ensures that it will find nothing else. If no enzyme is present to match the substrate, nothing happens. Otherwise, the extent of the reaction of the substrate measures the concentration of the enzyme. In this section, we learn about some examples of this medical technology.

■ GPT is the transaminase introduced on page 602.

Viral Hepatitis Is Detected by the Appearance of GPT and GOT in Blood   Heart, muscle, kidney, and liver tissue all contain the enzyme glutamate : pyruvate aminotransferase or GPT, which we introduced earlier. The liver, however, has about three times as much GPT as any other tissue, so the appearance of GPT in the blood generally indicates liver damage or a virus infection of the liver, such as viral hepatitis.

The level of another enzyme, glutamate : oxaloacetate aminotransferase or GOT, also increases in viral hepatitis, but the GPT level goes much higher than the GOT level. The ratio of GPT to GOT in the serum of someone with viral hepatitis is typically 1.6, compared with a level of 0.7 to 0.8 in healthy individuals. (Notice that we speak here of *ratios,* not absolute amounts, which are normally very low.)

■ The popular term for this set of events is *heart attack.*

Heart Attacks Cause Increased Levels of Three Enzymes in Blood Serum   A *myocardial infarction* (MI) is the withering of a portion of the heart muscle following some blockage of the blood vessels that supply it with oxygen and nutrients. Such blockage can be caused by deposits, by hardening, or by a clot. If the patient survives, the withered muscle becomes scar tissue, and the outlook for a reasonably active life is generally good, particularly if treatment is started promptly. An infarction can be diagnosed with exceptionally high reliability by analyzing the serum for several enzymes and isoenzymes.

When a myocardial infarction occurs, the serum levels of three enzymes normally confined inside heart muscle cells begin to rise. See Figure 24.9. These enzymes are CK (page

Figure 24.9
The concentrations of three enzymes in blood serum increase after a myocardial infarction. Here CK is creatine kinase, GOT is glutamate : oxaloacetate aminotransferase, and LD is lactate dehydrogenase.

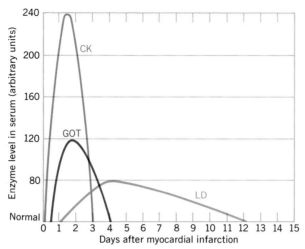

602), GOT (just described), and LD. LD stands for lactate dehydrogenase, which catalyzes the oxidation of lactate to pyruvate.

A clinical report from a patient with a myocardial infarction is shown in Table 24.1. You can see how sharply the levels of these three enzymes rose between day I and day II. The line of data labeled "CK(MB)" and the data in the columns headed by 'LD ISOENZYME' provided the clinching evidence for the infarction. As we learned on page 602, the CK enzyme occurs as three isoenzymes, CK(MM), CK(BB), and CK(MB). The technique that uses a chemical substrate to determine the serum CK level can't tell these isoenzymes apart, because all three catalyze the reaction with the substrate.

To be sure that the rise in serum CK level is caused by injury to the *heart* tissue, the clinical chemist has to analyze specifically for the CK(MB) isoenzyme common to heart muscle tissue. A technique called *electrophoresis,* described in Special Topic 24.2, is used. Electrophoresis separates the individual isoenzymes, and then each is analyzed separately. As you can see in the chart, the patient's serum CK(MB) level did rise.

As additional confirmation of an infarction, the serum LD fraction is further separated by electrophoresis into the five LD isoenzymes, and each is individually analyzed. The *relative serum concentrations of these five in a healthy person (Figure 24.10a) differ distinctively from their concentrations in one who has suffered an infarction (Figure 24.10b). Of particular importance are the relative levels of the LD$_1$ and the LD$_2$ isoenzymes.

Normally the LD$_1$ level is less than that of the LD$_2$, but following a myocardial infarction what is called an "LD$_1$-LD$_2$ flip" occurs. The relative concentrations of LD$_1$ and LD$_2$ become reversed and the level of LD$_1$ rises higher than that of LD$_2$. When both the CK(MB) band and the LD$_1$-LD$_2$ flip occur, the diagnosis of a myocardial infarction is essentially 100% certain.

■ The numbered subscripts of the LD isoenzymes are simply the order in which their molecules separate during electrophoresis.

The Blood Glucose Level Can Be Determined Enzymatically

The regular determination of the level of glucose in blood is important to people with diabetes, because when this

Figure 24.10
The lactate dehydrogenase isoenzymes. (a) The normal pattern of the relative concentrations of the five isoenzymes. (b) The pattern after a myocardial infarction. Notice the reversal in relative concentration between LD$_1$ and LD$_2$. This is the LD flip.

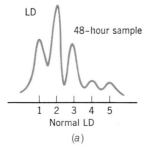

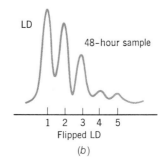

TABLE 24.1 Clinical Report: Myocardial Infarction

	DAY I		DAY II		DAY III
DATE	*5-25*	DATE	*5-26*	DATE	*5-27*
CK	*51*	CK	*552* *Moderate*	CK	*399* *Weak*
CK (MB)	*Negative*	CK (MB)	*Positive*	CK (MB)	*Positive*
GOT	*19*	GOT	*91*	GOT	*117*
LD	*88*	LD	*151*	LD	*247*

LD ISOENZYME		LD ISOENZYME		LD ISOENZYME	
% of Total LD activity		% of Total LD activity		% of Total LD activity	
LD_1	*28.3* %	LD_1	*33.8* %	LD_1	*37.9* %
LD_2	*32.9* %	LD_2	*32.3* %	LD_2	*32.8* %
LD_3	*19.7* %	LD_3	*16.3* %	LD_3	*15.7* %
LD_4	*11.6* %	LD_4	*9.1* %	LD_4	*7.6* %
LD_5	*7.5* %	LD_5	*8.5* %	LD_5	*6.0* %
CB		*CB*		*B.L.*	

	Normal Range		LD Isoenzymes Normals	
CK	Male	5–75 mU/ml	LD_1	14–29%
	Female	5–55 mU/ml	LD_2	29–40%
			LD_3	18–28%
GOT		5–20 mU/ml	LD_4	7–17%
			LD_5	3–16%
LD		30–110 mU/ml		

Source: Data courtesy of Dr. Gary Hemphill, Clinical Laboratories, Metropolitan Medical Center, Minneapolis, Minn.

Interpretation: The presence of a CK(MB) or an LD_1 greater than LD_2, or both, strongly suggest myocardial infarction. One International Unit (U) of activity is the reaction under standard conditions of one micromole per minute of a particular substrate used in the test.

level is poorly managed, several complications can occur. One commercially available test uses a combination of chemicals, including enzymes, that react with blood glucose to generate a dye. See Figure 24.11. The enzyme catalyzes the oxidation of glucose and generates some hydrogen peroxide in the process. This reacts with organic dye precursors. The intensity of the resulting dye is proportional to the blood glucose level.

Similar enzyme-based test are available to measure the serum levels of urea, triacylglycerols, bilirubin (a breakdown product of hemoglobin), and other compounds.

Enzymes Can Be Immobilized on Solid Supports   In some applications, enzymes are physically immobilized onto the surfaces of extremely tiny, inert plastic beads, which makes it easier to separate the products from the enzymes. Immobilized enzymes last longer, are less sensitive to temperature, and are less vulnerable to oxygen. Enzymes, for example, are used in filtering systems to remove bacteria and viruses from air and water.

In the CHEMSTRIP MatchMaker device, the blood glucose level is measured by the intensity of a dye produced enzymatically and converted into milligrams of glucose per deciliter (100 mL) of blood.

Molecules of proteins carry electrical charges, and both the numbers of charges and their signs depend on the pH of the medium. A procedure called *electrophoresis* that is used to separate a mixture of proteins is based on such charges and their pH dependence.

First, a surface is prepared from a porous but mechanically sturdy solid, such as filter paper, or a gel made from a polymer such as polyacrylamide. This surface is wetted with a solution that contains ions and whose pH has been adjusted to some predetermined value. Electrical poles or plates are attached at opposite ends of this wetted surface, as seen in the accompanying figure, and electricity can flow because ions are present to carry it.

Next, a solution of a mixture of proteins is deposited as a very narrow band across the middle of the strip. The molecules of proteins—they could be isoenzymes—begin to travel because they are also electrically charged. However, when they have different *kinds* of charge (positive or negative), they are bound to travel in opposite directions. And when they have different *quantities* of charge and possibly even different masses, they travel at different rates. Thus slowly the different proteins move out from the band where they were deposited, and they become increasingly separated, each into its own narrow zone or band. These bands can't be seen directly, but there are many techniques, including color tests, for locating them and measur-

ing the relative amounts of the individual proteins or isoenzymes in them.

Despite being *catalytically* the same, isoenzymes can be separated by electrophoresis. For example, the *MM*, *BB*, and *MB* isoenzymes of creatine kinase can be separated, and an increase in the CK(*MB*) band in blood serum helps to diagnose a myocardial infarction. The five isoenzymes of lactate dehydrogenase, LD, can also be separated and their relative amounts determined using electrophoresis.

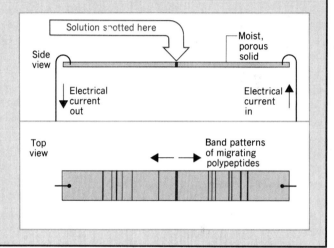

The enzyme heparinase is immobilized onto plastic beads that are then used to catalyze the breakdown of the heparin added to blood sent through a hemodialysis machine. The added heparin inhibits the clotting of the blood outside the body, but it has to be removed before the blood goes back into the body. The heparinase catalyzes this removal.

The enzyme bilirubin oxidase immobilized on plastic beads is used to catalyze the breakdown of bilirubin in blood channeled out of the body. This pigment forms normally from hemoglobin in all of us, but sometimes it occurs in infants at too high a level. They appear badly jaundiced. The excess bilirubin can cause mental retardation, deafness, or death.

Enzymes in Electrode Tips Make Possible Several Serum Assays   Clinical chemists have a variety of electrodes made with immobilized enzymes for analyses that resemble the use of pH electrodes to measure pH. The specificity of the enzyme, immobilized on the

Figure 24.11
The concentration of glucose in blood serum can be measured by this Ektachem clinical chemistry slide, seen here in cross section.

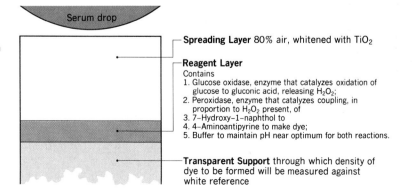

Spreading Layer 80% air, whitened with TiO_2

Reagent Layer
Contains
1. Glucose oxidase, enzyme that catalyzes oxidation of glucose to gluconic acid, releasing H_2O_2;
2. Peroxidase, enzyme that catalyzes coupling, in proportion to H_2O_2 present, of
3. 7–Hydroxy–1–naphthol to
4. 4–Aminoantipyrine to make dye;
5. Buffer to maintain pH near optimum for both reactions.

Transparent Support through which density of dye to be formed will be measured against white reference

■ The level of urea in the blood is called the BUN level (for blood urea nitrogen). A high BUN level indicates a kidney disorder.

electrode's tip, is a key factor in this technology. The level of urea in blood, for example, can be measured as a function of the concentration of the ammonium ions produced when urea is hydrolyzed. The tip of the urea electrode is lightly coated with a polymer that immobilizes urease, the enzyme that catalyzes the hydrolysis of urea.

$$NH_2-\overset{\overset{\displaystyle O}{\|}}{C}-NH_2+H_2O+2H^+\xrightarrow{\text{urease}}2NH_4^++CO_2$$

When this electrode is dipped into blood serum that contains urea, urea and water migrate into the polymer, the urea is promptly hydrolyzed (thanks to the urease), and the electrode helps to register the appearance of the newly formed ammonium ion. It is relatively easy to correlate the response of the electrode to the concentration of the urea.

Enzyme electrodes for the determination of glucose, uric acid, tyrosine, lactic acid, acetylcholine, cholesterol, and other substances have been developed.

A Natural Blood-Clot-Dissolving Enzyme Can Be Activated by Other Enzymes Three of the enzymes available to aid in dissolving blood clots that cause myocardial infarctions are streptokinase, tissue plasminogen activator (tPA), and a modified streptokinase, acylated plasminogen – streptokinase activator complex, called APSAC.

■ The commercial form of tPA, made by genetic engineering, is Activase. In the late 1980s it cost $2200 per treatment. (Streptokinase cost $200 per treatment.)

If you cut yourself, there is set in motion a huge cascade of enzyme-catalyzed reactions that bring about the formation of fibrin from a circulating polypeptide, fibrinogen. The long, stringy fibrin molecules form a brush-heap mat that entraps water and puts a seal, a blood clot, on the cut. After the wound heals, the clot must be dissolved. No part of a blood clot must break loose and circulate to the heart, because it will be stopped by tiny capillaries in heart muscle tissue. Such a blockage is one cause of a myocardial infarction.

■ About 150,000 people a year die from clots that start in their lungs.

To dissolve the fibrin of a clot, the body normally converts a zymogen, plasminogen, into the enzyme plasmin. We described the chemistry of this reaction in the previous section. Plasminogen actually is absorbed out of circulation by the fibrin as the clot forms. Its eventual activation, therefore, occurs exactly where its active form, plasmin, is needed. Plasmin, a protease, then catalyzes the hydrolysis of fibrin and the clot "dissolves."

■ This therapy is called *thrombolytic therapy* because it lyses (breaks down) thrombi (blood clots).

One of the interesting facts about plasminogen is that it becomes more susceptible to activation when bound to fibrin than when it is simply in circulation. In time, a circulating *tissue plasminogen activator* does what its name implies. It catalyzes the conversion of plasminogen to plasmin at the site of the blood clot.

Therapy for a myocardial infarction is intended to open blocked capillaries as rapidly as possible before the oxygen starvation of surrounding heart muscle tissue spreads the damage too widely. In the 1970s plasminogen activation therapy was introduced for this purpose, and it rapidly became essentially the only method for treating clot-related infarctions. Obviously, the sooner this therapy is applied following a myocardial infarction, the better the chances that long-term heart muscle damage will be slight.

■ Aspirin given with streptokinase doubles its effectiveness.

In this treatment one of the plasminogen-activating enzymes is introduced into circulation. Tissue plasminogen activator appears to be the best choice for acting on clots in heart tissue, but extensive clinical studies are in progress.

24.5 CHEMICAL COMMUNICATION—AN INTRODUCTION

Hormones and neurotransmitters are the chief methods by which cells communicate with one another.

Like any complex organism, the body is made up of highly specialized parts. Information, therefore, must flow among the parts to maintain a well-coordinated system. This flow is handled by chemical messengers, hormones or neurotransmitters, sent in response to a variety of signals.

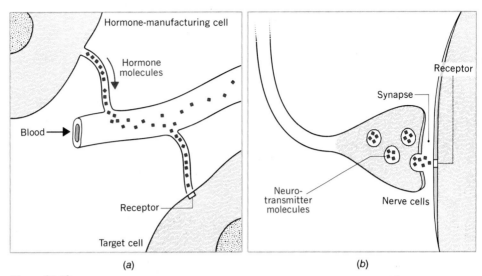

Figure 24.12
Chemical communication in the human body. (*a*) A hormone travels from an endocrine gland, where it is made, through the bloodstream to its target cell. (*b*) A neurotransmitter travels from one nerve cell to the next nerve cell across the synapse.

■ Greek *hormone,* arousing.

Hormones are compounds made in specialized organs, the endocrine glands, and secreted into the bloodstream and usually sent some distance away where they launch responses in their particular **target tissue** or **target cells.** The distance might be as close as another neighboring tissue or as far away as 15 to 20 cm. The signal for releasing a hormone might be something conveyed by one of our senses, such as light or an odor, or it might be a stress, or a variation in the level of a particular substance in the blood or in another fluid. Insulin, for example, is released when the level of glucose in blood increases.

Neurotransmitters are chemicals made in nerve cells, called neurons, and sent to the next nerve cells. Thus, as illustrated in Figure 24.12, the distinctions between hormones and neurotransmitters concern differences in how far they go to exert their action. How these two kinds of messengers cause what they do when they get there, however, bears many close similarities, as we will see.

Target Cell Receptors Identify Chemical Messengers At a target cell, a hormone or neurotransmitter delivers its messages by binding to a cell **receptor.** Each receptor has molecules so structured that it can accept just the messenger intended for it. It's another example of a lock-and-key mechanism at work to make interactions very specific.

The formation of a receptor–messenger complex changes the receptor structure, so that now it is activated to do something. It might be to activate a gene, or an enzyme, or to alter the permeability of a cell membrane so that certain ions or small molecules can move across it. In neurons, the activation of a receptor sends the nerve signal on. We'll consider specific examples later. We're after a broad overview here.

Chemical Messengers Enter Cells by Four Major Mechanisms Figure 24.13 outlines the principal ways by which signals enter cells. Some hormones, once "recognized" by the target cell, move directly through the cell membrane, enter the cytosol, and find a receptor inside the cell. Steroid hormones work in this way. See ①in Figure 24.13. They bind to receptors close to or inside the cell nucleus where they induce changes in the way the cell uses DNA.

Polypeptide hormones cannot migrate directly through cell membranes, so they bind to receptors that are integral parts of the membrane. See ②in Figure 24.13. Insulin and growth hormone work in this way.

Figure 24.13
The ways by which hormones get chemical messages into cells.

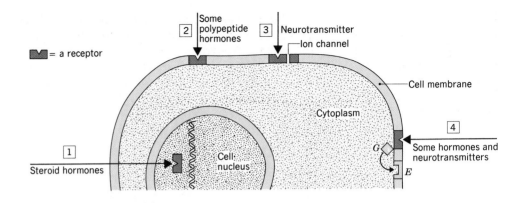

Neurotransmitters also bind to membrane-bound receptors, and this opens channels through the membrane for metal ions, ⟨3⟩. We have already seen how movements of the calcium ion can affect calmodulin or troponin and so activate a series of enzyme-catalyzed reactions.

Some receptors, in accepting neurotransmitters, hormones, or even light photons, release a small polypeptide called the *G-protein* that acts as a secondary messenger, ⟨4⟩ in Figure 24.13. The G-protein is what activates something inside the cell. Remarkably, a large variety of cells share just a few mechanisms for taking advantage of the action of the G-protein. We'll study two, the cyclic AMP and the inositol phosphate cascades.

■ The G in G-protein stands for *guanyl nucleotide binding protein.* Of its three small polypeptide subunits, only one actually migrates to activate adenylate cyclase.

■ *Cyclic* refers to the *extra* ring of the phosphate diester system.

The Formation and Hydrolysis of Cyclic AMP Is a Major Mechanism by Which Many Cells Pass on Messages
Cyclic nucleotides, particularly $3',5'$-cyclic AMP, are important secondary chemical messengers. How cyclic AMP works is sketched in Figure 24.14.

At the top of the figure we see a hormone—it could just as well be a neurotransmitter—that can combine with a receptor molecule at the surface of a cell. Because of a lock-and-key mechanism, the hormone bypasses all cells that do not have a matching receptor.

Figure 24.14
The activation of the enzyme adenylate cyclase by a hormone (or a neurotransmitter). The hormone–receptor complex releases a unit of the G-protein, which activates this enzyme. It then catalyzes the formation of cyclic AMP, which in turn, activates an enzyme inside the cell.

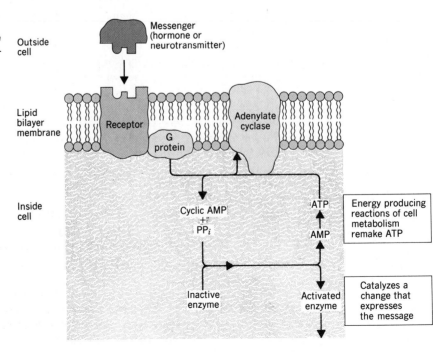

The complex that forms between hormone and receptor activates the release of a G-protein molecule bound on the cytosol side of the lipid bilayer. The G-protein finds a molecule of an inactive form of the enzyme adenylate cyclase and activates it. This enzyme is an integral part of the cell membrane.

Once adenylate cyclase is activated, the "message" is on the inside of the cell membrane, because now the enzyme promptly catalyzes the conversion of ATP into cyclic AMP and diphosphate ion, PP_i.

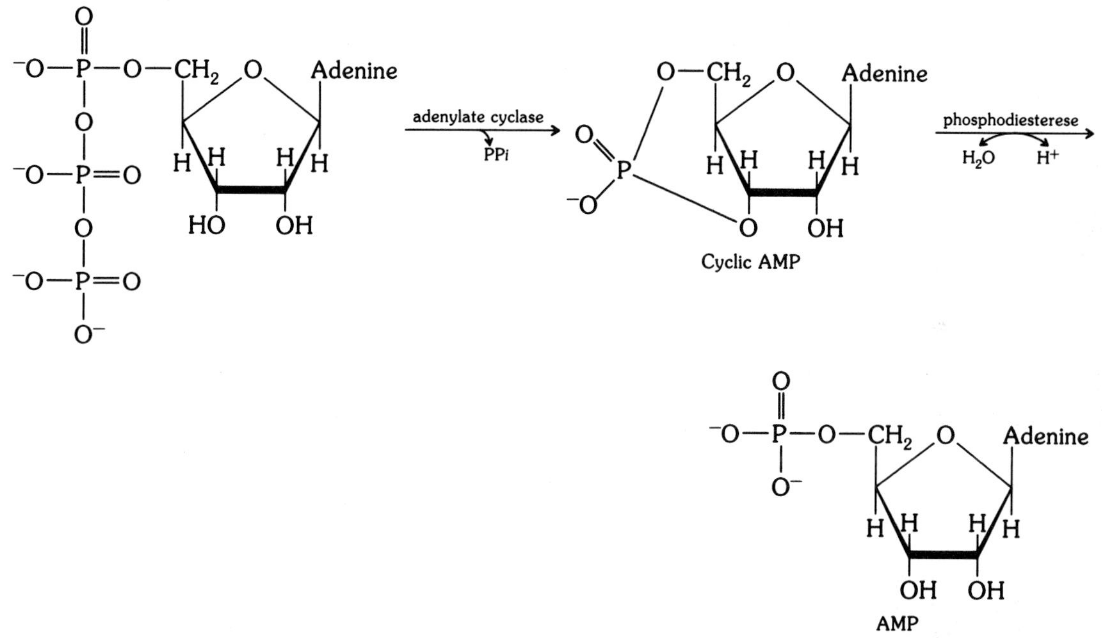

■ E. W. Sutherland, Jr., an American scientist, won the 1971 Nobel prize in physiology and medicine for his work on cyclic AMP.

Cyclic AMP

AMP

The newly formed cyclic AMP now activates an enzyme, which, in turn, catalyzes a reaction. This last event is what the original message was all about.

Finally, an enzyme called phosphodiesterase catalyzes the hydrolysis of cyclic AMP to AMP, and this shuts off the cycle. Energy-producing reactions in the cell will now remake ATP from the AMP.

Let's summarize the steps in this remarkable chemical cascade.

■ Hormones that work through the cyclic AMP cascade, which we will encounter later, include epinephrine, glucagon, norepinephrine, and vasopressin.

1. A signal releases the hormone or neurotransmitter.

2. It travels to its target cell, next door for a neurotransmitter but some farther distance away for a hormone.

3. The primary messenger molecule finds its target cell by a lock and key mechanism and binds to a receptor. The resulting complex releases a polypeptide unit of the G-protein.

4. The G-protein activates the enzyme adenylate cyclase.

5. Adenylate cyclase catalyzes the conversion of ATP to cyclic AMP.

6. Cyclic AMP, the secondary messenger, activates an enzyme inside the cell.

7. The enzyme catalyzes a reaction, one that corresponds to the primary message of the hormone or neurotransmitter.

8. Cyclic AMP is hydrolyzed to AMP, which is reconverted to ATP, and the system returns to the preexcited state.

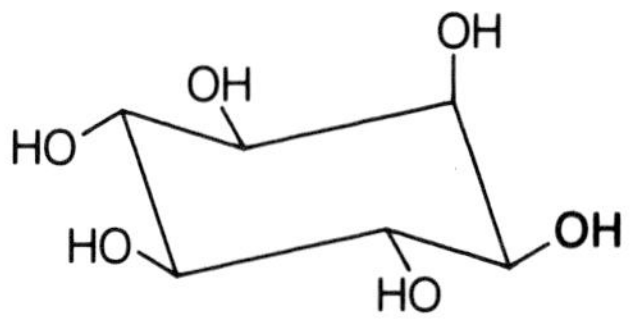

The Inositol Phosphate System Works in a Way Roughly Similar to the Cyclic AMP System

Inositol

Another of the G-protein communications systems used by cells involves phosphate and triphosphate esters of inositol, one of the stereoisomers of hexahydroxycyclohexane. We can follow it with the aid of Figure 24.15.

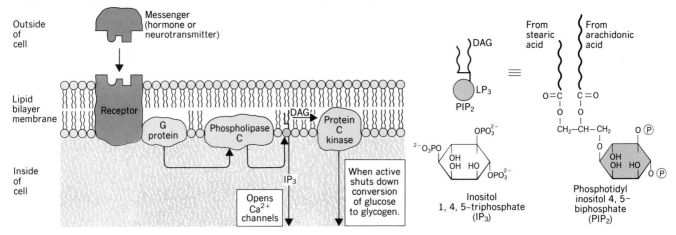

Figure 24.15
The inositol phosphate system which takes a message from a hormone or neurotransmitter and activates two enzymes to work cooperatively.

■ There are several variations of the G-protein.

■ The phosphoinositol cascade mediates the following activities:
glycogenolysis in the liver
insulin secretion
smooth muscle contraction
platelet aggregation

■ The cholera toxin is able to lock the G-protein into its active form, so adenylate cyclase cannot be shut off. This stimulates so much active transport of Na^+ ion into the gut, along with water, that massive diarrhea kills the victim.

The primary messenger binds to the receptor, the G-protein is released, and it activates an enzyme called phospholipase C. The pattern so far, as you can see, is quite similar to the cyclic AMP system. Phospholipase C now catalyzes the hydrolysis of a phosphate ester bond in a membrane-bound phospholipid, which we'll call PIP_2 (because its full name makes eyes glaze over). The products are two fragments *that are both messengers.* One we'll call IP_3 (an inositol triphosphate) and the other DAG (a diacyl glycerol).

DAG, being mostly hydrocarbon-like, stays in the lipid bilayer of the cell membrane where it activates a membrane-bound enzyme, protein kinase C. As we'll study under the metabolism of glucose, this enzyme aids the cell in developing a higher glucose level, which might be needed for energy.

The other fragment, IP_3, causes the rapid release of Ca^{2+} ion from intracellular storage systems. This ion might, for example, activate the contraction of a muscle. Of course, this is work requiring energy, so you can see that the two fragments, DAG and IP_3, work together. IP_3 tells the cell to do some work, DAG sees to the energy supply, and both are responses to one signal at the cell receptor.

Interestingly, malfunctions in the inositol phosphate system may be responsible for manic–depressive illness, one of the major psychiatric disorders. Lithium ion (as lithium carbonate) is used to treat this condition, and its action is evidently to shut down the inositol phosphate network in affected cells.

The inositol phosphate system may also be involved as a target for the action of chemicals, including errant genes, that cause tumors and cancer. Protein kinase C has a function in cell division and in the control of the proliferation of cells, so chemicals that interact with this enzyme in the wrong way can affect cell division.

24.6 HORMONES AND NEUROTRANSMITTERS

Interventions in the work of hormones and neurotransmitters are the bases of the action of a number of drugs, both licit and illicit.

Structurally, Hormones Come in Four Broad Types The principal endocrine glands of the human body and the major hormones they secrete are listed in Table 24.2. It is impossible to do justice to a subject as vast as hormones in one section of one chapter, so what follows is a very broad sketch of a few chemical aspects of hormone action. In later chapters we will mention specific hormones where they are particularly relevant to the metabolic

TABLE 24.2 The Principal Human Endocrine Glands and Their Hormones

Gland or Tissue	Hormone	Major Function of Hormone
Thyroid	Thyroxine	Stimulates rate of oxidative metabolism and regulates general growth and development
	Thyrocalcitonin	Lowers level of Ca^{2+} in blood
Parathyroid	Parathormone	Regulates the levels of calcium and phosphate ions in blood
Pancreas, β-cells	Insulin	Decreases blood glucose level
α-cells	Glucagon	Elevates blood glucose level
Adrenal medulla	Epinephrine	Elevates blood glucose level and heartbeat
Adrenal cortex	Cortisone and related hormones	Control carbohydrate, protein, mineral, salt, and water metabolism
Anterior pituitary	Thyrotropic hormone	Stimulates thyroid gland functions
	Adenocorticotropic hormone	Stimulates development and secretion of adrenal cortex
	Growth hormone	Stimulates body weight and rate of growth of skeleton
	Gonadotropic hormones	Stimulate gonads
	Prolactin	Stimulates lactation
Posterior pituitary	Oxytocin	Causes contraction of some smooth muscles
	Vasopressin	Inhibits secretion of water from the body by way of the urine
Ovary (follicle)	Estrogens	Influence development of sex organs and female characteristics
Ovary (corpus luteum)	Progesterone	Influences menstrual cycle, prepares uterus for pregnancy, maintains pregnancy
Uterus (placenta)	Estrogens and progesterone	Function in maintenance of pregnancy
Testes	Testosterone	Responsible for development and maintenance of sex organs and secondary male characteristics
Digestive system	Several gastrointestinal hormones	Integration of digestive processes

activity being studied. Let's first consider some features of hormone molecules. They come in four general types.

Some hormones, the steroid hormones, are made from cholesterol and so have largely hydrocarbon-like molecules. This feature enables them to slip easily through the lipid bilayers of their target cells. Inside they find their final receptors, and the hormone–receptor complexes move to DNA molecules where they bind and affect the transcriptions of genetic messages. The sex hormones like estradiol, progesterone, and testosterone work in this way.

Many growth factors as well as insulin, oxytocin, and thyroid-stimulating hormone consist of polypeptides or proteins. These are able to alter the permeabilities of their target cells to the migrations of small molecules. The growth factors, for example, help get amino acids inside cells where they are needed for growth. Insulin helps to get glucose inside its

TABLE 24.3 Neurotransmitters

Monoamines

Acetylchloline

$$(CH_3)_3\overset{+}{N}CH_2CH_2O\overset{\overset{\displaystyle O}{\|}}{C}CH_3$$

Dopamine

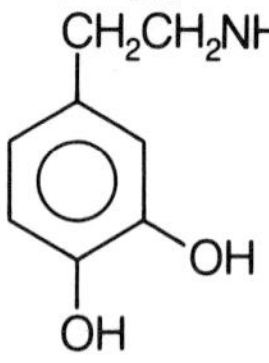

Norepinephrine

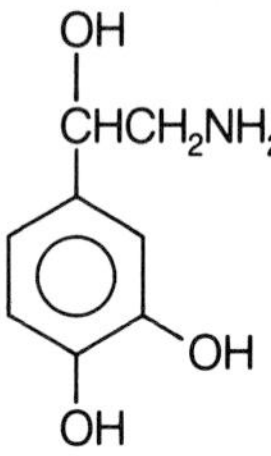

Serotonin

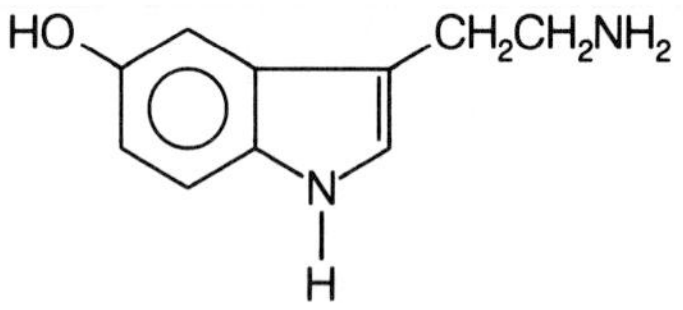

Amino Acids

Glycine	$^+NH_3CH_2CO_2^-$
γ-Aminobutyric acid	$^+NH_3CH_2CH_2CH_2CO_2^-$
Glutamic acid	$^+NH_3CHCO_2^-$
	$\quad\;\; \mid$
	$\quad\;\; CH_2CH_2CO_2H$

Neuropeptides

Met-Enkephalin   Tyr·Gly·Gly·Phe·Met

Leu-Enkephalin   Tyr·Gly·Gly·Phe·Leu

β-Endorphin   Tyr·Gly·Gly·Phe·Met·Thr·Ser·Glu·Lys·Ser
$\qquad\qquad\qquad\qquad\qquad\qquad\qquad\qquad\qquad\qquad\qquad\quad\mid$
Gln·Thr·Pro·Leu·Val·Thr·Leu·Phe·Lys·Asn
$\mid$
Ala·Ile·Val·Lys·Asn·Ala·His·Lys·Gly·Gln

Substance P   Arg·Pro·Lys·Pro·Gln·Gln·Phe·Phe·Gly·Leu·Met—NH₂

Angiotensin II   Asp·Arg·Val·Tyr·Ile·His·Pro·Phe—NH₂

Somatostatin

target cells. We'll have much more to say about insulin in a later chapter. Either the absence of insulin or the absence (or inactivity) of insulin-receptors results in the disease diabetes mellitus ("diabetes"). Several neurotransmitters are also polypeptides, and they alter the permeability of a neuron membrane to Ca^{2+} and Na^+. The cross-membrane movements of these ions are involved in the electrical signal that flows down a neuron.

Figure 24.16
One kind of neuron or nerve cell.

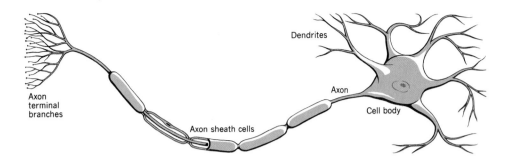

■ From *eicosane,* a C-20 hydrocarbon.

The prostaglandins, described in Special Topic 20.1, are now classified as hormones — as *local hormones* because they work where they are made. The *eicosanoids* is the technical name for this family of compounds.

Finally, a number of hormones are relatively simple amino compounds made from amino acids. These include epinephrine (page 460) and thyroxine. Some of these are also neurotransmitters.

Neurotransmitters Move Across the Narrow Synaptic Gap from One Neuron to the Next　A partial list of neurotransmitters is given in Table 24.3. Some are nothing more than simple amino acids. Others are β-phenylethylamines or catecholamines (Special Topic 17.1, page 460), and many are polypeptides.

Each nerve cell has a fiber-like part called an *axon* that reaches to the face of the next neuron or to one of its filament-like extensions called *dendrites* (Figure 24.16). A nerve impulse consists of a traveling wave of electrical charge that sweeps down the axon as small ions migrate at different rates between the inside and the outside of the neuron. The problem is how to get this impulse launched into the next neuron so that it can continue along the length of the nerve fiber. This is solved by a *chemical* communication from one neuron to the next. Neurotransmitters are the chemicals involved, and they are made from amino acids within the neuron and stored in sacs, called *vesicles,* located near the ends of the axons.

■ The traveling wave of electrical charge moves rapidly, but still not as rapidly as electricity moves in electrical wires.

Between the terminal of an axon and the end of the next neuron, there is a very narrow, fluid-filled gap called the *synapse.* Neurotransmitters move across the synapse when the electrical wave causes them to be released from their vesicles.

When neurotransmitter molecules lock to their receptors on the other side of the synapse, adenylate cyclase (or phospholipase C) is activated. (We'll use the adenylate cyclase system to illustrate the process.) See Figure 24.17. Now the formation of cyclic AMP is catalyzed, and newly formed cyclic AMP initiates whatever change is programmed by the chemicals in the target neuron. An enzyme then deactivates adenylate cyclase by catalyzing the release of the neurotransmitter molecule.

If the newly released neurotransmitter were a hormone, it would be swept away in the bloodstream, but it's not. It is still a neurotransmitter in the synapse, so unless the system wants it to act again, it must be removed or deactivated. A number of options are open, depending on the neurotransmitter.

■ The ANS nerves handle the signals that run the organs that have to work autonomously (without conscious effort), such as the heart and the lungs.

The Neurotransmitter Acetylcholine Is Swiftly Hydrolyzed　One method used to remove the neurotransmitter is to break it up by a chemical reaction. Acetylcholine, for example, a neurotransmitter in the autonomic nervous system or ANS, is catalytically hydrolyzed to choline and acetic acid. The enzyme is choline acetyltransferase.

$$\overset{+}{(CH_3)_3}NCH_2CH_2O\overset{\displaystyle O}{\overset{\|}{C}}CH_3 + H_2O \underset{\text{acetyltransferase}}{\overset{\text{choline}}{\rightleftharpoons}} \overset{+}{(CH_3)_3}NCH_2CH_2OH + HO\overset{\displaystyle O}{\overset{\|}{C}}CH_3$$

　　　　Acetylcholine　　　　　　　　　　　　　　　　　　　　Choline　　　　　Acetic acid

Figure 24.17

In neurotransmission the neurotransmitter molecules, released from vesicles of the presynaptic neuron, travel across the synapse. At the postsynaptic neuron they find their receptors, and the cyclic AMP system similar to that shown in Figure 24.14 becomes activated.

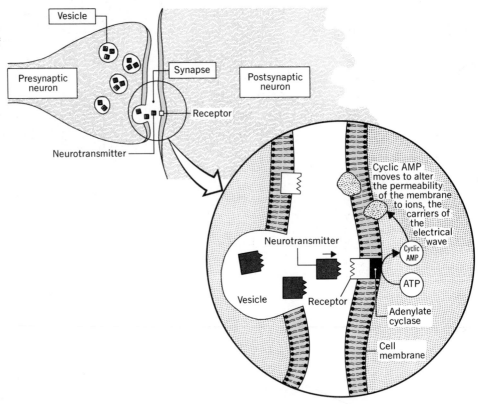

■ The ANS nerves that use acetylcholine are called the *cholinergic nerves.*

Within two milliseconds (2×10^{-3} s) of the release of acetylcholine in the synapse, all its molecules are all broken down. The synapse is now cleared for a fresh release of acetylcholine from the presynaptic neuron if the signal for its release continues. If the signal does not come, then the action is shut down.

The Botulinus Toxin Prevents a Neuron from Making Acetylcholine   The botulinus toxin is an extremely powerful toxic agent made by the food-poisoning botulinus bacillus and works by preventing the *synthesis* of acetylcholine. Without this neurotransmitter, the cholinergic nerves of the ANS can't work.

Nerve Poisons Deactivate Choline Acetyltransferase   The nerve gases act by deactivating the enzyme needed to break acetylcholine down after it has done its work. The absence of this enzyme means, therefore, that the signal transmitted by acetylcholine can't be turned off. It continues unabated until the heart fails, usually in a minute or two.

An antidote for nerve gas poisoning, atropine, works by blocking the receptor protein for acetylcholine, so despite the continuous presence of this neurotransmitter, it isn't able to complete the signal-sending work. This tones the system down, and other processes slowly restore the system to normal. (Given the extreme speed with which nerve gases work, atropine must obviously be used very promptly.)

Some organophosphate insecticides are mild nerve poisons and work in the same way. Other blockers of the receptor protein for acetylcholine are some local anesthetics like nupercaine, procaine, and tetracaine.

Drugs that block the action of a neurotransmitter are called **antagonists** to the neurotransmitter. The neurotransmitter itself is sometimes referred to as an **agonist.**

■ The nerves that use norepinephrine are called the *adrenergic nerves* (after an earlier name for norepinephrine, noradrenaline).

Some Neurotransmitters Are Reabsorbed by the Presynaptic Neuron   Norepinephrine, another neurotransmitter, is deactivated by being reabsorbed by the neuron that released it, where it is then degraded. (Some is also deactivated right within the synapse.) The degradation of norepinephrine is catalyzed by enzymes called the **monoamine oxidases** or MAO.

Drugs That Inactivate the Monoamine Oxidases Are Used to Treat Depression

One place where norepinephrine works is in the brain stem, where mood regulation is centered. If for any reason the monoamine oxidases are inactivated, then an excess of norepinephrine builds up in brain stem cells, and some spills back into the synapse and send signals on. In some mental states, like depression, an abnormally low level of norepinephrine develops, so now one would want to inactivate the monoamine oxidases. This would leave what norepinephrine there is to carry on its work. Thus some of the antidepressant drugs, such as iproniazid, word by inhibiting the monoamine oxidases.

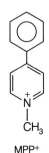

Chlorpromazine

Haloperidol

L-DOPA

MPTP

MPP⁺

$CHCH_2CH_2N(CH_3)_2$
Amitriptyline (Elavil)

$CH_2CH_2CH_2N(CH_3)_2$
Imipramine (Tofranil)

Other antidepressants, like amitriptyline (e.g., Elavil) and imipramine (e.g., Tofranil), inhibit the reabsorption of norepinephrine by the presynaptic neuron. Without this reabsorption into the degradative hands of the monoamine oxidases, the level of norepinephrine and its signal-sending work stays high.

Norepinephrine is both a hormone and a neurotransmitter. The adrenal medulla secretes it into the bloodstream in emergencies when it must be made available to all the nerve tissues that use it.

Dopamine Excesses Occur in Schizophrenia

Dopamine, like norepinephrine, is also a monoamine neurotransmitter. It occurs in neurons of the midbrain that are involved with feelings of pleasure and arousal as well as with the control of certain movements.

In schizophrenia the neurons that use dopamine are overstimulated, because either the releasing mechanism or the receptor mechanism is overactive. Drugs commonly used to treat schizophrenia such as chlorpromazine (e.g., Thorazine) and haloperidol (Haldol) bind to dopamine receptors and thus inhibit its signal-sending work.

Amphetamine Abuses Cause Schizophrenia-like Symptoms

Stimulants like the amphetamines (cf. Special Topic 17.1, page 460) work by triggering the release of dopamine into the arousal and pleasure centers of the brain. The effect is therefore a "high." But it's easy to abuse the amphetamines. When this occurs, there is the same kind of overstimulation associated with schizophrenia, causing such symptoms as delusions of persecution, hallucinations, and other disturbances of the thought processes.

Dopamine-Releasing Neurons Have Degenerated in Parkinson's Disease

When the dopamine-using neurons in the brain degenerate, as in Parkinson's disease, an extra supply of dopamine itself is then needed to compensate. This is why a compound called L-DOPA (levorotatory dihydroxyphenylalanine) is prescribed. The neurons that still work can use it to make extra dopamine.

In the mid-1980s a theory about the cause of Parkinson's disease emerged, and a large drug-testing operation has been started. By an accidental discovery, it was found that a contaminant in street heroin, called MPTP for short, rapidly destroys the same cells that degenerate in Parkinson's disease. The active agent is actually a metabolic breakdown product called MPP⁺. A drug, Deprenyl, which is a deactivator of monoamine oxidases, was found to block the conversion of MPTP to MPP⁺. If (and it's an if) Parkinson's disease is caused by some chemical in the environment that is similarly processed by monoamine oxidases, then perhaps Deprenyl might also protect susceptible brain cells against that chemical by the same mechanism. The five-year trial of this drug (and this theory) began in 1987.

$^+NH_3CH_2CH_2CH_2CO_2^-$

GABA

GABA Inhibits Nerve Signals   The normal function of some neurotransmitters is to *inhibit* signals instead of to initiate them. Gamma-aminobutyric acid (GABA) is an example, and as many as a third of the synapses in the brain have GABA available.

The inhibiting work of GABA can be made even greater by mild tranquilizers such as diazepam (e.g., Valium) and chlordiazepoxide hydrochloride (Librium), as well as by ethanol. The augmented inhibition of signals reduces anxiety, affects judgment, and induces sleep. Of course, you've probably heard of the widespread abuse of Valium and Librium, to say nothing of alcohol.

Diazepam (Valium)

Chlordiazepoxide
hydrochloride (Librium)

■ Greek, *chorea*, dance.

GABA Is Deficient in Huntington's Chorea   The victims of Huntington's chorea, a hereditary neurological disorder, suffer from speech disturbances, irregular movements, and a steady mental deterioration, all related to a deficiency in GABA. Unhappily, GABA can't be administered in this disease, because it can't move out of circulation and into the regions of the brain where it works.

Several Polypeptides Act as Painkilling Neurotransmitters   As we have said, some neurotransmitters are relatively small polypeptides. See Table 24.3. One type includes the *enkephalins;* another consists of the *endorphins.* Both types are powerful pain inhibitors. One of them, dynorphin, is the most potent painkiller yet discovered, being 200 times stronger than morphine, an opium alkaloid that is widely used to relieve severe pain. Sites in the brain that strongly bind molecules of morphine also bind those of the enkephalins, so these natural painkillers are now often referred to as the body's natural opiates.

■ *en-* or *end-,* within; *kephale,* brain; *-orph-,* from morphine.

The Enkaphalins Inhibit the Release of Substance P   Substance P is a pain-signaling, polypeptide neurotransmitter. According to one theory (see Figure 24.18), when a pain-transmitting neuron is activated, it releases substance P into the synapse. However, butting against such neurons are other neurons that can release enkephalin. And these, when released, inhibit the work of substance P. In this way, the intensity of the pain signal is toned down. The actions of enkephalin might explain the delay of pain that sometimes occurs during an emergency when the brain and the body must continue to function to escape the emergency.

Substance P might be involved in the link between the nervous system and the body's immune system. It is known that some forms of arthritis flare-up under stress, and stress deeply involves the nervous system. But arthritis is generally regarded as chiefly a disease of the immune system. In tests on rats with arthritis, flare-ups of the arthritis could be induced by injections of substance P. What interests scientists about this is the possibility of controlling the severity of arthritis by somehow diminishing levels of substance P in the affected joints.

One of the interesting developments in connection with the endorphins is that acupuncture, a pain-alleviating procedure developed in China many centuries ago, might work by stimulating the production and release of endorphins.

Figure 24.18
Inhibition of the release of substance P by enkephalin helps to reduce the intensity of the pain signal to the brain.

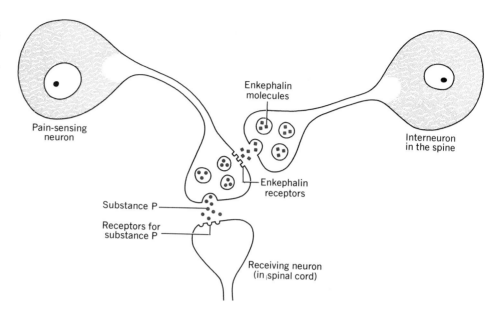

Many Neurotransmitters Exert More Than One Effect   Several neurotransmitters can be received by more than one kind of receptor. For example, at least three types of receptors for the opiates have been identified thus far. Such receptor multiplicity may explain how some neurotransmitters have multiple effects. Thus not only do opiates reduce pain, but they affect emotions; they induce sleep and they affect the appetite; and each of the opiate receptors handles a different one of these functions.

Calcium Channel Blockers Are Drugs That Reduce the Vigor of Heart Muscle Contractions   As we have often seen, calcium ions are major secondary chemical messengers and neurotransmitters are able to open channels for calcium ions through cell membranes. Heart muscle tissue receives such signals at a rate that paces the heart as its muscles contract and relax during the heartbeat. Calcium ions are what finally deliver the message to contract. Then the cell pumps them back out and the muscle relaxes until another cycle starts.

Drugs like nifedipine (Procardia, Adalat), diltiazem (Cardizem), and verapamil (Isoptin) find calcium ion channels in heart muscle and block them. Not all are blocked, of course, so the effect is to reduce the migrations of Ca^{2+} through cell membranes. These calcium channel blockers (also called calcium antagonists or slow channel blocking agents) thus make each heart muscle contraction less vigorous. This reduces the risk of heart attacks in people known to be at risk, like those who experience angina pectoris and cardiac arrhythmias (heartbeat irregularities).

What we have done in this section is look at some *molecular* connections between conditions of the nervous system and particular chemical substances. This whole field is one of the most rapidly moving areas of scientific investigation today, and during the next several years we may expect to see a number of dramatic advances both in our understanding of what is happening and in the strategies of treating mental and heart diseases.

SUMMARY

Enzymes   Enzymes are the catalysts in cells. Some consist wholly of one or more polypeptides and others include, besides polypeptides, a cofactor, which can be an organic coenzyme, a metal ion, or both. Some coenzymes are phosphate esters of B vitamins, and in these examples the vitamin unit usually furnishes the enzyme's active site.

Because they are mostly polypeptide in nature, enzymes are vulnerable to all of the conditions that denature proteins. The name of an enzyme, which almost always ends in *-ase*, usually discloses either the identity of its substrate or the kind of reaction it catalyzes.

Some enzymes occur as small families called isoenzymes in

which the polypeptide components vary slightly from tissue to tissue in the body.

An enzyme is very specific both in the kind of reaction it catalyzes and in its substrate. Enzymes make possible reaction rates that are substantially higher than the rates of uncatalyzed reactions.

Lock-and-key theory An enzyme is a reactant in the initial phase of the reaction as it functions catalytically. At a sufficiently high initial substrate concentration, the active sites on all the enzyme molecules become saturated by substrate molecules, so at still higher initial substrate concentrations, there is little further increase in the initial rate.

Some enzymes seem to respond sluggishly to small increases in substrate concentration when the latter is very low. These display a sigmoid rate curve, and they require activation by substrate molecules before they produce their dramatic rate enhancements.

When an enzyme–substrate complex forms, the active site is brought up to the part of the substrate that is to react. Binding sites on the enzyme guide the substrate molecule in, and sometimes a change in the conformation of the enzyme is induced by the substrate. The recognition of the enzyme by the substrate occurs as a lock-and-key model that involves complementary shapes and electrical charges.

Regulation of enzymes Enzymes that display a sigmoid rate curve can be activated allosterically either by their own substrates or by effectors. Some enzymes are activated by genes. Some enzymes that are parts of the membranes of cells (or small bodies within cells) are activated by the interaction between a hormone or a neurotransmitter and its receptor protein. The work of many of these is to cause changes in the calcium ion level in a cell.

Other enzymes, such as certain digestive enzymes, exist as zymogens (proenzymes) and are activated when some agent acts to remove a small part that blocks the active site. The kinase enzymes are activated by being phosphorylated.

Enzymes can be inhibited by competitive feedback that involves a product of the enzyme's action, or by a similar action by something that isn't a product. Some inhibitors act allosterically. Some of the most dangerous poisons bind to active sites and irreversibly block the work of an enzyme, or they carry enzymes out of solution by a denaturant action. Many antibiotics and other antimetabolites work by inhibiting enzymes in pathogenic bacteria.

Medical uses of enzymes The serum levels of many enzymes rise when the tissues or organs that hold these enzymes are injured or diseased. By monitoring these serum levels, and by looking for certain isoenzymes, we can diagnose many diseases—for example, viral hepatitis and myocardial infarctions.

When a blood clot threatens or causes a heart attack, any one of three enzymes—streptokinase, APSAC, or recombinant tissue plasminogen activator (tPA)—can be used to initiate the hydrolysis of the fibrin of the clot.

Enzymes are also used in analytical systems that measure concentrations of substrates, such as in tests for glucose. In some analytical systems, enzymes are immobilized on electrodes where they catalyze a reaction that produces a product; the electrode then senses and measures this product.

Chemical communication with hormones and neurotransmitters One common response to the formation of a complex between a chemical messenger and its receptor is the release of the G-protein. In the adenylate cyclase cascade, this activates adenylate cyclase, which then triggers the formation of cyclic AMP. In turn, cyclic AMP sets off other events, such as the activation of an enzyme that catalyzes a reaction, one that is ultimately what the "signal" of the neurotransmitter was all about.

When the G-protein is followed by the inositol phosphate cascade, it activates phospholipase C, which breaks up a phospholipid in the membrane into two enzyme-activators, PIP_2 and DAG. PIP_2 initiates the rapid release of Ca^{2+} from cytoplasm stores to cause muscle contraction, and DAG helps to keep the cell's glucose level high so that its metabolism can supply the energy.

Hormones Endocrine glands secrete hormones, and these primary chemical messengers travel to their target cells in the blood, where they activate a gene, or an enzyme, or affect the permeability of a cell membrane. They recognize their own target cells by a lock-and-key type of recognition that involves their receptor proteins.

The steroid hormones can move into a cell to its nucleus and there find a receptor. Polypeptide hormones lock to membrane-bound receptors to initiate their action.

Neurotransmitters In response to an electrical signal, vesicles in an axon release a neurotransmitter that moves across the synapse. Its molecules bind to a receptor protein on the next neuron, and then the pattern is much like that of hormones. The result, however, is to open channels through the cell membrane for the migration of ions.

Neurotransmitters include amino acids, monoamines, and polypeptides. Some neurotransmitters *activate* some response in the next neuron, whereas others *deactivate* some activity. A number of medications work by interfering with neurotransmitters or with the opening of calcium ion channels.

REVIEW EXERCISES

The answers to these Review Exercises are in the *Study Guide* that accompanies this book.

Nature of Enzymes

24.1 What are (a) the function and (b) the composition, in general terms only, of an *enzyme?*

24.2 To what does the term *specificity* refer in enzyme chemistry?

24.3 Define and distinguish among the following terms:
(a) apoenzyme (b) cofactor (c) coenzyme

24.4 Write the equation for the equilibrium catalyzed by carbonic anhydrase. What is particularly remarkable about the enzyme?

24.5 What in general does an enzyme do with an equilibrium?

Coenzymes

24.6 What B vitamin is involved in the $NAD^+/NADH$ system?

24.7 The active part of either FAD or FMN is furnished by which vitamin?

24.8 Complete and balance the following equation:

24.9 Complete and balance the following equation:

$$_____ + NADH + FAD \longrightarrow NAD^+ + _____$$

24.10 In what structural way do NAD^+ and $NADP^+$ differ? What formula can be used for the reduced form of $NADP^+$?

Kinds of Enzymes

24.11 What is most likely the substrate for each of the following enzymes?
(a) sucrase   (b) glucosidase
(c) protease   (d) esterase

24.12 What *kind* of reaction does each of the following enzymes catalyze?
(a) an oxidase   (b) transmethylase
(c) hydrolase   (d) oxidoreductase

24.13 What is the difference between lactose and lactase?

24.14 What is the difference between a hydrolase and hydrolysis?

24.15 What are isoenzymes (in general terms)?

24.16 What are the three isoenzymes of creatine kinase? Give their symbols and state where they are principally found.

Theory of How Enzymes Work

24.17 What name is given to the part of an enzyme where the catalytic work is carried out?

24.18 How is enzyme specificity explained?

24.19 What is the induced-fit theory?

24.20 How does the plot of initial rate versus initial [S] at constant [E] look when (a) an allosteric effect is occurring, and (b) no allosteric effect is observed? (Draw pictures.)

24.21 What happens to the initial rate of an enzyme-catalyzed reaction as the initial concentration of the substrate is increased to the point where all enzyme molecules are saturated with substrate molecules?

24.22 If the plot of initial reaction rate versus initial substrate concentration (at constant [E]) has a sigmoid shape, what does this signify about the active site(s) on the enzyme?

Enzyme Activation and Inhibition

24.23 What does *allosteric* mean?

24.24 How does a substrate molecule activate an enzyme whose rate curve is sigmoid?

24.25 How does an effector differ from a substrate in causing allosteric activation?

24.26 What are the names of two important effectors? Which one is used in muscle cells?

24.27 What are the approximate concentrations of calcium ion in the cytosol and the fluid just outside a cell? Why doesn't simple diffusion wipe out this concentration gradient?

24.28 Why must the concentration of Ca^{2+} be so low in the cytosol?

24.29 Does the concentration of Ca^{2+} in the cytosol measure the amount of Ca^{2+} in the whole cytoplasm? Explain.

24.30 What does Ca^{2+} do to calmodulin or troponin?

24.31 When Ca^{2+} combines with troponin, what happens with respect to other proteins in the cell? What then happens to Ca^{2+}?

24.32 What is the relationship of a zymogen to its corresponding enzyme? Give an example of an enzyme that has a zymogen.

24.33 What is enteropeptidase and what does it do?

24.34 What is plasmin and in what form does it normally circulate in the blood?

24.35 What role does a phosphorylation reaction have in connection with some enzymes?

24.36 How does competitive inhibition of an enzyme work?

24.37 Feedback inhibition of an enzyme works in what way?

24.38 Why is feedback inhibition an example of a homeostatic mechanism?

24.39 How do competitive inhibition and allosteric inhibition differ?

24.40 How do the following poisons work?
(a) CN^- (b) Hg^{2+}
(c) nerve gases or organophosphate insecticides

24.41 What are antimetabolites, and how are they related to antibiotics?

24.42 The following overall change is accomplished by a series of steps, each with its own enzyme:

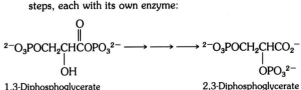

1,3-Diphosphoglycerate   2,3-Diphosphoglycerate
(1,3-DPG)   (2,3-DPG)

One of the enzymes in this series is inhibited by 2,3-DPG. What kind of control is exerted by 2,3-DPG on this series? (Name it.)

24.43 If you drink enough methanol, you will become blind or die. One strategy to counteract methanol poisoning is to give the victim a nearly intoxicating drink of dilute ethanol. As the ethanol floods the same enzyme that attacks the methanol, the methanol gets a lessened opportunity to react and it is slowly and relatively harmlessly excreted. Otherwise, it is oxidized to formaldehyde, the actual poison from an overdose of methanol:

$$CH_3OH \xrightarrow{\text{Dehydrogenase}} CH_2O$$
Methanol   Formaldehyde

What kind of enzyme inhibition might ethanol be achieving here? (Name it.)

Enzymes in Medicine

24.44 If an enzyme such as CK or LD is normally absent from blood, how can a *serum* analysis for either tell anything? (Answer in general terms.)

24.45 What is the significance of the CK(*MB*) band in trying to find out whether a person has had a heart attack and not just some painful injury in the chest region?

24.46 What CK band obtained by electrophoresis would increase if the injury in Review Exercise 24.45 were to skeletal muscle?

24.47 What is the LD flip, and how is it used in diagnosis?

24.48 What happens, chemically, in a positive blood test for glucose based on an enzyme? (Give the answer in terms of the steps in the series of changes that can be described by words, not equations.)

24.49 How is immobilized heparinase used?

24.50 Describe an example of an immobilized enzyme on an electrode tip and the function it serves.

24.51 What three enzymes are available to help dissolve a blood clot? Which one occurs in human blood and how is it obtained for therapeutic uses?

24.52 What substance makes up most of a blood clot, and what happens to it when tPA works?

Chemical Communication

24.53 What are the names of the sites of the synthesis of (a) hormones and (b) neurotransmitters?

24.54 What does the lock-and-key concept have to do with the work of hormones and neurotransmitters?

24.55 In what general ways do hormones and neurotransmitters resemble each other?

24.56 What general name is given to the substance on a target cell that recognizes a hormone or neurotransmitter?

24.57 Name the two kinds of "enzyme cascades" studied in this section.

24.58 Name the small polypeptide that both systems (Review Exercise 24.57) use to activate something inside the cell.

24.59 What function does adenylate cyclase have in the work of at least some hormones?

24.60 How is cyclic AMP involved in the work of some hormones and neurotransmitters?

24.61 After cyclic AMP has caused the activation of an enzyme inside a cell, what happens to the cyclic AMP that stops its action until more is made?

24.62 In what ways does the inositol "cascade" resemble the cyclic AMP cascade?

24.63 When the G-protein of the inositol cascade completes its work, it has produced *two* new messengers. In general terms, what does each one do next?

Hormones

24.64 What are the four broad types of hormones?

24.65 What structural fact about the steroid hormones makes it easy for them to get through a cell membrane?

24.66 In each case, what substance (or kind of substance) can enter a target cell more readily following the action of the named hormone?
(a) insulin   (b) growth hormone   (c) a neurotransmitter

24.67 Why are the prostaglandins called *local hormones*?

Neurotransmitters

24.68 What happens to acetylcholine after it has worked as a neurotransmitter? What is the name of the enzyme that catalyzes this change? In chemical terms, what specifically does a nerve gas poison do?

24.69 How does atropine counter nerve gas poisoning?

24.70 How does a local anesthetic such as procaine affect the functioning of acetylcholine as a neurotransmitter?

24.71 How does the botulinus toxin work?

24.72 What, in general terms, are the monoamine oxidases, and in what way are they important?

24.73 What does iproniazid do chemically in the neuron signaling that is carried out by norepinephrine?

24.74 In general terms, how do antidepressants such as amitriptyline or imipramine work?

24.75 Which neurotransmitter is also a hormone, and what is the significance of this dual character to the body?

24.76 The overactivity of which neurotransmitter is thought to be one biochemical problem in schizophrenia?

24.77 How do the drugs chlorpromazine and haloperidol work in controlling schizophrenia?

24.78 How can the amphetamines, when abused, give schizophrenia-like symptoms?

24.79 How does L-DOPA work in treating Parkinson's disease?

24.80 What is the theory behind the efforts to see if Deprenyl can be used in the treatment of Parkinson's disease?

24.81 Which common neurotransmitter in the brain is a signal inhibitor? How do such tranquilizers as Valium and Librium affect it?

24.82 Why is enkaphalin called one of the body's own opiates? How does it appear to work?

24.83 What does substance P do?

24.84 How do the calcium channel blockers reduce the risk of a heart attack?

Work of NAD$^+$, FMA, or FAD (Special Topic 24.1)

24.85 When NAD$^+$ is involved in the oxidation of an alcohol, what small pieces leave the alcohol molecule? Where does each go?

24.86 When FMN or FAD is involved in the oxidation of an alcohol, what small pieces leave the alcohol molecule? Where does each go?

24.87 What specifically makes the NAD$^+$ unit an attractor of H:$^-$?

24.88 What molecule finally gets the electrons of H:$^-$ at the end of the entire metabolic pathway?

Electrophoresis (Special Topic 24.2)

24.89 What is the overall result of electrophoresis?

24.90 Describe in general terms why electrophoresis works.

CHAPTER TWENTY-FIVE

Extracellular Fluids of the Body

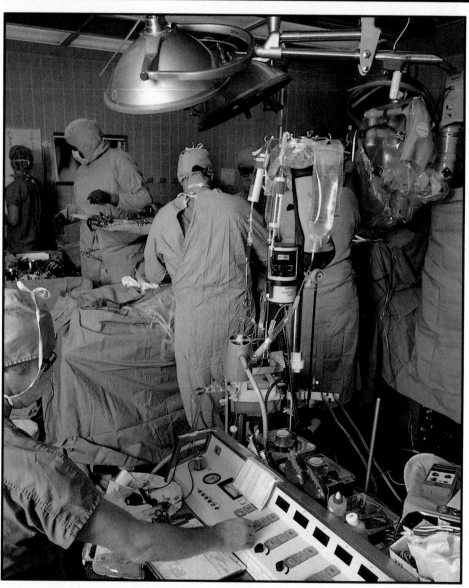

Many aspects of blood chemistry, a major topic in this chapter, must be closely monitored during open-heart surgery. A thicket of tubes and machines helps the anesthesiologist to accomplish this monitoring.

25.1 DIGESTIVE JUICES

The end products of the complete digestion of the nutritionally important carbohydrates, lipids, and proteins are monosaccharides, fatty acids, glycerol, and amino acids.

Life engages two environments, the outside environment we commonly think of, and the internal environment, which we usually take for granted. When healthy, our bodies have nearly perfect control over the internal environment, and so we are able to handle large changes outside more or less well: large temperature fluctuations, chilling winds, stifling humidity, and a fluctuating atmospheric tide of dust and pollutants.

■ The fluids of the internal environment make up about 20% of the mass of the body.

■ Synovial fluids are the viscous lubricants of joints.

Cells Exist in Contact with Interstitial Fluids and Blood   The **internal environment** consists of all the **extracellular fluids,** those that aren't actually inside cells. About three-quarters consists of the **interstitial fluid,** the fluid in the spaces or interstices *between* cells. The blood makes up nearly all the rest. The lymph, cerebrospinal fluid, digestive juices, and synovial fluids are also extracellular fluids.

The chemistry occurring inside cells, in the *intracellular fluid,* has been and will continue to be a major topic of our study. Here we will focus on two of the extracellular fluids, the digestive juices and the blood.

The Digestive Tract Is a Convoluted Tube Running Through the Body with Access to Several Solutions of Hydrolytic Enzymes   The principal parts of the digestive tract are given in Figure 25.1. The **digestive juices** are dilute solutions of electrolytes and hydrolytic enzymes (or zymogens) either in the cells lining the intestinal tract or in solutions that enter the tract from various organs.

■ Dextrins consist of slightly degraded starch molecules.

Saliva Provides α-Amylase, a Starch-Splitting Enzyme   The flow of **saliva** is stimulated by the sight, smell, taste, and even the thought of food. Besides water (99.5%), saliva includes a food lubricant called **mucin** (a glycoprotein) and an enzyme, **α-amylase.** This enzyme catalyzes the partial hydrolysis of starch to dextrins and maltose, and it works best at the pH of saliva, 5.8 to 7.1. Proteins and lipids pass through the mouth essentially unchanged.

■ The pH of gastric juice is normally in the range of 0.9 to 2.0.

Gastric Juice Starts the Digestion of Proteins with Pepsin   When food arrives in the stomach, the cells of the gastric glands are stimulated by hormones to release the fluids that combine to give **gastric juice.** One kind of gastric gland secretes mucin, which coats the stomach to protect it against its own digestive enzymes and its acid. Mucin is continuously produced and only slowly digested. If for any reason its protection of the stomach is hindered, part of the stomach itself could be digested, and this would lead to an ulcer.

Another gastric gland secretes hydrochloric acid at a concentration of roughly 0.1 mol/L, about a million times more acidic than blood. The acid coagulates proteins and activates a protease. Protein coagulation retains the protein in the stomach longer for exposure to the protease.

■ A *protease* is a enzyme that catalyzes the digestion of proteins.

The third gastric gland secretes the zymogen, **pepsinogen.** Pepsinogen is changed into **pepsin,** a protease, by the action of hydrochloric acid and traces of pepsin. The optimum pH of pepsin is in the range of 1 to 1.5, which is found in the stomach fluid. Pepsin catalyzes the only important digestive work in the stomach, the hydrolysis of some of the peptide bonds of proteins to make short polypeptides.

Adult gastric juice also has a lipase, but it does not start its work until it arrives in the higher pH medium of the upper intestinal tract.

The gastric juice of infants is less acidic than the adults. To compensate for the protein-coagulating work normally done by the acid, infant gastric juice contains rennin, a powerful protein coagulator. Because the pH of an infant's gastric juice is higher than that in the adult, its lipase gets an early start on lipid digestion.

Figure 25.1
Organs of the digestive tract.

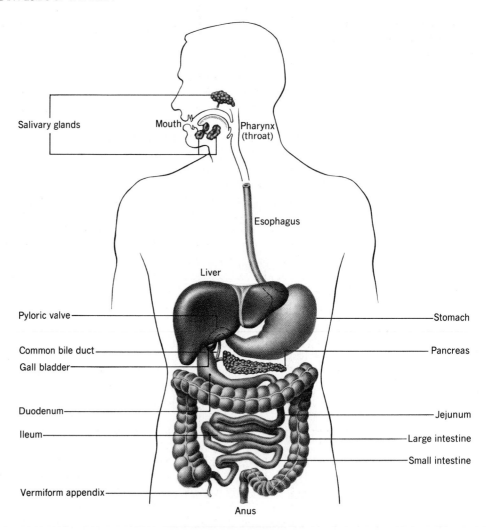

The churning and digesting activities in the stomach produce a liquid mixture called **chyme.** This is released in portions through the pyloric valve into the duodenum, the first 12 inches of the upper intestinal tract.

Pancreatic Juice Furnishes Several Zymogens and Enzymes As soon as chyme appears in the duodenum, hormones are released that circulate to the pancreas and induce this organ to release two juices. One is almost entirely dilute sodium bicarbonate, which neutralizes the acid in chyme. The other is the one usually called **pancreatic juice.** It carries enzymes or zymogens that become involved in the digestion of practically everything in food. It contributes an **α-amylase** similar to that present in saliva, a **lipase, nucleases,** and zymogens for protein-digesting enzymes.

■ The nucleases include ribonuclease (RNAase) and deoxyribonuclease (DNAase).

The conversion of the proteolytic zymogens to active enzymes begins with a "master switch" enzyme called **enteropeptidase,** which we mentioned in Section 24.3. It is released from cells that line the duodenum when chyme arrives, and it then catalyzes the formation of trypsin from its zymogen, trypsinogen.

■ Enteropeptidase used to be called enterokinase.

$$\text{Trypsinogen} \xrightarrow{\text{enteropeptidase}} \text{trypsin}$$

Trypsin then catalyzes the change of the other zymogens into their active enzymes.

$$\text{Procarboxypeptidase} \xrightarrow{\text{trypsin}} \text{carboxypeptidase}$$

■ These proteases must exist as zymogens first or they will catalyze the self-digestion of the pancreas, which does happen in acute pancreatitis.

$$\text{Chymotrypsinogen} \xrightarrow{\text{trypsin}} \text{chymotrypsin}$$

$$\text{Proelastase} \xrightarrow{\text{trypsin}} \text{elastase}$$

Trypsin, chymotrypsin, and **elastase** catalyze the hydrolysis of large polypeptides to smaller ones. **Carboxypeptidase,** working in from C-terminal ends of small polypeptides, carries the action further to amino acids and dipeptides or tripeptides.

Bile Salts Are Powerful Surfactants Necessary To Manage Dietary Lipids and Fat-Soluble Vitamins

■ The structure of a typical bile salt was given in Table 20.3, page 522.

In order to digest most lipids, the lipase in pancreatic juice needs the help of the powerful detergents in bile, called the **bile salts.** These help to emulsify water-insoluble fatty materials and so greatly increase the exposure of lipids to water and lipase. Triacylglycerols are hydrolyzed to fatty acids, glycerol, and some monoacylglycerols.

Bile is a juice that enters the duodenum from the gall bladder. Its secretion is stimulated by a hormone released when chyme contains fatty material. Bile is also an avenue of excretion, because it carries cholesterol and breakdown products of hemoglobin. These and additional breakdown products constitute the bile pigments, which give color to feces.

The bile salts also assist in the absorption of the fat-soluble vitamins (A, D, E, and K) from the digestive tract into the blood. This work reabsorbs some bile pigments, some of which eventually leave the body via the urine. Thus the bile pigments are responsible for the color of both feces and urine.

Cells of the Intestines Carry Several Digestive Enzymes

■ These intestinal cells last only about two days before they self-digest. They are constantly being replaced.

The term **intestinal juice** embraces not only a secretion but also the enzyme-rich fluids found inside certain kinds of cells that line the duodenum and jejunum. The secretion of some of these cells delivers an amylase and enteropeptidase, which we just described.

The other enzymes supplied by this region work within their cells as digestible compounds are already being absorbed. An **aminopeptidase,** working inward from N-terminal ends of small polypeptides, digests them to amino acids. The enzymes **sucrase, lactase,** and **maltase** handle the digestion of disaccharides: sucrose to fructose and glucose; lactose to galactose and glucose; and maltose to glucose. An intestinal lipase and enzymes for the hydrolysis of nucleic acids are also present.

As fatty acids, glycerol, and monoacylglycerols migrate through the cells of the duodenal lining, much is reconstituted into triacylglycerols, which are taken up by the lymph system rather than the blood.

Some Vitamins and Essential Amino Acids Are Made in the Large Intestine

No digestive functions are performed in the large intestine. Microorganisms in residence there, however, make vitamins K and B, plus some essential amino acids. These are absorbed by the body, but their contributions to overall nutrition in humans is not large.

Water and sodium chloride are reabsorbed from the ileum, and undigested matter (including fiber) and some water make up the feces.

25.2 BLOOD AND THE ABSORPTION OF NUTRIENTS BY CELLS

The balance between the blood's pumping pressure and its colloidal osmotic pressure tips at capillary loops.

■ The nervous system with its neurotransmitters is the other line of communication.

The circulatory system, Figure 25.2, is one of our two main lines of chemical communication between the external and internal environments. All the veins and arteries together are called the **vascular compartment.** The **cardiovascular compartment** includes this plus the heart.

The Blood Moves Nutrients, Oxygen, Messengers, Wastes, and Disease-Fighters Throughout the Body

Blood in the pulmonary branches moves through the

Figure 25.2
Human circulatory system. When oxygen-depleted venous blood (light areas) returns to the heart, it is pumped into the capillary beds of the alveoli in the lungs to reload oxygen and get rid ot carbon dioxide. Then the freshly oxygenated blood (dark areas) is distributed by the arteries throughout the body, including the heart muscle.

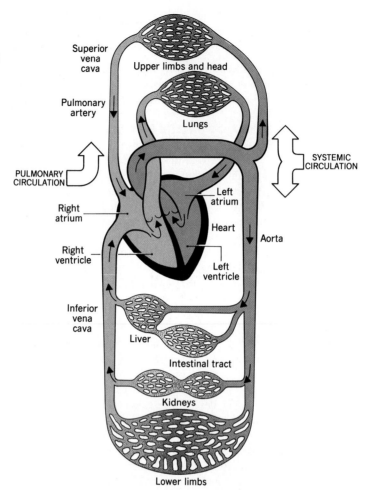

About 8% of the body's mass is blood. In the adult, the blood volume is 5 to 6 L.

lungs where waste carbon dioxide is exchanged for oxygen. The oxygenated blood then moves to the rest of the system via the systemic branches.

At the intestinal tract, the blood picks up the products of digestion. Most of these are immediately monitored at the liver and many alien chemicals are modified for elimination. In the kidneys, the blood replenishes its buffer supplies and eliminates waste nitrogen, mostly urea. The pH of blood and its electrolyte levels depend hugely on the kidneys. At endocrine glands, the blood picks up hormones whose secretions are often in response to something present in the blood.

White cells in blood provide protection against bacteria; red cells or **erythrocytes** carry oxygen and waste bicarbonate ion; and platelets are needed for blood clotting and other purposes. The blood also carries several zymogens that participate in the blood-clotting mechanism.

The Proteins in Blood Are Vital to Its Colloidal Osmotic Pressure   The principal types of substances in whole blood are summarized in Figure 25.3. Among the proteins, the **albumins** help carry hydrophobic molecules, like fatty acids, other lipids, and steroid hormones, and they contribute 75% to 80% of the osmotic effect of the blood. Some globulins carry ions (e.g., Fe^{2+} and Cu^{2+}) that otherwise are insoluble when the pH is greater than 7. The **gamma globulins** help to protect the body against infectious disease. **Fibrinogen** is converted to an insoluble form, **fibrin,** when a blood clot forms, as we discussed in Section 24.4.

About a quarter of the plasma proteins are replaced each day.

Figure 25.4 gives the levels of solutes, including proteins, in various components of the major body fluids. The higher level of protein in blood is the principal reason why blood has a

Figure 25.3
Major components of blood.

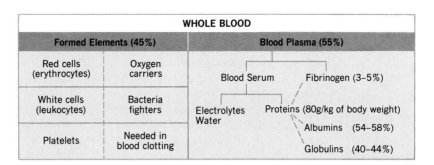

Figure 25.4
Electrolyte composition of body fluids.
(Adapted by permission from J. L.
Gamble, *Chemical Anatomy,
Physiology and Pathology of Extracel-
lular Fluids,* 6th ed, Harvard University
Press, Cambridge, Mass., 1954.)

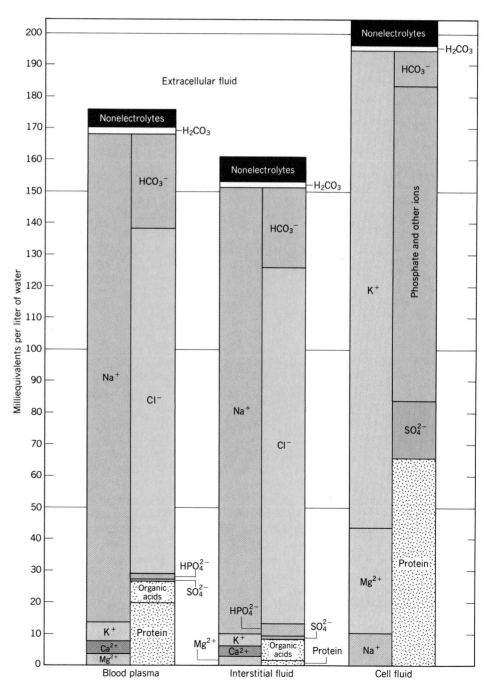

■ The osmolarity of plasma is about 290 mOsm/L.

higher osmotic pressure than interstitial fluid.[1] The *total* osmotic pressure of blood is caused, of course, by all the dissolved and colloidally dispersed solutes. The small ions and molecules, however, can dialyze back and forth between the blood and the interstitial compartment. The large protein molecules can't do this, so it is their presence that gives to blood a higher effective osmotic pressure than interstitial fluid. The margin of difference is the blood's colloidal osmotic pressure.

As a consequence of the higher osmotic pressure of blood, water tends to flow into the blood from the interstitial compartment. This cannot be allowed to happen *everywhere* and *continually*, however, or the interstitial space and then the cells would eventually become too dehydrated to maintain life. Before we see how this problem is managed, we need to survey some of the **electrolytes** in blood.

The Chief Ions in Blood Are Na⁺, Cl⁻, and HCO₃⁻   Figure 25.4 gives the levels of the electrolytes in body fluids. The sodium ion is the chief cation in both the blood and the interstitial fluid and the potassium ion is the major cation inside cells. A sodium–potassium pump, a special ATP-run protein complex, maintains these gradients. Both ions are needed to maintain osmotic pressure relationships, and both are a part of the regulatory system for acid–base balance. Both ions are also needed for the smooth working of the muscles and the nervous system.

■ Another word part is *-uria*, of the urine. Thus *glucosuria* means glucose in the urine.

Changes in the concentrations of sodium and potassium ion in blood can lead to serious medical emergencies, so a special vocabulary has been developed to describe various situations. We will see here how a technical vocabulary can be built on a few word parts, and we will use some of these word parts in later chapters, too. For example, we use *-emia* to signify "in the blood." *Hypo-* indicates a condition of a low concentration of something, and *hyper-* is the opposite, a condition of a high concentration of something. We can specify this something by a word part, too. Thus *-nat-* signifies sodium (from the Latin *natrium* for sodium), and *-kal-* designates potassium (from the Latin *kalium* for potassium). Putting these together gives us the following terms.

■ You'll see it called the "sodium level," not sodium *ion* level, in nearly all references, but sodium *ion* level is always intended.

Hyponatremia:	low level of sodium ion in blood
Hypokalemia:	low level of potassium ion in blood
Hypernatremia:	high level of sodium ion in blood
Hyperkalemia:	high level of potassium ion in blood

Na⁺ and K⁺ Levels Are Regulated in Tandem   Figure 25.5 shows the normal range for the sodium ion level in blood. Figure 25.6 does the same thing for the potassium ion level. Table 25.1 gives the normal ranges for these cations in various units.

If our kidneys cannot make urine or if we drink water faster than the kidneys can handle it, the sodium level of the blood decreases and we will display the signs of hyponatremia: flushed skin, fever, and a dry tongue (and a noticeable decrease in urine output).

Hypernatremia occurs from excessive losses of water under circumstances in which sodium ions are not lost, as in diarrhea, diabetes, and even in some high-protein diets.

Because the level of potassium ion in blood is so low, small changes are particularly dangerous. Severe hyperkalemia leads to death by heart failure. This danger exists in victims with crushing injuries, severe burns, or heart attacks — anything that breaks cells open so that they spill their K⁺ ions into general circulation.

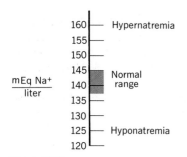

Figure 25.5
The sodium ion level in the blood.

At the other extreme, severe hypokalemia, caused by any unusual losses of body fluids including prolonged, excessive sweating, can lead to death by heart failure. Both body fluids *and electrolytes* have to be replaced during severe exercise.

■ Experienced backpackers use salt tablets that contain not only NaCl but also some KCl to supply K⁺.

The serum levels of sodium ions and potassium ions are regulated in tandem by the kidneys. If the intake of Na⁺ is high, there will be a loss of K⁺ from the body. If the intake of K⁺

[1] As a reminder and a useful memory aid, a high concentration of solute means high osmotic pressure; and solvent flows in osmosis or dialysis from a region where the solute is dilute to the region where it is concentrated. The "goal" of this flow is to even out the concentrations everywhere.

TABLE 25.1   Group IA Cations in the Human Body

Area	Na^+	K^+
Total body	2700–3000 meq	3200 meq
Plasma level	135–145 meq/L	3.5–5.0 meq/L
Intracellular level	10 meq/L	125 meq/L
Mass of 1 meq	23.0 mg	39.1 mg

TABLE 25.2   Group IIA Cations in the Human Body

Area	Ca^{2+}	Mg^{2+}
Total body	6×10^4 meq (1.2 kg)	1000 meq (24 g)
Plasma level	4.2–5.2 meq/L	1.5–2.0 meq/L
Intracellular level	(a)	35 meq/L
Mass of 1 meq	20.0 mg	12.2 mg

a Free in solution in the cytosol, about 10^{-7} mol/L.

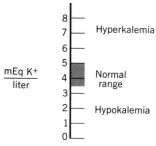

Figure 25.6
The potassium ion level in the blood.

is high, there will be a loss of Na^+ from the body. It's the total positive charge that must be maintained so as to balance the total negative charge. One reason we can't tolerate seawater (3% NaCl) and will die if we drink it is that it upsets the sodium–potassium balance in the body.

Mg^{2+} Is Second to K^+ as a Cation Inside Cells   The normal ranges for the levels of calcium ion and magnesium ion in the body are given in Table 25.2. The level of magnesium ion in the blood is even lower than that of K^+ (Figure 25.4), so small variations can mean large trouble. Hypomagnesemia, for example, is observed when the kidneys aren't working properly, or in alcoholism, or in untreated diabetes. Some of its signs are muscle weakness, insomnia, and cramps in the legs or the feet. Injections of isotonic magnesium sulfate solution are sometimes used to restore Mg^{2+} to the serum.

On the opposite side, hypermagnesemia can lead to cardiac arrest, and it can be brought on by the overuse of magnesium-based antacids such as milk of magnesia, $Mg(OH)_2$.

■ It's common among the elderly to suffer the loss of Ca^{2+} from bones, a condition called *osteoporosis*.

Nearly All the Body's Ca^{2+} Is in Bones and Teeth   The Ca^{2+} not in bones and teeth is absolutely vital, as we explained in the previous chapter. It is an important secondary chemical messenger involved in activating enzymes and in muscle contraction.

Hypocalcemia can be brought on by vitamin D deficiency, the overuse of laxatives, an impaired activity of the thyroid gland, and even by hypomagnesemia. Hypercalcemia, on the other hand, is caused by the opposite conditions: an overdose of vitamin D, the overuse of calcium ion-based antacids, or an overactive thyroid. In severe hypercalcemia, the heart functions poorly.

Cl^- and HCO_3^- Provide Almost All the Negative Charge to Balance the Cationic Charges in Blood   The chloride ion in blood helps to maintain osmotic pressure relationships, the acid–base balance, and the distribution of water in the body. It has a function in oxygen transport. The bicarbonate ion is the chief acid-neutralizing buffer in blood and the principal form in which waste CO_2 is carried.

■ In blood, the normal range for $[Cl^-]$ is 100 to 106 meq/L. (1 meq $Cl^- = 35.5$ mg)

In hypochloremia, there is an excessive loss of Cl^- from the blood. For every Cl^- lost, the blood either must lose one (+) charge, like Na^+, or retain one extra (−) charge on some other anion. Electrical neutrality dictates these simple facts. The chief ion retained is HCO_3^-. Because this ion tends to raise the pH of a fluid, *a condition of hypochloremia can cause alkalosis.*

By the same token, hyperchloremia, a rise in the level of Cl^-, could mean that HCO_3^- has to be dumped, which would mean a loss of base. Thus *hyperchloremia can cause acidosis.*

Fluids That Leave the Blood Must Return in Identical Volume   The blood vessels undergo extensive branching until the narrowest tubes called the capillaries are reached. Blood enters a capillary loop (Figure 25.7) as arterial blood, but it leaves on the other side of the loop as venous blood.

During the switch, fluids and nutrients leave the blood and move into the interstitial fluids and into the tissue cells themselves. *In the same volume* the fluids must return to the blood, but now they must carry the wastes of metabolism. The rate of this diffusion of fluids throughout

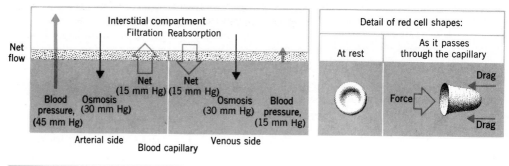

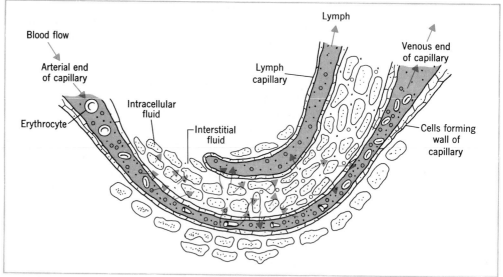

Figure 25.7
The exchange of nutrients and wastes at capillaries. As indicated at the top, on the arterial side of a capillary loop the blood pressure counteracts the pressure from dialysis and osmosis, and fluids are forced to leave the bloodstream. On the venous side of the loop, the blood pressure has decreased below that of dialysis and osmosis, so fluids flow back into the bloodstream. On the top right and the bottom is shown how a normal red cell distorts as it squeezes through a capillary loop. Red cells in sickle-cell anemia do not pass through as smoothly. The bottom drawing also shows how some fluids enter the lymph system.

■ The lymph system makes antibodies and it has white cells that help defend the body against infectious diseases.

the body is sizable, about 25 to 30 L/sec. Some fluids return to circulation by way of the lymph ducts, which are thin-walled, closed-end capillaries that bed in soft tissue.

Blood Pressure Overcomes Osmotic Pressure on the Arterial Side of a Capillary Loop Interstitial fluids have a natural tendency to dialyze into the bloodstream because the blood has the higher colloidal osmotic pressure. On the arterial side of a capillary loop, however, the blood pressure is sufficiently high to overcome this. Water and dissolved solutes are forced, instead, from the blood *into* the interstitial space. While they are there, exchanges of chemicals occur. Nutrients move into cells, and cells get rid of wastes.

Osmotic Pressure Overcomes Blood Pressure on the Venous Side of a Capillary Loop As blood emerges from the thin constriction of a capillary into the venous side, its pressure drops. Now it is too low to prevent the natural diffusion of fluids back into the bloodstream. By this time, of course, the fluids are carrying waste products. These relationships are illustrated in Figure 25.7. It shows how the colloidal osmotic pressure contributed by the dispersed macromolecules in blood, particularly the albumins, make the difference in determining the direction of diffusion.

Blood Loses Albumins in the Shock Syndrome   When the capillaries become more permeable to blood proteins, as they do in such trauma as sudden severe injuries, major surgery, and extensive burns, the proteins migrate out of the blood. Unfortunately, this protein loss also means the loss of the colloidal osmotic pressure that helps fluids to return from the tissue areas to the bloodstream. As a result, the total volume of circulating blood drops quickly, and this drastically reduces the blood's ability to carry oxygen and to remove carbon dioxide. The drop in blood volume and the resulting loss of oxygen supply to the brain sends the victim into traumatic **shock.**

■ The prompt restoration of blood volume is mandatory in the treatment of shock.

Blood Also Loses Proteins in Kidney Disease and Starvation   Sometimes the proteins in the blood are lost at malfunctioning kidneys. The effect, although gradual, is a slow but unremitting drop in the blood's colloidal osmotic pressure. Fluids accumulate in the interstitial regions. Because this takes place more slowly and water continues to be ingested, there is no sudden drop in blood volume as in shock. The victim appears puffy and water-logged, a condition called **edema.**

■ Greek *oidema*, swelling.

Edema can also appear at one stage of starvation, when the body has metabolized its circulating proteins to make up for the absence of dietary proteins.

Any obstruction in the veins can also cause edema, as in varicose veins and certain forms of cancer. Now it is the venous blood pressure that rises, creating a back pressure that reduces the rate at which fluids can return to circulation from the tissue areas. The localized swelling that results from a blow is a temporary form of edema caused by injuries to the capillaries.

25.3   BLOOD AND THE EXCHANGE OF RESPIRATORY GASES

The binding of oxygen to hemoglobin is allosteric, and it is affected by the pH, pCO_2, and the pO_2 of the blood.

■ Each red cell carries about 2.8×10^8 molecules of hemoglobin.

The carrier of oxygen in blood is **hemoglobin,** a complex protein found inside erythrocytes. It consists of four subunits, each with one molecule of heme, an organic group that holds an iron(II) ion and that is the actual oxygen-binding unit. Two of the subunits are identical and have the symbol α. The other two are also identical and have the symbol β.

$$^{2-}O_3POCH_2CHCO_2^-$$
$$|$$
$$OPO_3^{2-}$$

DPG (2,3-diphosphoglycerate)

When hemoglobin is oxygen-free, it is sometimes referred to as *deoxyhemoglobin;* in this state the molecule has a small cavity in which a small organic anion nestles. This is the **2,3-diphosphoglycerate** ion, called simply **DPG,** and it has an important function in oxygen transport.

The Subunits of Hemoglobin Cooperate in Its Oxygenation   We define the **oxygen affinity** of the blood as the percent to which the blood has all of its hemoglobin molecules saturated with oxygen. A fully laden hemoglobin molecule carries four oxygen molecules and is called **oxyhemoglobin.** For the maximum efficiency in moving oxygen from the lungs to tissues that need it, all hemoglobin molecules should leave the lungs in the form of fully loaded oxyhemoglobin. Let's see what factors ensure this.

First, the partial pressure of oxygen is higher in the lungs than anywhere else in the body; $pO_2 = 100$ mm Hg in freshly inhaled air in alveoli and only about 40 mm Hg in oxygen-depleted tissues. Because of this partial pressure gradient, oxygen naturally migrates from the lungs into the bloodstream. It's as though the higher partial pressure *pushes* oxygen into the blood. Second, newly arrived oxygen actually reacts with hemoglobin to form oxyhemoglobin, so this tends to *pull* oxygen into the blood.

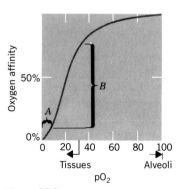

Figure 25.8
Hemoglobin–oxygen dissociation curve. Regions *A* and *B* are discussed in the text.

An allosteric effect also helps to load hemoglobin with oxygen. Figure 25.8 shows a plot of oxygen affinity versus the oxygen partial pressure. It has the sigmoid shape that in Chapter 24 we learned to associate with the allosteric effect among enzymes. At low values of pO_2, in region *A* of the plot, the ability of the blood to take up oxygen rises only slowly with increases in pO_2. But eventually the oxygen affinity takes off and rises very steeply with still more increases in pO_2, in region *B* of the plot. Eventually, the oxygen affinity starts to level off. It

■ We first learned about the allosteric effect on page 605.

■ This natural resistance is needed in working cells in which we want no restrictions on the deoxygenation of blood.

almost seems that a small "molecular dam" thwarts the efforts of oxygen molecules to be joined to hemoglobin at low partial pressure of oxygen.

What is thought to be happening is as follows. We'll represent deoxyhemoglobin by structure **1**, below. Each circle in **1** is a polypeptide subunit with its heme unit but without oxygen. The diamond figure centered within the structure represents one DPG anion. When the first O_2 molecule manages to bind (**1** → **2**), it induces a change in the shape of the affected subunit, which we have represented as a change from a circle to a square:

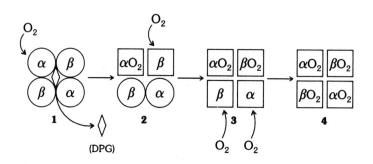

This change tends to squeeze out the DPG unit, and this "breaks the dam" that we just alluded to. The next oxygen molecule enters more readily (**2** → **3**). As its affected subunit changes its shape, the remaining two subunits allosterically change their shapes and become very receptive to the third and fourth molecules of oxygen. These two flood into this hemoglobin molecule (**3** → **4**) far more readily than either would bind to a completely deoxygenated hemoglobin molecule. Thus if a hemoglobin molecule accepts just one oxygen molecule, it's almost certain that it will soon accept three more to become fully oxygenated. Few if any partially oxygenated hemoglobin molecules leave the lungs.

■ Carbon monoxide binds 150 to 200 times more strongly to hemoglobin than oxygen does and thus prevents the oxygenation of hemoglobin and causes internal suffocation.

■ About 20% of a smoker's hemoglobin is more or less permanently tied up by carbon monoxide.

For the sake of the remaining discussion, we'll simplify what we have just described by letting the symbol HHb represent an entire hemoglobin molecule. The first H in HHb stands for a potential hydrogen ion, and we overlook the fact that more than one is actually present in hemoglobin. (We're now also overlooking the fact that *four* molecules of O_2 bind to one of hemoglobin.) With this in mind, we can represent the oxygenation of hemoglobin as the *forward* reaction in the following equilibrium where oxyhemoglobin is represented as the anion, HbO_2^-:

$$\underset{\text{Hemoglobin}}{HHb} + O_2 \rightleftharpoons \underset{\text{Oxyhemoglobin}}{HbO_2^-} + H^+ \tag{25.1}$$

Two facts indicated by this equilibrium are that HHb is a weak acid and that it becomes a stronger acid as it becomes oxygenated. Being stronger, it is produced in its ionized state as HbO_2^- and H^+. *The presence of H^+ in equilibrium 25.1 means that the equilibrium can be shifted one way or another simply by changing the pH,* a fact of enormous importance at the molecular level of life, as we'll see.

To understand the oxygenation of hemoglobin, we have to see how various stresses shift equilibrium 25.1 to the right in the lungs. One stress, as we've already noted, is the relatively high value of pO_2 (100 mm Hg) in the alveoli. This stress is on the left side of 25.1, so it helps to shift the equilibrium to the right.

$$\underset{\substack{\text{In the} \\ \text{red cell}}}{HHb} + \underset{\substack{\text{From} \\ \text{air}}}{O_2} \longrightarrow \underset{\substack{\text{In the} \\ \text{red cell}}}{HbO_2^-} + \underset{\substack{\text{In the} \\ \text{red cell}}}{H^+}$$

Another stress that isn't evident from 25.1 is the removal of H^+ *as it forms*. The red cell in the lungs is carrying waste HCO_3^-. The newly forming H^+ ions are therefore promptly equilibrated with HCO_3^- and CO_2 by carbonic anhydrase. (We write it as a forward reaction because that is how the equilibrium shifts when both H^+ and HCO_3^- are high.)

$$H^+ + HCO_3^- \xrightarrow{\text{carbonic anhydrase}} CO_2 + H_2O \qquad (25.2)$$

In the red cell   In the red cell   In the red cell

■ As we learned in the last chapter, carbonic anhydrase is the body's fastest-working enzyme, and it has to be fast because the red cells are always on the move.

This switch from the appearance of H^+ as a product to its disappearance as a reactant is called the **isohydric shift.**

We see here one of the beautiful examples of coordinated activity in the body, the coupling of the uptake of oxygen to the release of the carbon dioxide to be exhaled. The neutralization of the H^+ ions brought about by the uptake of O_2 produces CO_2. The loss of CO_2 from the red cell by exhaling pulls this and all previous equilibria to the right in the lungs.

$$CO_2 \text{ (in red cell)} \xrightarrow{\text{exhaling}} CO_2 \text{ (in exhaled air)}$$

Thus the uptake of O_2 as hemoglobin oxygenates, which pushes the equilibria to the right, simultaneously produces a chemical (CO_2) whose loss pulls the same equilibria to the right.

Let's now see how this waste is picked up at cells that have produced it and is carried to the lungs; and let's also see how this works cooperatively with the *release* of oxygen at cells that need it.

The Hemoglobin Subunits and DPG Cooperate in the Deoxygenation of Oxyhemoglobin in Metabolizing Tissues

Consider, now, a tissue that has done some chemical work, used up some oxygen, and made some waste carbon dioxide. When a fully oxygenated red cell arrives in such a tissue, some of the events we just described reverse themselves.

■ CO_2 molecules diffuse in body fluids 30 times more easily than O_2 molecules, so the partial pressure gradient for CO_2 need not be as steep as that for O_2.

We can think of this reversal as beginning with the diffusion of waste CO_2 from the tissue into the blood. An impetus for this diffusion is the higher pCO_2 (50 mm Hg) in active tissue versus its value in blood (40 mm Hg). Once the CO_2 arrives in the blood, it moves inside a red cell where it encounters carbonic anhydrase. Equation 25.2 is therefore run in reverse. It was part of the equilibrium managed by carbonic anhydrase, and it shifts to the left as more and more CO_2 arrives. In other words, the equilibrium now shifts to *make* HCO_3^-.

$$H_2O + CO_2 \xrightarrow{\text{carbonic anhydrase}} HCO_3^- + H^+ \qquad (25.2 \text{—reversed})$$

From the working tissue   In the red cell

Of course, this generates hydrogen ions, and if you'll look back to Equation 25.1, which is also part of an equilibrium, you will see that an increase in the level of H^+ (caused by the influx of waste CO_2) can only make Equation 25.1 run in reverse.

$$H^+ + HbO_2^- \longrightarrow HHb + O_2 \qquad (25.1 \text{—reversed})$$

Just made in the red cell at working tissue   In the red cell, just arrived   In the red cell   Will diffuse into the tissue

This reaction, another isohydric shift, not only neutralizes the acid generated by the arrival of waste CO_2 but also helps to force oxyhemoglobin to give up its oxygen. Notice the cooperation. The tissue that needs oxygen has made CO_2 and, hence, it has indirectly made the H^+ that is required to release this needed oxygen from newly arrived HbO_2^-.

■ The high negative charge on DPG keeps it from diffusing through the red cell's membrane.

The deoxygenation of HbO_2^- is also aided by the DPG anions that were pushed out when HbO_2^- formed. These anions are still inside the red cell, and as soon as an O_2 molecule leaves oxyhemoglobin, a DPG anion starts to move back in. The changes in shapes of the hemoglobin subunits now operate in reverse, and all oxygen molecules smoothly leave. It's all or nothing again, and the efficiency of the unloading of oxygen is so high that if one O_2 molecule leaves, the other three follow essentially at once. DPG helps this to happen. Partially deoxygenated hemoglobin units do not slip through and go back to the lungs.

■ No conditioning at a low altitude can get the cardiovascular system ready for a low pO_2 at a high altitude.

DPG and Hemoglobin Levels Are Higher in People Living at High Altitudes It's interesting that those who live and work at high altitudes, such as the populations in Nepal in the Himalayan Mountains, or the people in the Andes Mountains in Bolivia, have 20% higher levels of DPG in their blood and more red blood cells than those who live at sea level.

The extra red cells give them more hemoglobin to help them carry more oxygen per milliliter of blood, and the extra DPG increases the efficiencies of both loading and unloading oxygen. When lowlanders take trips to high altitudes, their bodies start to build more red cells and to make more DPG so that they can function better where the partial pressure of the atmospheric oxygen is lower. Those who patiently wait during the few days that it takes for these events to occur before they set off on strenuous backpacking expeditions are far less likely to suffer high altitude sickness, a condition that can cause death.

To summarize the chemical reactions we have just studied, we can write the following equations. The cancel lines show how we can arrive at the overall net results.

Oxygenation: $HHb + O_2 \longrightarrow HbO_2^- + \cancel{H^+}$

| In red cell | From air | Goes in red cell to tissues | In red cell |

■ CA is carbonic anhydrase.

$\cancel{H^+} + HCO_3^- \xrightarrow{CA} CO_2 + H_2O$

| Just made | In red cell (but from tissues) | In red cell (but will be exhaled) | |

■ **Net effect of oxygenating hemoglobin:**

$$HHb + O_2 + HCO_3^- \longrightarrow HbO_2^- + CO_2 + H_2O \qquad (25.3)$$

| In red cell | From air | In red cell (but from tissues) | Goes in red cell to tissues | Leaves the lungs in exhaled air | |

Deoxygenation: $CO_2 + H_2O \xrightarrow{CA} HCO_3^- + \cancel{H^+}$

| Waste from tissues | | In red cell (still by tissue but goes to the lungs) | In red cell |

$\cancel{H^+} + HbO_2^- \longrightarrow HHb + O_2$

| Just made | In red cell; by tissue | In red cell; will return to lungs | Goes into tissue needing it |

■ **Net effect of deoxygenating oxyhemoglobin:**

$$CO_2 + H_2O + HbO_2^- \longrightarrow HHb + HCO_3^- + O_2 \qquad (25.4)$$

| Waste from tissue | In red cell; by tissues | In red cell; will go to lungs | Goes in blood to lungs | Goes into tissue |

These summarizing equations omit two features. They do not show the importance of DPG and of the concentration of H^+ in both the loading and the unloading of oxygen. Concerning the concentration of H^+, Figure 25.9 shows the plots of oxygen affinity versus pO_2 at two different values of pH, one relatively low (pH 7.2) compared with the normal value of 7.35, and the other relatively high (pH 7.6). You can recall that the pO_2 in the vicinity of

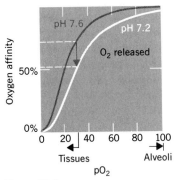

Figure 25.9
Hemoglobin–oxygen dissociation curves at two different values of the pH of blood.

oxygen-starved cells is around 30 to 40 mm Hg. Notice in Figure 25.9 that in this range of the partial pressure of oxygen, the blood's ability to hold oxygen is much less at the lower pH of 7.2 than it is at a pH of 7.6. In actively metabolizing cells, there is a localized drop in pH caused chiefly by the presence of the CO_2 that these cells have made. This drop in pH caused by CO_2 cannot help but to assist in the deoxygenation of HbO_2^-.

Thus precisely where O_2 should be unloaded there is a chemical signal (a lower pH) that makes it happen. It's an altogether beautiful example of how a set of interrelated chemical equilibria shift in just the directions that are required for health and life. Figure 25.9 will also help us understand in what ways both acidosis and alkalosis are serious threats.

Some CO_2 Is Carried to the Lungs on Hemoglobin There is another chemical reaction involving waste carbon dioxide that we must now mention. Not all the CO_2 made by metabolizing cells winds up as HCO_3^-. Some CO_2 reacts with the hemoglobin that has just been freed by deoxygenation:

$$CO_2 + HHb \longrightarrow Hb\!-\!CO_2^- + H^+ \tag{25.5}$$

Carbaminohemoglobin

Waste from tissues	Just released by deoxygenation	In red cells	Will react with HbO_2^-

This is actually the forward reaction of an equilibrium. The product, $Hb\!-\!CO_2^-$, is called **carbaminohemoglobin,** and it is one form in which some of the waste CO_2 travels in the blood back to the lungs.

Notice in Equation 25.5 that this reaction also produces H^+, just as did the reaction of water and waste CO_2. Thus whether waste CO_2 is changed to $H_2CO_3^-$ and H^+ or to $Hb\!-\!CO_2^- + H^+$, either fate helps to generate hydrogen ions that are needed to react with HbO_2^- and make it unload O_2.

When the red cell reaches the lungs, where H^+ will now be *generated* by

$$HHb + O_2 \longrightarrow HbO_2^- + H^+ \tag{25.1, again}$$

the reaction of Equation 25.5 will be forced to shift into reverse, because the added H^+ provides this kind of stress. Of course, this releases the CO_2 where it can be exhaled, and it gets hemoglobin ready to take on more oxygen.

Chloride Ion Is Also Needed to Deoxygenate Hemoglobin Still another factor we have not mentioned thus far and that helps to unload oxygen from oxyhemoglobin is the chloride ion. Hemoglobin, HHb, binds chloride ion, and it binds it better than does oxyhemoglobin. The following equilibrium exists along with all the others:

$$HHb(Cl^-) + O_2 \rightleftharpoons HbO_2^- + Cl^- + H^+ \tag{25.6}$$

Therefore to *unload* oxygen (do the reverse of 25.6), chloride ion must be available *inside* the red cell. The red cell obtains it by a mechanism called the *chloride shift.* Let's see how it occurs.

As chloride ions are drawn into the red cell to react with some of the HHb that is released in active tissue, negative ions have to move out so that there is electrical charge balance. The negative ions that leave are the newly forming bicarbonate ions. From 60% to 90% of all waste CO_2 returns to the lungs as the bicarbonate ion, but most of this makes the trip *outside* red cells.

For every chloride ion that enters the red cell, one HCO_3^- ion leaves, and this switch is called the **chloride shift.** When the red cell gets back to the lungs, the various new chemical stresses make all the equilibria, including the chloride shift, run in reverse.

If you're bewildered by all these equilibria and how they are made to shift in the correct directions, you're almost certainly not alone among your classmates. This isn't easy material, but it is so much at the heart of so many aspects of health and a person's ability to have an active life that the effort to master it is very worthwhile. As you make this effort, get the key

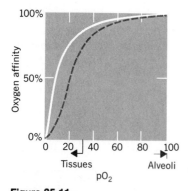

Figure 25.11
The myoglobin–oxygen dissociation curve is a solid line. The dashed line is the curve for hemoglobin. Over the entire range of pH in tissues that might need oxygen, the oxygen affinity of myoglobin is greater than that of hemoglobin.

■ HMy = myoglobin

equilibria down and memorized. For each one ask, What are the stresses that can make it shift, and where in the body is each stress important, in the lungs or at actively metabolizing cells?

The key stresses are the following: the relative partial pressures of O_2; the relative partial pressures of CO_2; and the changes in the levels of H^+ caused by the influx of CO_2 or by its loss by means of exhaling.

After you have studied the various equilibria from the stress point of view, and you can write all the equilibria and discuss the influence of various stresses, then you might find Figure 25.10 a useful way to review. Follow the direction of the large U-shaped arrow that curves around the legend, and use the boxed numbers in the legend to follow the events in the figure. Notice in particular that the reactions that occur in the red cell when it is in metabolizing tissue are just the reverse of those that happen when the cell is in the lungs.

Myoglobin Binds O_2 More Strongly Than Hemoglobin Myoglobin is a heme-containing protein in red muscle tissue such as heart muscle. Its function is to bind and store oxygen for the needs of such tissue. Unlike hemoglobin, myoglobin has only one polypeptide unit and only one heme unit per molecule. Moreover, there is no allosteric effect when it binds oxygen, as the shape of the myoglobin–oxygen dissociation curve (Figure 25.11) indicates.

Myoglobin's oxygen affinity is greater than that of hemoglobin, especially in the range of pO_2 associated with actively metabolizing tissues. Consequently, *myoglobin is able to take oxygen from oxyhemoglobin:*

$$HbO_2^- + HMy \longrightarrow HHb + MyO_2^-$$

This ability is vital to heart muscle which, as much as the brain, must have an assuredly continuous supply of oxygen. When oxymyoglobin, MyO_2^-, gives up its oxygen for the cell's needs, it can at once get a fresh supply from the circulating blood. Not only does this cell now have CO_2 and H^+ available to deoxygenate HbO_2^-, but it also has the superior oxygen affinity of its own myoglobin to draw more O_2 into the cell.

Fetal Hemoglobin Binds Oxygen More Strongly Than Adult Hemoglobin The hemoglobin in a fetus is slightly different from that of an adult, and it has a higher oxygen affinity than adult hemoglobin. This helps to ensure to the fetus successfully pulls oxygen from the mother's oxyhemoglobin to satisfy its own needs.

25.4 ACID–BASE BALANCE OF THE BLOOD

The proper treatment of acidosis or of alkalosis depends on knowing whether the underlying cause is a metabolic or a respiratory disorder.

Acid–base balance exists when the pH of blood is in the range of 7.35 to 7.45. A decrease in pH, acidosis, or an increase, alkalosis, is serious and requires prompt attention, because all the equilibria that involve H^+ in the oxygenation or the deoxygenation of blood are sensitive to pH. If the pH falls below 6.8 or rises above 7.8, life is not possible.

■ Acidosis is sometimes called *acidemia,* and alkalosis is called *alkalemia.*

Disturbances in Either Metabolism or Respiration Can Upset the Blood's Acid–Base Balance. In general, acidosis results from either the retention of acid or the loss of base by the body, and these can be induced by disturbances in either metabolism or respiration. Similarly, alkalosis results either from the loss of acid or from the retention of base, and some disorder in either metabolism or respiration can be the underlying cause.

A malfunction in respiration can be caused by any kind of injury to the *respiratory centers.* These are units in the brain that sense changes in the pH and pCO_2 of the blood and instruct the lungs to breathe either more rapidly or more slowly. Another cause of a malfunction of respiration is any kind of injury or disease of the lungs.

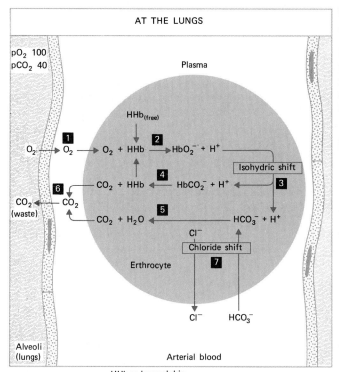
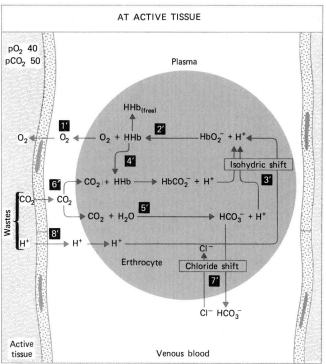
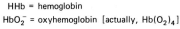

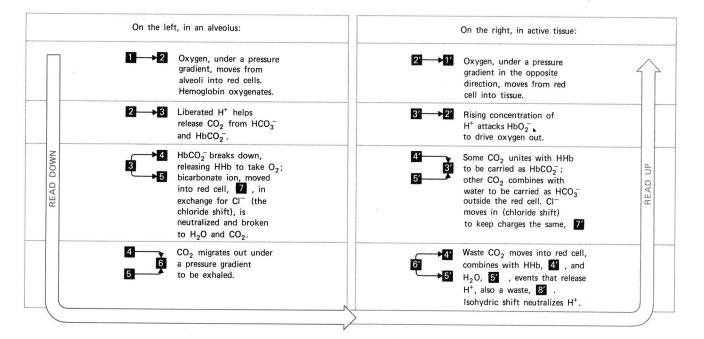

Figure 25.10

Oxygen and carbon dioxide exchange in the blood.

■ Normal values (arterial blood):
$$pCO_2 = 35-45 \text{ mm Hg}$$
$$[HCO_3^-] = 19-24 \text{ meq/L}$$
$$(1.0 \text{ meq } HCO_3^- = 61 \text{ mg } HCO_3^-)$$

What we'll do in this section is study four situations, metabolic and respiratory acidosis as well as metabolic and respiratory alkalosis. We will learn how the values of pH, pCO_2, and serum $[HCO_3^-]$ change in each situation. (Normal values are given in the margin.)

Metabolic Acidosis Receives a Respiratory Compensation, Hyperventilation In **metabolic acidosis,** the lungs and the respiratory centers are working, and the problem is metabolic. Acids are being produced faster than they are neutralized, or they are being exported too slowly.

Excessive loss of base, such as from severe diarrhea, can also result in metabolic acidosis. (In diarrhea, the alkaline fluids of the duodenum leave the body, and as base migrates to replace them, there will be a depletion of base somewhere else, such as in the blood, at least for a period of time.)

As the pH of the blood falls and the molar concentration of H^+ rises, there are parallel *but momentary* increases in the values of pCO_2 and $[HCO_3^-]$. The value of pCO_2 starts to increase because the carbonate buffer, working hard to neutralize the extra H^+, manufactures CO_2:

$$\underset{\substack{\text{From} \\ \text{acidosis}}}{H^+} + HCO_3^- \longrightarrow H_2O + CO_2$$

The kidneys work harder during this situation to try to keep up the supply of HCO_3^-.

The chief compensation for metabolic acidosis, however, involves the respiratory system. The respiratory centers, which are sensitive to changes in pCO_2, instruct the lungs to blow the CO_2 out of the body. The lungs, in other words, hyperventilate. As the equation just given shows, the loss of each molecule of CO_2 means a net neutralization of one H^+ ion.

Hyperventilation, however, is overdone. So much CO_2 is blown out that pCO_2 actually decreases. Thus as the blood pH decreases, so too do the values of pCO_2 (from hyperventilation) and $[HCO_3^-]$ (from the reaction with H^+). We can summarize the range of a number of clinical situations that involve metabolic acidosis as follows.

Clinical Situations of Metabolic Acidosis

■ (↓) means a decrease from a normal and (↑) means an increase. Some typical values are in parentheses. Note that some changes do not necessarily bring values outside the normal ranges.

Lab Results:	pH↓ (7.20); pCO_2↓ (30 mm Hg); $[HCO_3^-]$↓ (12 meq/L)
Typical Patient:	An adult male comes to the clinic with a severe infection. He does not know that he has diabetes.
Range of Causes:	Diabetes mellitus; severe diarrhea (with loss of HCO_3^-); kidney failure (to export H^+ or to make HCO_3^-); prolonged starvation; severe infection; aspirin overdose, alcohol poisoning.
Symptoms:	Hyperventilation (because the respiratory centers have told the lungs to remove excess CO_2 from the blood); increased urine output (to remove H^+ from the blood); thirst (to replace water lost as urine); drowsiness; headache; restlessness; disorientation.
Treatment:	If the kidneys function, use isotonic HCO_3^- intravenously to restore HCO_3^- level, thereby neutralizing H^+ and raising pCO_2. In addition, restore water. In diabetes, use insulin therapy. If the kidneys do not function, hemodialysis must be tried.

Respiratory Acidosis Is Compensated by a Metabolic Response In **respiratory acidosis,** either the respiratory centers or the lungs have failed, and the lungs are hypoventilating *because they cannot help it.* The blood now cannot help but retain CO_2. But the retention of CO_2 means the retention of its acid, H_2CO_3. It is the source of the hydrogen ions that lower the pH and give rise to respiratory acidosis.

Clinical Situations of Respiratory Acidosis

Lab Results:	pH↓ (7.21); pCO_2↑ (70 mm Hg); $[HCO_3^-]$↑ (27 meq/L)
Typical Patient:	Chain smoker with emphysema or anyone with chronic obstructive pulmonary disease.
Range of Causes:	Emphysema, severe pneumonia, asthma, anterior poliomyelitis, or any cause of shallow breathing such as an overdose of narcotics, barbiturates, or general anesthesia; severe head injury.
Symptoms:	Shallow breathing (which is involuntary)
Treatment:	Underlying problem must be treated; possibly intravenous sodium bicarbonate; possibly hemodialysis.

The body responds metabolically as best it can to respiratory acidosis by using HCO_3^- to neutralize the acid, by making more in the kidneys, and by exporting H^+ via the urine.

Metabolic Alkalosis Also Receives a Respiratory Compensation, Hypoventilation

■ An overdose of "bicarb" ($NaHCO_3$) can result from a too aggressive use of this home remedy for "heartburn."

In **metabolic alkalosis,** the system has lost acid, or it has retained base (HCO_3^-), or it has been given an overdose of base (e.g., antacids). Metabolic alkalosis can also be caused by a kidney-associated decrease in the serum levels of K^+ or Cl^-. The loss of these ions means the retention of Na^+ and HCO_3^- ions, because these work in tandem and oppositely. The loss of acid could be from prolonged vomiting, which removes the gastric acid. This is followed by an effort to borrow serum H^+ to replace it, and the pH of the blood increases. Improperly operated nasogastric suction can also remove too much gastric acid.

Whatever the cause, the respiratory centers sense an increase in the level of base in the blood (as the level of acid drops), and they instruct the lungs to retain the most readily available neutralizer of base it has, namely CO_2, which removes OH^- as follows.

$$CO_2 + OH^- \longrightarrow HCO_3^-$$
Retained   From
           alkalosis

■ Compensation by hypoventilation is obviously limited by the fundamental need of the body for some oxygen.

To help retain CO_2, so that it can neutralize base, the lungs hypoventilate. Thus metabolic alkalosis leads to hypoventilation.

Notice carefully that hypoventilation alone cannot be used to tell whether the patient has metabolic *alkalosis* or respiratory *acidosis*. Either condition means hypoventilation. But one condition, respiratory acidosis, could be treated by intravenous sodium bicarbonate, a base. This would aggravate metabolic alkalosis.

You can see that the lab data on pH, pCO_2, and $[HCO_3^-]$ must be obtained to determine which kind of condition is actually present. Otherwise, the treatment used could be just the opposite of what should be done. People working in emergency-care situations get the requisite lab data rapidly, and they must be able to interpret the data on the spot.

Clinical Situations of Metabolic Alkalosis

Lab Results:	pH↑ (7.53); pCO_2↑ (56 mm Hg); $[HCO_3^-]$↑ (45 meq/L)
Typical Patient:	Postsurgery patient with persistent vomiting.
Range of Causes:	Prolonged loss of stomach contents (vomiting or nasogastric suction); overdose of bicarbonate or of medications for stomach ulcers; severe exercise, or stress, or kidney disease (with loss of K^+ and Cl^-); overuse of a diuretic.

■ Ammonium ion acts as a neutralizer as follows:

$$NH_4^+ + OH^- \longrightarrow NH_3 + H_2O$$

Symptoms:	Hypoventilation (to retain CO_2); numbness, headache, tingling; possibly convulsions.
Treatment:	Isotonic ammonium chloride (a mild acid), intraveneously with great care. Replace K^+ loss.

Respiratory Alkalosis Is Compensated Metabolically by a Reduced Bicarbonate Level In **respiratory alkalosis,** the body has lost acid usually by some involuntary hyperventilation — hysterics, prolonged crying, or overbreathing at high altitudes — or by the mismanagement of a respirator. The respiratory centers have lost control, and the body expels CO_2 too rapidly. The loss of CO_2 means the loss of base-neutralizer from the blood. Hence, the level of base rises; the pH rises. To compensate, the kidneys excrete base, HCO_3^-, so the serum level of HCO_3^- falls.

■ Tissue that gets too little O_2 is in a state of **hypoxia**. If it gets none at all, it is in a state of **anoxia**.

Extreme respiratory alkalosis can occur to climbers of high mountains, such as climbers of Mount Everest (8848 m, 29,030 ft). At its summit, the barometric pressure is 253 mm Hg and the pO_2 of the air is only 43 mm Hg (as compared to 149 mm Hg at sea level). Hyperventilation brings their arterial pCO_2 down to only 7.5 mm Hg (compared to a normal of 40 mm Hg) and the blood pH is above 7.7!

Clinical Situations of Respiratory Alkalosis

Lab Results:	pH↑ (7.56); pCO_2↓ (23 mm Hg); $[HCO_3^-]$↓ (20 meq/L)
Typical Patient:	Someone nearing surgery and experiencing anxiety.
Range of Causes:	Prolonged crying; rapid breathing at high altitudes; hysterics; fever; disease of the central nervous system; improper management of a respirator.
Symptoms:	Hyperventilation (that can't be helped). Convulsions may occur.
Treatment:	Rebreathe one's own exhaled air (by breathing into a sack, like Lucy in the *Peanuts* cartoon); administer carbon dioxide; treat underlying causes.

Take careful notice that hyperventilation alone cannot be used to tell what the condition is. Either metabolic *acidosis* or respiratory *alkalosis* is accompanied by hyperventilation, but the treatments are opposite in nature.

Combinations of Primary Acid–Base Disorders Are Possible We have just surveyed the four *primary acid–base disorders.* Combinations of these are often seen, and health care professionals have to be alert to the ways in which the lab data vary in such combinations. Someone with diabetes, for example, might also suffer from an obstructive pulmonary disease. Diabetes causes metabolic acidosis and a *decrease* in $[HCO_3^-]$. The pulmonary disease causes respiratory acidosis with an *increase* in $[HCO_3^-]$. In combination, then, the lab data on bicarbonate level will not be in the expected pattern for either. We will not carry the

study of such complications further. We mention them only to let you know that they exist. There are standard ways to recognize them.[2]

25.5 BLOOD AND THE FUNCTIONS OF THE KIDNEYS

Both filtration and chemical reactions in the kidneys help to regulate the electrolyte balance of the blood.

Diuresis is the formation of urine in the kidneys, and it is an integral part of the body's control of the electrolyte and buffer levels in blood. Figure 25.12 shows the parts of the kidneys that participate.

Urea Is the Chief Nitrogen Waste Exported in the Urine   Huge quantities of fluids leave the blood by diffusion each day at the hundreds of thousands of filtering units, the glomeruli. Substances in solution but not those in colloidal dispersions (e.g., proteins) leave in these fluids. Then active transport processes in kidney cells pull all of any escaped glucose, any amino acids, and most of the fluids and electrolytes back into the blood. Most of the wastes are left in the urine that is being made.

■ The net urine production is 0.6 to 2.5 L/day.

Urea is the chief nitrogen waste (30 g/day), but creatinine (1 to 2 g/day), uric acid (0.7 g/day), and ammonia (0.5 g/day) are also excreted with the urine. If the kidneys are injured or diseased and cannot function, wastes build up in the blood, which leads to a condition known as *uremic poisoning*.

■ *Ur-*, of the urine; *-emia,* of the blood. *Uremia* means substances of the urine present in the blood.

The Hormone Vasopressin Helps Control Water Loss   A nonapeptide hormone, **vasopressin,** instructs the kidneys to retain or excrete water and thus helps to regulate the overall levels of solutes in blood. The hypophysis, where vasopressin is made, releases it when the osmotic pressure of blood increases by as little as 2%. At the kidneys, vasopressin promotes the reabsorption of water, and therefore it is often called the *antidiuretic hormone* or ADH.

[2] See for example, H. Valtin and F. J. Gennari, *Acid–Base Disorders, Basic Concepts and Clinical Management,* Little, Brown, Boston, 1987.

Figure 25.12
The kidneys. (*a*) Principal parts. (*b*) Location of the nephrons. (*c*) Details of a nephron and its associated capillary bed. Each kidney has about a million nephrons. In the renal glomerulus, fluids and their solutes leave the blood, enter Bowman's capsule, and start to move down the tubules. The kidney now works to put most of the electrolytes and organic molecules back into the blood and to leave certain wastes in the urine. The final adjustments of concentrations are made in the distal tubule.

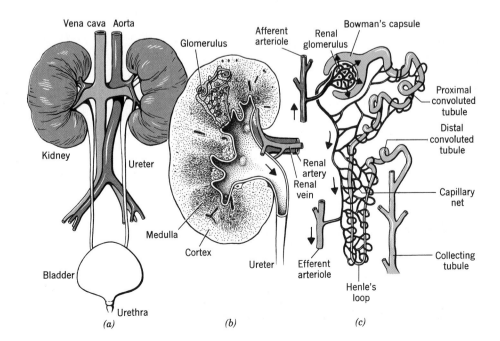

■ In *diabetes insipidus,* vasopressin secretion is blocked and unchecked diuresis can make from 5 to 12 L of urine a day.

An osmotic pressure that is higher than normal (hypertonicity) means a higher concentration of solutes and colloids in blood. The released vasopressin therefore helps the blood to retain water and thus keeps the solute levels from going still higher. In the meantime, the thirst mechanism is stimulated to bring in water to dilute the blood.

Conversely, if the osmotic pressure of blood decreases (becomes hypotonic) by as little as 2%, the hypophysis retains vasopressin. None reaches the kidneys, so the water that has left the bloodstream at the glomeruli does not return as much. Remember that a low osmotic pressure means a low concentration of solutes, so the absence of vasopressin at the kidneys when the blood is hypotonic lets urine form. This reduces the amount of water in the blood and thereby raises the concentrations of its dissolved matter. You can see that with the help of vasopressin a normal individual can vary the intake of water widely and yet preserve a stable, overall concentration of substances in blood.

The Hormone Aldosterone Helps the Blood Retain Sodium Ion The adrenal cortex makes **aldosterone,** a hormone that works to stabilize the sodium ion level of the blood. This steroid hormone is secreted if the blood's sodium ion level drops. When aldosterone arrives at the kidneys, it initiates reactions that make sodium ions that have left the blood return again. Of course, to keep things isotonic in the blood, the return of sodium ions also requires the return of water.

Conversely, if the sodium ion level of the blood increases, aldosterone is not secreted, and sodium ions that have migrated out of the blood at glomeruli are permitted to stay out. They remain in the urine being made, together with some extra water.

The Kidneys Make HCO_3^- for the Blood's Buffer System We have seen that breathing is the body's most direct means of controlling acid as it removes or retains CO_2. The kidneys are the body's means of controlling base, as they make or remove HCO_3^-.

The kidneys also adjust the blood's levels of HPO_4^{2-} and $H_2PO_4^-$, the anions of the phosphate buffer. Moreover, when acidosis develops, the kidneys can put H^+ ions into the urine. Some neutralization of these ions by HPO_4^{2-} and by NH_3 takes place, but the urine becomes definitely more acidic as acidosis continues, as we've mentioned before.

Figure 25.13 shows the various reactions that take place in the kidneys, particularly during acidosis. (The numbers in the following boxes refer to this figure.) The breakdown of metabolites, $\boxed{1}$, makes carbon dioxide, which enters the equilibrium whose formation is catalyzed by carbonic anhydrase, $\boxed{2}$. The ionization of carbonic acid, $\boxed{3}$, makes both bicarbonate ion and hydrogen ion. The bicarbonate ion goes into the bloodstream, $\boxed{4}$, but the hydrogen ion is put into the tubule, $\boxed{5}$, where urine is accumulating. This urine already contains sodium ions and monohydrogen phosphate ions, but to make step $\boxed{5}$ possible, *some* positive ion has to go with the HCO_3^-. Otherwise, there would be no net electrical balance. The kidneys have the ability to select Na^+ to go with HCO_3^- at $\boxed{4}$. The kidneys can make Na^+ travel one way and H^+ the other. Newly arrived H^+ can be buffered by HPO_4^{2-} in the developing urine, $\boxed{6}$. Moreover, the kidneys have an ability not generally found in other tissues to synthesize ammonia and use it to neutralize H^+, $\boxed{7}$. Thus the ammonium ion also appears in the urine.

■ Urine taken after several hours of fasting normally has a pH of 5.5 to 6.5.

The Kidneys Excrete Organic Anions When acidosis has a metabolic origin, the serum level of the anions of organic acids increases. Organic acids are made at accelerated rates in metabolic disorders, like diabetes or starvation, and are the chief cause of the pH change in metabolic acidosis. The base in the blood buffer has to neutralize them.

The kidneys let organic anions stay in the urine, but only by letting increasing quantities of water stay, too. There is a limit to how concentrated the urine can become, so as solutes stay in the urine, water must also stay. Someone with metabolic acidosis, therefore, can experience a general dehydration as the system borrows water from other fluids to make urine. The thirst mechanism normally brings in replacement water, so the individual drinks copious amounts of fluids.

■ In severe acidosis, the pH of urine can go as low as 4.

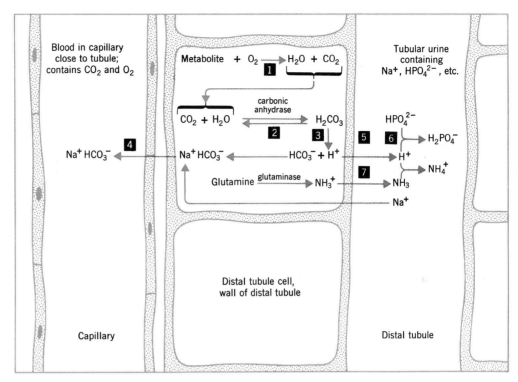

Figure 25.13
Acidification of the urine. The numbers refer to the text discussion.

The Kidneys Can Export HCO₃⁻ In alkalosis, the kidneys can put bicarbonate ion into the urine, and it no longer uses HPO_4^{2-} to neutralize H^+. Both actions raise the pH of the urine, and in severe alkalosis it can go over a pH of 8.

The Kidneys Also Help To Regulate Blood Pressure If the blood pressure drops, as in hemorrhaging, the kidneys secrete a trace of renin into the blood. Renin is an enzyme that acts on one of the zymogens in blood, angiotensinogen, to convert it to the enzyme, angiotensin I. This, in turn, helps to convert still another protein in blood to angiotensin II, a neurotransmitter.

Angiotensin II is the most potent vasoconstrictor known. When it makes blood capillaries constrict, the heart has to work harder, and this makes the blood pressure increase. This helps to ensure that some semblance of proper filtration continues at the kidneys.

Angiotensin II also triggers the release of aldosterone, which we've already learned helps the blood to retain water. This is important because the maintenance of the overall blood volume is needed to sustain a proper blood pressure.

SUMMARY

Digestion α-Amylase in saliva begins the digestion of starch. Pepsin in gastric juice starts the digestion of proteins. In the duodenum, trypsinogen (from the pancreas) is activated by enteropeptidase (from the intestinal juice) and becomes trypsin, which helps to digest proteins. It also activates chymotrypsin (from chymotrypsinogen) and carboxypeptidase (from procarboxypeptidase). These also help to digest proteins. The pancreas supplies an important lipase, which,

with the help of the bile salts, catalyzes the digestion of saponifiable lipids. The bile salts also aid in the absorption of the fat-soluble vitamins, A, D, E, and K.

Intestinal juice supplies enzymes for the digestion of disaccharides, nucleic acids, small polypeptides, and lipids.

The end products of the digestion of proteins are amino acids; of carbohydrates, glucose, fructose, and galactose; and of the triacylglycerols, fatty acids and glycerol. Complex lipids are also hydrolyzed, and nucleic acids yield phosphate, pentoses, and side-chain bases.

Blood Proteins in blood give it a colloidal osmotic pressure that assists in the exchange of nutrients at capillary loops. Albumins are carriers for hydrophobic molecules and serum-soluble metallic ions. Gamma globulin helps to defend the body against bacterial infections. Fibrinogen is the precursor of fibrin, the protein of a blood clot.

Among the electrolytes, anions of carbonic and phosphoric acid are involved in buffers, and all ions are involved in regulating the osmotic pressure of the blood. The chief cation in blood is Na^+, and the chief cation inside cells is K^+. The balances between Na^+ and K^+ as well as between Ca^{2+} and Mg^{2+} are tightly regulated. Ca^{2+} is vital to the operation of muscles, including heart muscle. Mg^{2+} is involved in a number of enzyme systems.

The blood transports oxygen and products of digestion to all tissues. It carries nitrogen wastes to the kidneys. It unloads cholesterol and heme breakdown products at the gall bladder. And it transports hormones to their target cells. Lymph, another fluid, helps to return some substances to the blood from tissues.

Sudden failure to retain the protein in blood causes an equally sudden loss in blood volume and brings on a condition of shock. Slower losses of protein, as in kidney disease or starvation, lead to edema.

Respiration The relatively high pO_2 in the lungs helps to force O_2 into HHb. This creates HbO_2^- and H^+. In an isohydric shift, the H^+ is neutralized by HCO_3^-, which is returning from working tissues that make CO_2. The resulting CO_2 leaves during exhaling. Some of the H^+ also converts $HbCO_2^-$ to HHb and CO_2.

In deoxygenating HbO_2^- at cells that need oxygen, the influx of CO_2 makes HCO_3^- and H^+. The H^+ then moves (isohydric shift) to HbO_2^- and breaks it down to HHb and O_2. Both Cl^- and DPG help to ease the last of the four O_2 molecules out of oxyhemoglobin. The low oxygen affinity of blood in tissues where pCO_2 is high also helps in the release of oxygen.

In red muscle tissue, myoglobin's superior oxygen affinity ensures that such tissue can obtain oxygen from the deoxygenation of oxyhemoglobin. Fetal hemoglobin also has an oxygen affinity superior to that of adult hemoglobin.

Acid – base balance The body uses the bicarbonate ion of the carbonate buffer to inhibit acidosis by irreversibly removing H^+ when the lungs release CO_2. HCO_3^- is replaced by the kidneys, which can also put excess H^+ into the urine. H_2CO_3 (or aqueous CO_2) in the carbonate buffer works to control alkalosis by neutralizing OH^-. Metabolic acidosis, with hyperventilation, and metabolic alkalosis, with hypoventilation, arise from dysfunctions in metabolism. Respiratory acidosis, with hypoventilation, and metabolic alkalosis, with hyperventilation, occur when the respiratory centers or the lungs are not working.

Diuresis The kidneys, with the help of hormones and changes in blood pressure, blood osmotic pressure, and concentrations of ions, monitor and control the concentrations of solutes in blood. Vasopressin tells the kidneys to keep water in the bloodstream. Aldosterone tells the kidneys to keep sodium ion (and therefore water also) in the bloodstream. A drop in blood pressure tells the kidneys to release renin, which activates a vasoconstrictor, and aldosterone, which helps to raise blood pressure and retain water. In acidosis the kidneys transfer H^+ to the urine and replace some of the HCO_3^- lost from the blood. In alkalosis the kidneys put some HCO_3^- into urine.

REVIEW EXERCISES

The answers to these Review Exercises are in the *Study Guide* that accompanies this book.

Digestion

25.1 What are the names of the two chief extracellular fluids?

25.2 Name the fluids that have digestive enzymes or digestive zymogens.

25.3 What enzymes or zymogens are there, if any, in each of the following?
(a) saliva   (b) gastric juice
(c) pancreatic juice   (d) bile
(e) intestinal juice

25.4 Name the enzymes that catalyze the digestion of each of the following, and the digestive juices that supply them (or their zymogens).
(a) large polypeptides   (b) triacylglycerols
(c) amylose   (d) sucrose
(e) dipeptides and tripeptides (f) nucleic acids

25.5 What are the end products of the complete digestion of each of the following?
(a) proteins   (b) carbohydrates
(c) triacylglycerols

25.6 What functional groups are hydrolyzed when each of the substances in Review Exercise 25.5 is digested? (Refer back to earlier chapters if necessary.)

25.7 In what way does enteropeptidase function as a "master switch" in digestion?

25.8 What would happen if the pancreatic zymogens were activated within the pancreas?

25.9 What services do the bile salts render in digestion?

25.10 What does mucin do (a) for food in the mouth and (b) for the stomach?

25.11 What is the catalyst for each of the following reactions?
(a) Pepsinogen $\rightarrow$ pepsin
(b) Trypsinogen $\rightarrow$ trypsin
(c) Chymotrypsinogen $\rightarrow$ chymotrypsin

(d) Procarboxypeptidase → carboxypeptidase

(e) Proelastase → elastase

25.12 Rennin does what for an infant?

25.13 Why is gastic lipase unimportant to digestive processes in the adult stomach but useful in the infant stomach?

25.14 In terms of where they work, what is different about intestinal juice compared to pancreatic juice?

25.15 What secretion neutralizes chyme, and why is this work important?

25.16 What happens to the molecules of glycerol and fatty acids that form from digestion?

25.17 In a patient with a severe obstruction of the bile duct the feces appear clay-colored. Explain why the color is light.

25.18 When the gall bladder is surgically removed, lipids of low formula weight are the only kinds that can be easily digested. Explain.

Substances in Blood

25.19 In terms of their general composition, what is the greatest difference between blood plasma and interstitial fluid?

25.20 What is the largest contributor to the net osmotic pressure of the blood as compared to that of the interstitial fluid?

25.21 What is fibrinogen? Fibrin?

25.22 What services are performed by albumins in blood?

25.23 What does gamma globulin do?

25.24 In what two different regions are Na^+ and K^+ ions mostly found?

25.25 What are the major functions of Na^+ and K^+?

25.26 In hypernatremia, the sodium ion level of blood is above what value?

25.27 The sodium ion level of blood is below what value in hyponatremia?

25.28 What causes the hyperkalemia in crushing injuries?

25.29 Above what level is the blood described as hyperkalemic?

25.30 Excessive drinking of water tends to cause what condition, hyponatremia or hypernatremia?

25.31 The overuse of milk of magnesia can lead to what condition that involves Mg^{2+}?

25.32 Inside cells, what is a function that Mg^{2+} serves?

25.33 Where is most of the calcium ion in the body?

25.34 What does Ca^{2+} do in cells?

25.35 What condition is brought on by an overdose of vitamin D, hypercalcemia or hypocalcemia?

25.36 Injections of magnesium sulfate would be used to correct which condition, hypomagnesemia or hypermagnesemia?

25.37 What is the principal anion in both the blood and the interstitial fluid?

25.38 Explain how hypochloremia leads to alkalosis.

25.39 What is the normal range of concentration of Cl^- in blood?

Exchange of Nutrients at Capillary Loops

25.40 What two opposing forces are at work on the arterial side of a capillary loop? What is the net result of these forces, and what does the net force do?

25.41 On the venous side of a capillary loop there are two opposing forces. What are they, what is the net result, and what does this cause?

25.42 Explain how a sudden change in the permeability of the capillaries can lead to shock.

25.43 Explain how each of the following conditions leads to edema.
(a) kidney disease (b) starvation
(c) a mechanical blow

Exchange of Respiratory Gases

25.44 What are the respiratory gases?

25.45 What compound is the chief carrier of oxygen to actively metabolizing tissues?

25.46 The binding of oxygen to hemoglobin is said to be allosteric. What does this mean, and why is it important?

25.47 Write the equilibrium expression for the oxygenation of hemoglobin. In what direction does this equilibrium shift when
(a) The pH decreases?
(b) The pO_2 decreases?
(c) The red cell is in the lungs?
(d) The red cell is in a capillary loop of an actively metabolizing tissue?
(e) CO_2 comes into the red cell?
(f) HCO_3^- ions flood into the red cell?

25.48 Using chemical equations, describe the isohydric shift when a red cell is (a) in actively metabolizing tissues and (b) in the lungs.

25.49 In what two ways does the oxygenation of hemoglobin in red cells in alveoli help to release CO_2?

25.50 In what way does waste CO_2 at active tissues help to release oxygen from the red cell?

25.51 In what way does extra H^+ at active tissue help release oxygen from the red cell?

25.52 Where is carbonic anhydrase found in the blood, and what function does it have in the management of the respiratory gases in (a) an alveolus and (b) actively metabolizing tissues?

25.53 How does DPG help in the process of oxygenating hemoglobin?

25.54 In what way is DPG involved in helping to deoxygenate HbO_2^-?

25.55 What are some changes involving the blood that occur when the body remains at a high altitude for a period of time, and how do these changes help the individual?

25.56 It has been reported that some long-distance Olympic runners have trained at high altitudes and then had some of their blood withdrawn and frozen. Days or weeks after returning to lower altitudes and just prior to a long race, they have used some of this blood to replace an equal volume of what they are carrying. This is supposed to help them in the race. How would it work?

25.57 How would the net equations for the oxygenation and the deoxygenation of blood be changed to include the function of DPG?

25.58 What are the two main forms in which waste CO_2 moves to the lungs?

25.59 How is oxygen affinity affected by pCO_2, and how is this beneficial?

25.60 What is the chloride shift and how does it aid in the exchange of respiratory gases?

25.61 In what way is the superior oxygen affinity of myoglobin over that of hemoglobin important?

25.62 Aquatic diving animals are known to have much larger concentrations of myoglobin in their red muscle tissue than humans. How is this important to their lives?

25.63 Fetal hemoglobin has a higher oxygen affinity than adult hemoglobin. Why is this important to the fetus?

Acid–Base Balance of the Blood

25.64 Construct a table using arrows ($\uparrow$) or ($\downarrow$) and typical lab data that summarize the changes observed in respiratory and metabolic acidosis and alkalosis. The column headings should be as follows:

Condition	pH	pCO_2	$[HCO_3^-]$

25.65 With respect to the *directions* of the changes in the values of pH, pCO_2, and $[HCO_3^-]$ in both respiratory acidosis and metabolic acidosis, in what way are the two types of acidosis the same? In what way are they different?

25.66 Hyperventilation is observed in what two conditions that relate to the acid–base balance of the blood? In one, giving carbon dioxide is sometimes used, and in the other, giving isotonic HCO_3^- can be a form of treatment. Which treatment goes with which condition and why?

25.67 In what two conditions that relate to the acid–base balance of the blood is hypoventilation observed? Isotonic ammonium chloride or isotonic sodium bicarbonate are possible treatments. Which treatment goes with which condition, and how do they work?

25.68 In which condition relating to acid–base balance does hyperventilation have a beneficial effect? Explain.

25.69 Hyperventilation is part of the *cause* of the problem in which condition relating to the acid–base balance of the blood?

25.70 Hypoventilation is the body's way of helping itself in which condition that relates to the acid–base balance of the blood?

25.71 In which condition that concerns the acid–base balance of the blood is hypoventilation part of the *problem* rather than the cure?

25.72 How can a general dehydration develop in metabolic acidosis?

25.73 Which condition, metabolic or respiratory acidosis or alkalosis, results from each of the following situations?
(a) hysterics
(b) overdose of bicarbonate
(c) emphysema
(d) narcotic overdose
(e) diabetes
(f) overbreathing at a high altitude
(g) severe diarrhea
(h) prolonged vomiting
(i) cardiopulmonary disease
(j) barbiturate overdose

25.74 Referring to Review Exercise 25.73, which is happening in each situation, hyperventilation or hypoventilation?

25.75 Why does hyperventilation in hysterics cause alkalosis?

25.76 Explain how emphysema leads to acidosis.

25.77 Prolonged vomiting leads to alkalosis. Explain.

25.78 Uncontrolled diarrhea can cause acidosis. Explain.

Blood Chemistry and the Kidneys

25.79 If the osmotic pressure of the blood has increased, what, in general terms, has changed to cause this?

25.80 How does the body respond to an increase in the osmotic pressure of the blood?

25.81 If the sodium ion level of the blood falls, how does the body respond?

25.82 What is the response of the kidneys to a decrease in blood pressure?

25.83 Alcohol in the blood suppresses the secretion of vasopressin. How does this affect diuresis?

25.84 In what ways do the kidneys help to reduce acidosis?

CHAPTER TWENTY-SIX

Biochemical Energetics

- ■ ENERGY FOR LIVING
- ■ OXIDATIVE PHOSPHORYLATION AND THE CHEMIOSMOTIC THEORY
- ■ THE CITRIC ACID CYCLE

In a short-distance race, the body must rely on its glucose reserves for energy. How this is done is introduced in this chapter.

26.1 ENERGY FOR LIVING

High-energy phosphates, such as ATP, are the body's means of trapping the energy of the oxidation of the products of digestion.

■ *Catabolism* is from the Greek *cata-*, down; *ballein*, to throw or cast.

We cannot use solar energy directly, like plants. We cannot use steam energy, like a locomotive. We need *chemical* energy for living. We obtain it from food, and we use it to make high-energy molecules. Then these drive the chemical engines behind muscular work, signal sending, and chemical manufacture in tissue. Our principal source of chemical energy is the **catabolism** (i.e., the breaking down) of carbohydrates and fatty acids, although we can also use proteins for energy.

Heats of Combustion Disclose the Energy Available from Catabolism The heat energy from the *combustion* of 1 mol of glucose to CO_2 and H_2O is exactly the same as the energy available from any other method to convert glucose to the same products, 673 kcal/mol. The difference is that our cells don't *burn* glucose and so receive its energy solely as heat. We metabolize it by a number of small steps, some of which make other high-energy compounds. Thus some of the energy available from changing glucose to CO_2 and H_2O is used to run chemical reactions, and the rest of the energy is released as heat.

If we were to burn 1 mol of palmitic acid, $CH_3(CH_2)_{14}CO_2H$, a typical fatty acid, we could obtain 2400 kcal. In the body, we can also change this compound to CO_2 and H_2O, and we obtain exactly the same energy per mole. However, as with glucose, not all this energy is released as heat. Some is used to make high-energy compounds, like the high-energy phosphates.

Each Organophosphate Has a Potential for Transferring Its Phosphate Unit to Another Molecule In Section 16.6 we first learned about the existence of energy-rich triphosphate esters. These and many similar high-energy compounds are involved in the mobilization of chemical energy in the body. Table 26.1 gives the names and structures of the principal phosphates we'll encounter. They are arranged in the order of their **phosphate group transfer potentials,** their relative abilities to transfer a phosphate group to an acceptor, as in the following equation[1]:

■ The bond in color denotes the P—O bond that breaks in an energy-releasing reaction of a high-energy phosphate.

$$R—O—PO_3^{2-} + R'—O—H \longrightarrow R—O—H + R'—O—PO_3^{2-} \qquad (26.1)$$

Higher
potential

Lower
potential

The numbers in the last column of Table 26.1 are measures of the actual potentials the compounds possess to transfer their phosphate groups under standard conditions. (We don't need to know anything about these conditions, just that they supply a common reference.)

We can use the positions of compounds in Table 26.1 to predict whether a particular transfer is possible. A compound with a higher phosphate group transfer potential can, in principal, always be used to make one with a lower potential (assuming that the right enzyme and any other needed reactants are available).

PRACTICE EXERCISE 1

Using Table 26.1, tell whether each reaction can occur.

(a) ATP + glycerol 3-phosphate → ADP + glycerol 1,3-diphosphate
(b) ATP + glucose → ADP + glucose 1-phosphate
(c) Glucose 1-phosphate + creatine → glucose + creatine phosphate

Adenosine Triphosphate (ATP) Is the Body's Chief Energy Broker One compound in Table 26.1, **adenosine triphosphate** or **ATP,** is so important that we must review

---

[1] We will usually write the phosphate group as PO_3^{2-}, but its state of ionization varies with the pH of the solution. At physiological pH, the group is mostly in the singly and doubly ionized forms, PO_3H^- and PO_3^{2-}.

TABLE 26.1 Some Organophosphates in Metabolism

Phosphate	Structure	Phosphate Group Transfer Potential
Phosphoenolpyruvate	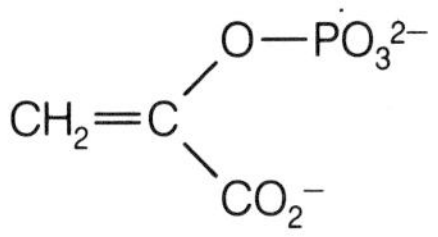 $CH_2{=}C$ with $O{-}PO_3^{2-}$ and CO_2^-	14.8
1,3-Diphosphoglycerate	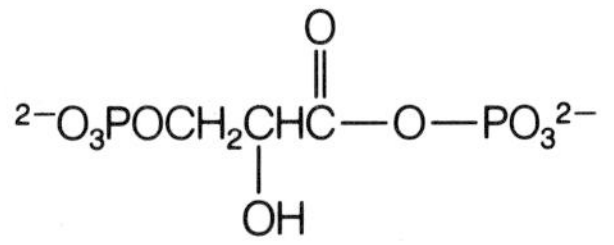 $^{2-}O_3POCH_2CHC{-}O{-}PO_3^{2-}$ (with =O and OH)	11.8
Creatine phosphate	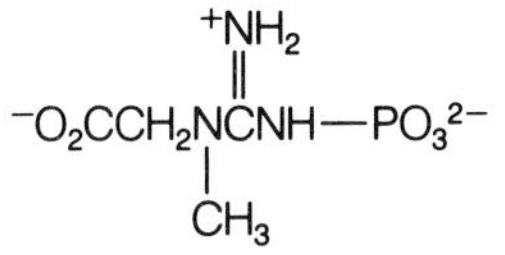 $^-O_2CCH_2NCNH{-}PO_3^{2-}$ with $^+NH_2$ and CH_3	10.3
Acetyl phosphate	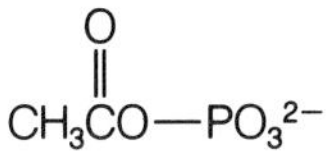 $CH_3CO{-}PO_3^{2-}$ (with =O)	10.1
Adenosine triphosphate ATP	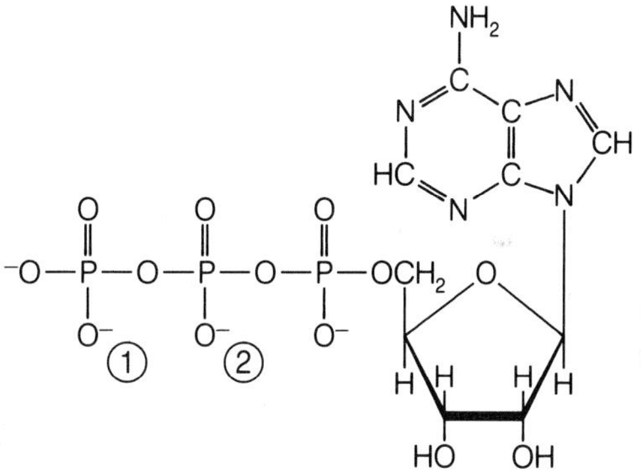 adenine–ribose–triphosphate structure with positions ① and ②	7.3 (at ①) 7.3 (at ②)
Glucose 1-phosphate	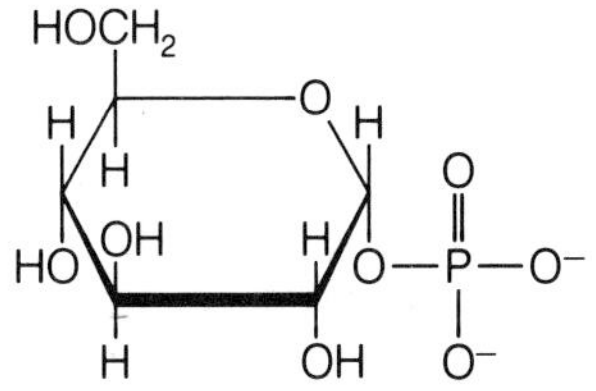 pyranose ring structure	5.0
Fructose 6-phosphate	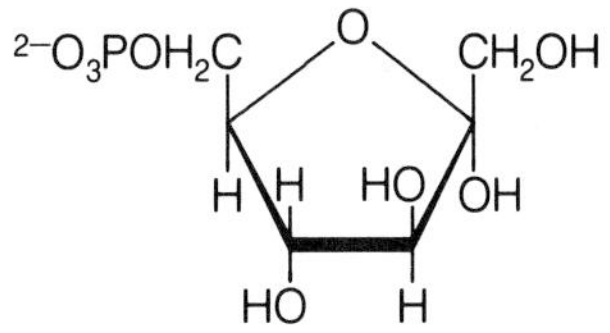 $^{2-}O_3POH_2C$ — furanose ring — CH_2OH	3.8
Glucose 6-phosphate	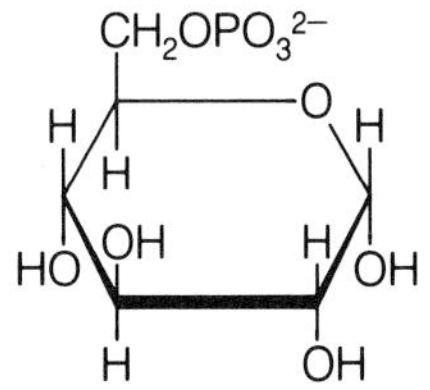 $CH_2OPO_3^{2-}$ pyranose ring structure	3.3
Glycerol 1-phosphate	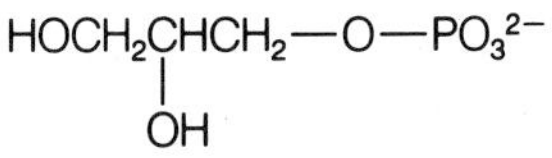 $HOCH_2CHCH_2{-}O{-}PO_3^{2-}$ with OH	2.2

what we learned about it in Section 16.6. From the lowest to the highest forms of life, ATP is universally used as the principal carrier of energy for bodily functions. It is the chief means used by the body to trap energy available by oxidations. Virtually all biochemical energetics comes down to the synthesis and uses of this compound.

Almost any energy-demanding activity of the body consumes ATP. The adult human *at rest* consumes about 40 kilograms of ATP per day. When engaged in exercise, the rate of consumption can be as high as 0.5 kg per minute. We saw in Section 16.6, for example, that muscle contraction can be very simply written as a chemical reaction of ATP with the proteins in relaxed muscle (or with something within the proteins):

$$\text{``Relaxed'' muscle} + \text{ATP} \longrightarrow \text{``contracted'' muscle} + \text{ADP} + \text{P}_i$$

This reaction causes changes in tertiary structures of muscle proteins that cause the fibers made from these proteins to contract. Simultaneously, ATP changes to **ADP,** which is **adenosine diphosphate,** plus inorganic phosphate, P_i.

ATP has two phosphate bonds, either of whose rupture can release much useful energy. Occasionally the second bond (see Table 26.1) is broken in some transfer of chemical energy, and the products then are **AMP, adenosine monophosphate,** and the inorganic diphosphate ion, PP_i.

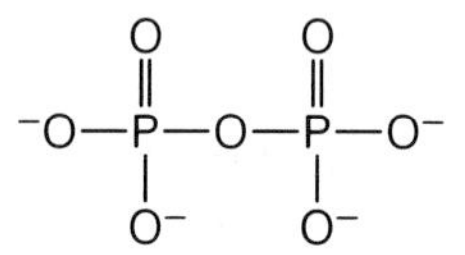

Occasionally triphosphates other than ATP are the carriers of energy. Guanosine triphosphate, GTP, is an example that we'll encounter later in this chapter.

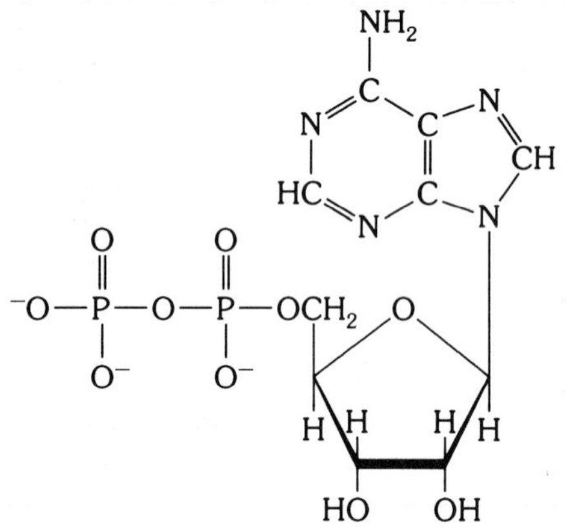

PP$_i$

ADP
(adenosine
diphosphate)

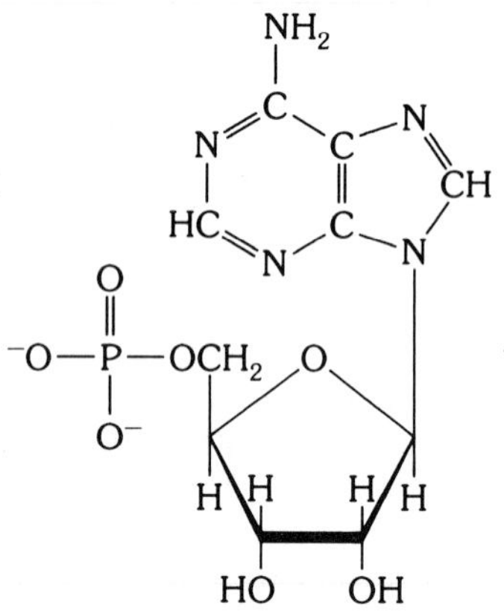

AMP
(adenosine
monophosphate)

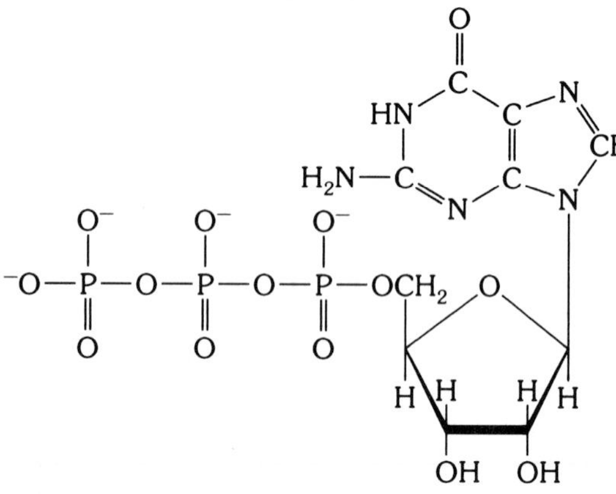

GTP
(guanosine
triphosphate)

By convention, the phosphates ATP and higher in Table 26.1 are called **high-energy phosphates.** Notice that ATP is not at the head of the list. This means that ATP can be *made from* ADP by the transfer of phosphate from those above ATP/ADP in the list. Then the ATP can *make* any phosphates lower on the list. This intermediate position of the ATP/ADP system is therefore one reason why it is so useful as an energy broker. This system can accept chemical energy from the phosphates with higher potential and then pass it on by phosphorylations that make compounds lower on the list.

The Resynthesis of ATP Is a Major Goal of Catabolism   Once ATP is used, it must be remade or no more internal work can be done. This resynthesis of ATP goes on continuously. One of the major purposes of catabolism is to transfer chemical energy in such a way that ATP is resynthesized from ADP and P_i.

Sometimes, one of the compounds in Table 26.1 *above* ATP is first made by catabolism, and then its phosphate group is made to transfer to ADP to give ATP. When this happens, the overall ATP synthesis is called **substrate phosphorylation** (where the substrate is ADP). The transfer is direct from an organic phosphate donor to ADP.

In substrate phosphorylation, the phosphate group doesn't come directly from a phosphate ion in solution. Not that inorganic phosphate can't be pinned directly to ADP. This happens in another kind of phosphorylation, **oxidative phosphorylation,** done by a series of reactions called the **respiratory chain,** which we'll study in the next section.

Creatine Phosphate Phosphorylates ADP in Muscles As you saw in Table 26.1, not all high-energy phosphates are triphosphates. Creatine phosphate, for example, is as important to muscle contraction as ATP. The ATP that is actually present in rested muscle can sustain muscle activity for only a fraction of a second. To provide for the immediate regeneration of ATP, muscle tissue makes and stores creatine phosphate (phosphocreatine) during periods of rest. Then, as soon as some ATP is used, and ADP + P_i is made, creatine phosphate regenerates ATP. The enzyme is creatine kinase, the CK enzyme we studied in Chapter 24.

> ■ When the level of ATP drops and the levels of ADP + P_i rise, the rate of breathing is also accelerated.

What actually happens is that an increase in the supply of ADP shifts the following equilibrium to the right, to raise the concentration of ATP. (The high value of K_{eq} tells us that the forward reaction is favored.)

$$\text{Creatine phosphate} + \text{ADP} \xrightarrow{\text{CK}} \text{creatine} + \text{ATP} \qquad K_{eq} = 162$$

Then, during periods of rest when the ATP level is substantially raised by other reactions, this equilibrium shifts back to the left to recharge the creatine phosphate reserves.

Although muscle tissue has three to four times as much creatine phosphate as ATP, even this reserve won't supply the high-energy phosphate needs for long, no more than what a sprinter needs for a 100 to a 200-m sprint. For a long period of work, the body uses other methods to make ATP. We'll now take an overview of all the pathways for ATP synthesis, and then we will look closely at the respiratory chain.

All Bioenergetic Pathways Converge on the Citric Acid Cycle and the Respiratory Chain Our first concern is what *initiates* ATP synthesis. This process is under feedback control, and if the supply of ATP is high, no more needs to be made. Only as ATP is used up is first one mechanism and then another thrown into action. Generally, it's the appearance of ADP that triggers these actions.

Figure 26.1 is a broad outline of the metabolic pathways that can generate ATP. Think of the last one mentioned, the respiratory chain, as being at the bottom of a tub, nearest the drain through which ATP will leave for some use. As in water that leaves a tub, the first to leave is at the plug. This activates the motions of water at higher levels.

By analogy, the next pathway to be thrown into action once the respiratory chain is launched, is the next one from the bottom in Figure 26.1, the citric acid cycle. The chief purpose of the **citric acid cycle** is to supply the chemical needs of the respiratory chain.

The citric acid cycle also requires a "fuel," and this need is filled by an acetyl derivative of a coenzyme called coenzyme A. **Acetyl coenzyme A,** often written as acetyl CoA, is the "fuel" for the citric acid cycle. The catabolism of molecules from all three major foods — carbohydrates, lipids, and proteins — can produce acetyl coenzyme A.

Fatty acids are a major source of acetyl CoA, particularly during periods of sustained activities. A series of reactions called the **fatty acid cycle** breaks fatty acids into acetyl units. We will study this pathway in Chapter 28.

Most amino acids can also be catabolized to acetyl units or to intermediates of the citric acid cycle itself, and we'll survey these reactions in Chapter 29.

From starch or glucose a pathway called **glycolysis** breaks glucose units down to the pyruvate ion. Then a short pathway converts this to acetyl CoA.

Glycolysis Can Make ATP When a Cell Is Deficient in Oxygen Glycolysis makes some ATP by substrate phosphorylation independently of the respiratory chain. Even when a cell is temporarily starved for oxygen, glycolysis is able to make some ATP for a while. Glycolysis is thus an important backup source of ATP for cells running low on oxygen.

When glycolysis has to run without oxygen, its end product is the lactate ion, not the pyruvate ion. Once the cell gets oxygen, however, it converts lactate to pyruvate.

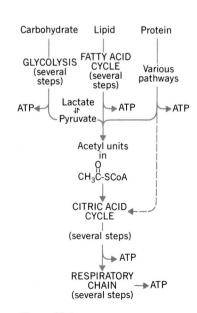

Figure 26.1
The major pathways for making ATP.

■ The pyruvate ⇌ lactate equilibrium is discussed in Chapter 27.

$$C_6H_{12}O_6 \xrightarrow[\text{not balanced}]{\text{(Several steps;}} 2CH_3\overset{\displaystyle O}{\overset{\|}{C}}CO_2^- \underset{\text{(With O}_2)}{\overset{\text{(If no O}_2)}{\rightleftharpoons}} 2CH_3\overset{\displaystyle OH}{\overset{|}{C}H}CO_2^-$$

Glucose   Pyruvate   Lactate

$$2CH_3\overset{\displaystyle O}{\overset{\|}{C}}-S-CoA$$

Acetyl coenzyme A

Thus glycolysis can end either with lactate or with pyruvate, depending on the oxygen supply. We will study details of glycolysis in the next chapter.

The full sequence of oxygen-consuming reactions from glucose units to pyruvate ions to acetyl CoA and on through the respiratory chain is sometimes called the **aerobic sequence** of glucose catabolism. The sequence that runs without oxygen from glucose units to lactate ions is called the **anaerobic sequence** of glucose catabolism.

■ *Aerobic* signifies the use of air. *Anaerobic,* stemming from "not air," means in the absence of the use of oxygen.

Our interest in this chapter is in the pathways that can accept breakdown products from any food, namely, the citric acid cycle and the respiratory chain.

26.2   OXIDATIVE PHOSPHORYLATION AND THE CHEMIOSMOTIC THEORY

The flow of electrons to oxygen in the respiratory chain creates a proton gradient in mitochondria that drives the synthesis of ATP.

The term *respiration* refers to more than just breathing. It includes the chemical reactions that use oxygen in cells. Oxygen is reduced to water, and the following equation is the most basic statement we can write for what happens:

$$(\!:\!) \quad + 2H^+ \; + \cdot\overset{\cdot\cdot}{\underset{\cdot\cdot}{O}}\cdot \; \longrightarrow H-\overset{\cdot\cdot}{\underset{\cdot\cdot}{O}}-H + \text{energy}$$

Pair of   Pair of   Atom of   Molecule
electrons   protons   oxygen   of water

■ The gain of e^- or of e^- carriers such as $H\!:^-$ is *reduction;* the loss of e^- or of $H\!:^-$ is *oxidation.*

The electrons and protons come mostly from intermediates in the catabolism of sugars and fats. Generally, the electrons of C—H bonds are used, and sometimes the hydride ion $H\!:^-$ is the vehicle for carrying the electrons. Hydride ions can be passed directly from organic donors to organic receptors. Sometimes just electrons are passed. Remember, now, that when any molecule loses electrons it is oxidized, and the acceptor is reduced.

The Chief Agents of Electron Transfer Are the Respiratory Enzymes   The respiratory chain is one long series of oxidation–reduction reactions. The flow of electrons from the initial donor is down an energy hill all the way to oxygen, and it is irreversible.

The cell's principal site of ATP synthesis is the *inner* membrane of a mitochondrion, Figure 26.2. Some tissues have thousands of these tiny organelles in the cytoplasm of a single cell. The inner membrane of a mitochondrion has built into it innumerable clusters of the **respiratory enzymes,** the set of enzymes that operate the respiratory chain. One very important property of this membrane is that it is permeable to chemical species, like H^+, only at particular channels.

■ A cell in the flight muscle of a wasp has about a million mitochondria.

Figure 26.3 gives an outline of which enzyme interacts with which together with an indication of the favorable drops in energy that impel the overall sequence. Since these are all redox reactions, they have their own cell potentials, which are discussed in Special Topic 26.1.

The Respiratory Chain Normally Creates a Proton Gradient across the Inner Mitochondrial Membrane   The first enzyme of the respiratory chain carries NAD^+ as the

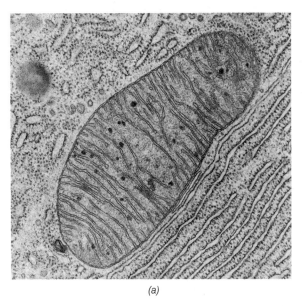

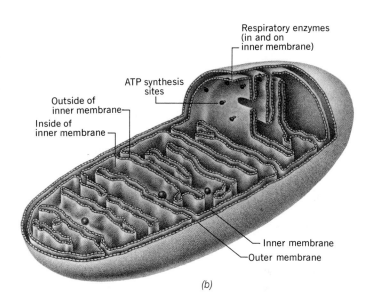

(a)

(b)

Figure 26.2

A mitochondrion. (a) Electron micrograph ($\times 53,000$) of a mitochondrion in a pancreas cell of a bat. (b) Perspective showing the interior. The respiratory enzymes are incorporated into the inner membrane. On the inside of this membrane are enzymes that catalyze the synthesis of ATP. (Micrograph courtesy of Dr. Keith R. Porter.)

■ Think of MH_2 as M:H, which becomes M when H:$^-$ and H$^+$ leave.

coenzyme, and it accepts H:$^-$ from a donor molecule. The donor is frequently an intermediate in the citric acid cycle. We studied how H:$^-$ transfers to NAD$^+$ in Section 24.1 and Special Topic 24.1. If we let MH_2 represent any metabolite that can donate H:$^-$ to NAD$^+$, we can write the following equation for the first step in the respiratory chain.

$$MH_2 + NAD^+ \longrightarrow M + NADH + H^+$$

The electron flow has now started toward oxygen. The electron pair has moved from MH_2 to NADH.

The next enzyme in the chain is FMN, which carries the vitamin riboflavin as part of its coenzyme. (We studied this enzyme in Section 24.1 and Special Topic 24.1.) The hydride in NADH now transfers to FMN, so we can write the following equation.

$$NADH + H^+ + FMN \longrightarrow FMNH_2 + NAD^+$$

■ Think of NADH as NAD:H, in which the dots in boldface are those that move along the respiratory chain from MH_2.

Figure 26.3

The enzymes of the respiratory chain and the energy drop from NAD$^+$ to reduced oxygen (water). The figures for energy refer to the portion of the energy change that is not unavoidably dissipated as heat. The symbols for the enzymes are as follows. (See also Figure 26.4.)

MH_2 = a metabolite; a donor of (H:$^-$ + H$^+$)

NAD$^+$ = enzyme with nicotinamide cofactor

FMN = enzyme with riboflavin phosphate cofactor

FeS—P = iron–sulfur protein

Q = enzyme with coenzyme Q cofactor

Cyt = enzyme of the cytochrome family

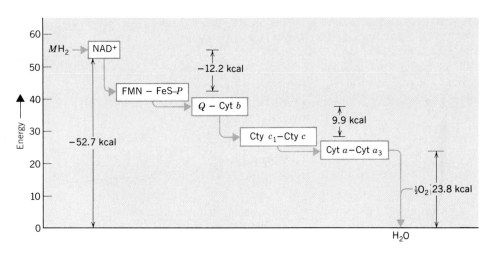

SPECIAL TOPIC 26.1   REDOX POTENTIALS AND BIOLOGICAL OXIDATIONS

Each step in the respiratory chain has its own potential for proceeding to completion. The first step, for example, in which NAD^+ accepts $H:^-$ from some donor is a redox reaction. We'll suppose that the donor is something simple, like ethyl alcohol. In Special Topic 24.1 we showed how NAD^+ could accept $H:^-$ from this alcohol and be reduced to NADH as the alcohol became oxidized to ethanal:

$$CH_3CH_2OH + NAD^+ \longrightarrow CH_3CH{=}O + NADH + H^+$$
$$\text{Ethanol} \qquad\qquad\qquad \text{Ethanal}$$

We'll now use what we studied in Chapter 10 to assess the extent to which this reaction spontaneously runs from left to right.

In Chapter 10 we learned how we can separate a redox reaction into two half-reactions, each with its own reduction potential. The half-reaction with the more positive reduction potential is able to force the other half-reaction to run in reverse, as an oxidation. Recall that we begin with the half-reactions *both* written as reductions. For the oxidation of ethanol by NAD^+ (or the reduction of NAD^+ by ethanol) we have the following two half-cell reactions with their reduction potentials.

$$NAD^+ + H^+ + 2e^- \longrightarrow NADH \quad E^{\circ\prime} = -0.32 \text{ V}$$
$$CH_3CH{=}O + 2H^+ + 2e^- \longrightarrow CH_3CH_2OH \quad E^{\circ\prime} = -0.20 \text{ V}$$

The Standard State Is Different When Working with Cellular Reactions We now have a prime (′) added to E. to indicate a change in the definition of a standard state. Earlier, we defined a standard state as involving all chemicals at concentrations of 1 M. In living systems this is unrealistic, particularly for H^+. The molarity of H^+ in cells is closer to 1×10^{-7} mol/L. In using reduction potentials for living systems, therefore, scientists define the standard state as one in which $[H^+] = 1.0 \times 10^{-7}$ M with a temperature of 25 °C.

The Reduction of Ethanal, Not the Oxidation of Ethanol, Is Favored Getting back to the two half-reactions, we see that the reduction *of the aldehyde has the more positive (less negative) reduction potential*. This half-reaction, therefore, is able to force the other to run as an oxidation. The two half-reactions, set up for combining them in the normal way, are now

$$CH_3CH{=}O + 2H^+ + 2e^- \longrightarrow CH_3CH_2OH$$
$$\underline{NADH \longrightarrow NAD^+ + H^+ + 2e^-}$$
$$CH_3CH{=}O + NADH + H^+ \longrightarrow CH_3CH_2OH + NAD^+$$
$$\text{(Equation A)}$$

The cell potential for this (by Equation 10.2, page 281) is

$$E^{\circ\prime}_{(cell)} = (-0.20 \text{ V}) - (-0.32 \text{ V})$$
$$= 0.12 \text{ V}$$

We learned in Chapter 10 that even very small cell potentials correspond to huge equilibrium constants, and 0.12 V means that if we treat the reduction of ethanal as an equilibrium *under the original definitions of standard conditions*, K_{eq} is roughly 10^5! How in the world, we might ask, can ethanol be *oxidized* by NAD^+, if the reverse reaction is so overwhelmingly favored? There are two pieces to the explanation.

First, we're not under standard conditions. The molarity of H^+ is not 1 M but 1×10^{-7} M. We'd have to use the Nernst equation (10.4, page 286) to calculate the cell potential under nonstandard conditions, and for this we would need data on the concentrations of all species at equilibrium. We do not have these data. But the second piece in the explanation makes this lack unimportant.

NAD^+ Does Not Act Alone, So the Oxidation of Ethanol Is Favored The second reason why NAD^+ can participate in the *oxidation* of ethanol is that NAD^+ is just the first enzyme in a series leading to the final step, the reduction of oxygen. NAD^+ does not have to work alone. The whole respiratory chain pulls electrons from ethanol toward oxygen. Thus it is the reduction of oxygen, not the reduction of NAD^+, that we should use in setting up the half-reactions leading to the cell reaction. With this in mind, let's go back and redo the oxidation of ethanol. The two half-reactions, written as reductions and with their reduction potentials, are

$$CH_3CH{=}O + 2H^+ + 2e^- \longrightarrow CH_3CH_2OH$$
$$E^{\circ\prime} = -0.20 \text{ V}$$
$$(\tfrac{1}{2})O_2 + 2H^+ + 2e^- \longrightarrow H_2O$$
$$E^{\circ\prime} = +0.82 \text{ V}$$

Now it's the oxygen reduction that has the more positive reduction potential, and it is well able to force the other half-reaction to run as an oxidation. Rewriting the two, on the way to the cell reaction, we have

$$CH_3CH_2OH \longrightarrow CH_3CH{=}O + 2H^+ + 2e^-$$
$$\underline{\tfrac{1}{2}O_2 + 2H^+ + 2e^- \longrightarrow H_2O}$$
$$CH_3CH_2OH + \tfrac{1}{2}O_2 \longrightarrow CH_3CH{=}O + H_2O$$

The cell potential for this is

$$E^{\circ\prime}_{(cell)} = (+0.82 \text{ V}) - (-0.20 \text{ V})$$
$$= 1.02 \text{ V}$$

This cell potential indicates an overwhelming driving force for the oxidation of ethanol to ethanal as oxygen is reduced to water.

The Reduction of Oxygen Has a Very Favorable Reduction Potential The same reduction of oxygen to water is the largest driving force in biological oxidations, too. Figure 26.3 shows the "energy cascade" along the respiratory chain until this last step, the largest energy drop, is accomplished. The sizes of the steps in this figure are proportional to the cell potentials of the individual reactions.

We have illustrated that when the body causes an overall change by a series of small steps, like the oxidation of ethanol, one (or more) steps can be energetically quite unfavorable if at least one step (particularly the last step) is very favorable.

Small Steps Enable a Long Sequence To Trap Energy in ATP We have also, very indirectly, suggested something else about biological oxidations. You would think that the oxidation of an alcohol group in a cell, so overwhelmingly favored, would go extremely rapidly, almost like a combus-

tion. So we get here a hint of the reason why the cell uses many steps.

Several steps provide two needs, the need for the control of overall rate being only one. The other need is to use at least some steps to run energy-consuming reactions. Direct combustion cannot provide such steps. It can produce *only* heat, which would be fine if we were steam engines. Instead, some of the energy of the oxidation of an alcohol group is used to create the proton gradient and the charge gradient, discussed in Section 26.2, that is so vital to the synthesis of ATP.

This restores the NAD^+ enzyme and moves the electron pair one more step down the respiratory chain.

What happens next is the transfer of just the pair of electrons while the hydrogen nucleus of $H:^-$ leaves the carrier as H^+. It induces conformational changes in an inner membrane protein that makes protons move outside the inner membrane. This step begins the most critical work of the respiratory chain, the buildup of an H^+ gradient across the inner mitochondrial membrane. The two electrons of $H:^-$ are accepted by an *iron–sulfur protein*, which we'll symbolize by $FeS—P$. The iron in $FeS—P$ occurs as Fe^{3+}. By accepting one electron, it is reduced to the Fe^{2+} state, so we need two units of $FeS—P$ to handle the pair of electrons now about to leave $FMNH_2$. This step can be written as

■ Think of $FMNH_2$ as $FMN:H$, with an H, which becomes FMN when it loses $H:^-$ and H^+.

$$FMNH_2 + 2FeS—P \longrightarrow FMN + 2FeS—P\cdot + 2H^+$$

where we use $FeS—P\cdot$ to represent the reduced form of the iron–sulfur protein in which Fe^{2+} occurs.

Before we go on, we will introduce a new way of writing these equations that helps to emphasize both the oxidation and the reduction aspects, as well as the restoration of each enzyme to its original condition. For example, the last three reactions we have studied can be represented as follows:

■ Visualize these enzymes and their reactions as occurring in the structure of the inner membrane itself.

2H⁺
Will promote the migration
of protons to the outside
of the inner mitochondrial membrane

Reading from left to right, at the point where the first pair of curved arrows touch, we see that as MH_2 changes to $M:$, it passes $H:^-$ to NAD^+ to change it to NADH. H^+ is also released. At the second pair of curved arrows, we read that as $NADH + H^+$ are changed back to NAD^+, the system passes one unit of $H:^- + H^+$ across to FMN to change it to $FMNH_2$. At the third pair of curved arrows, the display shows that as $FMNH_2$ changes back to FMN, it passes two electrons to two $FeS—P$ molecules and expels two protons (H^+) into the surroundings. Let's now pause to see where we are and where we are headed.

At this stage, two electrons have moved from MH_2 to two molecules of the iron–sulfur protein, and two hydrogen ions have been generated. These protons, like those released earlier, cause conformational changes in inner membrane proteins that makes them expel protons to the fluid on the *outside* of the inner mitochondrial membrane.

Between three and four protons, on the average, are moved out by each pair of H^+ ions released by the oxidation. Eventually the fluid just outside the inner membrane will have a pH 1.4 units lower than inside. In other words, the flow of electrons in the respiratory chain has started to establish a proton gradient that will eventually drive the synthesis of ATP. (And remember, the inner membrane is not permeable to protons except at certain channels. Protons can't diffuse back just anywhere along this inner membrane.)

What we are studying here is the **chemiosmotic theory,** first proposed in 1961 by Peter Mitchell of England (Nobel prize, 1981). As a way of seeing where we are heading, let's list the basic principles of this theory and then go back to pick up the trail of the electrons flowing in the respiratory chain.

Principles of the Chemiosmotic Theory

1. The synthesis of ATP occurs at an enzyme located on the *inside* of the inner mitochondrial membrane.

2. ATP synthesis is driven by a flow of protons that occurs from the outside to the inside of the inner membrane.

3. The flow of protons is through special channels in the membrane and down a concentration gradient of protons that exists across the inner membrane.

4. The energy that creates the proton gradient and the (+) charge gradient is provided by the flow of electrons within the respiratory chain whose enzymes make up integral packages in the inner membrane.

5. The inner membrane is a closed envelope except for the special channels for the flow of protons and special transport systems that let needed solutes move into or out of the innermost mitochondrial compartment.

Getting back to the respiratory chain, its entire function is to transport electrons from a metabolite, MH_2, to oxygen while setting up the gradients of H^+ and (+) charge.

As you have seen, the respiratory chain is quite complicated, and from this point on it becomes even more so. What follows next are additional transfers of electrons through a series of enzymes including several called the cytochromes. These are designated, in the order in which they participate, as cytochromes b, c_1, c, a, and a_3.

■ *Cyto-,* cell; *-chrome,* pigment. The cytochromes are colored substances.

Cytochromes a and a_3 are collectively known as the enzyme *cytochrome oxidase.* It is the enzyme that catalyzes the reduction of oxygen we described earlier. Cytochrome a_3 carries a copper ion that alternates between the Cu^{2+} and the Cu^+ states.

We will have to pass over the details of the rest of the respiratory chain. Figure 26.4 does show them, including a branch in the chain that involves an enzyme whose coenzyme is FAD. This enzyme can also help to feed electrons into the main chain, and we'll see an example of its operation in the next section.

The Respiratory Chain Oxidizes Metabolites, Reduces Oxygen, and Makes Protons Relocate   Figure 26.5 places the events of the respiratory chain into the context of the inner membrane, and it shows one of the portals through which protons can move back into the innermost part of the mitochondrion. As the figure as well as the previous net equation indicates, the net result of the operation of the respiratory chain, starting with MH_2 and NAD^+, can be expressed by the following equation.

$$MH_2 + nH^+ \quad + \tfrac{1}{2}O_2 \xrightarrow{\text{respiratory chain}} M + H_2O + nH^+$$

From inside the inner membrane

Drive the proton flow that makes the proton gradient

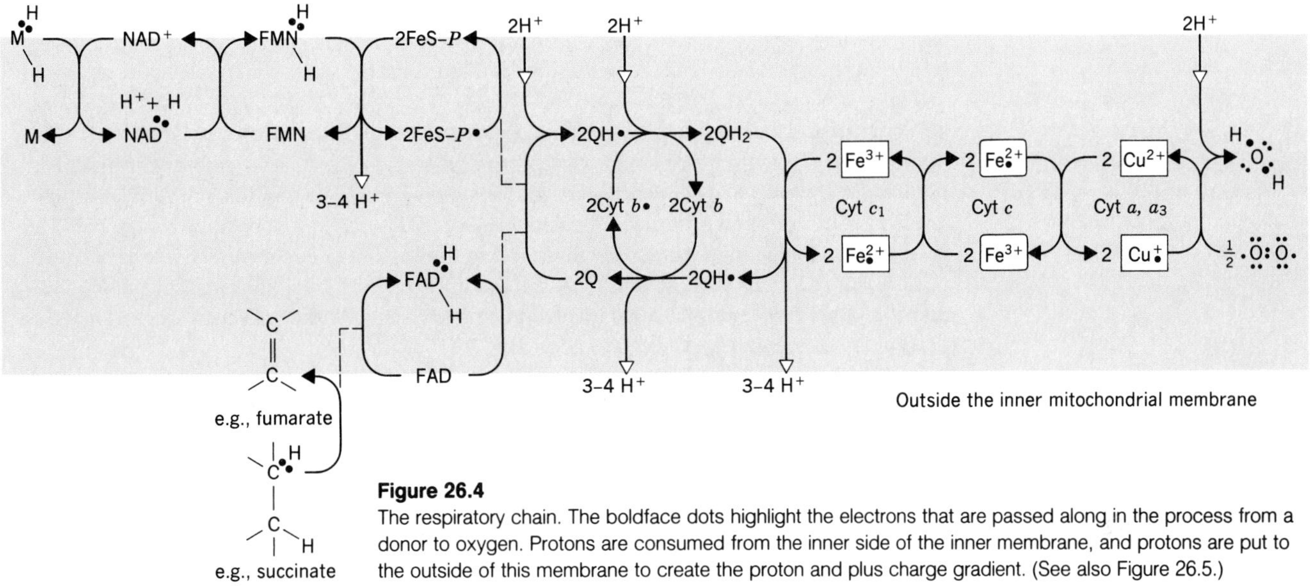

Figure 26.4

The respiratory chain. The boldface dots highlight the electrons that are passed along in the process from a donor to oxygen. Protons are consumed from the inner side of the inner membrane, and protons are put to the outside of this membrane to create the proton and plus charge gradient. (See also Figure 26.5.)

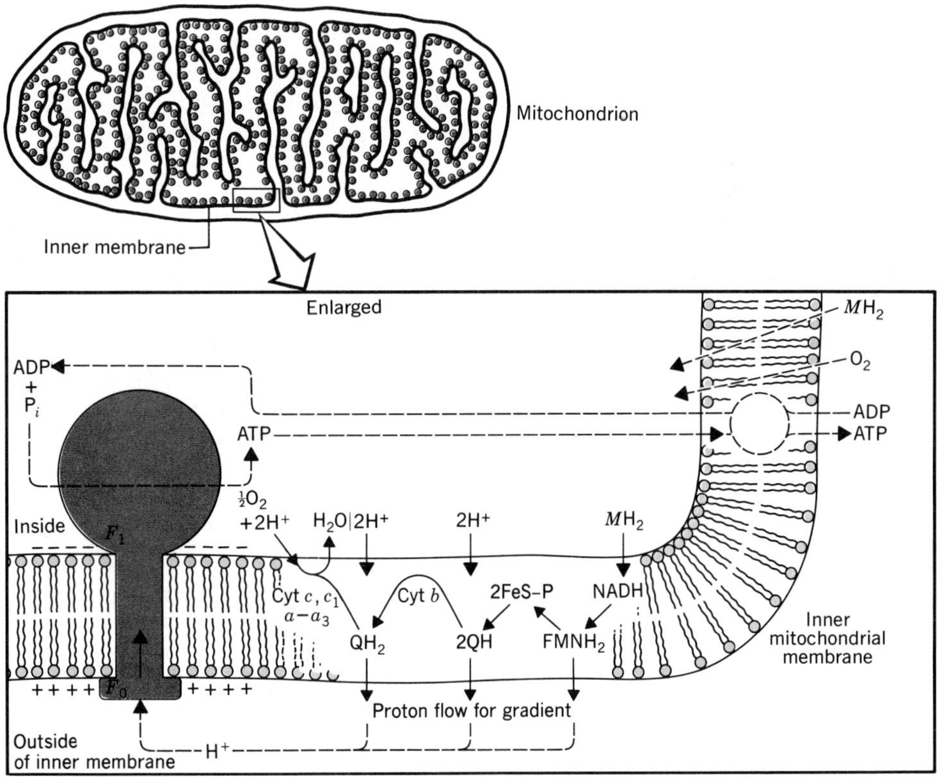

Figure 26.5

Cutaway of a portion of the inner mitochondrial membrane showing one respiratory chain and one proton conduit — labeled as F_0–F_1. This conduit includes the enzyme that catalyzes the formation of ATP from ADP and P_i. As indicated on the right, ADP can move inside only if ATP moves outside; the movements of these two are coupled.

The generation of the protons by the oxidation of one molecule of MH_2 forces conformational changes in membrane proteins that *expel roughly twelve* H^+ *ions to the fluid just outside the inner membrane.* The overall change from the branch that involves FAD places fewer H^+ ions into the gradient. (This branch isn't shown in Figure 26.5.)

Two Gradients Are Established, a Proton and a Plus Charge Gradient The operation of the respiratory chain pumps protons outside the inner membrane *without also putting the equivalent in negatively charged ions there, too.* Two gradients are thus set up, a gradient of H^+ ions and a gradient of positive charge. The gradient of positive charge could be erased either by the migration of negative ions to the outside *or by the migration of any kind of positive ion to the inside.* Calcium ions, for example, might move, and precisely such movements of Ca^{2+} ions are intimately involved with nerve signals and muscular work. Thus this theory helps us understand events other than ATP synthesis.

■ Because chemical reactions create the gradients, we have the *chemi-* part of the term *chemiosmotic.*

The Proton Channels of the Inner Mitochondrial Membrane Include an Enzyme for Making ATP from ADP and P_i Embedded in the inner mitochondrial membrane are complexes of proteins that form a tube through it. One tube exists for every unit of respiratory enzymes.

■ This migration through a semipermeable membrane explains the *-osmotic* part of the term *chemiosmotic.*

The tube is a conduit for protons, and it terminates on the inside of the inner membrane with an enzyme called ATP-ase that catalyzes the formation of ATP from ADP and P_i. This enzyme makes ATP and then holds it tightly to itself. As protons flow through one of the conduits, they cause conformational changes in polypeptides of the enzyme, and these force it to release the ATP.

Each molecule of MH_2 that enters the chain at NAD^+ can lead to a maximum of three ATPs. Each metabolite that donates hydrogen to FAD can lead to just two ATPs.

Because a series of oxidations establishes the proton gradient that makes this ATP synthesis possible, the overall synthesis is called **oxidative phosphorylation.** You'll also see this called *respiratory chain phosphorylation.*

A Transport Protein in the Mitochondrial Membrane Moves ADP Inside as It Carries ATP Out Both ATP and ADP are highly charged species and so could not easily get through a lipid bilayer membrane. A transport protein in the mitochondrial membrane called ATP–ADP translocase solves this problem. The migration of ATP to the outside is coupled to the movement of ADP inside.

Some Antibiotics and Poisons Inhibit Oxidative Phosphorylation One of the barbiturates, amytal sodium, blocks the respiratory chain between NAD^+ and cytochrome *b*. The powerful insecticide, rotenone, does the same thing. The cyanide ion blocks the chain at its very end, at cytochrome a_3. The antibiotic antimycin A stops the chain between cytochromes *b* and *c*.

■ Rotenone is a naturally occurring insecticide.

Now that we've taken a careful look at the "plug" end of the energy mobilization "tub," the respiratory chain and oxidative phosphorylation, we will move back one major step to the supplier of electrons for the respiratory chain, the citric acid cycle.

26.3 THE CITRIC ACID CYCLE

■ Hans Krebs won a share of the 1953 Nobel prize in medicine and physiology for his work on the citric acid cycle.

Acetyl CoA is used to make the citrate ion, which is then broken down bit by bit to CO_2 as units of $(H:^- + H^+)$ are sent into the respiratory chain.

Figure 26.6 gives the reactions of the citric acid cycle, a series of reactions that break down acetyl groups.[2] The two carbon atoms of this group end up in molecules of CO_2, and the

---

[2] You should be aware that the citric acid cycle goes by two other names as well: the *tricarboxylic acid cycle* and the *Krebs cycle*. You might encounter any of these names in other references.

hydrogen atoms are fed into the respiratory chain. These reactions occur in the innermost part of a mitochondrion, inside the inner membrane, in what is called the *mitochondrial matrix*.

Coenzyme A Is the Common Carrier of Acetyl Units   For an acetyl group to enter the citric acid cycle, it must be joined to coenzyme A, which we represent as CoA—SH.

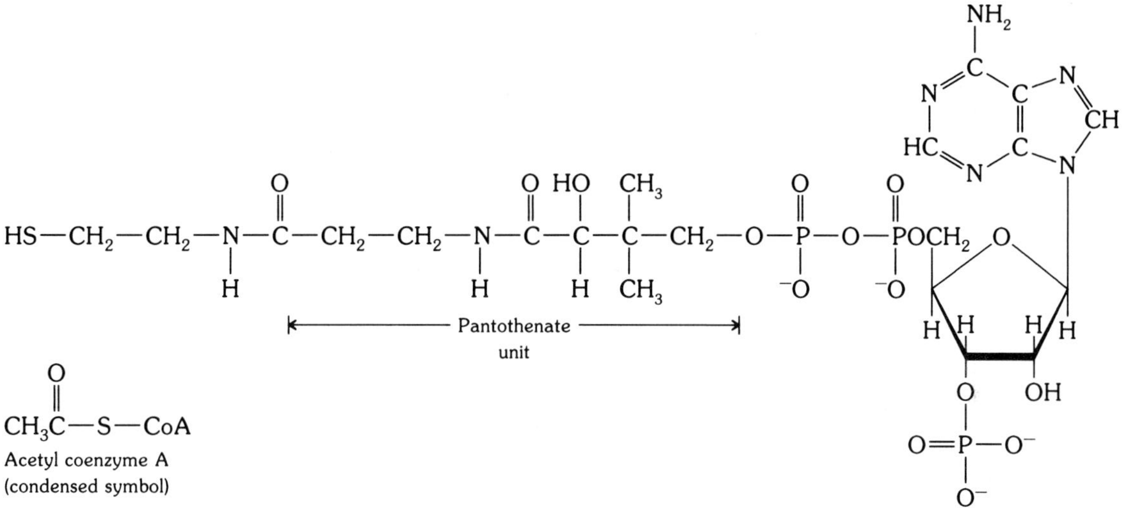

$$CH_3C(=O)-S-CoA$$

Acetyl coenzyme A
(condensed symbol)

Coenzyme A (CoA – SH)

This coenzyme requires pantothenic acid, one of the B vitamins.

The conversion of a pyruvate ion to acetyl coenzyme A involves both a decarboxylation and an oxidation. The overall equation for this complicated step is as follows, but we'll not study any details.

$$CH_3C(=O)-CO_2^- + CoA-S-H + NAD^+ \longrightarrow CH_3C(=O)-S-CoA + CO_2 + NADH$$

Pyruvate   Coenzyme A   Acetyl coenzyme A

Acetyl coenzyme A is a thio ester, which means an ester in which an oxygen atom has been replaced by a sulfur atom. A carbon–sulfur bond is far more reactive than a carbon–oxygen bond, particularly when the carbon is part of a carbonyl group. Therefore acetyl CoA is a particularly active transfer agent for the acetyl group. And just such a transfer of an acetyl group launches one turn of the citric acid cycle.

The Citric Acid Cycle Dismantles Acetyl Groups, Sending Hydrogen to the Respiratory Chain and CO$_2$ to Waste Disposal   In the first step of the citric acid cycle, the acetyl group of acetyl coenzyme A transfers to oxaloacetate ion, an ion that has two carboxylate groups and a keto group. The acetyl unit adds across the keto group in a type of reaction that we have not studied before. For background to this reaction see Special Topic 26.2.

The product is the citrate ion. Now begins a series of reactions by which the citrate ion is degraded bit by bit until another oxaloacetate ion is recovered. The numbers of the following steps match those in Figure 26.6.

■ At physiological pH, the acids in the cycle exist largely as their anions.

1. Citrate is dehydrated to give the double bond of *cis*-aconitate. (This is the dehydration of an alcohol.)

2. Water adds to the double bond of *cis*-aconitate to give an isomer of citrate called isocitrate. Thus the net effect of steps 1 and 2 is to switch the alcohol group in citrate to a different carbon atom. However, this changes the alcohol from tertiary to secondary, from one that can't be oxidized to one that can.

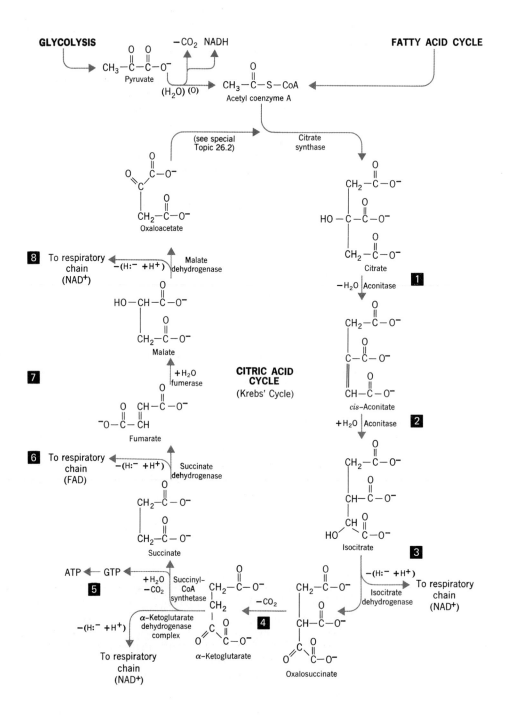

Figure 26.6

The citric acid cycle. The boxed numbers refer to the text discussion. The names of the enzymes for each step are given by the arrows.

3. The secondary alcohol group in isocitrate is dehydrogenated (oxidized) to give oxalosuccinate. NAD^+ accepts the hydrogen, so three ATPs can now be made as NAD:H passes its electron pair down the respiratory chain.

4. Oxalosuccinate loses a carboxyl group — it decarboxylates — to give α-ketoglutarate.

5. α-Ketoglutarate now undergoes a very complicated series of reactions, all catalyzed by one team of enzymes that includes coenzyme A. The results are the loss of a carboxyl group and another dehydrogenation. The hydrogen is accepted by NAD^+, so three more ATPs can now be made by the respiratory chain.

    The product, not shown in Figure 26.6, is the coenzyme A derivative of succinic acid. It is converted to the succinate ion, which is in Figure 26.6, in a reaction that also generates guanosine triphosphate, GTP. This is another high-energy triphosphate, which we mentioned on page 656 as being similar to ATP. GTP is able to phosphorylate ADP to make one ATP. Thus the citric acid cycle includes one substrate phosphorylation.

6. Succinate donates hydrogen to FAD (not to NAD^+), and the fumarate ion forms. Two ATPs (not three) can be made via FAD's involvement in the respiratory chain.

7. Fumarate adds water to its double bond, and malate forms.

8. The secondary alcohol in malate gives up hydrogen to NAD^+, and three more ATPs can be made.

The cycle is now closed. We have remade one molecule of the carrier, oxaloacetate. It can accept another acetyl group from acetyl coenzyme A. If the demand for ATP is still high enough, another turn of the cycle can now occur.

Oxidative Phosphorylation Makes a Maximum of Twelve ATP Molecules Using Intermediates of the Citric Acid Cycle The data in Table 26.2 show where ATP production is generated as the citric acid cycle runs. If, to the twelve ATPs made in this way, we add the three ATPs made possible by the conversion of pyruvate to acetyl CoA, then fifteen ATPs can be made by the degradation of one pyruvate ion.

Keep in mind that pyruvate isn't the only raw material either for acetyl coenzyme A or for other metabolites (MH_2) that can fuel the respiratory chain. Also remember that the energy of the respiratory chain can be used to run other operations besides making ATP — for example, the operation of nerves. Thus Table 26.2 has to be viewed as giving the upper limits to ATP production from pyruvate by the respiratory chain.

TABLE 26.2 ATP Production by Oxidative Phosphorylation

Steps	Receiver of $(H:^- + H^+)$ in the Respiratory Chain	Molecules of ATP Formed
Isocitrate $\longrightarrow$ α-ketoglutarate	NAD^+	3
α-Ketoglutarate $\longrightarrow$ succinyl CoA	NAD^+	3
Succinyl CoA $\longrightarrow$ succinate (via GTP)	—	1
Succinate $\longrightarrow$ fumarate	FAD	2
Malate $\longrightarrow$ oxaloacetate	NAD^+	3
Total ATP via citric acid cycle		12 ATP
Pyruvate $\longrightarrow$ acetyl CoA	NAD^+	3
Total ATP from pyruvate via citric acid cycle		15 ATP

SPECIAL TOPIC 26.2   **CONDENSING ESTERS—A MAJOR C—C BOND MAKING REACTION**

The reaction by which an acetyl group enters the citric acid cycle is just one example of many reactions of two carbonyl compounds in which an acyl group of one becomes joined to an alpha position of another. The product is a much larger molecule. We'll first explain how this happens under laboratory conditions with a very simple system, two molecules of the same ester, ethyl acetate. Organic chemists call the reaction the *Claisen ester condensation.*

The Alpha Hydrogen of a Carbonyl Compound Is "Mobile"   The acid ionization constant of an alkane is estimated to be about 10^{-40}; clearly, no one would call an alkane an acid! The ionization constant (of the α H—CH_2CO— unit) in ethyl acetate is roughly 10^{-18}, making it a billion trillion times as strong an acid (but still nothing we'd call an acid in water).

The reason for this greater acidity is the presence of the two nearby electronegative oxygen atoms. This greater acidity (mobility) of a hydrogen on a carbon alpha to oxygens is all we need to understand how the Claisen condensation and similar reactions in the body can occur.

With ethyl acetate, the reaction is as follows, where $B:^-$ is a powerful base, so powerful that the reaction cannot be run in water. (Usually it is run in ethyl alcohol.) In living systems, reactions like this use enzymes to handle necessary proton exchanges.

$$2CH_3-\overset{\overset{O}{\|}}{C}-O-CH_2CH_3 + \overset{B:^-}{\longrightarrow}$$

$$CH_3-\overset{\overset{O}{\|}}{C}-CH_2-\overset{\overset{O}{\|}}{C}-O-CH_2CH_3 + CH_3CH_2OH$$

Notice that an acetyl group (in color) has been joined to the alpha carbon of the second ester molecule. A new C—C bond has been made. Let's see how a strong base handles this reaction.

Step 1. The base takes the mobile H^+ from the alpha H—C position.

$$H-CH_2-\overset{\overset{O}{\|}}{C}-O-CH_2CH_3 + B:^- \longrightarrow$$
Ethyl acetate

$$^-CH_2-\overset{\overset{O}{\|}}{C}-O-CH_2CH_3 + B:H$$

Step 2. The new anion attacks the carbonyl carbon of another ester molecule. (This carbon has a partial positive charge on it.)

$$CH_3-\overset{\overset{:O:}{\|}}{C} + :CH_2-\overset{\overset{O}{\|}}{C}-O-CH_2CH_3 \longrightarrow$$
$$\underset{OCH_2CH_3}{}$$

$$CH_3-\overset{\overset{:O:^-}{|}}{\underset{\underset{CH_2CH_3}{O}}{C}}-CH_2-\overset{\overset{O}{\|}}{C}-O-CH_2CH_3$$

Step 3. The product of this reaction expels $CH_3CH_2O^-$, which takes H^+ from B:H (and the base is thus regenerated).

$$CH_3-\overset{\overset{:O:^-}{|}}{\underset{\underset{CH_2CH_3}{O}}{C}}-CH_2-\overset{\overset{O}{\|}}{C}-O-CH_2CH_3 \longrightarrow$$

B:H

$$CH_3-\overset{\overset{O}{\|}}{C}-CH_2-\overset{\overset{O}{\|}}{C}-OCH_2CH_3 + HOCH_3CH_3 + B:^-$$
Ethyl acetoacetate

This overall reaction is formally very similar to the initial reactions the body uses for several biosyntheses: to make long hydrocarbon chains from acetate units, and to make cholesterol and the sex hormones. So we'll meet this kind of reaction in later chapters.

Citrate Synthase Manages a Claisen-like Condensation of Acetyl CoA with Oxaloacetate   If we take acetyl CoA and oxaloacetate through the same steps, we have the following in which the services of a base, still represented by $B:^-$, are provided by the enzyme citrate synthase. Realize that what follows is a considerable simplification of a series of steps in which the way charges are managed by the enzyme are not indicated.

Step 1. Acetyl CoA gives up a proton.

$$H-CH_2-\overset{\overset{O}{\|}}{C}-S-CoA + B:^- \longrightarrow$$
Acetyl CoA

$$^-:CH_2-\overset{\overset{O}{\|}}{C}-S-CoA + B:H$$

Step 2. The new anion attacks the keto group in oxalo-acetate. The new C—C bond forms.

ordinary esters. In fact, this hydrolysis is part of the driving force of the overall reaction.)

Oxaloacetate

Step 3. The CoA–S group is hydrolyzed, and a proton is donated so that the 3° alcohol group can form. (The CoA–S unit is similar to an ordinary ester. It is a *thio* ester, and these hydrolyze more readily than

Citrate

Thus a Claisen-like condensation launches the acetyl group of acetyl CoA into the citric acid cycle.

SUMMARY

High-energy compounds Organophosphates whose phosphate group transfer potentials equal or are higher than that of ATP are classified as high-energy phosphates. A lower-energy phosphate can be made by phosphate transfer from a higher-energy phosphate, a process called substrate phosphorylation.

Respiratory chain A series of electron transfer enzymes called the respiratory enzymes occur together as groups called respiratory assemblies in the inner membranes of mitochondria. These enzymes process metabolites (MH_2), which often are obtained by the operation of the citric acid cycle. Either NAD^+ or FAD can accept $(H:^- + H^+)$ from a metabolite. Their reduced forms, NADH or $FADH_2$, then pass on the electrons until cytochrome oxidase uses them (together with H^+) to reduce oxygen to water.

Oxidative phosphorylation As electrons flow from NADH to oxygen in the respiratory chain, protons are released. These cause conformational changes in membrane proteins, which force protons

to the outside of the inner membrane, making a proton gradient and a positive charge gradient across the inner mitochondrial membrane. As protons flow back at the allowed conduits of this membrane, ATP made by an enzyme in each conduit is released. In some systems, other kinds of positive ions migrate, as in the operation of nerves. Various drugs and antibiotics can block the respiratory chain.

Citric acid cycle Acetyl groups from acetyl coenzyme A are joined to a four-carbon carrier, oxaloacetate, to make citrate. This six-carbon salt of a tricarboxylic acid then is degraded bit by bit as $(H:^- + H^+)$ is fed to the respiratory chain. Each acetyl unit leads to the synthesis of a maximum of twelve ATP molecules.

Fatty acids and glucose are important suppliers of acetyl groups. In glycolysis, glucose units are broken to pyruvate units, and the oxidative decarboxylation of pyruvate does two things. It leads to the synthesis of one NADH (which leads to the formation of three ATPs), and it supplies acetyl units to the citric acid cycle from which twelve more ATPs are made.

REVIEW EXERCISES

The answers to these Review Exercises are in the *Study Guide* that accompanies this text.

Energy Sources

26.1 What products of the digestion of carbohydrates, triacylglycerols, and the polypeptides can be used as souces of biochemical energy to make ATP?

26.2 The complete catabolism of glucose gives what products?

26.3 The identical products form when glucose is burned in open air as when it is fully catabolized in the body. How, then, do these two processes differ in their overall accomplishments?

26.4 What are the end products of the complete catabolism of fatty acids?

High-Energy Phosphates

26.5 Complete the following structure of ATP:

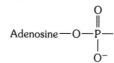

26.6 Write the structures of ADP and of AMP in the manner started by Review Exercise 26.5.

26.7 At physiological pH, what does the term *inorganic phosphate* stand for? (Give formulas and names.)

26.8 Why are phosphoenolpyruvate and ATP called high-energy phosphates but glycerol 3-phosphate is not?

26.9 If the organophosphate of *M* has a *lower* phosphate group transfer potential than *that of N*, in which direction does the following reaction tend to go spontaneously, to the left or to the right?

$$M-OPO_3^{2-} + N \underset{}{\overset{?}{\rightleftharpoons}} N-OPO_3^{2-} + M$$

26.10 Using data in Table 26.1, tell (yes or no) whether ATP readily transfers a phosphate group to each of the following possible compounds. (Assume, of course, that the right enzyme is available.)
(a) glycerol   (b) fructose
(c) creatine   (d) acetic acid

26.11 All the possible phosphate transfers in Review Exercise 26.10 are classified as *substrate* phosphorylations. What does this mean?

26.12 What is the function of creatine phosphate in muscle tissue?

26.13 Whether or not creatine phosphate is used in muscle tissue is under *feedback control*. Explain.

Overview of Metabolic Pathways

26.14 In the general area of biochemical energetics, what is the purpose of each of the following pathways?
(a) respiratory chain   (b) anaerobic glycolysis
(c) citric acid cycle   (d) fatty acid cycle

26.15 What prompts the respiratory chain to go into operation?

26.16 In general terms, the intermediates that send electrons down the respiratory chain come from what metabolic pathway that consumes acetyl groups?

26.17 Arrange the following sets of terms in sequence in the order in which they occur or take place. Place the identifying letter of the first sequence of a set to occur on the left of the row of numbers.

(a) Citric acid cycle   pyruvate   respiratory chain

      1   **2**   **3**

  glycolysis   acetyl CoA

      4   **5**

(b) Respiratory chain   fatty acid cycle

     1   **2**

  citric acid cycle   acetyl CoA

      3   **4**

26.18 The *aerobic sequence* begins with what metabolic pathway and ends with which pathway?

Respiratory Chain

26.19 What is missing in the following basic expression for what must happen in the respiratory chain?

$$\tfrac{1}{2}O_2 + 2H^+ \longrightarrow H_2O$$

26.20 What general name is given to the set of enzymes involved in electron transport?

26.21 Write the following display in the normal form of a chemical equation:

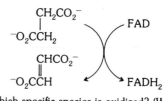

(a) Which specific species is oxidized? (Write its structure.)
(b) Which species is reduced?

26.22 Write the following equation in the form of a display like that shown in Review Question 26.21.

$$\underset{\displaystyle CH_3\overset{\displaystyle OH}{\underset{|}{C}}HCO_2^-}{} + NAD^+ \longrightarrow \underset{\displaystyle CH_3\overset{\displaystyle O}{\overset{\|}{C}}CO_2^-}{} + NADH + H^+$$

26.23 Arrange the following in the order in which they receive and pass on electrons.

      FMN   Cyt *a*   NAD$^+$ FeSP

26.24 What does cytochrome oxidase do?

26.25 What is FAD, and where is it involved in the respiratory chain?

Chemiosmotic Theory

26.26 Across which cellular membrane does the respiratory chain establish a gradient of H$^+$ ions? On which side of this membrane is the value of the pH lower?

26.27 According to the chemiosmotic theory, the flow of what particles most directly leads to the synthesis of ATP?

26.28 If the inner mitochondrial membrane is broken, the respiratory chain can still operate, but the phosphorylation of ADP that normally results stops. Explain this in general terms.

26.29 Complete and balance the following equation. (Use $\tfrac{1}{2}$ as the coefficient of oxygen as shown.)

$$MH_2 + H^+ \; + \; \tfrac{1}{2}O_2 \longrightarrow$$

From inside
the inner
membrane

26.30 What is the difference between substrate and oxidative phosphorylation?

26.31 Besides a gradient of H^+ ions, what other gradient exists in mitochondria as a result of the operation of the respiratory chain? In terms of helping to explain how cations other than H^+ move across a membrane, of what significance is this gradient?

26.32 Briefly describe the theory presented in this chapter that explains how a flow of protons across the inner mitochondrial membrane initiates the synthesis of ATP from ADP and P_i.

Citric Acid Cycle

26.33 What makes the citric acid cycle start up?

26.34 What chemical unit is degraded by the citric acid cycle? Give its name and structure.

26.35 How many times is a secondary alcohol group oxidized in the citric acid cycle?

26.36 Water adds to a carbon–carbon double bond how many times in one turn of the citric acid cycle?

26.37 The conversion of pyruvate to an acetyl unit is both an oxidation and a decarboxylation.
(a) If *only* decarboxylation occurred, what would form from pyruvate? Write the structure of the other product in

$$CH_3-\overset{\overset{\displaystyle O}{\|}}{C}-\overset{\overset{\displaystyle O}{\|}}{C}-O^- + H^+ \longrightarrow \underline{\hspace{2cm}} + O{=}C{=}O$$

(b) If this product is oxidized, what is the name and the structure of the product of such oxidation?
(c) Referring to Figure 26.6, which specific compound undergoes an oxidative decarboxylation similar to that of pyruvate? (Give its name.)

26.38 One cofactor in the enzyme assembly that catalyzes the oxidative decarboxylation of pyruvate requires thiamine, one of the B vitamins. Therefore in beriberi, the deficiency disease for this vitamin, the level of what substance can be expected to rise in blood serum (and for which an analysis can be made as part of the diagnosis of beriberi)?

26.39 The enzyme for the conversion of isocitrate to oxalosuccinate (Figure 26.6) is stimulated by one of these two substances, ATP or ADP. Which one is the likelier activator? Explain.

26.40 What is the maximum number of ATP molecules that can be made from the use of respiratory chain phosphorylation to break down
(a) pyruvate?
(b) an acetyl group in acetyl CoA?

26.41 Glutamic acid, one of the amino acids, can be converted to α-ketoglutarate (Figure 26.6). How many ATP molecules can be made from the entry of α-ketoglutarate into the citric acid cycle?

Redox Potentials (Special Topic 26.1)

26.42 What are *standard conditions* for reduction potentials when working with biological oxidations, and why are they different from the regular standard conditions.

26.43 Write the half-cell reaction for the reduction of acetate ion to ethanal. Its value of E' is -0.60 V.

26.44 Using the data and equation of Review Exercise 26.43 plus such data as needed from Special Topic 26.1, what would be the cell reaction if the acetate–ethanal system were coupled with the NAD^+–NADH system? Calculate the cell potential. What is the spontaneous reaction, the oxidation of ethanal or the reduction of acetate ion according to your answers here?

26.45 Repeat Review Exercise 26.44, only this time couple the acetate–ethanal system to the $\tfrac{1}{2}O_2$–H_2O system.

26.46 What is one reason why one step in a series can be quite unfavored and yet made to happen?

26.47 What is one reason why the body uses so many steps to bring about an overall oxidation of a metabolite?

Ester Condensations (Special Topic 26.2)

26.48 Which would be more acidic, acetone or propane? Explain.

26.49 Suppose that ethyl propanoate went through the steps of the Claisen condensation. Write the structure of the final product.

CHAPTER TWENTY-SEVEN

Metabolism of Carbohydrates

- ■ GLYCOGEN METABOLISM
- ■ GLUCOSE TOLERANCE
- ■ THE CATABOLISM OF GLUCOSE
- ■ GLUCONEOGENESIS

We can't give the molecular basis of mouth watering, but in this chapter we can go into the metabolism of carbohydrates.

27.1   GLYCOGEN METABOLISM

Much of the body's control over the blood sugar level is handled by its regulation of the synthesis and breakdown of glycogen.

The digestion of the starch and disaccharides in the diet gives glucose, fructose, and galactose, but their catabolic pathways all converge very quickly to that of glucose itself. Galactose, for example, is changed by a few steps in the liver to glucose 1-phosphate. Fructose is changed to a compound that occurs early in glycolysis. For these reasons, this chapter concentrates on the metabolism of glucose, and we'll begin with the glucose in circulation.

Wide Variations in the Blood Sugar Level Signal Something Wrong

■ mg/dL = milligrams per deciliter, where 1 dL = 100 mL.

The concentration of monosaccharides in whole blood, expressed in milligrams per deciliter (mg/dL), is called the **blood sugar level.** This is very close to the glucose level, because glucose is overwhelmingly the major monosaccharide. When determined after several hours of fasting, the blood sugar level, called the **normal fasting level,** is 65 to 95 mg/dL (70 to 110 mg/dL in plasma). In a condition of **hypoglycemia,** the blood sugar level is *below* normal, and in **hyperglycemia** it is *above* the normal fasting level.

■ *-glyc-*, sugar
-emia, in blood
hypo-, under, below
hyper-, above, over
renal, of the kidneys
-uria, in urine

When the blood sugar level become too hyperglycemic (becomes high), the kidneys are unable to put back into the blood all the glucose that left it in a glomerulus. Glucose then appears in the urine, a condition called **glucosuria.** The blood sugar level above which this happens is called the **renal threshold** for glucose, and it is in the range of about 140 to 160 mg/dL, sometimes higher.

Hypoglycemia Can Make You Faint

Your brain relys almost entirely on glucose for its chemical energy, so if hypoglycemia develops rapidly, you can experience dizziness and may faint. People with diabetes who unknowingly take too much insulin experience this in a severe form known as *insulin shock.* The brain consumes about 120 g/day of glucose, and a quick onset of hypoglycemia starves the brain cells. They do have the ability to switch over to other nutrients, but brain cells can't do this very rapidly.

Persistent Hyperglycemia Indicates Diabetes

Whenever hyperglycemia develops and tends to persist, something is wrong with the mechanisms for withdrawing glucose from circulation. Diabetes is a common cause of hyperglycemia, but there are other possible causes.

In an individual with a sustained hyperglycemia, some glucose combines with hemoglobin to give glycohemoglobin (or glycosylated hemoglobin). The measurement of the level of this substance has become the best way to monitor the average blood sugar level of a diabetic, better than any direct measurements of blood glucose. Its level doesn't fluctuate as widely as the blood sugar level, and it doesn't have to be determined as frequently.

Excess Blood Glucose Normally Is Withdrawn from Circulation

When there is more than enough glucose in circulation to meet energy needs, the body does not eliminate the excess but conserves its chemical energy. There are two ways to do this. One is to convert glucose to fat, and we'll study how this is done in the next chapter. The other is to synthesize glycogen, which we'll discuss here. (We studied glycogen on page 504.)

Liver and muscle cells can convert glucose to glycogen by a series of steps called **glycogenesis** ("glycogen creation"). The liver holds 70 to 110 g of glycogen, and the muscles, taken as a whole, contain 170 to 250 g. When muscles need glucose, they take it back out of glycogen. When the blood needs glucose because the blood sugar level has dropped too much, the liver hydrolyzes as much of its glycogen reserves as needed and then puts the glucose into circulation. The overall series of reactions in either tissue that hydrolyzes glycogen is called **glycogenolysis** (lysis or hydrolysis of glycogen). This process is controlled by several hormones.

Epinephrine Launches a Multiple-Enzyme Glycogenolysis Cascade

When muscular work is begun, the adrenal medulla secretes the hormone **epinephrine.** In muscle tissue, and to some extent in the liver, epinephrine activates glycogenolysis by the steps outlined in Figure 27.1. It first activates the enzyme adenylate cyclase, which catalyzes the conversion of some ATP to cyclic AMP in the manner we studied in Section 24.5.

Cyclic AMP then activates still another enzyme, and this still another enzyme, and so on in a cascade of events shown in Figure 27.1. Each molecule of epinephrine, by activating adenylate cyclase, triggers the formation of dozens of molecules of cyclic AMP. *Each* of these activates a succeeding enzyme, and so on until the final enzyme appears not only suddenly but in a relatively large quantity. Thus one epinephrine molecule triggers the rapid mobilization of thousands of glucose units. And these are now ready to supply energy that the body needs.

While the epinephrine "cascade" proceeds to release glucose from glycogen, the affected tissue simultaneously shuts down a team of enzymes called glycogen synthetase that otherwise would do the opposite, change glucose to glycogen. This is done at the step in Figure 27.1 where the enzyme called active protein kinase catalyzes the phosphorylation of *two* systems. One is inactive phosphorylase kinase and the other is active glycogen synthetase. The first action continues the epinephrine cascade, until glucose units are obtained from glycogen. The second action, the phosphorylation of glycogen synthetase, *shuts down an enzyme that would remake glycogen.* The potential competition, therefore, cannot develop. It's a remarkable aspect of this system.

The end product of glycogenolysis isn't actually glucose but glucose 1-phosphate. Cells that can do glycogenolysis also have an enzyme called phosphoglucomutase, which catalyzes the conversion of glucose 1-phosphate to its isomer, glucose 6-phosphate:

■ An estimated 30,000 molecules of glucose are released from glycogen for each molecule of epinephrine that initiates glycogenolysis.

Glucose 1-phosphate   phosphoglucomutase   Glucose 6-phosphate

Glucose Is Trapped in the Muscle Cell When It Is in the Form of Glucose 6-Phosphate

Glucose 6-phosphate, rather than glucose, is the form in which a glucose unit must be to enter a pathway that produces ATP. *It is also in a form that can't migrate out of muscle cells.* It won't be lost from tissue needing it during exercise. Thus glycogenolysis in muscle tissue is an important supplier of energy. When the supply of muscle glycogen is low, muscle cells can take glucose from circulation, *trap it as glucose 6-phosphate,* and then convert this to glycogen.

Glucagon Activates Liver Glycogenolysis and Thus Affects the Blood Sugar Level

The α-cells of the pancreas make a polypeptide hormone, **glucagon,** which helps to maintain a normal blood sugar level. When the blood sugar level drops, these cells release glucagon. Its target tissue is the liver, where it is an excellent activator of glycogenolysis.

Glucagon works by a cascade process very similar to that initiated by epinephrine. Like epinephrine, glucagon activates adenylate cyclase. Unlike epinephrine, glucagon also inhibits glycolysis, so this action helps to keep the supply of glucose up. Glucagon, also unlike epinephrine, does not cause an increase in blood pressure or pulse rate, and it is longer-acting than epinephrine.

Liver Cells Can Release Glucose to Circulation

Glucose units released from liver glycogen as glucose 6-phosphate are converted to glucose by an enzyme that the liver has, but not the muscles, glucose 6-phosphatase. It catalyzes the hydrolysis of glucose 6-phosphate to glucose and inorganic phosphate.

SPECIAL TOPIC 27.1   GLYCOGEN STORAGE DISEASES

A number of inherited diseases involve the storage of glycogen. For example, in **Von Gierke's disease,** the liver lacks the enzyme glucose 6-phosphatase, which catalyzes the hydrolysis of glucose 6-phosphate. Unless this hydrolysis occurs, glucose units cannot leave the liver. They remain as glycogen in such quantities that the liver becomes very large. At the same time, the blood sugar level falls, the catabolism of glucose accelerates, and the liver releases more and more pyruvate and lactate.

In **Cori's disease,** the liver lacks an enzyme needed to catalyze the hydrolysis of 1,6-glycosidic bonds, the bonds that give rise to the many branches of a glycogen molecule.

Without this enzyme, only a partial utilization of the glucose in glycogen is possible. The clinical symptoms resemble those of Von Gierke's disease, but they are less severe.

In **McArdle's disease,** the muscles lack phosphorylase, the enzyme needed to obtain glucose 1-phosphate from glycogen (see Figure 27.6). Although the individual is not capable of much physical activity, physical development is otherwise relatively normal.

In **Andersen's disease,** both the liver and the spleen lack the enzyme for putting together the branches in glycogen. Liver failure from cirrhosis usually causes death by age 2.

■ The letter P is often used to represent the whole phosphate group in the structures of phosphate ester intermediates in metabolism.

■ The glucagon molecule has 29 amino acid residues.

$$\text{glucose 6-P} + H_2O \xrightarrow{\text{glucose 6-phosphatase}} \text{glucose} + P_i$$

Glucose can now leave the liver and so help raise the blood sugar level. During periods of fasting, therefore, the overall process in the liver from glucose 1-phosphate to glucose 6-phosphate to glucose is a major supplier of glucose for the blood. Glucagon, which triggers this, is thus an important regulator of the blood sugar level.

The brain depends on the liver during fasting to maintain its favorite source of chemical energy, circulating glucose. (We are beginning to see in chemical terms how vital the liver is to the performance of other organs.) When circulating glucose is taken up by a brain cell, it is promptly trapped in the cell by being converted to glucose 6-phosphate.

Several hereditary diseases involve the glucose–glycogen interconversion, and some are discussed in Special Topic 27.1.

Figure 27.1
The epinephrine "cascade."

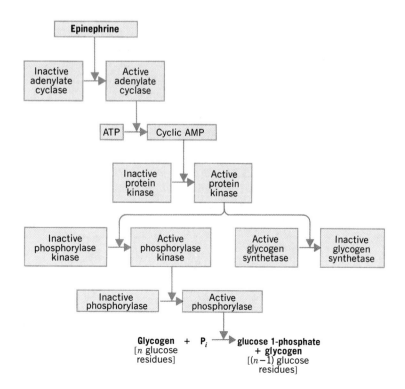

■ Acromegaly is sometimes called *giantism* because the flat bone structures of victims are enlarged. The nose, lips, tongue, hand and feet broaden progressively, and so do the visceral organs.

Human Growth Hormone Stimulates the Release of Glucagon   Growth requires energy, so the action of glucagon that helps to supply a source of energy — glucose — aids in the work of the human growth hormone. In some situations, such as a disfiguring condition known as acromegaly, there is an excessive secretion of human growth hormone which promotes too high a level of glucose in the blood. This is undesirable because a prolonged state of hyperglycemia from any cause can lead to diabetes and to some of the blood-capillary related complications of diabetes.

■ Adipose tissue is the fatty tissue that surrounds internal organs.

■ Life-saving first aid for someone in insulin shock is sugared fruit juice or candy to counter the hypoglycemia.

Insulin Strongly Lowers the Blood Sugar Level   The β-cells of the pancreas make and release **insulin,** a polypeptide hormone. Its release is stimulated by an increase in the blood sugar level, such as normally occurs after a carbohydrate-rich meal. As insulin moves into action, it finds its receptors at the cell membranes of muscle and adipose tissue. The insulin-receptor complexes somehow make it possible for glucose molecules to move easily into the cells, and this, of course, lowers the blood sugar level.

Not all cells depend on insulin to take up glucose. Brain cells, for example, and cells in the kidneys, the intestinal tract, red blood cells, and in the lenses of the eyes take up glucose directly. If too much insulin gets into circulation, as from an error in insulin therapy, the individual's blood sugar level falls too low, which leads to insulin shock, as we've already mentioned.

Somatostatin Inhibits Glucagon and Slows the Release of Insulin   The hypothalamus, a specific region in the brain, makes **somatostatin,** another hormone that participates in the regulation of the blood sugar level. When the β-cells of the pancreas secrete insulin, which helps to *lower* the blood sugar level, the α-cells should not at the same time release glucagon, which helps to *raise* this level. Somatostatin acts at the pancreas to inhibit the release of glucagon as well as to slow down the release of insulin. It thus helps to prevent a wild swing in the blood sugar level that insulin alone might cause.

27.2   GLUCOSE TOLERANCE

The ability of the body to tolerate swings in the blood sugar level is essential to health.

Your **glucose tolerance** is the ability of your body to manage its blood sugar level within the normal range. We'll take an overview here of the many factors that contribute to glucose tolerance.

■ Carl Cori and Gerti Cori shared the 1947 Nobel prize in physiology and medicine.

The Cori Cycle Describes the Distributions and Uses of Glucose   The strategies used by the body to maintain its blood sugar level within the normal range form a cycle of events called the **Cori cycle,** outlined in Figure 27.2.

At the bottom of the figure we see glucose as it enters the bloodstream from the intestinal tract. Its molecules either stay in circulation or are soon removed by various tissues. Two are shown in the figure, those of muscle and liver. Muscle cells can trap glucose molecules and use them either to make ATP by glycolysis or to replenish the muscle's glycogen reserves. Liver cells can similarly trap glucose, and the liver is able to release glucose back into the bloodstream when the blood sugar level must be raised.

When glucose is used in glycolysis, the end product is either pyruvate or lactate, depending on the oxygen supply, as we learned in the last chapter. Either can be used to make

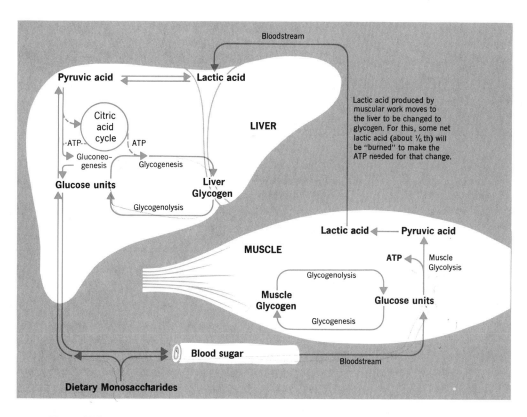

Figure 27.2
The Cori cycle.

more ATP by means of the citric acid cycle and the respiratory chain. However, when extensive anaerobic glycolysis is carried out in a tissue, the lactate level rises considerably.

Because lactate still has C—H bonds, it continues to have useful chemical energy, so instead of simply excreting excess lactate at the kidneys, the body recycles it. It converts a fraction of it—about five-sixths—to glucose. This synthesis of glucose from smaller molecules is called **gluconeogenesis,** and it requires ATP energy. Thus the remaining one-sixth of the lactate is catabolized to make the needed ATP. This process completes the Cori cycle. (We go into more details about gluconeogenesis later in this chapter.)

We can see from all these processes that many factors affect the blood sugar level. Some tend to raise it and some do the opposite. Figure 27.3 summarizes them in a different kind of display.

■ *Neo,* new; *-neogenesis,* new creation; *gluconeogenesis,* the synthesis of new glucose.

The Glucose Tolerance Test Measures Glucose Tolerance In the **glucose tolerance test,** the individual is given a drink that contains glucose, generally 75 g for an adult and 1.75 g per kilogram of body weight for children, and then the blood sugar level is checked at regular intervals.

Figure 27.4 gives typical plots of this level versus time. The lower curve is that of a person with normal glucose tolerance, and the upper curve is of one whose glucose tolerance is typical of diabetes. In both, the blood sugar level rises sharply at first. The healthy person, however, soon manages the high level and brings it back down with the help of a normal flow of insulin and somatostatin. In the diabetic, the level comes down only very slowly and remains essentially in the hyperglycemic range throughout.

Figure 27.3
Factors that affect the blood sugar level.

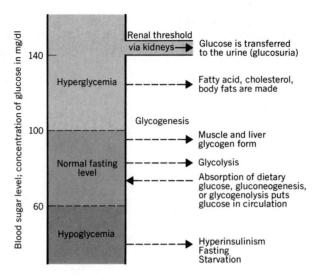

Figure 27.4
Glucose tolerance curves.

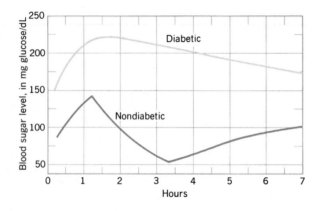

■ Unhappily, most people with midmorning sag go into another round of sugared coffee and sugared rolls. The glucose gives a short lift, but then an oversupply of insulin restores the mild hypoglycemia of the sag.

Notice that in the normal individual, the blood sugar level can sometimes drop to a mildly hypoglycemic level. Such hypoglycemia is possible also in someone who has eaten a carbohydrate-rich breakfast. With glucose pouring into the bloodstream, the release of a bit more insulin than needed can occur. This leads to the overwithdrawal of glucose from circulation, and midmorning brings dizziness and sometimes even fainting (even falling asleep in class). The prevention isn't more sugared doughnuts but a balanced breakfast.

Glucose Tolerance Is Poor in Diabetes The subject of glucose tolerance is nowhere more discussed than in connection with diabetes. **Diabetes** is defined clinically as a disease in which the blood sugar level persists in being much higher than warranted by the dietary and nutritional status of the individual. Invariably, a person with untreated diabetes has glucosuria, and the discovery of this condition often triggers the clinical investigations that are necessary to rule diabetes in or out.

As discussed in Special Topic 27.2, there are two broad kinds of diabetes, type I and type II. Type I diabetics are unable to manufacture insulin (at least not enough), and they need daily insulin therapy to manage their blood sugar levels. Maintaining a relatively even and normal blood sugar level is the best single strategy that such diabetics have for the prevention of some of the vascular and neural problems that can complicate their health later. Most type II diabetics are able to manage their blood sugar levels by a good diet, weight control, exercise, and sometimes the use of oral medications.

SPECIAL TOPIC 27.2   DIABETES MELLITUS

The name for this disorder is from the Greek *diabetes*, to pass through a siphon, and *mellitus*, honey-sweet— meaning to pass urine that contains sugar. We'll call it diabetes for short. In severe, untreated diabetes, the victim's body wastes away despite efforts to satisfy a powerful thirst and hunger. To the ancients, it seemed as though the body were dissolving from within.

In the United States there are nearly 6.5 million known cases of diabetes, and almost as many others are believed to have this disease. It ranks third behind heart disease and cancer as the cause of death.

Fewer than 10% of all cases of diabetes are of the severe, insulin-dependent variety in which the β-cells of the pancreas are unable to make and secrete insulin. This is **type I diabetes,** and insulin therapy is essential. It is also called **insulin-dependent diabetes mellitus** or **IDDM.** In the past, because most victims contracted it before they were 20, it was called *juvenile-onset diabetes.*

The rest of all those with diabetes have a form called **type II diabetes,** or **non-insulin-dependent diabetes mellitus, NIDDM.** Most victims are able to manage their blood sugar levels by diet and exercise alone, without insulin injections. Their problem is actually not a lack of insulin but rather a breakdown in the machinery for taking advantage of it. Most get type II diabetes when they are over 40, so it has been called *adult-onset diabetes.*

Type I Diabetes Develops in Six Stages   D. S. Eisenbarth, a diabetes specialist, divides the onset of type I diabetes into six stages. We'll review them as background for illustrations of equilibrium chemistry and factors that shift equilibria.

The first stage is simply a genetic condition. Both people and experimental animals who develop type I diabetes have at least one defective gene, almost certainly more, that contributes to their susceptibility to this disease. At least one such gene is among the major histocompatibility genes that code for the antigens of tissue transplantation. (An *antigen* is an alien chemical that the immune system's *antibodies* destroy.) This genetic problem can now be recognized by various assays before the individual has any other symptoms of diabetes.

The second stage is a triggering incident. It can be a viral infection. The mumps virus, for example, causes diabetes in some. Usually, the onset of virus-caused type I diabetes occurs slowly over a few years.

The third stage is the appearance in the blood of certain antibodies. A virus, for example, can alter substances on the membranes of the pancreatic β-cells so that the body's immune system sees them as foreign antigens and so makes antibodies against them. In this sense, type I diabetes might be caused by antibodies against its own pancreatic β-cells and so be an autoimmune disease. This means that the body's immune system fails to recognize

the proteins of its own body and sets out to destroy them and, therefore, itself. The presence of such antibodies can also be detected before diabetes happens.

The fourth stage in the onset of type I diabetes is the gradual loss of the ability to secrete insulin. How well the pancreas of a person in a fasting state secretes insulin in response to a dose of glucose can be measured, and this ability shows a decline before the traditional symptoms of diabetes appear.

The fifth stage is diabetes and persistent hyperglycemia. Most of the pancreatic β-cells have disappeared.

In the sixth stage the destruction of β-cells is complete.

Immune-Suppressant Therapy Works If the Problem Is Caught in Its Early Stages   Because the immune system becomes involved with an autoimmune reaction during the onset of type I diabetes, one type of treatment might be to use drugs, like cyclosporin, that suppress the immune system. Cyclosporine is used to suppress the rejection of transplanted organs, like kidney transplants. When used in the early stages of the onset of type I diabetes, cyclosporine prevents insulin dependence in a significant fraction of individuals tested.

Insulin Receptors Are a Problem in Type II Diabetes   The onset of type II diabetes is much slower than that for type I, and obesity is a factor in most cases. The number of insulin-receptor proteins on the surfaces of target cells declines in obesity. Obesity usually involves a diet that is far richer in sugars and other carbohydrates than normal, and some scientists believe these substances evoke such a continuous presence of insulin that the receptor proteins literally wear out faster than they can be replaced. When the weight is reduced, particularly through physical exercise, the relative numbers of receptor proteins rebound.

A mutation of the insulin receptor protein has been found to occur in some with non-insulin-dependent diabetes. This renders the receptor less effective and the victims have a high insulin resistance.

Glucosylation of Proteins May Cause the Long-Term Complications of Diabetes   The immediate complications are an elevated blood sugar level, metabolic acidosis, and eventual death from coma and uremic poisoning. Insulin therapy corrects these immediate problems, but it deals less well with the longer-term complications.

The continuous presence of a high level of blood glucose shifts certain chemical equilibria in favor of glucosylated compounds. The aldehyde group of the open form of glucose, for example, can react with amino groups to form products called *Schiff bases.*

$$-CH{=}O + H_2N- \rightleftharpoons -CH{=}N- + H_2O$$

Aldehyde   Amino   A Schiff
group   group   base

Hemoglobin, for example, gives this reaction, and a high level of glucose shifts this equilibrium to the right. The level of glucosylated hemoglobin thus increases. (As we have mentioned, the measurement of the level of this compound is now regarded as the best way to monitor how well a person is managing his blood sugar level.)

Any material to which glucose has access and which has NH_2 groups — all proteins and genes, for example — can be glucosylated. Since the reaction is reversible, when the glucose level is brought down and kept within a normal range, the Schiff base level also declines.

The problem with the Schiff bases in the long term is that they undergo molecular rearrangements that give more permanent products, called Amadori compounds, in which the C=N double bond has migrated to C=C positions. After a time, the formation of the Amadori compounds is not reversible.

One such complication that probably is caused by these reactions occurs in the basement membranes of blood capillaries. They thicken as diabetes progresses; the condition is called *microangiopathy*. (The basement membrane is the protein support structure that encases the single layer of cells of a capillary.) Microangiopathy is believed to lead to the other complications, most of which involve the vascular system or the neural networks: kidney problems, gangrene of the lower limbs, and blindness.

Diabetes is the leading cause of new cases of blindness in the United States, and it is the second most common cause of blindness, overall. (During an eye examination ophthalmologists can detect the development of microangiopathy in the retina of the eye before other symptoms of diabetes are recognized.)

Blindness from Diabetes May Also Reflect the Reduction of Glucose to Sorbitol Glucose is reduced by the enzyme aldose reductase to sorbitol. It's a minor reaction in cells of the lens of the eye, but an abundance of glucose shifts equilibria in favor of too much sorbitol. Sorbitol, unlike glucose, tends to be trapped in lens cells, and as the sorbital concentration rises so does the osmotic pressure in the fluid. This draws water into the lens cells, which generates pressure and leads to cataracts.

The same kinds of swelling might occur in peripheral nerve cells, too, and cause them to deteriorate and become unable to assist in motor nerve functions. The osmotic swelling might also be the cause of poorer circulation into peripheral capillaries, which eventually opens the way for gangrene or for a breakdown of the filtration mechanisms in the kidneys.

Diet Control Is Mandatory The nature of the diet — both quality and quantity — does appear to be a decisive factor in the onset of type II diabetes. In countries with very low levels of refined sugars in the national diets, the incidence of type II diabetes is rare.

The best single treatment of diabetes is any effort that keeps an absolutely strict control on the blood sugar level. What must at all costs be avoided are the episodes of upward surges followed by precipitous declines as either the diet or the insulin treatments are not well managed.

β-Cell Transplants May Bring a Cure to Type I Diabetes In the early 1980s, scientists discovered that β-cells, stripped of neighboring cells, can be transplanted. They need not even be inserted into the receiver's pancreas, and they start to make insulin in a few weeks. Apparently the cells *adjacent to* the β-cells are responsible for inducing the body's immune-centered rejection process.

Human β-cells work best, of course, but those from pigs and cows also appear to be usable provided that they are encapsulated in very small spheres. These spheres have microscopic holes large enough to let insulin molecules escape but not large enough to let antibodies inside. These techniques have cured type I diabetes in experimental animals.

27.3 THE CATABOLISM OF GLUCOSE

Glycolysis and the pentose phosphate sequence are the chief catabolic pathways open to glucose.

■ Greek *glykos,* sugar or sweet; *-lysis,* dissolution.

Glycolysis, as we noted in the previous chapter, is a series of reactions that change glucose to pyruvate or to lactate while a small but important amount of ATP is made. Other monosaccharides eventually enter the same glycolysis pathway as glucose, as seen in Figure 27.5, so when we study glycolysis we cover most bases.

Anaerobic Glycolysis Ends in Lactate When a cell receives oxygen at a rate slower than needed, glycolysis can still operate, but it ends in lactate, not pyruvate. The overall equation for this *anaerobic glycolysis,* or the **anaerobic sequence** is

Figure 27.5
Convergence of the pathways in the metabolism of dietary carbohydrates.

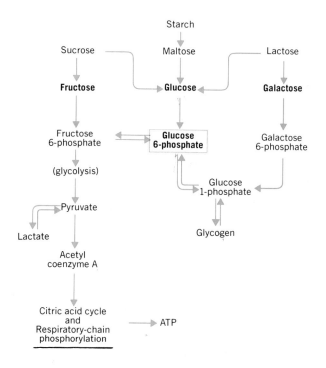

$$C_6H_{12}O_6 + 2ADP + 2P_i \xrightarrow[\text{glycolysis}]{\text{anaerobic}} 2CH_3\overset{\overset{\displaystyle OH}{|}}{C}HCO_2^- + 2H^+ + 2ATP$$

Glucose   Lactate

Except during extensive exercise, glycolysis is operated with sufficient oxygen, and it is aerobic. Its overall equation is

$$C_6H_{12}O_6 + 2ADP + 2P_i + 2NAD^+ \longrightarrow 2CH_3\overset{\overset{\displaystyle O}{\|}}{C}CO_2^- + 2ATP + 2NADH + 2H^+ + 2H_2O$$

Glucose   Pyruvate

The NADH is part of the respiratory chain, so more ATP will be made by using its $H:^-$ as NAD^+ is regenerated.

Glycolysis Begins with ATP Consumption But Then Generates More   Figure 27.6 outlines the steps to pyruvate (or lactate) that can begin with either glucose or glycogen. The steps that lead to fructose 1,6-diphosphate are actually up an energy hill, because they consume ATP. But this is like pushing a sled or bike up the short backside of a long hill, because the investment in energy is more than repaid by the long, downhill slide to lactate and more ATP. When glycolysis starts with glycogen instead of glucose, this initial investment in ATP is slightly smaller.

■ The numbers in this discussion refer to Figure 27.6.

1. Glucose is phosphorylated by ATP under catalysis by hexokinase to give glucose 6-phosphate.

2. Glucose 6-phosphate changes to its isomer, fructose 6-phosphate. The enzyme is phosphoglucose isomerase. This may seem to be a major structural change, but it involves little more than some shifts of bonds and hydrogens, as the arrows in the following sequence show:

■ These equilibria shift constantly to the right as long as later reactions continuously remove products as they form.

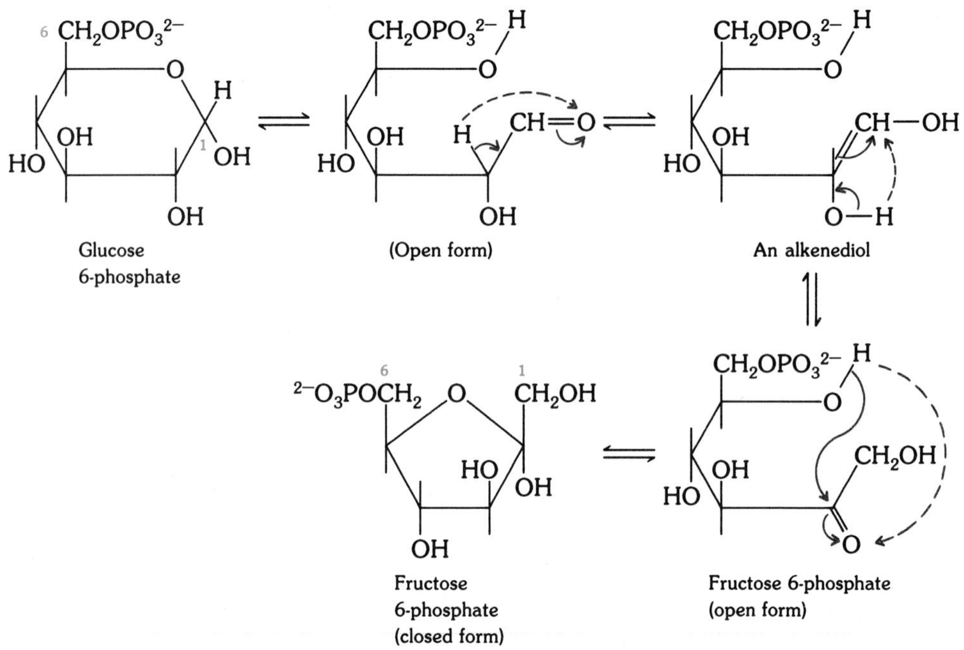

Glucose
6-phosphate

(Open form)

An alkenediol

Fructose
6-phosphate
(closed form)

Fructose 6-phosphate
(open form)

3. ATP phosphorylates fructose 6-phosphate to make fructose 1,6-diphosphate. The enzyme is phosphofructokinase. This step is essentially irreversible, and it ends the energy-using phase of glycolysis.

4. Fructose 1,6-diphosphate breaks apart into two triose monophosphates. The reaction is catalyzed by aldolase. We can visualize this reaction in terms of a few simple and reasonable shifts of electrons and protons.

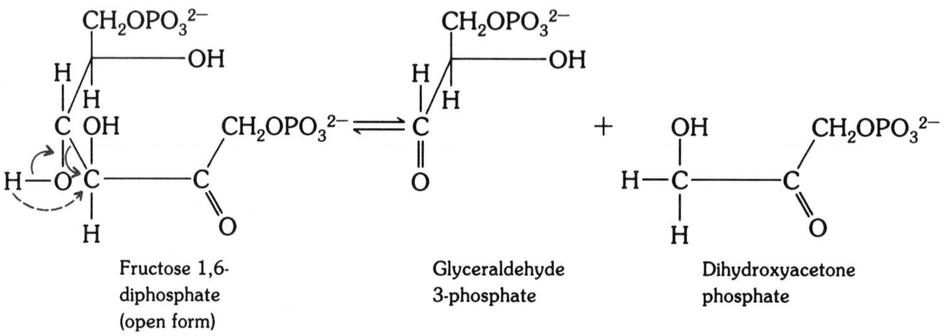

Fructose 1,6-
diphosphate
(open form)

Glyceraldehyde
3-phosphate

Dihydroxyacetone
phosphate

5. Dihydroxyacetone phosphate, in the presence of triose phosphate isomerase, changes to its isomer, glyceraldehyde 3-phosphate.

■ The continuous removal of glyceraldehyde 3-phosphate by its subsequent reaction shifts the dihydroxyacetone phosphate equilibrium to the right.

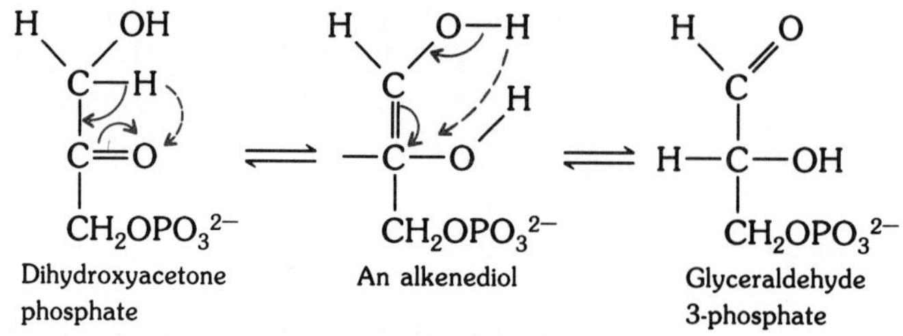

Dihydroxyacetone
phosphate

An alkenediol

Glyceraldehyde
3-phosphate

This change ensures that all the chemical energy in glucose will be obtained, because the main path of glycolysis continues with glyceraldehyde 3-phosphate. All dihydroxyacetone shuttles through glyceraldehyde 3-phosphate.

Figure 27.6
Glycolysis.

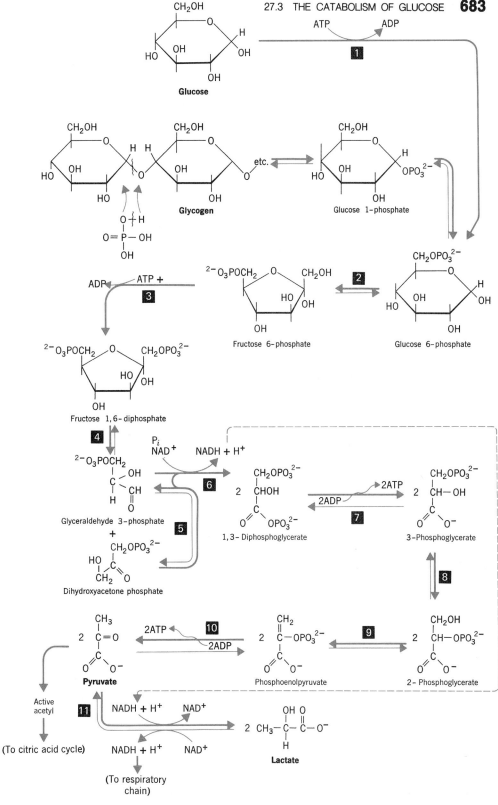

6. Glyceraldehyde 3-phosphate is simultaneously oxidized and phosphorylated. The enzyme has NAD^+ as a cofactor, and an SH group on the enzyme participates. Inorganic phosphate is the source of the new phosphate group. We can visualize how it happens as follows.

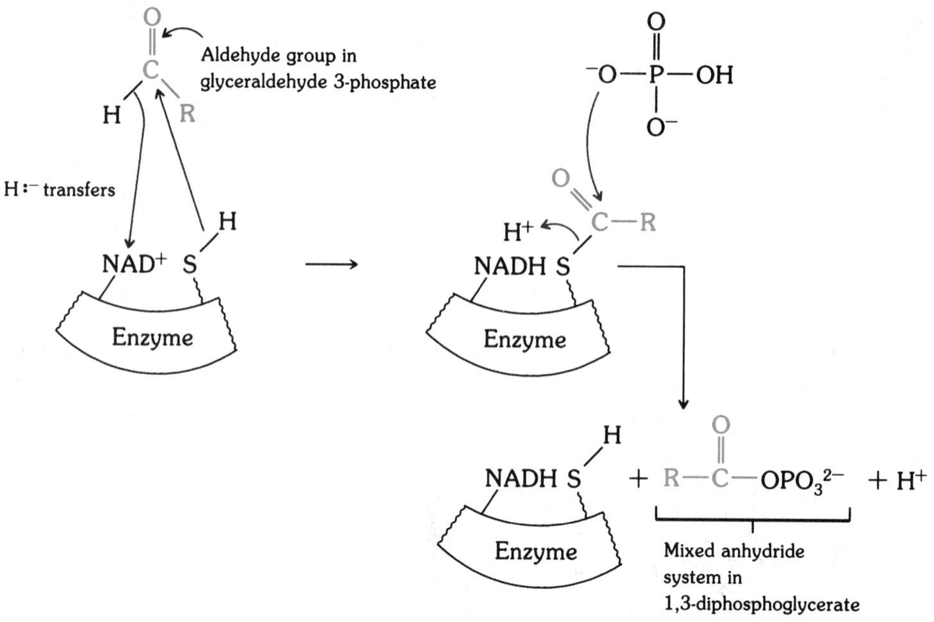

7. 1,3-Diphosphoglycerate has a higher phosphate group transfer potential than ATP. With the help of phosphoglycerate kinase, it transfers a phosphate to ADP, so this gives us back the original investment of ATP. (Remember that each glucose molecule with six carbons is processed through *two* three-carbon molecules, so *two* ATPs are made here for each original single glucose molecule.)

8. The phosphate group in 3-phosphoglycerate shifts to the 2-position, catalyzed by phosphoglyceromutase.

9. The dehydration of 2-phosphoglycerate to phosphoenolpyruvate is catalyzed by enolase. This step has been compared to cocking a huge bioenergetic gun. A simple, low-energy reaction, dehydration, converts a low-energy phosphate into the highest-energy phosphate in all of metabolism, the phosphate ester of the enol form of pyruvate, phosphoenolpyruvate.[1]

10. More ATP is made as the phosphate group in phosphoenolpyruvate transfers to ADP. The enzyme is pyruvate kinase. The enol form of pyruvate that is stranded promptly and irreversibly rearranges to the keto form of the pyruvate ion. The instability of enols (see footnote 1) is the driving force for this entire step.

11. If the mitochondrion is running aerobically when pyruvate is made, the pyruvate ion changes to acetyl coenzyme A, from which an acetyl group can enter the citric acid cycle (or be used in another way).

Anaerobic Glycolysis Provides a Way To Restore an Enzyme Vital to Continued Glycolysis in the Absence of Oxygen   The enzyme at step 6 now has its coenzyme, NAD^+, in its reduced form as NADH. As long as the $H:^-$ unit is on NADH, this enzyme is

---

[1] When a carbon atom of an alkene group holds an OH group, the compound is called an *enol* ("ene" + "-ol"). Enols are unstable alcohols that spontaneously rearrange into carbonyl compounds:

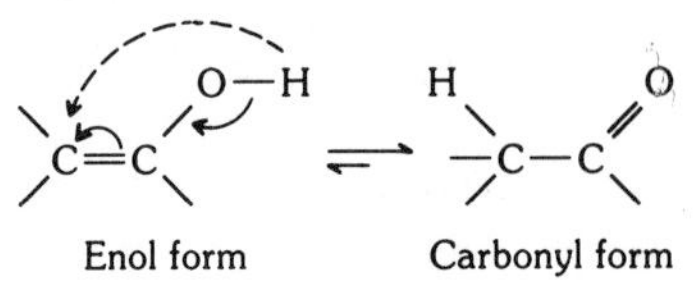

Enol form   Carbonyl form

No reaction in the body is truly complete until its enzyme is fully restored.

plugged and glycolysis is blocked at step 6. When the cell has sufficient oxygen, NADH simply gives its hydride unit to the respiratory chain, and glycolysis can run again. But when the cell is lacking oxygen, perhaps because of excessive work, glycolysis would shut down quickly without an alternative mechanism for changing NADH back to NAD^+. This is where pyruvate changes to lactate.

When oxygen isn't available, the $H\!:^-$ in NADH is unloaded into the keto group in pyruvate, which thereby changes to the alcohol group in lactate. This is why lactate is the end product of anaerobic glycolysis. Lactate serves to store $H\!:^-$ made at step 6 until the cell once again becomes aerobic.

The importance of anaerobic glycolysis is that the cell can continue to make some ATP even when insufficient oxygen is available to run the respiratory chain. Of course, there are limits. The longer the cell operates anaerobically and the more that lactate accumulates, the more the cell runs an increasing **oxygen debt.** Eventually the system has to slow down to let respiration bring back oxygen to metabolize lactate.

Excessive Exercise Causes Lactic Acid Acidosis By describing the production of lactate rather than lactic acid, we have obscured the generation of acid during glycolysis. Lactic acid, however, is promptly neutralized by the buffer so that the lactate ion is the product. Of course, extensive physical exercise that forces tissue to operate anaerobically can overtax the buffer. A form of metabolic acidosis called *lactic acid acidosis* is the result. Hyperventilation is initiated to blow out carbon dioxide and thus help to remove acid.

The Pentose Phosphate Pathway Makes NADPH The biosyntheses of some substances in the body require a reducing agent. Fatty acids, for example, are almost entirely alkane-like, and alkanes are the most reduced types of organic compounds. The reducing agent used in the biosynthesis of fatty acids is NADPH, the reduced form of $NADP^+$.

$NADP^+$ is a phosphate derivative of NAD^+.

The body's principal route to NADPH is the **pentose phosphate pathway** of glucose catabolism. This complicated series of reactions (which we'll not study in detail) is very active in adipose tissue, where fatty acid synthesis occurs. Skeletal muscles have very little activity in this pathway.

The pentose phosphate pathway also goes by the names *hexose monophosphate shunt* and *phosphogluconate pathway.*

The oxidative reactions in the pentose phosphate pathway convert a hexose phosphate into a pentose phosphate, hence, the name of the series. There are two broad sequences, one oxidative and the other nonoxidative. The overall equation for the oxidative sequence is

Glucose 6-phosphate $+ 2NADP^+ + H_2O \longrightarrow$
$$\text{ribose 5-phosphate} + 2NADPH + 2H^+ + CO_2$$

The ribose 5-phosphate can now be used to make the pentose systems in the nucleic acids, if they are needed. If not, ribose 5-phosphate undergoes a series of isomerizations and group transfers that make up the nonoxidative phase of the pentose phosphate pathway. These reactions have the net effect of converting three pentose units into two hexose units (glucose) and one triose unit (glyceraldehyde).

The hexoses can be catabolized by glycolysis, or they can be recycled to the oxidative series of the pentose phosphate pathway. Glyceraldehyde, as we'll soon see, can be converted to glucose and recycled as well. Thus glycolysis, the pentose phosphate reactions, and the resynthesis of glucose all interconnect, and specific bodily needs of the moment determine which pathway is operated.

Overall, with pentose recycled, the balanced equation for the complete oxidation of one glucose molecule via the pentose phosphate pathway is as follows.

6 Glucose 6-phosphate $+ 12NADP^+ \xrightarrow{\text{pentose phosphate pathway}}$
$$\text{5 glucose 6-phosphate} + 6CO_2 + 12NADPH + 12H^+ + P_i$$

27.4 GLUCONEOGENESIS

Some of the steps in gluconeogenesis are the reverse of steps in glycolysis.

The overall scheme of gluconeogenesis, by which glucose is made from smaller molecules, is given in Figure 27.7. Excess lactate can be used as a starting material, as we have already mentioned. Just as important, several amino acids can be degraded to molecules that can be used to make glucose, too.

You'll recall that the brain normally uses circulating glucose for energy. Therefore the ability of the body to manufacture glucose from noncarbohydrate sources such as amino acids — even those from the body itself — is an important backup during times when glucose either isn't in the diet (starvation) or cannot be effectively used (untreated diabetes).

Gluconeogenesis Is Not the Exact Reverse of Glycolysis   There are three steps in glycolysis that cannot be directly reversed: steps 1, 3, and 10 of Figure 27.6. However, the liver and the kidneys have special enzymes that create bypasses.

In the bypass that gets back and around step 10 of glycolysis, the synthesis of phosphoenolpyruvate from pyruvate, carbon dioxide is used as a reactant; ATP energy is used to drive the steeply uphill reaction; and pyruvate carboxylase is the enzyme. Pyruvate is changed to oxaloacetate:

■ The enzyme for this step requires the vitamin biotin.

$$CH_3-\overset{\overset{\text{O}}{\|}}{C}-CO_2^- + CO_2 + ATP + H_2O \longrightarrow$$

Pyruvate

$$^-O_2C-CH_2-\overset{\overset{\text{O}}{\|}}{C}-CO_2^- + ADP + P_i + 2H^+$$

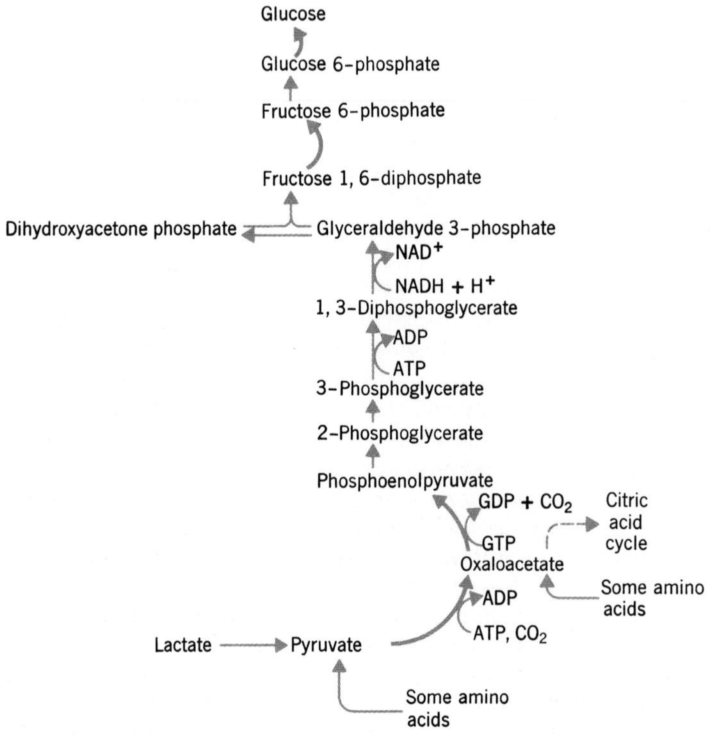

Oxaloacetate

Figure 27.7
Gluconeogenesis. The straight arrows signify steps that are the reverse of corresponding steps in glycolysis. The heavy, curved arrows denote steps that are unique to gluconeogenesis.

Oxaloacetate then reacts with another triphosphate, guanosine triphosphate (GTP), as carbon dioxide splits out and bonds rearrange:

Oxaloacetate   GTP

Phosphoenol-
pyruvate

Because each glucose to be made requires two pyruvates, and because each pyruvate uses two high-energy phosphates in gluconeogenesis, this bypass costs the equivalent of four ATPs (2ATP + 2GTP) per glucose molecule to be made.

At the reversal of step 7 (Figure 27.6), two more ATPs are used per molecule of glucose made. Thus a total of six ATPs is needed to make one glucose molecule by gluconeogenesis that starts from pyruvate. This may be compared with two ATPs that are produced by anaerobic glycolysis (which begins with glucose).

The bypasses to the reverses of steps 3 and 1 of glycolysis require only specific enzymes that catalyze the hydrolysis of phosphate ester groups, not high-energy boosters. Such enzymes are integral parts of the enzyme team for gluconeogenesis.

The other steps in gluconeogenesis are run as reverse shifts in equilibria that occur in the opposite direction in glycolysis.

SUMMARY

Glycogen metabolism The regulation of glycogenesis and glycogenolysis is a part of the machinery for glucose tolerance in the body. Hyperglycemia stimulates the secretion of insulin and somatostatin, and insulin helps cells of adipose tissue to take glucose from the blood. Somatostatin helps to suppress the release of glucagon (which otherwise stimulates glycogenolysis and leads to an increase in the blood sugar level).

When glucose is abundant, the body either replenishes its glycogen reserves or makes fat. In muscular work, epinephrine stimulates a cascade of enzyme activations that begins with the activation of adenylate cyclase and ends with the release of many glucose molecules from glycogen.

When glucose is in short supply, the body makes its own by gluconeogenesis from noncarbohydrate molecules, including several amino acids. In diabetes, some cells that are starved for glucose make their own, also. Such cells are unable to obtain glucose from circulation, so the blood sugar level is hyperglycemic to a glucosuric level. The glucose tolerance test is used to see how well the body handles an overload of glucose. In the management of diabetes, the maintenance of a reasonably steady blood sugar level in the normal range is vital. The measurement of the glycohemoglobin in circulation serves to monitor how well the normal range is kept over a long period of time.

Following strenuous exercise, when lactate is plentiful, the liver makes glucose from lactate. The many pathways that involve glycogen and glucose form a cycle of events called the Cori cycle.

Glycolysis Under anaerobic conditions, glucose can be catabolized to lactate ion. (Galactose and fructose enter this pathway, too.) When lactate is used to store $H:^-$, one of the enzymes in glycolysis can be regenerated in the absence of oxygen, and glycolysis can be run to make some ATP without the involvement of the respiratory chain. Then, when the cell is aerobic again, the $H:^-$ that this enzyme must shed to work again is given directly into the respiratory chain, and pyruvate instead of lactate becomes the end product of glycolysis.

Pentose phosphate pathway The body's need for NADPH to make fatty acids is met by catabolizing glucose through the pentose phosphate pathway.

Gluconeogenesis Most of the steps in gluconeogenesis are simply the reverse of steps in glycolysis, but there are a few that require rather elaborate bypasses. Special teams of enzymes and supplies of high-energy phosphate are used for these. Many amino acids can be used to make glucose by gluconeogenesis.

REVIEW EXERCISES

The answers to these Review Exercises are in the *Study Guide* that accompanies this book.

Blood Sugar

27.1 What are the end products of the complete digestion of the carbohydrates in the diet?

27.2 Why can we treat the catabolism of carbohydrates as almost entirely that of glucose?

27.3 What is meant by *blood sugar level*? By *normal fasting level*?

27.4 What is the range of concentrations in mg/dL for the normal fasting level of whole blood?

27.5 What characterizes the following conditions?
(a) glucosuria   (b) hypoglycemia
(c) hyperglycemia   (d) glycogenolysis
(e) gluconeogenesis   (f) glycogenesis

27.6 Explain how severe hypoglycemia can lead to disorders of the central nervous system.

Hormones and the Blood Sugar Level

27.7 When epinephrine is secreted, what soon happens to the blood sugar level?

27.8 At which one tissue is epinephrine the most effective?

27.9 What does epinephrine directly activate at its target cell?

27.10 Arrange the following in the correct order in which they work in epinephrine-initiated glycogenolysis.

phosphorylase kinase   phosphorylase   cyclic-AMP
1   **2**   **3**

adenylate cyclase   protein kinase
4   **5**

27.11 One epinephrine molecule triggers the ultimate formation of how many glucose units, 1, 10^1, 10^2, or 10^3?

27.12 What might be the result if phosphorylase and glycogen synthetase were both activated at the same time?

27.13 What switches glycogen synthetase off when glycogenolysis is activated?

27.14 What is the end product of glycogenolysis, and what does phosphoglucomutase do to it?

27.15 Why can liver glycogen but not muscle glycogen be used to resupply blood sugar?

27.16 What is glucagon, what does it do, and what is its chief target tissue?

27.17 Which is probably better at increasing the blood sugar level, glucagon or epinephrine? Explain.

27.18 How does human growth hormone manage to promote the supply of the energy needed for growth?

27.19 What is insulin, where is it released, and what is its chief target tissue?

27.20 What triggers the release of insulin into circulation?

27.21 If brain cells are not insulin-dependent cells, how can too much insulin cause insulin shock?

27.22 What is somatostatin, where is it released, and what kind of effect does it have on the pancreas?

Glucose Tolerance and the Cori Cycle

27.23 What is meant by *glucose tolerance*?

27.24 For what chief purpose is a glucose tolerance test performed, and how is it carried out?

27.25 Describe what happens when each of the following persons takes a glucose tolerance test.
(a) a nondiabetic individual
(b) a diabetic individual

27.26 Describe a circumstance in which hyperglycemia might arise in a nondiabetic individual.

27.27 In general terms, what happens to excess lactate produced in muscles during exercise?

27.28 Suppose that a sample of glucose is made using some atoms of carbon-13 in place of the common isotope, carbon-12. Suppose further that this is fed to a healthy, adult volunteer and that all of it is taken up by the muscles.
(a) Will some of the original molecules be able to go back out into circulation? Explain.
(b) Can we expect any carbon-13 compounds to end up in the liver? Explain.
(c) Can we ever expect to see carbon-13-labeled glucose molecules in circulation again? Explain.

Catabolism of Glucose

27.29 Fill in the missing substances and balance the following incomplete equation:

$$C_6H_{12}O_6 + 2ADP + \text{_____} \longrightarrow$$
Glucose

$$2C_3H_5O_3^- + 2H^+ + \text{_____}$$
Lactate

27.30 What particular significance does glycolysis have when a tissue is running an oxygen debt?

27.31 Why is the rearrangement of dihydroxyacetone phosphate into glyceraldehyde 3-phosphate important?

27.32 What happens to pyruvate (a) under aerobic conditions and (b) under anaerobic conditions?

27.33 What happens to lactate when an oxygen debt is repaid?

27.34 What is the maximum number of ATPs that can be made by the complete catabolism of (a) one molecule of glucose and (b) one glucose residue in glycogen?

27.35 The pentose phosphate pathway uses $NADP^+$, not NAD^+. What forms from $NADP^+$, and how does the body use it (in general terms)?

Gluconeogenesis

27.36 In a period of prolonged fasting or starvation, what does the system do to try to maintain its blood sugar level?

27.37 Amino acids are not excreted, and they are not stored in the same way that glucose residues are stored in a polysaccharide. What probably happens to the excess amino acids in a high-protein diet of an individual who does not exercise much?

27.38 The amino groups of amino acids can be replaced by keto groups. Which amino acids could give the following keto acids that participate in carbohydrate metabolism?
(a) pyruvic acid   (b) oxaloacetic acid

27.39 Referring to data in the previous chapter: (a) How much ATP can be made from the chemical energy in one pyruvate? (b) The conversion of one lactate to one pyruvate transfers one $H:^-$ to NAD^+. How many ATP molecules can be made just from the operation of this step? (c) If all the possible ATP that can be obtained from the complete catabolism of lactate were made available for gluconeogenesis, how many molecules of glucose could be made? (Assume that ATP can substitute for GTP.)

Glycogen Storage Diseases (Special Topic 27.1)

27.40 For each of the following diseases, name the defective (or missing) enzyme, and state the biochemical and physiological consequences.

(a) Von Gierke's disease
(b) Cori's disease
(c) McArdle's disease
(d) Andersen's disease

Diabetes Mellitus (Special Topic 27.2)

27.41 What is the biochemical distinction between type I and type II diabetes?

27.42 Juvenile-onset diabetes is usually which type?

27.43 Adult-onset diabetes is usually which type?

27.44 Briefly state the six stages in the onset of type I diabetes.

27.45 Viruses that cause diabetes attack which target cells?

27.46 There is some evidence that diabetes is an autoimmune disease. What does this mean, as applied to diabetes?

27.47 A sustained, elevated blood glucose level causes damage to which specific tissue, damage that might be responsible for other complications?

27.48 How is glucose involved in the formation of a Schiff base? What other kinds of compounds react with glucose in this way?

27.49 When the glucose level in blood drops, what happens to the level of glucosylated hemoglobin? Why?

27.50 What happens to the Schiff bases involving glucose if given enough time? Why is this serious?

27.51 Describe a theory that explains how the hydrogenation of glucose may contribute to blindness.

CHAPTER TWENTY-EIGHT

Metabolism of Lipids

By the end of the marathon, these racers have long since exhausted their reserves of carbohydrates and are now drawing on stored lipids for energy. How the body uses fatty acids to make ATP is studied in this chapter.

28.1 ABSORPTION AND DISTRIBUTION OF LIPIDS

Several lipoprotein complexes in the blood transport triacylglycerols, fatty acids, cholesterol, and other lipids from tissue to tissue.

The complete digestion of triacylglycerols, as we learned in Chapter 25, produces glycerol and a mixture of long-chain fatty acids. These, together with some monoacylglycerols (from incomplete digestion), leave the digestive tract, and as they migrate across the intestinal barrier they are extensively reconstituted into triacylglycerols. What is delivered to circulation consists mostly of these triacylglycerols.

Lipids Are Carried in Lipoprotein Complexes   Lipids are insoluble in water, and they are carried in blood by proteins in packages called **lipoprotein complexes.** Because defects in this system can cause heart disease, we'll look more closely at these species.

Lipoproteins are classified according to their densities, and each class has its own functions. They range in densities from 0.93 g/cm³ to 1.21 g/cm³, and the lipoproteins with the lowest density are called **chylomicrons.** They are only 2% protein or less and are put together in the liver. Figure 28.1 shows what happens to them. The numbers that follow refer to the numbers in this figure. Some of the carrier units in Figure 28.1 have letters, like E, C, B-48, and B-100. They represent polypeptides, and they participate not only as lipid carriers

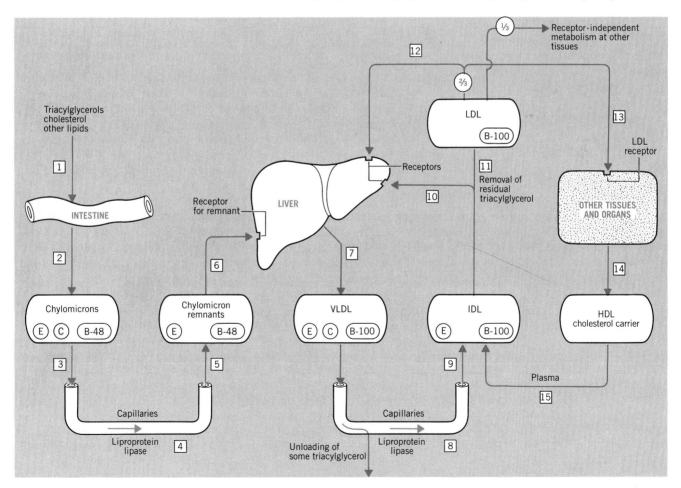

Figure 28.1
The transport of cholesterol and triacylglycerols by lipoprotein complexes. (Adapted by permission from J. L. Goldstein, T. Kita, and M. S. Brown, *New England Journal of Medicine,* August 4, 1983, page 289.)

but as the species that receptor proteins of other tissues, like the liver, can recognize. B-100, for example, is the polypeptide recognized by one key receptor at the liver.

Chylomicrons Carry Lipids to the Liver Where lipids from the processes of digestion, [1], enter circulation, [2], chylomicrons form around them: triacylglycerols, cholesterol, and free fatty acids. They transport these lipids, [3], and while they are in capillaries of adipose tissue, they unload some of the triacylglycerols, [4]. (A lipoprotein lipase catalyzes the hydrolysis of triacylglycerols. The resulting fatty acids and glycerol are absorbed by adipose tissue and reconstituted as triacylglycerols that are then stored until needed.)

This process leaves chylomicron remnants, [5], which are now richer in cholesterol, and the liver has special receptor proteins that recognize and help the liver absorb these remnants, [6].

- Remember that cholesterol is a nonsaponifiable lipid so it can't be hydrolyzed by digestion.

Liver Cholesterol Is Assigned to Various Needs The liver sees cholesterol from two sources, the diet and its own cholesterol-making cells. It can excrete cholesterol by way of the bile, which goes from the gall bladder into the intestinal tract. It can make bile salts from cholesterol, and these are needed to help digest lipids and absorb fat-soluble vitamins. Finally, the liver can send cholesterol out into circulation to be used in tissue for making cell membranes and steroid hormones.

- Cholesterol ($d = 1.05$ g/cm³) is denser than triacylglycerols (density of about 0.9 g/cm³).

The Liver Packages Cholesterol into VLDL Complexes The cholesterol to be sent into circulation, both as free cholesterol and as fatty acid esters of cholesterol, is organized into another lipoprotein complex designated very low density lipoprotein, or VLDL, for short, [7]. This has a slightly higher density than the chylomicrons.

The liver, as we said, can both receive and make cholesterol, and it also receives and makes triacylglycerols, as we'll study later in this chapter. Thus the VLDL complexes that are now put together by the liver carry, besides a small amount of protein, cholesterol, cholesterol esters, and triacylglycerols, regardless of their origins, to adipose tissue and muscles, [8].

These tissues remove most of the triacylglycerols from the VLDL units (again via hydrolysis and reconstitution), which leaves a lipoprotein complex, [9], of slightly higher density. It is mostly cholesterol in one form or another, and the complex is now designated as an intermediate-density lipoprotein complex, or IDL for short.

- J. L. Goldstein and M. S. Brown shared the 1985 Nobel prize in medicine for their work on LDL receptor proteins and how they help to control blood cholesterol levels.

Liver Receptor Proteins Accept Back about Half of the IDL The liver has special receptor proteins that recognize the B-100 protein in IDL, which helps take IDL packages back into the liver, [10]. The IDL that is not reabsorbed here experiences further losses of triacylglycerol. This causes a further increase in its density, and now the particles are classified as low-density lipoproteins, or LDL, [11].

A good portion of the LDL is captured for the liver by receptor proteins. In fact, transporting cholesterol back to the liver, [12], is one function of LDL. However, about a third of the LDL reaches peripheral tissues, [13], including the adrenal glands. Thus LDL carries cholesterol wherever cholesterol is needed to make cell membranes or to make steroid hormones. Some of these tissues carry special receptor proteins, but others can obtain cholesterol from LDL by other means.

HDL Units Carry Unused Cholesterol Back to the Liver Any leftover cholesterol must now be removed from the extrahepatic tissues (tissues other than the liver), and this job is handled by the high-density lipoprotein complexes, or HDL, [14], which the liver makes for this purpose. The chief function of the HDL is to carry cholesterol back to the liver, [15].

- The genetic condition is described as *homozygous* when mutant genes for it come from both parents.

The Absence of Liver Receptor Proteins Causes Atherosclerosis The receptor proteins for the IDL and LDL have a crucial function. If they are reduced in number or are absent, the liver has little ability to remove excess cholesterol and export it via the bile. The level of cholesterol in the blood, therefore, becomes too high, and this is a cause of atherosclerosis. Atherosclerosis is a disease in which several substances, including collagen, elastic fibers, triacylglycerols, but chiefly cholesterol and its esters, form plaques in the arterial wall. It is the chief cause of heart attacks.

Some people have a genetic defect that bears specifically on the livers receptors. Two genes are involved. Those who carry two mutant genes have *familial hypercholesterolemia*, a genetically caused high level of cholesterol in the blood. Even on a zero-cholesterol diet, the victims have very high cholesterol levels. Their cholesterol slowly comes out of the blood at valves and other sites and reduces the dimensions of the blood capillaries, which restricts blood flowage. Atherosclerosis has set in.

The heart must now work harder, and eventually arteries and capillaries in the heart itself are no longer able to bring oxygen to heart tissue. The victims generally have their first heart attacks as children and are dead by their early twenties. People with one defective gene and one normal gene for the LDL receptor proteins generally have blood cholesterol levels that are two or three times higher than normal. Although they number only about 0.5% of all adults, they have 5% of all heart attacks among those younger than 60.

High blood cholesterol levels also occur in many other people, even those with normal genes for the receptor proteins, and the causes have not been fully unraveled. High-cholesterol foods appear to contribute, and there is some evidence that as the liver receives more and more cholesterol from the diet, it loses more and more of the receptor proteins. This forces more and more cholesterol to linger in circulation. Smoking, obesity, and lack of exercise contribute to the cholesterol problem also. Later in the chapter we'll study how cholesterol is made, how this synthesis normally is controlled, and how certain medications offer significant help.

- About 1 person in 500 is heterozygous for familial hypercholesterolemia (received the mutant gene from just one parent).

- The desirable blood cholesterol level is below 200 mg/dL. Someone with a level between 200 and 240 is at some risk, and anyone with a level above 240 has too high a cholesterol level, according to the U.S. Surgeon General.

28.2 STORAGE AND MOBILIZATION OF LIPIDS

Triacylglycerols are the most weight-efficient means of storing chemical energy in the body.

The large number of C—H bonds per molecule make triacylglycerols particularly rich in chemical energy. These are the bonds that, in much modified molecules, finally send $H:^-$ units into the respiratory chain. We make about 120 ATP molecules from a single fatty acid molecule but only 38 from one of glucose. The mostly hydrocarbon-like nature of triacylglycerols also makes them good storage depots for chemical energy.

The High-energy Density of Stored Triacylglyerol Makes It a Choice Form for Storing Energy The energy stored per gram of tissue or solution is called the *energy density* of the material. Isotonic glucose solution, for example, carries only about 0.2 kcal per gram. When the glucose is changed into glycogen, however, *and no longer is in solution*, there is little associated water. Now we can get more energy into storage in 1 g; the energy density of wet glycogen is about 1.7 kcal/g. Triacylglycerol, in sharp contrast, has an energy density of about 7.7 kcal/g.

A 70-kg adult male has about 12 kg of triacylglycerol in storage. If he had to exist on no food, just water and a vitamin–mineral supplement, and if he needed 2500 kcal/day, this fat would supply his caloric needs for 43 days. Of course, during this time the body proteins would also be wasting away, and metabolic acidosis would be a problem of growing urgency.

- Because lipids are water-insoluble, they attract the least amount of associated water in storage.

- These data are for information; they're certainly not recommendations!

Adipose Tissue Is the Principal Lipid Storage Depot The chief depot for the storage of fatty acids is adipose tissue, a very metabolically active tissue. There are two kinds, brown and white. Both types are associated with internal organs, where they cushion the organs against mechanical bumps and shocks and insulate them from swings in temperature. For a discussion of how brown adipose tissue uses the respiratory chain to generate heat, not ATP, see Special Topic 28.1. The discussion that continues concerns the metabolic activities of white adipose tissue. White adipose tissue stores energy as triacylglycerols, chiefly on behalf of the energy budgets of other tissues.

SPECIAL TOPIC 28.1   **BROWN FAT AND THERMOGENESIS**

Both kinds of adipose tissue, white and brown, store triacylglycerols, but white adipose tissue does not metabolize them except to break them down to free fatty acids and glycerol. The fatty acids from white adipose tissue are then exported to other tissues for catabolism.

Respiratory Chain Oxidation and ATP Synthesis Are Uncoupled in Brown Adipose Tissue   The triacylglycerols in brown adipose tissue are catabolized within this tissue for little other use than to generate heat. This is possible because cells of brown adipose tissue can switch off the capability of the inner mitochondrial membranes to accept and hold a proton gradient. Recall that the chemiosmotic process in mitochondria normally uses the respiratory chain to establish a proton gradient across the inner mitochondrial membrane, and that as protons flow back through selected channels, they trigger the synthesis of ATP from ADP and P_i.

When the respiratory chain runs but cannot set up the proton gradient, the chemical energy released by the chain emerges only as heat. Such generation of heat is called *thermogenesis.* Two stimuli, both mediated by the neurotransmitter norepinephrine, trigger this heat-generating activity, exposure to cold and the ingestion of food.

The advantage to the body of thermogenesis induced by a cold outside temperature is that the body can oxidize its own fat to help keep itself warm.

The advantage of food-induced thermogenesis is that the individual is protected from getting fat by too much eating in relation to exercise. Thermogenesis in brown adipose tissue removes fat by catabolism, rather than by exercise, as new calories (in the food) are imported.

A Body in Dietary Balance Uses Fatty Acids as Well as Glucose for Energy

Some tissues, like heart muscle and the renal cortex, use breakdown products of fatty acids in preference of glucose for energy. Skeletal muscles can use both fatty acids and short molecules made from them for energy. In fact, most of the energy needs of resting muscle tissue are met by intermediates of fatty acid catabolism, not from glucose. Given enough time for adjustment, even brain cells can obtain some energy from fatty acid breakdown products.

Lipid material, consequently, comes and goes from adipose tissue, and the balance between its receiving or releasing lipids is struck by the energy requirements elsewhere. Sometimes either glucose is in very low supply (as in starvation) or what is available can't be used (as in diabetes), and the body now must turn to its fatty acids for energy.

Figure 28.2 outlines the many steps involved in tapping the lipid reserves for their energy. Triacylglycerol molecules in adipose tissue are first hydrolyzed to free fatty acids and glycerol. The lipase needed for this is activated by a process involving cyclic AMP and such hormones as epinephrine and glucagon. The fatty acids are carried as lipoprotein complexes to the liver, the chief site for their catabolism.

Insulin suppresses the lipase that releases fatty acids from adipose tissue. Thus when insulin is in circulation, and it's there only because there is a good supply of blood glucose, the fatty acids are less needed for energy.

The glycerol that is produced when the fatty acids are released is changed to dihydroxyacetone phosphate, and it enters the pathway of glycolysis.

28.3   THE CATABOLISM OF FATTY ACIDS

Acetyl groups are produced by the beta oxidation of fatty acids and are fed into the citric acid cycle and respiratory chain.

■ Although the whole series isn't exactly a cycle of a true variety, like the citric acid cycle, it's still referred to as the fatty acid *cycle.*

The degradation of fatty acids takes place inside mitochondria by a repeating series of steps known as the **fatty acid cycle,** or as the **beta-oxidation pathway.** Figure 28.3, page 696, outlines its chief steps.

A Fatty Acid Is First Joined to Coenzyme A

To enter the fatty acid cycle, a fatty acid has to be joined to coenzyme A. It costs one ATP to do this, but now the fatty acyl unit is activated. The ATP itself breaks down to AMP and PP_i. The subsequent hydrolysis of the diphosphate is the driving force for the overall change, but this means that the actual cost in high-energy phosphate is *two* high-energy phosphate bonds.

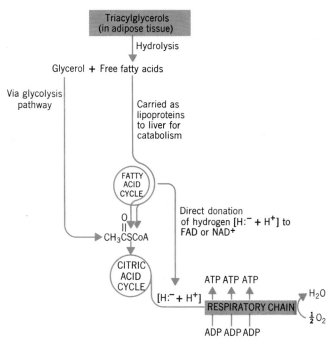

Figure 28.2
Pathways for the mobilization of energy reserves in the triacylglycerols of adipose tissue.

By being joined to coenzyme A, the fatty acyl unit is activated for catabolism. This is done on the outside of a mitochondrion, and then the fatty acyl coenzyme A is transported inside for oxidation.

Fatty Acyl CoA Is Catabolized by Two Carbons for Each Turn of the Cycle   The repeating sequence of the fatty acid cycle consists of four steps. Each turn of the cycle produces one molecule of $FADH_2$, one of NADH, and one of acetyl coenzyme A.

The now shortened fatty acyl unit is carried again through the four steps, and the process is repeated until no more two-carbon acetyl units can be made. The $FADH_2$ and the NADH fuel the respiratory chain. The acetyl groups pass into the citric acid cycle, or they enter the general pool of acetyl coenzyme A that the body draws from to make other substances (e.g., cholesterol). Let's now look at the four steps in greater detail. The numbers that follow refer to Figure 28.3.

■ Franz Knoop directed much of the research on the fatty acid cycle, so this pathway is sometimes called *Knoop oxidation*.

1. The first step is dehydrogenation. FAD accepts ($H:^- + H^+$) from the α- and the β-carbons of the fatty acyl unit.

$$CH_3(CH_2)_{12}\overset{\beta}{C}H_2 - \overset{\alpha}{C}H_2 - \overset{O}{\overset{\|}{C}} - SCoA + FAD \xrightarrow{\boxed{1}}$$

Palmityl coenzyme A

$$CH_3(CH_2)_{12}CH = CH - \overset{O}{\overset{\|}{C}} - SCoA + FADH_2 \longrightarrow (H:^- + H^+) \dashv$$

An α,β-unsaturated acyl derivative of coenzyme A

FAD

To respiratory chain

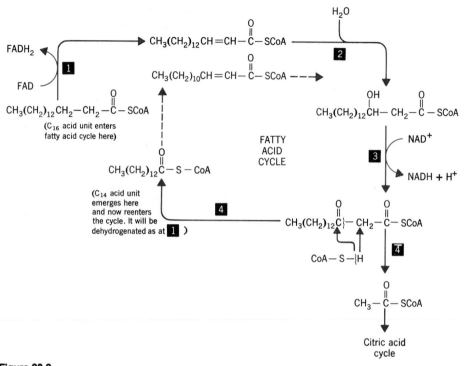

Figure 28.3
The fatty acid cycle (β-oxidation pathway). The numbers refer to the numbered steps discussed in the text.

2. The second step is hydration. Water adds to the alkene double bond and a secondary alcohol group forms.

$$CH_3(CH_2)_{12}CH{=}CH{-}\overset{\overset{\displaystyle O}{\|}}{C}{-}SCoA + H_2O \xrightarrow{\boxed{2}} CH_3(CH_2)_{12}\overset{\overset{\displaystyle OH}{|}}{C}H{-}CH_2{-}\overset{\overset{\displaystyle O}{\|}}{C}{-}SCoA$$

β-Hydroxyacyl derivative of coenzyme A

3. The third step is another dehydrogenation—a loss of ($H{:}^- + H^+$). This oxidizes the secondary alcohol to a keto group. Notice that these steps end in the oxidation of the β-position of the original fatty acyl group to a keto group. This is why the fatty acid cycle is sometimes called *beta oxidation*.

$$CH_3(CH_2)_{12}\overset{\overset{\displaystyle OH}{|}}{C}H{-}CH_2{-}\overset{\overset{\displaystyle O}{\|}}{C}{-}SCoA + NAD^+ \xrightarrow{\boxed{3}}$$

$$CH_3(CH_2)_{12}\overset{\overset{\displaystyle O}{\|}}{C}{-}CH_2{-}\overset{\overset{\displaystyle O}{\|}}{C}{-}SCoA + \underline{NADH + H^+}$$

β-Keto acyl coenzyme A

$\longrightarrow (H{:}^- + H^+)$

NAD^+

To respiratory chain

4. The fourth step breaks the bond between the α-carbon and the β-carbon. This bond has been weakened by the stepwise oxidation of the β-carbon, and now this bond breaks to release one unit of acetyl coenzyme A.

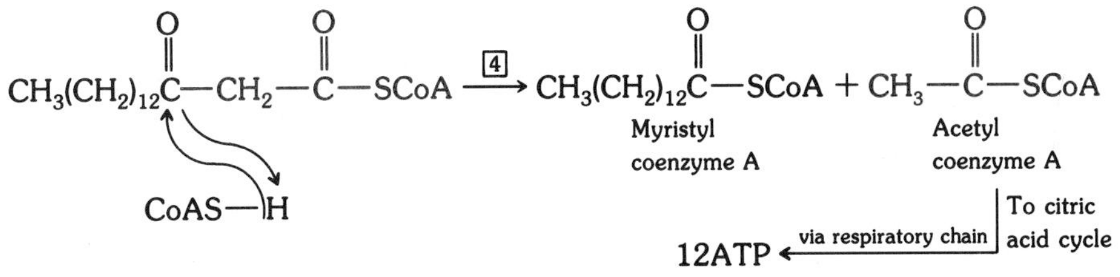

$$CH_3(CH_2)_{12}\overset{O}{\underset{}{C}}-CH_2-\overset{O}{\underset{}{C}}-SCoA \xrightarrow{\boxed{4}} CH_3(CH_2)_{12}\overset{O}{\underset{}{C}}-SCoA + CH_3-\overset{O}{\underset{}{C}}-SCoA$$

CoAS—H

Myristyl coenzyme A

Acetyl coenzyme A

To citric acid cycle

$12ATP \xleftarrow{\text{via respiratory chain}}$

The remaining acyl unit, the original shortened by two carbons, now goes through the cycle of steps again: dehydrogenation, hydration, dehydrogenation, and cleavage. After seven such cycles, one molecule of palmityl coenzyme A is broken into eight molecules of acetyl coenzyme A.

One Palmityl Unit Yields 129 ATP Molecules   Table 28.1 shows how the maximum yield of ATP from the oxidation of one unit of palmityl coenzyme A adds up to 131 ATPs. The net from palmitic acid is two ATP fewer, or 129 ATP, because the activation of the palmityl unit — joining it to coenzyme A — requires this initial investment, as we mentioned earlier.

28.4 BIOSYNTHESIS OF FATTY ACIDS

Acetyl CoA molecules that are not needed to make ATP can be made into fatty acids.

Acetyl CoA stands at a major metabolic crossroads. It can be made from any monosaccharide in the diet, from virtually all amino acids, and from fatty acids. Once made, it can be shunted into the citric acid cycle where its chemical energy can be used to make ATP; or its acetyl group can be made into other compounds that the body needs. In this section we'll see how acetyl CoA can be made into long-chain fatty acids by a series of steps called **lipigenesis.**

Lipigenesis Begins with the Activation of Acetyl CoA   Whenever acetyl CoA molecules are made within mitochondria but aren't needed for the citric acid cycle and respiratory chain, they are exported to the cytosol. The enzymes for lipigenesis are found there, not

TABLE 28.1   Maximum Yield of ATP from Palmityl CoA

Seven Turns of the Cycle Produce	ATP from Each Energy-Rich Intermediate	Total ATP Produced
7 FADH$_2$	2	14
7 NADH	3	21
8 CH$_3$$\overset{O}{\underset{}{C}}$—SCoA	12	96 131 ATP
Deduct two high-energy phosphate bonds for activating the acyl unit		−2
Net ATP yield per palmityl unit		129 ATP

Figure 28.4
The lipigenesis cycle. At the top, an acetyl group is activated and joined as a malonyl unit to an arm of the acyl carrier protein, ACP. Another acetyl group transfers from acetyl CoA to site E. In a second transfer, this acetyl group is then joined to the malonyl unit as CO_2 splits back out. This gives a β-ketoacyl system whose keto group is reduced to CH_2 by the next series of steps. One turn of the cycle adds a CH_2CH_2 unit to the growing acyl chain.

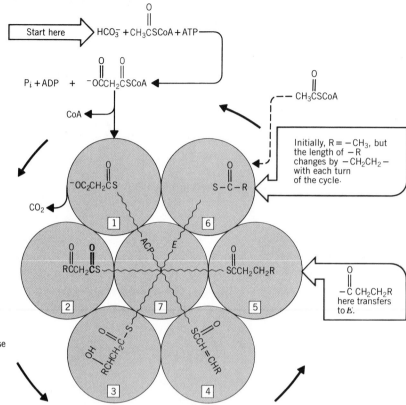

Enzymes

1. Malonyl transferase
2. 3-Ketoacyl-ACP synthase
3. 3-Ketoacyl-ACP reductase
4. 3-Hydroxyacyl-ACP dehydratase
5. Enoyl-ACP reductase
6. Acetyl transferase
7. Acyl carrier protein

within the mitochondria, which illustrates the general rule that the body segregates its sequences of catabolism from those of anabolism.

As might be expected, because lipigenesis is in the direction of climbing an energy hill, the cell has to invest some energy of ATP to make fatty acids from smaller molecules. The first payment occurs in the first step in which the bicarbonate ion reacts with acetyl CoA.

■ The enzyme for this step, acetyl CoA carboxylase, requires the vitamin biotin.

$$CH_3 - \overset{\overset{\displaystyle O}{\|}}{C} - SCoA + HCO_3^- + ATP \longrightarrow$$

Acetyl CoA

$$^-O - \overset{\overset{\displaystyle O}{\|}}{C} - CH_2 - \overset{\overset{\displaystyle O}{\|}}{C} - SCoA + 2H^+ + ADP + P_i$$

Malonyl CoA

This activates the acetyl system for lipigenesis.

The Growing Fatty Acyl Unit Is Moved from Enzyme to Enzyme by a Construction Boom Molecular Unit   The enzyme that now builds a long-chain fatty acid is actually a huge complex of seven enzymes called *fatty acid synthase*. See Figure 28.4. In the center of this complex is a molecular unit long enough to serve as a swinging arm carrier. It's called the *acyl carrier protein*, or ACP, and like the boom of a construction crane, this arm swings from site to site in the synthase. Thus the arm brings what it carries over first one enzyme and then another, and at each stop a reaction is catalyzed that contributes to chain lengthening. Let's see how it works.

The malonyl unit in malonyl CoA, which we just made, transfers to the swinging arm of ACP:

$$\underset{\text{Malonyl ACP}}{^-\text{OCCH}_2\text{C}-\text{S}-\text{CoA} + \text{ACP} \longrightarrow {^-\text{OCCH}_2\text{C}-\text{S}-\text{ACP}} + \text{CoA}}$$

In the meantime, a similar reaction occurs to another molecule of acetyl CoA at a different unit of the synthase, a unit that we'll call simply E:

$$\underset{\text{Acetyl } E}{\text{CH}_3\text{C}-\text{S}-\text{CoA} + E \longrightarrow \text{CH}_3\text{C}-\text{S}-E + \text{CoA}}$$

Next, the acetyl group of acetyl E is transferred to the malonyl group of malonyl ACP as carbon dioxide, the initial activator, is ejected. Its loss, in fact, is the driving force for the reaction, a driving force initially put in place by energy from ATP. A four-carbon derivative of ACP, forms. The E unit is vacated.

$$\underset{\text{Acetoacetyl ACP}}{\text{CH}_3\text{C}-\text{S}-E + {^-\text{OCCH}_2\text{C}-\text{S}-\text{ACP}} \longrightarrow \text{CH}_3\text{CCH}_2\text{C}-\text{S}-\text{ACP} + \text{CO}_2 + E}$$

The ketone group in acetoacetyl ACP is next reduced to a secondary alcohol. Then this alcohol is dehydrated to introduce a double bond. And the double bond is next reduced to give butyryl ACP. The overall effect of these steps is to reduce the keto group to CH_2. Notice that NADPH, the reducing agent manufactured by the pentose phosphate pathway of glucose catabolism, is used here, not NADH.

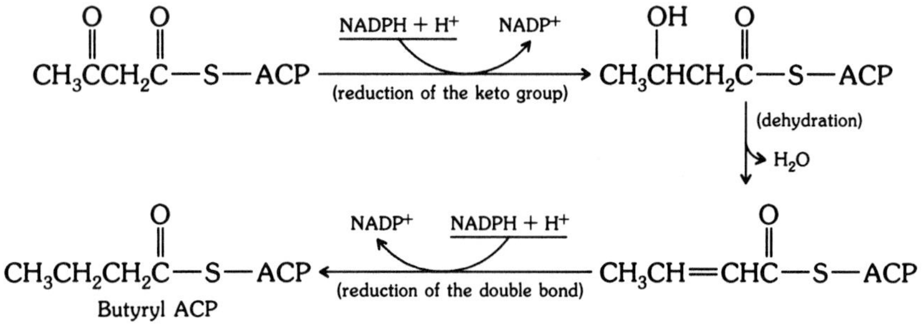

$$\text{CH}_3\text{CCH}_2\text{C}-\text{S}-\text{ACP} \xrightarrow[\text{(reduction of the keto group)}]{\text{NADPH} + \text{H}^+ \quad \text{NADP}^+} \text{CH}_3\overset{\text{OH}}{\text{CH}}\text{CH}_2\text{C}-\text{S}-\text{ACP}$$

$$\downarrow \text{(dehydration)} \quad \rightarrow \text{H}_2\text{O}$$

$$\underset{\text{Butyryl ACP}}{\text{CH}_3\text{CH}_2\text{CH}_2\text{C}-\text{S}-\text{ACP}} \xleftarrow[\text{(reduction of the double bond)}]{\text{NADP}^+ \quad \text{NADPH} + \text{H}^+} \text{CH}_3\text{CH}=\text{CHC}-\text{S}-\text{ACP}$$

The butyryl group is now transferred to the *vacant E* unit of the synthase, the unit that initially held an acetyl group. This ends one complete turn of the cycle. To recapitulate, we have gone from two two-carbon acetyl units to one four-carbon acyl unit.

The steps now repeat as shown in Figure 28.4. A new malonyl unit is joined to the ACP. Then the newly made *butyryl* group is made to transfer to the malonyl unit as CO_2 is again ejected. This elongates the fatty acyl chain to six carbons in length, positions it on the swinging arm, and gets it ready for the several-step reduction of the keto group to CH_2. The swinging arm mechanism and the enzymes of the synthase complex go to work until the chain

is that of the hexanoyl group, $\text{CH}_3\text{CH}_2\text{CH}_2\text{CH}_2\text{CH}_2\overset{\text{O}}{\text{C}}-$.

In the next turn, this six-carbon acyl group will be elongated to an eight-carbon group.

And the process will repeat until the chain is sixteen carbons long. Overall, the net equation for the synthesis of the palmitate ion from acetyl CoA is

■ Because the symbols ATP, ADP, and P$_i$ are not given with their electrical charges, we can't provide an electrical balance to equations such as this.

$$8CH_3\overset{O}{\overset{\|}{C}}SCoA + 7ATP + 14NADPH \longrightarrow$$
$$CH_3(CH_2)_{14}CO_2^- + 7ADP + 7P_i + 8CoA + 14NADP^+ + 6H_2O$$

If longer acids are needed, or acids with double bonds, additional steps using different enzymes are taken.

28.5 BIOSYNTHESIS OF CHOLESTEROL

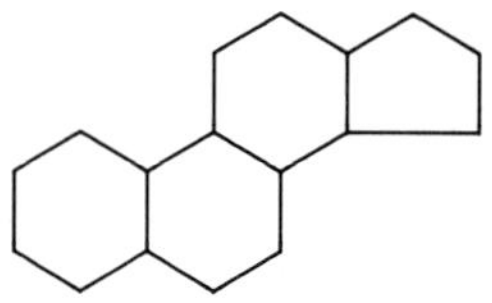

Steroid nucleus

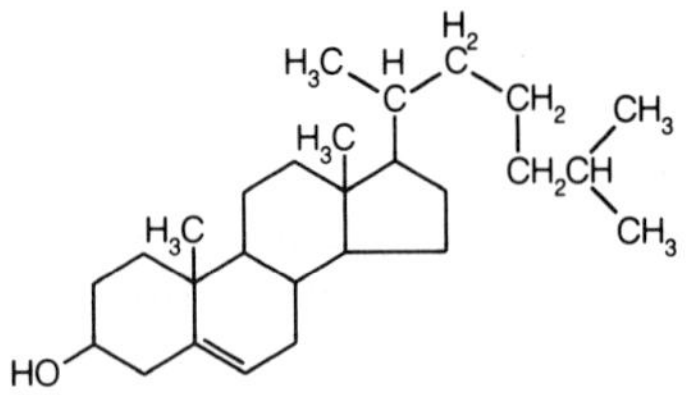

Cholesterol

Excessive cholesterol can inhibit the formation of a key enzyme required in the multistep synthesis of cholesterol.

In addition to serving as a raw material for making fatty acids, acetyl CoA can be used to make the steroid nucleus. Cholesterol, an alcohol with this nucleus, is the end product of a long, multistep process, and once it is made the body produces various bile salts and sex hormones.

In mammals, about 80% to 95% of all cholesterol synthesis takes place in cells of the liver and the intestines. We won't go into all the details, but we will go far enough to learn more about how the body normally controls the process. If sufficient cholesterol is provided by the diet for use in making cell membranes or to make other steroids, then the body's synthesis should be shut down. Let's see how this is done.

Cholesterol Is Made from Acetyl Units When the level of acetyl CoA builds up in the liver, the following equilibrium shifts to the right:

■ Le Chatelier's principle is again at work. The stress in this equilibrium is an increase in the concentration of acetyl CoA, so the shift is in the direction that uses it up.

$$2CH_3\overset{O}{\overset{\|}{C}}-SCoA \rightleftharpoons CH_3\overset{O}{\overset{\|}{C}}CH_2\overset{O}{\overset{\|}{C}}-SCoA + CoA-SH$$

Acetyl CoA   Acetoacetyl CoA

When cholesterol synthesis is switched on, then acetoacetyl CoA combines with another acetyl CoA:

■ This and the previous reaction are examples of ester condensations, which were discussed in Special Topic 26.2, page 668.

$$CH_3\overset{O}{\overset{\|}{C}}CH_2\overset{O}{\overset{\|}{C}}-SCoA + CH_3\overset{O}{\overset{\|}{C}}-SCoA \xrightleftharpoons{\text{HMG—CoA synthase}}$$

$$^-O\overset{O}{\overset{\|}{C}}CH_2\overset{OH}{\underset{CH_3}{\overset{|}{C}}}CH_2\overset{O}{\overset{\|}{C}}-SCoA + CoA-SH$$

HMG—CoA
(β-Hydroxy-β-methyl-glutaryl CoA)

■ Thirteen Nobel prizes have gone to scientists who invested the better parts of their careers to various aspects of cholesterol and its uses in the body.

The Reduction of HMG—CoA Commits the Cell to the Complete Cholesterol Synthesis Both a reduction and a hydrolysis occur in the next step, which is a complex change catalyzed by HMG—CoA reductase, a key enzyme.

$$HMG{-}CoA + 2NADPH + 2H^+ \xrightarrow[\text{reductase}]{\text{HMG}{-}\text{CoA}}$$

$$HOCH_2CH_2\overset{\overset{\displaystyle OH}{|}}{\underset{\underset{\displaystyle CH_3}{|}}{C}}CH_2CO_2^- + 2NADP^+ + CoA{-}SH$$

Mevalonate

Mevalonate is next carried through a long series of reactions until cholesterol is made. As we said, we'll not take it that far, but consider, instead, how cholersterol synthesis is controlled.

Cholesterol Is a Natural Inhibitor of HMG—CoA Reductase The control of HMG—CoA reductase is the major factor in the overall control of the biosynthesis of cholesterol. Cholesterol itself is one inhibitor, and it works by inhibiting both the *synthesis of the enzyme* and the *enzymic activity* of any of its existing molecules. In the presence of cholesterol the enzyme isn't totally deactivated. There is just *less* of it free to do catalytic work. Thus if the diet is relatively rich in cholesterol, the body tends to make less of it. If the diet is very low in cholesterol, the body makes more of it. Of course, another control mechanism over the cholesterol level in the blood is the efficiency with which excess cholesterol can be exported via the lower intestinal tract, as we discussed in Section 28.1.

Lovastatin and Gemfibrozil Lower Blood Cholesterol Levels A drug that lowers the cholesterol level, lovastatin (Mevacor), was approved in 1987 and has proved to be extraordinarily effective in suppressing the body's natural synthesis of cholesterol. It works partly as a competitive inhibitor of the enzyme HMG—CoA reductase, which is a key choke point in cholesterol synthesis. Lovastatin also increases the synthesis of the *m*RNA responsible for making the liver LDL receptors. With more of these, the liver is better able to reabsorb cholesterol and export it in the bile. In some people, lovastatin also enhances the levels of the HDL units that carry cholesterol back to the liver for removal.

Another drug, gemfibrozil, has been found effective in both increasing the HDL component of the circulating lipoprotein complexes and lowering the LDL component. Since HDL helps the system remove cholesterol, any improvement in the HDL level over the LDL level also contributes to the lowering of blood cholesterol.

Figure 28.5 provides a summary of much of what we have covered in this and the previous chapter about the chief uses of acetyl CoA and its relationship to carbohydrate and lipid catabolism. One point emphasized by this figure is that triacylglycerols can be made from any of the three dietary components: carbohydrates, lipids, and proteins.

■ On a low-cholesterol diet, an adult makes about 800 mg/day of cholesterol.

28.6 KETOACIDOSIS

An acceleration of the fatty acid cycle tips some equilibria in a direction that leads to ketoacidosis.

Cells of certain tissues have to engage in gluconeogenesis in two serious conditions, starvation and uncontrolled diabetes mellitus. In starvation, the blood sugar level drops because of nutritional deficiencies, so the body (principally the liver) tries to compensate by making glucose. The consequences are fatal unless the underlying causes are treated.

The Level of Acetyl CoA Increases When Gluconeogenesis Is Accelerated If you look back to Figure 27.7, you will see that gluconeogenesis consumes oxaloacetate, the

■ Figure 27.7 was on page 686.

Figure 28.5
Principal sources of triacylglycerols for adipose tissue and the chief uses of acetyl CoA.

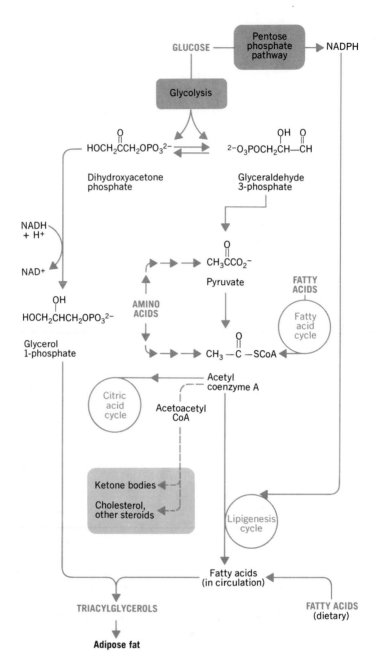

■ Figure 26.6 was on page 666.

carrier of acetyl units in the citric acid cycle (Figure 26.6). When oxaloacetate is diverted from the citric acid cycle, acetyl coenzyme A cannot put its acetyl group into the cycle. Yet acetyl coenzyme A continues to be made by the fatty acid cycle, so acetyl CoA levels build up.

As the supply of acetyl CoA rises in the liver, the following equilibrium shifts to the right to make acetoacetyl CoA.

$$2CH_3\overset{\overset{\displaystyle O}{\|}}{C}-SCoA \rightleftharpoons CH_3\overset{\overset{\displaystyle O}{\|}}{C}CH_2\overset{\overset{\displaystyle O}{\|}}{C}-SCoA + CoA-SH$$

Acetyl CoA   Acetoacetyl CoA

As the level of acetoacetyl CoA builds up, the following equilibrium shifts to the right. It's

■ Again we see applications of Le Chatelier's principle.

the same reaction that occurs early in the body's synthesis of cholesterol, so HMG—CoA synthase is the catalyst.

$$CH_3CCH_2C\!-\!SCoA + CH_3C\!-\!SCoA \xrightleftharpoons{\text{HMG-CoA synthase}}$$

$$^-OCCH_2CCH_2C\!-\!SCoA + CoA\!-\!SH$$
$$\underset{CH_3}{|}$$

HMG-CoA
(β-Hydroxy-β-methyl-
glutaryl CoA)

As the level of HMG—CoA increases (and little if any is being diverted to the synthesis of cholesterol), a liver enzyme splits it to acetoacetate ion and acetyl CoA:

$$HMG\!-\!CoA \longrightarrow CH_3CCH_2CO^- + HS\!-\!CoA$$

Acetoacetate

The net effect of these steps, starting from acetyl CoA, is the following:

$$2\ Acetyl\ CoA + H_2O \longrightarrow CH_3CCH_2CO_2^- + 2CoA + H^+$$

Acetoacetate

Notice the hydrogen ion. It makes the situation very dangerous, and an increased synthesis of "new" glucose was the cause.

Accelerated Acetoacetate Production Leads to Acidosis The acid produced by the formation of acetoacetate must be neutralized by the buffer. Under an increasingly rapid production of acetoacetate and hydrogen ion, the blood buffer slowly loses ground. A condition of acidosis sets in. It is a *metabolic* acidosis, because the cause lies in a disorder of metabolism. Because the chief species responsible for this acidosis has a keto group, the condition is often called **ketoacidosis.**

Blood Levels of the Ketone Bodies Increase in Starvation and Diabetes The *acetoacetate ion* is called one of the **ketone bodies.** The two others are *acetone* and the *β-hydroxybutyrate ion*. Both are produced from the acetoacetate ion. Acetone arises from acetoacetate by the loss of the carboxyl group:

$$H_2O + CH_3CCH_2CO^- \longrightarrow CH_3CCH_3 + HCO_3^-$$

Acetoacetate   Acetone

■ β-Hydroxybutyrate is called a *ketone* body not because it has a keto group but because it is made from and is found together with one that does.

β-Hydroxybutyrate is produced when the keto group of acetoacetate is reduced by NADH:

$$CH_3CCH_2CO_2^- + NADH + H^+ \longrightarrow CH_3CHCH_2CO_2^- + NAD^+$$

Acetoacetate   β-Hydroxybutyrate

■ The vapor pressure of acetone at body temperature is nearly 400 mm Hg, so it readily evaporates from the blood in the lungs.

The ketone bodies enter general circulation. Because acetone is volatile, most of it leaves the body via the lungs, and individuals with severe ketoacidosis have "acetone breath," the noticeable odor of acetone on the breath.

Acetoacetate and β-hydroxybutyrate can be used in skeletal muscles to make ATP. Heart muscle uses these two for energy in preference to glucose. Even the brain, given time, can adapt to using these ions for energy when the blood sugar level drops in starvation or prolonged fasting. The ketone bodies are thus not in themselves abnormal constituents of blood. Only when they are produced at a rate faster than the blood buffer can handle them are they a problem.

The Conditions of Ketonemia, Ketonuria, and "Acetone Breath" Collectively Constitute Ketosis

■ 1 μmol = 1 micromole = 10^{-6} mol

Normally, the levels of acetoacetate and β-hydroxybutyrate in the blood are, respectively, 2 μmol/dL and 4 μmol/dL. In prolonged, undetected, and untreated diabetes, these values can increase as much as 200-fold. The condition of excessive levels of ketone bodies in the blood is called **ketonemia.**

As ketonemia becomes more and more advanced, the ketone bodies begin to appear in the urine, a condition called **ketonuria.** When there is a combination of ketonemia, ketonuria, and acetone breath, the overall state is called **ketosis.** The individual will be described as *ketotic.* As unchecked ketosis becomes more severe, the associated ketoacidosis worsens and the pH of the blood continues its fatal descent.

The Urinary Removal of Organic Anions Means the Loss of Base from the Blood

Condition	$[HCO_3^-]_{blood}$ in mmol/L
Normal	22–30
Mild acidosis	16–20
Moderate acidosis	10–16
Severe acidosis	<10

To leave the ketone body anions in the urine, the kidneys have to leave positive ions with them to keep everything electrically neutral. Na^+ ions, the most abundant cations, are used. One Na^+ ion has to leave with each acetoacetate ion, for example. This loss of Na^+ is often referred to as the "loss of base" from the blood, although Na^+ is not a base. But the loss of one Na^+ stems from the appearance of one acetoacetate ion *plus one* H^+ *ion* that the blood had to neutralize. Thus each Na^+ that leaves the body corresponds to the loss of one HCO_3^- ion, the true base, consumed in neutralizing one H^+. Hence, the loss of Na^+ is taken as an indicator of the loss of this true base.

Another way to understand the urinary loss of Na^+ as the loss of base from the blood is that a Na^+ ion has to accompany a bicarbonate ion when it goes from the kidneys into the blood. The kidneys manufacture HCO_3^- ions normally in order to replenish the blood buffer system. The greater the number of Na^+ ions that have to be left in the *urine* in order to clear ketone bodies from the blood, the less the amount of true base, HCO_3^-, that can be put into the *blood.*

Diuresis Must Accelerate To Handle Ketosis

The solutes that are leaving the body in the urine cannot, of course, be allowed to make the urine too concentrated. Otherwise, osmotic pressure balances are upset. Therefore increasing quantities of water must be excreted. To satisfy this need, the individual has a powerful thirst. Other wastes, such as urea, are also being produced at higher than normal rates, because amino acids are being sacrificed in gluconeogenesis. These wastes add to the demand for water to make urine.

■ **Polyuria** is the technical name for the overproduction of urine.

Internal Water Shortages in Ketosis Spell Dehydration of Critical Tissues

If, during a state of ketosis, insufficient water is drunk, then water is simply taken from extracellular fluids. The blood volume therefore tends to drop, and the blood becomes more concentrated. It also thickens and becomes more viscous, which makes the delivery of blood more difficult.

Figure 28.6
The principal sequence of events in
untreated diabetes.

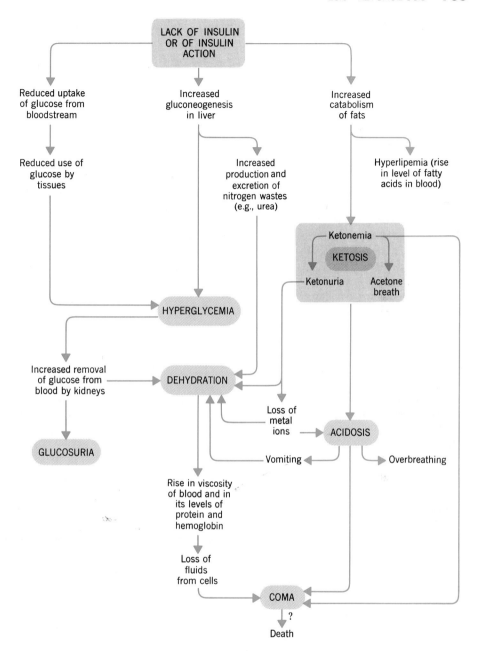

Because the brain has the highest priority for blood flow, some of this flow is diverted
from the kidneys to try to ensure that the brain gets what it needs. This only worsens the
situation in the kidneys, and they have an increasingly difficult time clearing wastes. As the
water shortage worsens, some water is borrowed from the intracellular supply. This, in
addition to a combination of other developments, leads to coma and eventually death.

Figure 28.6 outlines the succession of events in untreated type I diabetes. It is nothing
short of remarkable how the absence of one chemical, insulin, can release such a vast train of
biochemical events. But at the molecular level of life, this is the kind of story that occurs very
often.

SUMMARY

Lipid absorption and distribution As fatty acids and glycerol migrate out of the digestive tract, they become reconstituted as triacylglycerols. These, in addition to cholesterol and other lipids, are picked up by chylomicrons. As they migrate through the vascular compartment, they unload some of their triacylglycerols and finally are taken up by the liver. The liver organizes the remaining lipids together with those that the liver makes itself, which include cholesterol and triacylglycerols, and then sends very low density lipoprotein complexes, VLDL, into circulation. Triacylglycerols are again unloaded where they are needed, and the VLDL become slightly more dense and change into intermediate-density complexes, IDL. Much of these are reabsorbed by the liver. Those that aren't become denser and change over to low-density lipoprotein complexes, LDL. Some of the LDL finds its way to extrahepatic tissues, including endocrine glands that need cholesterol to make steroid hormones, and much of the LDL is reabsorbed by the liver to recycle its lipids. Any extra cholesterol not needed in extrahepatic tissue is carried back to the liver by high-density lipoprotein complexes, HDL. The liver excretes excess cholesterol via the bile, or it makes bile salts. Severe hypercholesterolemia is experienced by individuals who have inherited an inability to make enough of the receptor proteins for IDL and LDL.

Storage and mobilization of lipids The favorable energy density of triacylglycerol means that more energy is stored per gram of this material than can be stored by any other chemical system. The adipose tissue is the principal storage site, and fatty material comes and goes from this tissue according to the energy budget of the body. When the energy of fatty acids is needed, they are liberated from triacylglycerols and carried to the liver, the chief site of fatty acid catabolism.

Catabolism of fatty acids Fatty acyl groups, after being pinned to coenzyme A, are catabolized by the fatty acid cycle. By a succession of four steps — dehydrogenation, hydration of a double bond, oxidation of the resulting alcohol, and cleavage of the bond from the α-carbon to the β-carbon — one turn of the cycle removes one two-carbon acetyl group. The cycle then repeats as the shortened fatty acyl group continues to be degraded. Each turn of the cycle produces one $FADH_2$ and one NADH, which pass $H:^-$ to the respiratory chain for the synthesis of ATP. Each turn also sends one acetyl group into the citric acid cycle which, via the respiratory chain, leads to several more ATPs. The net ATP production is 129 ATPs per palmityl residue.

Biosynthesis of fatty acids Fatty acids can be made by a repetitive cycle of steps called the lipigenesis cycle. It begins by building one butyryl group from two acetyl groups. The four-carbon butyryl group is attached to an acyl carrier protein which acts as a swinging arm on the enzyme complex. This arm moves the growing fatty acyl unit first over one enzyme and then another as additional two-carbon units are added. The process consumes ATP and NADPH.

Biosynthesis of cholesterol Cholesterol is made from acetyl groups by a long series of reactions. The synthesis of one of the enzymes is inhibited by excess cholesterol, which gives the system a mechanism for keeping its own cholesterol synthesis under control.

Ketoacidosis Acetoacetate, β-hydroxybutyrate, and acetone build up in the blood — ketonemia — in starvation or in diabetes. The first two are normal sources of energy in some tissues. When they are made faster than they can be metabolized, however, there is an accompanying increased loss of bicarbonate ion from the blood's carbonate buffer. This leads to a form of metabolic acidosis called ketoacidosis. The kidneys try to leave the anionic ketone bodies in the urine, but this takes Na^+, too (for electrical neutrality), and water (for osmotic pressure balances). The excessive loss of Na^+ in the urine is interpreted as a loss of "base." With Na^+ leaving the body in the urine, less is available to accompany replacement HCO_3^-, made by the kidneys, when this base should be going into the blood. Under developing ketoacidosis, the kidneys have extra nitrogen wastes and, in diabetes, extra glucose to leave in the urine being made. This also demands an increased volume of water. Unless this is brought in by the thirst mechanism, it has to be sought from within. However, the brain has first call on blood flowage, so the kidneys suffer more. Eventually, if these events continue unchecked, the victim goes into a coma and dies.

REVIEW EXERCISES

The answers to these Review Exercises are in the *Study Guide* that accompanies this book.

Absorption and Distribution of Lipids

28.1 What are the end products of the digestion of triacylglycerols?

28.2 What happens to the products of the digestion of triacylglycerols as they migrate out of the intestinal tract?

28.3 What are chylomicrons and what is their function?

28.4 What happens to chylomicrons as they move through capillaries of, say, adipose tissue?

28.5 What happens to chylomicrons when they reach the liver?

28.6 What are the two chief sources of cholesterol that the liver exports?

28.7 What do the following symbols stand for?
(a) VLDL   (b) IDL
(c) LDL   (d) HDL

28.8 The loss of what kind of substance from the VLDL converts them into IDL?

28.9 What do IDL release as they change over to LDL?

28.10 What tissue can reabsorb IDL complexes?

28.11 What is the chief constitutent of LDL?

28.12 In extrahepatic tissue, what two general uses await delivered cholesterol?

28.13 If the liver lacks the key receptor proteins, which specific lipoprotein complexes can't be reabsorbed?

28.14 Explain the relationship between the liver's receptor proteins for lipoprotein complexes and the control of the cholesterol level of the blood.

28.15 What is the chief job of the HDL?

28.16 Some scientists believe that a relatively high level of HDL provides protection against atherosclerosis, and that one's risk of having heart disease declines when the level of HDL is raised by exercise and losing weight. Why would a low level of HDL tend to promote heart disease?

Storage and Mobilization of Lipids

28.17 With reference to the storage of chemical energy in the body, what is meant by *energy density?*

28.18 Arrange the following in their order of increasing quantity of energy that they store per gram.

Wet glycogen	Adipose lipids	Isotonic glucose
1	2	3

28.19 Briefly describe two conditions in which the body would have to turn to fatty acids for energy.

28.20 How does insulin suppress the mobilization of fatty acids from adipose tissue?

28.21 Arrange the following processes in the order in which they occur when the energy in storage in triacylglycerols is mobilized.

Fatty acid cycle	Oxidative phosphorylation	Citric acid cycle
1	2	3

Lipoprotein formation	Lipolysis in adipose tissue
4	5

28.22 What specific function does the fatty acid cycle have in obtaining energy from fatty acids?

28.23 What specific function does the citric acid cycle have in the use of fatty acids for energy?

28.24 Name two hormones that activate the lipase in adipose tissue. Referring to the previous chapter, what does the presence of these hormones do for the blood sugar level?

28.25 Explain how a rise in the blood sugar level indirectly inhibits the mobilization of energy from adipose tissue.

28.26 When lipolysis occurs in adipose tissue, what happens to the glycerol?

Catabolism of Fatty Acids

28.27 How are long-chain fatty acids activated for entry into the fatty acid cycle?

28.28 Complete the following equations for one turn of the fatty acid cycle by which a six-carbon fatty acyl group is catabolized.

(a) $CH_3CH_2CH_2CH_2CH_2\overset{\displaystyle O}{\overset{\|}{C}}{-}SCoA + FAD \longrightarrow$
　　＿＿＿＿＿＿ + ＿＿＿＿＿＿

(b) ＿＿＿＿＿＿ $+ H_2O \longrightarrow$ ＿＿＿＿＿＿

(c) ＿＿＿＿＿＿ $+ NAD^+ \longrightarrow$
　　＿＿＿＿＿＿ $+ NADH + H^+$

(d) ＿＿＿＿＿＿ $+ CoA{-}SH \longrightarrow$
　　＿＿＿＿＿＿ + ＿＿＿＿＿＿

28.29 Write the equations for the four steps in the fatty acid cycle as it operates on butyryl CoA. How many more turns of the cycle are possible after this one?

28.30 How is the FAD-enzyme recovered from its reduced form, $FADH_2$, when the fatty acid cycle operates?

28.31 How is the reduced form of the NAD^+ enzyme used in the fatty acid cycle restored to its oxidized form?

28.32 Why is the fatty acid cycle sometimes called beta oxidation?

28.33 Myristic acid, $CH_3(CH_2)_{12}CO_2H$, can be catabolized by the fatty acid cycle just like palmitic acid.
(a) How many units of acetyl CoA can be made from it?
(b) In producing this much acetyl CoA, how many times does $FADH_2$ form and then deliver its hydrogen to the respiratory chain?
(c) Referring again to part (a), how many times does NADH form as acetyl CoA is produced and then deliver its hydrogen to the respiratory chain?
(d) Complete the following table by supplying the missing numbers of molecules that are involved in the catabolism of myristic acid to acetyl CoA.

Intermediate	Maximum Number of ATP from Each	Total Number of ATP Possible from Each as Acetyl CoA Forms
＿＿＿ $FADH_2$	＿＿＿	＿＿＿
＿＿＿ NADH	＿＿＿	＿＿＿
＿＿＿ $CH_3\overset{\displaystyle O}{\overset{\|}{C}}{-}SCoA$	＿＿＿	
	Sum =	＿＿＿

Deduct ＿＿＿ high-energy phosphate bonds for activating the myristyl group　− ＿＿＿

Net ATP produced for each myristyl group as it changes to acetyl CoA　＿＿＿

Biosynthesis of Fatty Acids

28.34 Where are the principal sites for each activity in a liver cell?
(a) fatty acid catabolism
(b) lipigenesis

28.35 Outline the steps that make butyryl ACP out of acetyl CoA.

28.36 What metabolic pathway in the body is the chief supplier of NADPH for lipigenesis?

Biosynthesis of Cholesterol

28.37 The enzyme for the formation of which intermediate in cholesterol synthesis is the major control point in this pathway?

28.38 How does cholesterol itself work to inhibit the activity of the enzyme referred to in Review Exercise 28.37?

Ketoacidosis

28.39 What species is diverted from the citric acid cycle to gluconeogenesis?

28.40 Why does this diversion lead to an increase in the level of acetyl CoA?

28.41 Two molecules of acetyl CoA can combine to give the coenzyme A derivative of what keto acid? Give its structure.

28.42 In two steps, the compound of Review Exercise 28.41 gives one unit of a ketone body and one other significant species (besides recovered CoA). What is it? Why is it a problem?

28.43 Give the names and structures of the ketone bodies.

28.44 What is ketonemia?

28.45 What is ketonuria?

28.46 What is meant by acetone breath?

28.47 Ketosis consists of what collection of conditions?

28.48 What is ketoacidosis? What form of acidosis is it, metabolic or respiratory?

28.49 The formation of which particular compound most lowers the supply of HCO_3^- in ketoacidosis?

28.50 What are the reasons for the increase in the volume of urine that is excreted in someone with untreated, type I diabetes?

28.51 If the ketone bodies (other than acetone) can normally be used by heart and skeletal muscle, what makes them dangerous in starvation or in diabetes?

28.52 Why does the rate of urea production increase in untreated type I diabetes?

28.53 When a physician refers to the loss of Na^+ as the loss of *base*, what is actually meant?

Brown Adipose Tissue (Special Topic 28.1)

28.54 With respect to the catabolism of fatty acids, how do white and brown adipose tissue differ?

28.55 In the ordinary operation of the respiratory chain, the chain is coupled to the synthesis of ATP because of what condition concerning mitochondria?

28.56 What happens to the energy released by the respiratory chain when it isn't used to make ATP?

28.57 What is meant by *thermogenesis?*

CHAPTER TWENTY-NINE

Metabolism of Nitrogen Compounds

Big cats are carnivores and obtain their proteins from prey, which these two mountain lions have obviously just sighted. In this chapter we study how proteins and amino acids are used in metabolism.

29.1 THE BIOSYNTHESIS OF AMINO ACIDS

The body can manufacture a number of amino acids from intermediates that appear in the catabolism of nonprotein substances.

Amino acids, the end products of protein digestion, are rapidly transported across the walls of the small intestine. Some very small, simple peptides can also be absorbed. Once amino acids enter circulation, they become part of what is called the **nitrogen pool.**

The Nitrogen Pool Consists of All Nitrogenous Compounds Anywhere in the Body Figure 29.1 illustrates the various compartments of the nitrogen pool and how they are interrelated. Amino acids enter the nitrogen pool not only as digestive products but also as products of the breakdown of proteins in body fluids and tissues. These are undergoing constant turnover, fairly rapidly among the liver proteins and those in the blood and quite slowly among muscle proteins.

As indicated in Figure 29.1, individual amino acids can be used in any one of the following ways, depending on the body's needs of the moment.

1. The synthesis of new or replacement proteins.

2. The synthesis of such nonprotein nitrogen compounds as heme, creatine, nucleic acids, and certain hormones and neurotransmitters.

3. The production of ATP or of glycogen and fatty acids, substances with the potential for making ATP.

4. The synthesis of any needed nonessential amino acids.

The Body Uses Both Essential and Nonessential Amino Acids To Make Proteins In Chapter 23 we learned that we do not need all the 20 amino acids in the diet, that we can make roughly half of them. We labeled those that *must* be in the diet as the *essential amino acids.* The others, the *nonessential amino acids,* can be synthesized in the body. Be sure to remember that *nonessential* in this context refers *only* to a dietary need. In a larger context, the body must have all the amino acids to make polypeptides. We'll broadly study how the body makes nonessential amino acids next. Figure 29.2 gives an overview to which we'll refer as we go along.

The Reductive Amination of α-Ketoglutarate To Give Glutamate Makes the Ammonium Ion a Source of Nitrogen for Nonessential Amino Acids Many of the syntheses of nonessential amino acids outlined in Figure 29.2 depend on the availability of glutamic acid (actually, at body pH, the glutamate ion). It is made from α-ketoglutarate by a reaction called **reductive amination,** in which the ammonium ion is the source of nitrogen and NADPH is the reducing agent. (In some cells, NADH enzymes can also work.) We need a

 The polypeptides in proteins that serve as enzymes have a particularly rapid turnover.

 In both starvation and diabetes the body draws down its amino acid pool to make glucose.

Figure 29.1
The nitrogen pool.

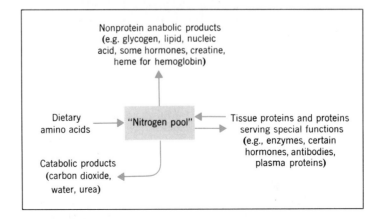

Nonprotein anabolic products
(e.g. glycogen, lipid, nucleic acid, some hormones, creatine, heme for hemoglobin)

Dietary amino acids → "Nitrogen pool" ← Tissue proteins and proteins serving special functions (e.g., enzymes, certain hormones, antibodies, plasma proteins)

Catabolic products (carbon dioxide, water, urea)

Figure 29.2
The biosynthesis of some nonessential amino acids.

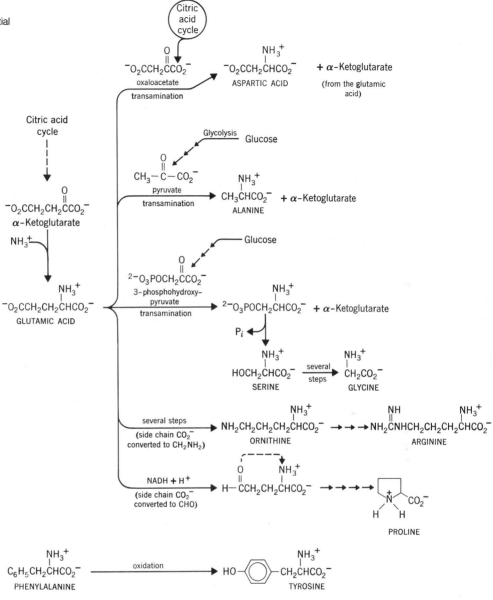

reducing agent because the keto group (of α-ketoglutarate) is in a higher oxidation state than the CH—NH$_2$ unit in glutamate, the product. The overall result is

$$^-O_2CCH_2CH_2\overset{\overset{\textstyle O}{\|}}{C}CO_2^- + NH_4^+ + NADPH + H^+ \rightleftharpoons$$

α-Ketoglutarate

$$^-O_2CCH_2CH_2\overset{\overset{\textstyle NH_3^+}{|}}{C}HCO_2^- + NADP^+ + H_2O$$

Glutamate

Glutamate Supplies the Amino Group To Make Many Nonessential Amino Acids Special aminotransferase enzymes (sometimes called transaminases) are able to catalyze the transferral of an amino group from glutamate to the keto carbonyl group of a keto acid. The reaction is called **transamination.** The required ketone compounds can come from the catabolism of glucose, as you can see in Figure 29.2. We'll illustrate the general case of what happens in a transamination:

$$G-\overset{\overset{\textstyle O}{\|}}{C}-CO_2^- + {}^-O_2CCH_2CH_2\overset{\overset{\textstyle NH_3^+}{|}}{C}HCO_2^- \rightleftharpoons$$

A keto acid   Glutamate

$$G-\overset{\overset{\textstyle NH_3^+}{|}}{C}H-CO_2^- + {}^-O_2CCH_2CH_2\overset{\overset{\textstyle O}{\|}}{C}CO_2^-$$

An amino acid α-Ketoglutarate

The amino transferases require the B vitamin pyridoxal to make their cofactors.

29.2 THE CATABOLISM OF AMINO ACIDS

The breakdown products of amino acid catabolism eventually enter the pathways of catabolism of either carbohydrates or lipids.

There is no special storage system for amino acids analogous to glycogen or to fat in adipose tissue. Amino acids in the nitrogen pool that aren't needed to make other amino acids or other nitrogen compounds are catabolized. Most of this work is done in the liver (indicating once again how important this organ is).

When Stripped of Amino Groups, Amino Acids Are Used To Make Glucose or They Enter the Citric Acid Cycle   The ultimate end products of the complete catabolism of amino acids are urea, carbon dioxide, and water. On the way to these compounds, however, there are several intermediates that can enter other pathways. In fact, all the pathways for the use of carbohydrates, lipids, and proteins are interconnected in one way or another.

Figure 29.3 shows this in broad outline, and it provides an overall summary of what we have been studying in these later chapters. Notice the central importance of two small molecules, acetyl CoA and pyruvate. Notice also that there is no route from acetyl CoA to pyruvate, which means that (in all animals, at least) glucose cannot be made from fatty acids. (We'll return to this shortly.)

$$NH_2-\overset{\overset{\textstyle O}{\|}}{C}-NH_2$$

Urea

We won't study in detail how each amino acid is catabolized, because each requires its own particular scheme, usually quite complicated. Early in each scheme, however, the amino acid gets rid of its nitrogen, which is shuttled into the synthesis of urea. The nonnitrogen fragment then eventually enters a pathway we have already studied. There are three kinds of reactions, besides transamination, that occur often: oxidative deamination, direct deamination, and decarboxylation. We'll study these and how they apply to certain selected amino acids.

Amino Groups Are Shuttled Through the α-Ketoglutarate–Glutamate Switch Toward Urea Synthesis   One of the steps in the catabolic process that removes amino groups of amino acids is **oxidative deamination.** It is actually the reverse of reductive amination, which we studied on page 710. In the display that follows, the step on the left is a transamination. The next step is oxidative deamination, and the arrowheads are in the direction of catabolism.

Figure 29.3
Interrelationships of major metabolic pathways.

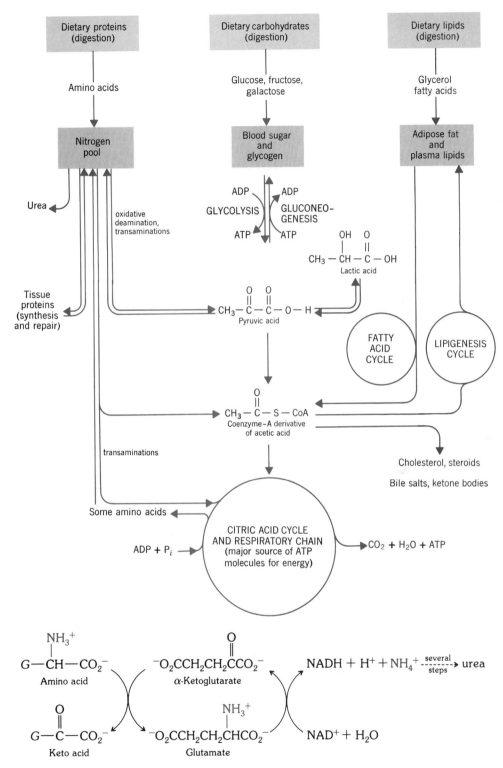

Notice that the nitrogen of the amino acid on the upper left ends up in urea, and that the α-ketoglutarate – glutamate pair provides a switching mechanism to convey this nitrogen in the right direction for catabolism.

Alanine Catabolizes to Pyruvate   The transamination of alanine gives pyruvate, which can go into the citric acid cycle, be used in gluconeogenesis, or be used for the biosynthesis of fatty acids.

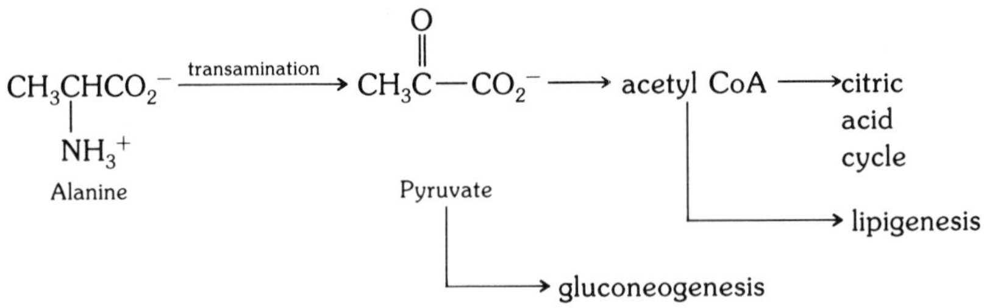

$$CH_3CHCO_2^- \xrightarrow{\text{transamination}} CH_3\overset{\overset{\displaystyle O}{\|}}{C}-CO_2^- \longrightarrow \text{acetyl CoA} \longrightarrow \begin{array}{l}\text{citric} \\ \text{acid} \\ \text{cycle}\end{array}$$

$$\underset{\substack{| \\ NH_3^+}}{}$$

Alanine   Pyruvate

→ lipigenesis

→ gluconeogenesis

Aspartic Acid Catabolizes to Oxaloacetate   The transamination of aspartic acid gives oxaloacetate, an intermediate in both gluconeogenesis and the citric acid cycle.

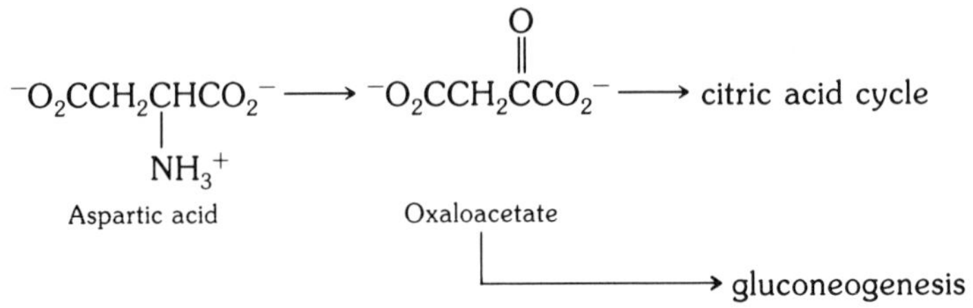

$$^-O_2CCH_2CHCO_2^- \longrightarrow {}^-O_2CCH_2\overset{\overset{\displaystyle O}{\|}}{C}CO_2^- \longrightarrow \text{citric acid cycle}$$

$$\underset{\substack{| \\ NH_3^+}}{}$$

Aspartic acid   Oxaloacetate

→ gluconeogenesis

Direct Deamination Removes Amino Groups Without Oxidation   Two amino acids, serine and threonine, have OH groups which make possible a nonoxidative loss of NH_2, called **direct deamination.** They are able to undergo the simultaneous loss of water and ammonia because their OH groups are strategically located on the carbon adjacent to the one that holds an amino group. Here's how direct deamination happens with serine.

◼ Imine groups easily hydrolyze because they can add water and then split out ammonia.

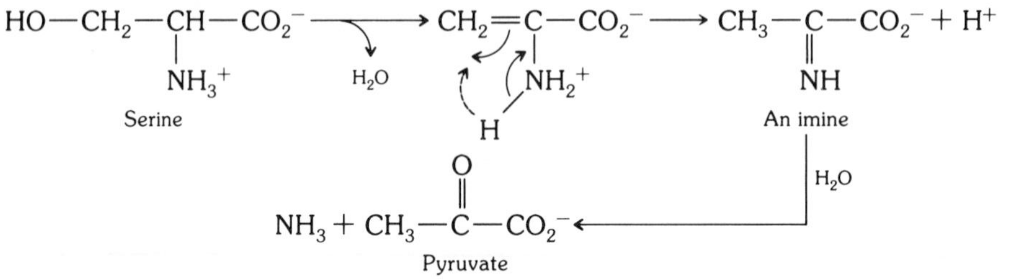

$$HO-CH_2-\underset{\substack{| \\ NH_3^+}}{CH}-CO_2^- \longrightarrow CH_2{=}\underset{\substack{| \\ NH_2^+ \\ | \\ H}}{C}-CO_2^- \longrightarrow CH_3-\underset{\substack{\| \\ NH}}{\overset{\displaystyle}{C}}-CO_2^- + H^+$$

Serine H_2O An imine

H_2O

$$NH_3 + CH_3-\overset{\overset{\displaystyle O}{\|}}{C}-CO_2^- \longleftarrow$$

Pyruvate

The first step is the dehydration of the alcohol system of serine to give an unsaturated amine. This spontaneously rearranges into an imine, a compound with a carbon–nitrogen double bond. Water can add to this double bond, but the product spontaneously breaks up, so the net effect is the hydrolysis of the imine group to a keto group and ammonia. Thus serine breaks down to pyruvate, which, as we now well know, can send an acetyl group into the citric acid cycle, or can contribute an acetyl group to lipigenesis, or can be used to make glucose.

Sustained Gluconeogenesis Necessarily Consumes Body Proteins   Figure 29.4 broadly outlines how the reactions just surveyed are involved in the catabolism of several amino acids. Notice particularly that oxaloacetate occurs in two places, as an intermediate in the citric acid cycle and as the product of the oxidative deamination of aspartate. This oxaloacetate, which has ultimately a protein source, has two options, to be used to make ATP or to make glucose by gluconeogenesis. Oxaloacetate thus connects the catabolism of amino acids to carbohydrate synthesis.

Because of the occurrence of oxaloacetate in the citric acid cycle, and because its carbons can originate in fatty acids (by way of acetyl coenzyme A), we might think that fatty acids could also be used to make glucose. Not so, not on a *net gain of glucose* basis. The removal of oxaloacetate from the citric acid cycle for gluconeogenesis means the removal of what carries acetyl units (of any origin) into the cycle. This leads to a backup of acetyl CoA (as we learned in Section 28.6) and a buildup of the ketone bodies.

Figure 29.4
The catabolism of some amino acids.

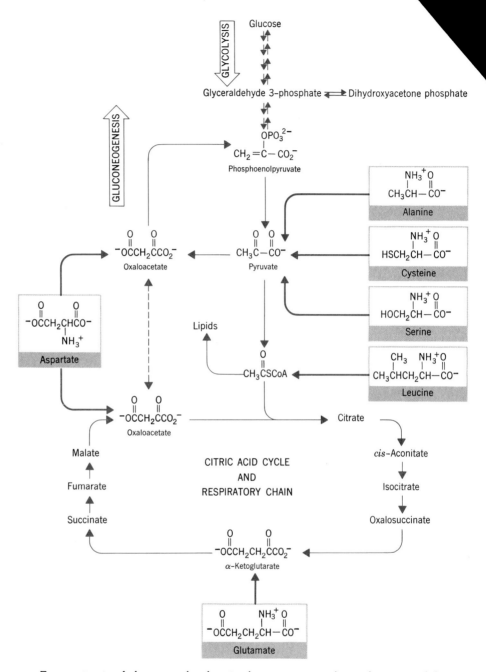

For a *net gain* of glucose molecules via gluconeogenesis, the oxaloacetate of the citric acid cycle can't be counted as available. Only oxaloacetate made from amino acids can give a net gain of glucose this way. This is why gluconeogenesis under conditions of starvation or diabetes necessarily breaks down body proteins. It needs some of their amino acids to make oxaloacetate to be able to make glucose.

The Decarboxylation of Some Amino Acids Leads to Neurotransmitters
Some special enzymes can split out just the CO_2^- groups from amino acids and make amines. This reaction is called **decarboxylation,** and it is used to make some neurotransmitters and hormones. Dopamine, norepinephrine, and epinephrine all are made by steps that begin with the decarboxylation of dihydroxyphenylalanine, which the body makes from the amino acid tyrosine.

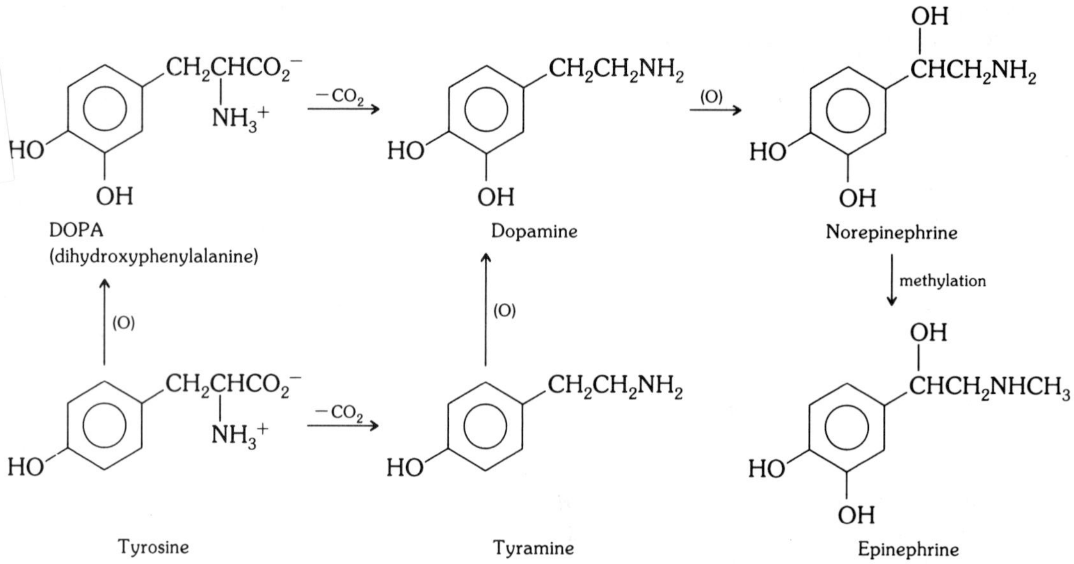

The chemical structures showing the metabolic pathway from DOPA to Dopamine to Norepinephrine to Epinephrine, and from Tyrosine to Tyramine.

DOPA
(dihydroxyphenylalanine)

Dopamine

Norepinephrine

Tyrosine

Tyramine

Epinephrine

methylation

29.3 THE FORMATION OF UREA

Ammonia and amino groups are converted into urea by a complex cycle of reactions called the urea cycle.

Urea, as we have learned, is the chief nitrogen waste made by the body. Most of its nitrogen indirectly comes from amino acids, but some comes (also indirectly) from two of the side-chain bases of nucleic acids.

Oxaloacetate Shuttles Nitrogen from Glutamate to Aspartate and Then into the Synthesis of Urea   There are two direct sources for the nitrogen atoms in urea. One is the ammonium ion produced by the oxidative deamination of glutamate (page 712). Recall that the amino group of this glutamate unit can come from the amino group of any other amino acid by way of another shuttle.

The other nitrogen atom in urea comes from a specific amino acid, aspartate. But because aspartate can be made from glutamate by a transamination, you can see that glutamate is close to being the direct source of both nitrogens in urea. Here is the shuttle from glutamate to aspartate just described.

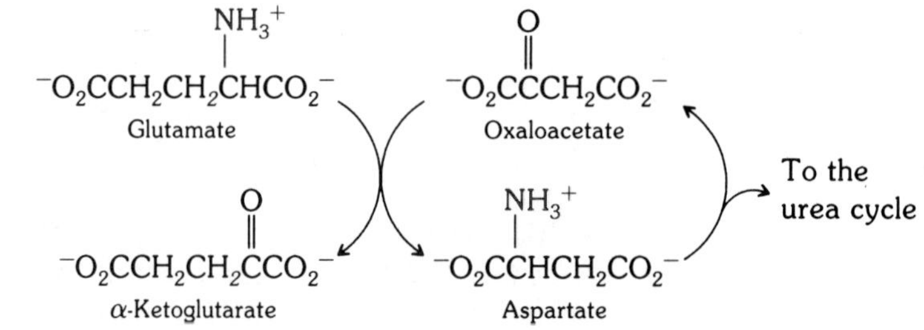

The reaction cycle showing:
Glutamate ($^-O_2CCH_2CH_2CHCO_2^-$ with NH_3^+) → Oxaloacetate ($^-O_2CCCH_2CO_2^-$ with O) → To the urea cycle

α-Ketoglutarate ($^-O_2CCH_2CH_2CCO_2^-$ with O) → Aspartate ($^-O_2CCHCH_2CO_2^-$ with NH_3^+)

The Urea Cycle Is the Only Way the Body Has To Make Urea   A series of reactions called the **urea cycle** manufactures urea from ammonium ion, carbon dioxide, and aspartate. Figure 29.5 displays its steps, and the boxed numbers in this figure refer to the following discussion.

■ The urea cycle is sometimes called the Krebs ornithine cycle.

Figure 29.5
The urea cycle. The boxed numbers refer to the text discussion. The dashed-line circle is the aspartate–oxaloacetate shuttle also discussed in the text.

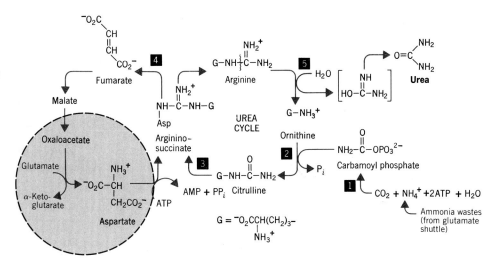

■ This step occurs inside a mitochondrion.

■ Steps 2 through 5 occur in the cell's cytosol.

1. Ammonia, with the help of ATP, reacts with CO_2 to form carbamoyl phosphate, a high-energy phosphate. In a sense, this is an activation of ammonia that launches it into the next step that takes it into the cycle.

2. The carbamoyl group transfers to the carrier unit, ornithine, as P_i is ejected. This consumes energy from high-energy phosphate. Citrulline forms.

3. Citrulline condenses with the α-amino group of aspartate to give argininosuccinate.

4. Fumarate forms from the original aspartate as the amino group stays with the arginine that emerges. Fumarate is an intermediate in the citric acid cycle. By a transamination that involves glutamate, it is reconverted to aspartate.

5. Arginine is hydrolyzed. Urea forms and ornithine is regenerated to start another turn of the cycle.

The overall result of the urea cycle is given by the following equation (which, as Figure 29.5 makes clear, is extremely simplified):

$$2NH_3 + H_2CO_3 \longrightarrow NH_2-\overset{\overset{\text{O}}{\|}}{C}-NH_2 + 2H_2O$$
$$\text{Urea}$$

To do justice to the overall event, we must factor in the ATP consumption, as follows:

$$NH_4^+ + CO_2 + 3ATP + \text{aspartate} + 3H_2O \longrightarrow$$
$$\text{urea} + 2ADP + \text{fumarate} + 4P_i + AMP$$

At Elevated Levels, the Ammonium Ion Is Toxic If an infant is born without any one of the enzymes needed for the five steps of the urea cycle just given, it will die soon after birth. It will be unable, on its own, to clear the ammonium ion from its blood. (Prior to birth, the mother's metabolism handled this.) The ammonium ion is toxic at sufficiently high levels.

Some inherited genetic defects produce enzymes for this cycle that have reduced activity. Such individuals have a condition called **hyperammonemia,** an elevated level of NH_4^+ in the blood. If the level is not high enough to cause death, it can be expected to cause mental retardation. Infants that have this genetic defect improve on low-protein diets.

Uric acid

Purine

29.4 THE CATABOLISM OF OTHER NITROGEN COMPOUNDS

Uric acid and the bile pigments are other end products of the catabolism of nitrogen compounds.

The nitrogen of the purine bases of nucleic acids, adenine (A) and guanine (G), is excreted as uric acid, which also has the purine nucleus. After studying how uric acid forms, we'll see how defects in this pathway can lead to gout or to a particularly difficult disease of children, the Lesch–Nyhan syndrome.

The Catabolism of AMP Gives the Urate Ion The numbered steps in Figure 29.6 are discussed next to show how the adenine unit of AMP can be used to make uric acid.

1. A transamination removes the amino group of the adenine side chain in adenosine monophosphate, AMP.
2. Ribose phosphate is removed and will enter the pentose phosphate pathway of carbohydrate catabolism. The product is hypoxanthine.
3. An oxidation produces xanthine. (The steps from guanine lead to xanthine, too.)
4. Another oxidation produces the keto form of uric acid, which exists partly in the form of a phenol. Actually, it's the salt of uric acid that forms, sodium urate, because the acid is neutralized by base in the buffer system.

Overproduction of the Urate Ion Causes Gout In the disease known as **gout,** the rate of formation of sodium urate is more rapid than its rate of elimination. Crystals of this salt precipitate in joints, where they cause painful inflammations and lead to a form of arthritis. Kidney stones may form as this salt comes out of solution in this organ.

Just why the formation of sodium urate accelerates isn't well understood, but genetic factors are involved. Normally, some of the hypoxanthine made in step 2 is recycled back to nucleotide bases that are needed to make nucleic acids or high-energy phosphates. Some individuals with gout are known to have a partial deficiency of the enzyme system required for this recycling of hypoxanthine. Hence, most if not all of their hypoxanthine ends up as more sodium urate than normal.

The Absence of One Enzyme Needed for Hypoxanthine Recycle Leads to Self-Mutilating Behavior in Infants In the Lesch-Nyhan syndrome, the enzyme for recycling

Figure 29.6
The catabolism of adenosine monophosphate, AMP. The boxed numbers refer to the discussion in the text.

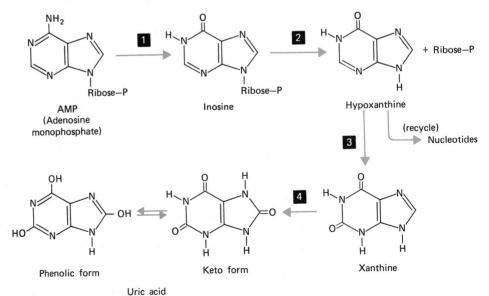

AMP
(Adenosine monophosphate)

Inosine

Hypoxanthine

(recycle) Nucleotides

Phenolic form

Keto form

Xanthine

Uric acid

JAUNDICE AND THE TETRAPYRROLE PIGMENTS

Jaundice (French *jaune,* yellow) is a condition that is symptomatic of a malfunction somewhere along the pathway of heme metabolism. If bile pigments accumulate in the plasma in concentrations high enough to impart a yellowish coloration to the skin, the condition of *jaundice* is said to exist. Jaundice can result from one of three kinds of malfunctions.

Hemolytic jaundice results when hemolysis takes place at an abnormally fast rate. Bile pigments, particularly bilirubin, form faster than the liver can clear them. Hepatic diseases such as infectious hepatitis and cirrhosis sometimes prevent the liver from removing bilirubin from circulation. The stools are usually clay-colored, because the pyrrole pigments do not reach the intestinal tract.

Obstructions of bile ducts can prevent release of bile into the intestinal tract, and the tetrapyrrole pigments in bile cannot be eliminated. Under these circumstances, they tend to reenter general circulation. The kidneys remove large amounts of bilirubin, but the stools are usually clay-colored. As the liver works harder and harder to handle its task of removing excess bilirubin, it can weaken and become permanently damaged.

■ The lack of one enzyme usually means great personal and family suffering.

hypoxanthine is totally lacking. The result is both bizarre and traumatic. Infants with this syndrome develop compulsive, self-destructive behavior at age 2 or 3. Unless their hands are wrapped in cloth, they will bite themselves to the point of mutilation. They act with dangerous aggression toward others. Some become spastic and mentally retarded. Kidney stones develop early, and gout comes later.

The Catabolism of Heme Produces the Bile Pigments Erythrocytes have life spans of only about 120 days. Eventually they split open. Their hemoglobin spills out and then is degraded. Its breakdown products are eliminated via the feces and, to some extent, in the urine. In fact, the characteristic colors of feces and urine are caused by partially degraded heme molecules called the **bile pigments.**

The degradation of heme begins before the globin portion breaks away. The heme molecule partly opens up to give a system that has a chain of four small rings called pyrrole rings. (This is why the bile pigments are sometimes called the *tetrapyrrole pigments*.)

Pyrrole skeleton

Carbon skeleton of the bile pigments

The rings have varying numbers of double bonds according to the state of oxidation of the pigment.

The slightly broken hemoglobin molecule, now called verdohemoglobin, then splits into globin, iron(II) ion, and a greenish pigment called **biliverdin** (Latin *bilis,* bile, + *virdus,* green). Globin enters the nitrogen pool. Iron is conserved in a storage protein called ferritin and is reused. Biliverdin is changed in the liver to a reddish-orange pigment called **bilirubin** (Latin *bilis,* bile + *rubin,* red). Bilirubin not only is made by the liver but is also removed from circulation by the liver, which transfers it to the bile. In this fluid it finally enters the intestinal tract.

■ Bile pigments are also responsible for the color of bile.

The pathway from hemoglobin to bilirubin after the rupture of an erythrocyte, as well as the fate of bilirubin, is shown in Figure 29.7.

Bilirubin is the principal bile pigment in humans. In the intestinal tract, bacterial enzymes convert bilirubin to a colorless substance called mesobilirubinogen. This is further processed to form a substance known as **bilinogen,** which usually goes by other names that describe differences in destination rather than structure. Thus bilinogen that leaves the body in the feces is called *stercobilinogen* (Latin *stercus,* dung). Some bilinogen is reabsorbed via the bloodstream, comes to the liver, and finally leaves the body in the urine. Now it is called *urobilinogen.* Some bilinogen is reoxidized to give **bilin,** a brownish pigment. Depending on its destination, bilin is called *stercobilin* or *urobilin.*

Special Topic 29.1 describes how the bile pigments are involved in jaundice.

Figure 29.7
The formation and the elimination of the products of the catabolism of hemoglobin.

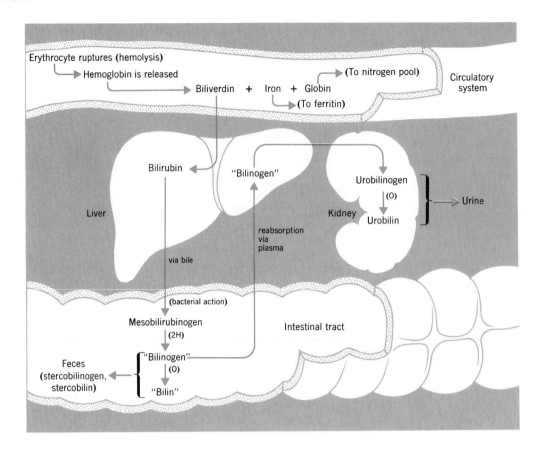

SUMMARY

Amino acid distribution The nitrogen pool receives amino acids from the diet, from the breakdown of proteins in body fluids or tissues, and from any synthesis of nonessential amino acids that occurs. Amino acids are used to build and repair tissue, replace proteins of body fluids, make nonprotein nitrogen compounds, provide chemical energy if needed, and supply molecular parts for gluconeogenesis or lipigenesis.

Amino acid metabolism By reactions of transamination, oxidative deamination, direct deamination, and decarboxylation, the α-amino acids shuffle amino groups between themselves and intermediates of the citric acid cycle, or the synthesis of urea and nonprotein nitrogen compounds.

Deaminated amino acids eventually become acetyl CoA, ace-
toacetyl CoA, pyruvate, or an intermediate in the citric acid cycle. The skeletons of most amino acids can be used to make glucose, or fatty acids, or the ketone bodies. Their nitrogen atoms become part of urea.

Metabolism of other nitrogen compounds The nitrogen atoms in some of the side-chain bases of nucleic acids end up in urea and those of the others are excreted as sodium urate. Urea is made by a complex cycle of reactions—the urea cycle.

Heme is catabolized to bile pigments and its iron is reused. The pigments—first, biliverdin (green), then bilirubin (red), then mesobilirubinogen (colorless), and finally bilinogen and bilin (brown)—become stercobilin or stercobilinogen, urobilin or urobilinogen, depending on the route of elimination.

REVIEW EXERCISES

The answers to these Review Exercises are in the *Study Guide* that accompanies this text.

Nitrogen Pool

29.1 What is the nitrogen pool?

29.2 What are four ways in which amino acids are used in the body?

29.3 When the body retains more nitrogen than it excretes in all
forms, the system is said to be on a *positive nitrogen balance*. Would this state characterize infancy or old age?

29.4 What happens to amino acids that are obtained in the diet but aren't needed to make any nitrogeneous compounds?

Biosynthesis of Amino Acids

29.5 Write the equation for the reductive amination that produces glutamate. (Use NADPH as the reducing agent.)

29.6 Write the structure of the keto acid that forms when phenylalanine undergoes transamination with α-ketoglutarate.

29.7 When valine and α-ketoglutarate undergo transamination, what new keto acid forms? Write its structure.

The Catabolism of Amino Acids

29.8 By means of two successive equations, one a transamination and the other an oxidative deamination, write the reactions that illustrate how the amino group of alanine can be removed as NH_4^+.

29.9 Arrange the following compounds in the order in which they would be produced if the carbon skeleton of alanine were to appear in one of the ketone bodies.

Pyruvate   Acetoacetyl CoA   Acetoacetate
   1   2   3

Alanine   Acetyl CoA
   4   5

29.10 In what order would the following compounds appear if some of the carbon atoms in glutamate were to become part of glycogen?

Oxaloacetate α-Ketoglutarate   Glucose
    1   2   3

Glycogen   Glutamate
    4   5

29.11 From a study of the figures in this chapter, can the carbon atoms of serine become a part of a molecule of palmitic acid? If so, write the names of the compounds, beginning with serine, in the sequence to the start of the lipigenesis cycle.

29.12 Can any of the carbon atoms of glucose become part of alanine? If so, explain (in general terms).

29.13 Write the structure of the keto acid that forms by the direct deamination of threonine.

29.14 When tyrosine undergoes decarboxylation, what forms? Write its structure.

29.15 Write the structure of the product of the decarboxylation of tryptophan.

29.16 In the conditions of starvation or diabetes, what can the amino acids be used for?

The Formation of Urea

29.17 In the biosynthesis of urea, what are the sources of (a) the two NH_2 groups and (b) the $C{=}O$ group?

29.18 What is hyperammonemia and, in general terms, how does it arise and how can it be handled in infants?

29.19 What is the overall equation for the synthesis of urea?

The Catabolism of Nonprotein Nitrogen Compounds

29.20 What compounds are catabolized to make uric acid?

29.21 What product of catabolism accumulates in the joints in gout?

29.22 Arrange the names of the following substances in the order in which they appear during the catabolism of heme.

Biliverdin   Heme   Hemoglobin   Bilirubin
    1   2   3   4

Mesobilirubinogen   Bilin   Bilinogen
        5   6   7

Tetrapyrrole Pigments and Jaundice (Special Topic 29.1)

29.23 Briefly describe what jaundice does to the body.

29.24 Describe how the following kinds of jaundice arise.
(a) hemolytic jaundice
(b) the jaundice of hepatic diseases

29.25 Why should an obstruction of the bile ducts cause jaundice?

Mathematical Concepts

A.1 EXPONENTIALS

When numbers are either very large or very small, it's often more convenient to express them in what is called *exponential notation*. Several examples are given in Table A.1, which shows how multiples of 10, such as 10,000, and submultiples of 10, such as 0.0001, can be expressed in exponential notation.

Exponential notation expresses a number as the product of two numbers. The first is a digit between 1 and 10, and this is multiplied by the second, 10 raised to some whole-number power or exponent. For example, 55,000,000 is expressed in exponential notation as 5.5×10^7, in which 7 (meaning $+7$) is the exponent.

Exponents can be negative numbers, too. For example, 3.4×10^{-3} is a number with a negative exponent. Now let's learn how to move back and forth between the exponential and the expanded expressions.

Positive Exponents A positive exponent is a number that tells how many times the number standing before the 10 has to be multiplied by 10 to give the same number in its expanded form. For example,

$$5.5 \times 10^7 = \underbrace{5.5 \times 10 \times 10 \times 10 \times 10 \times 10 \times 10 \times 10}_{10^7}$$

$$6 \times 10^3 = 6 \times 10 \times 10 \times 10 = 6000$$

$$8.576 \times 10^2 = 8.576 \times 10 \times 10 = 857.6$$

TABLE A.1

Number	Exponential Form
1	1×10^0
10	1×10^1
100	1×10^2
1,000	1×10^3
10,000	1×10^4
100,000	1×10^5
1,000,000	1×10^6
0.1	1×10^{-1}
0.01	1×10^{-2}
0.001	1×10^{-3}
0.0001	1×10^{-4}
0.00001	1×10^{-5}
0.000001	1×10^{-6}

The number before the 10 doesn't always have to be a number between 1 and 10. This is just a convention, which we sometimes might find useful to ignore. However, we can't ignore the rules of arithmetic in conversions from one form to another. For example,

$$0.00045 \times 10^5 = 0.00045 \times 10 \times 10 \times 10 \times 10 \times 10$$
$$= 45$$
$$87.5 \times 10^3 = 87.5 \times 10 \times 10 \times 10$$
$$= 87,500$$

In most problem-solving situations you find that the problem is given the other way around. You encounter a large number, and (after you've learned the usefulness of exponential notation) you know that the next few minutes of your life could actually be easier if you could quickly restate the number in exponential form. This is very easy to do. Just count the number of places that you have to move the decimal point to the *left* to put it just after the first digit of the given number. For example, you might have to work with a number such as 1500 (as in 1500 mL). You'd have to move the decimal point three places leftward from where it's understood to be (1500 = 1500.) to put it just after the first digit.

$$1 \underset{3 \quad 2 \quad 1}{,5\,0\,0}$$

Each of these leftward moves counts as one unit for the exponent. Three leftward moves mean an exponent of $+3$. Therefore 1500 can be rewritten as 1.500×10^3. A really huge number and one that you'll certainly meet somewhere during the course, is 602,000,000,000,000,000,000,000. It's called Avogadro's number, and you can see that manipulating it would be awkward. (How in the world does one even pronounce it?) In exponential notation, it's written simply as 6.02×10^{23}. Check it out. Do you have to move the decimal point leftward 23 places? (And now you could pronounce it: "six point oh two times ten to the twenty-third" — but saying "Avogadro's number" is easier.) Work these exercises for practice.

EXERCISE A.1   Expand each of these exponential numbers.

(a) 5.050×10^6 (b) 0.0000344×10^8 (c) 324.4×10^3

EXERCISE A.2   Write each of these numbers in exponential form.

(a) 422,045
(b) 24,000,000,000,000,000,000
(c) 24.32

Answers to Exercises A.1 and A.2

A.1   (a) 5,050,000   (b) 3,440   (c) 324,400
A.2   (a) 4.22045×10^5 (b) 2.4×10^{19} (c) 2.432×10^1

Negative Exponents   A negative exponent is a number that tells how many times the number standing before the 10 has to be *divided* by 10 to give the number in its expanded form. For example,

$$1 \times 10^{-4} = 1 \div 10 \div 10 \div 10 \div 10$$
$$= \frac{1}{10 \times 10 \times 10 \times 10} = \frac{1}{10,000} = \frac{1}{10^4}$$
$$= 0.0001$$
$$6 \times 10^{-3} = 6 \div 10 \div 10 \div 10$$
$$= \frac{6}{10 \times 10 \times 10} = \frac{6}{1000}$$
$$= 0.006$$

$$8.576 \times 10^{-2} = \frac{8.576}{10 \times 10} = \frac{8.576}{100} = 0.08576$$

You'll see negative exponents often when you study aqueous solutions that have very low concentrations.

Sometimes, you'll want to convert a very small number into its equivalent in exponential notation. This is also easy. This time we count *rightward* the number of times that you have to move the decimal point, one digit at a time, to place the decimal just to the right of the first nonzero digit in the number. For example, if the number is 0.00045, you have to move the decimal four times to the right to place it after the 4.

$$0.\underset{1\quad2\quad3\quad4}{0\ 0\ 0\ 4}\ 5$$

Therefore we can write $0.00045 = 4.5 \times 10^{-4}$. Similarly, we can write $0.0012 = 1.2 \times 10^{-3}$. And $0.00000000000000011 = 1.1 \times 10^{-16}$. Now try these exercises.

EXERCISE A.3 Write each number in expanded form.

(a) 4.3×10^{-2} (b) 5.6×10^{-10}
(c) 0.00034×10^{-2} (d) 4523.34×10^{-4}

EXERCISE A.4 Write the following numbers in exponential forms.

(a) 0.115   (b) 0.00005000041   (c) 0.000000000000345

Answers to Exercises A.3 and A.4

A.3   (a) 0.043   (b) 0.00000000056   (c) 0.0000034   (d) 0.452334
A.4   (a) 1.15×10^{-1} (b) 5.000041×10^{-5} (c) 3.45×10^{-13}

Now that we can write numbers in exponential notation, let's learn how to manipulate them.

How To Multiply Numbers Written In Exponential Form   Use the following two steps to multiply numbers that are expressed in exponential forms.

Step 1. Multiply the numbers in front of the 10s.

Step 2. *Add* the exponents of the 10s algebraically.

EXAMPLE A.1

$$(2 \times 10^4) \times (3 \times 10^5) = 2 \times 3 \times 10^{(4+5)}$$
$$= 6 \times 10^9$$

Usually, the problem you want to solve involves very large or very small numbers that aren't yet stated in exponential form. When this happens, convert the given numbers into their exponential forms first and then carry out the operation. The next example illustrates this and shows how exponentials can make a calculation easier.

EXAMPLE A.2

$$6576 \times 2000 = (6.576 \times 10^3) \times (2 \times 10^3)$$
$$= 13.152 \times 10^6$$
$$= 1.3152 \times 10^7$$

Work the following exercise to practice.

EXERCISE A.5 Calculate the following products after you have converted large or small numbers to exponential forms.

(a) $6,000,000 \times 0.0000002$　　(b) $10^6 \times 10^{-7} \times 10^8 \times 10^{-7}$

(c) $0.003 \times 0.002 \times 0.000001$　(d) $1,500 \times 3,000,000,000,000$

Answers: (a) 1.2　(b) 1　(c) 6×10^{-12}　(d) 4.5×10^{15}

How To Divide Numbers Written in Exponential Form　To divide numbers expressed in exponential forms, use the following two steps.

Step 1.　Divide the numbers that stand in front of the 10s.

Step 2.　*Subtract* the exponents of the 10s algebraically.

EXAMPLE A.3

$$(8 \times 10^4) \div (2 \times 10^3) = (8 \div 2) \times 10^{(4-3)}$$
$$= 4 \times 10^1$$

EXAMPLE A.4

$$(8 \times 10^4) \div (2 \times 10^{-3}) = (8 \div 2) \times 10^{[4-(-3)]}$$
$$= 4 \times 10^7$$

For practice, try the following exercise.

EXERCISE A.6 Do the following calculations using exponential forms of the numbers.

(a) $6,000,000 \div 1500$　　　　(b) $7460 \div 0.0005$

(c) $\dfrac{3,000,000 \times 6,000,000,000}{20,000}$　(d) $\dfrac{0.016 \times 0.0006}{0.000008}$

(e) $\dfrac{400 \times 500 \times 0.002 \times 500}{2,500,000}$

Answers: (a) 4×10^3　(b) 1.492×10^7　(c) 9×10^{11}　(d) 1.2　(e) 8×10^{-2}

How To Add and Subtract Numbers in Exponential Notation　We'll not spend too much time on this, because it doesn't come up very often. The only rule is that when you add or subtract exponentials, all the numbers must have the same exponents of 10. If they don't, we have to reexpress them to achieve this condition. Suppose you have to add 4.41×10^3 and 2.20×10^3. The result is simply 6.61×10^3.

$$(4.41 \times 10^3) + (2.20 \times 10^3) = [4.41 + 2.20] \times 10^3$$
$$= 6.61 \times 10^3$$

However, we can't add 4.41×10^3 to 2.20×10^4 without first making the exponents equal. We can do this in either of the following ways. In one, we notice that $2.20 \times 10^4 = 2.20 \times 10 \times 10^3 = 22.0 \times 10^3$, so we have

$$(4.41 \times 10^3) + (22.0 \times 10^3) = 26.41 \times 10^3 = 2.641 \times 10^4$$

Alternatively, we could notice that $4.41 \times 10^3 = 4.41 \times 10^{-1} \times 10^4 = 0.441 \times 10^4$, so we can do the addition as follows:

$$(0.441 \times 10^4) + (2.20 \times 10^4) = 2.641 \times 10^4$$

The result is the same both ways. The extension of this to subtraction should be obvious.[1]

The Pocket Calculator and Exponentials   The foregoing was meant to refresh your memory about exponentials, because you almost certainly have studied them in any course in algebra or some earlier course. You probably own a good pocket calculator, at least one that can take numbers in exponential form. Go ahead and use it, but be sure that you understand exponentials well, first. Otherwise, there are a great many pitfalls.

Most pocket calculators have a key marked *EE* or *EXP*. This is used to enter exponentials. Here is where an ability to *read* exponentials comes in handy. For example, the number 2.1×10^4 reads "two point one times ten to the fourth." The *EE* or *EXP* key on most calculators stands for ". . . times ten to the . . ." Therefore to enter 2.1×10^4, punch the following keys:

$$\boxed{2}\;\boxed{\cdot}\;\boxed{1}\;\boxed{EE}\;\boxed{4}$$

Try this on your own calculator and be sure to see that the display is correct. If it isn't, you may have a calculator that works differently than most, so recheck your operations of entering and then check your owner's manual.

To enter an exponential with a negative exponent, you have to use one more key, the $\boxed{+/-}$ key. This switches a positive number to its negative, and you *must* use it rather than the $\boxed{-}$ key in this situation. Thus the number 2.1×10^{-5} enters as follows:

$$\boxed{2}\;\boxed{\cdot}\;\boxed{1}\;\boxed{EE}\;\boxed{+/-}\;\boxed{5}$$

Try it and check the display. To see what happens if you use the $\boxed{-}$ key instead of the $\boxed{+/-}$ key, clear the display and enter this number only using the $\boxed{-}$ key instead of the $\boxed{+/-}$ key.

A.2   CROSS MULTIPLICATION

In this section we will learn how to solve for x in such expressions as

$$\frac{12}{x} = \frac{16}{25} \quad \text{or} \quad \frac{32.0}{11.2} = \frac{6.15x}{13.1}$$

The operation is called *cross multiplication,* and its object is to get x to stand alone, all by itself, on one side of the $=$ sign, and above any real or understood divisor line.

> To cross-multiply, move a number or a symbol both across the $=$ sign and across a divisor line, and then multiply.

EXAMPLE A.5

Problem: Solve for x in $\dfrac{25}{x} = 5$

Solution: Notice first the divisor lines; one is understood.

---

[1] Whenever these operations are with pure numbers and not with physical quantities obtained by measurements, we are not concerned about significant figures.

divisor line $\longrightarrow \dfrac{25}{x} = 5 \longleftarrow$ divisor line understood because $5 = \dfrac{5}{1}$

Remember, we want x to stand alone, on top of a divisor line (even if this line is understood). To make this happen, we carry out cross multiplication as indicated:

$$\dfrac{25}{x} = \boxed{5}$$

Notice that the arrows show moves that carry the quantities not only across the $=$ sign but also across their respective divisor lines. *It is essential that both crossing-overs be done.* Now we have x standing alone above its (understood) divisor line.

$$\dfrac{25}{5} = x$$

Now we can do the arithmetic, $x = 5$.

EXAMPLE A.6

Problem: Solve for x in $\dfrac{40}{4} = 5x$

Solution: For x to stand alone, only the 5 has to be moved. The result is

$$\dfrac{40}{4} = \boxed{5}\, x$$

$$\dfrac{40}{4 \times 5} = x \quad \text{or} \quad x = 2$$

EXAMPLE A.7

Problem: Solve for x in $\dfrac{25 \times 60}{12} = \dfrac{625}{x}$

Solution: To get x to stand alone, we carry out the following cross multiplication.

$$\dfrac{\boxed{25 \times 60}}{\boxed{12}} \quad \dfrac{625}{\boxed{x}}$$

The result is

$$x = \dfrac{625 \times 12}{25 \times 60}$$
$$= 5$$

Now try the following exercise for practice.

EXERCISE A.7   Solve for x in the following.

(a) $\dfrac{12}{x} = \dfrac{16}{25}$ (b) $\dfrac{32.0}{11.2} = \dfrac{6.15x}{13.1}$

Answers: (a) $x = 18.75$ (b) $x = 6.085946574$

In Example 2.3 on page 36, the problem was to solve for Δt in the equation

$$\frac{0.106 \text{ cal}}{\text{g} \text{ °C}} = \frac{115 \text{ cal}}{25.4 \text{ g} \times \Delta t}$$

Here is a problem with both units and numbers, so now we have to add one more and very important principle. *We cross-multiply units as well as numbers.*

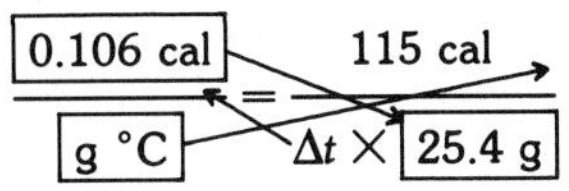

$$\boxed{0.106 \text{ cal}} \underset{=}{\diagdown} \boxed{115 \text{ cal}} \underset{\boxed{\text{g} \text{ °C}}}{\diagup} \overset{\diagdown}{\Delta t \times} \boxed{25.4 \text{ g}}$$

The result is the following, in which the cancel lines show how the units cancel.

$$\Delta t = \frac{(115 \text{ cal}) \times (\text{g} \text{ °C})}{(25.4 \text{ g}) \times (0.106 \text{ cal})} = 42.7 \text{ °C} \quad \text{(correctly rounded)}$$

How To Do Chain Calculations with the Pocket Calculator Sometimes the steps in solving a problem lead to something like the following:

$$x = \frac{24.2 \times 30.2 \times 55.6}{2.30 \times 18.2 \times 4.44}$$

Many people will first calculate the value of the numerator and write it down. Then they'll compute the denominator and write it down. Finally, they'll divide the two results to get the final answer. There's no need to do this much work. All you have to do is enter the first number you see in the numerator, 24.2 in our example. Then use the $\boxed{\times}$ key for any number in the numerator and the $\boxed{\div}$ key for any number in the denominator. *Each number in the denominator is entered with the $\boxed{\div}$ key.* Any of the following sequences work. Try them.

$$24.2 \times 30.2 \times 55.6 \div 2.30 \div 18.2 \div 4.44 = 218.632 \ldots$$

Or

$$24.2 \div 2.30 \times 30.2 \div 18.2 \times 55.6 \div 4.44 = 218.632 \ldots$$

A.3 LOGARITHMS

The **common logarithm** or the **log** of a number N to the base 10 is the exponent to which 10 must be raised to give N. In other words, when

$$N = 10^x$$

then the log of N is simply x. For example, when

$N = 10$	$\log N = 1$	because	$10 = 10^1$
$= 100$	$= 2$		$100 = 10^2$
$= 1000$	$= 3$		$1000 = 10^3$
$= 0.1$	$= -1$		$0.1 = 10^{-1}$
$= 0.001$	$= -2$		$0.1 = 10^{-2}$
$= 0.0001$	$= -3$		$0.001 = 10^{-3}$

Usually finding the value of $\log N$ is not this simple. Suppose, for example, that $N = 7.35$ rather than some simple multiple or submultiple of 10. By our definitions, to find the log of 7.35 (usually written log 7.35), we have to find the value of x in

$$7.35 = 10^x$$

The exponent x cannot now be a simple number. To analyze this we have to recognize that if

$$a = b$$

then it must be true that

$$\log a = \log b$$

So if

$$7.35 = 10^x$$

then, taking the logarithms of both sides, must give us

$$\log 7.35 = \log 10^x$$

But the definition of a log tells us that $\log 10^x = x$, so we can now write

$$\log 7.35 = x$$

There are two ways to determine x; use a table of logarithms or use a pocket calculator. A pocket calculator with a $\boxed{\log}$ key, in fact, has a built in table of logarithms. Just enter the number, 7.35, and hit the $\boxed{\log}$ key, and you will see 0.866287339 come up on the screen. This number has far more digits than we need. Let's round it to 0.866. Thus

$$\log 7.35 = 0.866$$

This result means that

$$7.35 = 10^{0.866}$$

Notice that this makes some rough sense. If $10 = 10^1$ and log 10 is therefore 1, the log of a number slightly smaller than 10, like 7.35, should correspond to 10 raised to a power somewhat smaller than 1. Maybe you can see now why logarithms were invented. They wouldn't be needed were all numbers simple, whole-number powers of 10, but there is an infinity of numbers with decimal places. Logarithms enable us to deal with any of them. For practice, try these exercises.

EXERCISE A.8 Find the logs of the following numbers. Round the calculator results as we did earlier. (We learned how to enter exponential numbers into the calculator at the end of Section A.1.)

(a) 125.34   (b) 0.00063   (c) 6.02×10^{23} (d) 5.778×10^{-6}
Answers: (a) 2.098   (b) −3.201   (c) 23.780   (d) −5.238

The only situation in this book in which logarithms must be used is in connection with pH or pK_a problems in Sections 9.2 and 9.5 and with Henderson–Haselbalch buffer problems in Section 9.7. For pH problems, Example 9.2 (page 239) gave detailed directions for using the pocket calculator to solve problems that require finding the log of a number. By definition, pH is given as follows.

$$pH = -\log [H^+]$$

If $[H^+] = 3.5 \times 10^{-8}$ mol/L, for example, the log of this value is (correctly rounded) -7.46. The pH is the negative of this number, so the pH = 7.46.

If the pH of a solution is given and the question asks you to find the value of $[H^+]$ in the solution, we can follow the directions of Example 9.3 (page 240). Now the alternative definition of pH is useful, which was given as Equation 9.4 (page 237).

$$[H^+] = 1 \times 10^{-pH}$$

Thus if an aqueous solution has a pH of 4.66, we enter 4.66 and change the sign with the $\boxed{+/-}$ key. We have now entered x for the equation

$$N = 10^x$$

where N is $[H^+]$ and $-x$ is the pH. We now use the $\boxed{10^x}$ key to find N. Correctly rounded,

$$N = 2.2 \times 10^{-5}$$

So

$$[H^+] = 2.2 \times 10^{-5} \text{ mol/L}$$

Footnote 2 on page 237 explains how to round physical data that involve logarithms. Now do the following exercise for more practice.

EXERCISE A.9   What are the concentrations of H^+ in solutions having the following values of pH?

(a) 1.34   (b) 5.65   (c) 6.65   (d) 7.35
Answers: (a) 4.57×10^{-2} mol/L   (b) 2.24×10^{-6} mol/L   (c) 2.24×10^{-7} mol/L
(d) 4.47×10^{-8} mol/L

Electron Configurations of the Elements

Atomic Number	Element	1s	2s	2p	3s	3p	3d	4s	4p	4d	4f	5s	5p	5d	5f	5g
1	H	1														
2	He	2														
3	Li	2	1													
4	Be	2	2													
5	B	2	2	1												
6	C	2	2	2												
7	N	2	2	3												
8	O	2	2	4												
9	F	2	2	5												
10	Ne	2	2	6												
11	Na	2	2	6	1											
12	Mg	2	2	6	2											
13	Al	2	2	6	2	1										
14	Si	2	2	6	2	2										
15	P	2	2	6	2	3										
16	S	2	2	6	2	4										
17	Cl	2	2	6	2	5										
18	Ar	2	2	6	2	6										
19	K	2	2	6	2	6		1								
20	Ca	2	2	6	2	6		2								
21	Sc	2	2	6	2	6	1	2								
22	Ti	2	2	6	2	6	2	2								
23	V	2	2	6	2	6	3	2								
24	Cr	2	2	6	2	6	5	1								
25	Mn	2	2	6	2	6	5	2								
26	Fe	2	2	6	2	6	6	2								
27	Co	2	2	6	2	6	7	2								
28	Ni	2	2	6	2	6	8	2								
29	Cu	2	2	6	2	6	10	1								
30	Zn	2	2	6	2	6	10	2								
31	Ga	2	2	6	2	6	10	2	1							
32	Ge	2	2	6	2	6	10	2	2							
33	As	2	2	6	2	6	10	2	3							
34	Se	2	2	6	2	6	10	2	4							
35	Br	2	2	6	2	6	10	2	5							
36	Kr	2	2	6	2	6	10	2	6							
37	Rb	2	2	6	2	6	10	2	6			1				
38	Sr	2	2	6	2	6	10	2	6			2				
39	Y	2	2	6	2	6	10	2	6	1		2				
40	Zr	2	2	6	2	6	10	2	6	2		2				
41	Nb	2	2	6	2	6	10	2	6	4		1				
42	Mo	2	2	6	2	6	10	2	6	5		1				
43	Tc	2	2	6	2	6	10	2	6	5		2				
44	Ru	2	2	6	2	6	10	2	6	7		1				
45	Rh	2	2	6	2	6	10	2	6	8		1				
46	Pd	2	2	6	2	6	10	2	6	10						
47	Ag	2	2	6	2	6	10	2	6	10		1				
48	Cd	2	2	6	2	6	10	2	6	10		2				
49	In	2	2	6	2	6	10	2	6	10		2	1			
50	Sn	2	2	6	2	6	10	2	6	10		2	2			
51	Sb	2	2	6	2	6	10	2	6	10		2	3			
52	Te	2	2	6	2	6	10	2	6	10		2	4			
53	I	2	2	6	2	6	10	2	6	10		2	5			
54	Xe	2	2	6	2	6	10	2	6	10		2	6			

Atomic Number	Element	K	L	M	4s	4p	4d	4f	5s	5p	5d	5f	5g	6s	6p	6d	7s
55	Cs	2	8	18	2	6	10		2	6				1			
56	Ba	2	8	18	2	6	10		2	6				2			
57	La	2	8	18	2	6	10		2	6	1			2			
58	Ce	2	8	18	2	6	10	1	2	6	1			2			
59	Pr	2	8	18	2	6	10	3	2	6				2			
60	Nd	2	8	18	2	6	10	4	2	6				2			
61	Pm	2	8	18	2	6	10	5	2	6				2			
62	Sm	2	8	18	2	6	10	6	2	6				2			
63	Eu	2	8	18	2	6	10	7	2	6				2			
64	Gd	2	8	18	2	6	10	7	2	6	1			2			
65	Tb	2	8	18	2	6	10	9	2	6				2			
66	Dy	2	8	18	2	6	10	10	2	6				2			
67	Ho	2	8	18	2	6	10	11	2	6				2			
68	Er	2	8	18	2	6	10	12	2	6				2			
69	Tm	2	8	18	2	6	10	13	2	6				2			
70	Yb	2	8	18	2	6	10	14	2	6				2			
71	Lu	2	8	18	2	6	10	14	2	6	1			2			
72	Hf	2	8	18	2	6	10	14	2	6	2			2			
73	Ta	2	8	18	2	6	10	14	2	6	3			2			
74	W	2	8	18	2	6	10	14	2	6	4			2			
75	Re	2	8	18	2	6	10	14	2	6	5			2			
76	Os	2	8	18	2	6	10	14	2	6	6			2			
77	Ir	2	8	18	2	6	10	14	2	6	7			2			
78	Pt	2	8	18	2	6	10	14	2	6	9			1			
79	Au	2	8	18	2	6	10	14	2	6	10			1			
80	Hg	2	8	18	2	6	10	14	2	6	10			2			
81	Tl	2	8	18	2	6	10	14	2	6	10			2	1		
82	Pb	2	8	18	2	6	10	14	2	6	10			2	2		
83	Bi	2	8	18	2	6	10	14	2	6	10			2	3		
84	Po	2	8	18	2	6	10	14	2	6	10			2	4		
85	At	2	8	18	2	6	10	14	2	6	10			2	5		
86	Rn	2	8	18	2	6	10	14	2	6	10			2	6		
87	Fr	2	8	18	2	6	10	14	2	6	10			2	6		1
88	Ra	2	8	18	2	6	10	14	2	6	10			2	6		2
89	Ac	2	8	18	2	6	10	14	2	6	10			2	6	1	2
90	Th	2	8	18	2	6	10	14	2	6	10			2	6	2	2
91	Pa	2	8	18	2	6	10	14	2	6	10	2		2	6	1	2
92	U	2	8	18	2	6	10	14	2	6	10	3		2	6	1	2
93	Np	2	8	18	2	6	10	14	2	6	10	4		2	6	1	2
94	Pu	2	8	18	2	6	10	14	2	6	10	6		2	6		2
95	Am	2	8	18	2	6	10	14	2	6	10	7		2	6		2
96	Cm	2	8	18	2	6	10	14	2	6	10	7		2	6	1	2
97	Bk	2	8	18	2	6	10	14	2	6	10	9		2	6		2
98	Cf	2	8	18	2	6	10	14	2	6	10	10		2	6		2
99	Es	2	8	18	2	6	10	14	2	6	10	11		2	6		2
100	Fm	2	8	18	2	6	10	14	2	6	10	12		2	6		2
101	Md	2	8	18	2	6	10	14	2	6	10	13		2	6		2
102	No	2	8	18	2	6	10	14	2	6	10	14		2	6		2
103	Lr	2	8	18	2	6	10	14	2	6	10	14		2	6	1	2

Some Rules for Naming Inorganic Compounds

Only rules considered sufficient to meet most of the needs of the users of this text are in this Appendix. The latest edition of the *Handbook of Chemistry and Physics,* published annually by the CRC Publishing Company, Cleveland, Ohio, under the general editorship of R. C. Weast, has a section on all the rules. Virtually all college libraries have this reference.

I. **Binary Compounds** — those made from only two elements
   A. One element is a metal and the other is a nonmetal
      1. The name of the metal is written first in the name of the compound, and its symbol is placed first in the formula.
      2. The name ending of the nonmetal is changed to *-ide.* Thus the names of the simple ions of groups VIA and VIIA of the periodic table are

Group VIIA	Group VIA
Fluoride	Oxide
Chloride	Sulfide
Bromide	Selenide
Iodide	Telluride

      3. If the metal and the nonmetal each have just one oxidation number, a binary compound of the two is named simply by writing the name of the metal and then that of the nonmetal with its ending modified by *-ide,* as shown above. Greek prefixes such as mono-, di-, tri-, etc., are not necessary. Examples are

Some Compounds Between Elements of Groups IA and VIIA		Some Compounds Between Elements of Groups IA and VIA	
NaF	Sodium fluoride	Na_2O	Sodium oxide (not disodium oxide)
KCl	Potassium chloride	K_2S	Potassium sulfide
LiBr	Lithium bromide	Li_2O	Lithium oxide
RbI	Rubidium iodide	Cs_2S	Cesium sulfide
CsCl	Cesium chloride	Rb_2O	Rubidium oxide

Some Compounds Between Elements of Groups IIA and VIIA		Some Compounds Between Elements of Groups IIA and VIA	
$BeCl_2$	Beryllium chloride	BeO	Beryllium oxide
$MgBr_2$	Magnesium bromide	MgS	Magnesium sulfide
CaF_2	Calcium fluoride	CaO	Calcium oxide
SrI_2	Strontium iodide	SrS	Strontium sulfide
$BaCl_2$	Barium chloride	BaO	Barium oxide

Some Compounds Between Elements of Groups IIIA and VIIA		Some Compounds Between Elements of Groups IIIA and VIA	
$AlCl_3$	Aluminum chloride	Al_2O_3	Aluminum oxide
AlF_3	Aluminum fluoride	Al_2S_3	Aluminum sulfide

4. If the metal has more than one oxidation number, but the nonmetal has just one, the formal name of the compound includes a roman numeral in parentheses following the name of the metal. This numeral stands for the oxidation number of the metal. Greek prefixes such as mono-, di-, etc., are not needed.

EXAMPLE C.1   **COMPOUNDS OF IRON IN OXIDATION STATES OF 2+ OR 3+**

	Formal Name	Common Name
$FeCl_2$	Iron(II) chloride[a]	ferrous chloride
FeO	Iron(II) oxide	ferrous oxide
Fe_2O_3	Iron(III) oxide	ferric oxide
$FeCl_3$	Iron(III) chloride	ferric chloride

[a] Pronounced "iron two chloride."

EXAMPLE C.2   **COMPOUNDS OF COPPER IN OXIDATION STATES OF 1+ AND 2+**

	Formal Name	Common Name
Cu_2O	Copper(I) oxide	cuprous oxide
CuBr	Copper(I) bromide	cuprous bromide
$CuCl_2$	Copper(II) chloride	cupric chloride
CuS	Copper(II) sulfide	cupric sulfide

5. Molecular compounds of two elements. Greek prefixes such as mono-, di-, and so on, are used, sometimes for *both* elements.
   (a) Oxides of Nonmetals
       (1) Oxides of Carbon   (2) Oxides of Sulfur

CO	Carbon monoxide	SO_2	Sulfur dioxide
CO_2	Carbon dioxide	SO_3	Sulfur trioxide

(3) Oxides of Nitrogen (Older Names in Parentheses)

N_2O	Dinitrogen monoxide (nitrous oxide)
NO	Nitrogen oxide (nitric oxide)
N_2O_3	Dinitrogen trioxide
NO_2	Nitrogen dioxide
N_2O_4	Dinitrogen tetroxide
N_2O_5	Dinitrogen pentoxide

(4) Oxides of Some Halogens

F_2O	Difluorine monoxide
Cl_2O	Dichlorine monoxide
Cl_2O_7	Dichlorine heptoxide

(b) Some Halides of Carbon

CCl_4	Carbon tetrachloride
CBr_4	Carbon tetrabromide

(c) Some Exceptions

H_2O	Water	NH_3	Ammonia	CH_4	Methane

II. **Compounds of Three or More Elements**

A. A positive and a negative ion are combined

1. The name of the positive ion is first followed by the name of the negative ion, just as with binary compounds between metals and nonmetals. Greek prefixes are not needed except where they occur in the name of an ion. (Older names are shown in parentheses.)

Li_2SO_4	Lithium sulfate	$MgSO_4$	Magnesium sulfate
Na_2SO_4	Sodium sulfate	$CaSO_4$	Calcium sulfate
K_2SO_4	Potassium sulfate	$Al_2(SO_4)_3$	Aluminum sulfate
$LiHCO_3$	Lithium hydrogen carbonate (lithium bicarbonate)[a]		
$NaHCO_3$	Sodium hydrogen carbonate (sodium bicarbonate)		
Li_2CO_3	Lithium carbonate	$KMnO_4$	Potassium permanganate
Na_2CO_3	Sodium carbonate	Na_2CrO_4	Sodium chromate
$CaCO_3$	Calcium carbonate	$Mg(NO_3)_2$	Magnesium nitrate
$Al_2(CO_3)_2$	Aluminum carbonate	$NaNO_2$	Sodium nitrite
$NaHSO_4$	Sodium hydrogen sulfate (sodium bisulfate)		
NaH_2PO_4	Sodium dihydrogen phosphate		
K_2HPO_4	Potassium monohydrogen phosphate		
$MgHPO_4$	Magnesium monohydrogen phosphate		
$(NH_4)_2HPO_4$	Ammonium monohydrogen phosphate		
Na_3PO_4	Sodium phosphate		
$Ca_3(PO_4)_2$	Calcium phosphate		

[a] *Bicarbonate* instead of *hydrogen carbonate* is used in this text because it is judged to be the more commonly used name for this ion, particularly among health scientists.

B. Molecular compounds of two or more elements. Most are organic compounds, so their rules of nomenclature are given in the chapters on organic compounds.

III.   **Important Inorganic Acids and Their Anions**

Formula	Name	Formula	Name
H_2CO_3	Carbonic acid	HCO_3^-	Hydrogen carbonate ion (bicarbonate ion)
		CO_3^{2-}	Carbonate ion
HNO_3	Nitric acid	NO_3^-	Nitrate ion
HNO_2	Nitrous acid	NO_2^-	Nitrite ion
H_2SO_4	Sulfuric acid	HSO_4^-	Hydrogen sulfate ion (bisulfate ion)
		SO_4^{2-}	Sulfate ion
H_2SO_3	Sulfurous acid	HSO_3^-	Hydrogen sulfite ion (bisulfite ion)
		SO_3^{2-}	Sulfite ion
H_3PO_4	Phosphoric acid (orthophosphoric acid)	$H_2PO_4^-$	Dihydrogen phosphate ion
		HPO_4^{2-}	Monohydrogen phosphate ion
		PO_4^{3-}	Phosphate ion
$HClO_4$	Perchloric acid	ClO_4^-	Perchlorate ion
$HClO_3$	Chloric acid	ClO_3^-	Chlorate ion
$HClO_2$	Chlorous acid	ClO_2^-	Chlorite ion
$HClO$	Hypochlorous acid	ClO^-	Hypochlorite ion
HCl	Hydrochloric acid[a]	Cl^-	Chloride ion

[a] The name of the aqueous solution of gaseous HCl.

Some generalizations about names of acids and their anions

1.   Names of ions from acids whose names end in *-ic* all end in *-ate.*

2.   When a nonmetal forms an oxyacid whose name ends in *-ic* also forms an acid with one fewer oxygen atoms, the name of the latter acid ends in *-ous.* (Compare nitric acid, HNO_3, and nitrous acid, HNO_2.)

3.   When a nonmetal forms an oxyacid with one fewer oxygen atoms than are in an *-ous* acid, then the prefix *hypo-* is used. (Compare chlorous acid, $HClO_2$, and hypochlorous acid, $HClO$.)

4.   The binary hydrohalogen acids are called hydrogen halides when they occur as pure gases but are called hydrohalic acids when they occur as aqueous solutions. Thus hydrogen fluoride in water becomes hydrofluoric acid; hydrogen chloride in water becomes hydrochloric acid; and so on.

Answers to Practice Exercises and Selected Review Exercises

Practice Exercises, Chapter 1

1. 310 K

2. (a) 5.45×10^8 (b) 5.67×10^{12}
    (c) 6.454×10^3 (d) 2.5×10^1
    (e) 3.98×10^{-5} (f) 4.26×10^{-3}
    (g) 1.68×10^{-1} (h) 9.87×10^{-12}

3. (a) 10^{-6} (b) 10^{-9}
    (c) 10^{-6} (d) 10^3

4. (a) mL   (b) μL   (c) dL
    (d) mm   (e) cm   (f) kg
    (g) μg   (h) mg

5. (a) kilogram   (b) centimeter   (c) deciliter
    (d) microgram   (e) milliliter   (f) milligram
    (g) millimeter   (h) microliter

6. (a) 1.5 Mg   (b) 3.45 μL   (c) 3.6 mg
    (d) 6.2 mL   (e) 1.68 kg   (f) 5.4 dm

7. (a) 275 kg   (b) 62.5 μL   (c) 82 nm or 0.082 μm

8. (a) 95   (b) 11.36   (c) 0.0263
    (d) 1.3000   (e) 16.1   (f) 3.8×10^2
    (g) 9.31   (h) 9.1×10^2

9. (a) $\dfrac{1 \text{ g}}{1000 \text{ mg}}$ or $\dfrac{1000 \text{ mg}}{1 \text{ g}}$

    (b) $\dfrac{1 \text{ kg}}{2.205 \text{ lb}}$ or $\dfrac{2.205 \text{ lb}}{1 \text{ kg}}$

10. 0.324 g of aspirin

11. (a) 324 mg of aspirin
    (b) 3.28×10^4 ft
    (c) 18.5 mL
    (d) 17.73 g
    (e) 4.78×10^3 μL

12. 40.0 °C

13. 59 °F (Quite cool.)

14. 20.7 mL

15. 32.1 g

Review Exercises, Chapter 1

1.31 273 K and 373 K

1.33 410 °F

1.35 88 °F

1.37 42.8 °C. No, regardless of the temperature *scale*, it's just as hot.

1.55 (a) 192 cm   (b) 111 lb avdp

1.57 16.9 liq oz

1.59 Do not cross; 2.1×10^3 kg $> 1.5 \times 10^3$ kg (the limit).

1.61 3.5 g/pat

1.63 8.8477×10^3 m; 8.8477 km

1.71 23.7 lb avdp of lead

1.73 28.3 mL of acetic acid

Practice Exercises, Chapter 2

1. Na_2S

2. Potassium, carbon, and oxygen in an atom ratio of $2:1:3$.

3. Final temperature = 24.5 °C.   ($\Delta t = 4.54$ °C)

4. 5.8×10^2 kcal

5. 2.99×10^4 cal
   29.9 kcal

6. 8.86 kcal

7. 4.0×10^3 kcal/day

Review Exercises, Chapter 2

2.21 $2:1$, a ratio of small whole numbers.

2.44 (a) KE = $\frac{1}{2}mv^2 = 5.86 \times 10^5$ J
    (b) KE = 1.40×10^5 cal
       = 1.40×10^2 kcal

2.51 For 1.00 g of water, heat capacity = 1.00 cal/°C.
    For 10.00 g of water, heat capacity = 10.0 cal/°C.

2.53 When ice melts at 0 °C and when liquid water boils at 100 °C.

2.65 $t = 282$ °C   (2.8×10^2 °C when properly rounded).

2.67 265 g of ethyl alcohol

2.81 4.0×10^3 kcal

2.83 1.7×10^2 kcal/cup milk   (rounded from 168 kcal).

Practice Exercises, Chapter 3

1. $^{16}_{8}O$

2. (a) 9 n   (b) 7 n   (c) 20 n   (d) 18 n
    8 p   7 p   17 p   17 p

3. The atomic number of carbon is 6, not 7.

4. (a) $1s^2 2s^2 2p_x^2 2p_y^2 2p_z^2 3s^2$
  (b) $1s^2 2s^2 2p_x^2 2p_y^2 2p_z^2 3s^2 3p_x^2 3p_y^2 3p_z^1$
  (c) $1s^2 2s^2 2p_x^2 2p_y^2 2p_z^2 3s^2 3p_x^2 3p_y^2 3p_z^2$
  (d) $1s^2 2s^2 2p_x^2 2p_y^2 2p_z^2 3s^2 3p_x^2 3p_y^2 3p_z^2 4s^2$

5. (a) Sn   (b) Cl   (c) Rb   (d) Mg   (e) Ar

6. (a) 1   (b) 6   (c) 5   (d) 7

Review Exercises, Chapter 3

3.9 (a) 4.03186 amu/He nucleus (calculated)
  (b) 4.001507 amu/He nucleus (observed)
  (c) 0.030356 amu/He nucleus (mass loss)
  (d) 4.54364×10^{-12} J/He nucleus
  (e) $2.7318 \times ^{12}$ J per 4 g of helium that forms by fusion.

3.41 Twelve times heavier.

3.42 (a) 1.33 times as heavy.
  (b) 16.0 g of oxygen atoms.

Practice Exercises, Chapter 4

1. (a) AgBr   (b) Na_2O (c) Fe_2O_3 (d) $CuCl_2$

2. (a) Copper(II) sulfide   (cupric sulfide)
  (b) Sodium fluoride
  (c) Iron(II) iodide   (ferrous iodide)
  (d) Zinc bromide
  (e) Copper(I) oxide   (cuprous oxide)

3. (a) 3+   (b) 2+   (c) 2+

4. (a) $1s^2 2s^2 2p_x^2 2p_y^2 2p_z^2 3s^2 3p_x^2 3p_y^2 3p_z^2 4s^1$ Ion's charge $= 1+$
  (b) $1s^2 2s^2 2p_x^2 2p_y^2 2p_z^2 3s^2 3p_x^2 3p_y^1 3p_z^1$ Ion's charge $= 2-$
  (c) $1s^2 2s^2 2p_x^2 2p_y^2 2p_z^2 3s^2 3p_x^1 3p_y^1$ No ion exists.

5. (a) $1s^2 2s^2 2p_x^2 2p_y^2 2p_z^2 3s^2 3p_x^2 3p_y^2 3p_z^2$
  (b) $1s^2 2s^2 2p_x^2 2p_y^2 2p_z^2 3s^2 3p_x^2 3p_y^2 3p_z^2$
  (c) No ion exists.

6. (a) Cs^+ (b) F^- (c) No ion.   (d) Sr^{2+}

7. (a) Mg is oxidized; S is reduced.
    Mg is the reducing agent; S is the oxidizing agent.
  (b) Zn is oxidized; Cu^{2+} is reduced.
    Zn is the reducing agent; Cu^{2+} is the oxidizing agent.

8. ·Na ·Mg· ·Al· ·Si· ·P· ·S· :Cl· :Ar:

9. ·Sb·

10. ·Ca· + ·Ö· → Ca^{2+} + [:Ö:]²⁻

11.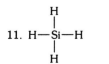

12. (a) $KHCO_3$ (b) Na_2HPO_4 (c) $(NH_4)_3PO_4$

13. (a) Sodium cyanide
  (b) Potassium nitrate

(c) Sodium hydrogen sulfite
(d) Ammonium carbonate
(e) Sodium acetate

14.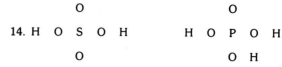

15. 32

16.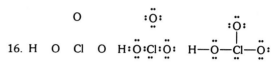
    skeletal structure   Lewis structures
    (requires 26
    valence electrons)

17.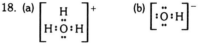

18. (a)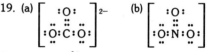

19. (a)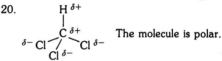

20.   The molecule is polar.

Practice Exercises, Chapter 5

1. $3O_2 \rightarrow 2O_3$

2. $4Al + 3O_2 \rightarrow 2Al_2O_3$

3. (a) $2Ca + O_2 \rightarrow 2CaO$
  (b) $2KOH + H_2SO_4 \rightarrow 2H_2O + K_2SO_4$
  (c) $Cu(NO_3)_2 + Na_2S \rightarrow CuS + 2NaNO_3$
  (d) $2AgNO_3 + CaCl_2 \rightarrow 2AgCl + Ca(NO_3)_2$
  (e) $2Al + 3H_2SO_4 \rightarrow Al_2(SO_4)_3 + 3H_2$
  (f) $CH_4 + 2O_2 \rightarrow 2H_2O + CO_2$

4. 8.68×10^{22} atoms of gold per ounce

5. (a) 180   (b) 58.3   (c) 859

6. 0.500 mol of H_2O.   500 mmol of H_2O

7. 4.20 mol of N_2 and 4.20 mol of O_2

8. 450 mol of H_2 and 150 mol of N_2

9. 408 g of NH_3

10. 0.0380 mol of aspirin

11. 11.5 g of O_2

12. 18.4 g of Na

13. (a) 2.45 g of H_2SO_4
  (b) 9.00 g of $C_6H_{12}O_6$

14. 156 mL of 0.800 M Na_2CO_3 solution

15. 9.82 mL of 0.112 M H_2SO_4, when calculated step by step with rounding after each step.
9.84 mL of 0.112 M H_2SO_4, when found by a chain calculation.

16. 20.0 mL of 0.200 M $K_2Cr_2O_7$.

17. Dilute 14 mL of 18 M H_2SO_4 to a final volume of 250 mL.

Review Exercises, Chapter 5

5.8 2.01×10^{23} formula units of H_2O

5.10 0.150 g of medication

5.13 (a) 40.0   (b) 100   (c) 98.1
      (d) 106   (e) 158   (f) 128

5.20 (a) 100 g   (b) 250 g   (c) 245 g
      (d) 265 g   (e) 395 g   (f) 320 g

5.22 (a) 1.88 mol   (b) 0.750 mol   (c) 0.765 mol
      (d) 0.708 mol   (e) 0.475 mol   (f) 0.586 mol

5.24 (a) $\dfrac{4 \text{ mol Fe}}{3 \text{ mol } O_2}$ and $\dfrac{3 \text{ mol } O_2}{4 \text{ mol Fe}}$

      (b) $\dfrac{4 \text{ mol Fe}}{2 \text{ mol } Fe_2O_3}$ and $\dfrac{2 \text{ mol } Fe_2O_3}{4 \text{ mol Fe}}$

      (c) $\dfrac{3 \text{ mol } O_2}{2 \text{ mol } Fe_2O_3}$ and $\dfrac{2 \text{ mol } Fe_2O_3}{3 \text{ mol } O_2}$

5.26 (a) 26 mol of O_2
      (b) 50 mol of H_2O
      (c) 26 mol of O_2

5.28 (a) 75.0 mol of H_2
      (b) 43 mol of CH_4

5.30 (a) 1.28×10^3 g of NaCl
      (b) 872 g of NaOH (stepwise calculation with rounding after each step).
      873 g of NaOH (when found by a chain calculation).
      (c) 21.8 g of H_2 (using 2.00 g/mol for H_2).

5.32 48.7 g of Na_2CO_3 (stepwise calculation with rounding after each step).
      48.6 g of Na_2CO_3 (when found by a chain calculation).

5.40 (a) 5.85 g of NaCl
      (b) 5.63 g of $C_6H_{12}O_6$
      (c) 0.981 g of H_2SO_4
      (d) 11.2 g of KOH

5.42 2.5×10^2 mL of 0.10 M HCl solution

5.44 1.0×10^2 mL of 0.010 M $NaHCO_3$ solution

5.46 250 mL of 1.00 M NaOH solution

5.48 167 mL of 0.150 M Na_2SO_4 solution

5.50 998 mL of 0.100 M HCl solution

5.52 Dissolve 12 mL of 17 M $HC_2H_3O_2$ in water and make the final volume equal to 100 mL.

Practice Exercises, Chapter 6

1. 1.31×10^3 mL of helium

2. 2.6 L

3. 52 mm Hg

4. Partial pressure of $N_2 = 720$ mm Hg
   Volume of $N_2 = 308$ mL

5. 547 mL of cyclopropane

6. 1.29×10^{-2} mol of O_2

7. Initially, $R = P_1V_1/nT_1$, and
   finally, $R = P_2V_2/nT_2$.
   Since $R = R$,
   $$P_1V_1/nT_1 = P_2V_2/nT_2$$
   The n's cancel, so
   $$P_1V_1/T_1 = P_2V_2/T_2$$

8. 2.63×10^4 mL of oxygen

9. $R = 0.0821$ L atm/mol K

Review Exercises, Chapter 6

6.10 2.08 lb/in.²

6.12 350 mm Hg or 350 torr

6.14 735 mm Hg

6.28 829 mm Hg

6.30 73 mm Hg

6.34 257 mL of wet O_2

6.36 1.84 L of O_2

6.44 (a) 3.54×10^{-2} mol of gas
      (b) 32.1
      (c) oxygen

6.46 (a) 2.00 mol of H_2
      (b) 200 L of H_2
      (c) 1.55×10^5 mL of H_2

Practice Exercises, Chapter 7

1. 1.47 mg N_2/100 g H_2O

2. 10.2 g of 96% H_2SO_4

3. 1.25 g of glucose and 499 g of water (rounded from 498.75, and assuming that the density of water is 1.00 g/mL).

4. 1.67×10^4 mm Hg

5. (a) 0.020 Osm   (b) 0.015 Osm
   (c) 0.100 Osm   (d) 0.150 Osm

Review Exercises, Chapter 7

7.39 $Z \cdot 10H_2O$

7.41 0.0207 g/L

7.52 (a) 0.500 g NaI
      (b) 1.25 g KBr
      (c) 6.25 g glucose
      (d) 15.0 g H_2SO_4

7.54 (a) 12.5 g of $Mg(NO_3)_2$
      (b) 5.00 g of NaBr
      (c) 2.50 g of KI
      (d) 1.68 g of $Ca(NO_3)_2$

7.56 25.0 mL of ethyl alcohol

7.58 (a) 11.0 mL of KOH solution

(b) 30.0 mL of HCl solution
(c) 650 mL of NaCl solution
(d) 281 mL of KOH solution

7.60 24.7 g of $Na_2SO_4 \cdot 10H_2O$

7.62 12.5 g of stock solution, or 11.9 mL of stock solution

7.64 (a) 71.0% (w/w) HNO_3
(b) 24.8 mL of concentrated solution

7.73 10% NaCl, which has 1.7 mmol/100 g solution versus only 0.67 mmol/100 g solution for 10% NaI.

7.76 372 mm Hg

Practice Exercises, Chapter 8

1. (a) $KBr(s) \rightarrow K^+(aq) + Br^-(aq)$
(b) $Na_2SO_4(s) \rightarrow 2Na^+(aq) + SO_4^{2-}(aq)$
(c) $CaCl_2(s) \rightarrow Ca^{2+}(aq) + 2Cl^-(aq)$

2. $H\!:\!\overset{..}{\underset{H}{O}}\!: + H\!:\!\overset{..}{\underset{..}{Br}}\!: \rightarrow \left[H\!:\!\overset{..}{\underset{H}{O}}\!:\!H \right]^+ + [\,:\!\overset{..}{\underset{..}{Br}}\!:\,]^-$

$H\!:\!\overset{..}{\underset{H}{O}}\!: + H\!:\!\overset{..}{\underset{..}{I}}\!: \rightarrow \left[H\!:\!\overset{..}{\underset{H}{O}}\!:\!H \right]^+ + [\,:\!\overset{..}{\underset{..}{I}}\!:\,]^-$

3. $H_2O + H_2SO_3(aq) \rightleftharpoons H_3O^+(aq) + HSO_3^-(aq)$
$H_2O + HSO_3^-(aq) \rightleftharpoons H_3O^+(aq) + SO_3^{2-}(aq)$

4. $HNO_3(aq) + KOH(aq) \rightarrow H_2O + KNO_3(aq)$
$H^+(aq) + NO_3^-(aq) + K^+(aq) + OH^-(aq) \rightarrow$
$ H_2O + K^+(aq) + NO_3^-(aq)$
$H^+(aq) + OH^-(aq) \rightarrow H_2O$

5. $Mg(OH)_2(s) + 2HCl(aq) \rightarrow 2H_2O + MgCl_2(aq)$
$Mg(OH)_2(s) + 2H^+(aq) \rightarrow 2H_2O + Mg^{2+}(aq)$

6. K_2SO_4

7. $2NaHCO_3(aq) + H_2SO_4(aq) \rightarrow$
$ 2CO_2(g) + 2H_2O + Na_2SO_4(aq)$
$2Na^+(aq) + 2HCO_3^-(aq) + 2H^+(aq) + SO_4^{2-}(aq) \rightarrow$
$ 2CO_2(g) + 2H_2O + 2Na^+(aq) + SO_4^{2-}(aq)$
$HCO_3^-(aq) + H^+(aq) \rightarrow CO_2(g) + H_2O$

8. $K_2CO_3(aq) + H_2SO_4(aq) \rightarrow CO_2(g) + H_2O + K_2SO_4(aq)$
$2K^+(aq) + CO_3^{2-}(aq) + 2H^+(aq) + SO_4^{2-}(aq) \rightarrow$
$ CO_2(g) + H_2O + 2K^+(aq) + SO_4^{2-}(aq)$
$CO_3^{2-}(aq) + 2H^+(aq) \rightarrow CO_2(g) + H_2O$

9. $MgCO_3(s) + 2HNO_3(aq) \rightarrow CO_2(g) + H_2O + Mg(NO_3)_2(aq)$
$MgCO_3(s) + 2H^+(aq) + 2NO_3^-(aq) \rightarrow$
$ CO_2(g) + H_2O + Mg^{2+}(aq) + 2NO_3^-(aq)$
$MgCO_3(s) + 2H^+(aq) \rightarrow CO_2(g) + H_2O + Mg^{2+}(aq)$

10. (a) $NH_3(aq) + HBr(aq) \rightarrow NH_4Br(aq)$
$NH_3(aq) + H^+(aq) \rightarrow NH_4^+(aq)$
(b) $2NH_3(aq) + H_2SO_4(aq) \rightarrow (NH_4)_2SO_4(aq)$
$NH_3(aq) + H^+(aq) \rightarrow NH_4^+(aq)$

11. $Mg(s) + 2HCl(aq) \rightarrow H_2(g) + MgCl_2(aq)$
$Mg(s) + 2H^+(aq) \rightarrow H_2(g) + Mg^{2+}(aq)$

12. (a) HNO_3 (b) HSO_3^- (c) HCO_3^-
(d) HSO_4^- (e) HCl   (f) H_3O^+
(g) H_2O

13. (a) CO_3^{2-} (b) PO_4^{3-} (c) HSO_4^-
(d) SO_4^{2-} (e) Br^- (f) H_2O
(g) OH^-

14. All are weak Brønsted bases.

15. (a) Weak   (b) Weak   (c) Strong   (d) Strong

16. Yes. $H^+(aq) + NO_2^-(aq) \rightleftharpoons HNO_2(aq)$
The product is favored.

17. $Cu(NO_3)_2(aq) + Na_2S(aq) \rightarrow CuS(s) + 2NaNO_3(aq)$
$Cu^{2+}(aq) + S^{2-}(aq) \rightarrow CuS(s)$

18. The acetate ion, $C_2H_3O_2^-(aq)$, binds H^+ ions from $HCl(aq)$ because $C_2H_3O_2^-$ is a relatively strong Brønsted base:
$C_2H_3O_2^-(aq) + H^+(aq) \rightleftharpoons HC_2H_3O_2(aq)$

19. (a) $Ag^+(aq) + Cl^-(aq) \rightarrow AgCl(s)$
(b) $CaCO_3(s) + 2H^+(aq) \rightarrow Ca^{2+}(aq) + H_2O + CO_2(g)$
(c) No reaction

Review Exercises, Chapter 8

8.55   0.250 mol of $NaHCO_3$

8.57   6.68 g of Na_2CO_3

8.59   4.91 g of $NaHCO_3$

8.61   29.5 mL of NaOH solution

8.63 $CaCO_3(s) + 2HCl(aq) \rightarrow CO_2(g) + H_2O + CaCl_2(aq)$
$ CaCO_3(s) + 2H^+(aq) \rightarrow CO_2(g) + H_2O + Ca^{2+}(aq)$
$ 47.8$ g of $CaCO_3$
$ 191$ mL of 5.00 M HCl

8.90   3.76 g or 3.76×10^3 mg of Cl^-

8.92   5.01 meq of K^+

8.108 Anion gap = 10 meq/L. This is in the normal range of 5 to 14 meq/L, so no serious disturbance in metabolism is indicated.

Practice Exercises, Chapter 9

1. (a) 2.5×10^{-6} mol OH^-/L, basic
(b) 9.1×10^{-8} mol OH^-/L, acidic
(c) 1.1×10^{-7} mol OH^-/L, basic

2. (a) pH = 1.60, pOH = 12.40
(b) pH = 10.40, pOH = 3.60
(c) pH = 10.70, pOH = 3.30

3. 7.14, basic.

4. (a) 4.6×10^{-7} mol/L, acidic.
(b) 1.3×10^{-8} mol/L, basic.

5. 5.25×10^{-8} mol/L

6. 3.6×10^{-10} mol/L

7. $HC_2H_3O_2(aq) \rightleftharpoons H^+(aq) + C_2H_3O_2^-(aq)$
$$K_a = \frac{[H^+][C_2H_3O_2^-]}{[HC_2H_3O_2]}$$

8. $HCO_3^-(aq) \rightleftharpoons H^+(aq) + CO_3^{2-}(aq)$
$$K_a = \frac{[H^+][CO_3^{2-}]}{[HCO_3^{2-}]}$$

9. $NH_4^+(aq) \rightleftharpoons H^+(aq) + NH_3(aq)$

$$K_a = \frac{[H^+][NH_3]}{[NH_3]}$$

10. Ascorbic acid

11. Cyanide ion

12. (a) $CO_3^{2-}(aq) + H_2O \rightleftharpoons HCO_3^-(aq) + OH^-(aq)$

$$K_b = \frac{[HCO_3^-][OH^-]}{[CO_3^{2-}]}$$

(b) $C_2H_3O_2^-(aq) + H_2O \rightleftharpoons HC_2H_3O_2(aq) + OH^-(aq)$

$$K_b = \frac{[HC_2H_3O_2][OH^-]}{[C_2H_3O_2^-]}$$

(c) $NH_3(aq) + H_2O \rightleftharpoons NH_4^+(aq) + OH^-(aq)$

$$K_b = \frac{[NH_4^+][OH^-]}{[NH_3]}$$

13. (a) Yes, basic.   (b) Yes, basic.
    (c) Yes, basic.   (d) Yes, acidic.
    (e) Yes, basic.   (e) Yes, basic.

14. Basic.

15. Acidic.

16. Yes, decrease the pH because NH_4^+ hydrolyzes to give some H^+.

17. 10.33

18. Acetic acid

19. 6.80

20. NH_3, $K_b = 1.8 \times 10^{-5}$

21. 4.8
    $CN^-(aq) + H_2O \rightleftharpoons HCN(aq) + OH^-(aq)$

$$K_b = \frac{[HCN][OH^-]}{[CN^-]}$$

22. 3.89

23. 3.86

24. (a) $pH = pK_a + 1$
    (b) $pH = pK_a - 1$

25. (a) 7.00
    (b) 7.18
    (c) A greater change in pH occurred.

26. 7.75. No

27. 0.105 M NaOH

28. 0.125 M H_2SO_4

Review Exercises, Chapter 9

9.8 2.43×10^{-14}. Neutral.

9.21 $pOH = 1.30$, $pH = 12.70$

9.37 (a) 3.17   (b) 7.52

9.39 (a) $pK_b = 10.83$
         $K_b = 1.5 \times 10^{-11}$
      (b) $pK_b = 6.48$
         $K_b = 3.3 \times 10^{-7}$

9.41 Y is the stronger acid. X has the stronger conjugate base.

9.64 4.83

9.66 (a) 5.22   (b) 5.06   (c) 5.38
      (d) $pH = 1.40$ after the addition of 0.020 mol of strong acid and $pH = 12.60$ after the addition of 0.020 mol of strong base to 500 mL of pure water.

9.70 (a) 6.1   (b) 7.1
      (c) Hyperventilation, to remove more CO_2.
      (d) The kidneys make more HCO_3^-.

9.79 400.0

9.81 (a) 9.125 g of HCl   (b) 5.434 g of HNO_3
      (c) 0.7357 g of H_2SO_4

9.83 (a) 0.04456 M Na_2CO_3 (b) 4.724 g of Na_2CO_3/L

Practice Exercises, Chapter 10

1. (a) H, +1   (b) S, +4   (c) H, +1
       S, −2   O, −2   O, −2
                                   S, +4

   (d) O, −2   (e) H, +1   (f) O, −2
       S, +6   O, −2   S, +6
                     S, +6

2. (a) H, +1   (b) H, +1   (c) H, +1
       C, −4   C, −2   C, 0
                     O, −2   O, −2

   (d) H, +1   (e) H, +1
       C, +2   C, +4
       O, −2   O, −2

3. (a) −1   (b) −2   (c) −3
   Reduction.

4. $Cu(s) + 4H^+(aq) + 2NO_3^-(aq) \rightarrow Cu^{2+}(aq) + 2NO_2(g) + 2H_2O$

5. $3C_2H_6O + 4MnO_4^-(aq) \rightarrow$
   $3C_2H_3O_2^-(aq) + 4MnO_2(s) + OH^-(aq) + 4H_2O$

6. $Zn(s) + Fe^{2+}(aq) \rightarrow Zn^{2+}(aq) + Fe(s)$

7. No, the reduction potential for $2H^+/H_2$ is not more positive than that of Cu^{2+}/Cu.

8. $E^\circ_{cell} = +0.29$ V

Review Exercises, Chapter 10

10.2 (a) O, −2   (b) O, −2   (c) O, −2
          N, +1   N, +2   N, +4
      (d) O, −2   (e) O, −2
          N, +4   N, +5

10.4 (a) H, +1   (b) H, +1   (c) H, +1
          S, −2   S, +4   S, +6
                        O, −2   O, −2

10.7 (a) $MnO_4^- + 8H^+ + 5e^- \rightarrow Mn^{2+} + 4H_2O$ (reduction)
      (b) $2Fe^{2+} + 3H_2O \rightarrow Fe_2O_3 + 6H^+ + 2e^-$ (oxidation)
      (c) $H_2C_2O_4 \rightarrow 2CO_2 + 2H^+ + 2e^-$ (oxidation)
      (d) $2NO_2 + 8H^+ + 8e^- \rightarrow N_2 + 4H_2O$ (reduction)

10.9 (a) $3Cu + 2NO_3^- + 8H^+ \rightarrow 3Cu^{2+} + 2NO + 4H_2O$
      (b) $Zn + SO_4^{2-} + 4H^+ \rightarrow Zn^{2+} + SO_2 + 2H_2O$
      (c) $3BiO_3^- + 2Cr^{3+} + 4H^+ \rightarrow 3Bi^{3+} + Cr_2O_7^{2-} + 2H_2O$
      (d) $5OCl^- + I_2 + H_2O \rightarrow 5Cl^- + 2IO_3^- + 2H^+$

10.11 (a) $CH_4O + 2MnO_4^- \rightarrow CO_2 + 2MnO_2 + 2OH^- + H_2O$
(b) $2CrO_4^{2-} + 3S^{2-} + 4H_2O \rightarrow 2CrO_2^- + 3S + 8OH^-$

10.14 (a) $Ca^{2+}(aq) + 2e^- \rightleftharpoons Ca(s)$ (b) Lesser   (c) H^+

10.20 $4I^- + O_2 + 4H^+ \rightarrow 2I_2 + 2H_2O$

10.22 Yes

10.24 1.51 V

10.26 1.0×10^{51}

Practice Exercises, Chapter 11

1. $^{131}_{53}I \rightarrow {}^{131}_{54}Xe + {}^{0}_{-1}e + {}^{0}_{0}\gamma$

2. $^{239}_{94}Pu \rightarrow {}^{235}_{92}U + {}^{4}_{2}He + {}^{0}_{0}\gamma$

3. 10,000 units

4. 8.5 m

Review Exercises, Chapter 11

11.11 (a) $^{241}_{94}Pu$ (b) $^{22}_{10}Ne$

11.13 (a) $^{252}_{99}Es \rightarrow {}^{4}_{2}He + {}^{248}_{97}Bk$
(b) $^{28}_{12}Mg \rightarrow {}^{0}_{-1}e + {}^{28}_{13}Al$
(c) $^{20}_{8}O \rightarrow {}^{0}_{-1}e + {}^{20}_{9}F$
(d) $^{251}_{98}Cf \rightarrow {}^{4}_{2}He + {}^{247}_{96}Cm + {}^{0}_{0}\gamma$

11.17 0.750 ng

11.30 15.1 m

11.46 Iron-55. $^{55}_{25}Mn + {}^{1}_{1}H \rightarrow {}^{1}_{0}n + {}^{55}_{26}Fe$

11.48 $^{113}_{49}In \rightarrow {}^{111}_{49}In + 2\,{}^{1}_{0}n$

11.50 $^{67}_{31}Ga + {}^{0}_{-1}e \xrightarrow{\text{electron capture}} {}^{67}_{30}Zn$

11.52 $^{10}_{5}B + {}^{4}_{2}He \rightarrow {}^{13}_{7}N + {}^{1}_{0}n$

11.54 A lithium nucleus. $^{27}_{13}Al + {}^{6}_{3}Li \rightarrow {}^{32}_{15}P + {}^{1}_{1}H$

11.56 10 J/kg

Practice Exercises, Chapter 12

1. (a) $CH_3{-}CH_2{-}CH_3$ (b) 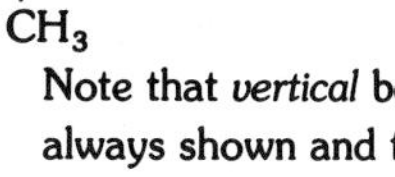 $CH_3{-}\underset{\underset{CH_3}{|}}{CH}{-}CH_3$

(c) 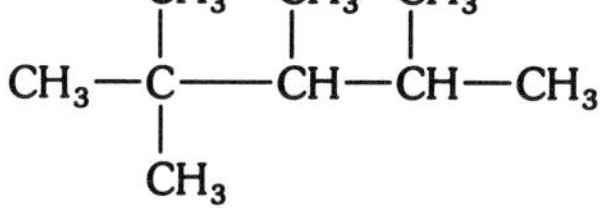 $CH_3{-}\overset{\overset{CH_3}{|}}{\underset{\underset{CH_3}{|}}{C}}{-}\overset{\overset{CH_3}{|}}{CH}{-}\overset{\overset{CH_3}{|}}{CH}{-}CH_3$

2. (a) $CH_3CH_2CH_3$ (b) 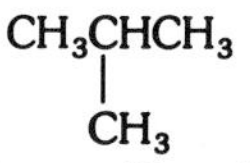 $CH_3\underset{\underset{CH_3}{|}}{CH}CH_3$

(c) 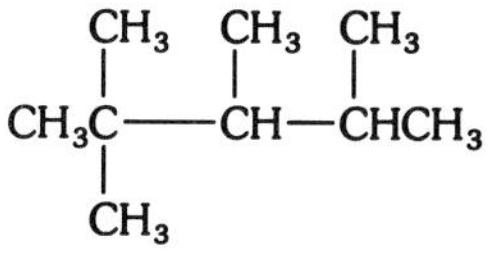 $CH_3\overset{\overset{CH_3}{|}}{\underset{\underset{CH_3}{|}}{C}}{-}\overset{\overset{CH_3}{|}}{CH}{-}CHCH_3$

Note that *vertical* bonds are always shown and that sometimes horizontal bonds are left in so that there will be room for other groups.

3. (a) 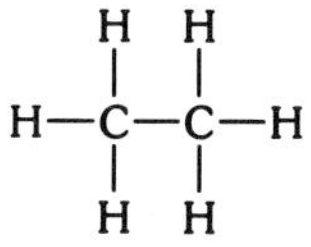 $H{-}\overset{\overset{H}{|}}{\underset{\underset{H}{|}}{C}}{-}\overset{\overset{H}{|}}{\underset{\underset{H}{|}}{C}}{-}H$

(b) [structural formula]

(c) [structural formula]

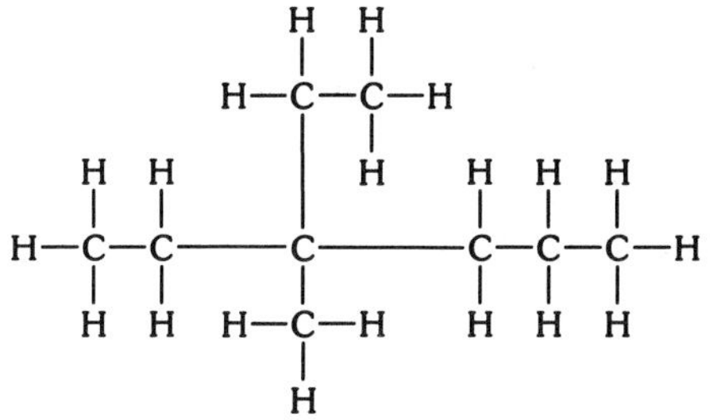

4. Structures b and c cannot represent real compounds.

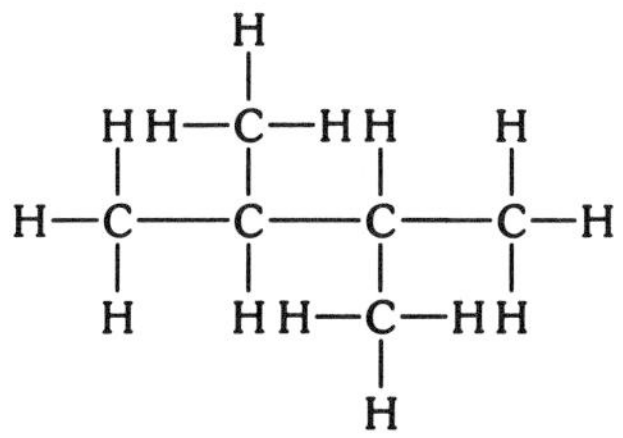

5. (a) 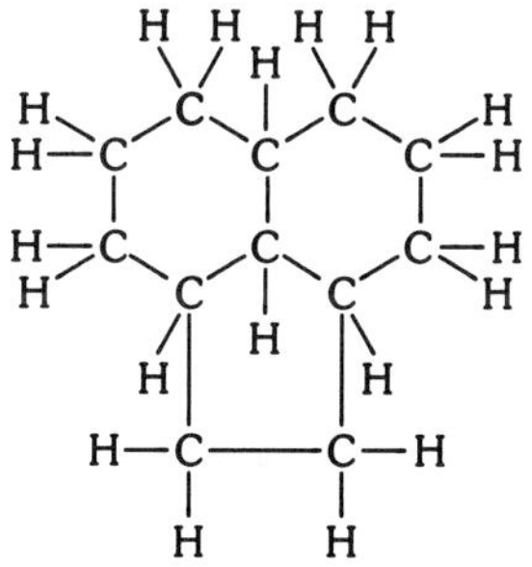 [structural formula]

(b) 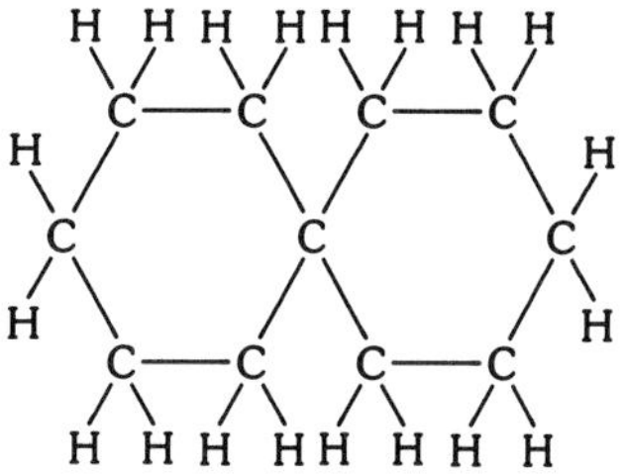 [structural formula]

6. 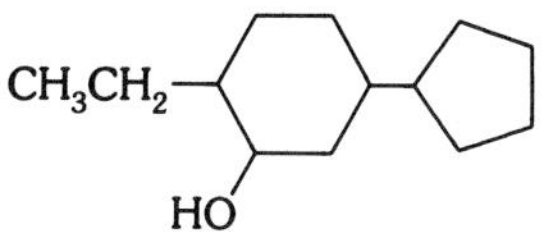 CH_3CH_2 — [cyclohexane ring with HO] — [cyclopentane ring]

7. (a) Identical.
(b) Isomers.
(c) Identical.
(d) Isomers.
(e) Different in another way.

8. The second structure. It has fewer polar —OH groups.

9. (a) 3-Methylhexane
(b) 4-*t*-Butyl-2,3-dimethylheptane
(c) 5-*sec*-Butyl-2,4-dimethylnonane
(d) 2-Bromo-1-chloro-3-iodopropane
(e) 5-*t*-Butyl-4-isopropyloctane or 4-*t*-butyl-5-isopropyloctane
(f) 1,3-Dinitro-2,2-dimethylpropane
(g) 1-Chloro-2,3-dimethylpentane
(h) 3-Ethyl-2,6-dimethylheptane

10. (a) 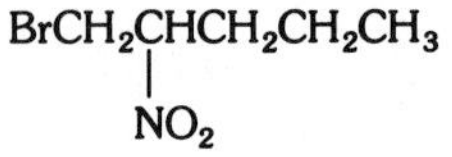 $BrCH_2CHCH_2CH_2CH_3$
          $\quad\quad\;\; |$
          $\quad\quad\; NO_2$

(b) 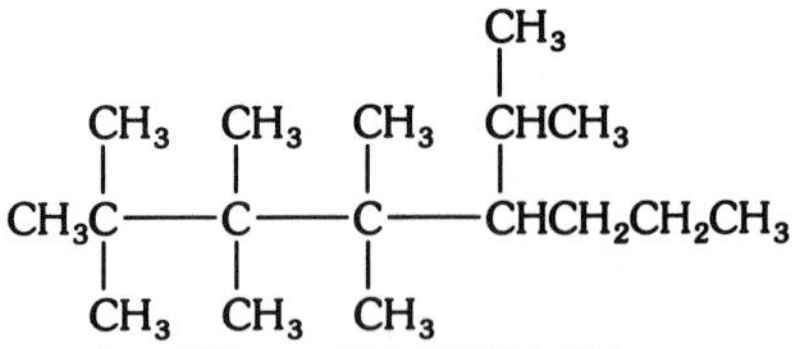
$$CH_3C \!-\! C \!-\! C \!-\! CHCH_2CH_2CH_3$$
with CH_3 groups and a $CHCH_3$ / CH_3 substituent

(c)
$$CH_3C \!-\! CH \!-\! CH \!-\! CH \!-\! CHCH_2CH_2CH_3$$
with I, I, CH_3, $CH_3CHCH_2CH_3$, $CHCH_3$, CH_3CCH_3, CH_3, CH_3 substituents

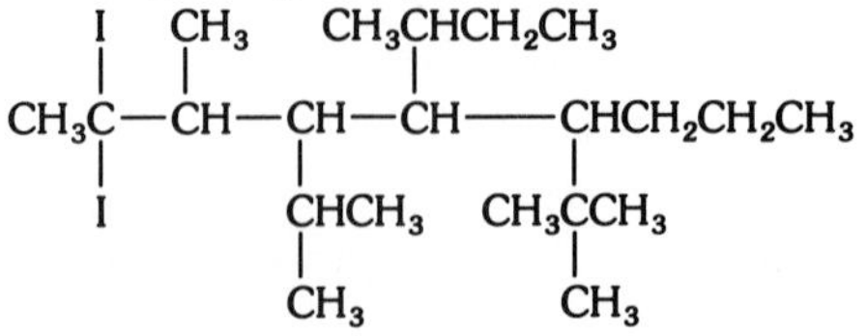

(d) 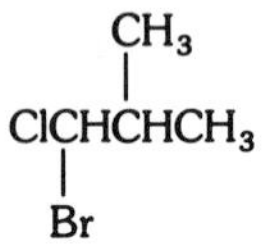
$$ClCHCHCH_3$$
$\quad\; |$
$\quad\; Br$
with CH_3 above

(e) 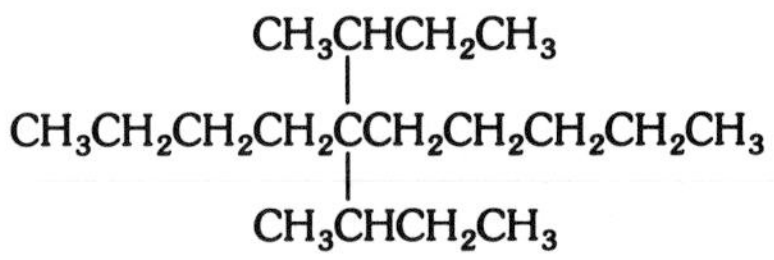 $CH_3CH_2CH_2CH_2CCH_2CH_2CH_2CH_3$
with $CH_3CHCH_2CH_3$ and $CH_3CHCH_2CH_3$ substituents

11. 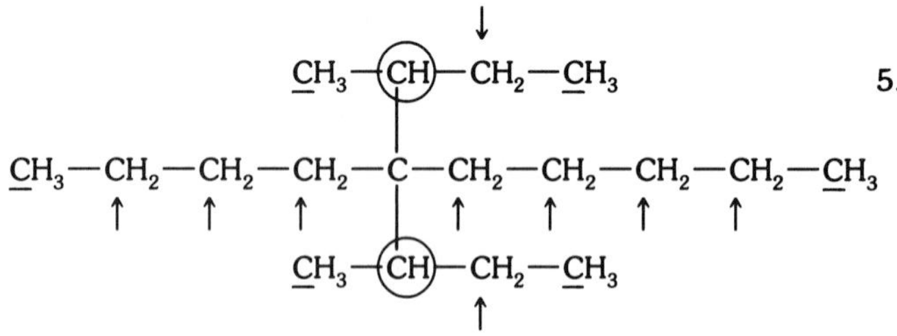
$$CH_3-CH_2-CH_2-CH_2-C-CH_2-CH_2-CH_2-CH_2-CH_3$$
with $CH_3-(CH)-CH_2-CH_3$ groups above and below

12. (a) Ethyl chloride
    (b) Butyl bromide
    (c) Isobutyl chloride
    (d) t-Butyl bromide

13. (a) Two. Butyl chloride or 1-chlorobutane and *sec*-butyl chloride or 2-chlorobutane
    (b) Two. Isobutyl chloride or 1-chloro-2-methylpropane and t-butyl chloride or 2-chloro-2-methylpropane

Practice Exercises, Chapter 13

1. (a) 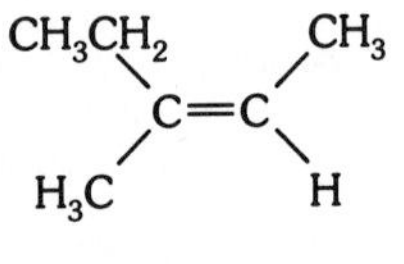
$$\underset{H_3C}{\overset{CH_3CH_2}{>}}C\!=\!C\overset{CH_3}{\underset{H}{<}} \quad\text{and}\quad \underset{H_3C}{\overset{CH_3CH_2}{>}}C\!=\!C\overset{H}{\underset{CH_3}{<}}$$

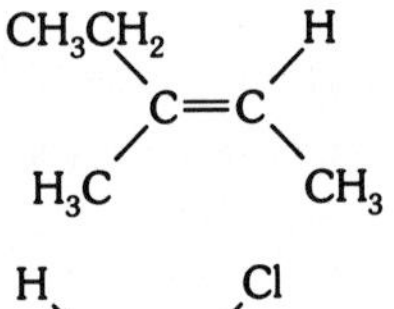

(b) 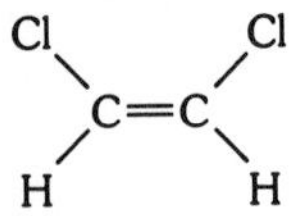
$$\underset{H}{\overset{Cl}{>}}C\!=\!C\overset{Cl}{\underset{H}{<}} \quad\text{and}\quad \underset{Cl}{\overset{H}{>}}C\!=\!C\overset{Cl}{\underset{H}{<}}$$

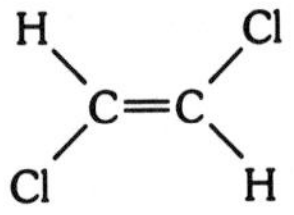

(c) None
(d) None

2. (a) 2-Methylpropene
   (b) 4-Isobutyl-3,6-dimethyl-3-heptene
   (c) 1-Chloropropene
   (d) 3-Bromopropene

(e) 4-Methyl-1-hexene   (f) 4-Methylcyclohexene

3. (a) 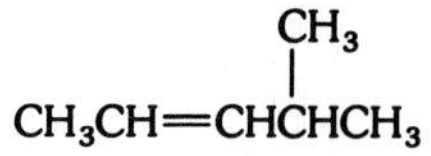 $CH_3CH\!=\!CHCHCH_3$ (with CH_3)
   (b) 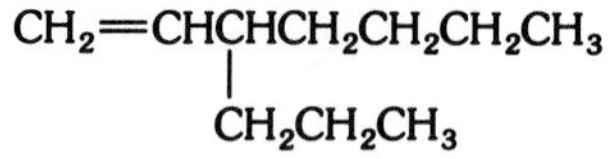 $CH_2\!=\!CHCHCH_2CH_2CH_3$ (with $CH_2CH_2CH_3$)
   (c) 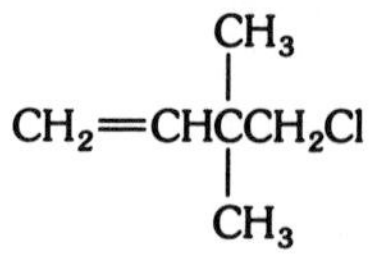 $CH_2\!=\!CHCCH_2Cl$ (with CH_3)
   (d) 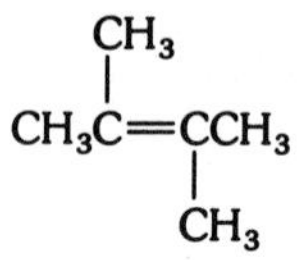 $CH_3C\!=\!CCH_3$ (with CH_3 and CH_3)

4. (a) $CH_3CH_2CH_3$
   (b) No reaction.
   (c) 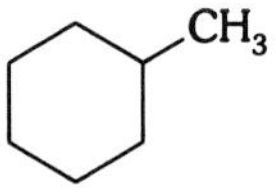 cyclohexane with CH_3
   (d) $CH_3(CH_2)_{16}CO_2H$

5. (a) 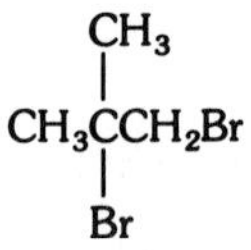 CH_3CCH_2Br (with CH_3 and Br)
   (b) No reaction. (*Substitution* can occur only if UV light or heat is used.)
   (c) 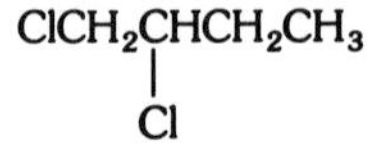 $ClCH_2CHCH_2CH_3$ (with Cl)
   (d) $CH_3CH_2CH_2CH_3$

6. (a) 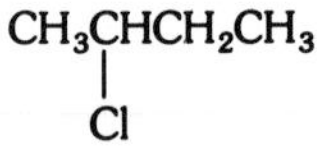 $CH_3CHCH_2CH_3$ (with Cl)
   (b) 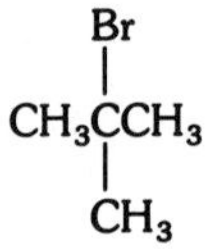 CH_3CCH_3 (with Br and CH_3)
   (c) 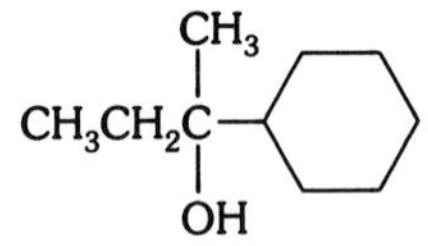 CH_3CH_2C—cyclohexane (with CH_3 and OH)
   (d) 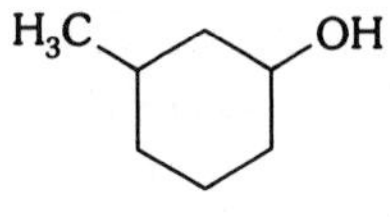 methylcyclohexanol + methylcyclohexanol
   (e) No reaction.

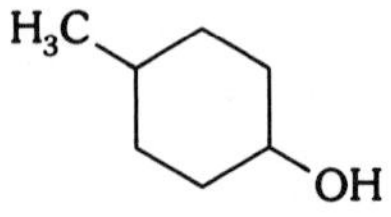

7. (a) $CH_3CH_2\overset{+}{C}HCH_3$, not $CH_3CH_2CH_2\overset{+}{C}H_2$
       (Preferred)

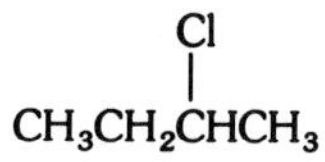

   $$CH_3CH_2CHCH_3$$
   $\quad\quad\quad |$
   $\quad\quad\quad Cl$
   (Product)

(b) 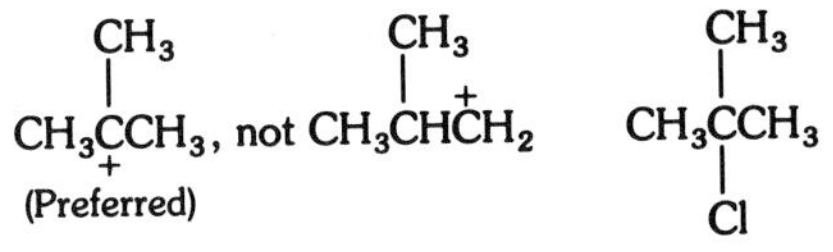 $CH_3\overset{CH_3}{\underset{+}{C}}CH_3$, not $CH_3\overset{CH_3}{\underset{+}{C}H}CH_2$ $CH_3\overset{CH_3}{\underset{\underset{Cl}{|}}{C}}CH_3$

(Preferred)   (Product)

(c) 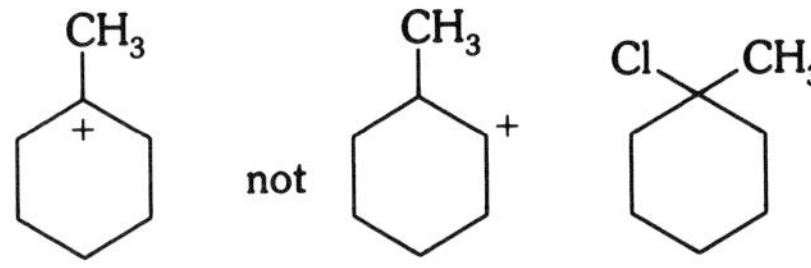   not

(Preferred)   (Product)

(d) $CH_3\overset{+}{C}HCH_2CH_3$ (the only cation) $CH_3\overset{\underset{Cl}{|}}{C}HCH_2CH_3$

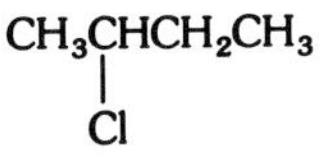

(e) $CH_3\overset{+}{C}HCH_2CH_2CH_3$ and $CH_3CH_2\overset{+}{C}HCH_2CH_3$ 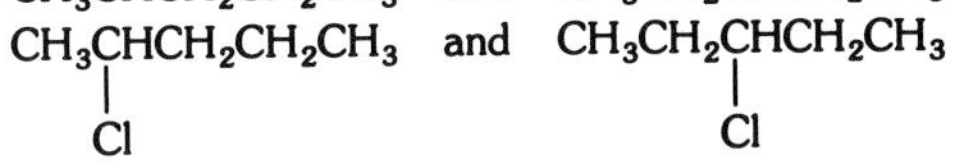
$CH_3\overset{\underset{Cl}{|}}{C}HCH_2CH_2CH_3$ and $CH_3CH_2\overset{\underset{Cl}{|}}{C}HCH_2CH_3$
(Both are equally stable.)

(f) 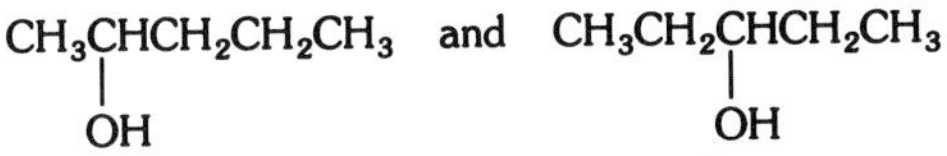 $CH_3\overset{\underset{OH}{|}}{C}HCH_2CH_2CH_3$ and $CH_3CH_2\overset{\underset{OH}{|}}{C}HCH_2CH_3$

The two possible cations, $CH_3\overset{+}{C}HCH_2CH_2CH_3$ and $CH_3CH_2\overset{+}{C}HCH_2CH_3$, are about equally stable, so both can and do form. This leads to the mixture of alcohols.

Practice Exercises, Chapter 14

1. (a) Monohydric, secondary
   (b) Monohydric, secondary
   (c) Dihydric, unstable
   (d) Dihydric
   (e) Monohydric, primary
   (f) Monohydric, primary
   (g) Monohydric, tertiary
   (h) Monohydric, secondary
   (i) Trihydric, unstable

2. (a) Alcohol   (b) Phenol
   (c) Carboxylic acid   (d) Alcohol
   (e) Alcohol   (f) Alcohol

3. (a) 4-Methyl-1-pentanol
   (b) 2-Methyl-2-propanol
   (c) 2-Ethyl-2-methyl-1-pentanol
   (d) 2-Methyl-1,3-propanediol

4. In 1,2-propanediol. Its boiling point is 189 °C, much higher than that of 1-butanol (b.p. 117 °C). 1,2-Propanediol is more soluble in water.

5. (a) $CH_3CH=CH_2$ (b) $CH_3CH=CH_2$
   (c) 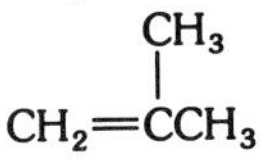 $CH_2=\overset{\underset{CH_3}{|}}{C}CH_3$ (d)

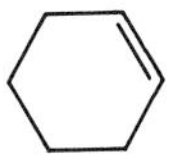

6. (a) 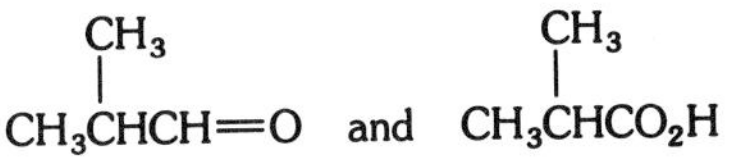 $CH_3\overset{\underset{CH_3}{|}}{C}HCH=O$ and $CH_3\overset{\underset{CH_3}{|}}{C}HCO_2H$

(b) 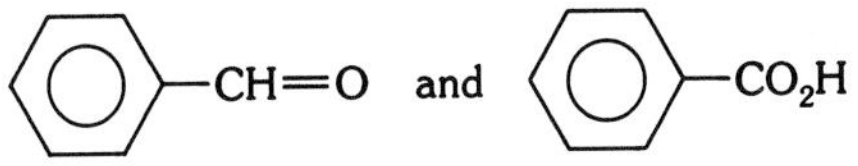 —CH=O and —CO₂H

(c) $CH_2=O$ and HCO_2H

7. (a) 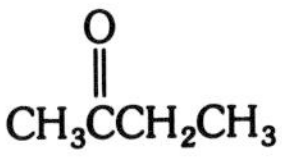 $CH_3\overset{\underset{\|}{O}}{C}CH_2CH_3$ (b)

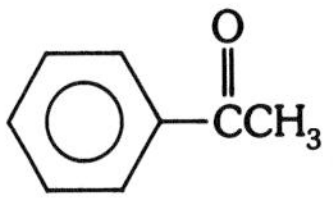

(c)

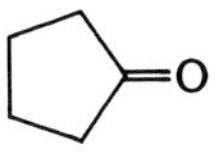

8. (a) 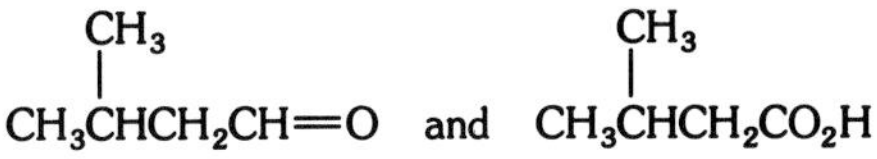 $CH_3\overset{\underset{CH_3}{|}}{C}HCH_2CH=O$ and $CH_3\overset{\underset{CH_3}{|}}{C}HCH_2CO_2H$
   (b) No reaction.
   (c) 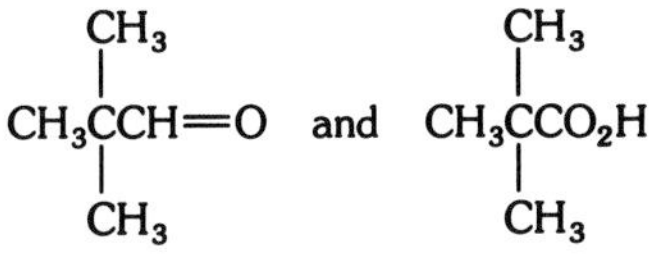 $CH_3\overset{\underset{CH_3}{|}}{C}CH=O$ and $CH_3\overset{\underset{CH_3}{|}}{C}CO_2H$, with $\overset{|}{CH_3}$ below each

   (d) 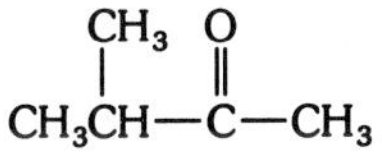 $CH_3\overset{\underset{CH_3}{|}}{C}H-\overset{\underset{\|}{O}}{C}-CH_3$

9. (a) $2CH_3SH$
   (b) $(CH_3)_2CH-S-S-CH(CH_3)_2$
   (c) $HSCH_2CH_2CH_2SH$
   (d)

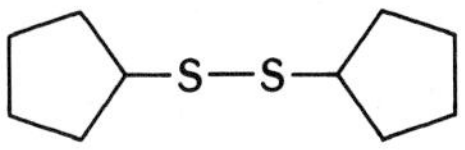

10. (a) CH_3-O-CH_3
    (b) $CH_3CH_2CH_2-O-CH_2CH_2CH_3$
    (c)

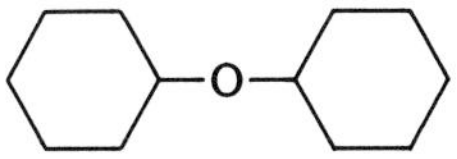

Practice Exercises, Chapter 15

1. (a) 2-Methylpropanal
   (b) 3-Bromobutanal
   (c) 4-Ethyl-2,4,6-trimethylheptanal

2. 2-Isopropylpropanal would have the structure.

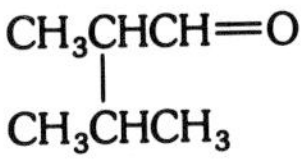

   $CH_3\overset{\underset{\overset{\underset{CH_3}{|}}{C}HCH_3}{|}}{C}HCH=O$

   and it should be named 2,3-dimethylbutanal.

3. (a) 2-Butanone (or simply butanone)
   (b) 6-Methyl-2-heptanone
   (c) 2-Methylcyclohexanone

4. (a) 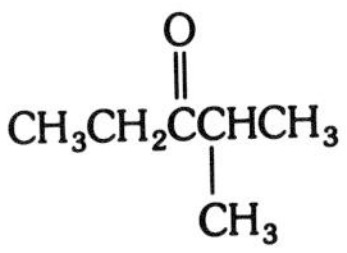 $CH_3CH_2\overset{\underset{\overset{\underset{CH_3}{|}}{}}{\overset{\|}{C}}}{C}HCH_3$ (b) $CH_3\overset{\underset{\|}{O}}{C}$—

   (c) $CH_3CH_2CH_2\overset{\underset{\|}{O}}{C}CH_2CH_2CH_3$

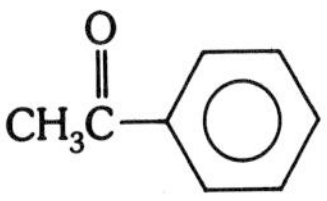

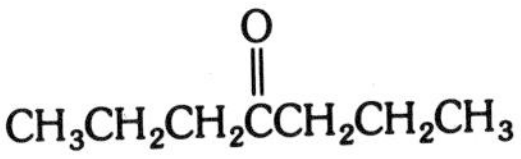

(d) 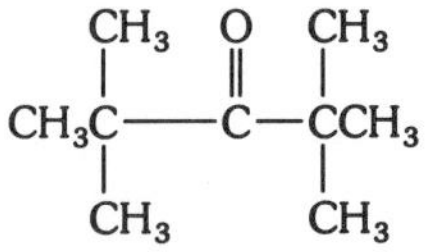
$$CH_3C\!-\!\overset{\overset{\displaystyle O}{\|}}{C}\!-\!CCH_3$$
with CH_3 groups

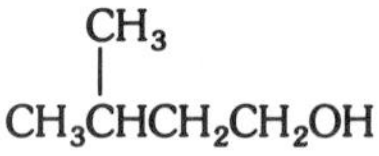

5. (a) 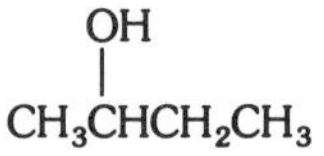 $CH_3\overset{\overset{\displaystyle OH}{|}}{C}HCH_2CH_3$ (b) $CH_3\overset{\overset{\displaystyle CH_3}{|}}{C}HCH_2CH_2OH$

(c) cyclohexyl—OH

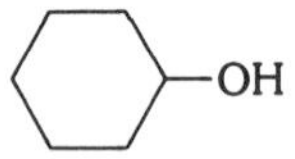

6. (a) Not a hemiacetal.   (b) Not a hemiacetal.
   (c) $HO\!-\!CH_2\!-\!O\!-\!CH_2CH_3$
   (d) 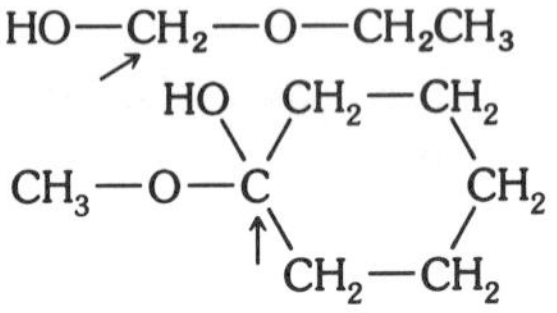
   $CH_3\!-\!O\!-\!C$ ring structure with HO and $CH_2\!-\!CH_2$

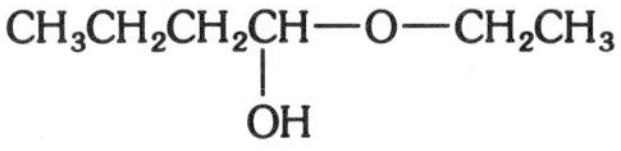

7. (a) 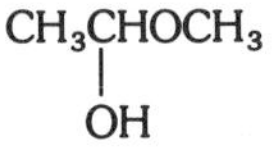 $CH_3\overset{\overset{\displaystyle }{}}{C}HOCH_3$ with OH (b) $CH_3CH_2CH_2CH\!-\!O\!-\!CH_2CH_3$ with OH

(c) phenyl—$CH\!-\!O\!-\!CH_2CH_2CH_3$ with OH

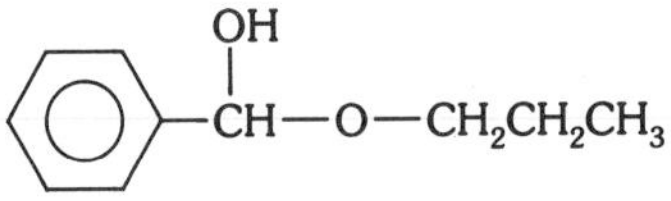

(d) $HO\!-\!CH_2\!-\!O\!-\!CH_3$

8. (a) $CH_3CH_2CH\!=\!O + HOCH_3$
   (b) $CH_3CH_2OH + O\!=\!CHCH_2CH_3$

9. (a) Not a hemiketal.   (b) 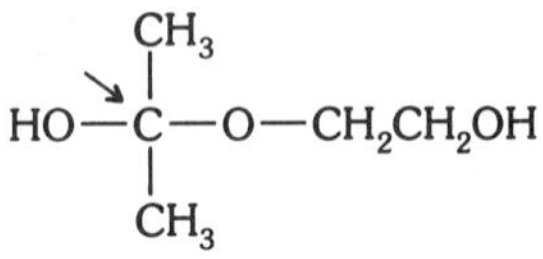 $HO\!-\!\overset{\overset{\displaystyle CH_3}{|}}{\underset{\underset{\displaystyle CH_3}{|}}{C}}\!-\!O\!-\!CH_2CH_2OH$

10. 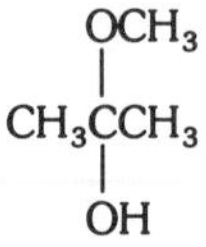 $CH_3\overset{\overset{\displaystyle OCH_3}{|}}{\underset{\underset{\displaystyle OH}{|}}{C}}CH_3$

11. 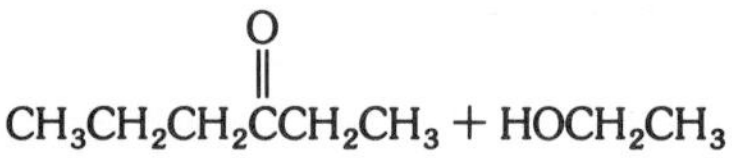 $CH_3CH_2CH_2\overset{\overset{\displaystyle O}{\|}}{C}CH_2CH_3 + HOCH_2CH_3$

12. (a) Neither
    (b) A ketal,

$CH_3CH_2\!-\!O\!-\!\overset{\overset{\displaystyle CH_3}{|}}{\underset{\underset{\displaystyle CH_3}{|}}{C}}\!-\!O\!-\!CH_2CH_3$

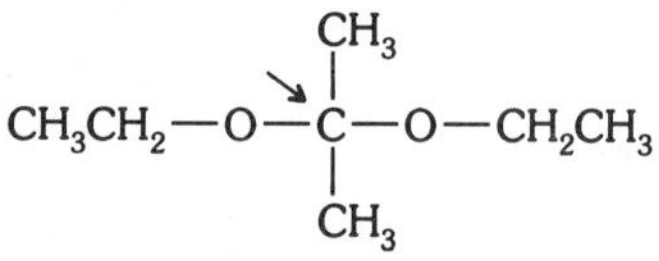

13. (a) $2CH_3OH + CH_2\!=\!O$
    (b) No reaction.
    (c) 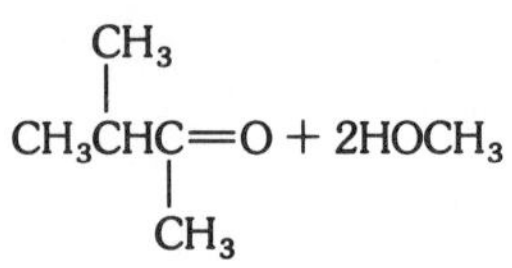 $CH_3\overset{\overset{\displaystyle CH_3}{|}}{C}HC\!=\!O + 2HOCH_3$ with CH_3

Practice Exercises, Chapter 16

1. (a) 2,2-Dimethylpropanoic acid
   (b) 5-Ethyl-5-isopropyl-3-methyloctanoic acid

(c) Sodium ethanoate
(d) Sodium 5-chloro-3-methylheptanoate

2. Pentanedioic acid
3. 9-Octadecenoic acid
4. (a) $CH_3CH_2CO_2^-$

   (b) 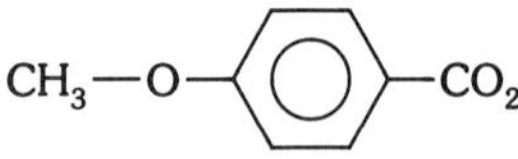 $CH_3\!-\!O\!-\!$ phenyl $\!-\!CO_2^-$

   (c) $CH_3CH\!=\!CHCO_2^-$

5. (a) 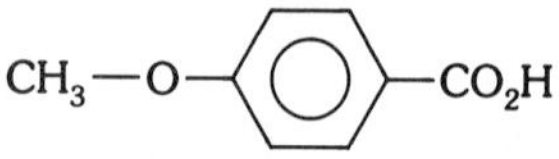 $CH_3\!-\!O\!-\!$ phenyl $\!-\!CO_2H$

   (b) $CH_3CH_2CO_2H$
   (c) $CH_3CH\!=\!CHCO_2H$

6. (a) $CH_3CO_2CH_3$
   (b) $CH_3CO_2CH_2CH_2CH_3$
   (c) 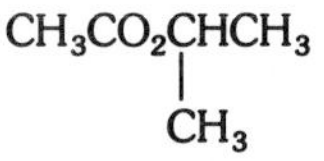 $CH_3CO_2\overset{\overset{\displaystyle }{}}{C}HCH_3$ with CH_3

7. (a) $HCO_2CH_2CH_3$
   (b) $CH_3CH_2CO_2CH_2CH_3$
   (c) 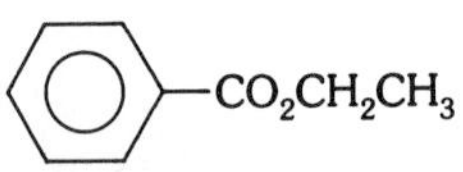 phenyl $\!-\!CO_2CH_2CH_3$

8. (a) Methyl propanoate
   (b) Propyl 3-methylpentanoate
9. (a) t-Butyl acetate
   (b) Ethyl butyrate
10. (a) $CH_3CO_2H + CH_3OH$
    (b) 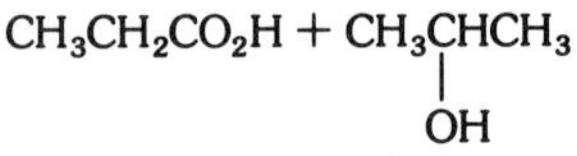 $CH_3CH_2CO_2H + CH_3\overset{\overset{\displaystyle }{}}{C}HCH_3$ with OH

    (c) $CH_3\overset{\overset{\displaystyle CH_3}{|}}{C}HCO_2H + CH_3CH_2CH_2OH$

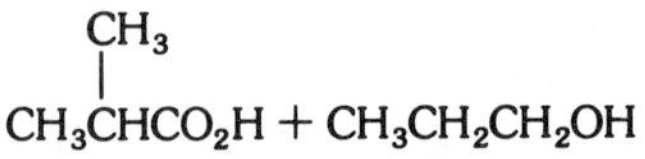

11. (a) 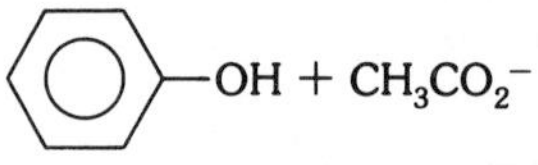 phenyl $\!-\!OH + CH_3CO_2^-$

    (b) 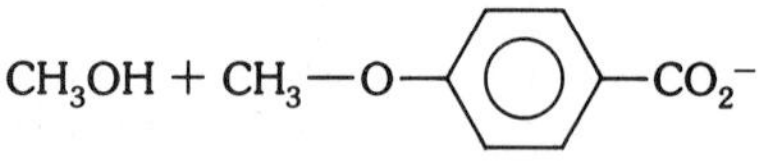 $CH_3OH + CH_3\!-\!O\!-\!$ phenyl $\!-\!CO_2^-$

Practice Exercises, Chapter 17

1. (a) Dimethylisopropylamine
   (b) Cyclohexylamine
   (c) Isobutyl-t-butylamine

2. (a) 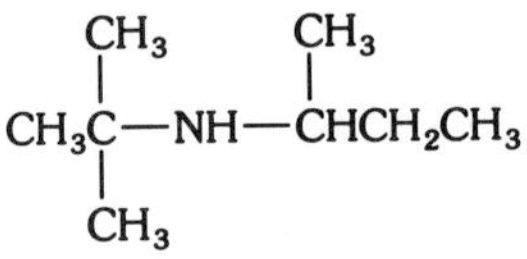 $CH_3\overset{\overset{\displaystyle CH_3}{|}}{\underset{\underset{\displaystyle CH_3}{|}}{C}}\!-\!NH\!-\!\overset{\overset{\displaystyle CH_3}{|}}{C}HCH_2CH_3$

   (b) 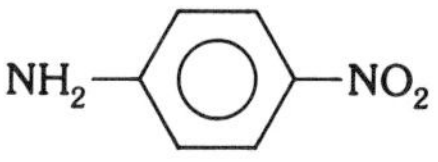 $NH_2\!-\!$ phenyl $\!-\!NO_2$

(c) 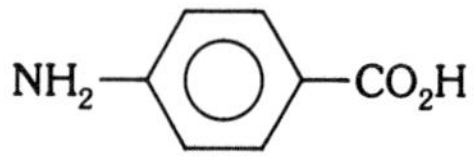 NH_2—⟨benzene ring⟩—CO_2H

3. (a) 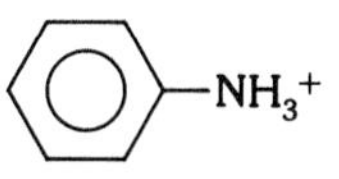 ⟨benzene ring⟩—NH_3^+

(b) 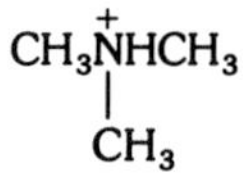 $CH_3\overset{+}{N}HCH_3$
    |
    CH_3

(c) $^+NH_3CH_2CH_2NH_3^+$

4. (a)

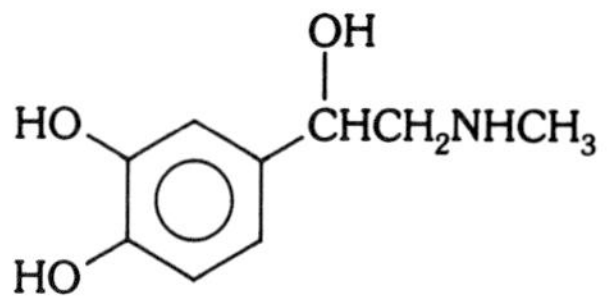

HO, HO—⟨benzene ring⟩—$\overset{OH}{\overset{|}{C}}HCH_2NHCH_3$

(b)

CH_3O, CH_3O—⟨benzene ring⟩—$CH_2CH_2NH_2$, CH_3O

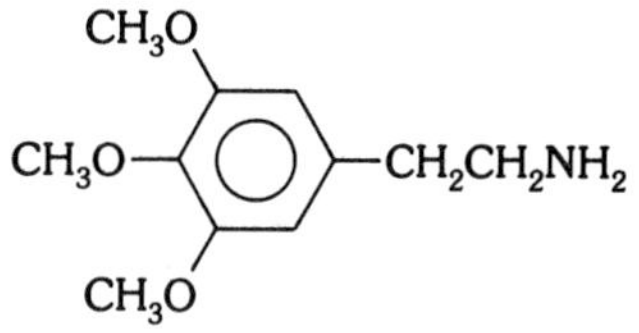

5. (a) 4-Methylhexanamide
   (b) 2-Ethylbutanamide

6. (a)  $CH_3\overset{\overset{CH_3}{|}}{C}HCONHCH_3$ (b) 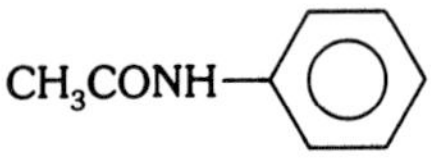 CH_3CONH—⟨benzene ring⟩

   (c) No amide can form.   (d) No amide can form.

7. (a) 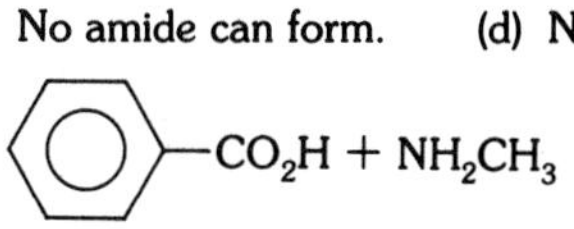 ⟨benzene ring⟩—$CO_2H + NH_2CH_3$

   (b) No hydrolysis can occur.

   (c) $CH_3CO_2H +$ ⟨benzene ring⟩—NH_2

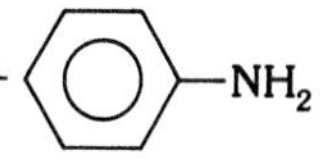

   (d) $2CH_3CO_2H + NH_2CH_2CH_2NH_2$

8. 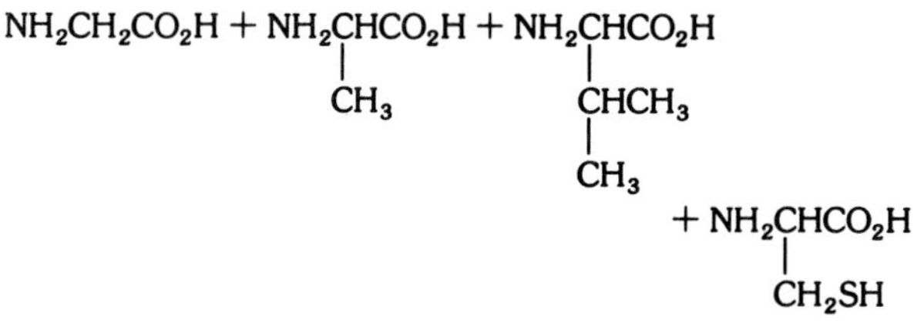 $NH_2CH_2CO_2H + NH_2\overset{\overset{}{|}}{C}HCO_2H + NH_2\overset{\overset{}{|}}{C}HCO_2H$
                           CH_3 $\overset{}{C}HCH_3$
                                          CH_3

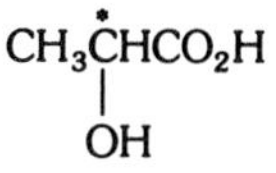

   $+ NH_2\overset{\overset{}{|}}{C}HCO_2H$
          CH_2SH

Practice Exercises, Chapter 18

1. (a)

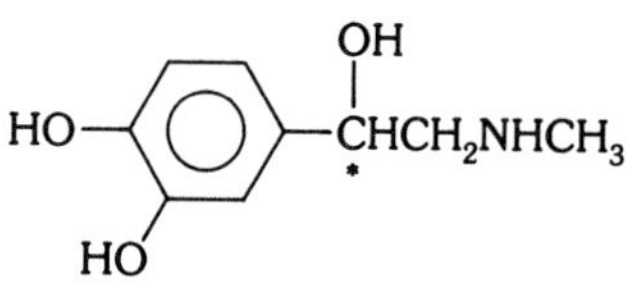

HO—⟨benzene ring⟩—$\overset{OH}{\overset{|}{\overset{*}{C}}}HCH_2NHCH_3$, HO

(b) $CH_3\overset{*}{C}HCO_2H$
        |
        OH

(c) $CH_3\overset{*}{C}H\overset{*}{C}HCO_2^-$
        | |
        HO NH_3^+

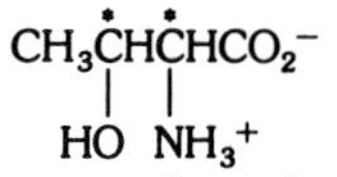

(d) 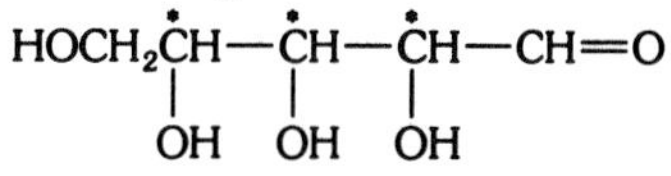 $HOCH_2\overset{*}{C}H$—$\overset{*}{C}H$—$\overset{*}{C}H$—$CH{=}O$
              | | |
              OH OH OH

2. (a) Three.
   (b) $2^3 = 8$ optical isomers.
   (c) Four pairs of enantiomers.

3. 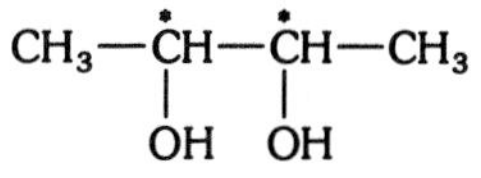 CH_3—$\overset{*}{C}H$—$\overset{*}{C}H$—CH_3
            | |
            OH OH

   No, they are not different. Each chiral carbon holds the identical set of four different groups.

Review Exercises, Chapter 18

18.19 3.01 g/dL

18.21 $[\alpha] = -139°$. The unknown is strychnine.

Practice Exercises, Chapter 19

1. (a) = (b), (c) = (e)
   (a) and (d) are enantiomers.
   (c) = (e) = a meso compound.

2.

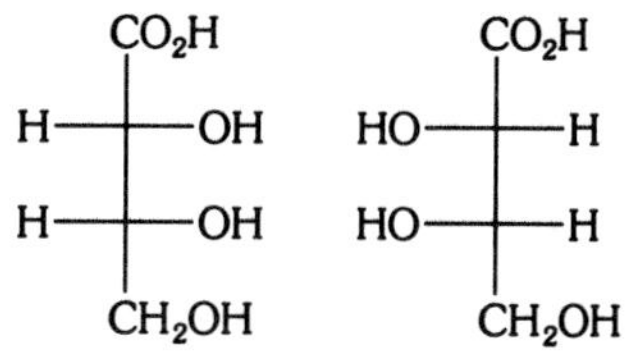

CO_2H	CO_2H
H——OH	HO——H
H——OH	HO——H
CH_2OH	CH_2OH

One pair of enantiomers

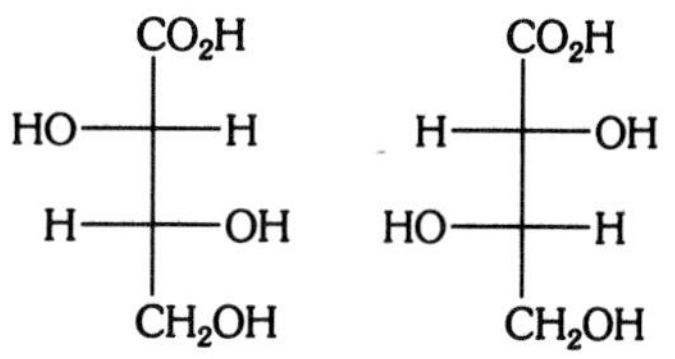

CO_2H	CO_2H
HO——H	H——OH
H——OH	HO——H
CH_2OH	CH_2OH

Another pair of enantiomers

Practice Exercises, Chapter 20

1.  $CH_3(CH_2)_{26}\overset{\overset{O}{\parallel}}{C}O(CH_2)_{25}CH_3$

2. $CH_3(CH_2)_7 \quad (CH_2)_7CO_2H$
         $C{=}C$
       $H \quad\quad H$

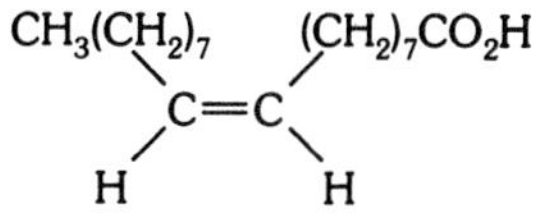

3. **1** $+ 3NaOH \rightarrow$
   $HOCH_2CHCH_2OH + NaO_2C(CH_2)_7CH{=}CH(CH_2)_7CH_3$
        | $+ NaO_2C(CH_2)_{14}CH_3$
        OH

   $+ NaO_2C(CH_2)_7CH{=}CHCH_2CH{=}CH(CH_2)_4CH_3$

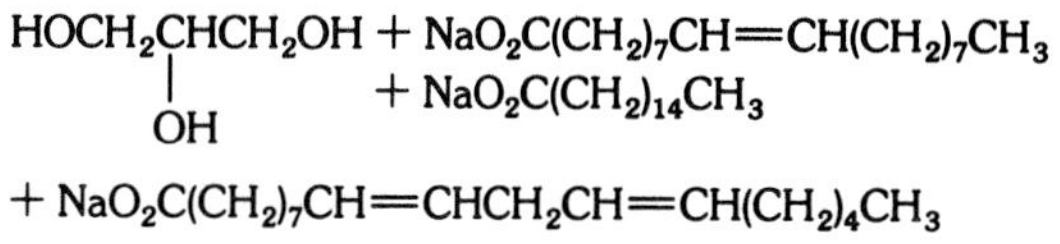

4. 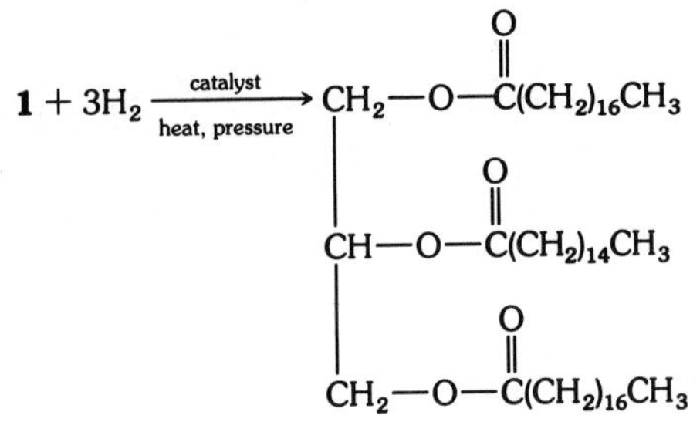 $1 + 3H_2 \xrightarrow[\text{heat, pressure}]{\text{catalyst}}$

$$CH_2-O-\overset{\overset{O}{\|}}{C}(CH_2)_{16}CH_3$$

$$CH-O-\overset{\overset{O}{\|}}{C}(CH_2)_{14}CH_3$$

$$CH_2-O-\overset{\overset{O}{\|}}{C}(CH_2)_{16}CH_3$$

Practice Exercises, Chapter 21

1. Glycine: $^{+}NH_3CH_2CO_2^{-}$

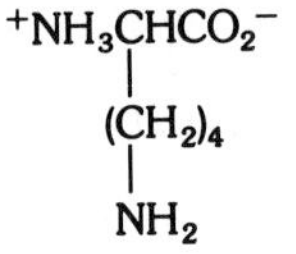

   Alanine: $^{+}NH_3CHCO_2^{-}$
   $\quad\quad\quad\quad | $
   $\quad\quad\quad\quad CH_3$

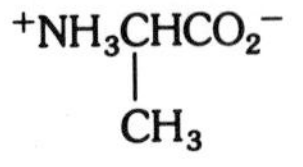

   Lysine: $^{+}NH_3CHCO_2^{-}$
   $\quad\quad\quad\quad | $
   $\quad\quad\quad\quad (CH_2)_4$
   $\quad\quad\quad\quad | $
   $\quad\quad\quad\quad NH_2$

   Glutamic acid: $^{+}NH_3CHCO_2^{-}$
   $\quad\quad\quad\quad\quad\quad | $
   $\quad\quad\quad\quad\quad\quad (CH_2)_2$
   $\quad\quad\quad\quad\quad\quad | $
   $\quad\quad\quad\quad\quad\quad CO_2H$

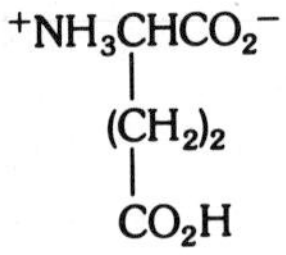

2. (a) 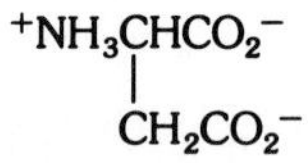 $^{+}NH_3CHCO_2^{-}$
   $\quad\quad\quad | $
   $\quad\quad\quad CH_2CO_2^{-}$

   (b) 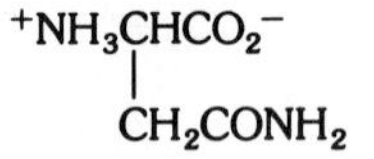 $^{+}NH_3CHCO_2^{-}$
   $\quad\quad\quad | $
   $\quad\quad\quad CH_2CONH_2$

3. 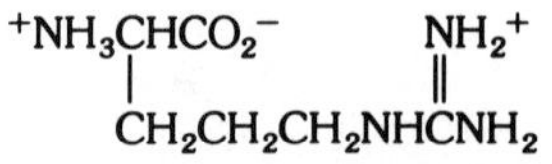 $^{+}NH_3CHCO_2^{-}$ $\quad\quad NH_2^{+}$
   $\quad | \quad\quad\quad\quad\quad\quad\quad \|$
   $\quad CH_2CH_2CH_2NHCNH_2$

4. Hydrophilic; neutral side chain.

5. 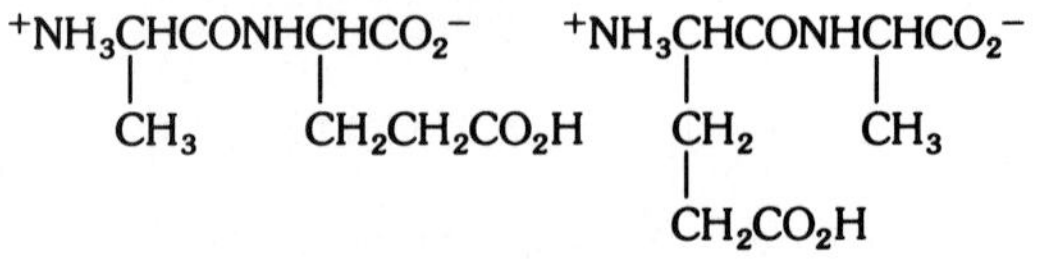 $^{+}NH_3CHCONHCHCO_2^{-}$ $\quad\quad ^{+}NH_3CHCONHCHCO_2^{-}$
   $\quad\quad | \quad\quad\quad\quad\quad | \quad\quad\quad\quad\quad\quad\quad | \quad\quad\quad\quad\quad | $
   $\quad\quad CH_3 \quad\quad CH_2CH_2CO_2H \quad\quad CH_2 \quad\quad CH_3$
   $\quad\quad\quad\quad\quad\quad\quad\quad\quad\quad\quad\quad\quad\quad\quad\quad\quad | $
   $\quad\quad\quad\quad\quad\quad\quad\quad\quad\quad\quad\quad\quad\quad\quad\quad\quad CH_2CO_2H$

Practice Exercises, Chapter 22

1. (a) Proline   (b) Arginine
   (c) Glutamic acid   (d) Lysine

2. (a) Serine   (b) CT (chain termination)
   (c) Glutamic acid   (d) Isoleucine

Practice Exercise, Chapter 26

1. (a) Yes   (b) Yes   (c) No

Glossary

Absolute Configuration The actual arrangement in space about each chiral center in a molecule.

Accuracy In science, the degree of conformity to some accepted standard or reference; freedom from error or mistake; correctness.

Acetal Any organic compound in which two ether linkages extend from one CH unit, as in

$$R—O—\overset{|}{C}H—O—R'$$

Acetyl Coenzyme A The molecule from which acetyl groups are transferred into the citric acid cycle or into the lipigenesis cycle.

$$CH_3\overset{\overset{O}{\|}}{C}—S—CoA$$

Achiral Not possessing chirality; the quality of a molecule (or other object) that allows it to be superimposed on its mirror image.

Acid Any substance that can donate a proton.

Acid – Base Indicator See *Indicator*.

Acid Anhydride In organic chemistry, a compound formed by splitting water out between two —OH groups of the acid function of an organic acid. The structural features are

$$—\overset{\overset{O}{\|}}{C}—O—\overset{\overset{O}{\|}}{C}— \qquad —\overset{\overset{O}{\|}}{P}—O—\overset{\overset{O}{\|}}{P}—$$
$$\qquad\qquad\qquad\quad \overset{|}{OH}\quad \overset{|}{OH}$$

Carboxylic acid anhydride system

Phosphoric acid anhydride system

Acid – Base Neutralization The reaction of an acid with a base.

Acid Chloride A derivative of an acid in which the —OH group of the acid has been replaced by —Cl.

$$R—\overset{\overset{O}{\|}}{C}—Cl$$

Acid Derivative Any organic compound that can be made from an organic acid or that can be changed back to the acid by hydrolysis. (Examples are acid chlorides, acid anhydrides, esters, and amides.)

Acid Ionization Constant (K_a) A modified equilibrium constant for the following equilibrium: $HA + H_2O \rightleftharpoons H_3O^+ + A^-$.

$$K_a = \frac{[H_3O^+][A^-]}{[HA]}$$

Acid Rain Rain made acidic by air pollutants such as oxides of sulfur and nitrogen.

Acidic Solution A solution in which the molar concentration of hydronium ions is greater than that of hydroxide ions.

Acidosis A condition in which the pH of the blood is below normal. *Metabolic acidosis* is brought on by a defect in some metabolic pathway. *Respiratory acidosis* is caused by a defect in the respiratory centers or in the mechanisms of breathing.

Active Site The region of an enzyme molecule most directly responsible for the catalytic effect of the enzyme.

Active Transport The movement of a substance through a biological membrane against a concentration gradient; caused by energy-consuming chemical changes that involve parts of the membrane.

Activity Series A list of elements (or other substances) in the order of the ease with which they release electrons under standard conditions and become oxidized.

Acyl Group

$$R—\overset{\overset{O}{\|}}{C}—$$

Acyl Group Transfer Reaction Any reaction in which an acyl group transfers from a donor to an acceptor.

Addition Reaction Any reaction in which two parts of a reactant molecule add to a double or a triple bond.

Adenosine Diphosphate (ADP) A high-energy diphosphate ester obtained from adenosine triphosphate (ATP) when part of the chemical energy in ATP is tapped for some purpose in a cell.

Adenosine Monophosphate (AMP) A low-energy phosphate ester that can be obtained by the hydrolysis of ATP or ADP; a monomer for the biosynthesis of nucleic acids.

Adenosine Triphosphate (ATP) A high-energy triphosphate ester used in living systems to provide chemical energy for metabolic needs.

Adequate Protein A protein that, when digested, makes available all the essential amino acids in suitable proportions to satisfy both the amino acid and total nitrogen requirements of good nutrition without providing excessive calories.

ADP See *Adenosine Diphosphate*.

Aerobic Sequence An oxygen-consuming sequence of catabolism that starts with glucose or with glucose units in glycogen, and proceeds through glycolysis, the citric acid cycle, and the respiratory chain.

Agonist A compound whose molecules can bind to a receptor on a cell membrane and cause a response by the cell.

Albumin One of a family of globular proteins that tend to dissolve in water, and that in blood contribute to the blood's colloidal osmotic pressure and aid in the transport of metal ions, fatty acids, cholesterol, triacylglycerols, and other water-insoluble substances.

Alcohol Any organic compound whose molecules have the —OH group attached to a saturated carbon; R—OH.

Alcohol Group The —OH group when it is joined to a saturated carbon.

Aldehyde An organic compound that has a carbonyl group joined to H on one side and C or H on the other; R—CH=O.

Aldehyde Group —CH=O

Aldohexose A monosaccharide whose molecules have six carbon atoms and an aldehyde group.

Aldose A monosaccharide whose molecules have an aldehyde group.

Aldosterone A steroid hormone, made in the adrenal cortex, and secreted into the bloodstream when the sodium ion level is low. It signals the kidneys to leave sodium ions in the bloodstream.

Aliphatic Compound Any organic compound whose molecules lack a benzene ring or a similar structural feature.

Alkali A strongly basic substance such as sodium hydroxide or potassium hydroxide.

Alkali Metals The elements of group IA of the periodic table: lithium, sodium, potassium, rubidium, cesium, and francium.

Alkaline Earth Metals The elements of group IIA of the periodic table: beryllium, magnesium, calcium, strontium, barium, and radium.

Alkaloid A physiologically active, heterocyclic amine isolated from plants.

Alkalosis A condition in which the pH of the blood is above normal. *Metabolic alkalosis* is caused by a defect in metabolism. *Respiratory alkalosis* is caused by a defect in the respiratory centers of the brain or in the apparatus of breathing.

Alkane Any saturated hydrocarbon, one that has only single bonds. A *normal* alkane is any whose molecules have straight chains.

Alkene Any hydrocarbon whose molecules have one or more double bonds.

Alkyl Group A substituent group that is an alkane minus one H atom.

Alkyne A hydrocarbon whose molecules have triple bonds.

Allosteric Activation The activation of an enzyme's catalytic site by the binding of some molecule at a position elsewhere on the enzyme.

Allosteric Inhibition The inhibition of the activity of an enzyme caused by the binding of an inhibitor molecule at some site other than the enzyme's catalytic site.

Alloy A mixture of two or more metals made by mixing them in their molten states.

Alpha (α) Particle The nucleus of a helium atom; $^4_2$He.

Alpha (α) Radiation A stream of high-energy alpha particles.

Amide Any organic compound whose molecules have a carbonyl–nitrogen unit,

$$\underset{\underset{\displaystyle |}{}}{\overset{\overset{\displaystyle O}{\parallel}}{}}$$
$$\text{—C—N—}$$

Amide Bond The single bond that holds the carbonyl group to the nitrogen atom in an amide.

Amine Any organic compound whose molecules have a trivalent nitrogen atom, as in R—NH_2, R—NH—R, or R_3N.

Amine Salt Any organic compound whose molecules have a positively charged, tetravalent, protonated nitrogen atom, as in RNH_3^+, $R_2NH_2^+$, or R_3NH^+.

Amino Acid Any organic compound whose molecules have both an amino group and a carboxyl group.

Amino Acid Residue A structural unit in a polypeptide, —NH—CH—CO—, furnished by an amino acid, in which G
is a side-chain group.

Aminoacyl Group NH_2CHC—, in which G is one of the amino acid side chains.

Aminopeptidase An enzyme that catalyzes the hydrolysis of N-terminal amino acid residues from small polypeptides.

AMP See *Adenosine Monophosphate*.

Amphipathic Compound A substance whose molecules have both hydrophilic and hydrophobic groups.

α-Amylase An enzyme that catalyzes the hydrolysis of amylose.

Anaerobic Sequence The oxygen-independent catabolism of glucose or of glucose units in glycogen to lactate ion.

Anhydrous Without water.

Anion A negatively charged ion.

Anion Gap

$$\text{Anion gap} = \frac{\text{meq of Na}^+}{\text{L}} - \left(\frac{\text{meq of Cl}^-}{\text{L}} + \frac{\text{meq of HCO}_3^-}{\text{L}} \right)$$

Anode The positive electrode to which negatively charged ions— anions—are attracted during electrolysis.

Anoxia A condition of a tissue in which it receives no oxygen.

Antagonist A compound that can bind to a membrane receptor without causing any response by the cell.

Antibiotics Antimetabolites made by bacteria and fungi.

Anticodon A sequence of three adjacent side-chain bases on a molecule of *t*RNA that is complementary to a codon and that fits to its codon on an *m*RNA chain during polypeptide synthesis.

Antimetabolite A substance that inhibits the growth of bacteria.

Apoenzyme The wholly polypeptide part of an enzyme.

Aromatic Compound Any organic compound whose molecules have a benzene ring (or a feature very similar to this).

Atmosphere, Standard See *Standard Atmosphere*.

Atom A small particle with one nucleus and zero charge; the smallest particle of a given element that bears the chemical properties of the element.

Atomic Mass Number See *Mass Number*.

Atomic Mass Unit (amu) 1.66066×10^{-24} g. A mass very close to that of a proton or a neutron.

Atomic Number The positive charge on an atom's nucleus; the number of protons in an atom's nucleus.

Atomic Orbital A region in space close to an atom's nucleus in which one or two electrons can reside.

Atomic Symbol A one- or two-letter symbol for an element or one of its atoms.

Atomic Weight The average mass, in amu, of the atoms of the isotopes of a given element as they occur naturally.

ATP See *Adenosine Triphosphate.*

Aufbau Rules The rules for constructing electron configurations.

Avogadro's Law Equal volumes of gases contain equal numbers of moles when they are compared at identical temperatures and pressures.

Avogadro's Number 6.023×10^{23}. The number of formula units in one mole of any element or compound.

Background Radiation Cosmic rays plus the natural atomic radiation emitted by the traces of radioactive isotopes in soils and rocks.

Balanced Equation See *Equation, Balanced.*

Barometer An instrument for measuring atmospheric pressure.

Basal Activities The minimum activities of the body needed to maintain muscle tone, control body temperature, circulate the blood, handle wastes, breathe, and carry out other essential activities.

Basal Metabolic Rate The rate at which energy is expended to maintain basal activities.

Basal Metabolism The total of all the chemical reactions that support basal activities.

Base *Arrhenius theory:* A compound that provides the hydroxide ion. *Brønsted theory:* A proton-acceptor; a compound that neutralizes hydrogen ions.

Base, Heterocyclic A heterocyclic amine obtained from the hydrolysis of nucleic acids: adenine, thymine, guanine, cytosine, or uracil.

Base Ionization Constant (K_b) For the equilibrium (in which B is some base) $B + H_2O \rightleftharpoons BH^+ + OH^-$

$$K_b = \frac{[BH^+][OH^-]}{[B]}$$

Base Pairing In nucleic acid chemistry, the association by means of hydrogen bonds of two heterocyclic, side-chain bases — adenine with thymine (or uracil) and guanine with cytosine.

Base Quantity A fundamental quantity of physical measurement such as mass, length, and time; a quantity used to define derived quantities such as mass/volume for density.

Base Unit A fundamental unit of measurement for a base quantity — such as the kilogram for mass, the meter for length, the second for time, the kelvin for temperature degree, and the mole for quantity of chemical substance; a unit to which derived units of measurement are related.

Basic Solution A solution in which the molar concentration of hydroxide ions is greater than that of hydronium ions.

Becquerel (Bq) The SI unit for the activity of a radioactive source; one nuclear disintegration (or other transformation) per second.

$$1 \text{ curie} = 3.7 \times 10^{10} \text{ Bq}$$

Benedict's Reagent A solution of copper(II) sulfate, sodium citrate, and sodium carbonate that is used in the Benedict's test.

Benedict's Test The use of Benedict's reagent to detect the presence of any compound whose molecules have easily oxidized functional groups — α-hydroxyaldehydes and α-hydroxy-

ketones — such as those present in monosaccharides. In a positive test the intensely blue color of the reagent disappears and a reddish precipitate of copper(I) oxide separates.

Beta Oxidation The fatty acid cycle of catabolism.

Beta (β) Particle A high-energy electron; $_{-1}^{0}e$.

Beta (β) Radiation A stream of high-energy electrons.

Bile A secretion of the gall bladder that empties into the upper intestine and furnishes bile salts; a route of excretion for cholesterol and bile pigments.

Bile Pigment Colored products of the partial catabolism of heme that are transferred from the liver to the gall bladder for secretion via the bile.

Bile Salts Steroid-base detergents in bile that emulsify fats and oils during digestion.

Bilin The brownish pigment that is the end product of the catabolism of heme and that contributes to the characteristic colors of feces and urine.

Bilinogen A product of the catabolism of heme that contributes to the characteristic colors of feces and urine and some of which is oxidized to bilin.

Bilirubin An reddish-orange substance that forms from biliverdin during the catabolism of heme, enters the intestinal tract via the bile, and is eventually changed into bilinogen and bilin.

Biliverdin A greenish pigment that forms when partly catabolized hemoglobin (as verdohemoglobin) is broken down further. It is changed in the liver to bilirubin.

Binding Site The part of an enzyme molecule that holds the substrate molecule and positions it over the active site.

Biochemistry The study of the structures and properties of substances found in living systems.

Biological Value In nutrition, the percentage of the nitrogen of ingested protein that is absorbed from the digestive tract and retained by the body when the total protein intake is less than normally required.

Biotin A water-soluble vitamin needed to make enzymes used in fatty acid synthesis.

Blood Sugar The carbohydrates — mostly glucose — that are present in blood.

Blood Sugar Level The concentration of carbohydrate — mostly glucose — in the blood; usually stated in units of mg/dL.

Binary Compound A compound made from just two elements.

Binding Sites Parts of enzyme molecules that bind substrate molecules

Bohr Model of the Atom The solar system model for the structure of an atom, proposed by Niels Bohr. It pictures the electrons circling the nucleus in discrete energy states called orbits.

Boiling The turbulent behavior in a liquid when its vapor pressure equals the atmospheric pressure and when the liquid absorbs heat while experiencing no rise in temperature.

Boiling Point, Normal The temperature at which a substance boils when the atmospheric pressure is 760 mm Hg (1 atm).

Bond, Chemical A net electrical force of attraction that holds atomic nuclei near one another within compounds.

Bond Angle The angle between two covalent bonds at an atom in a molecule.

Boyle's Law See *Pressure–Volume Law.*

Branched Chain A sequence of atoms to which additional atoms are attached at points other than the ends.

Brønsted Theory An acid is a proton-donor and a base is a proton-acceptor.

Brownian Movement The random, chaotic movements of particles in a colloidal dispersion that can be seen with a microscope.

Buffer A combination of solutes that holds the pH of a solution relatively constant even if small amounts of acids or bases are added.

Calorie The amount of heat that raises the temperature of 1 gram of water by 1 degree Celsius, from 14.5 °C to 15.5 °C.

Carbaminohemoglobin Hemoglobin that carries chemically bound carbon dioxide.

Carbocation Any cation in which a carbon atom has just six outer-level electrons; a carbonium ion.

Carbohydrate Any naturally occurring substance whose molecules are polyhydroxyaldehydes or polyhydroxyketones or can be hydrolyzed to such compounds.

Carbon Family The group IVA elements in the periodic table: carbon, silicon, germanium, tin, and lead.

Carbonate Buffer A mixture or a solution that includes bicarbonate ions and carbonic acid (dissolved carbon dioxide) in which the bicarbonate ion can neutralize added acid and carbonic acid can neutralize added base.

Carbonyl Group $C=O$.

Carboxylic Acid A compound whose molecules have the carboxyl group, $—CO_2H$.

Carboxypeptidase A digestive enzyme that catalyzes the hydrolysis of C-terminal amino acid residues from small polypeptides.

Carcinogen A chemical or physical agent that induces the onset of cancer or the formation of a tumor which might or might not become cancerous.

Cardiovascular Compartment The entire network of blood vessels and the heart.

Catabolism The reactions of metabolism that break molecules down.

Catalysis The phenomenon of an increase in the rate of a chemical reaction brought about by a relatively small amount of a chemical—the catalyst—that is not permanently changed by the reaction.

Catalyst A substance that is able, in relatively low concentrations, to accelerate the rate of a chemical reaction without itself being permanently changed. (In living systems, the catalysts are called enzymes.)

Catalytic Sites Parts of enzyme molecules that provide the catalytic function.

Cathode The negative electrode to which positively charged ions —cations—are attracted during electrolysis.

Cation A positively charged ion.

Cell Potential, Standard (E_{cell}°) The difference between the standard reduction potentials of the two half-cells of a redox reaction.

Centimeter (cm) A length equal to one-hundreth of the meter. 1 cm = 0.01 m = 0.394 in.

Charles' Law See *Temperature-Volume Law.*

Chemical Bond See *Bond, Chemical.*

Chemical Energy The potential energy that substances have because their arrangements of electrons and atomic nuclei are not as stable as are alternative arrangements that become possible in chemical reactions.

Chemical Equation A shorthand representation of a chemical reaction that uses formulas instead of names for reactants and products; that separates reactant formulas from product formulas by an arrow; that separates formulas on either side of the arrow by plus signs; and that expresses the mole proportions of the chemicals by simple numbers (coefficients) placed before the formulas.

Chemical Property Any chemical reaction that a substance can undergo and the ability to undergo such a reaction.

Chemical Reaction Any event in which substances change into different chemical substances.

Chemiosmotic Theory An explanation of how oxidative phosphorylation is related to the flow of protons in a proton gradient that is established by the respiratory chain, and that extends across the inner membrane of a mitochondrion.

Chemistry The study of the compositions and structures of substances and their ability to change into other substances.

Chiral Having handedness in a molecular structure. See also *Chirality.*

Chiral Carbon A carbon that holds four different atoms or groups.

Chirality The quality of handedness of a molecular structure that prevents this structure from being superimposible on its mirror image.

Chloride Shift An interchange of chloride ions and bicarbonate ions between a red blood cell and the surrounding blood serum.

Choline A compound needed to make complex lipids and acetylcholine; classified as a vitamin.

Chromosome Small thread-like bodies in a cell nucleus that carry genes in a linear array and that are microscopically visible during cell division.

Chylomicron A microdroplet of lipid material with a trace amount of protein that carries lipids picked up from the digestive tract to adipose tissue and to the liver.

Chyme The mixture of partially digested food, brought to this state by the activity of gastric juices in the stomach and then released through the pyloric valve into the duodenum.

Chymotrypsin A digestive enzyme that catalyzes the hydrolysis of peptide bonds in large polypeptides.

Citric Acid Cycle A series of reactions that dismantle acetyl units and send electrons (and protons) into the respiratory chain; a major source of metabolites for the respiratory chain.

Codon A sequence of three adjacent side-chain bases in a molecule of *m*RNA that codes for a specific amino acid residue when the *m*RNA participates in polypeptide synthesis.

Coefficient of Digestibility The proportion of an ingested protein's nitrogen that enters circulation rather than being eliminated (in feces); the difference between the nitrogen ingested and the nitrogen in the feces divided by the nitrogen ingested.

Coefficients Numbers placed before formulas in chemical equations to indicate the mole proportions of reactants and products.

Coenzyme An organic compound needed to make a complete enzyme from an apoenzyme.

Cofactor A nonprotein compound or ion that is an essential part of an enzyme.

Collagen The fibrous protein of connective tissue that changes to gelatin in boiling water.

Colligative Property A property of a solution that depends only on the concentrations of the solute and the solvent and not on their chemical identities (e.g., osmotic pressure).

Colloidal Dispersion A relatively stable, uniform distribution in some dispersing medium of colloidal particles — those with at least one dimension between 1 and 1000 nm.

Colloidal Osmotic Pressure The contribution made to the osmotic pressure of a solution by substances colloidally dispersed in it.

Combustion A rapid chemical reaction with oxygen that produces heat, light, a flame, and mostly gaseous products.

Common Ion Effect The reduction in the solubility of a salt in some solution by the addition of another solute that furnishes one of the ions of this salt.

Competitive Inhibition The inhibition of an enzyme by the binding of a molecule that can compete with the substrate for the occupation of the catalytic site.

Complex Ion An ion consisting of a central metal ion associated with electron-rich species, like ammonia or certain negative ions.

Compound A substance made from the atoms of two or more elements which are present in a definite proportion by mass and by atoms.

Concentration The quantity of some component of a mixture in a unit of volume or a unit of mass of the mixture.

Condensation The physical change of a substance from its gaseous state to its liquid state.

Condensed Structure See *Structural Formula.*

Conduction In the science of heat energy, the transfer of heat from a region of higher temperature to a region of lower temperature by means of the transfer of the kinetic energy of atoms, ions, or molecules to their neighbors. In the science of electrical energy, the movement of electrons in a conductor.

Configuration Any one of the many geometric forms that molecules can have by means of cis-trans or optical isomerism. *Absolute configuration* is the actual configuration at a chiral center.

Configurational Isomer An optical isomer. See *Optical Isomer.*

Conformation One of the infinite number of contortions of a molecule that is permitted by free rotations around single bonds.

Conjugate Acid-Base Pair Two particles whose formulas differ by only one H^+, such as NH_4^+ and NH_3, or HCl and Cl^-.

Convection In the science of heat energy, the transfer of heat by the circulation of a warmer fluid throughout the remainder of the fluid.

Conversion Factor A fraction that expresses a relationship between quantities that have different units, such as 2.54 cm/in.

Coordinate Covalent Bond A covalent bond in which both of the electrons of the shared pair originated from one of the atoms involved in the bond.

Cori Cycle The sequence of chemical events and transfers of substances in the body that describes the distribution, storage, and mobilization of blood sugar, including the reconversion of lactate to glycogen.

Cosmic Radiation A stream of ionizing radiations, from the sun and outer space, that consists mostly of protons but also includes alpha particles, electrons, and the nuclei of atoms up to atomic number 28.

Covalent Bond The net force of attraction that arises as two atomic nuclei share a pair of electrons. One pair is shared in a single bond, two pairs are shared in a double bond, and three electrons pairs are shared in a triple bond.

Crenation The shrinkage of red blood cells when they are in contact with a hypertonic solution.

Crick – Watson Theory A theory that uses the double-helix structure of DNA to explain how genes store genetic information and how this information is translated into sequences of amino acids in proteins.

Curie (Ci) A unit of activity of a radioactive source. 1 Ci $= 3.70 \times 10^{10}$ disintegrations/s

Dalton's Law See *Law of Partial Pressures.*

Dalton's Theory A theory that accounts for the laws of chemical combination by postulating that matter consists of indestructible atoms; that all atoms of the same element are identical in mass and other properties; that the atoms of different elements are different in mass and other properties; and that in the formation of a compound, atoms join together in definite, whole-number ratios.

Deamination The removal of an amino group from an amino acid.

Decarboxylation The removal of a carboxyl group.

Degree Celsius One hundredth (1/100) of the interval on a thermometer between the freezing point and the boiling point of water.

Degree Fahrenheit One one-hundred-and-eightieth (1/180) of the interval on a thermometer between the freezing point and the boiling point of water.

Deliquescence The ability of a substance to attract water vapor to itself to form a concentrated solution.

Denaturation The loss of the natural shape and form of a protein molecule together with its ability to function biologically, but not necessarily accompanied by the rupture of any of its peptide bonds.

Density The ratio of the mass of an object to its volume; the mass per unit volume. Density $=$ mass/volume (usually expressed in g/mL).

Deoxyribonucleic Acid (DNA) The chemical of a gene; one of a large number of polymers of deoxyribonucleotides. Its sequences of side-chain bases constitute the genetic messages of genes.

Deoxyribonucleotides The monomers of deoxyribonucleic acids (DNA) that consist of deoxyribose – phosphate esters with each deoxyribose unit carrying a side-chain base (one of four heterocyclic amines, adenine, thymine, guanine, or cytosine).

Derived Quantity A quantity based on a relationship that involves one or more base quantities of measurement, such as volume (length^3) or density (mass/volume).

Derived Unit A unit of a derived quantity such as g/mL (density).

Desiccant A substance that combines with water vapor to form a hydrate and thereby reduces the concentration of water vapor in the air space around the substance.

Dextrorotatory The property of an optically active substance by which it can cause the plane of plane-polarized light to rotate clockwise.

D-Family; L-Family The names of the two optically active families to which substances can belong when they are considered solely according to one kind of molecular chirality (molecular handedness) or the other.

Diabetes Mellitus A disease in which there is an insufficiency of effective insulin and an impairment of glucose tolerance.

Dialysis The passage through a dialyzing membrane of water and particles in solution, but not of particles that have colloidal size.

Diastereomer One of a pair of stereoisomers not related as an object is to its mirror image.

Diatomic Molecule A molecule made of two atoms.

Dietetics The application of the findings of the science of nutrition to the feeding of individual humans, whether well or ill.

Diffusion A physical process whereby particles, by random motions, intermingle and spread out so as to erase concentration gradients.

Digestive Juice A secretion into the digestive tract that consists of a dilute aqueous solution of digestive enzymes (or their zymogens) and inorganic ions.

Dihydric Alcohol An alcohol with two —OH groups, a glycol.

Dipeptide A compound whose molecules have two α-amino acid residues joined by a peptide (amide) bond.

2,3-Diphosphoglycerate (DPG) An organic ion that nestles within the hemoglobin molecule in deoxygenated blood but is expelled from the hemoglobin molecule during oxygenation.

Dipolar Ion A molecule that carries one plus charge and one minus charge, such as an α-amino acid.

Dipole, Electrical A pair of equal but opposite (and usually partial) electrical charges separated by a small distance in a molecule.

Diprotic Acid An acid with two protons available per molecule to neutralize a base (e.g., H_2SO_4).

Disaccharide A carbohydrate that can be hydrolyzed into two monosaccharides.

Dissociation The separation of preexisting ions from one another as an ionic compound dissolves or melts.

Disulfide Link The sulfur – sulfur covalent bond in polypeptides.

Disulfide System —S—S— as in R—S—S—R.

DNA See *Deoxyribonucleic Acid*; *Double Helix DNA Model*.

Double Bond A covalent bond in which two pairs of electrons are shared.

Double Helix DNA Model A spiral arrangement of two intertwining DNA molecules held together by hydrogen bonds between side-chain bases.

Double Replacement A reaction in which a compound is made by the exchange of partner ions between two salts.

DPG See *2,3-Diphosphoglycerate*.

Duodenum The upper 12 in. of the intestinal tract immediately below the stomach.

Dynamic Equilibrium See *Equilibrium*.

Dyspnea Air hunger; difficult or labored respiration.

Edema The swelling of tissue caused by the retention of water.

Effector A chemical other than a substrate that can allosterically activate an enzyme.

Elastase An enzyme that catalyzes the hydrolysis of elastin.

Elastin The fibrous protein of tendons and arteries.

Electrical Balance The condition of a net ionic equation wherein the algebraic sum of the positive and negative charges of the reactants equals that of the products.

Electrode A metal object, usually a wire, suspended in an electrically conducting medium through which electricity passes to or from an external circuit.

Electrolysis A procedure in which an electrical current is passed through a solution that contains ions, or through a molten salt, for the purpose of bringing about a chemical change.

Electrolyte Any substance whose solution in water conducts electricity; or the solution itself of such a substance.

Electrolytes, Blood The ionic substances dissolved in the blood.

Electron A subatomic particle that bears one unit of negative charge and has a mass that is 1/1836 the mass of a proton.

Electron Cloud A mental model that views the one or two rapidly moving electrons of an orbital as creating a cloud-like distribution of negative charge.

Electron Configuration The most stable arrangement (i.e., the arrangement of lowest energy) of the electrons of an atom, ion, or molecule.

Electronegativity The ability of an atom joined to another by a covalent bond to attract the electrons of the bond toward itself.

Electron Sharing The joint attraction of two atomic nuclei toward a pair of electrons situated between the nuclei and between which, therefore, a covalent bond exists.

Electron Shell An alternative name for *principal energy level*.

Electron Volt (eV) A very small unit of energy used to describe the energy of a radiation.

$$1 \ eV = 1.6 \times 10^{-19} \ joule$$
$$1 \ eV = 3.8 \times 10^{-20} \ calorie$$
$$1000 \ eV = 1 \ KeV \quad (1 \ kiloelectron \ volt)$$
$$1000 \ keV = 1 \ MeV \quad (1 \ megaelectron \ volt)$$

Element A substance that cannot be broken down into anything that is both stable and more simple; a substance in which all the atoms have the same atomic number and the same electron configuration; one of the three broad kinds of matter, the others being compounds and mixtures.

Emulsion A colloidal dispersion of tiny microdroplets of one liquid in another liquid.

Enantiomer One of a pair of stereoisomers that are related as an object is related to its mirror image but that cannot be superimposed one on the other.

End Point The stage in a titration when the operation is stopped.

Endergonic Describing a change that needs a constant supply of energy to happen.

Endocrine Gland An organ that makes one or more hormones.

Endothermic Describing a change that needs a constant supply of heat energy to happen.

Energy A capacity to cause a change that can, in principle, be harnessed for useful work.

Energy Density The energy per gram of stored glycogen or fat.

Energy Level A principal energy state in which electrons of an atom can be.

Energy of Activation The minimum energy that must be provided by the collision between reactant particles to initiate the rearrangement of electrons relative to nuclei that must happen if the reaction is to occur.

Enteropeptidase An enzyme of intestinal juice that changes trypsinogen into trypsin.

Enzyme A catalyst in a living system.

Enzyme Induction The initiation of the use of a gene to participate in transcription that will lead to the synthesis of an enzyme.

Enzyme – Substrate Complex The temporary combination that an enzyme must form with its substrate before catalysis can occur.

Epinephrine A hormone of the adrenal medulla that activates the enzymes needed to release glucose from glycogen.

Equation, Balanced A chemical equation in which all the atoms represented in the formulas of the reactants are present in identical numbers among the products, and in which any net electrical charge provided by the reactants equals the same charge indicated by the products. See also *Chemical Equation*.

Equilibrium A situation in which two opposing events occur at identical rates so that no net change happens.

Equilibrium Constant The value that the mass action expression has when a chemical system is at equilibrium.

Equilibrium Law $K_{eq} = \dfrac{[C]^c[D]^d}{[A]^a[B]^b}$ for the equilibrium

$$aA + bB \rightleftharpoons cC + dD$$

Equivalence Point The stage in a titration when the reactants have been mixed in the exact molar proportions represented by the balanced equation; in an acid – base titration, the stage when the moles of hydrogen ions furnished by the acid match the moles of hydroxide ions (or other proton acceptor) supplied by the base.

Equivalent For an ion, usually its mass in grams divided by the amount of its electrical charge.

Equivalent Weight A synonym for *Equivalent*.

Erythrocyte A red blood cell.

Essential Amino Acid An α-amino acid that the body cannot make from other amino acids and that must be supplied by the diet.

Essential Fatty Acid A fatty acid that must be supplied by the diet.

Ester A derivative of an acid and an alcohol that can be hydrolyzed to these parent compounds. Esters of carboxylic acids and phosphoric acid occur in living systems.

System in an ester of   System in an ester of
a carboxylic acid   phosphoric acid

Esterase An enzyme that catalyzes the hydrolysis of an ester.

Esterification The formation of an ester.

Ether An organic compound whose molecules have an oxygen attached by single bonds to separate carbon atoms, neither of which is a carbonyl carbon atom: R—O—R'.

Evaporation The conversion of a substance from its liquid to its vapor state.

Exergonic Describing a change by which energy of any form is released from the system.

Exon A segment of a DNA strand that eventually becomes expressed as a corresponding sequence of aminoacyl residues in a polypeptide.

Exothermic Describing a change by which heat energy is released from the system.

Extensive Property Any property whose value is directly proportional to the size of the sample, such as volume or mass.

Extracellular Fluids Body fluids that are outside of cells.

Fact In science, something that has physical existence, that can be experienced or observed, and that can be measured by independent observers.

Factor-Label Method A strategy for solving computational problems that uses conversion factors and the cancellation of the units of physical quantities as an aid in working toward the solution.

Fatty Acid Any carboxylic acid that can be obtained by the hydrolysis of animal fats or vegetable oils.

Fatty Acid Cycle The catabolism of a fatty acid by a series of repeating steps that produce acetyl units (in acetyl CoA).

Feedback Inhibition The competitive inhibition of an enzyme by a product of its own action.

Fibrin The fibrous protein of a blood clot that forms from fibrinogen during clotting.

Fibrinogen A protein in blood that is changed to fibrin during clotting.

Fibrous Proteins Water-insoluble proteins found in fibrous tissues.

Fission The splitting of the nucleus of a heavy atom approximately in half, accompanied by the release of one or a few neutrons and energy.

Folacin A vitamin supplied by folic acid or pteroylglutamic acid and needed to prevent megaloblastic anemia.

Food A material supplying one or more nutrients without contributing materials that, either in kind or in quantity, would be harmful to most healthy people.

Formula, Chemical A special symbol for a compound that uses the symbols of its constituent atoms.

Formula, Empirical A chemical symbol for a compound that gives just the ratios of the atoms and not necessarily the composition of a complete molecule.

Formula, Molecular A chemical symbol for a substance that gives the composition of a complete molecule.

Formula, Structural A chemical symbol for a substance that uses atomic symbols and lines to describe the pattern in which the atoms are joined together in a molecule.

Formula Unit A small particle—an atom, a molecule, or a set of ions — that has the composition given by the chemical formula of the substance.

Formula Weight The sum of the atomic weights of the atoms represented in a chemical formula.

Free Rotation The absence of a barrier to the rotation of two groups with respect to each other when they are joined by a single, covalent bond.

Functional Group An atom or a group of atoms in a molecule that is responsible for the particular set of reactions common to all compounds having this group.

Gamma (γ) In pharmaceutical work, one microgram; 1×10^{-6} g.

Gamma Radiation A natural radiation similar to but more powerful than X rays.

Gas Any substance that must be contained in a wholly closed space and whose shape and volume is determined entirely by the shape and volume of its container; a state of matter.

Gas Constant, Universal (R) The ratio of PV to nT for a gas, where $P =$ the gas pressure, $V =$ volume, $n =$ number of moles, and $T =$ the Kelvin temperature. When P is in mm Hg and V is in mL,

$$R = 6.24 \times 10^4 \text{ mm Hg mL/mol K}$$

Gas Tension The partial pressure of a gas over its solution in some liquid when the system is in equilibrium.

Gastric Juice The digestive juice that is secreted into the stomach and contains pepsinogen, hydrochloric acid, and gastric lipase.

Gay-Lussac's Law See *Pressure-Temperature Law.*

Gel A colloidal dispersion of a solid in a liquid that has adopted a semisolid form.

Gene A unit of heredity carried on a cell's chromosomes and consisting of DNA.

Genetic Code The set of correlations that specifies which codons on *m*RNA chains are responsible for which aminoacyl residues when the latter are steered into place during the *m*RNA-directed synthesis of polypeptides.

Genetic Engineering The use of recombinant DNA to manufacture substances or to repair genetic defects.

Geometric Isomerism Stereoisomerism caused by restricted rotation that gives different geometries to the same structural organization; cis-trans isomerism.

Geometric Isomers Stereoisomers whose molecules have identical atomic organizations but different geometries; cis-trans isomers.

Globular Proteins Proteins that are soluble in water or in water containing certain dissolved salts.

Globulins Globular proteins in the blood that include gamma-globulin, an agent in the body's defense against infectious diseases.

Glucagon A hormone secreted by the α-cells of the pancreas in response to a decrease in the blood sugar level. It stimulates the liver to release glucose from its glycogen stores.

Gluconeogenesis The synthesis of glucose from compounds with smaller molecules or ions.

Glucose Tolerance The ability of the body to manage the intake of dietary glucose while keeping the blood sugar level from fluctuating widely.

Glucose Tolerance Test A series of measurements of the blood sugar level after the ingestion of a considerable amount of glucose; used to obtain information about an individual's glucose tolerance.

Glucoside An acetal formed from glucose (in its cyclic, hemiacetal form) and an alcohol.

Glucosuria The presence of glucose in urine.

Glycogenesis The synthesis of glycogen.

Glycogenolysis The breakdown of glycogen to glucose.

Glycol A dihydric alcohol.

Glycolipid A lipid whose molecules include a glucose unit, a galactose unit, or some other carbohydrate unit.

Glycolysis A series of chemical reactions that break down glucose or glucose units in glycogen until pyruvate remains (when the series is operated aerobically) or lactate forms (when the conditions are anaerobic).

Glycoside An acetal or a ketal formed from the cyclic form of a monosaccharide and an alcohol.

Glycosidic Link The oxygen bridge between one monosaccharide unit and another in a disaccharide or a polysaccharide.

Gout A disease of the joints in which deposits of salts of uric acid accumulate and cause inflammation, swelling, and pain.

Gradient The presence of a change in value of some physical quantity with distance, as in a *concentration* gradient in which the concentration of a solute is different in different parts of the system.

Gram (g) A mass equal to one-thousandth of the kilogram mass, the SI standard mass.

$$1 \text{ g} = 0.001 \text{ kg} = 1000 \text{ mg}; \quad 1 \text{ lb} = 454 \text{ g}$$

Gray (Gy) The SI unit of absorbed dose of radiation equal to one joule of energy absorbed per kilogram of tissue.

Group A vertical column in the periodic table; a family of elements.

Half-Life The time needed for half of the atoms in a sample of a particular radioactive isotope to undergo radioactive decay.

Half-Reaction A net ionic equation that includes electrons either as reactants or as products and that is used to describe either the reduction or the oxidation part of a redox reaction.

Halogens The elements of group VIIA of the periodic table: fluorine, chlorine, bromine, iodine, and astatine.

Hard Water Water that contains one or more of the metallic ions Mg^{2+}, Ca^{2+}, Fe^{2+} or Fe^{3+}. The negative ions present are usually Cl^- and SO_4^{2-}. If HCO_3^- is the chief negative ion, the water is said to be *temporary hard water;* otherwise it is *permanent hard water*.

Heat The form of energy that transfers between two objects that are in contact but initially have different temperatures.

Heat Capacity The quantity of heat that a given object can absorb (or release) per degree Celsius change in temperature,

$$\text{Heat capacity} = \text{heat}/\Delta t$$

where Δt is the change in temperature.

Heat of Fusion The quantity of heat that one gram of a substance absorbs when it changes from its solid to its liquid state at its melting point.

Heat of Reaction The net energy difference between the reactants and the products of a reaction.

Heat of Vaporization The quantity of heat that one gram of a substance absorbs when it changes from its liquid to its gaseous state.

Heisenberg Uncertainty Principle It is impossible simultaneously to determine with precision and accuracy both the position and the velocity of an electron.

α-Helix One kind of secondary structure of a polypeptide in which its molecules are coiled.

Heme The deep-red, iron-containing prosthetic group in hemoglobin and myoglobin.

Hemiacetal Any compound whose molecules have both an —OH group and an ether linkage coming to a —CH— unit:

$$\underset{\overset{|}{\text{—CH—O—C—}}}{\overset{\text{OH} \qquad \text{OH}}{}} \qquad \text{as in} \qquad \text{R—CH—O—R}'$$

Hemiketal Any compound whose molecules have both an —OH group and an ether linkage coming to a carbon that otherwise bears no H atoms:

$$\underset{\text{R}}{\overset{\text{OH} \qquad\qquad \text{OH}}{\text{—C—O—C—} \qquad \text{as in} \qquad \text{R—C—O—R}'}}$$

Hemoglobin (HHb) The oxygen-carrying protein in red blood cells.

Hemolysis The bursting of a red blood cell.

Henderson–Hasselbalch Equation An equation used in buffer calculations,

$$\text{pH} = \text{p}K_a + \log \frac{[\text{anion}]}{[\text{acid}]}$$

Henry's Law See *Pressure-Solubility Law.*

Heterocyclic Compound A compound whose molecules have a ring in which one or more atoms is not carbon.

High-Energy Phosphate An organophosphate with a phosphate group transfer potential equal to or higher than that of ADP or ATP.

Homeostasis The response of an organism to a stimulus that restores the organism to its prestimulated state.

Homogeneous Mixture A mixture in which the composition and properties are uniform throughout.

Homolog Any member of a homologous series of organic compounds.

Homologous Series A series of organic compounds in the same family whose successive members differ by individual CH_2 units.

Hormone A primary chemical messenger made by an endocrine gland and carried by the bloodstream to a target organ where a particular chemical response is initiated.

Human Growth Hormone One of the hormones that affects the blood sugar level; a stimulator of the release of the hormone glucagon.

Hund's Rule Electrons become distributed among *different* orbitals of the same principal energy level insofar as there is room.

Hybrid Orbital An atomic orbital obtained by mixing two or more pure orbitals (those of the *s*, *p*, *d*, or *f* types).

Hydrate A compound in which intact molecules of water are held in a definite molar proportion to the other components.

Hydration The association of water molecules with dissolved ions or polar molecules.

Hydrocarbon Any organic compound that consists entirely of carbon and hydrogen.

Hydrogen Bond The force of attraction between a $\delta+$ charge on a hydrogen held by a covalent bond to oxygen or nitrogen (or fluorine) and a $\delta-$ charge on a nearby atom of oxygen or nitrogen (or fluorine).

Hydrolysis of Anions Reactions in which anions (other than OH^-) react with water and increase the pH of a solution.

Hydrolysis of Cations Reactions in which cations (other than H_3O^+) react with water and decrease the pH of a solution

Hydronium Ion H_3O^+

Hydrophilic Group Any part of a molecular structure that attracts water molecules; a polar or ionic group such as —OH, $-CO_2^-$, $-NH_3^+$, or $-NH_2$.

Hydrophobic Group Any part of a molecular structure that has no attraction for water molecules; a nonpolar group such as any alkyl group.

Hydroxide Ion OH^-

Hygroscopic Describing a substance that can reduce the concentration of water vapor in the surrounding air by forming a hydrate.

Hyperammonemia An elevated level of ammonium ion in the blood.

Hypercalcemia An elevated level of calcium ion in blood—above 5.2 meq/L.

Hyperglycemia An elevated level of sugar in the blood—above 110 mg/dL in whole blood.

Hyperkalemia An elevated level of potassium ion in blood—above 5.0 meq/L.

Hypermagnesemia An elevated level of magnesium ion in blood—above 2.0 meq/L.

Hypernatremia An elevated level of sodium ion in blood—above 145 meq/L.

Hyperthermia An elevated body temperature.

Hypertonic Having an osmotic pressure greater than some reference; having a total concentration of all solute particles higher than that of some reference.

Hyperventilation Breathing considerably faster and deeper than normal.

Hypocalcemia A low level of calcium ion in blood—below 4.2 meq/L.

Hypoglycemia A low level of glucose in blood—below 70 mg/dL of whole blood.

Hypokalemia A low level of potassium ion in blood—below 3.5 meq/L.

Hypomagnesemia A low level of magnesium ion in blood—below 1.5 meq/L.

Hyponatremia A low level of sodium ion in blood—below 135 meq/L.

Hypothermia A low body temperature.

Hypothesis A conjecture, subject to being disproved, that explains a set of facts in terms of a common cause and that serves as the basis for the design of additional tests or experiments.

Hypotonic Having an osmotic pressure less than some reference; having a total concentration of dissolved solute particles less than that of some reference.

Hypoventilation Breathing more slowly and less deeply than normal; shallow breathing.

Hypoxia A condition in which the supply of oxygen is low.

Ideal Gas A hypothetical gas that obeys the gas laws exactly.

Indicator A dye that, in solution, has one color below a measured pH range and a different color above this range.

Induced Fit Theory Certain enzymes are induced by their substrate molecules to modify their shapes to accommodate the substrate.

Inducer A substance whose molecules remove repressor molecules from operator genes and so open the way for structural genes to direct the overall syntheses of particular polypeptides.

Inducible Gene A gene that can be made to serve in polypeptide synthesis by the action of an inducer substance.

Inertia The resistance of an object to a change in its position or its motion.

Inhibitor A substance that interacts with an enzyme to prevent its acting as a catalyst.

Inner Transition Elements The elements of the lanthanide and actinide series of the periodic table.

Inorganic Compound Any compound that is not an organic compound.

Insensible Perspiration The loss of water from the body with no visible sweating; evaporative losses from the skin and the lungs.

Insulin A protein hormone made by the pancreas, released in response to a rise in the blood sugar level, and used by certain tissues to help them take up glucose from circulation.

Insulin Shock Shock brought on by a drastic reduction in the blood sugar level, usually after an overdose of insulin.

Intensive Property Any property whose value is independent of the size of the sample, such as temperature and density.

Internal Environment Everything enclosed within an organism.

International System of Units (SI) The successor to the metric system, with new reference standards for the base units but with the same names for the units and the same decimal relationships.

International Union of Pure and Applied Chemistry System (IUPAC System) A set of systematic rules for naming compounds, designed to give each compound one unique name. For each compound only one structure can be drawn. The Geneva system of nomenclature.

Interstitial Fluids Fluids in tissues but not inside cells.

Intestinal Juice The digestive juice that empties into the duodenum from the intestinal mucosa. Its enzymes also work within the intestinal mucosa as molecules migrate through.

Intron A segment of a DNA strand that separates exons and that does not become expressed as a segment of a polypeptide.

Inverse-Square Law The intensity of radiation varies inversely with the square of the distance from its source.

Invert Sugar A $1:1$ mixture of glucose and fructose.

Iodine Test A test for starch by which a drop of iodine produces an intensely purple color if starch is present.

Ion An electrically charged, atomic or molecular-sized particle; a particle that has one or a few atomic nuclei and either one or two (seldom, three) too many or too few electrons to render the particle electrically neutral.

Ionic Bond The force of attraction between oppositely charged ions in an ionic compound.

Ionic Compound A compound consisting of an orderly aggregation of oppositely charged ions that assemble in whatever ratio ensures overall electrical neutrality.

Ionic Equation A chemical equation that explicitly shows all the particles—ions, atoms, or molecules—that are involved in a reaction, even if some are only spectator particles. See also *Net Ionic Equation; Equation, Balanced.*

Ionization A change, usually involving solvent molecules, whereby molecules change into ions.

Ionizing Radiation Any radiation that can create ions from molecules within the medium that it enters, such as alpha, beta, gamma, X, and cosmic radiation.

Ion Product Constant of Water (K_w) The product of the molar concentrations of hydrogen ions and hydroxide ions in water at a given temperature.

$$K_w = [\text{H}^+][\text{OH}^-]$$
$$= 1.0 \times 10^{-14} \quad \text{(at 25 °C)}$$

Isoelectric Molecule A molecule that has an equal number of positive and negative sites.

Isoelectric Point (pI) The pH of a solution in which a specified amino acid or a protein is in an isoelectric condition; the pH at which there is no net migration of the amino acid or protein in an electric field.

Isoenzymes Enzymes that have identical catalytic functions but are made of slightly different polypeptides.

Isohydric Shift In actively metabolizing tissue, the use of a hydrogen ion released from newly formed carbonic acid to react with and liberate oxygen from oxyhemoglobin. In the lungs, the use of hydrogen ion released when hemoglobin oxygenates to combine with bicarbonate ion and liberate carbon dioxide for exhaling.

Isomerism The phenomenon of the existence of two or more compounds with identical molecular formulas but different structures.

Isomers Compounds with identical molecular formulas but different structures.

Isotonic Having an osmotic pressure identical to that of a reference; having a concentration equivalent to the reference with respect to the ability to undergo osmosis.

Isotope A substance in which all the atoms are identical in atomic number, mass number, and electron configuration.

Isozyme An isoenzyme.

IUPAC System See *International Union of Pure and Applied Chemistry System.*

K_a See *Acid Dissociation Constant.*

K_b See *Base Dissociation Constant.*

K_w See *Ion Product Constant of Water*.

Kelvin The SI unit of temperature degree; one-hundredth (1/100) of the interval between the freezing point and the boiling point of water when measured under standard conditions.

Keratin The fibrous protein of hair, fur, fingernails, and hooves.

Ketal A substance whose molecules have two ether linkages joined to a carbon that also holds two hydrocarbon groups as in

$$R_2C(OR')_2$$

Ketoacidosis The acidosis caused by untreated ketonemia.

Keto Group The carbonyl group when it is joined on each side to carbon atoms.

Ketohexose A monosaccharide whose molecules contain six carbon atoms and have a keto group.

Ketone Any compound with a carbonyl group attached to two carbon atoms, as in $R_2C{=}O$.

Ketone Bodies Acetoacetate, β-hydroxybutyrate — or their parent acids — and acetone.

Ketonemia An elevated concentration of ketone bodies in the blood.

Ketonuria An elevated concentration of ketone bodies in the urine.

Ketose A monosaccharide whose molecules have a ketone group.

Ketosis The combination of ketonemia, ketonuria, and acetone breath.

Kilocalorie (kcal) The quantity of heat equal to 1000 calories.

Kilogram (kg) The SI base unit of mass; 1000 g; 2.205 lb.

Kilometer (km) A length equal to 1000 meters or 0.621 mile.

Kinase An enzyme that catalyzes the transfer of a phosphate group.

Kindling Temperature The temperature at which a substance spontaneously bursts into flame in air.

Kinetic Energy The energy of an object by virtue of its motion.

$$\text{Kinetic energy} = \tfrac{1}{2}(\text{mass})(\text{velocity})^2$$

Kinetic Theory of Gases A set of postulates about the nature of an ideal gas: that it consists of a large number of very small particles in constant, random motion; that in the collisions the particles lose no frictional energy; that between collisions the particles neither attract nor repel each other; and that the motions and collisions of the particles obey all the laws of physics.

Kinetics The field of chemistry that deals with the rates of chemical reactions.

Krebs Cycle The citric acid cycle.

Lactase A digestive enzyme that catalyzes the hydrolysis of lactose.

Lambda (λ) In pharmaceutical work, one microliter; 1×10^{-6} L.

Law of Conservation of Energy Energy can be neither created nor destroyed but only transformed from one form to another.

Law of Conservation of Mass Matter is neither created nor destroyed in chemical reactions; the masses of all products equal the masses of all reactants.

Law of Definite Proportions The elements in a compound occur in definite proportions by mass.

Law of Mass Action (Law of Guldberg and Waage) The molar proportions of the interacting substances in a chemical equilibrium are related by the following equation (in which the ratio on the left is called the *mass action expression* for the system).

$$\frac{[C]^c[D]^d}{[A]^a[B]^b} = K_{eq}$$

The symbols refer to the following generalized equilibrium,

$$aA + bB \rightleftharpoons cC + dD$$

and the brackets, [ ], denote molar concentrations. (When an equilibrium involves additional substances, the equation for the equilibrium constant is adjusted accordingly.)

Law of Multiple Proportions When two elements can combine to form more than one compound, the different masses of the first that can combine with the same mass of the second are in the ratio of small whole numbers.

Law of Partial Pressures (Dalton's Law) The total pressure of a mixture of gases is the sum of their individual partial pressures.

Le Chatelier's Principle If a system is in equilibrium and a change is made in its conditions, the system will change in whichever way most directly restores equilibrium.

Length The base quantity for expressing distances or how long something is.

Levorotatory The property of an optically active substance that causes a counterclockwise rotation of the plane of plane-polarized light.

Lewis Structure A structural formula of a particle (atom, ion, or molecule) that shows all valence shell electrons in their correct places.

Like-Dissolves-Like Rule Polar solvents dissolve polar or ionic solutes and nonpolar solvents dissolve nonpolar or weakly polar solutes.

Limiting Amino Acid The essential amino acid most poorly provided by a dietary protein.

Lipase An enzyme that catalyzes the hydrolysis of lipids.

Lipid A plant or animal product that tends to dissolve in such nonpolar solvents as ether, carbon tetrachloride, and benzene.

Lipid Bilayer The sheet-like array of two layers of lipid molecules, interspersed with molecules of cholesterol and proteins, that make up the membranes of cells in animals.

Lipigenesis The synthesis of fatty acids from two-carbon acetyl units.

Lipoprotein Complex A combination of a lipid molecule with a protein molecule that serves as the vehicle for carrying the lipid in the bloodstream.

Liquid A state of matter in which a substance's volume but not its shape is independent of the shape of its container.

Liter (L) A volume equal to 1000 cm³ or 1000 mL or 1.057 liquid quart.

Lock-and-Key Theory The specificity of an enzyme for its substrate stems from the need for the substrate molecule to fit snugly to the enzyme's surface, much as a key fits to and turns only one tumbler lock.

London Force A net force between molecules that arises from temporary polarities induced in the molecules by collisions or near-collisions with neighboring molecules.

Macromolecule Any molecule with a very high formula weight — generally several thousand or more.

Maltase A digestive enzyme that catalyzes the hydrolysis of maltose.

Manometer A device for measuring gas pressure.

Markovnikov's Rule In the addition of an unsymmetrical reactant to an unsymmetrical double bond of a simple alkene, the positive part of the reactant molecule (usually H^+) goes to the carbon with the greater number of hydrogen atoms and the negative part goes to the other carbon of the double bond.

Mass A quantitative measure of inertia based on an artifact at Sèvres, France, called the standard kilogram mass; a measure of the quantity of matter in an object relative to this reference standard.

Mass Number The sum of the numbers of protons and neutrons in one atom of an isotope.

Material Balance The condition of a chemical equation in which all the atoms present among the reactants are also found in the products.

Matter Anything that occupies space and has mass.

Measurement An operation by which we compare an unknown physical quantity with one that is known.

Melting Point The temperature at which a solid changes into its liquid form; the temperature at which equilibrium exists between the solid and liquid forms of a substance.

Mercaptan A thioalcohol; R—S—H.

Meso Compound One of a set of optical isomers whose own molecules are not chiral and which, therefore, is optically inactive.

Messenger RNA (*mRNA*) RNA that carries the genetic code as a specific series of codons for a specific polypeptide from the cell's nucleus to the cytoplasm.

Metabolism The sum total of all the chemical reactions that occur in an organism.

Metal Any element that is shiny, conducts electricity well, and (if a solid) can be hammered into sheets and drawn into wires.

Metalloids Elements that have some metallic and some nonmetallic properties.

Meter (m) The base unit of length in the International System of Measurements (SI).

$$1 \text{ m} = 100 \text{ cm} = 39.37 \text{ in.} = 3.280 \text{ ft} = 1.093 \text{ yd}$$

Metric System A decimal system of weights and measures in which the conversion of a base unit of measurement into a multiple or a submultiple is done by moving the decimal point; the predecessor to the International System of Measurements (SI).

Microangiopathy A change in the thickness, composition, and metabolism of the basement membrane of blood capillaries.

Microgram (μg) A mass equal to one-thousandth of a milligram.

$$1 \text{ μg} = 0.001 \text{ mg} = 1 \times 10^{-6} \text{ g}$$

(Its symbol is sometimes given as mcg or as γ in pharmaceutical work.)

Microliter (μL) A volume equal to one-thousandth of a milliliter.

$$1 \text{μL} = 0.001 \text{ mL} = 1 \times 10^{-6} \text{ L}$$

(Its symbol is sometimes given as λ in pharmaceutical work.)

Milliequivalent (meq) A quantity of substance equal to one-thousandth of an equivalent.

Milligram (mg) A mass equal to one-thousandth of a gram.

$$1 \text{ mg} = 0.001 \text{ g} \quad 1000 \text{ mg} = 1 \text{ g} \quad 1 \text{ grain} = 64.8 \text{ mg}$$

Milliliter (mL) A volume equal to one-thousandth of a liter.

$$1 \text{ mL} = 0.001 \text{ L} = 16.23 \text{ minim} = 1 \text{ cm}^3$$

$$1 \text{ liquid ounce} = 29.57 \text{ mL} \quad 1 \text{ liquid quart} = 946.4 \text{ mL}$$

Millimeter (mm) A length equal to one-thousandth of a meter.

$$1 \text{ mm} = 0.001 \text{ m} = 0.0394 \text{ in.}$$

Millimeter of Mercury (mm Hg) A unit of pressure equal to 1/760 atm.

Millimole (mmol) One-thousandth of a mole. 1000 mmol = 1 mol

Minerals Ions that must be provided in the diet at levels of 100 mg/day or more; Ca^{2+}, Mg^{2+}, Na^+, K^+, Cl^-, and phosphate.

Mitochondrion A unit inside a plant or animal cell in which the machinery for making high-energy phosphates by oxidative phosphorylation is located.

Mixture One of the three kinds of matter (together with elements and compounds); any substance made up of two or more elements or compounds combined physically in no particular proportion by mass and separable into its component parts by physical means.

Model, Scientific A mental construction, often involving pictures or diagrams, that is used to explain a number of facts.

Moderate Acid An acid with a K_a in the range of 1 to 10^{-3}.

Molar Concentration (*M*) A solution's concentration in units of moles of solute per liter of solution; molarity.

Molar Mass The number of grams per mole of a substance.

Molar Volume The volume occupied by one mole of a gas under standard conditions of temperature and pressure; 22.4 L at 273 K and 1 atm.

Molarity See *Molar Concentration*.

Mole (mol) A mass of a compound or of an element that equals its formula weight in grams; Avogadro's number of a substance's formula units.

Molecular Compound A compound whose smallest representative particle is a molecule; a covalent compound.

Molecular Equation An equation that shows the complete formulas of all the substances present in a mixture undergoing a reaction. See also *Net Ionic Equation; Equation, Balanced*.

Molecular Orbital A region in the space that envelopes two (or sometimes more) atomic nuclei where a shared pair of electrons of a covalent bond resides.

Molecular Weight The formula weight of a substance.

Molecule An electrically neutral (but often polar) particle made up of the nuclei and electrons of two or more atoms and held together by covalent bonds; the smallest representative sample of a molecular compound.

Monoamine Oxidase An enzyme that catalyzes the inactivation of neurotransmitters or other amino compounds of the nervous system.

Monohydric Alcohol An alcohol whose molecules have one —OH group.

Monomer Any compound that can be used to make a polymer.

Monoprotic Acid An acid with one proton per molecule that can neutralize a base.

Monosaccharide A carbohydrate that cannot be hydrolyzed.

Mucin A viscous glycoprotein, released in the mouth and the stomach, that coats and lubricates food particles and protects the stomach from the acid and pepsin of gastric juice.

Mutagen Any chemical or physical agent that can induce the mutation of a gene without preventing the gene from replicating.

Mutarotation The gradual change in the specific rotation of a substance in solution but without a permanent, irreversible chemical change occurring.

Myosins Proteins in contractile muscle.

Net Ionic Equation A chemical equation in which all spectator particles are omitted so that only the particles that participate directly are represented.

Neurotransmitter A substance released by one nerve cell to carry a signal to the next nerve cell.

Neutral Solution A solution in which the molar concentration of hydronium ions exactly equals the molar concentration of hydroxide ions.

Neutralization, Acid-Base A reaction between an acid and a base.

Neutralizing Capacity The capacity of a solution or a substance to neutralize an acid or a base — expressed as a molar concentration.

Neutron An electrically neutral subatomic particle with a mass of 1 amu.

Niacin A water-soluble vitamin needed to prevent pellagra and essential to the coenzymes in NAD^+ and $NADP^+$; nicotinic acid or nicotinamide.

Nitrogen Balance A condition of the body in which it excretes as much nitrogen as it receives in the diet.

Nitrogen Family The elements of group VA of the periodic table: nitrogen, phosphorus, arsenic, antimony, and bismuth.

Nitrogen Pool The sum total of all nitrogen compounds in the body.

Noble Gases The elements of group 0 of the periodic table: helium, neon, argon, krypton, xenon, and radon.

Nomenclature The system of names and the rules for devising such names, given structures, or for writing structures, given names.

Nonelectrolyte Any substance that cannot furnish ions when dissolved in water or when melted.

Nonfunctional Group A section of an organic molecule that remains unchanged during a chemical reaction at a functional group.

Nonmetal Any element that is not a metal. (See *Metal*.)

Nonsaponifiable Lipid Any lipid, such as the steroids, that cannot be hydrolyzed or similarly broken down by aqueous alkali.

Nonvolatile Liquid Any liquid that has a very low vapor pressure at room temperature and does not readily evaporate.

Normal Fasting Level The normal concentration of something in the blood, such as blood sugar, after about 4 hours without food.

Nuclear Chain Reaction The mechanism of nuclear fission by which one fission event makes enough fission initiators (neutrons) to cause more than one additional fission event.

Nuclear Equation A representation of a nuclear transformation in which the chemical symbols of the reactants and products include mass numbers and atomic numbers.

Nuclease An enzyme that catalyzes the hydrolysis of nucleic acids.

Nucleic Acid A polymer of nucleotides in which the repeating units are pentose phosphate esters, each pentose unit bearing a side-chain base (one of four heterocyclic amines); polymeric compounds that are involved in the storage, transmission, and expression of genetic messages.

Nucleotide A monomer of a nucleic acid that consists of a pentose phosphate ester in which the pentose unit carries one of five heterocyclic amines as a side-chain base.

Nucleus In chemistry and physics, the subatomic particle that serves as the core of an atom and that is made up of protons and neutrons. In biology, the organelle in a cell that houses DNA.

Nutrient Any one of a large number of substances in food and drink that is needed to sustain growth and health.

Nutrition The science of the substances of the diet that are necessary for growth, operation, energy, and repair of bodily tissues.

Octet, Outer A condition of an atom or ion in which its highest occupied energy level has eight electrons — a condition of stability.

Octet Rule The atoms of a reactive element tend to undergo the chemical reactions that most directly give them the electron configuration of the noble gas that stands nearest the element in the periodic table (all but one of which have outer octets).

Olefin An alkene.

One-Substance – One-Structure Rule If two samples of matter have identical physical and chemical properties, they have identical molecules.

Optical Activity The ability of a substance to rotate the plane of polarization of plane-polarized light.

Optical Isomer One of a set of compounds whose molecules differ only in their chiralities.

Optical Rotation The degrees of rotation of the plane of plane-polarized light caused by an optically active solution; the observed rotation of such a solution.

Orbital See *Atomic Orbital*.

Orbital Hybridization The mixing of two or more ordinary atomic orbitals to give an equal number of modified atomic orbitals, called *hybrid orbitals*, each of which possesses some of the characteristics of the originals.

Orbital Overlap The interpenetration of one atomic orbital by another from an adjacent atom to form a molecular orbital.

Organic Chemistry The study of the structures, properties, and syntheses of organic compounds.

Organic Compounds Compounds of carbon other than those related to carbonic acid and its salts, or to the oxides of carbon, or to the cyanides.

Osmolarity (Osm) The molar concentration of all osmotically active solute particles in a solution.

Osmosis The passage of water only, without any solute, from a less concentrated solution (or pure water) to a more concentrated solution when the two solutions are separated by a semipermeable membrane.

Osmotic Membrane A semipermeable membrane that permits only osmosis, not dialysis.

Osmotic Pressure The pressure that would have to be applied to a solution to prevent osmosis if the solution were separated from water by an osmotic membrane.

Outer Octet See *Octet, Outer.*

Outside Level In an atom, the highest principal energy level that holds at least one electron.

Oxidase An enzyme that catalyzes an oxidation.

Oxidation A reaction in which the oxidation number of one of the atoms of a reactant becomes more positive; in organic chemistry, the loss of hydrogen or the gain of oxygen.

Oxidation Number For simple monoatomic ions, the quantity and sign of the electrical charge on the ion.

Oxidation – Reduction Reaction A reaction in which oxidation numbers change.

Oxidative Deamination The change of an amino group to a keto group with loss of nitrogen.

Oxidative Phosphorylation The synthesis of high-energy phosphates such as ATP from lower-energy phosphates and inorganic phosphate by the reactions that involve the respiratory chain.

Oxidizing Agent A substance that can cause an oxidation.

Oxidoreductase An enzyme that catalyzes the formation of an oxidation – reduction equilibrium.

Oxygen Affinity The percentage to which all the hemoglobin molecules in the blood are saturated with oxygen molecules.

Oxygen Debt The condition in a tissue when anaerobic glycolysis has operated and lactate has been excessively produced.

Oxygen Family The elements in group VIA of the periodic table: oxygen, sulfur, selenium, tellurium, and polonium.

Oxyhemoglobin Oxygenated hemoglobin.

P_i Inorganic phosphate ion(s) of whatever mix of PO_4^{3-}, HPO_4^{2-}, $H_2PO_4^{-}$, and possibly even traces of H_3PO_4, is possible at the particular pH of the system, but almost entirely HPO_4^{2-} + $H_2PO_4^{-}$.

Pancreatic Juice The digestive juice that empties into the duodenum from the pancreas.

Pantothenic Acid A water-soluble vitamin needed to make coenzyme A.

Partial Pressure The pressure contributed by an individual gas in a mixture of gases.

Parts per Billion (ppb) The number of parts in a billion parts. (Two drops of water in a railway tank car that holds 34,000 gallons of water correspond roughly to 1 ppb.)

Parts per Million (ppm) The number of parts in a million parts. (Two drops of water in a large 32-gallon trash can correspond roughly to 1 ppm.)

Pascal (Pa) The SI derived unit of pressure. 133.3224 Pa = 1 mm Hg.

Pauli Exclusion Principle No more than two electrons can occupy the same orbital at the same time, and two can be present only if they have opposite spin.

Pentose Phosphate Pathway The synthesis of NADPH that uses chemical energy in glucose 6-phosphate and that involves pentoses as intermediates.

Pepsin A digestive, proteolytic enzyme in gastric juice that forms by the action of acid on pepsinogen.

Pepsinogen The zymogen of pepsin.

Peptidase A digestive enzyme that catalyzes the hydrolysis of a peptide.

Peptide Bond The amide linkage in a protein; a carbonyl-to-nitrogen bond.

Percent (%) A measure of concentration. *Vol/vol percent:* The number of volumes of solute in 100 volumes of solution. *Wt/wt percent:* The number of grams of solute in 100 g of the solution. *Wt/vol percent:* The number of grams of solute in 100 mL of the solution. *Milligram percent:* The number of milligrams of the solute in 100 mL of the solution.

Period A horizontal row in the periodic table.

Periodic Law Many properties of the elements are periodic functions of their atomic numbers.

Periodic Table A display of the elements that emphasizes the family relationships.

pH The negative power to which the base 10 must be raised to express the molar concentration of hydrogen ions in an aqueous solution.

$$[H^+] = 1 \times 10^{-pH}$$

or

$$-\log [H^+] = pH$$

Phenol Any organic compound whose molecules have an —OH group attached to a benzene ring.

Phenyl Group The benzene ring minus one H atom; C_6H_5—.

Phosphate Buffer Usually a mixture or a solution that contains dihydrogen phosphate ions ($H_2PO_4^{-}$) to neutralize OH^- and monohydrogen phosphate ions (HPO_4^{2-}) to neutralize H^+.

Phosphate Group Transfer Potential The relative ability of an organophosphate to transfer a phosphate group to some acceptor.

Phosphoglyceride A phospholipid such as a plasmalogen or a lecithin whose molecules include a glycerol unit.

Phospholipid Lipids such as the phosphoglycerides, the plasmalogens, and the sphingomyelins whose molecules include phosphate ester units.

Photon A package of energy released when an electron in an atom moves from a higher to a lower energy state; a unit of light energy.

Photosynthesis The synthesis in plants of complex compounds from carbon dioxide, water, and minerals with the aid of sunlight captured by the plant's green pigment, chlorophyll.

Physical Property Any observable characteristic of a substance other than a chemical property, such as color, density, melting point, boiling point, temperature, and quantity.

Physical Quantity A property of something to which we assign both a numerical value and a unit, such as mass, volume, or temperature; physical quantity = number $\times$ unit.

Physiological Saline Solution A solution of sodium chloride with an osmotic pressure equal to that of blood.

pI See *Isoelectric Point.*

Pi Bond (π Bond) A covalent bond formed when two electrons fill a molecular orbital created by the side-to-side overlap of two p orbitals.

Pi (π) Electrons The pair of electrons in a pi bond.

pK_a $pK_a = -\log K_a$

pK_b $pK_b = -\log K_b$

Plane-Polarized Light Light whose electrical field vibrations are all in the same plane.

Plasmalogens Glycerol-based phospholipids whose molecules also include an unsaturated fatty alcohol unit.

Plasmid A circular molecule of supercoiled DNA in a bacterial cell.

β-Pleated Sheet A secondary structure for a polypeptide in which the molecules are aligned side by side in a sheet-like array with the sheet partially pleated.

pOH The negative power to which the base 10 must be raised to express the concentration of hydroxide ions in an aqueous solution in mol/L.

$$[OH^-] = 1 \times 10^{-pOH}$$

or

$$-\log [OH^-] = pOH$$

At 25 °C,

$$pH + pOH = 14.00$$

Poison A substance that reacts in some way in the body to cause changes in metabolism that threaten health or life.

Polar Bond A bond at which we can write $\delta+$ at one end and $\delta-$ at the other end, the end that has the more electronegative atom.

Polar Molecule A molecule that has sites of partial positive and partial negative charge and a permanent electrical dipole.

Polarimeter An instrument for detecting and measuring optical activity.

Polarization Any increase in the polarity of a molecule.

Polyatomic Ion Any ion made from two or more atoms, such as OH^-, SO_4^{2-}, and CO_3^{2-}.

Polymer Any substance with a very high formula weight whose molecules essentially consist of repeating structural units.

Polymerization A chemical reaction that makes a polymer from a monomer.

Polypeptide A polymer with repeating α-aminoacyl units joined by peptide (amide) bonds.

Polysaccharide A carbohydrate whose molecules are polymers of monosaccharides.

Potential Energy Stored or inactive energy.

PP$_i$ Inorganic diphosphate ion(s).

Ppb See *Parts per Billion.*

Ppm See *Parts per Million.*

Precipitate A solid that separates from a solution as the result of a chemical reaction.

Precipitation The formation and separation of a precipitate.

Precision The fineness of a measurement or the degree to which successive measurements agree with one another when several are taken one after the other. See also *Accuracy.*

Pressure Force per unit area.

Pressure – Solubility Law (Henry's Law) The concentration of a gas in a liquid at any given temperature is directly proportional to the partial pressure of the gas on the solution.

Pressure – Temperature Law (Gay-Lussac's Law) The pressure of a gas is directly proportional to its Kelvin temperature when the gas volume is constant.

Pressure – Volume Law (Boyle's Law) The volume of a gas is inversely proportional to its pressure when the temperature is constant.

Primary Alcohol An alcohol in whose molecules an —OH group is attached to a primary carbon, as in RCH_2OH.

Primary Carbon In a molecule, a carbon atom that is joined directly to just one other carbon, such as the end carbons in $CH_3CH_2CH_3$.

Primary Structure The sequence of aminoacyl residues held together by peptide bonds in a polypeptide.

Primary Transcript RNA (*pt*RNA) RNA made directly at the guidance of DNA and from which messenger RNA (*m*RNA) is made.

Principal Energy Level A space near an atomic nucleus where there are one or more sublevels and orbitals in which electrons can reside; an electron shell.

Principle of Maximum Overlap The more that two atomic orbitals overlap or interpenetrate, the stronger is the bond that arises from the resulting molecular orbital.

Procarboxypeptidase The zymogen of carboxypeptidase.

Product A substance that forms in a chemical reaction.

Proenzyme An inactive form of an enzyme; a zymogen.

Property A characteristic of something by means of which we can identify it.

Prosthetic Group A nonprotein molecule joined to a polypeptide to make a biologically active protein.

Protein A naturally occurring polymeric substance made up wholly or mostly of polypeptide molecules.

Proton A subatomic particle that bears one unit of positive charge and has a mass of 1 amu.

Pure Substances Elements and compounds.

Quantum A quantity of energy possessed by a photon.

Quaternary Structure An aggregation of two or more polypeptide strands, each with its own primary, secondary, and tertiary structure.

Racemic Mixture A 1 : 1 mixture of enantiomers that is therefore optically inactive.

Rad One rad equals 100 ergs (1×10^{-5} J) of energy absorbed per gram of tissue as a result of ionizing radiations.

Radiation A process whereby light or heat is emitted; also the emitted light or heat. In atomic physics, the emission of some ray such as an alpha, beta, or gamma ray.

Radiation Sickness The set of symptoms that develops following exposure to heavy doses of ionizing radiations.

Radical A particle with one or more unpaired electrons.

Radioactive The property of unstable atomic nuclei whereby they emit alpha, beta, or gamma rays.

Radioactive Decay The change of a radioactive isotope into another isotope by the emission of alpha rays or beta rays.

Radioactive Disintegration Series A series of isotopes selected and arranged in such a way that each isotope except the first is produced by the radioactive decay of the preceding isotope and the last isotope is nonradioactive.

Radioactive Element An element that emits dangerous radiation(s).

Radioactivity The ability to emit high energy radiations such as alpha, beta, or gamma rays.

Radiomimetic Substance A substance whose chemical effect in a cell mimics the effect of ionizing radiation.

Radionuclide A radioactive isotope.

Rate of Reaction The number of successful (product-forming) collisions that occur each second in each unit of volume of the reacting mixture.

Ratio A relationship between two numbers or two physical quantities expressed as a fraction.

Reactant One of the substances that reacts in a chemical reaction.

Reagent Any mixture of chemicals, usually a solution, that is used to carry out a chemical test.

Receptor Molecule A molecule of a protein built into a cell membrane that can accept a molecule of a hormone or a neurotransmitter.

Recombinant DNA DNA made by combining the natural DNA of plasmids in bacteria or the natural DNA in yeasts with DNA from external sources, such as the DNA for human insulin. Recombinant DNA is a step in a process that uses altered bacteria or yeasts to make specific proteins (e.g., interferons, human growth hormone, or insulin).

Recommended Dietary Allowance (RDA) The level of intake of a particular nutrient as determined by the Food and Nutrition Board of the National Research Council of the National Academy of Sciences to meet the known nutritional needs of most healthy individuals.

Redox Reaction Abbreviation of *reduction – oxidation;* a reaction in which oxidation numbers change.

Reducing Agent A substance that can cause another to be reduced.

Reducing Carbohydrate A carbohydrate that gives a positive Benedict's test.

Reductase An enzyme that catalyzes a reduction.

Reduction A reaction in which the oxidation number of one of the atoms of a reactant becomes less positive or more negative; in organic chemistry, the gain of hydrogen or the loss of oxygen.

Reduction Potential The quantitative measure of the tendency of a given half-reaction to proceed as a reduction relative to the standard hydrogen half-reaction.

Reduction Potential, Standard ($E°$) The reduction potential under standard conditions, 25 °C, 1 atm, and concentrations of 1 M.

Reductive Amination The conversion of a keto group to an amino group by the action of ammonia and a reducing agent.

Rem One rem is the quantity of a radiation that produces the same effect in humans as one roentgen of X rays or gamma rays.

Renal Threshold That concentration of a substance in blood above which it appears in the urine.

Replication The reproductive duplication of a DNA double helix.

Representative Element Any element in any A group of the periodic table; any element in groups IA to VIIA and those in group 0.

Repressor A substance whose molecules can bind to a gene and prevent the gene from directing the synthesis of a polypeptide.

Respiration The intake and chemical use of oxygen by the body and the release of carbon dioxide.

Respiratory Chain The reactions that transfer electrons from the intermediates made by other pathways to oxygen; the mechanism that creates a proton gradient across the inner membrane of a mitochondrion and that leads to ATP synthesis; the enzymes that handle these reactions.

Respiratory Enzymes The enzymes of the respiratory chain.

Respiratory Gases Oxygen and carbon dioxide.

Riboflavin A B vitamin needed to give protection against the breakdown of tissue around the mouth, the nose, and the tongue, as well as to aid in wound healing.

Ribonucleic Acids (RNA) Polymers of ribonucleotides that participate in the transcription and the translation of the genetic messages into polypeptides. See also *Messenger RNA, Primary Transcript RNA, Ribosomal RNA,* and *Transfer RNA.*

Ribonucleotides The monomers for ribonucleic acids that consist of ribose phosphate esters with each ribose unit carrying a side-chain base (one of four heterocyclic amines: adenine, uracil, guanine, and cytosine).

Ribosomal RNA (rRNA) RNA that is incorporated into cytoplasmic bodies called ribosomes.

Ribosome A granular complex of *r*RNA that becomes attached to a *m*RNA strand and that supplies some of the enzymes for *m*RNA-directed polypeptide synthesis.

Ring Compound A compound whose molecules contain three or more atoms joined in a ring.

RNA See *Ribonucleic Acid.*

Roentgen One roentgen is the quantity of X rays or gamma radiation that generates ions with an aggregate of 2.1×10^9 units of charge in 1 mL of dry air at normal pressure and temperature.

Saliva The digestive juice secreted in the mouth whose enzyme, amylase, catalyzes the partial digestion of starch.

Salt Any crystalline compound that consists of oppositely charged ions (other than H^+, OH^-, or O^{2-}).

Salt Bridge A force of attraction between (+) and (−) sites on polypeptide molecules.

Saponifiable Lipid Any lipid with ester groups.

Saponification The reaction of an ester with sodium or potassium hydroxide to give an alcohol and the salt of an acid.

Saturated Compound A compound whose molecules have only single bonds.

Saturated Solution A solution into which no more solute can be dissolved at the given temperature; a solution in which dynamic equilibrium exists between the dissolved and the undissolved solute.

Scientific Method A method of solving a problem that devises a hypothesis to explain the facts and suggests further tests or experiments designed to discover whether the hypothesis is true or false.

Scientific Notation The method of writing a number as the product of two numbers, one being 10^x, where x is some positive or negative whole number.

Second (s) The SI unit of time; 1/60th minute.

Secondary Alcohol An alcohol in whose molecules an —OH group is attached to a secondary carbon atom; $R_2CH—OH$.

Secondary Carbon Any carbon atom in an organic molecule that has two and only two bonds to other carbon atoms, such as the middle carbon atom in $CH_3CH_2CH_3$.

Secondary Structure A shape, such as the α-helix or a unit in a β-pleated sheet, that all or a large part of a polypeptide molecule adopts under the influence of hydrogen bonds or salt bridges after its peptide bonds have been made.

Semipermeable Descriptive of a membrane that permits only certain kinds of molecules to pass through and not others.

Sensible Perspiration Visible perspiration released by the sweat glands.

Shock, Traumatic A medical emergency in which relatively large volumes of blood fluid leave the vascular compartment and enter the interstitial spaces.

Side Chain An organic group that can be appended to a main chain or to a ring.

Sigma Bond (σ-Bond) A covalent bond associated with a molecular orbital whose shape is symmetrical about the bonding axis.

Significant Figures The number of digits in a numerical measurement or in the result of a calculation that are known with certainty to be accurate plus one more digit.

Simple Lipid A triacylglycerol; a triglyceride.

Simple Salt A salt that consists of just one kind of cation and one kind of anion.

Simple Sugar Any monosaccharide.

Single Bond A covalent bond involving one shared pair of electrons.

Soap A detergent that consists of the sodium or potassium salts of long-chain fatty acids.

Soft Water Water with a small amount if any of the hardness ions—Mg^{2+}, Ca^{2+}, Fe^{2+}, or Fe^{3+}.

Sol A colloidal dispersion of tiny particles of a solid in a liquid.

Solid A state of matter in which the visible particles of the substance have both definite shapes and definite volumes.

Solubility The extent to which a substance dissolves in a fixed volume or weight of a solvent at a given temperature.

Solute The component of a solution that is understood to be dissolved in or dispersed in a continuous solvent.

Solution A homogeneous mixture of two or more substances that are at the smallest sizes of their states of subdivision—at the ion, atom, or molecule level.

Solution, Aqueous A solution in which water is the solvent.

Solution, Concentrated A solution with a high ratio of solute to solvent.

Solution, Dilute A solution with a low ratio of solute to solvent.

Solution, Saturated See *Saturated Solution*.

Solution, Supersaturated An unstable solution that has a higher concentration of solute than that of the saturated solution.

Solution, Unsaturated A solution into which more solute could be dissolved without changing the temperature.

Solvent The component of a solution into which the solutes are considered to have dissolved; the component that is present as a continuous phase.

Somatostatin A hormone of the hypothalamus that inhibits or slows the release of glucagon and insulin from the pancreas.

Specific Gravity The ratio of the density of an object to the density of water.

Specific Heat The amount of heat that one gram of a substance can absorb per degree Celsius increase in temperature,

$$\text{Specific heat} = \frac{\text{heat}}{g\,\Delta t}$$

where Δt = the change in temperature. (The unit of heat is usually the calorie, but kilocalorie, joule, or kilojoule can be used.)

Specific Rotation [α] The optical rotation of a solution per unit of concentration per unit of path length,

$$[\alpha] = \frac{(100)(\alpha)}{(c)(\ell)}$$

where α = observed rotation; c = concentration in g/100 mL; and ℓ = path length in decimeters.

sp^2 Hybrid Orbital A hybrid orbital made by mixing one s orbital with two p orbitals to form three new, identical orbitals whose axes are in one plane and point to the corners of an equilateral triangle.

sp^3 Hybrid Orbital One of four equivalent hybrid orbitals formed by the mixing of one s orbital and three p orbitals and whose axes point to the corners of a regular tetrahedron.

Sphingolipid A lipid that, when hydrolyzed, gives sphingosine instead of glycerol, plus fatty acids, phosphoric acid, and a small alcohol or a monosaccharide; sphingomyelins and cerebrosides.

Spontaneous Combustion Combustion that follows the slow accumulation of oxidation-generated heat until the kindling temperature is reached.

Standard, Reference A physical description or embodiment of a base unit of measurement, such as the standard meter or the standard kilogram mass.

Standard Atmosphere (atm) The pressure that supports a column of mercury 760 mm high when the mercury has a temperature of 0 °C.

Standard Conditions of Temperature and Pressure (STP) 0 °C (or 273 K) and 1 atm (or 760 mm Hg).

Standard Solution Any solution for which the concentration is accurately known.

States of Matter The three possible physical conditions of aggregation of matter—solid, liquid, and gas.

Stereoisomer One of a set of isomers whose molecules have the same atom-to-atom sequences but different geometric arrangements; a geometric (cis-trans) or optical isomer.

Steroids Nonsaponifiable lipids such as cholesterol and several sex hormones whose molecules have the four fused rings of the steroid nucleus.

Stoichiometry The branch of chemistry that deals with the mole proportions of chemicals in reactions.

Straight Chain A continuous, open sequence of covalently bound carbon atoms from which no additional carbon atoms are attached at interior locations of the sequence.

Strong Acid An acid with a high percentage ionization and a high value of acid ionization constant, K_a.

Strong Base A metal hydroxide with a high percentage ionization in solution.

Strong Brønsted Acid Any species, molecule or ion, that has a strong tendency to donate a proton to some acceptor.

Strong Brønsted Base Any species, molecular or ionic, that binds an accepted proton strongly.

Strong Electrolyte Any substance that has a high percentage ionization in solution.

Structural Formula A formula that uses lines representing covalent bonds to connect the atomic symbols in the pattern that occurs in one molecule of a compound.

Structural Isomer One of a set of isomers whose molecules differ in their atom-to-atom sequence.

Structure Synonym for structural formula. See *Structural Formula.*

Subatomic Particle An electron, a proton, or a neutron; the atomic nucleus as a whole is also a subatomic particle.

Sublevel A region that makes up part (sometimes all) of a principal energy level and that can itself be subdivided into individual orbitals.

Subscripts Numbers placed to the right and a half space below the atomic symbols in a chemical formula.

Substances The materials in a sample of matter. See also *Pure Substances.*

Substitution Reaction A reaction in which one atom or group replaces another atom or group in a molecule.

Substrate The substance on which an enzyme performs its catalytic work.

Substrate Phosphorylation The direct transfer of a phosphate unit from an organophosphate to a receptor molecule.

Sucrase A digestive enzyme that catalyzes the hydrolysis of sucrose.

Superimposition An operation to see whether one molecular model can be made to blend simultaneously at exactly every point with another model.

Supersaturated Describing an unstable condition of a solution in which more solute is in solution than could be were there equilibrium between the undissolved and dissolved states of the solute.

Surface-Active Agent See *Surfactant.*

Surface Tension The quality of a liquid's surface by which it behaves as though it were a thin, invisible, elastic membrane.

Surfactant A substance, such as a detergent, that reduces the surface tension of water.

Suspension A homogeneous mixture in which the particles of at least one component have average diameters greater than 1000 nm.

Synapse The fluid-filled gap between the end of the axon of one nerve cell and dendrites of the next nerve cell.

Syndet A synthetic detergent that works in hard water.

Target Cell A cell at which a hormone molecule finds a site where it can become attached and then cause some action that is associated with the hormone.

Target Tissue The tissue whose cells are recognizable by the molecules of a particular hormone.

Temperature The measure of the hotness or coldness of an object. *Degrees* of temperature, such as those of the Celsius, Fahrenheit, or Kelvin scales, are intervals of equal separation on the thermometer.

Temperature – Volume Law (Charles' Law) The volume of a gas is directly proportional to its Kelvin temperature when the pressure is kept constant.

Teratogen Any chemical or physical agent that can cause birth defects in a fetus other than those defects that the fetus has inherited.

Tertiary Alcohol An alcohol in whose molecules an —OH group

is held by a carbon from which three bonds extend to other carbon atoms; R_3C—OH.

Tertiary Carbon Any carbon in an organic molecule that has three and only three bonds to adjacent *carbon* atoms.

Tertiary Structure The shape of a polypeptide molecule that arises from further folding or coiling of secondary structures.

Tetrahedral Descriptive of the geometry of bonds at a central atom that project from there to the corners of a regular tetrahedron.

Theory An explanation for a large number of facts, observations, and hypotheses in terms of one or a few fundamental assumptions of what the world (or some small part of the world) is like.

Thiamin A B vitamin needed to prevent beriberi.

Thioalcohol A compound whose molecules have the —SH group attached to a saturated carbon atom; a mercaptan.

Threshold Exposure The level of exposure to some toxic agent below which no harm is done.

Time A period during which something endures, exists, or continues.

Titration A procedure for determining the concentration of some species by adding from a buret a measurable volume of a standard solution of some reactant until the equivalence point of the reaction is reached.

Tollens' Reagent A slightly alkaline solution of the diammine complex of the silver ion, $Ag(NH_3)_2^+$, in water.

Tollens' Test The use of Tollens' reagent to detect an easily oxidized group such as the aldehyde group.

Torr A unit of pressure; 1 torr = 1 mm Hg; 1 atm = 760 torr

Trace Element Any element that the body needs each day in an amount of no more than 20 mg.

Transamination The transfer of an amino group from an amino acid to a receiver with a keto group in such a way that the keto group changes to an amino group.

Transcription The synthesis of messenger RNA under the direction of DNA.

Transfer RNA (*t*RNA) RNA that serves to carry an aminoacyl group to a specific acceptor site of a *m*RNA molecule at a ribosome where the aminoacyl group is placed into a growing polypeptide chain.

Transferase An enzyme that catalyzes the transfer of some group.

Transition Elements The elements between those of group IIA and those of group IIIA in the long periods of the periodic table; a metallic element other than one in group IA or IIA or in the actinide or lanthanide families.

Translation The synthesis of a polypeptide under the direction of messenger RNA.

Transmutation The change of an isotope of one element into an isotope of a different element.

Triacylglycerol A lipid that can be hydrolyzed to glycerol and fatty acids; a triglyceride; sometimes, simply called a glyceride.

Triglyceride See *Triacylglycerol.*

Trihydric Alcohol An alcohol with three —OH groups per molecule.

Triple Bond A bond in which three pairs of electrons are shared between two nuclei.

Triple Helix The quaternary structure of tropocollagen in whi'' three polypeptide chains are twisted together.

Triprotic Acid An acid that can supply three protons per molecule.

Trypsin A digestive enzyme, made from the trypsinogen of pancreatic juice by the action of enteropeptidase, that catalyzes the hydrolysis of proteins.

Tyndall Effect The scattering of light by colloidal-sized particles in a colloidal dispersion.

Universal Gas Law $PV = nRT$. See also *Gas Constant, Universal*.

Unsaturated Compound Any compound whose molecules have a double or a triple bond.

Unshared Pairs Pairs of valence-shell electrons not involved in covalent bonds.

Urea Cycle The reactions by which urea is made from amino acids.

Vacuum An enclosed space in which there is no matter.

Valence Shell The highest energy level of an atom that is occupied by electrons.

Valence-Shell Electron-Pair Repulsion Theory (VSEPR) Bond angles at a central atom are caused by the repulsions of the electron clouds of valence-shell electron pairs.

Vapor Pressure The pressure exerted by the vapor that is in equilibrium with its liquid state at a given temperature.

Vaporization The change of a liquid into its vapor.

Vascular Compartment The entire network of blood vessels and their contents.

Vasopressin A hypophysis hormone that acts at the kidneys to help regulate the concentrations of solutes in the blood by instructing the kidneys to retain water (if the blood is too concentrated) or to excrete water (if the blood is too dilute).

Ventilation The movement of air into and out of the lungs by breathing.

Virus One of a large number of substances that consist of nucleic acid (usually RNA) surrounded (usually) by a protein overcoat and that can enter host cells, multiply, and destroy the host.

Vital Force Theory A discarded theory that organic compounds could be made in the laboratory only if the chemicals possessed a vital force contributed by some living thing.

Vitamin An organic substance that must be in the diet; whose absence causes a deficiency disease; that is present in foods in trace concentrations; and that isn't a carbohydrate, lipid, protein, or amino acid.

Vitamin A Retinol; a fat-soluble vitamin in yellow-colored foods and needed to prevent night blindness and certain conditions of the mucous membranes.

Vitamin B$_6$ Pyridoxine, pyridoxal, or pyridoxamine; a vitamin needed to prevent hypochromic microcytic anemia and used in enzymes of amino acid catabolism.

Vitamin B$_{12}$ Cobalamin; A vitamin needed to prevent pernicious anemia.

Vitamin C Ascorbic acid; a vitamin needed to prevent scurvy.

Vitamin D Cholecalciferol (D_3) or ergocalciferol (D_2); a fat-soluble vitamin needed to prevent rickets and to ensure the formation of healthy bones and teeth.

Vitamin Deficiency Diseases Diseases caused not by bacteria or viruses but by the absence of specific vitamins, such as pernicious anemia (B$_{12}$), hypochromic microcytic anemia (B$_6$), pellagra (niacin), the breakdown of certain tissues (riboflavin), megaloblastic anemia (folacin), beriberi (thiamin), scruvy (C), hemorrhagic disease (K), rickets (D), and night blindness (A).

Vitamin E A mixture of tocopherols; a fat-soluble vitamin apparently needed for protection against edema and anemia (in infants) and possibly against dystrophy, paralysis, and heart attacks.

Vitamin K The antihemorrhagic vitamin that serves as a cofactor in the formation of a blood clot.

Volatile Liquid A liquid that has a high vapor pressure and readily evaporates at room temperature.

Volt The SI unit of electrical potential, the force that drives the stream of electrons when a current of electricity flows.

Volume The capacity of an object to occupy space.

Water of Hydration Water molecules held in a hydrate in some definite mole ratio to the rest of the compound.

Wax A lipid whose molecules are esters of long-chain monohydric alcohols and long-chain fatty acids.

Weak Acid An acid with a low percentage ionization in solution and with a low value of acid ionization constant, K_a.

Weak Base A base with a low percentage ionization in solution.

Weak Brønsted Acid Any species, molecule or ion, that has a weak tendency to donate a proton and poorly serves as a proton donor.

Weak Brønsted Base Any species, molecule or ion, that weakly holds an accepted proton and poorly serves as a proton-acceptor.

Weak Electrolyte Any electrolyte that has a low percentage ionization in solution.

Weight The gravitational force of attraction on an object as compared to that of some reference.

Zymogen A polypeptide that is changed into an enzyme by the loss of a few amino acid residues or by some other change in its structure; a proenzyme.

PHOTO CREDITS

Chapter 1
Opener: W. K. Almond/Stock, Boston.
Page 5: (left) Leif Skoogfors/Woodfin Camp.
        (right) Dan McCoy/Rainbow.
Page 7: Robert J. Capece.
Figure 1.1: National Bureau of Standards.
Page 8: (top) Ken Karp.
        (bottom) Ken Karp.
Figure 1.2: OPC, Inc.

Chapter 2
Opener: Yann Guichaoua/Agence Vandystadt/Photo Researchers.
Figure 2.2: Jim Brady and Kathy Bendo.
Figure 2.3: OPC, Inc.
Figure 2.4: OPC, Inc.
Page 28: Ken Karp.
Page 29: A. L. Smith, *John Dalton 1766–1844; A Bibliography by and About Him.* Manchester: The University Press, 1966. Courtesy AIP Neils Bohr Library.
Figure 2.5: OPC, Inc.
Page 34: (top) Ken Karp.
        (bottom) Ken Karp.

Chapter 3
Opener: Helmut Wimmer, The American Museum of Natural History—Hayden Planetarium.
Page 47: Larry Hamill.
Page 49: Drawing by William Numeroff.
Page 51: Courtesy Nobel Foundation, Stockholm.
Page 60: New York Public Library Picture Collection.

Chapter 4
Opener: Jane Burton/Bruce Coleman.
Page 72: M. Claye Jacana/Photo Researchers.
Page 74: Peter Lerman.
Figure 4.4: Ken Karp.

Chapter 5
Opener: Blair Seitz/Photo Researchers.
Figure 5.1: Peter Lerman.
Figure 5.2: Peter Lerman.
Figure 5.4: OPC, Inc.
Figure 5.5: Peter Lerman.
Figure 5.7: OPC, Inc.

Chapter 6
Opener: Diana Stratton.
Figure 6.15: OPC, Inc.

Chapter 7
Opener: Erwin and Peggy Bauer/Bruce Coleman.
Figure 7.6: OPC, Inc.

Chapter 8
Opener: Jack Fields/Photo Researchers.
Figure 8.2: OPC, Inc.
Figure 8.4: OPC, Inc.
Page 203: Robert J. Capece.
Page 207: OPC, Inc.

Page 475:   Robert J. Capece.

Figure 18.7:   Photograph Courtesy Polaroid Corporate Archives.

Chapter 19

Opener: Earl Roberge/Photo Researchers.

Chapter 20

Opener: Courtesy Staten Island Historical Society.

Chapter 21

Opener: Copyright © 1989, Robert Davenport, Department of Biology, Massachusetts Institute of Technology.

Page 542:   (left) Bill Longcore/Photo Researchers.
            (right) Bill Longcore/Photo Researchers.

Chapter 22

Opener: Toni Angermayer/Photo Researchers.

Figure 22.7:   Courtesy Richard J. Feldman, Division of Computer Research and Technology, National Institutes of Health.

Page 558:   Courtesy Lifecodes Corporation.

Page 561:   S. H. Kim, Duke University Medical Center.

Chapter 23

Opener: Michel Tcherevkoff/Image Bank.

Chapter 24

Opener: Auscape/Agence Vandystadt/Photo Researchers.

Figure 24.2:   Courtesy T. A. Steitz, Department of Molecular Biophysics and Biochemistry, Yale University.

Page 610:   Courtesy Boehringer Mannheim Diagnostics.

Chapter 25

Opener: Dan McCoy/Rainbow.

Page 646:   Reprinted by permission of United Features Syndicate, Inc.

Chapter 26

Opener: Focus on Sports.

Chapter 27

Opener: Catherine Karnow/Woodfin Camp.

Chapter 28

Opener: Neil Leifer/*Sports Illustrated*.

Chapter 29

Opener: Wolfgang Bauer/Bruce Coleman.

PERIODIC TABLE OF THE ELEMENTS[a]

Atomic number

| 1 |
| H |
| 1.00794 |

Atomic weight

Noble gases

Periods	IA	IIA	IIIB	IVB	VB	VIB	VIIB	VIII			IB	IIB	IIIA	IVA	VA	VIA	VIIA	0
1	1 H 1.00794																	2 He 4.00260
2	3 Li 6.941	4 Be 9.01218											5 B 10.811	6 C 12.011	7 N 14.00674	8 O 15.9994	9 F 18.99840	10 Ne 20.1797
3	11 Na 22.98977	12 Mg 24.3050											13 Al 26.98154	14 Si 28.0855	15 P 30.97376	16 S 32.066	17 Cl 35.4527	18 Ar 39.948
4	19 K 39.0983	20 Ca 40.078	21 Sc 44.95591	22 Ti 47.88	23 V 50.9415	24 Cr 51.9961	25 Mn 54.9380	26 Fe 55.847	27 Co 58.93320	28 Ni 58.69	29 Cu 63.546	30 Zn 65.39	31 Ga 69.723	32 Ge 72.61	33 As 74.92159	34 Se 78.96	35 Br 79.904	36 Kr 83.80
5	37 Rb 85.4678	38 Sr 87.62	39 Y 88.90585	40 Zr 91.224	41 Nb 92.90638	42 Mo 95.94	43 Tc 98.9072	44 Ru 101.07	45 Rh 102.90550	46 Pd 106.42	47 Ag 107.8682	48 Cd 112.411	49 In 114.82	50 Sn 118.710	51 Sb 121.75	52 Te 127.60	53 I 126.90447	54 Xe 131.29
6	55 Cs 132.90543	56 Ba 137.327	57 *La 138.9055	72 Hf 178.49	73 Ta 180.9479	74 W 183.85	75 Re 186.207	76 Os 190.2	77 Ir 192.22	78 Pt 195.08	79 Au 196.96654	80 Hg 200.59	81 Tl 204.3833	82 Pb 207.2	83 Bi 208.98037	84 Po 208.9824	85 At 209.9871	86 Rn 222.0176
7	87 Fr 223.0197	88 Ra 226.0254	89 †Ac 227.0278	104 Unq 261.11	105 Unp 262.114	106 Unh 263.118	107 Uns 262.12											

*	58 Ce 140.115	59 Pr 140.90765	60 Nd 144.24	61 Pm 144.9127	62 Sm 150.36	63 Eu 151.965	64 Gd 157.25	65 Tb 158.92534	66 Dy 162.50	67 Ho 164.93032	68 Er 167.26	69 Tm 168.93421	70 Yb 173.04	71 Lu 174.967
†	90 Th 232.0381	91 Pa 231.0359	92 U 238.0289	93 Np 237.0482	94 Pu 244.0642	95 Am 243.0614	96 Cm 247.0703	97 Bk 247.0703	98 Cf 242.0587	99 Es 252.083	100 Fm 257.0951	101 Md 258.10	102 No 259.1009	103 Lr 260.105

[a] Atomic weights are the 1985 values given in the Table of Atomic Weights and Numbers (opposite) but rounded, where appropriate to the fifth decimal place.

TABLE OF ATOMIC WEIGHTS AND NUMBERS

Based on the 1985 Report of the Commission on Atomic Weights of the International Union of Pure and Applied Chemistry and for the elements as they exist naturally on earth. Scaled to the relative atomic mass of carbon-12. The estimated uncertainties in values, between ±1 and ±9 units in the last digit of an atomic weight, are in parentheses after the atomic weight. (From *Pure and Applied Chemistry,* Vol. 58 (1986), pp. 1677–1692. Copyright © 1986 IUPAC)

Element	Symbol	Atomic Number	Atomic Weight		Element	Symbol	Atomic Number	Atomic Weight	
Actinium	Ac	89	227.0278	(L)	Neodymium	Nd	60	144.24(3)	(g)
Aluminum	Al	13	26.981539(5)		Neon	Ne	10	20.1797(6)	(g, m)
Americium	Am	95	243.0614	(L)	Neptunium	Np	93	237.0482	(L)
Antimony	Sb	51	121.75(3)		Nickel	Ni	28	58.69(1)	
Argon	Ar	18	39.948(1)	(g, r)	Niobium	Nb	41	92.90638(2)	
Arsenic	As	33	74.92159(2)		Nitrogen	N	7	14.00674(7)	(g, r)
Astatine	At	85	209.9871	(L)	Nobelium	No	102	259.1009	(L)
Barium	Ba	56	137.327(7)		Osmium	Os	76	190.2(1)	(g)
Berkelium	Bk	97	247.0703	(L)	Oxygen	O	8	15.9994(3)	(g, r)
Beryllium	Be	4	9.012182(3)		Palladium	Pd	46	106.42(1)	(g)
Bismuth	Bi	83	208.98037(3)		Phosphorus	P	15	30.973762(4)	
Boron	B	5	10.811(5)	(g, m, r)	Platinum	Pt	78	195.08(3)	
Bromine	Br	35	79.904(1)		Plutonium	Pu	94	244.0642	(L)
Cadmium	Cd	48	112.411(8)	(g)	Polonium	Po	84	208.9824	(L)
Calcium	Ca	20	40.078(4)	(g)	Potassium	K	19	39.0983(1)	
Californium	Cf	98	242.0587	(L)	Praseodymium	Pr	59	140.90765(3)	
Carbon	C	6	12.011(1)	(r)	Promethium	Pm	61	144.9127	(L)
Cerium	Ce	58	140.115(4)	(g)	Protactinium	Pa	91	231.03588(2)	(Z)
Cesium	Cs	55	132.90543(5)		Radium	Ra	88	226.0254	(L)
Chlorine	Cl	17	35.4527(9)		Radon	Rn	86	222.0176	(L)
Chromium	Cr	24	51.9961(6)		Rhenium	Re	75	186.207(1)	
Cobalt	Co	27	58.93320(1)		Rhodium	Rh	45	102.90550(3)	
Copper	Cu	29	63.546(3)	(r)	Rubidium	Rb	37	85.4678(3)	(g)
Curium	Cm	96	247.0703	(L)	Ruthenium	Ru	44	101.07(2)	(g)
Dysprosium	Dy	66	162.50(3)	(g)	Samarium	Sm	62	150.36(3)	(g)
Einsteinium	Es	99	252.083	(L)	Scandium	Sc	21	44.955910(9)	
Erbium	Er	68	167.26(3)	(g)	Selenium	Se	34	78.96(3)	
Europium	Eu	63	151.965(9)	(g)	Silicon	Si	14	28.0855(3)	
Fermium	Fm	100	257.0951	(L)	Silver	Ag	47	107.8682(2)	(g)
Fluorine	F	9	18.9984032(9)		Sodium	Na	11	22.989768(6)	
Francium	Fr	87	223.0197	(L)	Strontium	Sr	38	87.62(1)	(g, r)
Gadolinium	Gd	64	157.25(3)	(g)	Sulfur	S	16	32.066(6)	(r)
Gallium	Ga	31	69.723(4)		Tantalum	Ta	73	180.9479(1)	
Germanium	Ge	32	72.61(2)		Technetium	Tc	43	98.9072	(L)
Gold	Au	79	196.96654(3)		Tellurium	Te	52	127.60(3)	(g)
Hafnium	Hf	72	178.49(2)		Terbium	Tb	65	158.92534(3)	
Helium	He	2	4.002602(2)	(g, r)	Thallium	Tl	81	204.3833(2)	
Holmium	Ho	67	164.93032(3)		Thorium	Th	90	232.0381(1)	(g, r, Z)
Hydrogen	H	1	1.00794(7)	(g, m, r)	Thulium	Tm	69	168.93421(3)	
Indium	In	49	114.82(1)		Tin	Sn	50	118.710(7)	(g)
Iodine	I	53	126.90447(3)		Titanium	Ti	22	47.88(3)	
Iridium	Ir	77	192.22(3)		Tungsten	W	74	183.85(3)	
Iron	Fe	26	55.847(3)		(Unnilhexium)	(Unh)	106	263.118	(L, n)
Krypton	Kr	36	83.80(1)	(g, m)	(Unnilpentium)	(Unp)	105	262.114	(L, n)
Lanthanum	La	57	138.9055(2)	(g)	(Unnilquadium)	(Unq)	104	266.11	(L, n)
Lawrencium	Lr	103	260.105	(L)	(Unnilseptium)	(Uns)	107	262.12	(L, n)
Lead	Pb	82	207.2(1)	(g, r)	Uranium	U	92	238.0289(1)	(g, m, Z))
Lithium	Li	3	6.941(2)	(g, m, r)	Vanadium	V	23	50.9415(1)	
Lutetium	Lu	71	174.967(1)	(g)	Xenon	Xe	54	131.29(2)	(g, m)
Magnesium	Mg	12	24.3050(6)		Ytterbium	Yb	70	173.04(3)	(g)
Manganese	Mn	25	54.93805(1)		Yttrium	Y	39	88.90585(2)	
Mendelevium	Md	101	258.10	(L)	Zinc	Zn	30	65.39(2)	
Mercury	Hg	80	200.59(3)		Zirconium	Zr	40	91.224(2)	(g)
Molybdenum	Mo	42	95.94(1)						

(g) Geologically exceptional specimens of this element are known that have different isotopic compositions. For such samples, the atomic weight given here may not apply as precisely as indicated.

(L) This atomic weight is for the relative mass of the isotope of longest half-life. The element has no stable isotopes.

(m) Modified isotopic compositions can occur in commercially available materials that have been processed in undisclosed ways, and the atomic weight given here might be quite different for such samples.

(n) Name and symbol are assigned according to systematic rules developed by the IUPAC.

(r) Ranges in isotopic compositions of normal samples obtained on earth do not permit a more precise atomic weight for this element, but the tabulated value should apply to any normal sample of the element.

(Z) Despite having no stable isotopes, the terrestrial compositions of samples of the long-lived isotopes allow a meaningful atomic weight.